HUMAN GEOGRAPHY

PLACES AND REGIONS IN GLOBAL CONTEXT

THIRD CANADIAN EDITION

PAUL L. KNOX
VIRGINIA TECH

SALLIE A. MARSTON
UNIVERSITY OF ARIZONA

ALAN E. NASH
CONCORDIA UNIVERSITY

WITH CONTRIBUTIONS FROM

K. BRUCE NEWBOLD
(McMASTER UNIVERSITY)

WHO WROTE THE NEW "HUMAN GEOGRAPHY
AND CLIMATE CHANGE" FEATURES

Pearson Canada
Toronto

Library and Archives Canada Cataloguing in Publication

Knox, Paul L.
Human geography: places and regions in global context/Paul L. Knox,
Sallie A. Marston, Alan Eric Nash—3rd Canadian ed.

Includes index.
ISBN 978-0-13-206448-4

1. Human geography—Textbooks. I. Marston, Sallie A. II. Nash, Alan E. (Alan Eric), 1954– III. Title.
GF41.K56 2009   304.2   C2008-907378-9

ISBN-13: 978-0-13-206448-4
ISBN-10: 0-13-206448-0

Vice-President, Editorial Director: Gary Bennett
Acquisitions Editor: Cathleen Sullivan
Marketing Manager: Kimberly Ukrainec
Senior Developmental Editor: Eleanor MacKay
Production Editor: Imee Salumbides
Copy Editor: Cat Haggert
Proofreader: Claudia Forgas
Production Coordinator: Lynn O'Rourke
Compositor: Macmillan Publishing Solutions
Photo and Permissions Researcher: Christina Beamish
Art Director: Julia Hall
Cover and Interior Designer: Miguel Acevedo
Cover Image: Copyright Edward Burtynsky, Courtesy Nicholas Metivier Gallery, Toronto

4 5   13 12 11 10

Printed and bound in the United States of America.

This book is printed on recycled paper.

For Tina

—A.E.N.

Brief Contents

Contents

CHAPTER 3   Geographies of Population   88

CHAPTER 8   Agriculture and Food Production   350

Preface

A highly embroiled quarter, a network of streets that I had avoided for years, was disentangled at a single stroke when one day a person dear to me moved there. It was as if a searchlight set up at this person's window dissected the area with pencils of light.

Walter Benjamin, *One-Way Street and Other Writings*.
London: New Left Books, p. 85.

Most people have an understanding of what their own lives are like and some knowledge of their own areas—their neighbourhood, their city, their country. Yet, even as the countries and regions of the world become more interconnected, most of us still know very little about the lives of people in other societies or about the ways in which the lives of those people connect to our own.

The quotation from Walter Benjamin's book reminds us that to understand places, they must first be made meaningful to us. This book provides an introduction to human geography that will make places and regions meaningful. To study human geography, to put it simply, is to study the dynamic and complex relationships between peoples and the worlds they inhabit. Our book gives students the basic geographical tools and concepts needed to understand the complexity of places and regions and to appreciate the interconnections between their own lives and those of people in different parts of the world.

Objective and Approach

The objective of the book is to introduce the study of human geography by providing not only a body of knowledge about the creation of places and regions but also an understanding of the interdependence of places and regions in a globalizing world. The approach is aimed at establishing an intellectual foundation that will enable a life-long and life-sustaining geographical imagination.

The book takes a fresh approach to human geography, reflecting the major changes that have recently been impressed on global, regional, and local landscapes. These changes include the globalization of industry, the realignment of world powers, the upwelling of ethnic regionalisms on the heels of decolonization and the formation of new states, the physical restructuring of cities, the transformation of traditional agricultural practices throughout much of the world, and the emerging trend toward transnational political and economic organizations. The approach used in *Human Geography: Places and Regions in Global Context* provides access not only to the new ideas, concepts, and theories that address these changes but also to the fundamentals of human geography: the principles, concepts, theoretical frameworks, and basic knowledge that are necessary to more specialized studies.

The most distinctive feature of this approach is that it employs the concept of geographical scale and emphasizes the interdependence of both places and processes at different scales. In overall terms, this approach is designed to provide an understanding of relationships between the global and the local and the outcomes of these relationships. It follows that one of the chief organizing principles is how globalization frames the social and cultural construction of particular places and regions at various scales.

This approach has several advantages:

- It captures aspects of human geography that are among the most compelling in the contemporary world—the geographical bases of cultural diversity and their impacts on everyday life, for example.

- It encompasses the salient aspects of new emphases in academic human geography—geography's new focus on the social construction of spaces and places, for example.

- It makes for an easier connection between topical and regional material by emphasizing how processes link them—technological innovation and the varying ways technology is adopted and modified by people in particular places, for example.

- It facilitates meaningful comparisons between places in different parts of the world—how the core-generated industrialization of agriculture shapes gender relations in households both in the core and the periphery, for example.

In short, the textbook is designed to focus on geographical processes and to provide an understanding of the interdependence among places and regions without losing sight of their individuality and uniqueness.

Several important themes are woven into each chapter, integrating them into the overall approach:

- The relationship between global processes and their local manifestations

- The interdependence of people and places, especially the interactive relationships between core regions and peripheral regions

- The continuing transformation of the political economy of the world-system, and of nations, regions, cities, and localities

- The social and cultural differences that are embedded in human geographies (especially the differences that relate to ethnicity, gender, age, and class)

The preparation of an adaptation of *Places and Regions in Global Context* for the Canadian audience provided both an exciting opportunity and a formidable challenge. The opportunity was to make the book's exposition of the major themes of modern human geography more relevant to one particular audience—the Canadian one. The challenge was to do this without sacrificing the general approach, insight, and clarity of the original American text.

From the outset, it was clear that any worthwhile adaptation involved more than simply replacing a number of American examples with Canadian illustrations (for example, replacing Denver with Winnipeg, or Seattle with Vancouver). The reasons for this are obvious enough, but two can be highlighted here. First, since European contact, the country that we now call Canada has been developed according to a very different geographical set of principles than our neighbour to the south. This country's spatial economy, articulated to facilitate the export of staple commodities, has produced a geography of heartland–hinterland dependencies that contrast with ones developed on the basis of local manufacture for a large domestic market. Second, because Canada's population is made up of a far greater proportion of recent immigrants from a wider range of countries than is the population of the United States, it can be argued that Canada's interest in world affairs is of a far different nature. Many Canadians, for example, view the geographic processes of globalization through the prism of their local connections with other parts of the world—and not, as in an American case, from the geopolitical perspective of a superpower.

Therefore, to make the book truly relevant for Canadians, it was felt that an adaptation must also address the major themes that are of importance

- in understanding this country's geography
- in looking at the world from a Canadian perspective
- in interpreting this country's role in global affairs

These are the goals of this adaptation, and to the extent that they are met successfully, they will also each show how Canadian geography illustrates, in its own particular and nuanced way, the general principles that inform the study of human geography.

Thus, for the first Canadian edition, the entire text of *Human Geography: Places and Regions in Global Context* was extensively revised to meet the goals of adaptation, and a considerable amount of new Canadian-focused material was included. The main additions and their locations can be listed as follows:

- The development of geography in Canada (Chapter 1)
- A Canadian perspective on the world-system model (Chapter 2)
- Canadian population and immigration (Chapter 3)
- A discussion of Canadian medical geography (also in Chapter 3)
- Vernacular architectural regions in Canada (Chapter 5)
- The many dimensions of Canadian language geography (Chapter 5)
- Aesthetics and the design of Canadian gardens (Chapter 6)
- Canadian malls, ethnic restaurants, and the creation of "place" (Chapter 6)
- The economic impact of tourism in Canada (Chapter 7)
- Canadian agricultural geography (Chapter 8)
- A discussion of political geography from Canada's multicultural perspective (Chapter 9)
- Canada's electoral geography (Chapter 9)
- The Canadian urban hierarchy and its evolution (Chapter 10)
- The distinctiveness of Canadian cities (Chapter 11)
- The development of urban planning in Canada (Chapter 11)

The second Canadian edition of *Human Geography: Places and Regions in Global Context* continued the goal of expanding on topics relevant in Canada today by adding the following:

- Traditional Inuit methods of navigation (Chapter 1)
- Staples Thesis (Chapter 2)
- Case studies of two Canadian immigrant groups (Chapter 3)
    - The Petworth Emigration Society (1832–1837)
    - The Somali refugee community in Toronto (1991–2005)
- Migrant farm workers (Chapter 3)
- Fisheries decline and the changing meaning of "place" in Atlantic Canada (Chapter 4)
- The geography of religion in Canada (Chapter 5)
- Multiculturalism (Chapter 5)
- Mad cow disease (Chapter 8)
- The challenges of rural Canada (Chapter 8)
- Internet use in northern Canada (Chapter 12)

In addition, the following new topics of general interest were included:

- Lefebvre's theories of space (Chapter 1)
- Castells' notion of the Information Age (Chapter 1)
- Religion and the environment (Chapter 4)
- Exploitation of the world's fisheries (Chapter 4)
- The diets of hunter-gatherers (Chapter 4)
- Natural disasters (Chapter 4)
- Construction of gendered space (Chapter 5)

- Economic development and the environment (Chapter 7)
- Environmental security (Chapter 9)
- International debt relief (Chapter 12)
- The World Social Forum (Chapter 12)

The third Canadian edition of *Human Geography: Places and Regions in Global Context* provides a thorough revision of the entire text, in order to keep topics and data current and to improve the clarity of the text and graphics. New material on Canada and topics of relevance to Canadians were added throughout the text where relevant, and, in particular, include the following new topics:

- Changing recent birth rates in Canada and Europe (Chapter 3)
- New patterns of internal migration in Canada, 2001–2006 (Chapter 3)
- Deindustrialization and economic restructuring in Montreal in the context of Richard Florida's theory of the *creative economy* (Chapter 7)
- Aboriginal tourism (Chapter 7)
- British Columbia and the cruise industry (Chapter 7)
- "The 100-mile diet" (Chapter 8)
- The changing fortune of Canada's Prairie farmers, 2001–2008 (Chapter 8)
- Arctic sovereignty (Chapter 9)
- Homelessness: the "problem" as depicted by Vancouver's Downtown Eastside (Chapter 10) and possible solutions considered by Victoria (Chapter 11)
- "Sense in the city": an alternate approach to Canadian urban geography (Chapter 11)
- Computers and the virtual economy: the Ubisoft phenomenon (Chapter 12)

We are especially grateful to Dr. K. Bruce Newbold, professor of geography at the School of Geographical and Environmental Sciences at McMaster University in Hamilton, Ontario, and director of the McMaster Institute of Environment and Health (MIEH). Using the general theme of "Human Geography and Climate Change," Dr. Newbold has prepared six short essays for this edition that examine the consequences of environmental change, each focused on a different aspect of that general challenge and illustrating how the specific concerns of the individual chapters themselves both influence and are affected by wider issues of environmental change. These reflections may be read as "stand-alone" pieces, or as integral parts of the following chapters in which they are located:

- Human Geography and Climate Change: Population Displacement (Chapter 3)
- Human Geography and Climate Change: Population and Health (Chapter 3)
- Human Geography and Climate Change: Energy (Chapter 4)
- Human Geography and Climate Change: The Kyoto Protocol and Its Legacy (Chapter 4)
- Human Geography and Climate Change: Agriculture (Chapter 8)
- Human Geography and Climate Change: Climate Change and Social Actions (Chapter 12)

In addition, the following new topics of general interest have been included:

- The history of geographic thought: from Antiquity to the Enlightenment (Chapter 1)
- "New Geography," locational analysis and spatial science (Chapter 1)
- Geographers Jared Diamond and Carl Sauer on domestication (Chapter 4)
- Environmental change and civilization in the Mediterranean (Chapter 4)
- Hurricane Nargis and the Chinese earthquake, May 2008 (Chapter 4)

- Feminist geography and the geographical study of gender (Chapter 5)
- Stocks, resources, and reserves (Chapter 7)
- Replacement of technologies: the cellphone example (Chapter 7)
- Economic development: the role of war, peace, and security (Chapter 7)
- Weber's theory of industrial location (Chapter 7)
- Von Thünen's theory of agricultural location (Chapter 8)
- "Food miles" (Chapter 8)
- Decolonization: theory, history, and challenge (Chapter 9)
- Lagos and the shock city theory of Rem Koolhaas (Chapter 11)

These additions are supported by the inclusion of many new photographs, diagrams, maps, and graphics specially prepared for the Canadian adaptation.

The pedagogical structure of the text is unchanged since experience with previous editions has been very positive. The beginning of each chapter features a section on the main points, including those of relevance to a Canadian audience, that will be covered in the chapters. These main points are revisited at the end of each chapter to reinforce the most important points and themes from each chapter. All of the end-of-chapter exercises have been designed for Canadian students, and the website has been specially adapted for a Canadian audience. Lastly, each chapter now includes Canadian material in its list of suggested further readings.

Chapter Organization

The organization of the book is innovative in several ways. First, the chapters are organized in such a way that the conceptual framework—why geography matters in a globalizing world—is laid out in Chapters 1 and 2 and then deployed in thematic chapters (Chapters 3 through 11). The concluding chapter, Chapter 12, provides a coherent summary of the main points of the text by showing how future geographies may unfold, given what is known about present geographical processes and trends. Second, the conceptual framework of the book requires the inclusion of two introductory chapters rather than the usual one. The first describes the basics of a geographic perspective; the second explains the value of the globalization approach.

Third, the distinctive chapter ordering within the book follows the logic of moving from less complex to more complex systems of human social and economic organization, always highlighting the interaction between people and the world around them. The first thematic chapter (Chapter 3) focuses on human population. Its early placement in the book reflects the central importance of people in understanding geography. Chapter 4 deals with the relationship between people and the environment as it is mediated by technology. This chapter capitalizes on the growing interest in environmental problems and develops a central theme: all human geographical issues are about how people negotiate their environment—whether the natural or the built environment.

The six boxes by Dr. Newbold that examine this general theme are interspersed throughout the volume in order to emphasize the fact that the issue of environmental change intersects with all other concerns discussed in this textbook.

The chapter on nature, society, and technology is followed by Chapter 5 on cultural geography. The intention in positioning the cultural chapter here is to signal that culture is the primary medium through which people operate and understand their place in the world. In Chapter 6, the impact of cultural processes on the landscape is explored, together with the ways in which landscape shapes cultural processes.

In Chapter 7, the book begins to move toward more complex concepts and systems of human organization by concentrating on economic development. The focus of Chapter 8 is agriculture. The placement of agriculture after economic development reflects the overall emphasis on globalization. This chapter shows how processes of globalization and economic development have led to the industrialization of agriculture at the expense of more traditional agricultural systems and practices.

The final three thematic chapters cover political geography (Chapter 9), urbanization (Chapter 10), and city structure (Chapter 11). Devoting two chapters to urban geography, rather than a more conventional single chapter, is an important indication of how globalization increasingly leads to urbanization of the world's people and places. The final chapter, on future geographies (Chapter 12), gives a sense of how a geographic perspective might be applied to the problems and opportunities to be faced in the twenty-first century.

Features

To signal the freshness of the approach, the pedagogy of the book employs three different boxed features, "Visualizing Geography" "Geography Matters" and "Human Geography and Climate Change"; and more familiar pedagogical devices such as chapter overviews and end-of-chapter exercises.

Geography Matters: Geography Matters boxes examine one of the key concepts of the chapter, providing an extended example of its meaning and implications through both visual illustration and text. The Geography Matters features demonstrate to students that the focus of human geography is on real-world problems.

Visualizing Geography: Visualizing Geography boxes highlight key concepts of the chapter with a photographic essay. This feature helps students recognize that the visual landscape contains readily accessible evidence about the impact of globalization on people and places.

Human Geography and Climate Change: Each Human Geography and Climate Change box focuses on a different aspect of the general challenge of environmental change and illustrates how the specific concerns of the chapter both influence and are affected by it. These features help students realize how environmental change is a general theme that connects across almost all of the topics discussed in the chapters of the textbook, that issues of environmental concern affect various aspects of our daily lives, and show ways in which individual actions can shape the global environment.

Pedagogical Structure within Chapters: Each chapter opens with a brief vignette that introduces the theme of the chapter and illustrates why a geographical approach is important. A list of the Main Points that will be covered in the chapter follows this vignette. Throughout each chapter, key terms are printed in boldface as they are introduced, with capsule definitions of the term in the margin of the same page. These key terms are listed alphabetically, together with their location in the text, at the end of the chapter, and are compiled in the Glossary at the end of the text. Figures with extensive captions are provided to integrate illustration with text.

At the end of each chapter, there are five useful devices to help students review. First comes a chapter Conclusion that summarizes the overarching themes and concepts of the chapter. Next the Main Points of the chapter are listed again, but this time they are expanded to include a summary of the text discussion of each Main Point. Then there is a comprehensive list of Key Terms for the chapter, followed by a number of suggested Additional Readings on the topic of the chapter. Each chapter concludes with two sets of exercises, some internet based (On the Companion Website) and some more traditional (Unplugged). Both sets of exercises require students to put into practice several of the key concepts of a chapter.

As part of the set of On the Companion Website questions, you will find two new features for this edition. We have made our CBC Video Cases available to you online along with links to four thought-provoking video segments. CBC Videos and cases accompany Chapters 3, 5, 8, and 11. You will also be able to listen to and download five audio interviews our author, Alan Nash, conducted with four prominent Canadian human geographers. Interviews accompany Chapters 1, 4, 7, 10, and 12.

Supplements

The book includes a complete supplements program for both students and teachers.

For the Student

Companion Website: This site created specifically for the text, contains numerous review exercises (from which students get immediate feedback), chapter exercises to expand one's understanding of human geography, and additional internet resources for further research and exploration. We will also feature our CBC videos, two of which are new, and five entirely new audio interviews with human geographers that you can listen to and download.

CBC Videos: For Chapter 3, watch the CBC video, *Dying for Doctors—South African Doctors*, which highlights some of the cultural and economic issues of emigration and immigration.

For Chapter 5, watch the CBC video, *Inuktitut Survival*, which highlights some of the cultural and political issues of language use, decline, and retention.

For Chapter 8, watch the CBC video, *Made in Canada*, which highlights some of the issues around food's production, safety, and environmental impact.

For Chapter 11, watch the CBC video, *Big Thirst*, which highlights some of the challenges of environmental change for cities discussed in this chapter, particularly how the predicted decline of water supplies in the Prairies will affect both the urban and rural inhabitants of that region within the next 20 years.

Audio Interviews: For Chapter 1, listen to geographer, Dr George Lovell (Queen's University) talk about the history of geography.

For Chapter 4, listen to geographer, Dr George Lovell (Queen's University) talk about the cultural geography of the Maya in Guatemala, and the challenges geographers face when conducting field work.

For Chapter 7, listen to geographer, Dr Norma Rantisi (Concordia University) talk about her research on urban economies, Montreal's fashion industries, the benefits of a geographical training, and the challenges geographers face when conducting interviews.

For Chapter 10, listen to geographer, Dr Carlos Teixeira (University of British Columbia: Okanagan) talk about his work on the Portuguese community in Toronto, on urban social geography, immigration in Canada's cities, and the general value of a geographical education.

For Chapter 12, listen to geographer, Dr Quentin Chiotti (Pollution Probe) talk about the future environmental challenges that we face, and the reasons why a geographical education better enables us to understand such problems.

You can access our Companion Website in two ways. Visit us the traditional way by visiting **www.pearsoned.ca/knox**. You can also access our site by visiting us at **www.mygeoscienceplace.ca**—a 24/7 personal study portal. Our site provides an excellent platform from which to start using the internet for the study of human geography. You will need the access code that has been packaged with your copy of the text to register and log on to the Companion Website.

For the Instructor

Instructor's Resource CD-ROM (IRCD): All the supplements that instructors need to teach and test their students are now available in one easy-to-access CD-ROM. Instructors can view the supplement on their computers or print them out.

Included on the Instructor's Resource CD-ROM:

Instructor's Resource Manual: The Instructor's Resource Manual, intended as a resource for both new and experienced teachers, includes a variety of lecture outlines, additional source materials, teaching tips, advice on how to integrate visual supplements, answers to the end-of-chapter exercises, and various other ideas for the classroom.

Computerized Test Item File in TestGen Test-Generating Software: Pearson TestGen is a special computerized test item file that enables instructors to view and edit existing questions, add questions, generate tests, and print tests in a variety of formats. This test bank contains approximately 1400 questions, and includes multiple choice, short-answer, graphing, and scenario-based items. We identify a suggested answer, an associated learning objective, and a difficulty level of easy, moderate, or difficult for all questions. The Pearson TestGen is compatible with IBM or MacIntosh systems.

PowerPoint® Lecture Slides: The PowerPoint lecture slides include selected illustrations, maps, figures, and tables from the text.

Image Library: The Image Library will include selected illustrations, maps, figures, and tables from the text. The digital images will be available in PowerPoint.

CBC Videos: A one-hour and twenty minute video has been prepared to support this textbook. It features extracts from four CBC programs that examine the emigration of South African doctors to northern British Columbia, the future of Inuktitut as a living language, the real source of foods labelled "Made in Canada," and the problems of future water shortages in the cities and farms of the Prairies. Of relevance to Chapters 3, 5, 8, and 11, respectively, each video extract is supported by a video summary, study questions, and list of further resources, available on the Companion Website.

Conclusion

The idea for this book evolved from conversations between the authors and colleagues about how to teach human geography in colleges and universities. Our intent was to find a way not only to capture the exciting changes that are rewriting the world's landscapes and reorganizing the spatial relationships between people but also to convincingly demonstrate why the study of geography matters. Our aim was to show why a geographical imagination is important, how it can lead to an understanding of the world and its constituent places and regions, and how it has practical relevance in many spheres of life.

This adaptation now reinterprets these aims from a Canadian perspective by showing the relevance of a geographical imagination constituted in Canadian terms, and how a clearer understanding of geography is essential to comprehend not only the effects of global change on Canada but also this country's role in the world.

Acknowledgments

I am indebted to the following professors for their assistance, advice, and constructive criticism in the course of preparing this adaptation:

Jeff Boggs
Brock University

David W. Edgington
University of British Columbia

Michael Bunce
University of Toronto at Scarborough

Christopher Fullerton
Brock University

Brent Doberstein
University of Waterloo

Jocelyn Guindon
Dawson College

Michael Imort
Wilfrid Laurier University

Walter Peace
McMaster University

Bernard Momer
*University of British Columbia
Okanagan*

Michelle Rhodes
*University College of the
Fraser Valley*

Bruce Newbold
McMaster University

Robert J. Summers
University of Alberta

Bob Patrick
University of Alberta

Stephen Swales
Ryerson University

In addition, I would like to thank Pearson Education Canada for its commitment to this project, and especially the Toronto office team of Cathleen Sullivan (Acquisitions Editor), Kim Ukrainec (Marketing Manager), Eleanor MacKay (Developmental Editor), Imee Salumbides (Production Editor), and Cat Haggert (Copy Editor) for all of their help and support.

Finally, it is a privilege to record here my indebtedness to the many people who have helped me with advice and information over the period that the Canadian adaptation has been in preparation. In particular, I thank my Concordia University colleagues Robert Aiken, Jacqueline Anderson, Max Barlow, Pierre Deslauriers, Norma Rantisi, Richard Soare, Craig Townsend, and Patricia Thornton, who each gave unstintingly of their time and advice; and Damaris Rose (INRS), Clifford Hastings (Dawson College), Jane Barr (Commission for Environmental Cooperation), Quentin Chiotti (Pollution Probe), Robert Murdie and Carlos Teixeira (York University), and Iain Wallace (Carleton University), for their help with material in their fields of expertise. Sincere thanks are also due to Pauline Frost (Vanier College) who found me the map of Japanese–Canadian deportations, and to Philip Jones for his splendid photographs of Italian gardens. I am very grateful to the many undergraduate students who have sat through my classes and served as guinea pigs for the materials included in this adaptation, and to the community of Canadian geographers from whom I have learned so much, and am still learning.

In particular, I wish to thank all those who have been my teachers over the years, especially my old high school geography teacher Brian Alner, my undergraduate advisor Andy Cliff, my graduate supervisor Robin Glasscock, and Ron Johnston, Shirley Seward and David Frost, who have been valued mentors. Each of them has inspired many by their enthusiasm, guidance and integrity. I am delighted to acknowledge my thanks in this way.

The first edition of the Canadian adaptation was dedicated to the memory of Suzanne Mackenzie who first introduced me to the fascination of this country. The second edition was dedicated to the memory of my mother, who always encouraged my studies; my father, whose natural curiosity has taken me in many directions; and to my dearest Matina, who helped me to find my way again. Matina's encouragement has enabled me to complete this third edition, and it is therefore only fitting that it is dedicated to her. *Agape mou.*

Paul L. Knox
Sallie A. Marston
Alan E. Nash

About the Authors

Paul L. Knox

Paul Knox received his Ph.D. in Geography from the University of Sheffield, England. In 1985, after teaching in the United Kingdom for several years, he moved to the United States to take up a position as professor of urban affairs and planning at Virginia Tech. His teaching centres on urban and regional development, with an emphasis on comparative study. In 1989, he received a university award for teaching excellence. He has written several books on aspects of economic geography, social geography, and urbanization. He serves on the editorial board of several scientific journals and is co-editor on a series of books on World Cities. In 1996, he was appointed to the position of University Distinguished Professor at Virginia Tech, where he currently serves as dean of the College of Architecture and Urban Studies.

Sallie A. Marston

Sallie Marston received her Ph.D. in Geography from the University of Colorado, Boulder. She has been a faculty member at the University of Arizona since 1986. Her teaching focuses on the historical, social, and cultural aspects of American urbanization, with particular emphasis on race, class, gender, and ethnicity issues. She received the College of Social and Behavioral Sciences Outstanding Teaching Award in 1989. She is the author of numerous journal articles and book chapters and serves on the editorial board of several scientific journals. In 1994 and 1995, she served as Interim Director of Women's Studies and the Southwest Institute for Research on Women. She is currently a professor in, and serves as head of, the Department of Geography and Regional Development.

Alan E. Nash

Alan Nash received his Ph.D. in Geography from the University of Cambridge in England, and began his teaching career at the University of Sheffield. After moving to Canada in 1981, he taught at Queen's University, before becoming a research associate at the University of Western Ontario's Centre for Canadian Population Studies. From 1986 to 1989, he was a research associate at the Institute for Research on Public Policy in Ottawa. Since then, he has been a member of the Geography Department at Concordia University in Montreal, where he has served as Chair. His teaching focuses on human geography; his recent research activities and academic publications deal with the cultural geography of restaurants. From 2002 to 2005, he was Secretary-Treasurer of the Canadian Association of Geographers.

List of Maps

List of Special Elements

Geography Matters

Visualizing Geography

Human Geography and Climate Change

The following two features appear on the Companion Website.

CBC Video Cases

Interview with a Geographer

A Great Way to Learn and Instruct Online

The Pearson Education Canada Companion Website is easy to navigate and is organized to correspond to the chapters in this textbook. Whether you are a student in the classroom or a distance learner you will discover helpful resources for in-depth study and research that empower you in your quest for greater knowledge and maximize your potential for success in the course.

Companion
Website

[**www.pearsoned.ca/knox**]

Enter

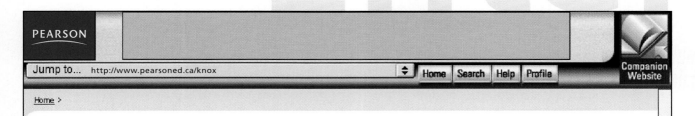

PEARSON

Jump to...   http://www.pearsoned.ca/knox   Home   Search   Help   Profile

Companion
Website

Home >

Companion Website

Human Geography: Places and Regions in Global Context,
Third Canadian Edition, by Knox, Marston, and Nash

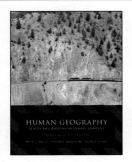

HUMAN GEOGRAPHY

The CW for the third Canadian edition has been thoroughly revised and updated.

Student Resources

This online study guide provides students with tools for learning course material. Each chapter may include:

- Chapter Objectives
- Quizzes
- Weblinks
- Flashcard Glossary
- Critical-Thinking Questions
- Thinking Spatially Questions
- CBC Videos and cases
- Audio Interviews

In the quiz modules students can send answers to the grader and receive instant feedback on their progress through the Results Reporter. In addition, this CW is enhanced with Gradetracker, which preserves the results from the quizzes you take for your later reference.

Instructor Resources on the Online Catalogue

The online catalogue provides instructors with additional teaching tools. The Instructor's Resource Manual, Test Generator, and PowerPoint Presentations are just some of the materials that may be available in this section. Where appropriate, this section will be password protected. To get a password, simply contact your Pearson Education Canada Representative or call Faculty Sales and Services at 1-800-850-5813.

1

Geography Matters

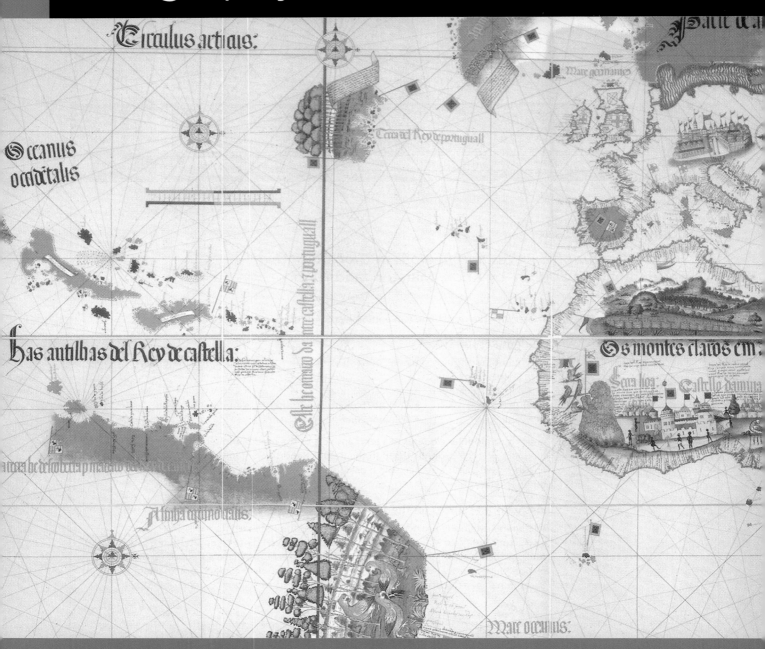

Portugal's claims to the New World   Alberto Contino's 1502 map shows how the New World was divided. Under the Treaty of Tordesillas (1494), Spain was given exclusive rights west of a line drawn 370 leagues west of the Cape Verde Islands. Portugal claimed all lands east of this line, including Newfoundland and Labrador (shown as a tree-covered island in the map's upper centre).

The study of human geography offers Canadians the opportunity to develop a better understanding of this vast country, to interpret the world more knowledgeably, and to grasp more fully the geographical processes that shape local, national, and global patterns. In today's world, where places are becoming increasingly interdependent, it is important to know something about human geography and to understand how places affect, and are affected by, one another.

At its simplest level, a knowledge of human geography helps us locate events that happen in Canada or elsewhere. Local events, such as the closure of a pulp mill in British Columbia or the increase in average temperatures in the Canadian Arctic, are obviously newsworthy in their own right. Events at an international level also attract attention from Canadians because so many of us have ties to other countries. We can understand each event more fully if we know something about the unique circumstances of each place—the characteristics of its culture and economy, for example.

All these events are also tied together by wider geographical processes (such as regional economic development or global environmental change), in which what happens in one place affects what happens elsewhere. An understanding of such wider geographical patterns enables us not only to interpret our daily news but also to set such events into a coherent analytic framework. We can then use these insights to interpret what is happening in Canada and the world.

Human geography is about recognizing and understanding the interdependence among places and regions, without losing sight of the individuality and uniqueness of specific places. Basic tools and fundamental concepts enable geographers to study the world in this way. Geographers learn about the world by finding out where things are and why they are there. Maps and mapping, of course, play a key role in how geographers analyze and portray the world. They are also key in introducing to others the geographers' ideas about the way that places and regions are made and altered.

MAIN POINTS

- Geography matters because specific places provide the settings for people's daily lives. It is in these settings that important events happen, and it is from them that significant changes spread and diffuse.
- Places and regions are highly *interdependent*, each filling specialized roles in complex and ever-changing networks of interaction and change.
- Some of the most important aspects of the interdependence between geographical scales are provided by the relationships between the *global* and the *local*.

- Human geography provides ways of understanding places, regions, and spatial relationships as the products of a series of interrelated forces that stem from nature, culture, and individual human action.

- The first law of geography is that "everything is related to everything else, but near things are more related than are distant things."

- Distance is one aspect of this law, but connectivity is also important, because contact and interaction are dependent on channels of communication and transportation.

WHY PLACES MATTER

human geography: the study of the spatial organization of human activity and of people's relationships with their environments

An appreciation of the diversity and variety of peoples and places is a theme that runs through the entire span of **human geography**, the study of the spatial organization of human activity and of people's relationships with their environments. This theme is inherently interesting to nearly all of us. Canadian magazines, such as *Canadian Geographic, Harrowsmith,* and *Equinox,* are popular because they draw on the wonder and endless fascination that Canadians have for this country (**Figure 1.1**). Yet, at the same time, many surveys show how little we really know about Canada or the world in general.

So, although most people are fascinated by different places, relatively few have a systematic knowledge of them. Fewer still have an understanding of how different places came to be the way they are or why places matter in the broader scheme of things. This lack of understanding is an important issue because geographic knowledge can take us far beyond simply glimpsing the inherently interesting variety of peoples and places.

Geographic knowledge is not, therefore, simply the result of famous explorers' exploits, and a task completed once a society considers all of the globe to be discovered—far from it. Each of us faces the task of learning about the world, and interpreting it for ourselves. We are each engaged in our own voyage of discovery, and each of us is therefore a "geographer." Our voyages may be very unspectacular, and the new places we find may be well known to others, but they are nevertheless part of our own geographic investigations and as meaningful to us as discoveries as anything for which Christopher Columbus achieved a wider fame or notoriety. This sense of our individual geographic imagination and creativity is well expressed by Miriam Waddington in the following lines from her 1992 poem "The Last Landscape" that now adorn the Canadian $100 note:

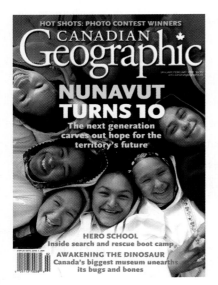

Figure 1.1   Geography's popularity
Canadian Geographic magazine is available on newsstands across this country and is sent out across the world to many subscribers. Focusing on Canada, it deals with the many geographical issues that affect Canada. Its popularity reflects Canadians' interest in the variety of landscapes and communities across this country.

Do we ever remember
that somewhere above the sky
in some child's dream perhaps
Jacques Cartier is still sailing,
always on his way always
about to discover a new Canada?

The importance of geography as a subject of study is becoming more widely recognized, however, as people everywhere struggle to understand a world that is increasingly characterized by instant global communications, unfamiliar international relationships, unexpected local changes, and growing evidence of environmental degradation.

Places are dynamic, with changing properties and fluid boundaries that are the product of the interplay of a wide variety of environmental and human factors. Dynamism and complexity are what make places so fascinating for readers of *Canadian Geographic* and *National Geographic.* They are also what make places so important in shaping people's lives and in influencing the pace and direction of change. Places provide the settings for people's daily lives. In these settings, people learn who and what they are and how they should think and behave.

Not only do these differences of emphasis result in rather different values, attitudes, and behaviours, but they also make it difficult for people raised in different settings to understand and appreciate one another. Moreover, people from different cultures will often have very different attitudes to spirituality, human relationships, religion, and other factors that contribute to making us who we are.

The Influence and Meaning of Places

Places exert a strong influence, for better or worse, on people's physical well-being, their opportunities, and their lifestyle choices. Living in a small town dominated by petrochemical industries, for example, means a higher probability than elsewhere of being exposed to air and water pollution, having only a limited range of job opportunities, and having a relatively narrow range of lifestyle options because of a lack of amenities, such as theatres, specialized stores and restaurants, and recreational facilities. Living in the central neighbourhoods of a large metropolitan area, however, usually means having a wider range of job opportunities and a greater choice of lifestyle options because of the variety of amenities accessible within a short distance.

Places contribute to people's collective memory and become powerful emotional and cultural symbols (**Figure 1.2**). And for many people, ordinary places have special meaning: a childhood neighbourhood, a university campus, a hockey arena, or a family vacation spot. This layering of meanings reflects the way that places are socially constructed—given different meanings by different groups for different purposes. Places exist, and are constructed by their inhabitants, from a subjective point of view. At the same time, though, the same places will likely be constructed rather differently by outsiders. Your own neighbourhood, for example, centred on yourself and your home, is probably heavily laden with personal

Figure 1.2   The power of place
Some places acquire a strong symbolic value because of the buildings, events, people, histories or myths, and images with which they are associated. For example, for many Canadians, the Peace Tower on Parliament Hill in Ottawa is a place that draws its meaning from its associations with important events in this country's political life. Other places in Canada evoke more general, but no less powerful, symbolic associations. For example, this picture of a canoe trip (on the Bloodvein River in Manitoba), has a much wider symbolic meaning because of its connotations with our images of a vast northern landscape and all the cultural values we associate with such a landscape. Indeed, for many people, especially those outside this country, such pictures are iconic of Canada and serve as a shorthand for tourist and other promotional literature.

meaning and sentiment. However, your neighbourhood may well be viewed very differently, and perhaps unsympathetically, from an outsider's perspective. This distinction is useful in considering the importance of understanding spaces and places from the viewpoint of the insider—the person who normally lives in and uses a particular place—as well as from the viewpoint of outsiders (including geographers).

Finally, places are the sites of innovation and change, of resistance and conflict. The unique characteristics of specific places can provide the preconditions for new agricultural practices (for example, the development of seed agriculture and the use of plow and draft animals, which sparked the first agricultural revolution in the Middle East in prehistoric times); new modes of economic organization (for example, the Industrial Revolution that began in England in the late eighteenth century); new cultural practices (the punk movement that began in disadvantaged British housing projects, for example); and new lifestyles (for example, the "hippie" lifestyle that began in San Francisco in the late 1960s). It is in specific locales that important events happen, and it is from them that significant changes spread.

The influence of places is by no means limited to the occasional innovative change. Because of their distinctive characteristics, places always modify and sometimes resist the imprint of even the broadest economic, cultural, and political trends. Consider, for example, the way that a global cultural trend—rock 'n' roll—was modified in Jamaica to produce reggae, while in Iran and North Korea rock 'n' roll has been resisted by the authorities, with the result that it has acquired an altogether different kind of value and meaning for the citizens of those countries. As an illustration, think of the way that some communities have declared themselves to be nuclear-free zones. They are, to use the slogan, thinking globally and acting locally. In doing so, they may influence thinking in other communities so that eventually their challenge could result in a reversal of established trends.

In summary, places are settings for social interaction that, among other things,

- structure the daily routines of people's economic and social life
- provide both opportunities and constraints in terms of people's long-term social well-being
- provide a context in which everyday, commonsense knowledge and experience are gathered
- provide a setting for processes of socialization
- provide an arena for contesting social norms

The Interdependence of Places

Places, then, have an importance of their own. Yet, at the same time, most places are *interdependent*, each filling specialized roles in complex and ever-changing geographies. Consider, for example, the way that Manhattan, New York, operates as a specialized global centre of corporate management, business, and financial services while relying on thousands of other places to satisfy its needs. For labour, it draws on analysts and managers from the nation's business schools, blue- and pink-collar workers from neighbouring boroughs, and skilled professional immigrants from around the world. For food, it draws on fruits and vegetables from Florida, dairy products from upstate New York, and specialty foods from Europe, the Caribbean, and Asia. For energy, it draws on coal from southwest Virginia to fuel its power stations. And for consumer goods, it draws on specialized manufacturing settings all over the world.

This interdependence means that individual places are tied into wider processes of change that are reflected in broader geographical patterns. An important issue for human geographers—and a central theme of this book—is to recognize these wider processes and broad geographical patterns without losing sight of the individuality and uniqueness of specific places. This means that we have to recognize another kind of interdependence: the interdependence that exists *between different geographical scales*, that is—as we will see in the next section—between different levels (or *scales*) of geographical analysis.

The Interdependence of Geographical Scales

In today's world, some of the most important aspects of the interdependence between geographical scales are provided by the relationships between the *global* and the *local* scales. The study of human geography shows not only how global trends influence local outcomes but also how events in particular localities can come to influence patterns and trends elsewhere.

We can illustrate this by taking the example of Canada's pulp and paper industry. *Global* effects, such as the European environmental movement's protests against clear-cutting in British Columbia's forests, adversely affect the industry *locally* by reducing demand for Canadian products. Indeed, the effect of reduced demand is felt throughout this country. Tree planters, forest managers, lumberjacks, and pulp and paper mill workers are all affected by the contraction of the industry in the wake of these actions. The economy of the small towns in which the mills are located will also feel the effects of such changes. Conversely, *locally induced* factors designed to boost lumber production in British Columbia could have *global* environmental effects if tree replanting were not practised to the extent it is and if the province's overall forest cover were reduced to a total area that could no longer maintain existing levels of carbon dioxide absorption.

Interdependence as a Two-Way Process

One of the most important tenets of human geography is that places are not just distinctive outcomes of geographical processes; they are part of the processes themselves. Think of any city neighbourhood, with its distinctive mix of buildings and people. This mix is the product of a combination of processes, including real estate development, the dynamics of the city's housing market, the successive occupancy of residential and commercial buildings by particular groups who move in and then out of the community, the services and upkeep provided by the city, and so on. Over time, these processes result in a distinctive physical environment with an equally distinctive population profile, social atmosphere, image, and reputation. Yet, these neighbourhood characteristics exert a strong influence, in turn, on the continuing processes of real estate redevelopment, housing market dynamics, and migration in and out of the neighbourhood. Places, then, are dynamic phenomena. They are created by people responding to the opportunities and constraints presented by their environments. As people live and work in places, they gradually impose themselves on their environment, modifying and adjusting it to suit their needs and express their values. At the same time, people gradually accommodate both to their physical environment and to the people around them. There is thus a *continuous two-way process* in which people create and modify places while being influenced by the settings in which they live and work (**Figure 1.3**).

Place making is always incomplete and ongoing, and it occurs simultaneously at different scales. Processes of geographic change are constantly modifying and reshaping places, and places are constantly coping with change. It is important for geographers to be sensitive to this kind of interdependence without falling into the trap of overgeneralization, or losing sight of the diversity and variety that constitute the heart of human geography. It is equally important not to fall into the trap of singularity, or treating places and regions as separate entities, the focus of study in and of themselves.

Figure 1.3 Place making People develop patterns of living that are attuned to the opportunities and constraints of the local physical environment. When this happens, distinctive regional landscapes are produced. This section of a topographic map and photo show part of the Qu'Appelle Valley, near Lumsden, Saskatchewan. As you can see, this prairie landscape is not flat. Largely the result of the most recent glaciations, it is made up of an undulating succession of low hills and shallow depressions (known as *sloughs*). Low rainfall, caused by the rain-shadow effect of the Rockies, originally supported a grassland ecology—one perhaps maintained by local fires set by Aboriginal peoples. Encouraged by a landscape that appeared so easy to clear for farming, thousands of nineteenth-century immigrants were drawn to Saskatchewan, establishing the regular pattern of farms and rectangular property divisions shown on the map. As the different place names and names for natural features show, these settlers had various origins ("Qu'Appelle"—French; "Longlaketon"—English). Occasionally, as here at Lumsden, rivers meander sluggishly through wide valleys (originally carved out by glacial meltwaters). Attracted to water, human settlement has focused on these rivers but generally avoids the valley bottoms with their risk of annual flooding following snow melt. Some settlements, because they are bridging points, have grown into larger centres.

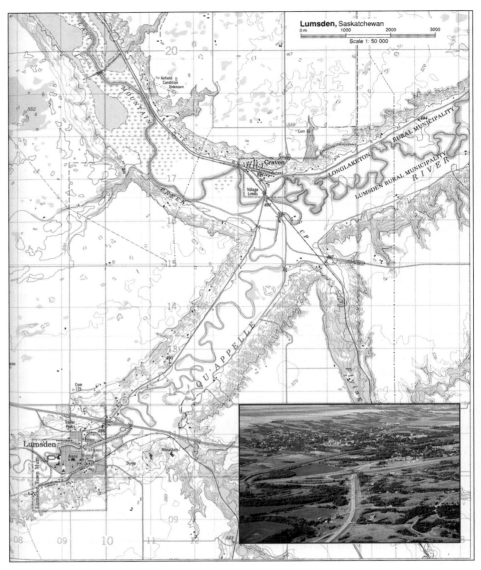

WHY GEOGRAPHY MATTERS

Geography matters because, quite simply, it enables us to understand our world and Canada's relationship with it. With such an understanding, it is possible not only to appreciate the diversity and variety of the world's peoples and places but also to be aware of their relationships to one another and to make positive contributions to local, national, and global development.

Given its importance, it is hardly surprising that we find an appreciation of what we would now call "geography" among the men, women, and children of all societies, whether from past eras or the present day, from Western or Eastern traditions, or from the developed or developing world. To take examples that we will consider in later chapters, the ancient Chinese practice of *feng-shui* paid close attention to the location of sites in the landscape and of "energy lines" across its surface, aided by the use of early lodestones. For thousands of years, Australia's Aborigines have celebrated their landscape in songs that record its sacredness and show how its mythological meanings can best be understood if places (all of which have associations with mythological creatures and creation stories) are visited in the order dictated by those stories. The Navaho align their houses (*hogans*) according to the cardinal directions and are just one of many groups with creation stories that describe specific territories being given to them.

As a further example, consider the navigational achievements of the Polynesians, who were able to travel around the Pacific Ocean aided only by their knowledge of star navigation (**Figure 1.4**) (for long-distance trips) and by an understanding of the behaviour of waves, clouds, and birds (when land was nearby). To help recognize wave activity around island groups with which they were familiar, the Polynesians constructed "stick charts," made from the ribs of palm leaves and cowrie shells. The palm ribs (or "sticks") indicated the particular pattern of waves and swells caused by winds, and the shells marked the position of the islands. As simple as these methods seem, great feats of navigation were undertaken. In an example that matches any modern achievement, Hawaii was first settled between A.D. 300 and A.D. 600 by Polynesians who had sailed from the Marquesas Islands, approximately 3200 kilometres to the south.

Moving around Canada's Arctic posed equally difficult but quite different navigational challenges for Inuit peoples. In his recent study of Inuit astronomy, John MacDonald of the Nunavut Research Institute at Igloolik writes that the

> impressive, almost uncanny ability of most Inuit hunters to find their way accurately over vast areas of frozen, seemingly featureless, terrain in virtually any weather, has long amazed and puzzled European visitors to the Arctic.[1]

Figure 1.4   Polynesian star navigation
Polynesian star navigation depends on an intimate knowledge of the night sky. In particular, it is important to know the relative location of stars that do not appear to move in the sky during the course of a night. These provide key reference points for navigators. As an illustration here, we consider a simple version of how Hawaii was first settled. The Polynesians, on setting out from the Marquesas Islands, took note of the stars that appeared immediately above them (Figure 1.4a). We can call these *reference stars* (in the illustration, only one is shown here for clarity). As the Polynesians sailed north, they observed that the reference stars appeared to shift their relative position in the sky, every night moving gradually farther southward. Once land was reached (in this case, Hawaii), the relative locations of the stars were memorized for the return voyage (in Figure 1.4b, note that the reference star now appears just above the horizon). To return to the Marquesas, the Polynesians had only to reverse the procedure. For local navigation—around familiar groups of islands—"stick charts" (Figure 1.4c) were used to record wind patterns and island locations.   (*Sources:* for (a) and (b): Author's summary based on Bishop Museum Planetarium, Hawaii; for (c): Adapted from Norman Thrower, *Maps and Man.* Englewood Cliffs, NJ: Prentice-Hall, 1972, p. 6.)

Polynesian star navigation

(a)

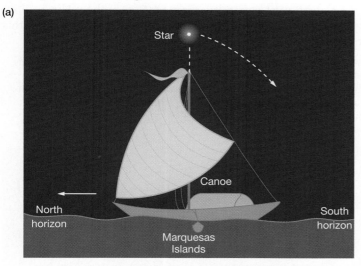

(b)

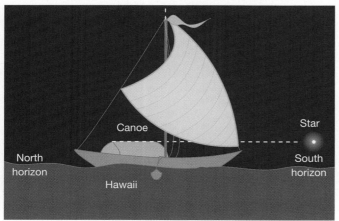

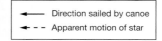

(c) "Stick chart" for local voyages

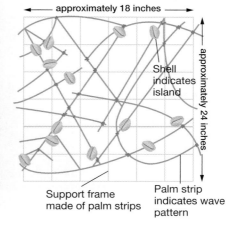

[1]John MacDonald, *The Arctic Sky: Inuit Astronomy, Star Lore and Legend.* Toronto: Royal Ontario Museum/Iqaluit: Nunavut Research Institute, 2000, ch. 6, p. 161.

This feat is extraordinary because the high latitudes of this region make star navigation impractical. (In the Arctic, the continuous daylight for five months of the year renders the stars invisible during that period.) The position of the sun cannot be relied on because over the period that it rises and sets in the polar realms, it appears to rise at all points of the compass (rather than only in the east, as in lower latitudes).

The fact that Inuit hunters did not use a rigorous system "in the sense usually applied to European or even Polynesian navigation" but rather relied on a "broad, innate-like approach to wayfinding, developed over generations and based on close and constant observation of the natural environment" only seemed to baffle European observers still further.[2]

In fact, as we now know, the Inuit developed an approach to navigation that relied on *all* the resources and cues at their disposal:

> When navigating, Inuit bring all their knowledge, experience, and senses to bear on every available environmental sign and circumstance including wind direction, the set of snowdrifts, landmarks, vegetation, sea currents, clouds, and various astronomical bodies [such as the Aurora Borealis]; clues are even derived from the behaviour of sled-dogs and other animals.[3]

Of particular interest is the use of snowdrifts to establish direction. In Igloolik, just west of Baffin Island, for example, the prevailing west-northwest winds form snow into drifts, which, because they are aligned to that wind's direction, provide the most dependable and frequently used navigational clue. These types of drifts are termed *uqalurait* (singular *uqaluraq*), after the elevated tongue-shaped form (or *uqaq*) found at their north-west extremity (**Figure 1.5**). Abraham Ulayuruluk, an Inuit elder interviewed by the Igloolik Research Centre in 1993, provides this description of their formation:

> During a blizzard the snowfall is usually soft. A type of snow mound, *uluangnaq*, is formed. The [prevailing wind] then erodes this mound, thereby forming a *uqaluraq*— a drift with a tip that resembles a tongue *(uqaq)*—which is pointed and elevated from the ground. . . . *Uqalurait* are formed by the *Uangnaq* [the west-northwest wind] . . . the strongest of all winds, at least in our homelands.[4]

Figure 1.5   Inuit snowdrift navigation
The Inuit make use of many aspects of their world for navigation. One of the most dependable and frequently used is the orientation of snowdrifts. These types of snowdrifts are called *uqalurait*, after the elevated tongue-shaped form found at their windward extremity.

[2]John MacDonald, *The Arctic Sky: Inuit Astronomy, Star Lore and Legend.* Toronto: Royal Ontario Museum/Iqaluit: Nunavut Research Institute, 2000, ch. 6, p. 162.
[3]Ibid, p. 161.
[4]Ibid, p. 174.

Directional information is then readily interpreted within the context of the Inuit's overall geographical knowledge of the local area to provide an exact location. Indeed, scholars have long recognized the Inuit people's ability to construct "cognitive maps," a skill aided by the detailed names given to landscape features and by the ability of the Inuit language, Inuktitut, to describe locations precisely by the use of certain word categories known as "localizers."

It is important to note here that this sophisticated grasp of location and navigation was not historically the preserve of Inuit men. A large amount of evidence attests to the importance of Inuit women's knowledge. For example, Sir William Parry was rescued on his second voyage of Arctic exploration (1821–1823) by a sketch map drawn for him by an Inuit woman called Iligliuk. "To her alone," John Barrow (secretary to the navy) later said, "is the merit due to the discovery of the extreme northern boundary of America."[5] Geographical knowledge in most early societies, as we might expect, is not the exclusive domain of either sex.

Turning to the Old World, the ancient Greeks were probably the first to demonstrate in detail the intellectual importance and utility of geographical knowledge, and their contributions were, in turn, built on by Roman scholars and leaders. During the Middle Ages—after the fall of the Roman Empire (A.D. 476) until around 1450—the most significant advances in geographical knowledge came from Chinese and Middle Eastern scholars. Then, in the fifteenth century, the focus of geographical scholarship shifted back to Europe (see **Geography Matters 1.1—The Development of Geographic Thought**). The timing is no coincidence: the foundations of modern geography were established in conjunction with the beginnings, in the fifteenth century, of a worldwide system of exploration and trade.

Geography and Exploration

The Portuguese, under the sponsorship of Dom Henrique (known as Prince Henry the Navigator), established a school of navigation and cartography and began to explore the Atlantic Ocean and the coast of Africa. **Cartography** is the name given to the system of practical and theoretical knowledge about making distinctive visual representations of Earth's surface in the form of maps. **Figure 1.6** shows the key voyages of discovery. Portuguese successes inspired other countries to attempt their own voyages of discovery, all of them in pursuit of commercial advantage and economic gain. Not to be left behind, the Venetian family of Cabot were recruited by Bristol merchants to explore Canadian waters as early as 1497 (**Figure 1.7**). These explorations enabled European navigators to develop an invaluable body of knowledge about ocean currents, wind patterns, coastlines, peoples, and resources.

Geographical knowledge acquired during this Age of Discovery was crucial to the expansion of European political and economic power in the sixteenth century. In societies that were becoming more and more commercially oriented and profit conscious, geographical knowledge became a valuable commodity in itself. Information about regions and places was a first step to control and influence, and this, in turn, was an important step to wealth and power. At the same time, every region began to be opened up to the influence of other regions as a result of the economic and political competition that was unleashed by geographical discovery. As the New World was being affected by European colonists, missionaries, and adventurers, the countries of the Old World found themselves pitched into competition with one another for overseas resources. Meanwhile, new crops, like maize and potatoes, introduced to Europe from the New World, profoundly affected local economies and ways of life.

cartography: the body of practical and theoretical knowledge about making distinctive visual representations of Earth's surface in the form of maps

---

[5]James P. Delgado, *Across the Top of the World: The Quest for the Northwest Passage.* Toronto: Douglas and MacIntyre, 2000, pp. 73, 76.

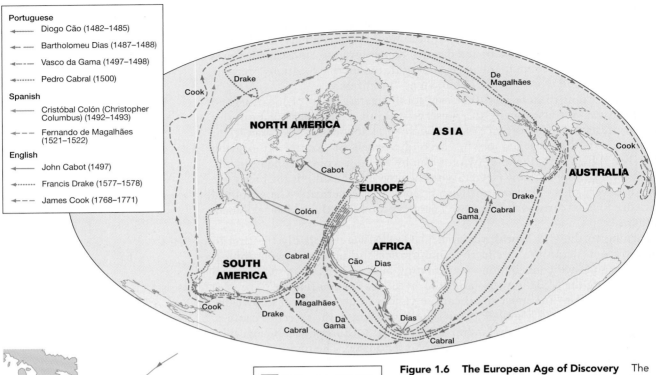

Portuguese
←——— Diogo Cão (1482–1485)
←— — Bartholomeu Dias (1487–1488)
←—·— Vasco da Gama (1497–1498)
←······ Pedro Cabral (1500)

Spanish
←——— Cristóbal Colón (Christopher Columbus) (1492–1493)
←— — Fernando de Magalhães (1521–1522)

English
←——— John Cabot (1497)
←······ Francis Drake (1577–1578)
←— — James Cook (1768–1771)

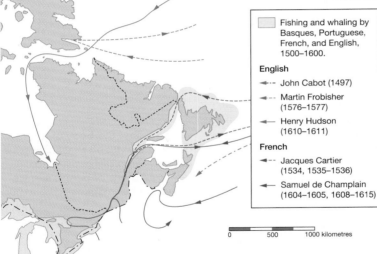

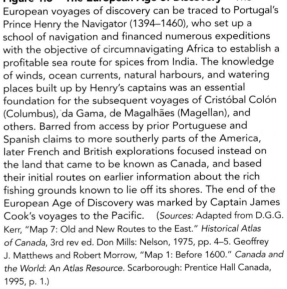

Fishing and whaling by Basques, Portuguese, French, and English, 1500–1600.

English
←·— John Cabot (1497)
←— Martin Frobisher (1576–1577)
←— Henry Hudson (1610–1611)

French
←·— Jacques Cartier (1534, 1535–1536)
←— Samuel de Champlain (1604–1605, 1608–1615)

0   500   1000 kilometres

Figure 1.6 The European Age of Discovery The European voyages of discovery can be traced to Portugal's Prince Henry the Navigator (1394–1460), who set up a school of navigation and financed numerous expeditions with the objective of circumnavigating Africa to establish a profitable sea route for spices from India. The knowledge of winds, ocean currents, natural harbours, and watering places built up by Henry's captains was an essential foundation for the subsequent voyages of Cristóbal Colón (Columbus), da Gama, de Magalhães (Magellan), and others. Barred from access by prior Portuguese and Spanish claims to more southerly parts of the America, later French and British explorations focused instead on the land that came to be known as Canada, and based their initial routes on earlier information about the rich fishing grounds known to lie off its shores. The end of the European Age of Discovery was marked by Captain James Cook's voyages to the Pacific. (*Sources:* Adapted from D.G.G. Kerr, "Map 7: Old and New Routes to the East." *Historical Atlas of Canada*, 3rd rev ed. Don Mills: Nelson, 1975, pp. 4–5. Geoffrey J. Matthews and Robert Morrow, "Map 1: Before 1600." *Canada and the World: An Atlas Resource*. Scarborough: Prentice Hall Canada, 1995, p. 1.)

Figure 1.7 The Cabot House in Venice John Cabot (1450–1498), the first European known to have reached North America since the Vikings, is believed to have made landfall in either Newfoundland or Cape Breton, Nova Scotia. Although his voyage was funded by Britain, Cabot was a citizen of Venice, and this photograph shows the house in that city where he is believed to have lived from the age of 11. A commemorative plaque on the house wall was placed by the Canadian government.

The Development of Geographic Thought

Although elementary geographical knowledge has existed since prehistoric times, the ancient Greeks were probably the first to demonstrate in detail the intellectual importance and utility of geographic knowledge. They showed that places embody fundamental relationships between people and the natural environment and that geography provides the best way of addressing the *interdependencies* among places and between people and nature. The Greeks were almost certainly among the first to appreciate the practical importance and utility of geographic knowledge, particularly in politics, business, and trade. Research reported as recently as July 2008 shows that a 2000-year-old device found in the Aegean Sea (and known as the *Antikythera Mechanism*) was likely used to predict solar eclipses. The word *geography* is, in fact, derived from the Greek language, the literal translation meaning "Earth writing" or "Earth describing." As Greek civilization developed, descriptive geographical writing came to be an essential tool for recording information about sea and land routes and for preparing colonists and merchants for the challenges and opportunities they would encounter in faraway places (**Figures 1.1.1** and **1.1.2**).

With the decline and fall of the ancient empires of the Greeks and Romans, however, geography and geographical

Figure 1.1.1 A reconstruction of one of the earliest maps of the world, by Anaximander of Miletus Almost no details remain of Anaximander's map, but from the written accounts of his contemporaries, we know roughly what it looked like. This version is attributed to the Greek geographer Hecataeus and dates from around 500 B.C. At about the same time as Anaximander drafted his map, Pythagoras was theorizing about the curvature of Earth's surface, speculating that Earth was spherical rather than flat. Some 300 years later, Eratosthenes (273–192 B.C.), who is supposed to have coined the term *geography*, was the first person to measure accurately the circumference of Earth. He also developed a system of latitude and longitude, which allowed the exact location of places to be plotted on the world's spherical surface. (*Source:* J.B. Harley and D. Woodward [eds.], *The History of Cartography*, vol. 1. Chicago: University of Chicago Press, fig. 8.5, p. 135.)

Figure 1.1.2 Ptolemy's map of the world Ptolemy began his *Guide to Geography* with an explanation of how to construct a globe, together with its parallels and meridians, and then showed how to project the world onto a plane surface. His map of the world stood for centuries as the basis for cartography. This example, published in 1482 by Leinhart Holle in Ulm, Germany, was typical of the basic map of the world in use at the time that Cristóbal Colón (Christopher Columbus) was considering the feasibility of going to China by sailing west.

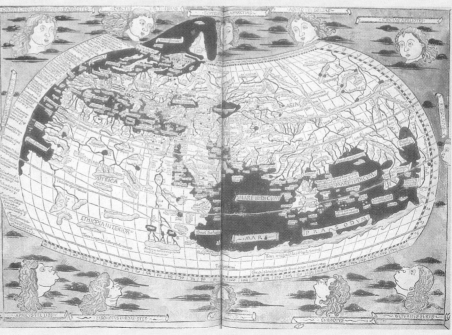

knowledge were neglected. In medieval Europe, from around A.D. 500 until after A.D. 1400, there was little use or encouragement of science or philosophy of any kind. Meanwhile, though, the base of geographical knowledge was preserved and expanded by Chinese and Islamic scholars (see **Figure 1.1.3**). Chinese maps of the world from the same period were more accurate than those of European cartographers because they were based on information brought back by imperial China's admirals, who are widely believed to have successfully navigated parts of the Pacific and Indian oceans. They showed, for example, that Africa was a southward-pointing triangle, whereas European and Arabic maps of the time always represented Africa as pointing eastward.

With the rise of Islamic power in the Middle East and the Mediterranean in the seventh and eighth centuries A.D., centres of scholarship emerged throughout these regions, including Baghdad, Damascus, Cairo, and Granada, Spain. Here, surviving Greek and Roman texts were translated into Arabic by scholars, such as Al-Battani, Al-Farghani, and Al-Khwarazmi. These Islamic scholars were also able to draw on Chinese geographical writing and cartography,

brought back by traders. The requirement that the Islamic religious faithful should undertake at least one pilgrimage to Mecca created a demand for travel guides. It also brought scholars from all over the Arab world into contact with one another, stimulating considerable debate over different philosophical views of the world and of people's relationship with nature.

This rich legacy is perhaps only now getting the wider attention that it deserves. For example, the travels of Ibn Battuta (1304–1377) have recently been recreated by Tim Mackintosh-Smith for a television documentary as *Travels with a Tangerine*. Ibn Fadlan's tenth-century journey from Baghdad to the Volga river has been examined in books by Richard Frye (2005) and Stewart Gordon (2008), and the astonishing story of al-Hasan al-Wazzan's *Description of Africa* (first published in 1550) explored by Toronto-based historian Natalie Zemon Davis in her 2006 study. (A Muslim from Granada and Morocco, al-Wazzan spent many years as a captive in Rome, and Davis shows how he endeavours to describe northern Africa to a medieval Italian audience in a way that he knows it can be comprehended.)

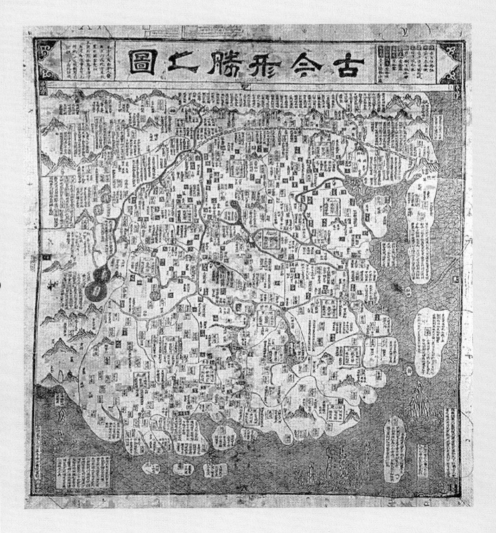

Figure 1.1.3 Early Chinese contributions to geography Chinese geographical writing dates back to the fifth century B.C., when Chinese writers began to compile travellers' guides. For a thousand years, between roughly A.D. 300 and A.D. 1300, cartographers slowly but steadily added to the body of knowledge about China and adjacent parts of Asia. This knowledge was summarized by Zhu Siben (1273–1337), whose map of China, prepared between 1311 and 1320, was a standard work of reference for more than 200 years. The map shown here, drawn by an anonymous cartographer in 1555 and based on Zhu's work, represents territory from Samarkand in Central Asia to Japan and from present-day Mongolia to Java and Sumatra in Southeast Asia. (*Source:* Archivo General de Indias, Seville, Spain. Plate 1, facing p. 324, in J.B. Harley and D. Woodward [eds.], *The History of Cartography*, vol. 2, bk. 2. Chicago: University of Chicago Press, 1994.)

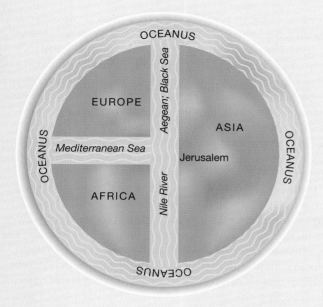

Figure 1.1.4 The medieval T-O map Maps such as these shaped Western Europe's view of the world during the Middle Ages. Traditionally these maps were oriented with Asia at the top of the diagram (a direction we now associate with "north") and Jerusalem in the middle.
(*Source*: This diagram is a simplified version of a T-O map prepared by the author to highlight basic generic features. Examples of T-O maps include Richard of Haldingham's *Mappa Mundi* of 1290 [now in Hereford Cathedral, United Kingdom].)

Despite such progress, geographical knowledge during the Middle Ages throughout Western Europe was dictated by the views of the Church, which taught that the world embodied Christian theology. This view, conveyed for example, in the form of what are known today as "T-O maps," stated that Jerusalem lay at the centre of the world and outwards from it radiated three continents (Europe, Africa, and Asia), separated by the waters of the Nile and Mediterranean (**Figure 1.1.4**). This is not to suggest that extensive travels were not undertaken by Europeans during this period, as the exploits of Marco Polo (1254–1324) clearly show, but they did not seek to challenge the prevailing geographical orthodoxy. Indeed, precisely because there was no mention of any other continent in this worldview, Christopher Columbus fully expected that he would reach China by sailing directly west across the Atlantic from Spain—a trip he believed lay easily within the reach of the small ships at his disposal because of his understanding of the ancient Greeks' calculations of Earth's circumference. Such information was was only then beginning to reach Western Europe from places such as the library of Alexandria (where Arab scholars had long recognized the value of such works), or Constantinople (from where a copy of Ptolemy's work was taken to Florence in 1400).

As we know, of course, Columbus was mistaken in his assumptions and one of the many repercussions of his voyage of 1492 was, perhaps ironically, to destroy the medieval European worldview upon which he had relied. In its place, the enormous amount of new geographical information about the world that now became available to Europeans as part of their Age of Discovery (see Figure 1.6) necessitated a new physical representation of the globe—provided to the next generation of explorers in 1569 by the Mercator projection (Figure 1.8). Not as easy, however, was a new set of theories which would make

sense of all of this new information, and the history of geographical thought over the succeeding centuries is marked by a search for such a framework—one that would do more than just record, but also interpret the world again.

Notable efforts in this search were made by Immanuel Kant (1724–1804) who agued that all knowledge could be divided into that which occurred in time (the *chronological*) or space (the *chorological*). Kant was an influential philosopher, and his belief in the intellectual importance of geography marked an important step in establishing it as a formal discipline. Certainly, geography (in common with many other disciplines) benefited from the more rational approaches to knowledge that characterized the Enlightenment, as University of Edinburgh geographer Charles Withers has shown in his 2007 study *Placing the Enlightenment*. The next significant steps to developing the analytical basis of this discipline were taken by the German geographer and aristocrat Baron Alexander von Humboldt (1769–1859), whose life's work emphasized the mutual interdependence between the people, flora, and fauna with their physical setting (he called it "the chain of connection"). In this way he showed how people have adapted to their environment and how their behaviours also affect the environment that surrounds them—in other words, he emphasized the mutual causality that exists among species and their environment.

Humboldt's considerable influence on the discipline is only now being fully realized, and work such as Aaron Sachs' 2006 book *The Humboldt Current* examines his influence on nineteenth-century American environmental thought. Certainly, his interest in studying how phenomena created distinctive regions was one important strand that led to the development of "regional geography" in the first part of the twentieth century, especially in France, the United Kingdom, and the United States.

A decisive development in modern geographical thought came in 1925 with a paper written by Carl Sauer, a professor of geography at the University of California, Berkeley. Sauer argued that landscapes should provide the focus for the scientific study of geography because they reflect the outcome, over time, of the interdependence of physical and human factors in the creation of distinctive places and regions. Sauer stressed that although everything in a particular landscape is interrelated, the physical elements do not necessarily determine the nature of the human elements. Sometimes they do, sometimes it is the other way around, and sometimes it is a bit of both. Sorting these relationships out and explaining how they constitute distinctive landscapes were the objectives of Sauer's geography.

Sauer's views received considerable support with the publication in 1939 of Richard Hartshorne's *The Nature of Geography,* which argued strongly that the focus of geography was "areal differentiation" (by which he meant the identification and description of regions). According to Hartshorne, the main purpose of geography was therefore the integration (or "synthesis") of information on a host of relevant phenomena to provide a total description of an area (or "region"), and the discipline's focus was, almost by definition, the uniqueness of place.

Such a view could not long be sustained as a rationale for a discipline—and certainly not for one, such as geography, that sought to provide for people's interpretations of their world. The solution came in the form of a paper by Fred Schaefer, published posthumously in 1953 in the *Annals of the Association of American Geographers,* in which he argued that the way forward was for geography to replace a search for the unique with the quest for generalization, to reject regional synthesis for spatial analysis, and to replace "mere" description with prediction (a hallmark of a true science, in his opinion). To do so required that geography become a "spatial science" and that it turn its attention to the underlying general processes that caused human activities to adopt the patterns that they did.

This clarion call brought in an era (known variously as "the Quantitative Revolution" or the "the New Geography") that focused on the "locational analysis" (or "spatial analysis") of human activities, and adopted the use of "scientific" research methods. (This kind of approach, using direct measurements of observable phenomena and established methods to verify hypotheses and construct universal laws and theories, is more formally known as *positivism.*) Important examples of locational analysis considered later in this book are Alfred Weber's theory of industrial location (Chapter 7), von Thünen's examination of agricultural location (Chapter 8), Christaller's analysis of settlement size and distribution (Chapter 10), and the various theories of urban structure discussed in Chapter 11.

Today, most geographers accept that such principles never actually work themselves out in pure form. There are always specific histories, unusual circumstances, and special local factors. The key issue thus becomes maintaining a perspective on general principles and broad outcomes without losing sight of the attributes of specific places. Recent developments in geographical thought have focused on understanding the uniqueness of individual places and regions within the context of other places and regions (and, indeed, the whole globe) and on understanding how general relationships play out within particular local settings.

These developments have introduced geographers to the study of *postmodernity* (which celebrates difference and rejects positivism's universal or general principles). They have also re-emphasized geography's traditional concerns with the environment and our place in it. In addition, they have opened up geography to a number of nontraditional approaches that pay more attention to difference and diversity in our use of space and place—the most important, perhaps, being the study of how gender differences affect and are affected by geography. Other examples include the examination of multiculturalism and identity, and the study of postcolonialism (a concept defined in Chapter 2).[6]

These advances, when added to the technological innovations that have seen the addition of geographic information systems (GIS) and remote sensing, have undoubtedly now made the study of geography one of the most exciting and rewarding pursuits in contemporary college and university curricula.

The growth of a commercial world economy meant that objectivity in cartography and geographical writing became essential. Navigation, political boundaries, property rights, and rights of movement all depended on accuracy and impartiality. Success in commerce depended on clarity and reliability in describing the opportunities and dangers presented by one region or another. International rivalries required sophisticated understanding of the relationships among nations, regions, and places. Geography became a key area of knowledge. The historical period in Europe known as the *Renaissance* (from the mid-fourteenth

---

[6]See, for example, Alison Blunt and Jane Wills, *Dissident Geographies: An Introduction to Radical Ideas and Practice.* Harlow: Prentice Hall, 2000.

to the mid-seventeenth centuries) saw an explosion of systematic mapmaking and the development of new **map projections** (**Figure 1.8**) and geographical description (**Figure 1.9**).

Throughout the seventeenth and eighteenth centuries, the body of geographical knowledge increased steadily as more and more of the world was explored using increasingly sophisticated techniques of survey and measurement. Some of the most important advances in scientific cartographic techniques took place in France, where Louis XIV appointed an official cartographer, Nicolas Sanson, to produce a set of accurate maps of French territory.

By the mid-nineteenth century, thriving geographical societies had been established in a number of cities, including Berlin, London, Frankfurt, Moscow,

map projection: a systematic rendering on a flat surface of the geographic coordinates of the features found on Earth's surface

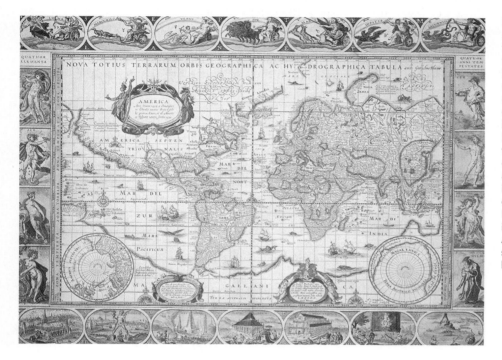

Figure 1.8   Renaissance cartography
Accurate mapping was important to the Europeans' ability to open up the world for commerce. Gerardus Mercator's world map was specially devised, in 1569, as a navigational chart of the world on which mariners could plot the exact compass distance between any two points as a straight line. The Mercator projection became very popular as a general-purpose map of the world. This example is from an atlas created by Willem Blau, published in 1635. The use of the term *atlas* for a collection of maps stems from Mercator himself, who used an illustration of the mythological figure Atlas holding the world on his shoulders to decorate one of his books of maps.

Figure 1.9   Dutch master Johannes Vermeer's painting *The Geographer* (1668–1669)   In Renaissance Europe, the study of geography not only contributed to the growth of scientific knowledge but also helped support European overseas expansion. Vermeer's geographer is surrounded by accurately rendered cartographic objects, including a wall chart of the seacoasts of Europe, published by Willem Blau in 1658, and a globe made by Jodocus Hondius in 1618.

New York, and Paris. By 1899, there were 62 geographical societies worldwide, and university chairs of geography had been created in many of the most prestigious universities around the world. Nevertheless, geography was interpreted first in narrow terms as the discipline of exploration and second as a servant of European expansion. Because the importance of geography was linked so clearly to European commercial and political ambitions, ways of geographical thinking also changed. Places and regions tended to be portrayed from a distinctly European point of view and from the perspective of particular national, commercial, and religious interests. Geography mattered but mainly as an instrument of colonialism.

The result was that geography began to develop a disciplinary tradition that was strongly influenced by ethnocentrism, imperialism, and masculinism. **Ethnocentrism** is the attitude that a person's own race and culture are superior to those of others. **Imperialism** is the extension of the power of a nation through direct or indirect control of the economic and political life of other territories. **Masculinism** is the assumption that the world is, and should be, shaped mainly by men for men. These trends became more and more explicit as European dominance increased, reaching a peak in the late nineteenth century, at the height of European geopolitical influence.

We should also note that most of the geographical writing in the nineteenth century was strongly influenced by environmental determinism, a view heavily influenced by Darwinian teachings on evolution. **Environmental determinism** is a doctrine holding that human activities are controlled by the environment. It rests on a belief that the physical attributes of geographical settings are the root not only of people's physical differences (skin colour, stature, and facial features, for example) but also of differences from place to place in people's economic vitality, cultural activities, and social structures. Environmental determinists thus tended to think in terms of the influence of the physical environment on people, rather than the other way around. The idea that peoples' social and economic development and their behaviour were fundamentally shaped by their physical environment was one that lasted well into the twentieth century. Geographers now regard it as misguided because it ignores people's ability to create their world in whatever environment they find themselves.

Interdependence in a Globalizing World

Today, in a world that is experiencing rapid changes in economic, cultural, and political life, geographic knowledge is especially important and useful. In a fast-changing world, when our fortunes and ideas are increasingly bound up with those of other peoples in other places, the study of geography provides an understanding of the crucial interdependencies that underpin all people's lives. One of the central themes throughout this book is the *interdependence* of people and places.

Another central theme of this book is globalization. **Globalization** is a process and a condition that involves the increasing interconnectedness of different parts of the world through common processes of economic, environmental, political, and cultural change. A world economy has been in existence for several centuries, and with it a comprehensive framework of sovereign nation-states and an international system of production and exchange have developed. This system has been reorganized several times. Each time it has been reorganized, however, major changes have resulted, not only in world geography but also in the character and fortunes of individual places.

The most recent round of reorganization has created a highly interdependent world. The World Bank has noted that "these are revolutionary times in the global economy"[7] and tellingly shows how globalization has affected the lives of

ethnocentrism: the attitude that a person's own race and culture are superior to those of others

imperialism: the extension of the power of a nation through direct or indirect control of the economic and political life of other territories

masculinism: the assumption that the world is, and should be, shaped mainly by men for men

environmental determinism: a doctrine holding that human activities are controlled by the environment

globalization: the increasing interconnectedness of different parts of the world through common processes of economic, environmental, political, and cultural change

---

[7]World Bank, *World Development Report*. Washington, DC: The World Bank, 1995, p. 1.

four very different people in very different places: a Vietnamese peasant, a Vietnamese city dweller, a Vietnamese immigrant to France, and a French garment worker.

Duong is a Vietnamese peasant farmer who struggles to feed his family. He earns the equivalent of US$10 a week for 38 hours of work in the rice fields, but he works full-time only six months of the year—during the off-season he can earn very little. His wife and four children work with him in the fields, but the family can afford to send only the two youngest to school. Duong's eleven-year-old daughter stays at home to help with housework, while his thirteen-year-old son works as a street trader in town. By any standard Duong's family is living in poverty. Workers like Duong, laboring in family farms in low- and middle-income countries, account for about 40 percent of the world's labor force.

Hoa is a young Vietnamese city dweller experiencing relative affluence for the first time. In Ho Chi Minh City she earns the equivalent of US$30 a week working 48 hours in a garment factory—a joint venture with a French firm. She works hard for her living and spends many hours looking after her three children as well; her husband works as a janitor. But Hoa's family has several times the standard of living of Duong's and, by Vietnamese standards, is relatively well off. There is every expectation that both she and her children will continue to have a vastly better standard of living than her parents had. Wage employees like Hoa, working in the formal sector in low- and middle-income countries, make up about 20 percent of the global labor force.

Françoise is an immigrant in France of Vietnamese origin who works long hours as a waitress to make ends meet. She takes home the equivalent of US$220 a week, after taxes and including tips, for 50 hours work. By French standards she is poor. Legally, Françoise is a casual worker and has no job security, but she is much better off in France than she would have been in Vietnam. Her wage is almost eight times that earned by Hoa in Ho Chi Minh City. Françoise and other service workers in high-income countries account for about 9 percent of the global workforce.

Jean-Paul is a 50-year-old Frenchman whose employment prospects look bleak. For ten years he has worked in a garment factory in Toulouse, taking home the equivalent of US$400 a week—twelve times the average in Vietnam's garment industry. But next month he will lose his job when the factory closes. Unemployment benefits will partly shield him from the shock, but his chances of matching his old salary in a new job are slim. Frenchmen of Jean-Paul's age who lose their jobs are likely to stay unemployed for more than a year, and Jean-Paul is encouraging his son to work hard in school so he can go to college and study computer programming. Workers in industry in high-income countries, like Jean-Paul, make up just 4 percent of the world's labor force.

These four families—two living in Vietnam, two in France—have vastly different standards of living and expectations for the future. Employment and wage prospects in Toulouse and Ho Chi Minh City are worlds apart, even when incomes are adjusted for differences in the cost of living. Françoise's poverty wage would clearly buy Hoa a vastly more affluent lifestyle. And much of the world's workforce, like Duong, works outside the wage sector, on family farms and in casual jobs, generally earning even lower incomes. The lives of all workers in different parts of the world, however, are increasingly intertwined. French consumers buy the product of Hoa's labour. Jean-Paul believes it is Hoa's low wages that are taking his job, while immigrant workers, like Françoise, feel the brunt of Jean-Paul's anger. Meanwhile, Duong struggles to save so that his children can be educated and leave the countryside for the city, where foreign companies advertise new jobs at better wages.

Geography in a Globalizing World

Recently, there has been a pronounced change in both the pace and the nature of globalization. New telecommunication technologies, new corporate strategies, and new institutional frameworks have all combined to create a dynamic new framework for real-world geographies. New information technologies have helped create a frenetic international financial system, while transnational corporations are now able to transfer their production activities from one part of the world to another in response to changing market conditions (**Figure 1.10**). This locational

Figure 1.10   The globalization of manufacturing industry   The globalization of the world economy has been made possible by the emergence of commercial corporations that are transnational in scope.

flexibility has meant that a high degree of functional integration now exists between economic activities that are increasingly dispersed so that products, markets, and organizations are both spread and linked across the globe. Governments, in their attempts to adjust to this new situation, have sought new ways of dealing with the consequences of globalization, including new international political and economic alliances.

The sheer scale and capacity of the world economy means that humans are now capable of altering the environment at the global scale. In addition to the spectre of global warming (a result of emissions of gaseous materials into the atmosphere), we also face the reality of serious global environmental degradation through deforestation, desertification, acid rain, loss of genetic diversity, smog, soil erosion, groundwater decline, and the pollution of rivers, lakes, and oceans (**Figure 1.11**).

All this adds up to an intensification of global connectedness and the beginnings of the world as one place. Or, to be more precise, this is how it adds up for the 800 million or so of the world's population who are directly tied to global systems of production and consumption and who have access to global networks of communication and knowledge. All of us in this globalizing world are in the middle of a major reorganization of the world economy and a radical change in our relationships to other people and other places.

At first glance, it might seem that globalization will render geography obsolete—especially in the more developed parts of the world. High-tech communications and the global marketing of standardized products seem as if they might soon wash away the distinctiveness of people and places, permanently

Figure 1.11   Environmental degradation   Many of the important issues facing modern society are the consequences—intended and unintended—of human modifications of the physical environment.

Industrial air pollutants include sulphur and nitrogen oxides, which form dilute acids in moist airstreams, leading to acid rain, which damages forests and pollutes lakes. Four thousand Swedish lakes are now devoid of fish because of acid rain.

Like this area on the southern shore, some 24 000 square kilometres (11 000 square miles) of former seabed in the Aral Sea have become a desert of sand and salt.

diminishing the importance of differences among places. Far from it. The new mobility of money, labour, products, and ideas actually increases the significance of place in the following very real and important ways:

- The more universal the diffusion of material culture and lifestyles, the more valuable regional and ethnic identities become. One example of this is the way that the French government has actively resisted the Americanization of French language and culture by banning the use of English words and phrases and by subsidizing France's domestic movie industry.

- The faster the information highway takes people into cyberspace, the more they feel the need for a subjective setting—a specific place or community— they can call their own. Examples are residential developments that have been carefully designed to create a sense of community and identity.

- The greater the reach of transnational corporations, the more easily they are able to respond to place-to-place variations in labour markets and consumer markets and the more often and more radically that economic geography has to be reorganized. Athletic shoe manufacturers, such as Nike, frequently switch production from one developing country to another in response to the changing international geography of wage rates and currencies.

- The greater the integration of transnational governments and institutions, the more sensitive people have become to localized cleavages of race, ethnicity, and religion. An example is the resurgence of nationalism and regionalism, as in the near separation of Quebec from Canada in 1995 and the emergence of the Lega Nord party in Italy in the early 1990s. Lega Nord (the Northern League) is a political party whose supporters in northern Lombardy and rural north-eastern Italy want to distance themselves from what they view as a distinctively different culture and society in the Italian South.

The reality is that globalization is variously embraced, resisted, subverted, and exploited as it makes contact with specific cultures and settings. In the process, places are modified or reconstructed rather than being destroyed or homogenized.

GEOGRAPHY IN CANADA

It could be said that geography has been practised by both women and men in Canada since people first came to this land. Of course, the needs placed on geographical knowledge have altered over time. The ways in which that knowledge has been enlarged and passed on to other generations has also changed. We now emphasize the university and college classroom, but we should not overlook the contributions made by earlier people to our understanding of this country's geography.

Pre-Confederation

A profound interest in geography considerably pre-dates the creation of Canada as a country in 1867. This country's Aboriginal peoples, European explorers, and immigrant settlers all had particular interests in acquiring geographical knowledge about the land they inhabited.

- Canada's Aboriginal peoples built a considerable store of information about this country's environments—knowledge necessary to support their population and to interpret their world. Maps, drawn from memory on the ground or in the snow, were an essential tool for nomadic peoples to cross this country's vast distances tracking food resources. Maps were also drawn by Aboriginal peoples on paper or animal skins to help the first Europeans find their way across Native lands (**Figure 1.12**). Ironically, however, despite this more permanent record, these widespread and well-developed maps were largely ignored by the history of cartography. (A welcome exception is the *Historical Atlas of*

Figure 1.12 Early Aboriginal maps
Canada's Aboriginal peoples possessed a well-developed sense of their surroundings. Evidence of this knowledge is preserved in the maps that they drew to guide Europeans on their voyages of "discovery" into this country. (*Source:* D. Wayne Moodie, "Indian Maps." *The Historical Atlas of Canada, Volume 1: From the Beginning to 1800.* Toronto: University of Toronto Press, 1987, plate 59. Reprinted with permission of the University of Toronto Press.)

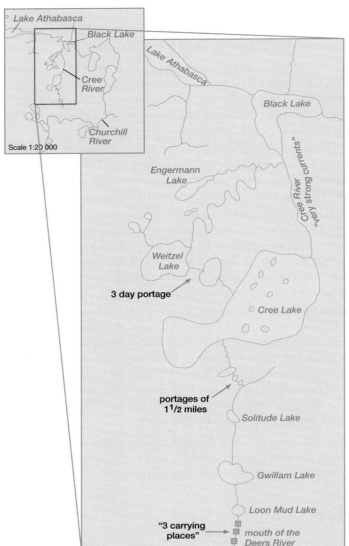

This map was drawn in 1810 by a Chipewyan Indian named Cot aw ney yaz zah. It provides essential information on canoe travel between Churchill River and Lake Athabasca. The map exaggerates scale to clarify important features, such as portages. It also conveys information on route choice: the original map indicated that those travelling north should take the fast-flowing Cree River and those travelling south should travel via Weitzel Lake to avoid struggling against the river's fast currents. The map was drawn for Peter Fidler of the Hudson's Bay Company, who (like all fur traders) depended on the local knowledge of Aboriginal peoples.

Note: The outline of the map preserves that of the original. Place names, however, have been modernized to aid in interpretation, and annotations by Peter Fidler have been omitted.

Canada, Volume 1, where a number of examples are reproduced.) As late as the eighteenth century, Aboriginal peoples were moving into lands freed up as glaciers continued their retreat in parts of the Yukon and Alaska, but this history had been largely overlooked until Julie Cruikshank's 2005 study examined the surviving oral testimony.

■ European explorers, keen to open up Canada as quickly as possible, often engaged in strenuous activity as they sought to find the best routes into the country, to record that information following Western cartographic practice, and to describe the new lands they had found. The French explorer Samuel de Champlain (1570–1635) illustrated his accounts of travels along the St. Lawrence River with his own paintings and maps. An *astrolabe* (a device used to measure latitude) he lost in the Ottawa Valley in about 1613 was subsequently found and is now on display in the National Museum of Civilization in Hull, Quebec. David Thompson (1770–1857), according to the *Canadian Encyclopedia,* "devoted most of his life to the study of geography and the practice of geography." An employee of the Hudson's Bay Company, Thompson mapped the company's vast western lands before they were transferred to Canada in 1869, and he mapped the entire route of the Columbia River.

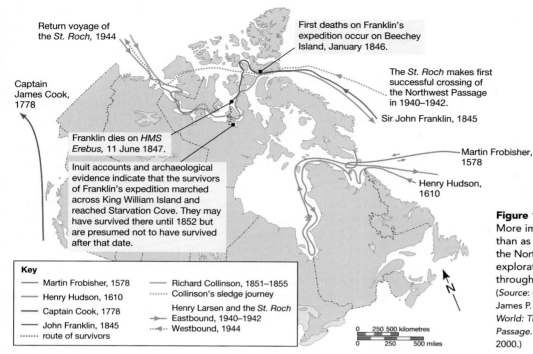

Return voyage of the *St. Roch*, 1944

First deaths on Franklin's expedition occur on Beechey Island, January 1846.

Captain James Cook, 1778

The *St. Roch* makes first successful crossing of the Northwest Passage in 1940–1942.

Sir John Franklin, 1845

Franklin dies on *HMS Erebus*, 11 June 1847.

Martin Frobisher, 1578

Inuit accounts and archaeological evidence indicate that the survivors of Franklin's expedition marched across King William Island and reached Starvation Cove. They may have survived there until 1852 but are presumed not to have survived after that date.

Henry Hudson, 1610

Key

—— Martin Frobisher, 1578	—— Richard Collinson, 1851–1855
······ Henry Hudson, 1610	········ Collinson's sledge journey
—— Captain Cook, 1778	Henry Larsen and the *St. Roch*
—— John Franklin, 1845	▶— Eastbound, 1940–1942
······· route of survivors	◀··· Westbound, 1944

0   250 500 kilometres
0   250   500 miles

Figure 1.13 The Northwest Passage
More important for its place in legend than as a practical route, the search for the Northwest Passage was a spur to the exploration of Canada's Arctic region throughout the nineteenth century. (*Source*: Compiled by author from maps in James P. Delgado, *Across the Top of the World: The Quest for the Northwest Passage*. Toronto: Douglas and MacIntyre, 2000.)

■ The Arctic has long held a special place in the imagination of Canadians, as writers Margaret Atwood and Rudy Wiebe have pointed out,[8] and the story of its exploration occupies an important place in the development of Canadian geography. A fascination with the Northwest Passage gripped Europe from the time of its first contacts with Canada, and many expeditions were launched to find the fabled route to the East (**Figure 1.13**). Few were ever successful, but Europe's geographical knowledge of the region increased through the attempts. Certainly, the 32 separate expeditions mounted between 1847 and 1859 to find Sir John Franklin, after his expedition party disappeared, resulted in a redrawing of Canada's north. Many scholars see Lady Franklin, Sir John's widow, as the single most important individual in this activity because she organized four separate expeditions of her own to find the vanished explorer.[9] As recently as August 2008, the Canadian government announced new efforts to locate Franklin's two ships in the High Arctic—an opportunity to stake Canada's claim to the sovereignty over this area at a time when rising oil prices and global warming have turned the attention of other nations toward the Northwest Passage.

■ The less daring but equally demanding work of detailed land surveying followed as the country was divided into and settled as farms and townsites, and lines of communications were opened up. Accurate work was essential but often impossible, given the dense cover of forest across the country. One account of survey work along the Rideau Canal (completed 1831) describes how surveyors would set fire to a distant tree to have an unambiguous point of reference for their sightlines.

■ Once they arrived, settlers expressed their own keen interest in knowing more about the resource potential and economic future of their farm, province, and

---

[8]Margaret Atwood, *Strange Things: The Malevolent North in Canadian Literature*. Oxford: Clarendon Press, 1995; Rudy Wiebe, *Playing Dead: A Contemplation Concerning the Arctic*. Edmonton: NeWest Press, 2003.

[9]The complete story is told by the director of the Vancouver Maritime Museum, James P. Delgado, in his book *Across the Top of the World: The Quest for the Northwest Passage*. Toronto: Douglas and MacIntyre, 2000. Data on expedition numbers are from pages 119 and 149.

country—interest that prompted government action. No less important was that these settlers, in their paintings and letters, began to record descriptions of the world they had made.

1870s to 1930s: An Immense Task

"Despite these promising beginnings," John Warkentin and Paul Simpson-Housley write in their account of the history of Canadian geography, "the task of geography remained immense in the 1870s. Knowledge of most parts of the country was thin and sketchy."[10] For the next 60 years or so, that immense task was in the hands of three main groups: the federal government, individual writers and artists, and interested citizens.

- Beginning in 1892, the federal government undertook Canada's first extensive topographic map series—a survey of the Prairies at the scale of 1 inch to 3 miles (2.5 centimetres to 4.8 kilometres), that is, 1:190 080. This was followed, in 1906, with the publication of the first sheet of a national topographic series at the scale of 1 inch to 1 mile (2.5 centimetres to 1.6 kilometres, or 1:63 360). In the same year, the first *National Atlas of Canada* was published, under the direction of James White, the government's chief geographer. White's office also had the responsibility of systematically recording all new place names, elevations, and natural features—of "cataloguing" Canada.

- Among the Canadian writers of travel and adventure books in this period were some who had great insights regarding the geographical development of Canada. Many of the themes they discussed are ones that remain important to this day, for example:
  - Canada's relations with the United States
  - the regional character of Canada
  - the European settlement of Canada
  - French-speaking Canada's relations with English-speaking Canada

  University economists and historians with an interest in geographical issues, such as Harold Innis and Donald Creighton, added the following themes:
  - the role of the St. Lawrence and the lower Great Lakes as an organizing axis of Canadian development
  - the importance of the **ecumene**, or total amount of habitable land, as a limit on agricultural settlement
  - the role of the frontier as a catalyst for development

  In some circumstances, a novel or poem described people's worlds more succinctly or captured underlying geographical truths not amenable to conscious analysis. Painters, such as the Group of Seven (1910–1930s), enabled Canadians to reinterpret the rugged landscape of the Canadian Shield by developing a new aesthetic for landscape painting. Emily Carr's paintings of Haida landscapes had a similarly profound effect on the way British Columbia's coastal forests and Aboriginal peoples were viewed.

- Individuals also grouped together to advance the cause of geographical research. In 1877, *la Société de géographie de Québec* was established, at that date only the third geographical society to be founded in all of North America. In 1905, the Champlain Society was founded to publish historical documents relating to Canada. The Canadian Geographical Society was founded in Ottawa in 1929

ecumene: the total habitable area of a country. Since it depends on the prevailing technology, the available ecumene varies over time. It is an important concept in Canada's case, since the ecumene is so much less than the country's total area.

---

[10]John Warkentin and Paul Simpson-Housley, "The Development of Geographical Study in Canada, 1870–2000." In Gary S. Dunbar (ed.), *Geography: Discipline, Profession and Subject since 1870.* Dordrecht: Kluwer, 2001, p. 282. This section draws substantially on their work.

(becoming the Royal Canadian Geographical Society in 1957) and began to publish *The Canadian Geographical Journal* (**Figure 1.14**) in 1930 (now *Canadian Geographic*).

1930s to Present: A Geography Truly Our Own

Geography had been taught since the late nineteenth century as a high-school subject in many parts of Canada. But it was not until the early part of the twentieth century that the discipline began to be taught at the university and college levels. Even then, recognition came very slowly. The Geology Department at the University of British Columbia was renamed in 1923 to include "Geography" in its title, and by the mid-1920s, geographers trained by the eminent French regional geographer Paul Vidal de la Blache lectured at the Université de Montréal. It was only in 1935 that the first fully fledged geography department in this country was established at the University of Toronto. Its founding head was Griffith Taylor, a geographer who had survived Scott's ill-fated Antarctic expedition of 1910–1912 and who had taught in Australia and Chicago before coming to Canada.

By 1951, the subject had grown enough that the need for a professional group was felt. As a result, the Canadian Association of Geographers (CAG) was founded with 65 members, and its journal *The Canadian Geographer* was established (**Figure 1.15**). The CAG fought strongly to get geography recognized as a legitimate subject in this country's universities. An important way to achieve this was to teach a geography that was "truly our own," in the words of Pierre Dagenais, an early president of the association. Consequently, the geography curricula of those years stressed such issues as Canadian regionalism and national distinctiveness.

On the occasion of the CAG's 50th anniversary, in 2001, there were departments or programs in geography in 48 Canadian universities and a nationwide membership of 750 professors. The subject's growth between these years was fuelled by two factors. First, there was a steady demand for geography graduates from the federal and provincial or territorial public services, which were eager to map Canada's resources and plan the post-war world. The development, by 1966, of the innovative technology needed for the Canadian Geographic Information System (CGIS) to inventory this country in detail is but one example of how government needs drew on university training and research. Indeed, close connections with Canada's public service have been an ongoing feature of Canadian university geography, and many geographers continue to be involved in public-policy issues.

Second, in keeping with a number of other newer disciplines (particularly those in the social sciences), Canadian geography benefited from the rapid increase in the number of universities in this country and the post-war desire to adapt university curricula to the challenges of the modern world. This led, in the 1960s and 1970s, to the recruitment of large numbers of professors from overseas. The influence of academics, trained mainly in the American and British geographical traditions, meant that a greater theoretical component was now added to Canadian geography. It also enabled Canadian geography to keep up-to-date with the latest developments in the discipline. Paradoxically, perhaps, it also led Canadian geographers, from the mid-1980s onward, to research work emphasizing this country's uniqueness. This is very much the spirit that informed the *Historical Atlas of Canada* project—a major collaborative research endeavour begun in these years involving many geographers across the country and resulting in the award-winning publication of a three-volume atlas, which has set new standards in both Canadian cartography and geography. In this continuing effort, geographers are increasingly turning to issues that now define Canada as a nation (such as immigration and multiculturalism) and to the geographies of Canada's cultural, social, political, and economic life.

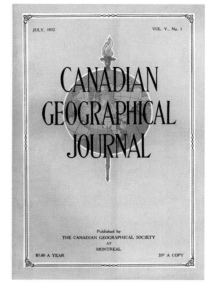

Figure 1.14 The *Canadian Geographical Journal* This issue of the journal was published in July 1932 and cost 35 cents a copy. It is clear that the publishers saw Canada, although an independent country, as still very much part of the British Empire (shown by the red shading on the globe behind the title lettering).

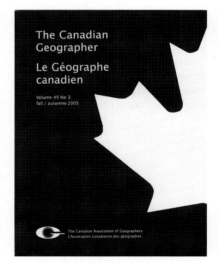

Figure 1.15 The *Canadian Geographer* Published since 1951, this journal is one of the leading outlets for the academic work of Canadian geographers and for geographers based elsewhere who write about this country.

Today, Canadian geography remains both a vibrant and an absorbing discipline for three main reasons:

1. Technological developments, such as GIS and remote sensing, have enabled geographers to deal with growing amounts of data in an increasingly sophisticated spatial manner.

2. Growing public concerns about environmental change have given heightened relevancy to many aspects of geographical research.

3. The addition of a number of new research themes in recent years has significantly increased Canadian geography's purchase on real-world issues. Examples include the introduction of feminist analysis and ideas of gendered place, the development of rural geography, and the growth of research into sustainable urban transportation.

One interesting way to get a sense of the character of today's geography in Canada is to look at the pages of the Canadian Association of Geographers' CAG *Newsletter,* a publication issued six times a year and designed to keep geographers up to speed with their discipline. Another would be to look at the contents of the association's academic publication *The Canadian Geographer* to get a sense of the latest research and methods of analysis that are used.[11]

Geographers at Work

Canadian geography graduates are employed in a wide range of occupations. This is because the skills that geographers possess are varied and include the abilities to integrate data from both the physical and the social sciences, to use statistics, and to write. Many continue to pursue such fields as urban planning and teaching and to serve in public administration at all levels. Geographers also find employment in marketing (using **geodemographic research**) or evaluating the most profitable location for stores, businesses, or factories. Increasingly, geographers have been employed in the environmental field (as industry consultants, researchers for non-governmental organizations, environmental impact analysts, or government scientists and field workers). Other skills, such as cartography, computer mapping, and the rapidly growing field of **geographic information system (GIS)** technology, have enabled many graduates to pursue careers in business and many other fields (see **Geography Matters 1.2—Geographic Information Systems**).

STUDYING HUMAN GEOGRAPHY

The study of geography involves the study of Earth as created by natural forces and as modified by human action. This, of course, covers an enormous amount of subject matter. There are two main branches of geography—physical geography and human geography. *Physical geography* deals with Earth's natural processes and their outcomes. It is concerned, for example, with climate, weather patterns, landforms, soil formation, and plant and animal ecology. *Human geography* deals with the spatial organization of human activity and with people's relationships with their environments. This focus necessarily involves looking at natural physical environments insofar as they influence, and are influenced by, human activity. This means that the study of human geography must cover a wide variety of phenomena. These phenomena include, for example, agricultural production and food security, population change, the ecology of human diseases, resource management, environmental pollution, regional planning, and the symbolism of places and landscapes. Regional geography combines elements of both physical and human geography. **Regional geography** is concerned with the way that unique combinations

geodemographic research: investigation using census data and commercial data (such as sales data and property records) about the populations of small districts to create profiles of those populations for market research

geographic information system (GIS): an organized collection of computer hardware, software, and geographical data that is designed to capture, store, update, manipulate, and display spatially referenced information

regional geography: the study of the ways in which unique combinations of environmental and human factors produce territories with distinctive landscapes and cultural attributes

---

[11]Both publications are accessible via the Canadian Association of Geographers' website at **www.cag-acg.ca.**

Geographic Information Systems (GIS)

Geographic information systems (GIS) have rapidly grown to become one of the most important methods of geographical analysis, particularly in the military and in the commercial world. A *geographic information system* is an organized collection of computer hardware, software, and geographical data that is designed to capture, store, update, manipulate, and display geographically referenced information. The software in GIS incorporates programs to store and access spatial data, to manipulate those data, and to draw maps.

The most important aspect of GIS, from an analytical point of view, is that they allow data from several different sources on different topics and at different scales to be merged. This allows analysts to emphasize the spatial relationships among the objects being mapped. A GIS makes it possible to link, or integrate, information that is difficult to associate through any other means. For example, using GIS technology and water-company billing information, it is possible to simulate the discharge of materials in the septic systems in a neighbourhood upstream from a wetland. The bills show how much water is used at each address. Because the amount of water a customer uses will roughly predict the amount of material that will be discharged into the septic systems, areas of heavy septic discharge can be located using a GIS.

The primary requirement for data to be used in GIS is that the locations for the variables are known. Location may be annotated by *x, y,* and *z* coordinates of longitude, latitude, and elevation, or by such systems as postal codes. Any variable that can be located spatially can be fed into a GIS.

Data capture—putting the information into the system—is the time-consuming component of GIS work. Identities of the objects on the map must be specified, as well as their location. Different sources of data, using different systems of measurement, different scales, and different systems of representation, must be integrated with one another. Changes must be tracked and updated. Editing of information that is automatically captured can also be difficult. Electronic scanners record blemishes on a map just as faithfully as they record the map features. For example, a fleck of dirt might connect two lines that should not be connected. All this means that although the costs of GIS hardware and software have fallen significantly (and will probably continue to do so), the costs of acquiring and updating reliable data continue to rise. Currently, for every dollar spent on GIS hardware, $10 must be spent on software and training and $100 on acquiring and updating data. As a result, it is only the more developed nations and the larger and more prosperous organizations that can take full advantage of GIS technologies.

Applications of GIS Technology

GIS technology can render visible many aspects of geography that were previously unseen. GIS can, for example, produce incredibly detailed maps based on millions of pieces of information—maps that could never be drawn by human hands. One example of such a map is the satellite image reconstruction of the land cover of part of Essex County in Ontario shown in **Figure 1.2.1**. At the other extreme of spatial scale, GIS can put places under the microscope, creating detailed new insights using huge databases and effortlessly browsable media.

Many advances in GIS have come from military applications: GIS allow infantry commanders to calculate line of sight from tanks and defensive emplacements, allow cruise missiles to fly below enemy radar, and provide a comprehensive basis for military intelligence. Beyond the military, GIS technology allows an enormous range of problems to be addressed. GIS can be used, for example, to decide how

Figure 1.2.1 Image of land cover
This image shows part of the intensive farming area of Essex County, south of Windsor, Ontario. GIS technology allows the interpretation of the satellite data to identify different types of land use. For example, Band 3 of the spectrum (near infrared) is displayed as red and indicates healthy, vigorous crops. In contrast, bare fields are shown as blue-white, water appears blue to black (depending on its depth), and the towns of Harrow and Kingsville are distinguished by their lack of colour.

best to route emergency vehicles to accidents, to monitor the spread of infectious diseases, to identify the locations of potential business customers, to identify the locations of potential criminals, and to provide a basis for urban and regional planning. To take another example, Environics Analytics, a Canadian GIS company, uses information from consumer surveys and censuses to develop likely behaviour "profiles" of postal code areas. These can then be used to target future marketing campaigns. See their website at **www.environicsanalytics.ca**.

Critiques of GIS Technology

Within the past decade, GIS technology has resulted in the creation of more maps than were created in all of previous human history. One result is that as maps have become more commonplace, more people and more businesses have become more spatially aware. Nevertheless, some critics have argued that GIS technology represents no real advances in geographers' understanding of places and regions. The results of GIS, they argue, may be useful but are essentially mundane. This misses the point that however routine their subject may be, all maps constitute powerful and influential ways of representing the world. A more telling critique, perhaps, is that the real impact of GIS technology has been to increase the level of surveillance of the population by those who already possess power and control. The fear is that GIS may be helping to create a world in which people are not treated and judged by who they are and what they do, but more by where they live. People's credit ratings, their ability to buy insurance, and their ability to secure a mortgage, for example, are all routinely judged, in part, by GIS-based analyses that take into account the attributes and characteristics of their neighbours.

Sources: This feature draws from the GIS page of the United States Geological Service (**www.usgs.gov/research/gis/title.html**) and from Chapter 7 in D. Dorling and D. Fairbairn, *Mapping: Ways of Representing the World.* London: Addison Wesley Longman, 1997.

---

region: a larger-sized territory that encompasses many places, all or most of which share similar attributes in comparison with the attributes of places elsewhere

of environmental and human factors produce territories with distinctive landscapes and cultural attributes. The concept of **region** is used by geographers to apply to larger-sized territories that encompass many places, all or most of which share similar attributes in comparison with the attributes of places elsewhere.

What is distinctive about the study of human geography is not so much the phenomena that are studied as the *way* they are approached. The contribution of human geography is to reveal, in relation to a wide spectrum of natural, social, economic, political, and cultural phenomena, *how and why geographical relationships are important.* Thus, for example, human geographers are interested not only in patterns of agricultural production but also in the geographical relationships and interdependencies that are both cause and effect of such patterns.

Basic Tools

In general terms, the basic tools employed by geographers are similar to those in other disciplines. Like other social scientists, human geographers usually begin with *observation*. Information must be collected and data recorded. This can involve many different methods and tools. Fieldwork (surveying, asking questions, using scientific instruments to measure and record things), laboratory experiments, and archival searches are all used by human geographers to gather information about geographical relationships. Geographers also use **remote sensing (Figure 1.16)** to obtain information about parts of Earth's surface by means of aerial photography or satellite imagery designed to collect data on visible, infrared, and microwave sensor systems. For example, agricultural productivity can be monitored by remotely sensed images of crops, and energy efficiency can be monitored by remotely sensed levels of heat loss from buildings.

remote sensing: the collection of information about parts of Earth's surface by means of aerial photography or satellite imagery designed to record data on visible, infrared, and microwave sensor systems

Once data have been obtained through some form of observation, the next important step is to portray and describe them through *visualization* or *representation*. This can involve a variety of tools, including written descriptions, charts, diagrams, tables, mathematical formulas, and maps. Visualization and representation are important activities because they allow large amounts of information to be explored, summarized, and presented to others. They are nearly always a first step in the analysis of geographical relationships, and they are important in conveying the findings and conclusions of geographical research.

At the heart of geographical research, as with other kinds of research, is the *analysis* of data. The objective of analysis, whether of quantitative or qualitative

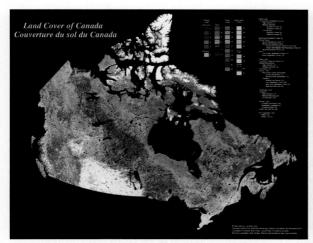

This image is based on data obtained from the SPOT 4 satellite. Prepared by the Canadian Centre for Remote Sensing, it shows the distribution of 31 different land cover types across Canada.

This Radarsat image shows the extent of the Red River flood on 27 April 1997. Areas of standing water are shown in blue. As can be seen, the floodway successfully diverted water around Winnipeg. Further south, toward Morris, localized flooding is evident. The interpretation of such images has enabled the Canadian Space Agency and the Manitoba Remote Sensing Agency to aid in flood preparedness.

Figure 1.16   Remotely sensed images   Remotely sensed images can provide new ways of seeing the world, as well as unique sources of data on all sorts of environmental conditions. Remotely sensed images can be helpful in explaining problems and processes that would otherwise require expensive surveys and detailed cartography.   (*Source:* Photos courtesy of Canada Centre for Remote Sensing, Natural Resources, Canada.)

data, is to discover patterns and establish relationships so that hypotheses can be established and models can be built. **Models**, in this sense, are simplifications of reality that help explain the real world. Such models require tools that allow us to generalize about things. Once again we find that geographers are like other social scientists in that they use a wide range of analytical tools, including conceptual and linguistic devices, maps, charts, and mathematical equations.

In many ways, therefore, the tools and methods of human geographers are parallel to those used in other sciences, especially the social sciences. In addition, geographers increasingly use some of the tools and methods of the humanities—interpretive analysis and inductive reasoning, for example—together with ethnographic research and textual analysis. The most distinctive tool in the geographer's kit bag is, of course, the map (see **Geography Matters 1.3—Understanding Maps**). As we have seen, maps can be used not only to describe data but also to serve as important sources of data and tools for analysis. Because of their central importance to geographers, they can also be objects of study in their own right.

model: often described as a theory or concept, a model is best thought of as "a simplification of reality" designed to help generalize our understanding of a particular process or set of phenomena; it can take the form of a diagram, equation, or simple verbal statement (such as a law), and may be used as a summary of past and present behaviour or to predict future events

Fundamental Concepts of Geography

The study of geography is easily distinguished by its fundamental concepts. *Region, location, distance, space, place, accessibility, spatial interaction,* and *scale* are eight important concepts that geographers have developed in their approach to the world. Although these concepts may be familiar from everyday language, they do require some elaboration. We have already encountered some of them in this chapter, and we will now be able to examine them more fully by considering them together as a group.

Region   As already noted, the concept of the region is used by geographers to apply to larger-sized territories that encompass many places, all or most of which share similar attributes in comparison with the attributes of places elsewhere. This definition is based on four important points:

■ *The concept of the "region" is used to distinguish one area from another.* If we think of regions that we know of in this country, we can see that the vast region known as the Canadian Shield is clearly very different from the Prairies or the Maritime provinces.

Understanding Maps

All maps are simplifications of the world because they cannot show everything and therefore must select what they do show. They also distort what they show because maps are usually two-dimensional, graphic representations that use lines and symbols to convey information or ideas about spatial relationships. Maps that are designed to represent the *form* of Earth's surface and to show permanent (or at least long-standing) features, such as buildings, highways, field boundaries, and political boundaries, are called *topographic maps* (see, for example, **Figure 1.3.1**). The usual device for representing the form of Earth's surface is the *contour*, a line that connects points of equal vertical distance above or below a zero data point, usually sea level. Maps that are designed to represent the spatial dimensions of particular conditions, processes, or events are called *thematic maps*. These can be based on any one of a number of devices that allow cartographers or mapmakers to portray spatial variations or spatial relationships. One of these is the *isoline*, a line (similar to a contour) that connects places of equal data value (for example, air pollution, as in **Figure 1.3.2**). Maps based on isolines are known as *isopleth maps*. Another common device used in thematic maps is the *proportional symbol*. For example, circles, squares, spheres, cubes, or some other shape can be drawn in proportion to the frequency of occurrence of some particular phenomenon or event at a given location. Symbols, such as arrows or lines, can also be drawn proportionally, to portray flows of things between particular places. **Figure 1.3.3** shows two examples of proportional symbols: flow lines and proportional circles. Simple distributions can be effectively portrayed through *dot maps*, in which

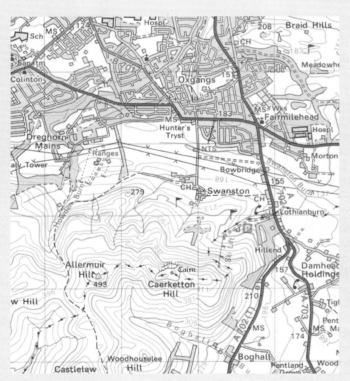

Figure 1.3.1 Topographic maps Topographic maps are maps that represent the form of Earth's surface in both horizontal and vertical dimensions. This extract is from a British Ordnance Survey map of the area just to the south of Edinburgh, Scotland. The height of landforms is represented by contours (lines that connect points of equal vertical distance above sea level), which on this map are drawn every 50 feet (15 metres), with contour values shown to the nearest metre. Features, such as roads, power lines, built-up areas, and so on, are shown by stylized symbols. Note how the closely spaced contours of the hill slopes are able to represent the shape and form of the land. (*Source:* Extract from Sheet 66, 1:50 000 Series, Ordnance Survey of the United Kingdom. Copyright © Crown copyright [87375M].)

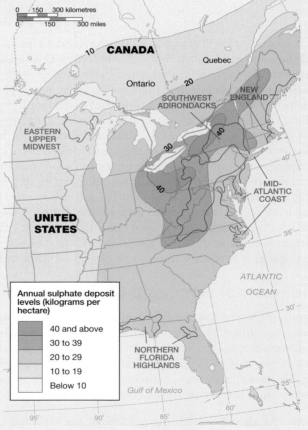

Annual sulphate deposit levels (kilograms per hectare)

- 40 and above
- 30 to 39
- 20 to 29
- 10 to 19
- Below 10

Figure 1.3.2 Isoline maps Isoline maps portray spatial information by connecting points of equal data value. Contours on topographic maps (see Figure 1.3.1) are isolines. This map shows air pollution in eastern North America. (*Source:* Reprinted with permission of Prentice Hall, from J.M. Rubenstein, *The Cultural Landscape: An Introduction to Human Geography*, 1996, p. 584. Adapted from William K. Stevens, "Study of Acid Rain Uncovers Threat to Far Wider Area." *New York Times*, 16 January 1990, p. 21, map.)

(a) Flow lines

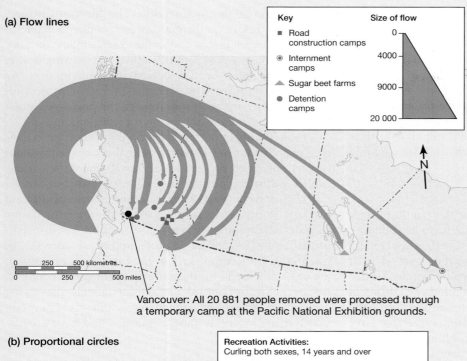

Key		Size of flow
■	Road construction camps	0
⊛	Internment camps	4000
▲	Sugar beet farms	9000
●	Detention camps	20 000

0 250 500 kilometres
0 250 500 miles

Vancouver: All 20 881 people removed were processed through a temporary camp at the Pacific National Exhibition grounds.

(b) Proportional circles

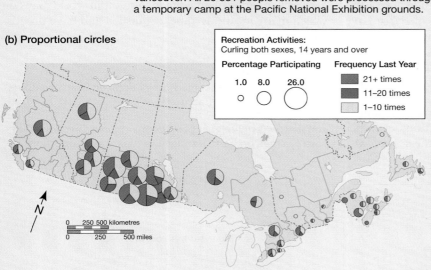

Recreation Activities:
Curling both sexes, 14 years and over

Percentage Participating
1.0 8.0 26.0
○ ○ ◯

Frequency Last Year
21+ times
11–20 times
1–10 times

0 250 500 kilometres
0 250 500 miles

Figure 1.3.3 Two examples of proportional symbols in thematic mapping   (a) *Flow lines*. In such maps, the magnitude of movement (or flow) to individual places or regions is expressed as a proportion of the total movement. This particular map shows the 1942 forced movement of 20 881 Japanese Canadians from their homes in coastal British Columbia to detention camps in the province's interior and to sugar beet farms in Alberta and Manitoba. (b) *Proportional circles*. In these types of maps, the size of the circles is proportional to the quantity or phenomenon being mapped. This particular map shows the percentage of people across the country who curled in 1975.   (*Sources:* (a) Map prepared by Sean Dougherty, Vanier College, Montreal. (b) Douglas J. Dudycha, Stephen L.J. Smith, Terry O. Stewart, and Barry D. McPherson, *The Canadian Atlas of Recreation and Exercise.* Department of Geography, University of Waterloo, 1983: Department of Geography Publication Series No. 21, p. 37.)

a single dot or other symbol represents a specified number of occurrences of some particular phenomenon or event (an example used later in this book is Figure 4.21). Yet another device is the *choropleth map*, in which tonal shadings are graduated to reflect area variations in numbers, frequencies, or densities (an example used later in this book is Figure 3.12). As such, choropleth maps use data that relate to the specific areas, or spatial units of measurement, that compose the map and from which the relevant information has been collected or recorded. Known more generally by geographers as **areal units**, these units may comprise areas as small as a city block or as large as a province or territory. Most large areal units of measurement are built up from smaller component

units. For example, Statistics Canada data for *Census Metropolitan Areas* (or CMAs, which are defined as having an urban core population of at least 100 000 people) are built up (or *spatially aggregated*) from small component areal units, known as *census tracts*, which individually comprise between 2500 and 8000 people. Finally, thematic maps can be based on *located charts*, in which graphs or charts are located by place or region. In this way, a tremendous amount of information can be conveyed in one single map.

Map Scales

A *map scale* is the ratio between linear distance on a map and linear distance on Earth's surface. It is usually expressed in terms of corresponding lengths, as in "one centimetre equals one kilometre," or as a *representative fraction* (in this case, 1/100 000) or ratio (1:100 000). *Small-scale* maps are maps based on small

areal units: spatial units of measurement, such as a city block or province, used for recording statistics

31

representative fractions (for example, 1/1 000 000 or 1/10 000 000). Small-scale maps cover a large part of Earth's surface on the printed page. A map drawn on this page to the scale of 1:10 000 000 would easily cover a third of Canada; a map drawn to the scale of 1:16 000 000 would cover the whole of Europe. *Large-scale* maps are maps based on larger representative fractions (e.g., 1/25 000 or 1/10 000). A map drawn on this page to the scale 1:10 000 would cover a typical suburban subdivision; a map drawn to the scale of 1:1000 would cover just a block or two of it.

Map Projections

A map projection is a systematic rendering on a flat surface of the geographical coordinates of the features found on Earth's surface. Because Earth is not a perfect sphere and its surface is curved, it is impossible to represent on a flat plane, sheet of paper, or monitor screen without some distortion. Cartographers have devised a number of different techniques of projecting latitude and longitude onto a flat surface, and the resulting representations of Earth have both advantages and disadvantages. None of them can represent distance correctly in all directions, though many can represent compass bearings or area without distortion. The choice of map projection depends largely on the purpose of the map.

Projections on which compass directions are rendered accurately are known as **conformal projections.** Another property of conformal projections is that the scale of the map is the same in any direction. The Mercator projection (**Figure 1.3.4**), for example, preserves directional relationships between places, and so the exact compass distance between any two points can be plotted as a straight line. As a result, it has been widely used in navigation. As Figure 1.3.4 shows, however, the Mercator projection distorts area more and more toward the poles—so much so that the poles cannot be shown as single points.

Projections that portray areas on Earth's surface in their true proportions are known as **equal-area** or **equivalent projections.** Such projections are used where the cartographer wants to compare and contrast distributions on Earth's surface, the relative area of different types of land use, for example. Examples of equal-area projections include Bartholomew's Nordic projection (used in Figure 1.6) and the Mollweide projection (see Figure 1.3.4). Equal-area projections, such as the Mollweide projection, are especially useful for thematic maps showing economic, demographic, or cultural data. Unfortunately, preserving accuracy in terms of area tends to result in world maps on which many locations appear squished and have unsatisfactory outlines.

conformal projections: map projections on which compass bearings are rendered accurately

equal-area (equivalent) projections: map projections that portray areas on Earth's surface in their true proportions

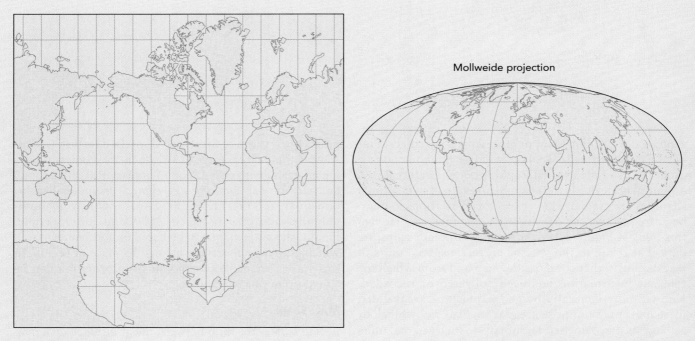

Mollweide projection

Mercator projection

Figure 1.3.4 Comparison of map projections Different map projections have different properties. On the Mercator projection, compass directions between any two points are true, and the shapes of land masses are true, but their relative sizes are distorted. On the Mollweide projection, relative sizes are true, but shapes are distorted.

32

For some applications, aesthetic appearance is more important than conformality, equivalence, or equidistance, and so cartographers have devised a number of other projections. Examples include the Times projection, which is used in many world atlases, and the Robinson projection, which is used by the National Geographic Society in many of its publications. The Robinson projection (**Figure 1.3.5**) is a compromise projection that distorts both area and directional relationships but provides a general-purpose world map. There are also political considerations. Countries may appear larger and therefore more important on one projection rather than on another. The Peters projection, for example (**Figure 1.3.6**), is a deliberate attempt to give prominence to the underdeveloped countries of the equatorial regions and the Southern Hemisphere. As such, it was officially adopted by the World Council of Churches, numerous agencies of the United Nations, and other international institutions. Its unusual shapes give it a shock value that gets people's attention. For some, however, its unusual shapes are ugly: it has been likened to laundry hung out to dry.

In this book, we sometimes use another striking projection, the Dymaxion projection devised by Buckminster Fuller (**Figure 1.3.7**). Fuller was a prominent modernist architect and industrial designer who wanted to produce a map of the world with no significant distortion to any of the major land masses. The Dymaxion projection does this, though it produces a world that at first may seem disorienting. This is not necessarily such a bad thing, for it can force us to take a fresh look at the world and at the relationships among places. Because Europe, North America, and Japan are all located toward the centre of this map projection, it is particularly useful for illustrating two of the central themes of this book: the relationships among these prosperous regions and the relationships between this prosperous core group and the less prosperous, peripheral countries of the world. Fuller's projection shows the economically peripheral countries of the world as being cartographically peripheral, too.

One particular kind of map projection that is sometimes used in small-scale thematic maps is the *cartogram*. In this kind of projection, space is transformed according to statistical factors, with the largest mapping units representing the greatest statistical values. **Figure 1.3.8** shows a cartogram of the world in which countries are represented as proportional to their population. This sort of projection is particularly effective in helping to visualize relative inequalities among the world's populations.

Finally, the advent of computer graphics has made it possible for cartographers to move beyond the use of maps as two-dimensional representations of Earth's surface.

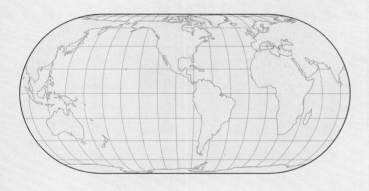

Figure 1.3.5   The Robinson projection   On the Robinson projection, distance, direction, area, and shape are all distorted in an attempt to balance the properties of the map. It is designed purely for appearance and is best used for thematic and reference maps at the world scale.   (*Source:* Reprinted with permission of Prentice Hall from E.F. Bergman, *Human Geography: Cultures, Connections, and Landscapes,* © 1995, p. 12.)

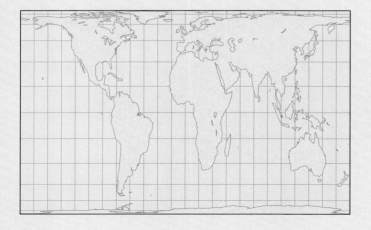

Figure 1.3.6   The Peters projection   This equal-area projection is an attempt to offer an alternative to traditional projections, which exaggerate the size and apparent importance of the higher latitudes—that is, the world's core regions—and so promote the "Europeanization" of Earth. While it has been adopted by the World Council of Churches, various agencies of the United Nations, and other international institutions, it has been criticized by cartographers on the grounds of aesthetics: one of the consequences of equal-area projections is that they distort the shape of land masses.   (*Source:* Reprinted with permission of Prentice Hall from E.F. Bergman, *Human Geography: Cultures, Connections, and Landscapes,* © 1995, p. 13.)

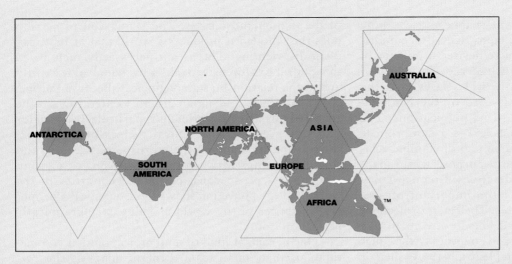

Figure 1.3.7 Fuller's Dymaxion projection This striking map projection was designed by Buckminster Fuller (1895–1983). As this figure shows, Fuller achieved his objective of creating a map with the minimum of distortion to the shape of the world's major land masses by dividing the globe into triangular areas. Those areas not encompassing major land masses were cut away, allowing the remainder of the globe to be "unfolded" into a flat projection. (*Source:* Buckminster Fuller Institute and Dymaxion Map Design, Santa Barbara, CA. The word *Dymaxion* and the Fuller Projection Dymaxion™ Map design are trademarks of the Buckminster Fuller Institute, Santa Barbara, California, © 1938, 1967 & 1992. All rights reserved).

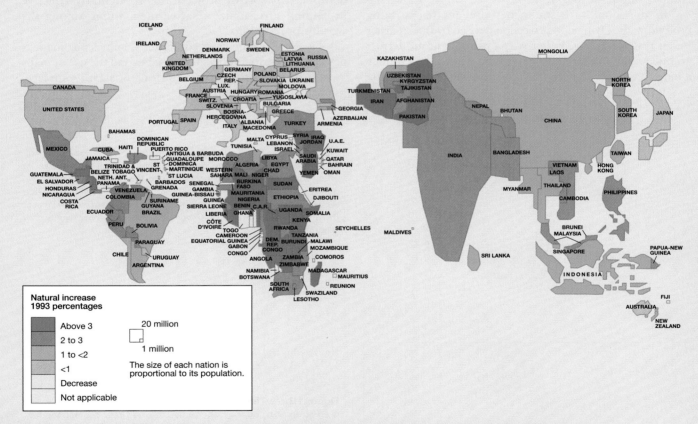

Figure 1.3.8 Example of a cartogram In a cartogram, space is distorted to emphasize a particular attribute of places or regions. This example shows the relative sizes of countries based on their populations rather than their areas; the cartographers have maintained the shape of each country as closely as possible to make the map easier to read. As you can see, population-based cartograms are very effective in demonstrating spatial inequality.
(*Source:* M. Kidron and R. Segal [eds.], *The State of the World Atlas*, rev. 5th ed. London: Penguin Reference, 1995, pp. 28–29.)

Computer software that renders three-dimensional statistical data onto the flat surface of a monitor screen or a piece of paper facilitates the **visualization** of many aspects of human geography in innovative and provocative ways (**Figure 1.3.9**).

visualization: a computer-assisted representation of spatial data, often involving three-dimensional images and innovative perspectives, that reveals spatial patterns and relationships more effectively

Figure 1.3.9 Visualization   This example shows the spatial structure of the Internet's multicast backbone that is the most popular way of transmitting real-time video and audio streams. (*Source:* T. Munzner, E. Hoffman, K. Claffy, and B. Fenner, "Visualizing the Global Topology of the MBone," *Proceedings of the 1996 IEEE Symposium on Information Visualization,* pp. 85–92, 1996, San Francisco, CA.)

■ *Regions are distinguished on the basis of specific characteristics, or attributes.* In everyday speech, we talk very imprecisely about regions. To be useful to a geographer, a region must be based on specific definitions to have any real meaning. Consider the example of the Canadian Shield. If we now try to think about the Shield in relation to a region we can call the Canadian North, the problem is evident. We can draw no clear boundary between these two regions because we have no clear basis on which to do so. We may even be unable to decide which region a particular place is in. Unless we clearly define what we mean by the *North* and the *Shield,* these terms have little useful meaning.

■ *Regions minimize the variation of the chosen attribute within their boundaries and maximize the variation of that attribute between themselves and their neighbouring regions.* This aspect of the definition of a region is one that geographers interested in statistics have used to show that regions can be *objectively* or *scientifically* defined. In more general terms, regions need to be as homogeneous as possible with respect to the factors used to define them. Or, to put it the other way round, each factor used to define a region must alter as little as possible across that region. For instance, it is only because the regions used on a weather map show areas of similar weather that such maps have any use for us.

■ *Regions can be defined on the basis of any attribute or combination of attributes.* The best known regions to us appear every day on the Weather Channel, where we see regions defined on the basis of one or more variables, such as temperature or precipitation. The examples used thus far have used physical factors, but we can also use cultural characteristics (or any others) to define regions. For example, if we carefully define the factors used (such as different regional accents and folk architecture), then we can distinguish the Acadian part of Maritime Canada as a cultural region. As a further illustration, in the 1960s, Professor Louis-Edmond Hamelin developed an *Index of Nordicity,* which uses a combination of six environmental criteria and four cultural factors to define Canada's North.

Geographers have traditionally divided regions into three types: *formal, functional,* and *vernacular.* A *formal region* is one that is uniform in terms of specific criteria—the Canadian Shield is an example if we consider geological characteristics. A *functional region* is an area that literally functions as a unit, economically or administratively, and is usually organized by transport routes focused on a dominant city. A *vernacular region* is the local region as identified by the region's own inhabitants.

Knowing how geographers define the concept of the region also enables us to understand more fully the definition of *regional geography,* previously introduced. Regional geographers are attracted by the interplay of physical and human factors in the creation of regions. Indeed, a number of the discipline's most famous geographers (such as Vidal de la Blache and Carl Sauer) have believed that regional geography *is* geography. Vidal de la Blache compared the way in which the physical and human aspects of a region mould each other to that of a "snail growing into its shell" so that the region becomes "a medal struck in the likeness of a people."

Location Often, location is *nominal,* or expressed solely in terms of the names given to regions and places. We speak, for example, of Vancouver, or of Gastown, a location within Vancouver. Location can be used also as an *absolute* concept, whereby locations are fixed mathematically through coordinates of latitude and longitude (**Figure 1.17**). **Latitude** refers to the angular distance of a point on Earth's surface, measured in degrees, minutes, and seconds north or south of the equator, which is assigned a value of 0°. Lines of latitude around the globe run parallel to the equator, which is why they are sometimes referred to as parallels. **Longitude** refers to the angular distance of a point on Earth's surface, measured in degrees, minutes, and seconds east or west from the *prime meridian* (the line that passes through both poles and through Greenwich, England, which is assigned a value of 0°). Lines of longitude, called *meridians,* always run from the North Pole (latitude 90° north) to the South Pole (latitude 90° south). Vancouver's coordinates are precisely 49°20′N, 123°10′W. A second example is to consider the map store World of Maps, an authorized regional distributor for all Canadian government maps and charts produced by the Canada Map Office. This business is located at 1235 Wellington Street in Ottawa, Ontario, and gives its coordinates as 45°23′N, 75°43′NW.

The ability to estimate latitude is, as we have already seen in this chapter, an ancient skill. Champlain's astrolabe measured latitude by estimating the angle of the sun in the sky, and we have seen how the Polynesians used the relative position of stars for the same purpose. Calculating longitude proved to be a great deal harder and, as Dava Sobel has recently explained, had to await eighteenth-century Europe's development of accurate clocks.[12] From this date onward, ships began to carry two clocks to calculate their longitude. One clock kept the time in the home port; the other was reset by the noonday sun to local time aboard the ship. The difference between the two clocks, in terms of time, could then be converted to a difference in terms of longitude. However, it was not until the 1760s that the types of clock accurate enough to keep time over long sea journeys were developed. The "Great Navigator," Captain Cook, was one of the first to test this new technology on his voyages of discovery across the Pacific.

Thanks to the Global Positioning System (GPS), it is now very easy to determine the latitude and longitude of any given point. The **Global Positioning System** consists of 21 satellites (plus 3 spares) that orbit Earth on precisely predictable paths, broadcasting highly accurate time and locational information. The GPS is owned by the U.S. government, but the information transmitted by the satellites is readily available at no cost to everyone around the world. All that is needed is a GPS receiver. Basic receivers cost less than $150 and can relay latitude, longitude,

latitude: the angular distance of a point on Earth's surface, *measured north or south* from the equator, which is 0°

longitude: the angular distance of a point on Earth's surface, *measured east or west* from the prime meridian (the line that passes through both poles and through Greenwich, England, and that has the value of 0°)

Global Positioning System (GPS): a system of satellites that orbit Earth on precisely predictable paths, broadcasting highly accurate time and locational information

---

[12]Dava Sobel, *Longitude.* New York: Penguin, 1995, p. 5.

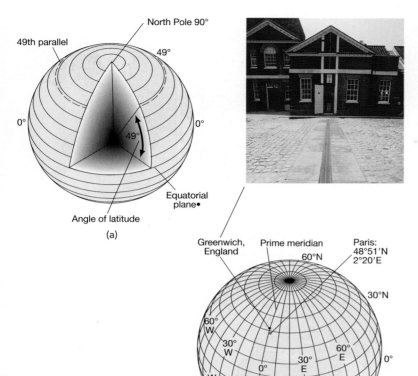

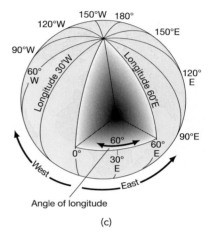

The prime meridian at the Royal Observatory in Greenwich, England—The observatory was founded by Charles II in 1675 with the task of setting standards for time, distance, latitude, and longitude—the key components of navigation.

Figure 1.17 Latitude and longitude Lines of latitude and longitude provide a grid that covers Earth, allowing any point on Earth's surface to be accurately referenced. Latitude is measured in angular distance (that is, degrees and minutes) north or south of the equator, as shown in (a). Longitude is measured in the same way, but east and west from the prime meridian, a line around Earth's surface that passes through both poles (North and South) and the Royal Observatory in Greenwich, just to the east of central London, in England. Locations are always stated with latitudinal measurements first. The location of Paris, France, for example, is 48°51′N and 2°20′E, as shown in (b). (*Sources:* (a) and (c): Reprinted with permission of Prentice Hall, from R.W. Christopherson, *Geosystems: An Introduction to Physical Geography*, 2nd ed., © 1994, pp. 13 and 15. (b): Reprinted with permission of Prentice Hall, from E.F. Bergman, *Human Geography: Cultures, Connections, and Landscapes*, © 1995, figs. 1-10 and 1-13.)

and height to within 100 metres day or night, in all weather conditions, in any part of the world. The most precise GPS receivers, costing thousands of dollars, are accurate to within a centimetre. The GPS has drastically increased the accuracy and efficiency of collecting spatial data. In combination with GIS technology and remote sensing, the GPS has revolutionized mapmaking and spatial analysis.

Location can also be *relative*, fixed in terms of site or situation. **Site** refers to the physical attributes of a location: its terrain, soil, vegetation, and water sources, for example. **Situation** refers to the location of a place relative to other places and human activities: its accessibility to routes, for example, or its nearness to population centres. For example, Stanley Park has a coastal site and is situated on a peninsula in the northwest of Vancouver.

Finally, location also has a *cognitive* dimension, in that people have cognitive images of places and regions, compiled from their own knowledge, experience, and impressions. **Cognitive images** (sometimes referred to as **mental maps**) are psychological representations of locations that spring from people's individual ideas and impressions of these locations. These representations can be based on people's direct experiences, on written or visual representations of actual locations, on hearsay, on people's imaginations, or on a combination of these sources. Location in these cognitive images is fluid, depending on people's changing information and

site: the physical attributes of a location—its terrain, soil, vegetation, and water sources, for example

situation: the location of a place relative to other places and human activities

cognitive images (mental maps): psychological representations of locations that are created from people's individual ideas and impressions of these locations

Figure 1.18 One person's cognitive image of Montreal This mental map was drawn by a geography student at Concordia University in Montreal as part of a class exercise. The student has included some (but not all) of Montreal's prominent landmarks, particularly "the mountain" in the city's centre. In addition, the shape of Montreal's island is distorted, emphasizing areas most familiar to the student.

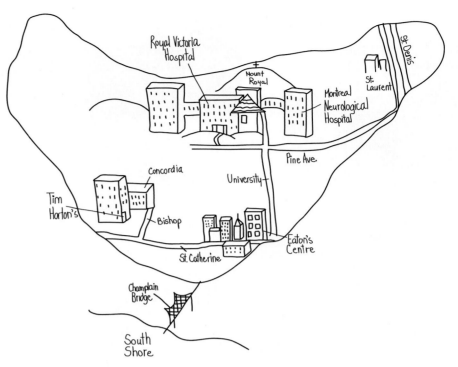

perceptions of the principal landmarks in their environment. **Figure 1.18** shows one person's cognitive image of Montreal. As the drawing shows, the relative importance of places affects our mental maps.

The Canadian architectural scholar Witold Rybczynski observes of his own years as a student at McGill University in Montreal that "the gym marked the northernmost edge of my campus world, just as Joe's Steak House circumscribed it to the south. The latter does not appear on the official map of the university, but each of us carries mental place maps within us—maps that often bear little resemblance to reality." Yet, for us, he concludes, "they are truer depictions than those of cartographers."[13]

Distance Distance is also useful as an *absolute* physical measure, whose units we may count in kilometres or miles, and as a *relative* measure, expressed in terms of time, effort, or cost. It can take more (or less) time, for example, to travel 10 kilometres from point A to point B than it does to travel 10 kilometres from point A to point C. Similarly, it can cost more (or less). Of course, relative distance can be measured in many ways. The distance (in social space) between social groups, known as *social distance,* is a very useful measure and has, for example, been used in explanations of how social areas within cities develop (see Chapter 11). Groups that are close together in terms of social distance will interact more frequently than groups that are socially very distant from each other—irrespective of the actual physical distance between them. In this way, social processes of assimilation and discrimination can also become powerful spatial processes shaping a city. Geographers also have to recognize that distance can sometimes be in the eye of the beholder. It can seem longer (or shorter) or more (or less) pleasant going from A to B than from A to C. This is **cognitive distance**, the distance that people perceive to exist in a given situation. Cognitive distance is based on people's personal judgments about the degree of spatial separation between points.

The importance of distance as a fundamental factor in determining real-world relationships is a central theme in geography. It was once described as the "first law" of geography: "Everything is related to everything else, but near things are

cognitive distance: the distance that people perceive to exist in a given situation

---

[13]Witold Rybczynski, *Looking Around: A Journey through Architecture.* Toronto: HarperCollins, 1992, p. 116.

more related than distant things." Waldo Tobler, the geographer from the University of California, Santa Barbara, who put it this way, is one of many who have investigated the **friction of distance**, the deterrent or inhibiting effect of distance on human activity. The friction of distance is a reflection of the time and cost of overcoming distance.

These geographers established that these effects are not uniform, that is, not directly proportional to distance itself. This is true whether distance is measured in absolute terms (kilometres, for example) or in relative terms (time- or cost-based measures, for example). The deterrent effects of extra distance tend to lessen as greater distances are involved. Thus, for example, although there is a big deterrent effect in having to travel 2 kilometres rather than 1 to get to a grocery store, the deterrent effect of the same extra distance (1 kilometre) after already travelling 10 kilometres is relatively small.

This sort of relationship creates what geographers call a distance-decay function. A **distance-decay function** describes the rate at which a particular activity or phenomenon diminishes with increasing distance. A typical distance-decay function is described by the graph in **Figure 1.19**, which shows how the measure of almost any aspect of human behaviour diminishes with increasing distance.

Distance-decay functions reflect people's behavioural response to opportunities and constraints in time and space. As such, they are a reflection of the utility of particular locations to people. The **utility** of a specific place or location refers to its usefulness to a particular person or group. In practice, utility is thought of in different ways by different people in different situations. The business manager of a supermarket chain, for example, will almost certainly decide on the utility of potential locations for a new store by weighing criteria based on the projected costs and revenues for each potential site. In deciding on the utility of potential locations in which to retire, however, that same manager will almost certainly decide on the utility of potential locations by weighing criteria based not only on costs but also on a wide range of quality-of-life aspects of potential retirement places.

The common unifying theme here is that in most circumstances, regardless of how people think of place utility, they tend to *seek to maximize the net utility of location*. The supermarket chain's business manager, for example, will seek to find the location for the chain's new store that is most likely to yield the greatest profit. On retirement, he or she will choose to live in the place that represents the best trade-off among housing costs, the cost of living, and the quality of life. Seeking to maximize the net utility of location means that a great deal of human activity is influenced by what University of Washington geographer Richard Morrill once called the "nearness principle." According to this principle—a more explicit version of Tobler's first law—people will seek to

- maximize the overall utility of places at minimum effort
- maximize connections among places at minimum cost
- locate related activities as close together as possible

As a result, patterns of behaviour, locational decisions, and interrelations between people and places come to take on fairly predictable, organized patterns.

Space Like distance, space can be measured in absolute, relative, and cognitive terms. Absolute space is a mathematical space, described through points, lines, areas, and planes whose relationships can be fixed precisely through mathematical reasoning. Several ways of analyzing space mathematically are useful to geographers. The conventional way is to view space as a container, defined by rectangular coordinates and measured in absolute units of distance (kilometres or miles, for example). Other mathematical conceptions of space that geographers sometimes find useful also exist, however. One example is **topological space**, defined as the connections between, or connectivity of, particular points in space (**Figure 1.20**). Topological space is measured not in terms of conventional measures of distance but rather by the nature and degree of connectivity between locations.

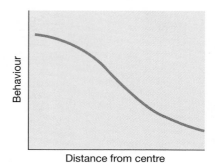

Distance from centre

Figure 1.19   The friction of distance
The effects of distance on people's behaviour can be charted on graphs like this one. The farther people have to travel, the less likely they are to do so.

friction of distance: the deterrent or inhibiting effect of distance on human activity

distance-decay function: the rate at which a particular activity or process diminishes with increasing distance

utility: the usefulness of a specific place or location to a particular person or group

topological space: the connections between, or connectivity of, particular points in space

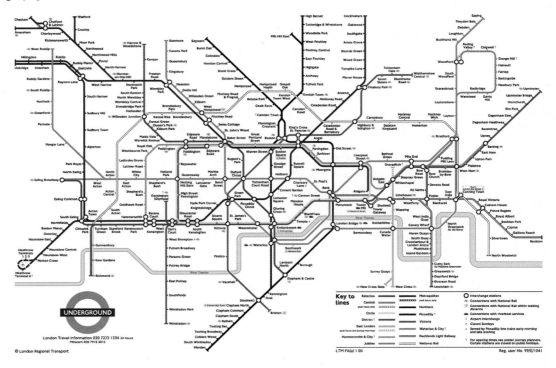

Figure 1.20 Topological space The map of the London Underground is a topological map, showing how specific points are joined within a particular network. The most important aspects of networks of any kind, from the geographer's viewpoint, are their connectivity attributes. These attributes determine the flow of people and things (goods, information) and the centrality of places. As most Londoners know, the Underground system gives Paddington a very high degree of connectivity because trains on the District, Circle, Bakerloo, and Hammersmith & City lines all stop there. Paddington is therefore relatively central within the "space of flows" of passenger traffic in central London. Edgeware Road—nearby in absolute terms—is much less central, however, and much less the focus of passenger flows. (*Source:* London Regional Transport, where updates and more information are available at **www.thetube.com**.)

cognitive space: space defined and measured in terms of the nature and degree of people's values, feelings, beliefs, and perceptions about locations, districts, and regions

Relative measurements of space can also take the form of socioeconomic space or of experiential or cultural space. *Socioeconomic space* can be described in terms of sites and situations, routes, regions, and distribution patterns. In these terms, spatial relationships have to be fixed through measures of time, cost, profit, and production, as well as through physical distance. Dividing the world into economic blocks, such as the West, or according to gross national product (GNP) are examples; in these cases, an economic scale replaces simple distance as a measure. *Experiential or cultural space* is the space of groups of people with common ties, and it is described through the places, territories, and settings whose attributes carry special meaning for these particular groups. Finally, **cognitive space** is defined and measured in terms of people's values, feelings, beliefs, and perceptions about locations, districts, and regions. Cognitive space can be described, therefore, in terms of behavioural space—landmarks, paths, environments, and spatial layouts.

When we begin to think about space in these relative terms, we can understand that space is much more than an objective "container" in which activity occurs; in many ways, space is itself created or called into being by that activity. This is not an easy point to grasp and is the focus of some of the latest research in geography. However, a simple example can illustrate the idea. Consider the history of settlement of the Prairies, and imagine being one of the first immigrants to establish a farm there. In the first phase of settlement, distance has no effect on us because we are isolated and self-sufficient. But once a settlement is established in that landscape, a "centre" is created and the location of our farm is now redefined in terms of its distance from that centre. This is extremely important if we begin to transport our grain to the grain elevator in that newly created settlement, from where it will be transported to a distant market by rail. In other words, *distance* and all of the effects of the *friction of distance* are created—in this case, by the form of economic exploitation being used to settle the Prairies—and *space* is itself produced. (This process is one of the reasons why the exact route of the Canadian Pacific Railway across the country was so hotly contested, and many speculators lost money gambling on the sites to be chosen for settlements.)

Contemporary geographical thinking about the concept of space owes a great deal to the work of the French scholar Henri Lefebvre (1901–1991) and, in particular, his 1974 book *The Production of Space* (translated from French in 1991).[14] In this work, Lefebvre explores what he believes are the three main processes societies use to constantly produce space:

1. *Spatial practice.* These are the spatial locations in which our social and economic activities are found and the ways in which they are linked to create space. In our example above, these relationships affect and are affected by the socioeconomic system, which, through the economic value given to distance, is able to "create" space. Lefebvre suggests that different socioeconomic systems (or modes of production) will be associated with different types of space. Certainly, in communist or cooperative economies, common ownership of land prevents the creation of a land market and the creation of rich and poor economic zones familiar in Western capitalist cities.

2. *Representations of space.* These are the ways in which power is, often invisibly, "inscribed" in space (for example, through municipal zoning regulations, which enforce one group's values across a multiethnic city).

3. *Representational space/spaces of representation.* These are the functions of spatial allusions in the common symbols used in any culture's literature or art. To illustrate this point, William New, a professor of English at the University of British Columbia, suggests that such words as *garden, valley,* or *mountain* carry with them a whole set of cultural and social attitudes that mean far more than simply descriptions of physical phenomena. In his words: "The language that alludes to gardens, mountains, and so on, constitutes, at the same time, an ongoing history of a culture's relations with place and space."[15]

Lefebvre's finding that space is a cultural and social creation is certainly a very stimulating one for modern geography; it holds the promise that many geographical problems are not, ultimately, rooted in physical space as much as they are in more abstract social spaces—spaces in which it might be possible to effect change for the better.

Place   Throughout this chapter, we have been considering the concept of **place**. As we have seen, places are objective locations that have both uniqueness and interdependent relations with other places. It is appropriate now to consider how to define this concept because its full meaning can only be understood in contrast to that of *space*.

Canadian author Mordecai Richler once described Canada as "justifiably better known for its spaces rather than its places."[16] At first sight, this seems a reasonable enough statement. But, in some respects, Richler may be quite wrong. If we follow the geographer Yi-Fu Tuan's memorable remark that "place is space filled with meaning," we will see that the concept of place draws its real meaning from us. Our lives in the world inevitably make certain small parts of that world unique and meaningful to us as individuals. We are also influenced in these assessments by our wider social and cultural frames of reference. Place, in this sense, is therefore defined subjectively as somewhere that has personal meaning to individuals or

place: a concept with two levels of meaning: (1) an objective location that has both uniqueness and interdependence with other places; (2) a subjective social and cultural construct—somewhere that has personal meaning for individuals or groups

---

[14]Alison Blunt and Jane Wills, *Dissident Geographies: An Introduction to Radical Ideas and Practice.* Harlow: Prentice Hall, 2000, pp. 75–79.

[15]H. William. *New Land Sliding: Imagining Space, Presence and Power in Canadian Writing.* Toronto: University of Toronto Press, 1997, p. 8.

[16]Mordecai Richler, "Quebec City's Prime Time." In A.M. Rosenthal and A. Gelb (eds.), *The Sophisticated Traveler. Winter: Love It or Leave It.* New York: Villard Books, 1984, p. 89.

place making: any activity, deliberate or unintentional, that enables space to acquire meaning

groups. In a more formal way, we can define it as a social and cultural construct. On the basis of this discussion, we can see that the term **place making** describes any activity, deliberate or unintentional, that enables space to develop meaning.

In this sense, Canada is full of places, for it is a land that embodies the lives and memories of Aboriginal peoples, of immigrants and their descendants who settled the land with farms and cities, and of tourists enraptured by our landscape. As Wallace Stegner, an American writer raised on the Saskatchewan–Montana border, has written:

> The geologist who surveyed southern Saskatchewan in the 1870s called it one of the most desolate and forbidding regions on earth. . . . Desolate? Forbidding? There was never a country that in its good moments was more beautiful. Even in drouth [drought] or dust storm or blizzard it is the reverse of monotonous, once you have submitted to it with all the senses.[17]

accessibility: the opportunity for contact or interaction from a given point or location in relation to other locations

Accessibility   Given that people tend to pursue the nearness principle, the concept of accessibility is very important. **Accessibility** is generally defined by geographers in terms of relative location: the opportunity for contact or interaction from a given point or location in relation to other locations. It implies proximity, or nearness, to something. Because it is a fundamental influence on the utility of locations, distance is an important influence on people's behaviour. Distance is one aspect of accessibility, but it is by no means the only important aspect.

Connectivity is also an important aspect of accessibility because contact and interaction are dependent on channels of communication and transportation: streets, highways, telephone lines, and wavebands, for example. Effective accessibility is thus a function not only of distance but also of the configuration of networks of communication and transportation.

Accessibility is often a function of economic, cultural, and social factors. In other words, relative concepts and measures of distance are often as important as absolute distance. A nearby facility, such as a health care clinic, is accessible to us only if we can actually afford the cost of getting there, if it seems close according to our own standards of distance, if we can afford to use the facility, if we feel that it is socially and culturally acceptable for us to use it, and so on. To take another example, a daycare centre may be located just a few blocks from a single-parent family, but the centre is not truly accessible if it opens after the parent has to be at work or if the parent feels that the staff, children, or other parents at the centre are from an incompatible social or cultural group.

Spatial Interaction   Interdependence between places and regions can be sustained only through movement and flows. Geographers use the term *spatial interaction* as shorthand for all kinds of movement and flows involving human activity. Freight shipments, commuting, shopping trips, telecommunications, electronic cash transfers, migration, and vacation travel are all examples of spatial interaction. The fundamental principles of spatial interaction can be reduced to four basic concepts: complementarity, transferability, intervening opportunities, and—most importantly—spatial diffusion.

- *Complementarity.* A precondition for interdependence between places is complementarity. For any kind of spatial interaction to occur between two places, there must be a demand in one place and a supply that matches, or complements it, in the other. This complementarity can be the result of several factors. One important factor is the variation in physical environments and resource endowments from place to place. For example, the flow of Canadian visitors to Florida, Mexico, and Cuba during the winter is the result of climatic complementarity. To take another example, the flow of crude oil from Saudi Arabia (with vast oil reserves) to Japan (with none) is a function of complementarity in natural resource endowments.

---

[17]W. Stegner, *Wolf Willow.* New York: Ballantine, 1973 [first published 1955], pp. 6, 8.

A second factor is the international division of labour that derives from the evolution of the world's economic systems. The more developed countries of the world have sought to establish overseas suppliers for their food, raw materials, and exotic produce, allowing the more developed countries to specialize in more profitable manufacturing and knowledge-based industries (see Chapter 2).

A third contributory factor to complementarity is the operation of principles of specialization and economies of scale. Places, regions, and countries can derive economic advantages from the efficiencies created through specialization, which allows for larger-scale operations. **Economies of scale** are cost advantages to manufacturers that accrue from high-volume production, since the average cost of production falls with increasing output (**Figure 1.21**).

■ *Transferability.* In addition to complementarity, another precondition for interdependence between places is *transferability*, which depends on the frictional or deterrent effects of distance. Transferability is a function of two things: the costs of moving a particular item, measured in real money or time, and the ability of the item to bear these costs. If, for example, the costs of moving a product from one place to another make it too expensive to sell successfully at its destination, then that product does not have transferability between those places.

■ *Intervening opportunities.* Although complementarity and transferability are preconditions for spatial interaction, intervening opportunities are more important in determining the *volume* and *pattern* of movements and flows. Intervening opportunities are simply alternative origins or destinations. Such opportunities are not necessarily situated directly between two points, or even along a route between them. Thus, for Scottish families considering a Mediterranean vacation in Greece, resorts in Spain, southern France, and Italy are all intervening opportunities because they can be reached more quickly and more cheaply than resorts in Greece.

The size and relative importance of alternative destinations are also important aspects of the concept of intervening opportunity. For our Scottish families, Spanish resorts probably offer the greatest intervening opportunity because they contain the largest aggregate number of hotel rooms and vacation apartments. We can state the principle of intervening opportunity as follows: spatial interaction between an origin and a destination will be proportional to the number of opportunities at that destination and inversely proportional to the number of opportunities at alternative destinations.

■ *Spatial diffusion.* Disease outbreaks, technological innovations, political movements, and new musical fads all originate in specific places and subsequently spread to other places and regions. The way that things spread through space and over time—**spatial diffusion**—is one of the most important aspects of spatial interaction and is crucial to an understanding of geographical change. In fact, because the study of diffusion involves the spread of phenomena over space *and* through time, it is a topic of special fascination to geographers.

Diffusion seldom occurs in an apparently random way, jumping unpredictably all over the map. Rather, it occurs as a function of statistical probability, which is often based on fundamental geographical principles of distance and movement. The diffusion of a contagious disease, for example, is a function of the probability of physical contact, modified by variations in individual resistance to the disease. The diffusion of an agricultural innovation, such as hybrid wheat, is a function of the probability of information flowing between members of the farming community (itself partly a function of distance), modified by variations in individual farmers' receptivity to innovative change. The result is typically a "wave" of diffusion that describes an S-curve, with a slow buildup, rapid spread, and final levelling off (**Figure 1.22**).

It is possible to recognize several different spatial tendencies in patterns of diffusion. In *expansion diffusion* (also called *contagious diffusion*—**Figure 1.23a**), a phenomenon spreads due to the proximity of carriers, or agents of change, who are fixed in their location. A good example is the spread of measles across a city

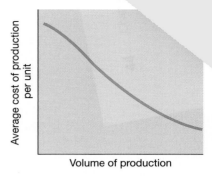

Figure 1.21 Economies of scale
In many manufacturing enterprises, the higher the volume of production, the lower the average cost of producing each unit. This relationship occurs partly because high-volume production allows for specialization and division of labour, which can increase efficiency and hence lower costs. It also occurs partly because most manufacturing activities have significant fixed costs (such as product design and the cost of renting or buying factory space) that must be paid for irrespective of the volume of production, and so the larger the output, the lower is the fixed cost per unit. These savings are known as economies of scale.

economies of scale: cost advantages to manufacturers that accrue from high-volume production, since the average cost of production falls with increasing output

spatial diffusion: the way that things spread through space and over time

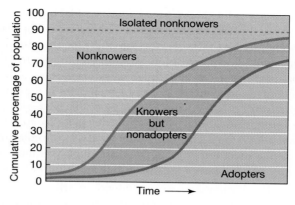

Figure 1.22   Spatial diffusion   The spatial diffusion of many phenomena (such as diseases or ideas) tends to follow an S-curve of slow buildup, rapid spread, and levelling off. In the case of the spread of a disease, such as measles, or the adoption of an innovation, for example, it usually takes a while for enough people to become exposed to the disease or for sufficient potential adopters to get to know about the innovation, and even longer for a critical mass of them to adopt it. After that, the disease or innovation spreads quite rapidly, until most of the susceptible population or potential adopters have been exposed to the disease or innovation. (*Source:* D.J. Walmsley and G.J. Lewis, *Human Geography: Behavioural Approaches.* London: Longman, 1984, fig. 5.3, p. 52. Reprinted by permission of Addison Wesley Longman Ltd.)

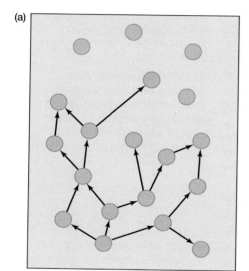

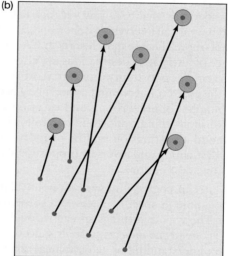

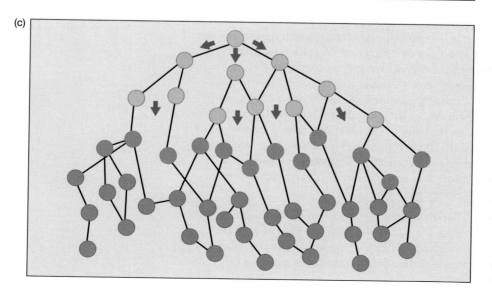

Figure 1.23   Patterns of spatial diffusion   (a) Expansion diffusion (for example, the spread of a contagious disease, such as cholera, across a city; the spread of an innovative agricultural practice, such as the use of hybrid seed stock, across a rural area); (b) relocation diffusion (for example, the movement of spices from Asia to Europe); (c) hierarchical diffusion (for example, the spread of a fashion trend from large metropolitan areas to smaller cities and towns).   (*Source:* L.A. Brown and E.G. Moore, "Diffusion Research: A Perspective." In C. Board, R.J. Chorley, P. Haggett, and D. Stoddart [eds.], *Progress in Geography.* London: Edward Arnold/ Hodder and Stoughton Educational, 1969.)

or region. With *relocation diffusion,* a phenomenon is spread as an initial carrier or group of carriers moves from one location to another, taking the phenomenon with it as it travels or migrates (**Figure 1.23b**). The long-distance movement of rare or precious commodities (such as spices along the Silk Road across Asia) provides an example of the physical relocation of articles from one place to another. The movement of exotic animals from tropical locations to zoos in Winnipeg or Toronto is a further illustration. However, the most important example is the movement, or relocation, of people themselves, as in the case of the original settling of the Americas or the nineteenth-century settling of the Prairies.

Last, with *hierarchical diffusion* (also known as *cascade diffusion*), a phenomenon can be diffused from one location to another without necessarily spreading to places in between (**Figure 1.23c**). This is because such phenomena first only spread *between* centres of equal rank in an urban hierarchy (between major world cities, for example), before spreading *down* the urban hierarchy (from city to town to village, for example). There are two important consequences of hierarchical diffusion. First, diffusion in hierarchical space results in phenomena spreading much more quickly around the world (and is one of the many features of a globalizing world), than they would if they had to rely on expansion diffusion alone. Second, phenomena spread last to places at the bottom of the urban hierarchy (small villages, for example)—a consequence that means that while hierarchical diffusion can be faster than expansion diffusion, it is not always as thorough in reaching everywhere quickly. This is because very small villages located close to large centres are going to receive news of an innovation, for example, much later than more distant but larger centres, which (while geographically further from the origin of innovation) are much closer in terms of hierarchical space. (This observation is a specific example of the much wider finding that phenomena close together in one type of space may be far apart in another, or vice versa, and the importance of recognizing this.) One example would be the initial spread of the HIV-1 virus, which rapidly spread from Central Africa to other parts of the world (**Figure 1.24**). Another would be the spread of severe acute respiratory syndrome (SARS) from China to Toronto in March 2003.

Actual patterns and processes of diffusion can reflect several of these tendencies, as different aspects of human interaction come into play at different times in

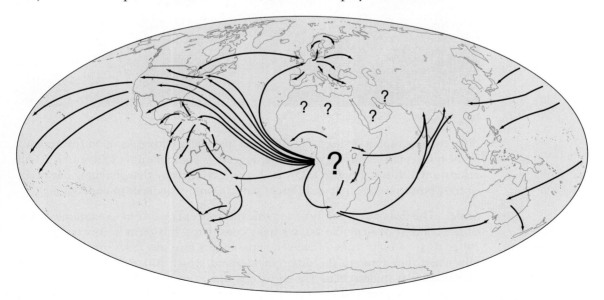

Figure 1.24   Diffusion of the HIV-1 virus   Medical geographers have concluded that the HIV-1 virus that causes AIDS spread in a hierarchical diffusion pattern from a hearth area in Central Africa in the late 1970s. The virus initially appeared almost simultaneously in the major metropolitan areas of North and South America, the Caribbean, and Europe. These areas then acted as localized diffusion poles for the virus, which next spread to major metropolitan areas in Asia and Oceania and to larger provincial cities in North and South America, the Caribbean, and Europe. Next in this "cascading" pattern of diffusion were provincial cities in Asia and Oceania and small towns in North and South America, the Caribbean, and Europe.   (*Source:* M. Smallman-Raynor, A. Cliff, and P. Haggett, *London International Atlas of AIDS.* Oxford: Blackwell Reference, 1992, fig. 4.1(c), p. 146.)

Figure 1.25 Diffusion of cholera in 1832 from Gross Île (Quebec) and New York (a) Nineteenth-century cholera epidemics followed a combination of hierarchical and relocation diffusion. The 1832 epidemic occurred when the urban system was loosely linked together by water transport, and the epidemic spread relatively slowly from its sources in Grosse Île (northeast of Quebec City, in the St. Lawrence) and New York. Both were important ports of entry for immigrants to Canada and to the United States, respectively. (b) Grosse Île, Quebec, served as a quarantine point for those afflicted with cholera in 1832. Sadly, however, the disease was able to spread from this point and diffused along the St. Lawrence to Montreal and its surroundings. (*Source for map:* "The Diffusion of Cholera in the United States in the Nineteenth Century," by G.F. Pyle, *Geographical Analysis*, vol. 1, no. 1. Reprinted by permission. Copyright © 1969 by the Ohio State University Press. All rights reserved.)

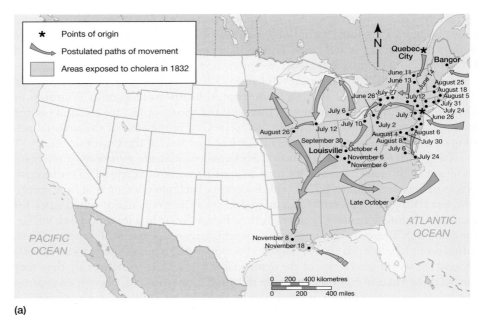

(a)

(b)

different geographic settings. The diffusion of cholera outbreaks in North America in the nineteenth century, for example, suggests a combination of hierarchical and relocation diffusion (**Figure 1.25**). It also reflects the way that changing networks of transportation resulted in different patterns and sequences of contagion.

Scale The last of geography's fundamental concepts we need to examine is that of the concept of **scale**. So far, we have considered this term in its cartographical context of *map scale*. However, geographers also use this term more generally when they refer to the different levels at which processes occur or when explanation is undertaken. The most obvious example is one we have already seen in this chapter and is summed up in the well-known slogan "think global, act local." Geographers have long understood that there are various scales (or levels) of analysis (local, regional, national, global), that they are linked, and that processes operating at one scale can have significance at other scales. Indeed, in some cases, processes operate in different ways at different scales. Consider again the example of the diffusion of the HIV-1 virus (see Figure 1.24). At a *global scale*, a hierarchical process of diffusion dominates, but at a very *local scale*, the expansion (or "contagious") diffusion process will be more important.

scale: the general concept that there are various scales of analysis (local, regional, national, global), that they are linked, and that processes operating at one scale can have significance at other scales

CONCLUSION

Human geography is the systematic study of the location of peoples and human activities across Earth's surface and of their relationships to one another. An understanding of human geography is important, both from an intellectual point of view (that is, understanding the world around us) and from practical points of view (for example, contributing to environmental quality, human rights, social justice, business efficiency, political analysis, and government policy-making).

Although modern ideas about the study of human geography developed from intellectual roots going back to the classical scholarship of ancient Greece, as the world itself has changed, our ways of thinking about it have also changed. What is distinctive about the study of human geography today is not so much the phenomena that are studied as the way they are approached. The contribution of human geography is to reveal, in relation to economic, social, cultural, and political phenomena, how and why geographical relationships matter in terms of cause and effect.

Geography matters because it is in specific places that people learn who and what they are and how they should think and behave. Places are a strong influence, for better or worse, on people's physical well-being, their opportunities, and their lifestyle choices. Places contribute to people's collective memory and become powerful emotional and cultural symbols. Places are the sites of innovation and change, of resistance and conflict.

To investigate specific places, however, we must be able to frame our studies of them within the context of the entire globe. This is important for two reasons. First, the world consists of a complex mosaic of places and regions that are interrelated and interdependent in many ways. Second, place-making forces—especially economic, cultural, and political forces that influence the distribution of human activities and the character of places—are increasingly operating at global and international scales. The interdependence of places and regions means that individual places are tied into wider processes of change that are reflected in broader geographical patterns. An important issue for human geographers is to recognize these wider processes and broad geographical patterns without losing sight of the individuality and uniqueness of specific places.

This global perspective leads to the following principles:

- Each place, each region, is largely the product of forces that are both local and global in origin.
- Ultimately, each place and region are linked to many other places and regions through these same forces.
- The individual character of places and regions cannot be accounted for by general processes alone. Some local outcomes are the product of unusual circumstances or special local factors.

MAIN POINTS REVISITED

- **Geography matters because specific places provide the settings for people's daily lives. It is in these settings that important events happen, and it is from them that significant changes spread and diffuse.**
  Places are settings for social interaction that, among other things, structure the daily routines of people's economic and social lives; provide both opportunities for and constraints to people's long-term social well-being; establish a context in which everyday, commonsense knowledge and experience are gathered; provide a setting for processes of socialization; and provide an arena for contesting social norms.

- **Places and regions are highly *interdependent,* each filling specialized roles in complex and ever-changing networks of interaction and change.**

Individual places are tied into wider processes of change that are reflected in broader geographical patterns. An important issue for human geographers is to recognize these wider processes and broad geographical patterns without losing sight of the individuality and uniqueness of specific places. Processes of geographical change are constantly modifying and reshaping places, and places are constantly coping with change.

- **Some of the most important aspects of the interdependence between geographic scales are provided by the relationships between the *global* and the *local*.**
  The study of human geography shows not only how global trends influence local outcomes but also how events in particular localities can come to influence patterns and trends elsewhere. With an understanding of these trends and outcomes,

it is possible not only to appreciate the diversity and variety of the world's peoples and places but also to be aware of their relationships to one another and to be able to make positive contributions to local, national, and global development.

■ **Human geography provides ways of understanding places, regions, and spatial relationships as the products of a series of interrelated forces that stem from nature, culture, and individual human action.**
Places are dynamic phenomena. They are created by people responding to the opportunities and constraints presented by their environments. As people live and work in places, they gradually impose themselves on their environment, modifying and adjusting it to suit their needs and express their values. At the same time, people gradually accommodate both to their physical environment and to the people around them. There is thus a continuous two-way process in which people create and modify places while being influenced by the settings in which they live and work. Places are not just distinctive outcomes of geographical processes; they are part of the processes themselves.

■ **The first law of geography is that "everything is related to everything else, but near things are more related than are distant things."**
A great deal of human activity is influenced by the "nearness principle," according to which people seek to maximize the overall utility of places at minimum effort, to maximize connections between places at minimum cost, and to locate related activities as close together as possible. In doing so, people are responding to the friction of distance, the deterrent or inhibiting effect of distance on human activity. A distance-decay function describes the rate at which a particular activity or phenomenon diminishes with increasing distance from a given point.

■ **Distance is one aspect of this law, but connectivity is also important because contact and interaction are dependent on channels of communication and transportation.**
Interdependence among places and regions can be sustained only through movement and flows. Accessibility and spatial interaction are two of the fundamental concepts that distinguish the study of human geography.

Key Terms

accessibility   (p. 42)
areal units   (p. 31)
cartography   (p. 11)
cognitive distance   (p. 38)
cognitive images
   (mental maps)   (p. 37)
cognitive space   (p. 40)
conformal projections   (p. 32)
distance-decay function   (p. 39)
economies of scale   (p. 43)
ecumene   (p. 24)
environmental determinism   (p. 18)
equal-area (equivalent)
   projections   (p. 32)

ethnocentrism   (p. 18)
friction of distance   (p. 39)
geodemographic
   research   (p. 26)
geographic information
   system (GIS)   (p. 26)
globalization   (p. 18)
Global Positioning
   System (GPS)   (p. 36)
human geography   (p. 4)
imperialism   (p. 18)
latitude   (p. 36)
longitude   (p. 36)
map projection   (p. 17)

masculinism   (p. 18)
model   (p. 29)
place   (p. 41)
place making   (p. 42)
region   (p. 28)
regional geography   (p. 26)
remote sensing   (p. 28)
scale   (p. 46)
site   (p. 37)
situation   (p. 37)
spatial diffusion   (p. 43)
topological space   (p. 39)
utility   (p. 39)
visualization   (p. 35)

Additional Reading

Agnew, J., D. Livingstone, and A. Rogers (eds.). *Human Geography: An Essential Anthology*. Cambridge, MA: Blackwell, 1996.

Andrey, J., and J. Gordon (eds.). *Public Issues: A Geographical Perspective*. Waterloo: Department of Geography, University of Waterloo, 1994.

Buttimer, A. *Geography and the Human Spirit*. Baltimore: Johns Hopkins University Press, 1993.

Cloke, P., C. Philo, and D. Sadler. *Approaching Human Geography: An Introduction to Contemporary Debates*. London: Chapman, 1991.

Davis, N.Z. *Trickster Tales: A Sixteenth-Century Muslim between Worlds*. New York: Hill and Wang, 2006.

Dear, M., and J. Wolch. "How Territory Shapes Social Life." In J. Wolch and M. Dear (eds.), *The Power of Geography*. Boston: Unwin Hyman, 1989, 3–18.

Delgado, J.P. *Across the Top of the World: The Quest for the Northwest Passage*. Toronto: Douglas and McIntyre, 2000.

Dorling, D., and D. Fairbairn. *Mapping: Ways of Seeing the World*. London: Addison Wesley Longman, 1997.

Frye, R. *Ibn Fadlun's Journey to Russia: A Tenth-Century Traveler from Baghdad to the Volga River*. Princeton NJ: Marcus Wiener, 2005.

Gaile, G., and C. Willmott (eds.). *Geography in America*. Columbus, OH: Merrill, 1989.

Gordon, S. *When Asia Was the World: Traveling Merchants, Scholars, Warriors and Monks Who Created the "Riches of the East."* Philadephia: Da Capo Press, 2008.

Gould, P. *The Geographer at Work*. Boston: Routledge & Kegan Paul, 1985.

Gregory, D. *Power, Knowledge, and Geography: An Introduction to Geographic Thought and Practice*. Oxford: Blackwell, 1999.

Hamelin, L. *Canadian Nordicity: It's Your North*. Montreal: Harvest House, 1979.

Harley, J.B., and D. Woodward. *The History of Cartography*. Chicago: University of Chicago Press, 1987.

Harris, R.C., and G.J. Matthews (eds.). *Historical Atlas of Canada. Volume 1: From the Beginning to 1800*. Toronto: University of Toronto Press, 1987.

Harvey, D.W. *Explanation in Geography*. London: Edward Arnold, 1969.

Helferich, G. *Humboldt's Cosmos: Alexander von Humboldt and the Latin American Journey That Changes the Way We See the World*. New York: Gotham Books, 2004.

Johnston, R.J. "The World Is Our Oyster." *Transactions, Institute of British Geographers* 9, 1984, 443–459.

Johnston, R.J., and J.D. Sidaway. *Geography and Geographers: Anglo-American Human Geography Since 1945*, 6th ed. London: Edward Arnold, 2004.

Kobayashi, A. "Truly Our Own: Canadian Geography 50 Years After," *Canadian Geographer* 45, 2001, 3–13.

Litalien, R., J.F. Palomino, and D. Vaugeois. *Mapping a Continent: Historical Atlas of North America, 1492–1814.* Montreal and Kingston: McGill-Queen's University Press, 2007.

Livingstone, D.N. *The Geographical Tradition: Episodes in the History of a Contested Enterprise.* Oxford: Blackwell, 1993.

MacEachern, A.M., and D. Taylor (eds.). *Visualization in Modern Cartography.* Oxford: Pergamon, 1994.

Mackintosh-Smith, T. *Travels with a Tangerine: A Journey in the Footsteps of Ibn Battutah.* London: John Murray, 2001.

Mackintosh-Smith, T. (ed.). *The Travels of Ibn Battutah.* London: Picador, 2002.

Massey, D., and J. Allen (eds.). *Geography Matters!* New York: Cambridge University Press, 1984.

Peet, R. *Modern Geographic Thought.* New York: Blackwell, 1998.

Pickles, J. (ed.). *Ground Truth: The Social Implications of Geographic Information Systems.* London: Longman, 1995.

Robinson, J.L. "Geography," *The Canadian Encyclopedia.* Edmonton: Hurtig, 1985, Volume 2, 725–726. [A revised online version by Lewis Robinson and Larry Bourne is now available at **www.thecanadianencyclopedia.com**, Historica Foundation of Canada: 2002.]

Royal Geographical Society. *Atlas of Exploration.* New York: Oxford University Press, 1997.

Sachs, A. *The Humboldt Current: Nineteenth-Century Exploration and the Roots of American Environmentalism.* New York: Viking Penguin, 2006.

Sack, R.D. *Place, Modernity, and the Consumer's World.* Baltimore: Johns Hopkins University Press, 1992.

Sanderson, M. *Griffith Taylor: Antarctic Scientist and Pioneer Geographer.* Ottawa: Carleton University Press, 1988.

Sauer, C.O. "Morphology of Landscape," *University of California Publications in Geography* 2, 1925, 19–54.

Unwin, T. *The Place of Geography.* London: Longman, 1992.

Walmsley, D.J., and G.J. Lewis. *People and Environment: Behavioural Approaches in Human Geography.* London: Longman, 1984.

Warkentin, J. *A Regional Geography of Canada: Life, Land, and Space.* Scarborough, ON: Prentice Hall, 2000.

Warkentin, J., and P. Simpson-Housley. "The Development of Geographical Study in Canada, 1870–2000." In G.S. Dunbar (ed.), *Geography: Discipline, Profession and Subject Since 1870.* Dordrecht: Kluwer, 2001, 281–315.

Withers, C.W.J. *Placing the Enlightenment: Thinking Geographically about the Age of Reason.* Chicago: University of Chicago Press, 2007.

Wood, D. *The Power of Maps.* New York: Guilford Press, 1992.

Exercises

Here you will find exercises and activities for each chapter. Unplugged exercises help you review chapter discussions, and pose ideas for your own human geography research. On the Companion Website exercises will require you have access to the internet.

Unplugged

1. List five geographic settings that have strong symbolic value for you, and state in 25 words or less why each setting has acquired such value.

2. Consider geographical interdependence from the point of view of your own life. Take an inventory of your clothes, noting, where possible, where each garment was manufactured. Where did you buy the garments? Was the store part of a regional, national, or international chain? What can you find out about the materials used in the garments? Where were they made?

3. The food we consume provides a good illustration of globalization and geographical interdependence. Try to establish all of the places involved in the ingredients of your next meal. Start with the regions or countries where the crops were grown (or animals reared). Next, find out where the ingredients went to be processed, warehoused, distributed, and so on. Finally, think about how and where you got them. Geographers call the

various steps involved in a foodstuff's journey a *commodity chain.* Think about how commodity chains might be different in shape or size depending on what part of the world or what time period we examine.

4. Describe, as exactly and concisely as possible, the *site* (see p. 37) of your campus. Then describe its *situation* (see p. 37). Can you think of any reasons why the campus is sited and situated just where it is? Would there be a better location; and, if so, why?

5. Choose a local landscape, one with which you are familiar, and write a short essay (500 words or two double-spaced, typed pages) on how you consider the landscape has evolved over time. Note especially any evidence that physical, environmental conditions have shaped any of the human elements in the landscape, together with any evidence of people having modified the physical landscape.

On the Companion Website

This book has its own Companion Website where you will find additional resources—maps, photographs, data—as well as exercises and activities that relate to each chapter. To complete the Companion Website exercises, go to **www.pearsoned.ca/knox**. The following is a summary of the types of exercises created for this chapter.

1. The exercises for this chapter are designed to reinforce the geographical concepts presented. For example, concept review exercises are provided for the major ideas introduced, and these exercises can be immediately graded electronically. The online Companion Website also focuses on several map exercises that will help you understand and compare map scale and projection. There is a critical-thinking exercise on the development of

geographical thought. Finally, to emphasize the idea that *geography matters,* we have created an exercise that allows you to explore geographic information systems (GIS) that are used to create digital maps, scaled from outer space to the smallest plot of land, that focus on such things as site and situation information.

2. The Audio Interview, Interview with George Lovell (Part 1), that accompanies this chapter has been conducted to highlight how the general study of human geography discussed in this chapter developed in North America under the influence of Carl Sauer. In addition, you will hear about the appeal of geography as a subject of study. You will find a link to the Audio Interview, interview summary, and questions on the Companion Website for this chapter.

2

The Changing
Global Context

McDonald's restaurant, Tokyo, Japan

The story is told of a little Japanese girl who arrives in Los Angeles, sees a McDonald's restaurant, tugs her mother's sleeve, and says, "Look, Mother, they have McDonald's in this country, too." With more than 2000 restaurants, McDonald's Japan is the biggest franchise outside the United States. It has become a cliché about the twenty-first century that everywhere will come to look like everywhere else, with the same McDonald's, Taco Bells, and Kentucky Fried Chickens, the same television programming with Hollywood movies and TV series, and the same malls selling the same Nike shoes, Sony electronics, and GAP clothing. Another cliché is that instantaneous global telecommunications, satellite television, and the internet will soon overthrow all but the last vestiges of geographical differentiation in human affairs. Companies, according to this view, will need no headquarters; they will be able to locate their activities almost anywhere in the world. Employees will work as effectively from home, car, or beach as they could in offices that need no longer exist. Events halfway across the world will be seen, heard, and felt with the same immediacy as events across town. National differences and regional cultures will disappear, the cliché has it, as a global marketplace brings a uniform dispersion of people, tastes, and ideas.

Such developments are, in fact, highly unlikely. Even in the Information Age, geography still matters, and it may well become more important than ever. Places and regions will undoubtedly change as a result of the new global context of the Information Age. But geography *still matters* because of several factors: transport costs, differences in resource endowments, fundamental principles of spatial organization, people's territorial impulses, the resilience of local cultures, and the legacy of the past. An editorial in the *Economist* magazine, debunking the cliché of a spaceless information economy and pointing out that place and space *do* matter, explained, "The main reason is that history counts: where you are depends very much on where you started from."[1]

MAIN POINTS

- Places and regions are part of a "world-system" that has been created as a result of processes of private economic competition and political competition among states.
- Today, the world-system is highly structured and is characterized by three tiers: *core regions*, *semiperipheral regions*, and *peripheral regions*.
- The world-system is made up of a nested set of cores and peripheries.
- Canada is simultaneously part of the global core and semiperiphery.

---

[1]"Does It Matter Where You Are?" *Economist*, 30 July 1994, 13–14.

- The evolution of the modern world-system has exhibited distinctive stages, each of which has left its legacy in different ways on particular places, depending on their changing role within the world-system.

- At the end of the eighteenth century, the new technologies of the Industrial Revolution brought about the emergence of a global economic system that reached into almost every part of the world and into virtually every aspect of people's lives.

- The growth and internal colonization of the core regions could take place only with the foodstuffs, raw materials, and markets provided by the colonization of the periphery.

- Within each of the world's major regions, successive technological innovations have transformed regional geographies.

- Globalization has intensified the differences between the core and the periphery and has contributed to the emergence of a digital divide and an increasing division between a fast world (about 15 percent of the world's population) and a slow world (about 85 percent of the world's population) with contrasting lifestyles and levels of living.

THE CHANGING WORLD

The essential foundation for an informed human geography is an ability to understand places and regions as components of a constantly changing global system. We can best understand these changes and their consequences for different places and regions by thinking of the world as an evolving, competitive, political-economic system that we can call the *world-system*.

The modern world-system was first established over a long period that began in the late fifteenth century and lasted until the mid-seventeenth century. A **world-system** is an *interdependent* system of countries linked by political and economic competition. The hyphenation in the term *world-system*, which was coined by historian Immanuel Wallerstein in the 1970s, is meant to emphasize the interdependence of places and regions around the world.

world-system: an interdependent system of countries linked by economic and political competition

Although the exact reasons for its beginnings are still debated, the modern world-system had its origins in parts of fifteenth-century Europe, when exploration beyond European shores began to be seen as an important way of opening up new opportunities for trade and economic expansion. By the sixteenth century, new techniques of shipbuilding and navigation had begun to bind more and more places and regions together through trade and political competition. The decline of feudalism and its replacement by merchant capitalism also profoundly changed Europe's economy during this period. As a result, increasingly more peoples around the world became exposed to one another's technologies and ideas. Their different resources, social structures, and cultural systems resulted in quite different pathways of development, however. Some societies were incorporated into the new, European-based international economic system faster than others; some resisted incorporation; and some sought alternative systems of economic and political organization. Some parts of the world were barely penetrated, if at all, by the European world-system. Australia and New Zealand, for example, were not discovered by Europeans until the late eighteenth century. Such regions were an **external arena** to the world-system (**Figure 2.1**).

external arena: regions of the world not yet absorbed into the modern world-system

Since the seventeenth century, the world-system has been consolidated with stronger economic ties among countries. It has also been extended, with all the world's countries eventually becoming involved to some extent, in the interdependence of the capitalist system. There have, however, been many instances of resistance and adaptation, with some countries (Tanzania, for example) attempting to become self-sufficient and others (for example, China and Cuba) seeking to opt

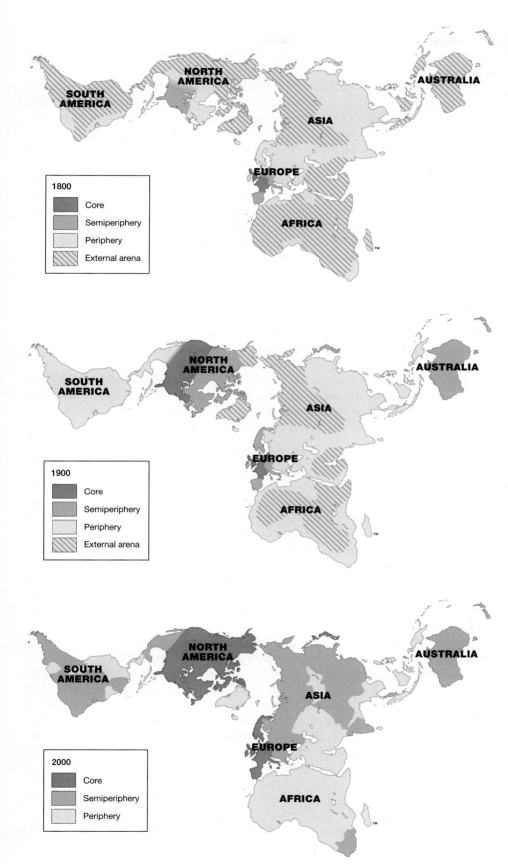

Figure 2.1   The world-system core, semiperiphery, and periphery in 1800, 1900, and 2000   Note how the Dymaxion projection (see Chapter 1) used in these maps emphasizes the relative proximity of core regions and accentuates the geographical isolation of the economically peripheral regions.   (*Source:* Map projection, Buckminster Fuller Institute and Dymaxion Map Design, Santa Barbara, CA. The word *Dymaxion* and the Fuller Projection Dymaxion™ Map design are trademarks of the Buckminster Fuller Institute, Santa Barbara, California, © 1938, 1967, & 1992. All rights reserved.)

states: independent political units with territorial boundaries that are internationally recognized by other political units

core regions: regions that dominate trade, control the most advanced technologies, and have high levels of productivity within diversified economies

colonialism: the establishment and maintenance of political and legal domination by a state over a separate and alien society

peripheral regions: regions with dependent and disadvantageous trading relationships, obsolete technologies, and undeveloped or narrowly specialized economies with low levels of productivity

semiperipheral regions: regions that are able to exploit peripheral regions but are themselves exploited and dominated by core regions

out of the system altogether to pursue a different path to development—that of communism. Today, the overall result is that a highly structured relationship between places and regions has emerged. This relationship is organized around three tiers: *core, semiperipheral,* and *peripheral regions.* These broad geographical divisions have been created through a combination of processes of private economic competition and competition among states. **States** are independent political units with territorial boundaries that are internationally recognized by other states (see the discussion of states, nations, and nation-states in Chapter 9).

The **core regions** of the world-system are those that dominate trade, control the most advanced technologies, and have high levels of productivity within diversified economies. As a result, they enjoy relatively high *per capita* incomes. The first core regions of the world-system were the trading hubs of Holland and England. Later, these were joined by manufacturing and exporting regions in other parts of Western Europe and in North America and, later still, by Japan and the Pacific Rim.

The success of these core regions depends on their dominance and exploitation of other regions. This dominance, in turn, depends on the participation of these other regions within the world-system. Initially, such participation was achieved by military enforcement, then by European colonialism, and finally by the sheer economic and political influence of the core regions. **Colonialism** involves the establishment and maintenance of political and legal domination by a state over a separate and alien society. This domination usually involves some colonization (that is, the physical settlement of people from the colonizing state) and always results in economic exploitation by the colonizing state.

Regions that have remained economically and politically unsuccessful throughout this process of incorporation into the world-system are peripheral. **Peripheral regions** are characterized by dependent and disadvantageous trading relationships, obsolete technologies, and undeveloped or narrowly specialized economies with low levels of productivity.

In between core regions and peripheral regions are semiperipheral regions. **Semiperipheral regions** are able to exploit peripheral regions but are themselves exploited and dominated by core regions. They consist mostly of countries that were once peripheral. This semiperipheral category underlines the fact that neither peripheral status nor core status is necessarily permanent. Canada, the United States, and Japan all achieved core status after having been peripheral; Spain and Portugal, part of the original core in the sixteenth century, became semiperipheral in the nineteenth century but are now once more part of the core. Quite a few countries, including Brazil, India, Mexico, South Korea, and Taiwan, have become semiperipheral after first having been incorporated into the periphery of the world-system and then developing a successful manufacturing sector that moved them into semiperipheral status.

So far, we have talked about core regions as if they are uniform, homogeneous areas. However, they are not. The same types of economic, political, social, and cultural processes that have created and that sustain core regions at a global level also operate at regional and local scales (**Figure 2.2**). The "global core," if we look at it more closely, is itself made up of a number of *regional cores, semiperipheries,* and *peripheries.* For example, Canada, with a gross national product (GNP) that places it in the G8 group of nations, is undoubtedly part of the global core. (The G8 actually has nine members: the world's seven most prosperous economies, the European Union, and Russia.) However, we know that not all of Canada's provinces and territories share uniformly in this prosperity. In fact, this country could be divided into the "heartland" and "hinterlands" as many Canadian geographers have come to call the regional core and its peripheries within this country.

Similarly, regional cores are themselves made up of *local cores* and *peripheries,* the result of more local processes of development. If we consider the megacity of Toronto, for example, we can agree that the city as a whole represents a highly developed region. But we also recognize that there are relatively wealthier and poorer sections of this city. The growing number of homeless people sleeping on

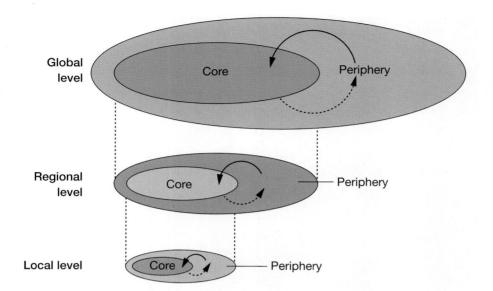

Figure 2.2   A simplified model of the world-system   The arrows indicate the various economic, political, military, and cultural means used by cores to dominate their peripheries. The diagram illustrates how the world-system is made up of a nested set of cores and peripheries.

the streets in the same blocks as the headquarters of our major banks is but one very sad example of these types of geographical differences. Another is that "Tent City" (an informal squatter settlement built on abandoned land) existed in one of the country's wealthiest cities.

We will be considering these regional and local levels in greater detail in later chapters (especially in Chapters 7 and 10). The important point to understand here is that the world-system is not made up of a few homogeneous regions. It is much more geographically varied than that. In fact, it is made up of a nested set of cores, semiperipheries, and peripheries at different scales of analysis.

We also need to understand that in certain cases—and Canada is one of them—a region can be simultaneously part of the global core and semiperiphery. As we have noted, Canada has a GNP and average per capita standard of living that places it in the global core. Canadian-owned businesses and banks make substantial profits from investments overseas, especially in the Caribbean periphery (**Figure 2.3**). Canada also acts as part of the global core in a military way (for example, its special forces [known as JTF2] fought in Afghanistan in support of the American invasion). Yet, at the same time, we recognize characteristics of the semiperiphery: large parts of the Canadian economy are American-owned, and Canada's political influence over the behemoth to its south is negligible. An appreciation of this dual position helps us understand the difficulties a middle power, such as Canada, faces on the world scene.

Because the world-system model is one that is so useful to geographers in understanding the world, it is well worth summarizing its most important features here.

- The world-system model states that the world can be divided into a series of cores, semiperipheries, and peripheries.

- In dividing the world in this way, we are using a relative concept of space, based on a socioeconomic measure of distance (see Chapter 1).

- The global core maintains its dominance through the exercise of the economic, political, military, and cultural forces at its disposal.

- The core also maintains its dominance through environmental and ecological means. (As examples, geographer Jared Diamond in his best-selling, 1997 study *Guns, Germs and Steel*, has argued that the initial centres of domestication secured a lasting advantage; Alfred Crosby has shown how the introduction of European crops overseas itself become an instrument of imperialism; and, in future, genetic modification may enable Western farmers to produce crops that could once only be grown in the tropics.)

Figure 2.3 A Canadian bank in the Caribbean This photograph shows a branch of the Royal Bank of Canada in Castries, the capital of Saint Lucia.

- The global periphery is maintained in a dependent position by the global core. (As an aside, because of this, some experts have suggested that the core actively "undevelops" the periphery; others point out how space is, in at least an economic or social sense, created by the inevitability of these interplays between the core and the periphery.)
- The global core and periphery have changed their locations over time.
- The world-system is made up of a nested series of cores and peripheries. In this, we see another of the concepts that we examined in Chapter 1, the concept of scale. In this way, local developments are transmitted to the regional and global levels, and the forces of globalization manifest themselves at the local level.

For the rest of this chapter, we will consider in more detail the evolution and operation of the world-system at the global scale.

GEOGRAPHIC EXPANSION, INTEGRATION, AND CHANGE

The world-system evolved in successive stages of geographic expansion and integration. This evolution has affected the roles of individual places and the nature of the interdependence among places. It also explains why places and regions have come to be distinctive and how this distinctiveness has formed the basis of geographic variability.

Mini-systems

mini-system: a society with a single cultural base and a reciprocal social economy

Systematically differentiated human geographies began with mini-systems. A **mini-system** is a society with a single cultural base and a *reciprocal* social economy.

That is, each individual specializes in particular tasks (tending animals, cooking, or making pottery, for example), freely giving any excess product to others, who reciprocate by giving up the surplus product of their own specialization. In prehistoric times, mini-systems were based on hunting and gathering societies that were finely tuned to local physical environments. They were all very small in geographical extent and very vulnerable to environmental change. After the first agricultural revolution between 9000 and 7000 B.C., mini-systems were both more extensive and more stable. These qualities eventually contributed to new forms of spatial organization, including urbanization and long-distance trading.

The transition to food-producing mini-systems had several important implications for the long-term evolution of the world's geographies. First, as we will see in Chapter 8, it allowed much higher population densities and encouraged the proliferation of settled villages. Second, it brought about a change in social organization, from loose communal systems to systems that were more highly organized on the basis of kinship. Kin groups provided a natural way of assigning rights over land and resources and of organizing patterns of land use. Third, it allowed some specialization in nonagricultural crafts, such as pottery, woven textiles, jewellery, and weaponry. This specialization led to a fourth development: the beginnings of barter and trade between communities, sometimes over substantial distances.

It is worth noting here that the first scholar to describe (and try to explain) the broad changes over time in the social economic bases of mini-systems (from reciprocity to redistribution) was Karl Polanyi (1886–1964). A Viennese-born economic historian, in his later life in Canada Polanyi endeavoured to show how ancient economies may have begun and then evolved over time. His work has influenced disciplines such as anthropology and political science, but has had less impact in the field of economics itself (where Polanyi's rejection of abstract theory in favour of the interpretation of historical evidence has been seen as a flaw). More recent research on ancient societies has itself questioned the ability of Polanyi's description to fit *all* such societies, and—we might add—it is obviously impossible for us to place ourselves into the minds of early peoples and make assumptions about how they interpreted their lives.

Most mini-systems vanished a long time ago, although some remnants of mini-systems have survived. Examples of these residual and fast-disappearing mini-systems are the bush people of the Kalahari, the hill tribes of Papua New Guinea, and the tribes of the Amazon rain forest. These mini-systems contribute powerfully to regional differentiation and sense of place in a few enclaves around the world, but their most important contribution to contemporary human geographies is that they provide a stark counterpoint to the landscapes and practices of the contemporary world-system.

The Growth of Early Empires

The higher population densities, changes in social organization, craft production, and trade brought about by the first agricultural revolution provided the preconditions for the emergence of several world-empires. A **world-empire** is a group of mini-systems that have been absorbed into a common political system while retaining their fundamental cultural differences. The social economy of world-empires can be characterized as redistributive-tributary. That is, wealth is appropriated from producer classes by an elite class in the form of taxes or tribute. This redistribution of wealth is most often achieved through military coercion, religious persuasion, or a combination of the two. The best-known world-empires are the largest and longest lasting of the ancient civilizations—Egypt, Greece, China, Byzantium, and Rome. **Figure 2.4** shows the geographical extent of one world-empire, the Chinese empire of the Qing dynasty. World-empires brought two important new elements to the evolution of the world's geographies. The first was the emergence of *urbanization* (see Chapter 10). Towns and cities became essential as centres of administration, military garrisons, and theological centres for the ruling classes, who were able to

world-empire: mini-systems that have been absorbed into a common political system while retaining their fundamental cultural differences

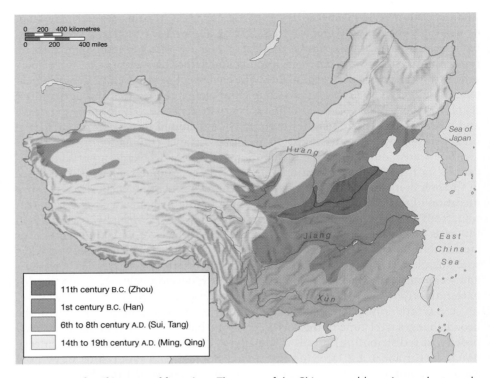

Figure 2.4 The Chinese world-empire The roots of the Chinese world-empire can be traced to the eleventh century B.C. and the Zhou culture that occupied the middle section of the north China plain, along the Huang (or Yellow) River. Recognizable Chinese civilization, however, is usually traced back to the Han dynasty of the first century B.C.: an Iron Age state with a population of about 60 million. Subsequently, the Chinese world-empire went through periods of expansion and contraction, with a major phase of expansion to the south during the Sui and Tang dynasties between the sixth and eighth centuries A.D. Between the fourteenth century and the nineteenth century, the Chinese world-empire was taken over by groups from the northern regions of present-day China, who established the Ming and Qing dynasties. The Qing dynasty was eventually overthrown in 1911, at which point the Chinese world-empire became absorbed into the modern world system.   (*Source:* F. Leeming, *The Changing Geography of China*. Oxford: Blackwell, 1993, fig. 3.1.)

law of diminishing returns: the tendency for productivity to decline, after a certain point, with the continued application of capital or labour or both to a given resource base

use a combination of military and theological authority to hold their empires together. As long as these early world-empires were successful, they gave rise not only to monumental capital cities but also to a whole series of secondary settlements, which acted as intermediate centres in the flow of tribute and taxes from colonized territories.

The second important contribution of world-empires to evolving world geographies was *colonization*. In part, this was an indirect consequence of the operation of the **law of diminishing returns**. This law refers to the tendency for productivity to decline, after a certain point, with the continued addition of capital, labour, or both to a given resource base. Because of the law of diminishing returns, world-empires could support growing populations only if overall levels of productivity could be increased. However, for each additional person working the land, the gain in production per worker was less. The usual response was to enlarge the resource base by colonizing nearby land. This colonization had immediate spatial consequences in terms of establishing dominant/subordinate spatial relationships between original areas of settlement within world-empires and colonies. It was also important in establishing hierarchies of settlements and creating improved transportation networks. The military underpinnings of colonization also meant that new towns and cities now came to be carefully sited for strategic and defensive reasons.

The legacy of these important changes is still apparent in many of today's landscapes (see **Visualizing Geography 2.1—The Legacy of World-Empires**).

The Legacy of World-Empires

Long after they have collapsed, the physical remains of imperial systems survive in today's landscape. Ruined defensive systems, cities, walls, and aqueducts provide some of the tangible signs that these places were once part of a previous economic and political system.

Known as the "abandoned city of the Mughals," Fatephur Sikr was built in the 1540s to serve a Muslim kingdom after the invasion of Central India.

This spectacular aqueduct was built in the time of Augustus (63 B.C. to A.D.14) to supply the city of Nîmes, in southern France, with water from Uzès, 50 kilometres (31 miles) away. The whole project is a testament to the surveying and engineering skills of the Romans. The water dropped only 17 metres (56 feet) over the whole distance.

The Maori peoples of New Zealand built defensive works known as *pa* to defend their territory. Usually built on hilltops, these earthworks required the excavation of massive banks and ditches to provide a secure refuge from attack.

Hadrian's Wall, a Roman defensive barrier guarding the northern frontier of the province of Britain. Completed in A.D. 136, it extended almost 110 kilometres (70 miles), with an original height of 6 metres (20 feet), a thickness of 2.5 metres (8 feet), and a flat-bottomed ditch that ran from the eastern coast to the western coast of northern England. The wall was protected by a series of small forts, but it was evacuated in A.D. 383 after several incursions by northern tribes.

Figure 2.5 Terraced landscapes
This landscape in Sikkim is the legacy of a hydraulic society—a world-empire in which despotic rulers once organized labour-intensive irrigation schemes that allowed for significant increases in agricultural productivity. The photo shows rice cultivation in Sikkim, formerly a kingdom but now an Indian state.

Some world-empires were exceptional in that they were based on a particularly strong central state, with totalitarian rulers who were able to organize large-scale, communal land improvement schemes using forced labour. Their dependency on large-scale land improvement schemes (particularly irrigation and drainage schemes) as the basis for agricultural productivity has led Wittfogel and other scholars to characterize them as *hydraulic societies*. Today, their legacy can be seen in the landscapes of terraced fields that have been maintained for generations in such places as Sikkim, India, and East Java, Indonesia (**Figure 2.5**).

The Geography of the Pre-modern World

Figure 2.6 shows the generalized framework of human geographies in the Old World as they existed around A.D. 1400. The following characteristics of this period are important. First, harsher environments in continental interiors were still peopled by isolated, subsistence-level, kin-ordered hunting and gathering mini-systems. Second, the dry belt of steppes and desert margins stretching across the Old World from the western Sahara to Mongolia was a continuous zone of kin-ordered pastoral mini-systems. Third, the areas where various forms of sedentary agricultural production extended in a discontinuous arc from Morocco to China, with two main outliers: in the central Andes and in Mesoamerica. The dominant centres of global civilization were China, northern India (both of them hydraulic variants of world-empires), and the Ottoman Empire of the eastern Mediterranean. Other important world-empires were based in Southeast Asia, in Muslim city-states of coastal North Africa, in the grasslands of West Africa, around the gold and copper mines of East Africa, and in the feudal kingdoms and merchant towns of Europe.

These more-developed realms were interconnected through trade, which meant that several emerging centres of capitalism existed. Port cities were particularly important, and among the leading centres were the city-state of Venice, the Hanseatic League of independent city-states in northwestern Europe, Cairo, Calicut, Canton, Malacca, and Sofala. Traders in these port cities began to organize the production of agricultural specialties, textiles, and craft products in their respective hinterlands. The **hinterland** of a town or city is its sphere of economic influence—the tributary area from which it collects products to be exported and throughout which it distributes imports. By the fifteenth century, several regions of budding capitalism existed: northern Italy, Flanders, southern England, the Baltic, the Nile Valley, Malabar, eastern coastal India (Coromandel), Bengal, northern Java, and southeast coastal China (**Figure 2.6**).

hinterland: the sphere of economic influence of a town or city

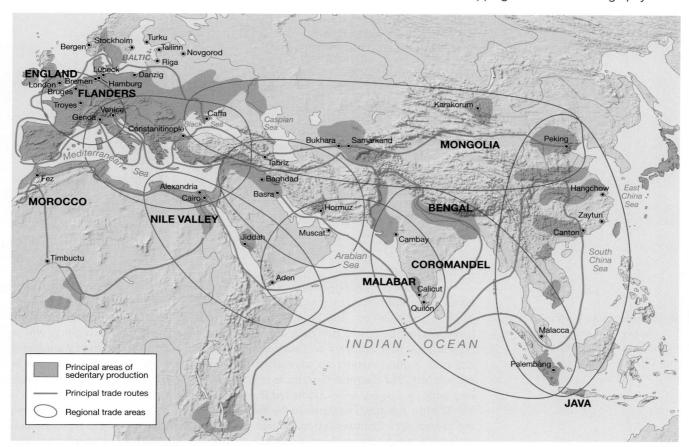

Figure 2.6   The precapitalist Old World, circa A.D. 1400   Principal areas of sedentary agricultural production are shaded. Some long-distance trade took place from one region to another, but for the most part, it was limited to a series of overlapping regional circuits of trade.   (*Sources:* R. Peet, *Global Capitalism: Theories of Societal Development.* New York: Routledge, 1991; J. Abu-Lughod, *Before European Hegemony: The World-System* A.D. *1200–1350.* New York: Oxford University Press, 1989; and E.R. Wolf, *Europe and the People without History.* Berkeley: University of California Press, 1983.)

MAPPING A NEW WORLD GEOGRAPHY

With the emergence of the modern world-system at the beginning of the sixteenth century, a whole new geography began to emerge. Although several regions of budding capitalist production existed and although imperial China could boast of sophisticated achievements in science, technology, and navigation, it was European merchant capitalism that reshaped the world. Several factors motivated European overseas expansion. A relatively high-density population and a limited amount of cultivable land meant that there was a continuous struggle to provide enough food. Meanwhile, the desire for overseas expansion was intensified by both competition among a large number of small monarchies and inheritance laws that produced large numbers of impoverished aristocrats with little or no land of their own. Many of these were eager to set out for adventure and profit.

Added to these motivating factors were the enabling factors of innovations in shipbuilding, navigation, and gunnery. In the mid-fifteenth century, for example, the Portuguese developed a cannon-armed ship—the caravel—that could sail anywhere, defend itself against pirates, pose a threat to those who were initially unwilling to trade, *and* carry enough goods to be profitable. The quadrant (1450) and the astrolabe (1480) enabled accurate navigation and mapping of ocean currents, prevailing winds, and trade routes (**Figure 2.7**). Naval power enabled the Portuguese and the Spanish to enrich their economies with capital from gold and silver plundered from the Americas.

Figure 2.7 Champlain's astrolabe
Lost soon after Champlain set out through the Ottawa Valley, this astrolabe was recovered in the nineteenth century. It is now on exhibit in the Canadian Museum of Civilization in Gatineau, Quebec.

plantations: large landholdings that usually specialize in the production of one particular crop for market

import substitution: the process by which domestic producers provide goods or services that formerly were bought from foreign producers

Europeans were able not only to send adventurers for gold and silver but also to take land, decide on its use, and exploit coerced labour to produce high-value crops (such as sugar, cocoa, and indigo) on **plantations**, large landholdings that usually specialized in the production of one particular crop for market. Some regions, whose populations were resistant to European disease and that also had high population densities, a good resource base, and strong states, were able to keep Europeans at arm's length. For the most part, these regions were in South and East Asia. Their dealings with Europeans were conducted through a series of coastal trading stations.

Within Europe, innovations in business and finance (banking, loan systems, credit transfers, commercial insurance, and courier services, for example) helped increase savings, investment, and commercial activity. European merchants and manufacturers also became adept at **import substitution**—copying and making goods previously available only by trading. The result was the emergence of Western Europe as the core region of a world-system that had penetrated and incorporated significant portions of the rest of the world.

For Europe, this overseas expansion stimulated further improvements in technology. These included new developments in nautical mapmaking, naval artillery, shipbuilding, and the use of sails. The whole experience of overseas expansion also provided a great practical school for entrepreneurship and investment. In this way, the self-propelling growth of merchant capitalism was intensified and consolidated.

For the periphery, European overseas expansion meant dependency (as it has ever since for many of the world's peripheral regions). In Canada's case, this situation was one that developed very slowly. Basque whalers from northeastern Spain were probably the first Europeans to exploit this country's natural resources on a regular basis. In their whaling stations on the lower St. Lawrence (such as the one at Red Bay in Labrador, established in the 1540s and recently re-created in the Canadian Museum of Civilization in Ottawa-Gatineau), whales were rendered into oil for the European market (**Figure 2.8**). From the early sixteenth century onward, French, Portuguese, and Basque fishing ships took increasingly large quantities of cod from the Grand Banks off Newfoundland and Labrador. Initially an annual undertaking from Europe, fishing by the 1680s by the French and British included overwintering on the coasts of Newfoundland and Labrador. Occasional exchanges of goods between sailors and Aboriginal groups led to the beginnings of the fur trade.

The subsequent development of an almost insatiable European market for Canadian furs drove itinerant French traders farther up the St. Lawrence and into the Great Lakes by the late seventeenth century to exploit the animal resources of those vast watersheds. An alternative method of fur trading was practised by the British. Using permanent bases (or "factories," such as Moose Factory), the Hudson's Bay Company was able to tap into the huge territory of Rupert's Land, which it had been granted in 1670, and to ship its furs out through northern waters (**Figure 2.9**).

Figure 2.8   Red Bay, Labrador
Archaeologists have found that this camp provided shelter for the production of whale oil and summer accommodation for the small Basque crews engaged in whaling in the 1540s.

Figure 2.9   Moose Factory   From its bases, such as this one at Moose Factory, the Hudson's Bay Company tapped the wealth of Rupert's Land and shipped furs to England.

In both cases, the real profits of the fur trade were realized in Europe, where furs were made into hats and garments. In addition, the Hudson's Bay Company was headquartered in London, where political and financial control over its Canadian resources was exercised. Only in the case of Montreal, where individual French traders based themselves and where the North West Company had its centre of operations from the 1780s to the 1820s, do we find any substantial profits from the fur trade being retained in Canada. Such merchant capital enabled the growth of Montreal's early business elite, which expressed itself in the mansions and built form of the city. That elite then invested in the early development of railroads in the Montreal region to profit from the encouragement of local trade and agriculture.

After 300 years of evolution, roughly between 1450 and 1750, the world-system had incorporated only parts of the world. The principal spheres of European influence were Mediterranean North Africa, Portuguese and Spanish colonies in the Americas, Indian ports and trading colonies (**Figure 2.10**), the East Indies, African and Chinese ports, the Greater Caribbean, and North America. The rest of the world functioned more or less as before, with slow-changing geographies

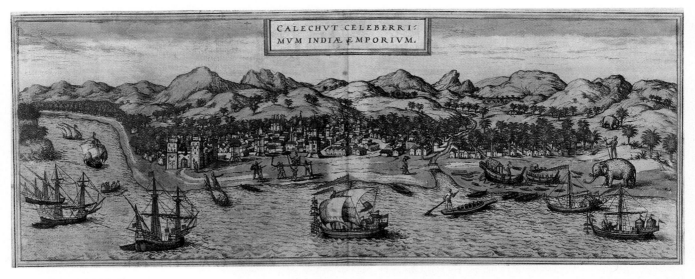

Figure 2.10 British, Portuguese, French, and Dutch ships in the harbour at Kolkata (Calcutta), India, around 1600 The expansion of European trade and the protection of trade routes required strong navies and a willingness to use them. England's Sir Walter Raleigh expressed the sentiment succinctly in 1608: "Whoso commands the sea commands the trade of the world; whoso commands the trade of the world commands the riches of the world."

leadership cycles: periods of international power established by individual states through economic, political, and military competition

hegemony: domination over the world economy exercised by one national state in a particular historical epoch through a combination of economic, military, financial, and cultural means

based around modified mini-systems and world-empires that were only partially and intermittently penetrated by market trading.

Industrialization and Geographic Change

With the new production and transportation technologies of the Industrial Revolution (from the late eighteenth century), capitalism truly became a global system that reached into virtually every part of the world and every aspect of people's lives. Human geographies were recast again, this time with a more interdependent dynamic. New production technologies, based on more concentrated forms of energy, such as coal, helped raise levels of productivity and create new and better products that stimulated demand, increased profits, and created a pool of capital for further investment. New transportation technologies triggered successive phases of geographic expansion, allowing for internal development as well as external colonization and *imperialism,* the deliberate exercise of military power and economic influence by core states to advance and secure their national interests (see Chapter 7).

The colonization and imperialism that accompanied the expansion of the world-system was closely tied to the evolution of world leadership cycles. **Leadership cycles** are periods of international power established by individual states through economic, political, and military competition. In the long term, success in the world-system depends on economic strength and competitiveness, which brings political influence and pays for military strength. With a combination of economic, political, and military power, individual states can dominate the world-system, setting the terms for many economic and cultural practices and imposing their particular ideology by virtue of their pre-eminence. This kind of dominance is known as hegemony. **Hegemony** refers to domination over the world economy exercised—through a combination of economic, military, financial, and cultural means—by one national state in a particular historical epoch. Over the long run, the costs of maintaining this kind of power and influence tend to weaken the dominant power, which brings the possibility of a new dominant world power (see **Geography Matters 2.2— World Leadership Cycles**).

Industrialization, meanwhile, resulted not only in the complete reorganization of the human geography of the original European core of the world-system but also in an extension of the world-system core to the United States and Japan.

Europe In Europe, three distinctive waves of industrialization occurred. The first, between 1790 and 1850, was based on the initial cluster of industrial technologies (steam engines, cotton textiles, and ironworking) and was very localized.

World Leadership Cycles

The modern world-system has so far experienced the following five full leadership cycles.

Portuguese dominance was established through initial advantages derived from Atlantic exploration, trade, and plunder. The Treaty of Tordesillas, arbitrated by Pope Alexander VI in 1494, consolidated these advantages by limiting direct competition with Portugal's chief rival, Spain. The treaty allowed Portugal to lay claim to any territory to the east of a line drawn north–south, 370 leagues (2075 kilometres, or 1290 miles) west of Cape Verde (that is, between 48° and 49°W), which included the eastern coast of Brazil (**Figure 2.2.1**). By 1550, Portugal had established many important outposts around the world.

Dutch dominance began with the defeat of the Portuguese-backed Spanish Armada (against England) in a decisive naval battle in 1588. Dutch ports and Dutch shipping dominated European trade, and the Dutch government coordinated trade through the Dutch East India Company and the Dutch West India Company (**Figure 2.2.2**). The hegemony of the United Provinces of the Netherlands (the so-called Dutch Republic) continued until the 1660s, when both the English and the French were able to mount a serious challenge.

Thereafter, *British dominance* was sustained, in spite of a relatively poor domestic resource base, by overseas trade and colonization, backed up by a powerful navy. A

Figure 2.2.2   Merchant vessels of the Dutch and English East India Companies   The English East India Company was established in 1600 as a monopolistic trading company and agent of British imperialism in India. In response, the Dutch East India Company was founded in 1602 by the government of the United Provinces of the Netherlands to protect its trading interests in the Far East.

series of Napoleonic Wars with France marked the competitive phase of the leadership cycle, which was brought to a close by decisive victories at Trafalgar (1805) and at Waterloo (1815). By then, the Industrial Revolution had given Britain an economic and military edge that proved decisive.

The second cycle of British dominance was based on the economic advantages of early industrialization, which allowed for an unprecedented degree of incorporation of the world under British imperial and economic hegemony. But from the 1860s onward, imperial overstretch and increasing economic competition from the United States and Germany put an end to hegemony and marked the beginning of a period of struggle. The German challenge culminated in the Great War of 1914–1918 (World War I), which left Germany defeated, Britain weakened, and the United States strengthened.

The *United States* was economically dominant within the world-system by 1920 but did not achieve hegemonic power because of a lack of political will to get involved in world affairs. After World War II, the United States was unquestionably the hegemonic power. Its economic and cultural dominance within the world-system has not yet been seriously challenged, though its political and military superiority was in question for several decades as the Soviet Union sought a noncapitalist path to modernization and power. This challenge disappeared in 1989, but by then, the economic foundation for U.S. hegemony had come under serious threat because of the resurgence of Japanese and European industries and the globalization of economic activity through transnational corporations (**Figure 2.2.3**).

Figure 2.2.1   Portugal's claims to the New World   The Treaty of Tordesillas (1494) gave Portugal control over what were the more accessible parts of the New World. This map, drawn in 1502 by Alberto Contino, shows Portuguese territories marked by flags with a blue interior and a red border. Spanish territories, farther west, are marked by the red, gold, and black flag of Spain.

Figure 2.2.3   The Gulf War   All hegemonic powers must protect the economic foundations of their power. They must also resist challenges to their political, cultural, and ideological dominance. Occasionally, this calls for military intervention. The Gulf War, fought in 1991, was an example of this sort of intervention. It was prompted by the invasion of Kuwait in 1990 by Iraq, where President Saddam Hussein had consolidated popularity through an aggressive stance toward American culture and business interests. The invasion of Kuwait not only threatened to disrupt the supply of crude oil to the world economy but also posed a threat to the U.S.-sponsored regional balance of power in the Middle East. In 1991, the United States led an international coalition of 500 000 troops (including 4500 Canadians) against Iraq, driving Iraqi troops out of Kuwait and destroying Iraq's military infrastructure.

The second wave, between 1850 and 1870, involved the diffusion of industrialization to most of the rest of Britain and to parts of northwest Europe, particularly the coalfield areas of northern France, Belgium, and Germany (**Figure 2.11**). New opportunities were created as railroads and steamships made more places accessible, bringing their resources and their markets into the sphere of industrialization. New materials and new technologies (for example, steel and machine tools) created opportunities to manufacture and market new products. These new activities brought some significant changes in the logic of industrial location. The importance of railway networks, for example, attracted industry away from smaller towns on the canal systems toward larger towns with good rail connections.

The third wave of industrialization, between 1870 and 1914, saw a further reorganization of the geography of Europe as yet another cluster of technologies

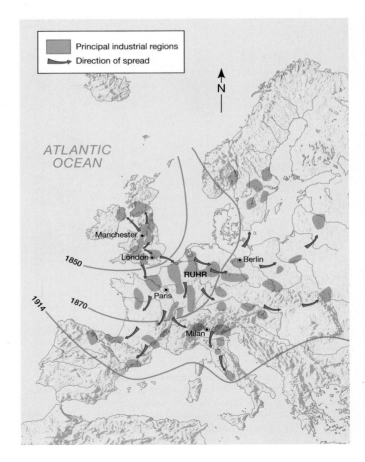

Figure 2.11   The spread of industrialization in Europe
European industrialization began with the emergence of small industrial regions in several different parts of Britain. As new rounds of industrial and transportation technologies emerged, industrialization spread to other regions with access to raw materials and energy sources, good communications, and large labour markets.

(including electricity, electrical engineering, and telecommunications) imposed different needs and created new opportunities. During this period, industrialization spread for the first time to other parts of Europe as Figure 2.11 illustrates. The overall result was to create a core within a core, an area of prosperity centred on the "Golden Triangle" stretching from London to Paris to Berlin.

The United States   By the end of the nineteenth century, the core of the world-system had itself extended to include the United States and Japan. The United States, politically independent just before the onset of the Industrial Revolution, was able to make the transition from the periphery to the core because of several favourable circumstances. Its vast natural resources of land and minerals provided the raw materials for a wide range of industries that could grow and organize without being hemmed in and fragmented by political boundaries. Its population, growing quickly through immigration, provided a large and expanding market and a cheap and industrious labour force. Its cultural and trading links with Europe provided business contacts, technological know-how, and access to capital for investment in a basic infrastructure of canals, railways, docks, warehouses, and factories.

As in Europe, industrialization developed around pre-existing centres of industrialization and population and was shaped by the resource needs and market opportunities of successive clusters of technology. America's industrial strength was established at the beginning of the twentieth century with the development of a new cluster of technologies that included the internal combustion engine, oil and plastics, electrical engineering, and radio and telecommunications (see Chapter 7). The outcome was a distinctive economic core (**Figure 2.12**)—another core within a core.

Canada   By 1900, Canada remained dependent on the global core, but it had become more integrated into the world-system. It had moved from periphery to semiperiphery status on a world scale (see Figure 2.1). Politically, much had changed. The conquest of New France in 1760 by Britain and the loss of Britain's colonies in America (the Revolutionary War of 1775–1783) now meant that Canada became the focus of British colonial activity in North America. With Confederation in 1867, Canada became, nominally at least, in charge of its own affairs. Nevertheless, by the century's end, the increasing involvement of U.S. financial interests in Canada's economy was causing another change: Canada was shifting from being a dependency of Britain to become dependent on the U.S. regional core. In 1900, for example, U.S. capital represented 15 percent of all foreign investment in Canada; by 1920, it totalled more than 50 percent.

Nineteenth-century developments were greatly aided by British and American investments in Canada's rail system and by the implementation of Canada's *National Policy* of 1879. This policy promoted the completion of a transcontinental link to tie the country together, encouraged immigration to the Prairies, and introduced tariffs to protect Canadian industry from cheaper American manufacturers. As a result, industrialization (which had begun by the 1850s) gathered pace, and by 1900, small manufacturing belts lay between Niagara (where hydro power was already in use) and Toronto, in the Montreal region, and around the Cape Breton coalfields of Nova Scotia.

To the existing Canadian staples of fish and furs, the nineteenth century added the development of a significant timber trade in Quebec and Ontario, the export of wheat from the Prairies to European markets, and, by the 1920s, the beginnings of pulp and paper production in British Columbia for American markets. The development, after 1945, of Alberta's substantial reserves of oil and gas, and the construction of the thousands of kilometres of pipelines needed to transport these hydrocarbons to market ensured that Canada's post-war economy remained heavily dependent on the export of raw materials.

Unlike the U.S. economy, Canada remained heavily dependent on the exploitation of its natural resources, or *staples,* for sale overseas. One danger of this was

Figure 2.12 The North American core and periphery, 1911
(*Source:* L. McCann and A. Gunn, *Heartland and Hinterland: A Regional Geography of Canada.* Scarborough: Prentice-Hall, 1998.)

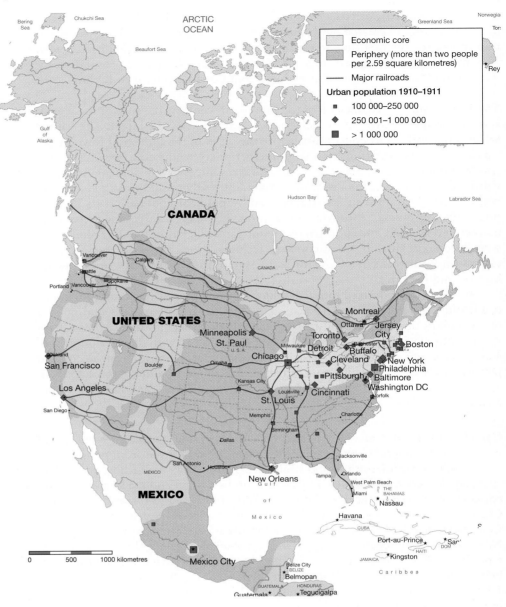

staples trap: an over-reliance on the export of staples makes an economy (national or regional) vulnerable to fluctuations in world prices and without alternatives when resource depletion occurs

staples thesis: a proposition arguing that the export of Canada's natural resources, or staples, had a pervasive impact on this country, one consequence being that Canada became locked into dependency as a resource hinterland for more advanced economies

the **staples trap,** which left Canada vulnerable to fluctuations in world prices and without alternatives when resource depletion occurred. Another problem was the paradox of how such a high level of exports could result in such low levels of economic growth in Canada itself. This question prompted scholars to develop the staples thesis in the 1920s—50 years before Immanuel Wallerstein advanced his more general world-system model.

The **staples thesis** argues that the export of Canada's natural resources, or staples (such as fur, fish, timber, grain, and oil), to more advanced economies has hindered the development of this country's economic, political, and social systems. As Canadian scholars, such as Harold Innis (1894–1952), have suggested, the economy's over-reliance on the export of staples to generate income locked Canada into being a resource hinterland. The value-added in the subsequent manufacture of products derived from those staples accrued not to this country but to the manufacturers in Britain and the United States.

In this view, domestic industry was stultified because it was cheaper and easier to export raw materials and then to use that income to purchase manufactured items from overseas. Escape from this over-reliance on the export of basic commodities would have required the establishment of locally owned factories and a widely diversified industry. But finance capital was limited in Canada, and locally produced products would be more expensive than were British or American imports (because of the small production runs). What this means, if we focus on outcomes rather than on principles, is that Canadian economic growth could only be achieved, according to the staples thesis, by the continual discovery of new forms of staples to export.

The staples thesis enables us to explain why many local economic activities in Canada (such as, for example, coal mining in Kimberley, British Columbia, or fishing along Newfoundland and Labrador's shores) have not produced sustained growth in other sectors of the local economy.

Innis's view may be, in the words of the economist Mel Watkins, "the most important single contribution to scholarship by Canadian social scientists and historians,"[2] but it is not without its critics, as it was in his day. Economic historian W.A. Mackintosh, a contemporary of Innis's, for example, believed that staple production was merely a stage in a country's economic evolution and that a mature economy would develop once investment from staple production stimulated the diversification of industry. An example of this alternative view is Ottawa (discussed more fully in Chapter 7), which was a lumber town in the early nineteenth century but now boasts a fully diversified local economy.

Internal Development of the Core Regions

Within the world's core regions, the transformation of regional geographies hinged on successive innovations in transport technology. These innovations opened up agrarian interiors and intensified interregional trading networks. Farmers were able to mechanize their equipment, while manufacturing companies were able to take over more resources and more markets.

Canals and the Growth of Industrial Regions   The first phase of this internal geographic expansion and regional integration was, in fact, based on an old technology, the canal. Merchant trade and the beginnings of industrialization in both Britain and France were underpinned by extensive navigation systems that joined one river system to another. By 1790, France had just more than 1000 kilometres (625 miles) of canals and canalized rivers; Britain had nearly 3590 kilometres (2230 miles). The Industrial Revolution provided both the need and the capital for a spate of additional canal building that began to integrate and extend emerging industrial regions.

In Canada, the main object of canal construction was to improve or protect navigation along the St. Lawrence–Great Lakes corridor, a project ultimately completed only with the opening of the St. Lawrence Seaway in 1959. The Lachine Canal (1821–1825) and the small canals at Grenville and Carillon on the Ottawa River (1819–1834) bypassed rapids west of Montreal. The Rideau Canal (1826–1832) was designed to enable canal traffic to avoid possible American attacks on the St. Lawrence itself. The most ambitious project, the Welland Canal (1829, 1845, 1887, and 1913–1932), was built to enable vessels to climb 100 metres from Lake Ontario to Lake Erie. The Trent–Severn Waterway (1833–1920), although now extremely popular for recreation, was never a commercial success because its hinterland was too thinly settled (**Figure 2.13**). Low population density was also the reason for the failure of Nova Scotia's Shubenacadie Canal (1826–1861), which connected Halifax to the Bay of Fundy.

Steamboats, Railroads, and Internal Development   The scale of North America was such that a network of canals was a viable proposition only in the more densely

---

[2]Mel Watkins, "Staples Thesis." *The Canadian Encyclopedia.* This authoritative source can now be consulted electronically. See the online edition at **www.thecanadianencyclopedia.com**.

Figure 2.13 The Trent–Severn Waterway's lift lock at Peterborough, Ontario The Trent–Severn Waterway connects Trenton (on Lake Ontario) with Port Severn (on Georgian Bay, Lake Huron), a distance of 386 kilometres (240 miles). Connecting a series of lakes and rivers, the waterway consists of 44 locks. Two of the locks, at Peterborough (illustrated here) and at Kirkfield, are hydraulic lift locks, which are unique in North America. Based on a design developed in Belgium and England, these structures were among the first to be built entirely of concrete in Canada. The waterway was built sporadically between 1833 and 1920 and was never a commercial success because of the low population density of its hinterland. The waterway has, however, experienced an increase in use in recent years as tourists have realized its recreational potential.

settled areas. The effective colonization of the interior could not take place until the development of steam-powered transportation—first riverboats and then railroads. The heyday of the river steamboat was between 1830 and 1850. During this period, vast areas of the U.S. interior were opened up to commercial, industrialized agriculture—especially cotton production for export to British textile manufacturers. At the same time, river ports, such as New Orleans, St. Louis, Cincinnati, and Louisville, grew rapidly, extending the frontiers of industrialization and modernization.

In western Canada, the heyday of the riverboat lasted much longer. Steamers ferried thousands of people into British Columbia during gold rushes to the Fraser Valley (1858), the Cariboo region around Barkerville (1862), and Yukon in 1898. A Saskatchewan River steamer took part in the defeat of Louis Riel, Gabriel Dumont, and the Métis at the Battle of Batoche in 1885. Stern paddle wheelers provided the only means of transport across the Kootenay lakes and continued in service into the 1950s. The last remaining vessel, the *S.S. Moyie*, is now preserved at Kaslo, British Columbia, as a heritage attraction (**Figure 2.14**).

By 1860, the railroads had taken over the task of internal development, further extending the frontier of settlement and industrialization and intensifying the use

Figure 2.14 The *S.S. Moyie* The last remaining sternwheeler on the Kootenay lakes is preserved at Kaslo, British Columbia. Before the construction of railroads or highways, these steamers (many of which transported trains on their decks) provided a vital link across many parts of Canada. Sternwheelers, for example, plied the Yukon, Mackenzie, and South Saskatchewan Rivers, and they were part of nineteenth-century transportation systems on Lake Winnipeg, the Great Lakes, and the St. Lawrence River.

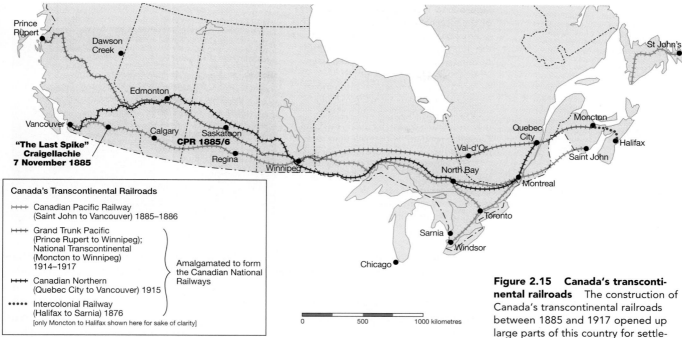

Figure 2.15   Canada's transcontinental railroads   The construction of Canada's transcontinental railroads between 1885 and 1917 opened up large parts of this country for settlement and economic development. (*Source:* Based on John Warkentin, *A Regional Geography of Canada; Life and Space*, 2nd ed. Scarborough: Prentice Hall, 2000, p. 108, map 4–5.)

of previously developed regions. The railroad originated in Britain, where George Stephenson engineered the world's first commercial railroad, a 20-kilometre (12.4-mile) line between Stockton and Darlington that was opened in 1825. In other core countries, where sufficient capital existed to license (or copy) the locomotive technology and install the track, railroad systems led to the first full stage of economic and political integration.

In Canada, as we have already noted, railroad construction was one of the pillars of nation building. Indeed, a completed transcontinental railroad was a condition of British Columbia joining Confederation in 1871. By 1885, this was achieved with the completion of the Canadian Pacific Railroad. The construction of such lines enabled British Columbia's timber and prairie agricultural products to be transported overseas and large numbers of immigrants to be moved to the frontiers of settlement (**Figure 2.15**). Cities that served as regional rail centres, such as Winnipeg, grew to substantial size during this period. Nevertheless, the Ontario–Quebec manufacturing region retained its primacy because it financed and controlled the rail network and because Montreal stood at the centre of Canada's rail and sea connections.

Although the railroads integrated the economies of entire countries and allowed vast territories to be colonized, they also brought some important regional and local restructuring and differentiation. In the United States, for example, the railroads led to the consolidation of the Manufacturing Belt. They also contributed to the mushrooming of Chicago as the focal point for railroads that extended the Manufacturing Belt's dominance over the West and South.

Tractors, Trucks, Road Building, and Spatial Reorganization   In the twentieth century, the internal combustion engine powered further rounds of internal development, integration, and intensification (**Figure 2.16**). The replacement of horse-drawn farm implements with lightweight tractors powered by internal combustion engines, beginning in the 1910s, amounted to a major revolution in agriculture (see Chapter 8). Productivity was increased, the frontiers of cultivable land were extended, and vast numbers of agricultural labourers, now replaced by mechanization, became available for industrial work in cities. The result was a parallel revolution in the geographies of both rural and urban areas.

Figure 2.16 The geographical impacts of the internal combustion engine The internal combustion engine revolutionized the geography of the more affluent and developed parts of the world. Between 1946 and 1961, the total length of surfaced roads (concrete or bituminous) increased in Canada from 39 267 kilometres (24 424 miles) to 125 525 kilometres (78 075 miles). By 2001, the total Canadian road network (excluding rural roads and roads within urban areas) was 215 000 kilometres (133 700 miles). With the eclipse of the railroads, the spatial organization of industries and land uses was radically reorganized, and a new round of geographical change took place.

The development of trucks in the 1910s and 1920s suddenly released factories from locations tied to railroads, canals, and waterfronts. Trucking allowed goods to be moved farther, faster, and cheaper than before. As a result, trucking made it feasible to locate factories on inexpensive land on city fringes and in smaller towns and peripheral regions where labour was cheaper. It also increased the market area of individual factories and reduced the need for large product inventories. This decentralization of industry, in conjunction with the availability of buses, private automobiles, and massive road-building programs, brought about another phase of spatial reorganization. In Canada, construction began on the Queen Elizabeth Way in the 1930s. This four-lane controlled access highway provided important links between Canada's economic heartland and the U.S. Manufacturing Belt. In addition to economic aims, the Trans-Canada Highway (7821 kilometres), opened in 1962, had the national goal of linking the entire country, this time by road. The outcomes of this phase were the specialized and highly integrated regions and urban systems of the modern core of the world-system. This integration was not simply an interconnectedness through highway systems; it also involved close economic linkages among manufacturers, suppliers, and distributors—linkages that enabled places and regions to specialize and develop economic advantages (see Chapter 7).

ORGANIZING THE PERIPHERY

Parallel with the internal development of core regions were changes in the geographies of the periphery of the world-system. Indeed, the growth and internal development of the core regions simply could not have taken place without the foodstuffs, raw materials, and markets provided by the colonization of the periphery and the incorporation of more and more territory into the sphere of industrial capitalism.

As soon as the Industrial Revolution had gathered momentum in the early nineteenth century, the industrial core nations embarked on the inland penetration of the world's midcontinental grassland zones to exploit them for grain or stock production. At the same time, as the demand for tropical plantation products increased, most of the tropical world came under the political and economic control—directly or indirectly—of one or another of the industrial core nations. In the second half of the nineteenth century, and especially after 1870, there was a vast increase in the number of colonies and the number of people under colonial rule.

The International Division of Labour

The fundamental logic behind all this colonization was economic: the need for an extended arena for trade, an arena that could supply foodstuffs and raw materials in return for the industrial goods of the core. The outcome was an international division of labour, driven by the needs of the core and imposed through its economic and military strength. This **division of labour** involved the specialization of different people, regions, and countries in certain kinds of economic activities.

The result was that colonial economies were founded on narrow specializations that were oriented to, and dependent on, the needs of core countries. Examples of these specializations include bananas in Central America; cotton in India; coffee in Brazil, Java, and Kenya; copper in Chile; cocoa in Ghana; tea in Ceylon (now Sri Lanka); tin in Bolivia; and bauxite in Guyana and Surinam. Most of these specializations have continued through to the present. Thus, for example, 48 of the 55 countries in sub-Saharan Africa still depend on just three products—tea, cocoa, and coffee—for more than half of their export earnings.

The international division of labour brought about a substantial increase in trade and a huge surge in the overall size of the capitalist world economy. The peripheral regions of the world contributed a great deal to this growth. By 1913, Africa and Asia provided more *exports* to the world economy than either North America or the British Isles. Asia alone was *importing* almost as much, by value, as North America. The industrializing countries of the core bought increasing amounts of foodstuffs and raw materials from the periphery, financed by profits from the export of machinery and manufactured goods. Britain, the hegemonic power of the period, drew on a trading empire that was truly global (**Figure 2.17**).

Patterns of international trade and interdependence became increasingly complex. Britain used its capital to invest not just in peripheral regions but also in profitable industries in other core countries, especially the United States. At the same time, these other core countries were able to export cheap manufactured goods to Britain. Britain financed the purchase of these goods, together with imports of food from its dominion states (Canada, South Africa, Australia, and New Zealand) and colonies, through the export of its own manufactured goods to peripheral countries. India and China, with large domestic markets, were especially important. Thus, there developed a widening circle of exchange and dependence, with constantly switching patterns of trade and investment.

Canadian interests benefited from this activity, particularly the transatlantic trade with Britain. In 1878, the total Canadian fleet of 7196 vessels was the third largest in the world (after Britain and the United States). Large sailing ships were built in small centres, such as Maitland, Nova Scotia. Samuel Cunard, of Halifax, operated the mail ships from Liverpool to Halifax, Quebec City, and Boston beginning in 1840.

division of labour: the specialization of different people, regions, or countries in particular kinds of economic activities

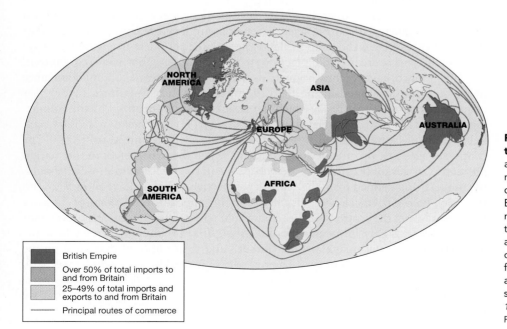

Figure 2.17   The British Empire in the late 1800s   Protected by the all-powerful Royal Navy, the British merchant navy established a web of commerce that collected food for British industrial workers and raw materials for its industries, much of them from colonies and dependencies appropriated by imperial might and developed by British capital. So successful was the trading empire that Britain also became the hub of trade for other states.   (*Source:* P. Hugill, *World Trade since 1431*. Baltimore: Johns Hopkins University Press, 1993, p. 136.)

Legend:
- British Empire
- Over 50% of total imports to and from Britain
- 25–49% of total imports and exports to and from Britain
- Principal routes of commerce

Imperialism: Imposing New Geographies on the World

The incorporation of the periphery was by no means entirely motivated by this basic logic of free trade and investment. Although Britain was the hegemonic power in the late nineteenth century, several other European countries (notably Germany, France, and the Netherlands) together with the United States—and later Japan—were competing for global influence. This competition developed into a scramble for territorial and commercial domination. The core countries engaged in pre-emptive geographical expansionism to protect their established interests and to limit the opportunities of others. They also wanted to secure as much of the world as possible—through a combination of military supervision, administrative control, and economic regulations—to ensure stable and profitable environments for their traders and investors. This combination of circumstances defined a new era of imperialism.

In the final quarter of the nineteenth century, a second wave of imperialism brought a competitive form of colonialism that resulted in a scramble for territory. Between 1870 and 1900, European countries added almost 16 million square kilometres (10 million square miles) and 150 million people to their spheres of control—20 percent of Earth's land surface and 10 percent of its population.

Africa, more than any other peripheral region, was given an entirely new geography. It was carved up into a patchwork of European colonies and protectorates in just 34 years, between 1880 and 1914, with little regard for either physical geography or the pre-existing human geographies of mini-systems and world-empires. Within just a few years, the whole of Africa became incorporated into the modern world-system, with a geography that consisted of a hierarchy of three kinds of space. One consisted of regions and localities organized by European colonial administrators and European investors to produce commodities for the world market. A second consisted of zones of production for local markets, where peasant farmers produced food for consumption by labourers engaged in commercial mining and agriculture. The third consisted of widespread regions of subsistence agriculture whose connection with the world-system was as a source of labour for the commercial regions.

The imprint of imperialism and colonization on the geographies of the newly incorporated peripheries of the world-system was immediate and profound. The periphery was brought to be almost entirely dependent on European and North American capital, shipping, managerial expertise, financial services, and news and communications. Consequently, it also became dependent on European cultural products: language, education, science, religion, architecture, and planning. All of these influences were etched into the landscapes of the periphery in a variety of ways as new places were created, old places were remade, and regions were reorganized.

Geographers have recently begun to examine the processes of cultural dominance using theories developed in the field of cultural studies. **Subaltern theory**, for example, examines the ways in which the periphery is marginalized by the colonizing centre. (The word *subaltern* in the theory's name literally means a military rank below that of captain but in this context means the "colonized subject.") The centre engages in a process of "othering," in which the experiences of the margin are seen as irrelevant because they are outside the norms of convention—*convention*, of course, being defined from the centre's perspective. Scholars have shown how, in this way, colonial voices are "disabled" by the imposition on them of "master narratives" from the centre. The best example of research on this process is Professor Edward Said's highly influential book *Orientalism*, in which he shows how the West created its own image of the "Orient" and then imposed that view on the Asian lands it came to dominate. The remedy, suggested by such scholars as Said, is to examine the centre *from* the margin. We can easily see that the terms *centre* and *margin* equate with the world-system terms of *core* and *periphery* that we have been using thus far.

subaltern theory: a theory examining the ways in which the colonized margin is culturally dominated by the colonizing centre

Subaltern theory is itself a part of a broader set of artistic, political, and research approaches collectively known as **postcolonialism**, or postcolonial theory, because it examines the consequences of the end of the European colonial system.[3] Leading scholars include Franz Fanon, whose 1960s' work saw nationalism as a necessary step in the breakup of an empire, and Gayatri Spivak, who has continued Edward Said's work on how colonial attitudes limit and affect imperialism.

Illustrations of cultural marginalization can also be found in the history of Canadian settlement. In the years before Canada's Aboriginal peoples were acknowledged, their cultures were reinterpreted through the eyes of the French and British colonizers. Similarly, in the past, immigrants from other parts of the world found that their own cultures were devalued in a Canadian milieu. Since the 1890s, however, high levels of immigration from other parts of the world have enabled a rich cultural mosaic to develop, especially in Canada's fast-growing metropolitan centres, in which Canadians have come to recognize the validity of the many different cultures they encounter in their day-to-day existence. Recent federal and provincial initiatives concerning policies of multiculturalism have also helped deal with this issue. Of course, as a country that is itself dependent on the core, Canada, over time, has had to bear the cultural imperialism of the major powers of the core—the cultures of France, Britain, and now the United States. Each has set standards of language, music, and literature that Canadian society has adopted.

Perhaps the Barbadian poet Kevyn Alan Arthur, who now lives in England, best expresses the sense of cultural disablement that neo-colonialism by a dominant core culture can bring. In his poem "England and Nowhere," he writes:

> They tried to make me understand, like them,
> that identity comes from History, Politics;
> and that they were of that Culture, History,
> in terms of which Life has its highest meaning;
> that my greatest aspirations could only lie
> in my assimilating their supremacy
> as best this bettered savage could.
> . . .
>
> They had robbed me one more time:
> had made me take too long to understand
> that I needed do no more than simply *feel*
> to know that Life itself was deep and meaningful
> before we stamped somebody's ethos on it,
> long before we coloured it
> in whosoever geography or history . . .[4]

postcolonialism: a broad set of artistic, political, and research approaches that examine the consequences of the end of European colonialism

GLOBALIZATION

The imperial world order began to disintegrate shortly after World War II. The United States emerged as the new hegemonic power, the dominant state within the world-system core. This core came to be called the "First World." The Soviet Union and China, opting for alternative paths of development for themselves and their satellite countries, were seen as a "Second World," withdrawn from the capitalist world economy. Their pursuit of alternative political economies was based on radically different values.

By the 1950s, many of the old European colonies began to seek political independence. Nevertheless, the newly independent states were still influenced by many of the old colonial links and legacies that remained intact. The result was

---

[3]A useful discussion of the term *postcolonialism* can be found in Craig Calhoun (ed.), *Dictionary of Social Sciences*. Oxford: Oxford University Press, 2002, pp. 373–374.
[4]Kevyn Alan Arthur, *England and Nowhere*. Leeds, UK: Peepal Tree Press, 1993, pp. 34–35.

neo-colonialism: economic and political strategies by which powerful states in core economies indirectly maintain or extend their influence over other areas or people

a neo-colonial pattern of international development. **Neo-colonialism** refers to economic and political strategies by which powerful states in core economies indirectly maintain or extend their influence over other areas or people. Instead of formal, direct rule (colonialism), controls are exerted through such strategies as international financial regulations, commercial relations, and covert intelligence operations. Because of this neo-colonialism, the human geographies of peripheral countries continued to be heavily shaped by the linguistic, cultural, political, and institutional influences of the former colonial powers and by the investment and trading activities of their firms.

At about the same time, a new form of imperialism was emerging. This was the commercial imperialism of giant corporations. These corporations had grown within the core countries through the elimination of smaller firms by mergers and takeovers. By the 1960s, quite a few of them had become so big that they were *transnational* in scope, having established overseas subsidiaries, taken over foreign competitors, or simply bought into profitable foreign businesses.

transnational corporations: companies with investments and activities that span international boundaries and with subsidiary companies, factories, offices, or facilities in several countries

These **transnational corporations** have investments and activities that span international boundaries, with subsidiary companies, factories, offices, or facilities in several countries. By the mid-1990s, nearly 40 000 transnational corporations were operating, 90 percent of which had headquarters in core states. Among them, these corporations control about 180 000 foreign subsidiaries and account for over US$6 trillion in worldwide sales.

The distinctive feature of globalization over the past 30 years or so is a decisive increase in the proportion of the world's economic and cultural activities that are international in scope. This increase is linked to a significant shift in the nature of international economic activity. Flows of goods, capital, and information that take place within and between transnational corporations are becoming more important than imports and exports between countries. The foreign affiliates of transnational corporations achieved more than US$10 trillion in sales in 1998, accounting for more than one-third of total world exports. At the same time, all these flows and activities have helped spread new values around the world. These new values range from consumer lifestyle preferences to altruistic concerns with global resources, global environmental changes, and famine relief.

commodity chains: networks of labour and production processes beginning with the extraction or production of raw materials and ending with the delivery of a finished commodity

The contemporary world economy is constituted through the myriad commodity chains that criss-cross global space. **Commodity chains** are networks of labour and production processes whose origin is in the extraction or production of raw materials and whose end result is the delivery and consumption of a finished commodity. These networks often span countries and continents, linking into vast global assembly lines the production and supply of raw materials, the processing of raw materials, the production of components, the assembly of finished products, and the distribution of finished products. As we willl see in Chapter 7, these global assembly lines are increasingly important in shaping places and regions.

This globalization of the contemporary world—its causes and effects on specific aspects of human geographies at different spatial scales—is a recurring theme through the rest of this book. For the moment, we need note only in broad outline its principal causes and outcomes.

Factors Contributing to Globalization

The globalization of the past quarter-century has been caused by four important and interrelated factors: a new international division of labour, an internationalization of finance, a new technology system, and a homogenization of international consumer markets.

The new international division of labour has involved three main changes. First, the United States has declined as an industrial producer, relative to the spectacular growth of Japan and the resurgence of Europe as industrial producers.

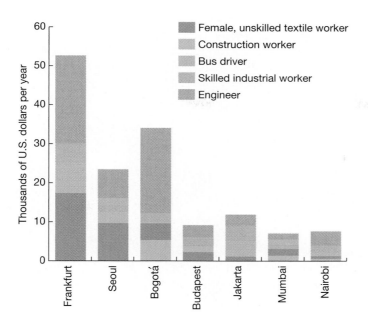

Figure 2.18 International differences in wage rates Wages vary substantially across countries and regions. The height of each bar segment in this chart indicates the range of salaries for several occupations in different cities. Adjusted for differences in their currencies' purchasing power, the earnings of engineers in Frankfurt, Germany, are seven times those of engineers in Mumbai (formerly Bombay), India. International differences in the pay of unskilled workers are even greater—unskilled female textile workers in Frankfurt are paid 18 times as much as their counterparts in Nairobi, Kenya. (*Source:* World Bank, *World Development Report 1995.* New York: Oxford University Press, 1996, p. 11.)

Second, manufacturing production has been decentralized from all of these core regions to some semiperipheral and peripheral countries. An important reason for this trend has been the prospect of keeping production costs low by exploiting the huge differential in wage rates around the world (**Figure 2.18**). Third, new specializations have emerged within the core regions of the world-system, specifically high-tech manufacturing and **producer services** (that is, such services as information services, insurance, and market research that enhance the productivity or efficiency of other firms' activities or that enable them to maintain specialized roles). One significant result of this new international division of labour is that global trade has grown much more rapidly over the past 30 years than global production—a clear indication of the increased economic integration of the world-system.

The second factor contributing to today's globalization is the internationalization of finance—the emergence of global banking and globally integrated financial markets. These changes are, of course, tied to the new international division of labour. In particular, they are a consequence of massive increases in levels of international direct investment. Between 1988 and 1998, the flow of investment capital from core to semiperipheral and peripheral countries increased more than twentyfold. All in all, about US$100 billion worth of currencies are traded every day. The volume of international investment and financial trading has created a need for banks and financial institutions that can handle investments on a large scale, across great distances, quickly and efficiently. The nerve centres of the new system are located in just a few places—London, Frankfurt, New York, and Tokyo, in particular. Their activities are interconnected round the clock (**Figure 2.19**), and their networks penetrate into every corner of the globe.

It is interesting to note that one of the Canadian Pacific Railway's leading engineers and surveyors, Sir Sandford Fleming, was instrumental in convening the International Prime Meridian Conference in Washington, DC, in 1884, at which the international standard time was adopted. The world was divided into 24 zones, each 15 degrees of longitude wide, starting at 0° on the Greenwich meridian. The standardization of time in this way is obviously a key to the smooth operation of financial transactions around the world.

The third factor contributing to globalization is a new technology system, which has required the geographical reorganization of the core economies. It has also extended the global reach of finance and industry and permitted a more

producer services: services that enhance the productivity or efficiency of other firms' activities or that enable them to maintain specialized roles

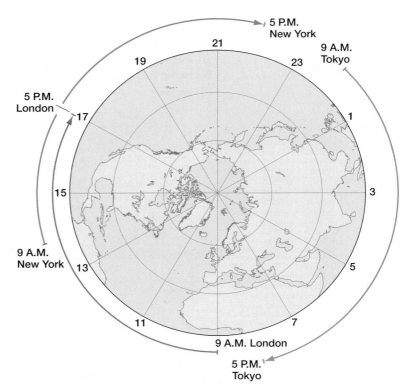

Figure 2.19   24-hour trading among major financial markets   Office hours in the most important financial centres—New York, London, and Tokyo—overlap one another because the three cities are situated in broadly separated time zones. This means that, among them, they span the globe with 24-hour trading in currencies, stocks, and other financial instruments.

flexible approach to investment and trade. Especially important in this regard have been new and improved technologies in transport and communications—the integration of shipping, railroad, and highway systems through containerization (**Figure 2.20**); the introduction of wide-bodied cargo jets (**Figure 2.21**); and the development of fax machines, fibre-optic networks, communications satellites, and electronic mail and information retrieval systems.

A fourth factor in globalization has been the growth of consumer markets. Among the more affluent populations of the world, similar trends in consumer taste have been created by similar social processes. The global market for popular cultural products is becoming concentrated, however. At the core of the entertainment industry—film, music, and television—there is a growing dominance of US products, and many countries have seen their home-grown industries wither. Hollywood obtains more than 50 percent of its revenues from overseas, up from just 30 percent in 1980. Movies made in the United States account for about 50 percent of the market share in Japan, 70 percent in Europe, and 85 percent in

Figure 2.20   The impact of containerization on world trade
Containerization revolutionized long-distance transport because it eliminated the need for slow, expensive, and unreliable loading and unloading of ships using manual labour. Before containerization, ships spent one day in port for every one day at sea; after containerization, they spent 1 day in port for every 10 days at sea. By 1965, an international standard for containers had been adopted, making it possible to transfer goods directly from ship to rail to road, and allowing for a highly integrated global transport infrastructure. Containerization requires a heavy investment in both vessels and dockside handling equipment, however. As a result, container traffic has quickly become concentrated in a few ports that handle high-volume transatlantic and transpacific trade.

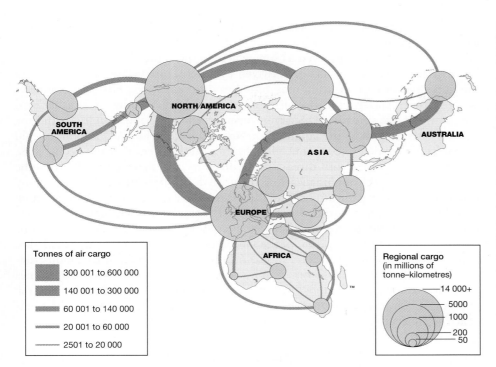

Figure 2.21 Global air cargo traffic in 1990 The introduction of wide-bodied cargo jets (such as the Boeing 747) in the 1970s was an important factor in contributing to the globalization of the world economy. Within a few years, specialized parcel services had established regular routes handling a high volume of documents and freight with a high value-to-weight ratio. This Dymaxion projection shows how the pattern of air freight reflects the three-cornered structure of the contemporary world economy, with the highest-volume flows among Western Europe, North America, and Japan. (*Source:* Map projection, Buckminster Fuller Institute and Dymaxion Map Design, Santa Barbara, CA. The word *Dymaxion* and the Fuller Projection Dymaxion™ Map design are trademarks of the Buckminster Fuller Institute, Santa Barbara, California, © 1938, 1967, & 1992. All rights reserved.)

Latin America. Similarly, U.S. television series have become increasingly prominent in the programming of other countries (**Figure 2.22**).

For this reason, Canada has sought, with varying degrees of success, to protect its cultural industries. Canadian content rules have had some success promoting Canadian talent on radio in this country. However, attempts to do the same for magazines published in Canada have met with NAFTA challenges from the United States. Canadian television and films are eligible for various federal and provincial or territorial subsidies. Nevertheless, despite world-class talent (such as directors Atom Egoyan and David Cronenberg) and productions (such as Torill Kove's 2007 Oscar-winning animated film *The Danish Poet*), the Canadian film and TV industries are simply too small to compete effectively against the United States.

With regard to Canadian access to U.S. and global film and TV audiences, the story is different. A large pool of Canadian acting talent (for example, Sandra Oh in ABC television's *Grey's Anatomy*) has become familiar to U.S. audiences. Until the Canadian dollar's increase in value beginning in early 2003, Vancouver, Montreal, and Toronto had become frequent locations for Hollywood productions. However, it is interesting to note that in the majority of cases, the identity

Figure 2.22 Global marketing of television programming The globalization of culture has been facilitated more than anything else by television broadcasting via satellite and by the sales of popular televison programs to markets around the world. This photograph shows a television fair held in Miami Beach, Florida.

of Canadian actors or locations is not acknowledged (for example, Vancouver and the lower mainland of British Columbia, the location for most of the *X-Files* episodes, was always portrayed as somewhere in the United States).

Just as globalization has been driven by several interrelated factors, so are the outcomes of globalization manifested in different ways. First, for example, is the commercial aspect of globalization: the commodity chains of transnational corporations, the spread of U.S.-style consumerism and popular culture, and the extension of English as the language of business the world over. Second, certain global issues are tied to economic globalization: the depletion of the ozone layer, for example, together with threats to biodiversity and marine life. Third is the cosmopolitan aspect of globalization: the growth of internationally and globally oriented groups, organizations, and alliances—Greenpeace, for example, along with hundreds of international professional organizations, international conferences, and web-based international virtual communities. Fourth are the various local outcomes of the operation of the international economy: resource depletion and environmental despoilation in some regions, ecotourism in others, industrialization in still others, and so on. Finally, there are other kinds of local outcomes of economic and cultural globalization: local reactions that sometimes involve the clashing of cultures, sometimes the mingling of cultures, and sometimes the emergence of alternative pathways to economic and cultural development.

The Fast World and the Slow World

The single most dramatic outcome of the globalization that has resulted from all these changes is the consolidation of the core of the world-system. The core is now a close-knit triad of the geographical centres of North America, the European Union, and Japan (**Figure 2.23**). These three geographical centres are connected through three main circuits, or flows, of investment, trade, and communication: between Europe and North America, between Europe and Asia, and among the regions of the Pacific Rim. **Figure 2.24**, for example, shows just how dominant North America has become in accounting for flows of international telephonic communication. As we shall see in Chapter 7, this consolidation of the core of the world-system is having some profound effects on economic geography. Within the core regions, for example, a new hierarchy of regional economic specialization has been imposed by the locational strategies of transnational corporations and international financial institutions.

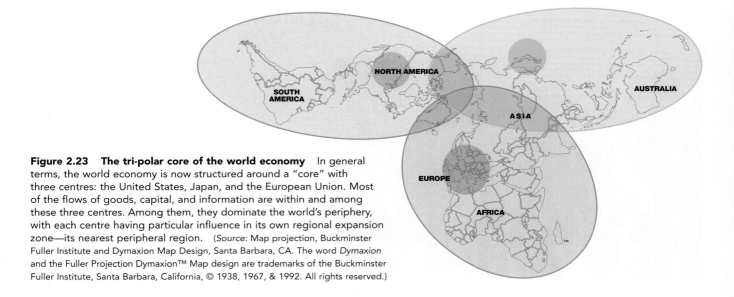

Figure 2.23   The tri-polar core of the world economy   In general terms, the world economy is now structured around a "core" with three centres: the United States, Japan, and the European Union. Most of the flows of goods, capital, and information are within and among these three centres. Among them, they dominate the world's periphery, with each centre having particular influence in its own regional expansion zone—its nearest peripheral region.   (*Source:* Map projection, Buckminster Fuller Institute and Dymaxion Map Design, Santa Barbara, CA. The word *Dymaxion* and the Fuller Projection Dymaxion™ Map design are trademarks of the Buckminster Fuller Institute, Santa Barbara, California, © 1938, 1967, & 1992. All rights reserved.)

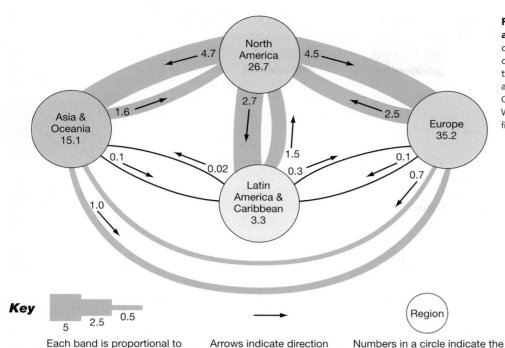

Figure 2.24 Communication flows among major world regions This diagram shows the flows, in billions of minutes of telecommunications traffic over public telephone networks, among major regions. (*Source:* G.C. Staple [ed.], *TeleGeography 1999*. Washington, DC: TeleGeography Inc., 1999, fig. 4, p. 255.)

Key

5   2.5   0.5

Each band is proportional to the total annual traffic from one region to another.

Arrows indicate direction of traffic between regions.

Region

Numbers in a circle indicate the total amount of international traffic for countries within a region.

Globalization, although incorporating more of the world more completely into the capitalist world-system, has intensified the differences between the core and the periphery. According to the United Nations Development Programme (UNDP), the gap between the poorest fifth of the world's population and the wealthiest fifth increased more than threefold between 1960 and 1999. Some parts of the periphery have almost slid off the economic map. In some countries—55 of them, in fact—per capita incomes actually fell during the 1990s. In sub-Saharan Africa, economic output fell by one-third during the 1980s and stayed low during the 1990s; people's standard of living there is now, on average, lower than it was in the early 1960s. By 2007, the UNDP observed that the poorest 20 percent of the world's population accounted for only 1.5 percent of world income. In contrast, nine out of 10 people in those countries that make up the Organisation for Economic Co-operation and Development (the OECD) are in the top 20 percent of the global income distribution.[5]

Such enormous differences lead many people to question the equity, or fairness, of geographical variations in people's levels of affluence and well-being. The concept of **spatial justice** is important here because it requires us to consider the distribution of society's benefits and burdens at different spatial scales, taking into account variations in both people's needs and their contributions to the production of wealth and social well-being. Thinking about spatial justice is an important aspect of the "geographic imagination" described in Chapter 1, and it is a recurring theme in the remainder of this book.

Meanwhile, differences between the core and the periphery are now less easily captured in terms of the framework of states. Economic and cultural globalization has not been matched by political globalization, or a system of governance that can cope with its powerful forces. Policy-makers everywhere lack an adequate framework for coping with the consequences of globalization. Trade policy has come to be governed by powerful transnational corporations, while national governments

spatial justice: the fairness of the distribution of society's burdens and benefits, taking into account spatial variations in people's needs and in their contributions to the production of wealth and social well-being

---

[5]United Nations, *Human Development Report 2006*. New York: United Nations Development Programme, 2007, p. 269. (Available on the web at **http://hdr.undp.org**.)

are unable to deal with large-scale environmental issues. Globalization has fuelled global economic expansion, but, in the process, it has widened the gap between rich and poor and made places and regions everywhere vulnerable to rapid and devastating change. As Ted Turner, then owner of CNN, observed in a 1999 United Nations report on international development, "It is as if globalization is in fast forward, and the world's ability to react to it is in slow motion."[6]

Ted Turner's observation points to an increasing division that now exists between the "fast world" and the "slow world." The **fast world** consists of people, places, and regions directly involved, as producers and consumers, in transnational industry, modern telecommunications, materialistic consumption, and international news and entertainment. The **slow world**, which accounts for about 85 percent of the world's population, consists of people, places, and regions whose participation in transnational industry, modern telecommunications, materialistic consumption, and international news and entertainment is limited. The slow world consists chiefly of the impoverished periphery, but it also includes many rural backwaters, declining manufacturing regions, and disadvantaged slums in core countries, all of them bypassed by this latest phase in the evolution of the modern world-system.

The centre of gravity of the fast world is the tri-polar core of the world-system. The United States, for example, with less than 5 percent of the world's population, accounts for more than 40 percent of the world's telephone stock. Similarly, the fast world also extends throughout the world to the more affluent regions, neighbourhoods, and households that are "plugged in" to the contemporary world economy, whether as producers or consumers of its products and culture. The leading edge of the fast world is the internet, the global web of computer networks that began in the United States in the 1970s as a decentralized communication system sponsored by the United States Department of Defense.

Today, those early networks have become absorbed into the internet, a loose confederation of thousands of small, locally run computer networks for which there is no clear centre of control or authority (**Figure 2.25**). The internet has been doubling in networks and users every year since 1990, but most internet users are still in the world's core regions. At the beginning of 2000, about 55 percent were in North America, and another 23 percent were in Europe. The rest were in Japan, Australia, and New Zealand, and in the fragmentary outposts of the fast world that are embedded within the larger metropolitan areas of the periphery and semiperiphery. Overall, more than 80 percent of all internet traffic originates in or is destined for North America. These particular inequalities between the fast world and the slow world are part of a **digital divide** that exists at every spatial scale.

This division between fast and slow worlds is, of course, something of a caricature. In fact, the fast world encompasses almost every*where* but not every*body*. As a result, human geography now has to contend with the apparent paradox of people whose everyday lives are lived partly in one world and partly in another. Consider, for example, the shantytown residents of Mexico City. With extremely low incomes, only makeshift housing, and little or no formal education, they somehow are knowledgeable about international soccer, music, film, and fashion and are even able to copy fast-world consumption through cast-offs and knock-offs. Increasingly, the use of cell phones is enabling people to "leap frog" technologies and avoid costly land lines. For many Canadians in rural and northern areas, this exciting possibility holds the promise of connection to the fast world, even at so great a distance. Very few regions, therefore, remain largely untouched by globalization.

fast world: people, places, and regions directly involved, as producers and consumers, in transnational industry, modern telecommunications, materialistic consumption, and international news and entertainment

slow world: people, places, and regions whose participation in transnational industry, modern telecommunications, materialistic consumption, and international news and entertainment is limited

digital divide: inequality of access to telecommunications and information technology, particularly the internet

---

[6]United Nations, *Human Development Report 1999*. New York: United Nations Development Programme, 1999, p. 100.

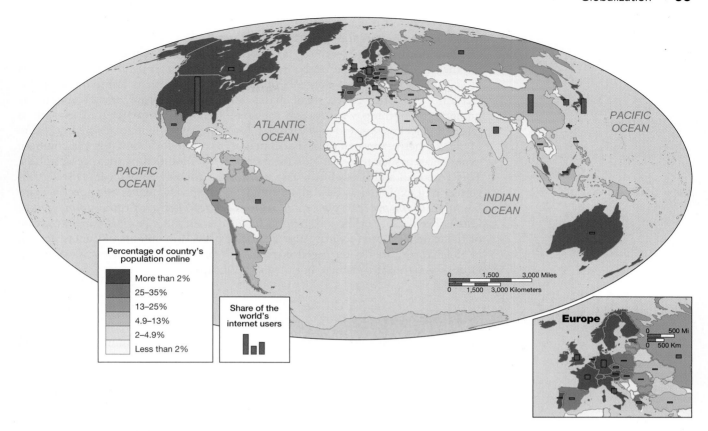

Figure 2.25 Global internet connectivity   Like all previous revolutions in transportation and communications, the internet is effectively reorganizing space. Although often spoken of as "shrinking" the world and "eliminating" geography, the internet is highly uneven in its availability and use. About 70 percent of all traffic on the internet originates from or is addressed to North America. In contrast, some peripheral countries have almost no internet connectivity, while in others the costs are prohibitive. Even in Europe, Japan, and North America, internet connectivity is decidedly uneven in socioeconomic terms. It is the medium of the "fast world" of big business and affluent consumers. This map shows the percentage of the total population in each country with access to the internet (indicated by the density of shading) and the relative share of the world's internet users accounted for by each country (indicated by the vertical bars).   (*Source:* M. Zook, **www.zookNIC.com/**.)

The differences between the fast and the slow worlds allow us to see what sociologist and planner Manuel Castells, in his monumental study *The Information Age*, has identified as spaces of social exclusion created by the uneven spatial development of "informational capitalism."[7] Since access to networks and people is so crucial in the Information Age, Castells argues that to be denied such access is to be excluded from "the powerhouse of global capitalism" and instead become part of the "Fourth World," a space he defines as "made up of multiple black holes of social exclusion throughout the planet." Castells uses the term "Fourth World" because he suggests that the Third World no longer has geopolitical relevance, that the Second World (of communism) has disintegrated, and that the First World of capitalism is not an all-encompassing world. He writes that the Fourth World "comprises large areas of the globe, such as much of sub-Saharan Africa, and impoverished rural areas of Latin America and Asia. But it is also present in literally every country, and city, in this new geography of social exclusion." It is, therefore, a space that includes the poor, the homeless, the sick, and the illiterate. And it is a world that will only get bigger if

[7]Manuel Castells, *The Information Age: Economy, Society and Culture. Volume 3, End of Millennium*, rev. ed. Oxford: Blackwell, 1999. The quotations are from pages 164 and 165.

Castells is correct in his assertion that "the rise of the Fourth World is inseparable from the rise of international, global capitalism."

This distinction between the fast world and the slow world brings us back to the themes of place, scale, and change that will recur throughout the rest of this book. At first glance, the emergence of the fast world—with its transnational architectural styles, dress codes, retail chains, and popular culture, and its ubiquitous immigrants, business visitors, and tourists—seems as if it might have brought a sense of placelessness and dislocation, a loss of territorial identity, and an erosion of the distinctive sense of place associated with certain localities. Yet, the common experiences associated with globalization are still modified by local geographies. The structures and flows of the fast world are variously embraced, resisted, subverted, and exploited as they make contact with specific places and specific communities. *In the process, places and regions are reconstructed rather than effaced.* Often, this involves deliberate attempts by the residents of a particular area to create or re-create territorial identity and a sense of place. Inhabitants of the fast world, in other words, still feel the need for enclaves of familiarity, centredness, and identity. Human geographies change, but they don't disappear.

CONCLUSION

Places and regions everywhere carry the legacy of a sequence of major changes in world geography. The evolution of world geography can be traced from the prehistoric beginnings of human settlement, through the trading systems of the precapitalist, pre-industrial world to the foundations of the geography of the modern world. These foundations were cast through industrialization, the colonization of the world, and the spread of an international market economy. As the *Economist* magazine pointed out, "History counts: where you are depends very much on where you started from." Today, these foundations can be seen in the geography of the Information Age, a geography that now provides a new, global context for places and regions.

Today's world is highly integrated. Places and regions have become increasingly interdependent, linked together through complex and rapidly changing commodity chains that are orchestrated by transnational corporations. Using new technology systems that allow for instantaneous global telecommunications and flexible patterns of investment and production, these corporations span the fast world of the core and the slow worlds of the periphery. This integration does tend to blur some national and regional differences as the global marketplace brings a dispersion of people, tastes, and ideas. The overall result, though, has been an intensification of the differences between the core and the periphery.

Within this new global context, local differences in resource endowments remain, and people's territorial impulses endure. Many local cultures continue to be resilient or adaptive. Fundamental principles of spatial organization also continue to operate. All this ensures that even as the world-system becomes more and more integrated, places and regions continue to be made and remade. The new global context is filled with local variety that is constantly changing, just as the global context itself is constantly responding to local developments.

MAIN POINTS REVISITED

- **Places and regions are part of a "world-system" that has been created as a result of processes of private economic competition and political competition among states.**
  Each place and region carries out its own particular role within the competitive world-system. Because of these different roles, places and regions are dependent on one another. The development of each place affects, and is affected by, the development of many other places.

- **Today, the world-system is highly structured and is characterized by three tiers: *core regions, semiperipheral regions,* and *peripheral regions.***

The core regions of the world-system are those that dominate trade, control the most advanced technologies, and have high levels of productivity within diversified economies. Peripheral regions are characterized by dependent and disadvantageous trading relationships, by primitive or obsolescent technologies, and by undeveloped or narrowly specialized economies with low levels of productivity. Semiperipheral regions are able to exploit peripheral regions but are themselves exploited and dominated by the core regions. This three-tiered system is fluid, providing a continually changing framework for geographical transformation within individual places and regions.

■ **The world-system is made up of a nested set of cores and peripheries.**
In this way, local developments are transmitted to the regional and global levels, and the forces of globalization affect the local level.

■ **Canada is simultaneously part of the global core and semiperiphery.**
Possessing many core characteristics (such as high GNP), Canada nevertheless is still heavily interdependent with such countries as the United States.

■ **The evolution of the modern world-system has exhibited distinctive stages, each of which has left its legacy in different ways on particular places, depending on their changing role within the world-system.**
The modern world-system was first established over a long period that began in the late fifteenth century. More and more peoples around the world became exposed to one another's technologies and ideas over the next five centuries. Their different resources, social structures, and cultural systems resulted in quite different pathways of development, however. Some societies were incorporated into the new, European-based international economic system faster than others; some resisted incorporation; and some sought alternative systems of economic and political organization.

■ **At the end of the eighteenth century, the new technologies of the Industrial Revolution brought about the emergence of a global economic system that reached into almost every part of the world and into virtually every aspect of people's lives.**
New transportation technologies triggered successive phases of geographic expansion, allowing for an intensive period of external colonization and imperialism. The core of the world-system grew to include the United States and Japan, while most of the rest of the world was systematically incorporated into the capitalist world-system as a dependent periphery.

■ **The growth and internal colonization of the core regions could take place only with the foodstuffs, raw materials, and markets provided by the colonization of the periphery.**
In the eighteenth and nineteenth centuries, the industrial core nations embarked on the inland penetration of the world's midcontinental grassland zones to exploit them for grain or stock production. At the same time, as the demand for tropical plantation products increased, most of the tropical world came under the political and economic control—directly or indirectly—of one or another of the industrial core nations. For these peripheral regions, European overseas expansion meant political and economic dependency.

■ **Within each of the world's major regions, successive technological innovations have transformed regional geographies.**
Each new system of production and transportation technologies has helped raise levels of productivity and create new and better products that have stimulated demand, increased profits, and created a pool of capital for further investment. This investment, however, has taken place in new or restructured geographical settings.

■ **Globalization has intensified the differences between the core and the periphery and has contributed to the emergence of a digital divide and an increasing division between a fast world (about 15 percent of the world's population) and a slow world (about 85 percent of the world's population) with contrasting lifestyles and levels of living.**
The leading edge of the fast world is the internet, which is now the world's single most important mechanism for the transmission of scientific and academic knowledge. Today, flows of goods, capital, and information that take place within and among transnational corporations are becoming more important than imports and exports among countries. At the same time, all these flows have helped spread new values—from consumer lifestyle preferences to altruistic concerns with global resources, global environmental changes, and famine relief—around the fast world.

Key Terms

colonialism (p. 54)
commodity chains (p. 76)
core regions (p. 54)
digital divide (p. 82)
division of labour (p. 73)
external arena (p. 52)
fast world (p. 82)
hegemony (p. 64)
hinterland (p. 60)
import substitution (p. 62)

law of diminishing returns (p. 58)
leadership cycles (p. 64)
mini-system (p. 56)
neo-colonialism (p. 76)
peripheral regions (p. 54)
plantations (p. 62)
postcolonialism (p. 75)
producer services (p. 77)
semiperipheral regions (p. 54)

slow world (p. 82)
spatial justice (p. 81)
staples thesis (p. 68)
staples trap (p. 68)
states (p. 54)
subaltern theory (p. 74)
transnational corporations (p. 76)
world-empire (p. 57)
world-system (p. 52)

Additional Reading

Angus, J.T. *A Respectable Ditch: A History of the Trent–Severn Waterway 1833–1920.* Montreal and Toronto: McGill-Queen's University Press, 1988.

Baum, G. *Karl Polanyi on Ethics and Economics.* Montreal and Kingston: McGill-Queens University Press, 1996.

Blaut, J. *The Colonizer's Model of the World: Geographic Diffusionism and Eurocentric History.* New York: Guilford Press, 1993.

Britton, J. (ed.). *Canada and the Global Economy: The Geography of Structural and Technological Change.* Montreal and Kingston: McGill-Queen's University Press, 1996.

Castells, M. *The Information Age. Volume 1, The Rise of the Network Society.* Oxford: Blackwell, 1996.

Castells, M. *The Information Age: Economy, Society and Culture, Volume 3, End of Millennium.* Oxford: Blackwell, 1999.

Christopher, A.J. *The British Empire at Its Zenith.* New York: Croom Helm, 1988.

Daniels, P., and W.F. Lever (eds.). *The Global Economy in Transition.* New York: Addison Wesley Longman, 1996.

De Alcantara, C.H. *Social Futures, Global Visions.* New York: United Nations Research Institute for Social Development, 1996.

Dicken, P. *Global Shift,* 3rd ed. New York: Harper & Row, 1998.

Gentilcore, R.L., and G.J. Matthews (eds.). *Historical Atlas of Canada. Volume 2: The Land Transformed 1800–1891.* Toronto: University of Toronto Press, 1993.

Harris, R.C., and G.J. Matthews (eds.). *Historical Atlas of Canada. Volume 1: From the Beginning to 1800.* Toronto: University of Toronto Press, 1987.

Harris, R.C., and J. Warkentin. *Canada before Confederation: A Study in Historical Geography.* Toronto: Oxford University Press, 1974.

Hugill, P. *World Trade since 1431.* Baltimore: Johns Hopkins University Press, 1993.

Johnston, R.J., P.J. Taylor, and M. Watts (eds.). *Geographies of Global Change.* Cambridge, MA: Blackwell, 1995.

Kerr, D. *Historical Atlas of Canada,* 3rd ed. Don Mills, ON: Nelson, 1975.

Kerr, D., D. Holdsworth, and G.J. Matthews (eds.). *Historical Atlas of Canada. Volume 3: Addressing the Twentieth Century.* Toronto: University of Toronto Press, 1990.

Knox, P.L., and J. Agnew. *The Geography of the World Economy,* 3rd ed. New York: Routledge, 1998.

Leacy, F.H. (ed.). *Historical Statistics of Canada,* 2nd ed. Ottawa: Minister of Supply and Services, 1983.

McCann, L., and A. Gunn. *Heartland and Hinterland: A Regional Geography of Canada,* 3rd ed. Scarborough, ON: Prentice Hall Canada, 1998.

Norcliffe, G. *The Ride to Modernity: The Bicycle in Canada, 1869–1900.* Toronto: University of Toronto Press, 2001.

Peet, R. *Global Capitalism: Theories of Societal Development.* New York: Routledge, 1991.

Ruggles, R.I. *A Country So Interesting: The Hudson's Bay Company and Two Centuries of Mapping, 1670–1870.* Montreal and Kingston: McGill-Queen's University Press, 1991.

Said, E. *Orientalism.* New York: Pantheon, 1978.

Seitz, J.L. *Global Issues: An Introduction.* Cambridge, MA: Blackwell, 1995.

Terlouw, C.P. *The Regional Geography of the World-System.* Utrecht: Faculteit Ruimtelijke Wetenschappen Rijksuniversiteit Utrecht, 1994.

Unwin, T. (ed.). *Atlas of World Development.* New York: John Wiley and Sons, 1994.

Wallace, I. *The Global Economic System.* London: Unwin Hyman, 1990.

Wallace, I. *A Geography of the Canadian Economy.* Toronto: Oxford University Press, 2002.

Wolf, E.R. *Europe and the People without History.* Berkeley: University of California Press, 1983.

Exercises

Here you will find exercises and activities for each chapter. Unplugged exercises help you review chapter discussions, and pose ideas for your own human geography research. On the Companion Website exercises will require you have access to the internet.

Unplugged

1. The present-day core regions of the world-system, shown in Figure 2.1, are those that dominate trade, control the most advanced technologies, have high levels of productivity within diversified economies, and enjoy relatively high *per capita* incomes. What statistical evidence can you find in your local library to support this characterization? Hint: Look for data in annual compilations of statistics published in annual reviews, such as the Encyclopaedia Britannica's *Yearbook,* and in the annual reports of organizations, such as the United Nations Development Programme (UNDP), the World Bank, and the World Resources Institute.

2. We quoted the *Economist* magazine as saying that places and regions are important because "where you are depends very much on where you started from." Illustrate this point with reference to any region with which you are familiar.

3. The idea of an international division of labour is based on the observation that different countries tend to specialize in the production or manufacture of particular commodities, goods, or services. In what product or products do the following countries specialize: Bolivia, Ghana, Guinea, Libya, Namibia, Peru, and Zambia? You will find the data you need in a good statistical yearbook, such as the Encyclopaedia Britannica's *Yearbook,* or in a world reference atlas or economic atlas.

On the Companion Website

This book has its own Companion Website where you will find additional resources—maps, photographs, data—as well as exercises and activities that relate to each chapter. To complete the Companion Website exercises, go to **www.pearsoned.ca/knox**. The following is a summary of the types of exercises created for this chapter.

The exercises for this chapter take you back to the time of Alexander the Great and, through a critical-thinking exercise, help you understand (through the actions of Alexander and the consequences of his empire) key geographical concepts, such as core and periphery regions, the development of transportation, and how the Greek culture managed to diffuse throughout the known world. The concept-review exercises will help your understanding of such concepts as world-system, semiperipheral regions, slow world, and commodity chain. There is a set of online map exercises that focus on industrialization, satellite images, transportation, trade, and more. You also have an opportunity to explore key terms in depth through internet search engines that provide examples of how these terms are used.

3

Geographies of Population

Crowded downtown street, Toronto

On 28 June 2008, the cover of the *New York Times Magazine* raised the question "Childless Europe: What happens to a continent when it stops making babies?" and contained a lengthy article that discussed what it called the "alarming" decline in birth rates. In Canada, a similar note of concern was sounded in 2004 by the Ottawa-based Vanier Institute of the Family in a report that noted that Canadian families are getting smaller and that there will be a larger number of older families in the future. Both are trends caused by Canada's declining birth rate, a decline that is happening across Western countries, and one that has caused some policy-makers (such as those quoted in the *New York Times Magazine*) to worry about the implications of a continued decline in the birth rate. Yet, Canada's population continues to rise—reaching a total of 33 223 840 in April 2008 according to a Statistics Canada estimate—and on a global scale, world population steadily increases, passing the 6.6 billion mark as of mid-2007, causing many to worry about issues such as the possible overpopulation of the planet and its environmental consequences. In August 2008, for example, Britain's *Guardian Weekly* newspaper summarized an editorial that had appeared in a recent issue of the *British Medical Journal* under the heading "Have fewer children and help save the planet . . .". The editorial suggested that since every new person born in Britain would produce 160 times more greenhouse emissions than a person born in Ethiopia, a decline in Britain's birth rate would obviously have beneficial environmental consequences.[1]

How can we resolve these two very different views—one which is concerned about a decline in births, the other about their continued increase? For geographers, as well as population experts, the most important point to be derived from these two opposing views about population is that both are true: they are true for different places and for different reasons in those places. In most core countries, population growth has slowed or stopped altogether, while in most peripheral countries, despite the fact that women there are having fewer children, population growth continues. Experts do agree that population growth is the result of the phenomenal decline of death rates in the twentieth century. Birth and death are the two variables that shape overall population growth and change. For population geographers, knowing the fertility (or birth) figures or the mortality (or death) figures is not enough, however: they also want

---

[1]Russell Shorto, "Childless Europe: What Happens to a Continent When It Stops Making Babies?" *New York Times Magazine*, 28 June 2008, pp. 34–41, 68–71; Ian Sample, "Have Fewer Children and Help Save the Planet, Britons Told." *Guardian Weekly*, 1 August 2008, p. 14. (It is worth adding, as the *Guardian* itself did, that a reduction in greenhouse gas emission through the decline in the birth rate would happen too slowly for it to have an immediate effect on projected levels of global warming.)

to know where births and deaths are occurring, why they are occurring, and what the consequences of changes in their rates are for the remaining population.

In this chapter, we examine population distribution and structure as well as the dynamics of population growth and change, with a special focus on spatial variations and implications. In short, we want to know the locations of population clusters, the numbers of men and women and old and young, and the ways these combine to create overall change, either as growth or decline. We also look at population movements and the models and concepts that population experts have developed to gain a better understanding of the potential and problems posed by human populations.

MAIN POINTS

- Population geographers depend on a wide array of data sources to assess the geography of populations. Chief among these sources is the census, although other sources include vital records and public health statistics.

- Population geographers are largely concerned with the same sorts of questions as other population experts study, but they also investigate "the why of where": *why* do particular aspects of population growth and change (and problems) occur *where* they do, and what are the implications of these factors for the future of places?

- Two of the most important factors that make up population dynamics are birth and death. These variables may be examined in simple or complex ways, but in either case, the reasons for the behaviour of these variables are as important as the numbers themselves.

- A third crucial force in population change is the movement of populations. The forces that push populations from particular locations as well as those that pull them to move to new areas are key to understanding the resulting new settlement patterns. Population migration may not always be a matter of choice.

- As a generalization, world demographic patterns are easily described within a world-system framework. They are an important aspect of the very different economic and social "spaces" that this model produces. High birth rates and death rates are a feature of today's periphery; low birth rates and death rates are a feature of the core. The discrepancy in economic and political terms between them generates substantial flows of migrants and refugees.

- Perhaps the most pressing issue facing scholars, policy-makers, and other interested individuals is the one articulated at the International Conference on Population and Development, held in Cairo in 1994: how many people can the world adequately accommodate with food, water, clean air, and other basic necessities for the enjoyment of happy, healthy, and satisfying lives?

- Whether at the world, country, or local scale of analysis, the work of those geographers studying the interactions among population, health, and the environment shows us that the principal explanation for varying spatial patterns of health is variation in income distribution.

THE DEMOGRAPHER'S TOOLBOX

Demography, or the study of the characteristics of human populations, is an interdisciplinary undertaking. Geographers study population to understand the areal distribution of Earth's population. They are also interested in the reasons for, and the consequences of, the distribution of population from the international to the local level. Historians study the evolution of demographic patterns and sociologists the social dynamics of human populations, but it is geographers who focus special attention on the spatial patterns of human populations, the implications of such patterns, and the reasons for them. Using many of the same tools and methods of analysis as other population experts, geographers think of population in terms of the places that populations inhabit. They also consider populations in terms of the way that places are shaped by populations and, in turn, shape the populations that occupy them.

demography: the study of the characteristics of human populations

Sources of Information

Population experts rely on a wide array of instruments and institutions to carry out their work. Governments, for example, collect information on births, deaths, marriages, immigration, and other aspects of population change. The most widely known instrument for assessing the state of the population is the census. At a simple level, a **census** is a straightforward count of the number of people in a country, region, or city. Censuses, however, are not usually so simple. Most are also directed at gathering other information about the population, such as previous residence, marital status, income, and other personal data.

census: the count of the number of people in a country, region, or city

In Canada, the earliest census dates from 1666 when the population of New France (Quebec) was recorded on the orders of Louis XIV. The first nationwide census dates from 1851. Since then, Canadian full censuses have been conducted every 10 years with, since 1956, a shorter mid-decade census. The next censuses in this country will therefore be taken in 2011 and 2016.

Undertakings of this sort are hugely expensive (the 2006 census cost $567 million to conduct) and will take several years to tabulate fully.[2] Even so, they are not completely error free. Estimates suggest an undercount of between 1 percent and 2 percent in recent censuses, mainly because of enumerator error. We also know that some groups are more under-represented than others. The homeless are, almost by definition, going to be hard to survey, and some of Canada's Native reserves have declined to participate in recent surveys. Nevertheless, the impressive quantity and quality of data collected more than compensate for these disadvantages.

In addition to the census, population experts also employ other data sources to assess population characteristics. One such source is **vital records** (from the Latin word *vita*, meaning "life"), which report births, deaths, marriages, divorces, and the incidences of certain infectious diseases. These data are collected and records of them kept by provincial and territorial levels of government. Schools, hospitals, and other public agencies, and international organizations, such as the World Health Organization, also collect demographic statistics that are useful to population experts.

vital records: information about births, deaths, marriages, divorces, and the incidences of certain infectious diseases

In parts of New France, parish registers (a form of vital record) date from the beginning of the seventeenth century. Quebec historians who have analyzed these records have been able to reconstruct the demographic experiences of entire communities, using the techniques of **family reconstitution**, and have provided us with a fascinating glimpse of life along the St. Lawrence River nearly 400 years ago.

family reconstitution: the process of reconstructing individual and family life histories by linking together separately recorded birth, marriage, and death data

Not all information that population experts use is as straightforward as census or vital records data. Nor are such data always available. In many cases, it is

---

[2]It is because of this unavoidable delay that more detailed information from each census is not published until some years later. Check Statistics Canada's website for the latest releases of census data and related statistics at **www.statcan.gc.ca**.

necessary to utilize numerous other types of data to say something about a past population's size and structure. Consider, for example, the Aboriginal populations of British Columbia. To be able to examine the terrible effects of European diseases, such as the 1792 smallpox epidemic, on the size of their populations, we need some way of estimating their numbers on the eve of contact with Europeans. However, turning Hudson's Bay Company head counts, archaeological evidence, or calculations of carrying capacities into population estimates with any degree of accuracy is virtually impossible. This problem would have only academic interest were it not for the practical need to establish the validity of Aboriginal title to territory in British Columbia. As Cole Harris, a historical geographer at the University of British Columbia, has recently observed, "as political debates about Native government and land claims intensify, and as appeals proceed through the courts, questions of disease and depopulation are explicitly repoliticized. . . . For a society preoccupied with numbers, scale, and progress, more people imply fuller, more controlled occupation of land."[3]

Generally speaking, to get a full picture of what is happening, most contemporary population experts prefer to use a combination of both census and vital record information. This is because census data can record only snapshot views (or cross-sections) of a population on the day the census was conducted. They cannot consider change over time; for this, the information from vital registration is invaluable. However, vital records can track only a limited number of variables over time; censuses give us a far richer data picture.

administrative record linkage: the linking together of a number of different government databases to build one database with much more detailed information on each individual

Administrative record linkage may provide the ideal solution. By linking together a number of different databases on individuals, governments are able to not only build up a very detailed picture of that individual but also update this picture very regularly. Canada is a world leader in this respect and has, for the purposes of research, combined tax files with records of employment and immigration data to produce a very rich source of information on large samples of the population. Only ethical issues of privacy prevent a greater use of this material and—as has happened in some Scandinavian countries—its eventual replacement of the census.

POPULATION DISTRIBUTION AND STRUCTURE

Because human geographers explore the interrelationships and interdependencies between people and places, they are interested in demography, or the systematic analysis of the numbers and distribution of human populations. Population geographers bring to demography a special perspective—the spatial perspective—that emphasizes description and explanation of the "where" of population distribution, patterns, and processes. For instance, the seemingly simple fact that as of mid-2007, the world was inhabited by 6.6 billion people is one that geographers like to think about in a more complex way. Although this number is undeniably phenomenal and, furthermore, increasing daily, its most important aspect for geographers is its uneven spatial expression from region to region and place to place. Equally important are the implications and impacts of these differences. Looking at population numbers, geographers ask themselves two questions: where are these populations concentrated, and what are the causes and consequences of such a population distribution?

Population Distribution

At a basic level, many geographical reasons exist for the distribution of populations throughout the globe. As the world population density map (**Figure 3.1**) demonstrates, some areas of the world are very heavily inhabited, while others are only sparsely.

Degree of accessibility, topography, soil fertility, climate and weather, water availability and quality, and type and availability of other natural resources are

---

[3]Cole Harris, *The Resettlement of British Columbia: Essays on Colonialism and Geographical Change.* Vancouver: UBC Press, 1997, pp. 3–4.

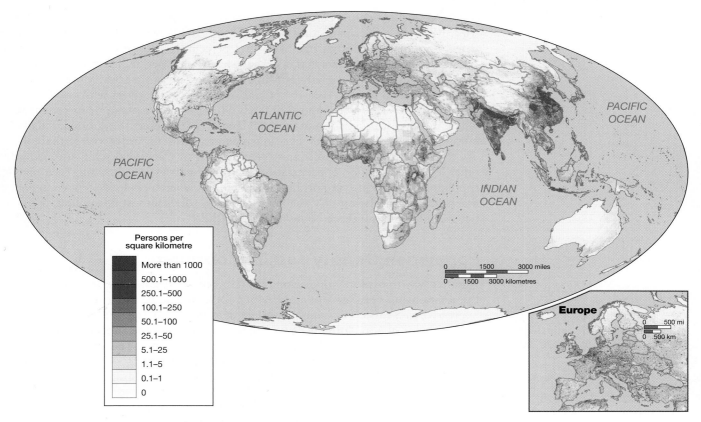

Figure 3.1   World population density, 2004   As this map shows, the world's population is not uniformly distributed across the globe. Such maps are useful in understanding the relationships between population distribution and the national contexts within which they occur. China and India are the largest countries in the world with respect to population, while the core countries have much smaller populations.   (After World Bank, *World Development Indicators, 2004.* Washington, DC: World Bank.)

some of the important factors that shape population distribution. Other factors are also crucial. First and foremost is a country's political and economic experiences and characteristics. For example, the high population concentrations along Brazil's Atlantic coast date back to the trade patterns set up during Portuguese colonial control in the sixteenth and seventeenth centuries.

Table 3.1 shows population estimates in terms of traditional continental distributions. From the table, it is clear that Asia is by far the most populous

TABLE 3.1	World Population Estimates by Continents	
Continent	**Number of Inhabitants (in millions)**	**% of Total Population**
Africa	944	14.2
Asia	4010	60.5
Australia, New Zealand, and the South Pacific Islands	35	0.5
Europe	733	11.1
North America	335	5.1
Latin America and the Caribbean	569	8.9
TOTAL	6625	100.0

Source: Population Reference Bureau website, **www.prb.org**, Mid-2007 World Population tables.
Note: Data and totals subject to rounding.

continent, including 60.5 percent of the world's inhabitants in more than 40 countries. Running a distant second and third are Africa, with 14.2 percent of the world's population, and Europe, with 11.1 percent, respectively.

The population clusters that take shape have a number of physical similarities. Almost all of the world's inhabitants live on 10 percent of the land. Most live near the edges of land masses, near the oceans or seas or along rivers with easy access to a navigable waterway. Approximately 90 percent live north of the equator, where the largest proportion of the total land area (63 percent) is located. Finally, most of the world's population lives in temperate, low-lying areas with fertile soils.

Population numbers are significant not only at the global scale but also at other levels. Population concentrations within countries, regions, and even metropolitan areas are also important for showing us where people are. For example, much of the population of Canada, which now totals almost 33 million, is distributed along its southern boundary (**Figure 3.2**).

Population Density and Composition

Another way to explore population is in terms of *density,* a numerical measure of the relationship between the number of people and some other unit of interest expressed as a ratio. For example, crude density is probably the most common measurement of population density. **Crude density**, also called **arithmetic density**, is the total number of people divided by the total land area. The limitation of the crude density ratio—and hence the reason for its "crudeness"—is that it is one-dimensional. It tells us very little about the opportunities and obstacles that the relationship between people and land contains.

In addition to exploring patterns of distribution and density, population geographers also examine population in terms of its composition, that is, the subgroups that constitute it. Understanding population composition enables geographers to gather important information about population dynamics. For example, knowing the composition of a population in terms of the total number of males and females, number and proportion of old people and children, and number and proportion of people active in the workforce provides valuable insights into the ways in which the population behaves.

Facing unique challenges are countries with a population that contains a high proportion of old people—a situation many core countries will soon be facing as their "baby boom" population ages. The **baby boom** population includes those individuals born in the two decades following World War II. Considerable amounts of these countries' resources and energies are necessary to meet the needs of a large number of people who may no longer be contributing significantly to the creation of the wealth necessary for their support. There might also be a need to import workers to supplement the small working-age population. Knowing the number of women of childbearing age in a population, along with other information about their status and opportunities, can provide valuable information about the future growth potential of that population.

For example, populations in core countries, such as Denmark, which has a small number of women of childbearing age relative to the total population size—women with high levels of education, socioeconomic security, and wide opportunities for work outside the home—will generally grow very slowly, if at all. Populations in peripheral countries, such as Kenya—where a large number of women of childbearing age have low levels of education and socioeconomic security and relatively few employment opportunities—will, however, continue to experience relatively high rates of population growth, barring unforeseen changes. The variety of social and economic opportunities that are available to groups within a country's population very much shapes the opportunities and challenges it must confront nationally, regionally, and locally.

Understanding population composition, then, not only can tell us much about the future demographics of regions but is also quite useful in the present. For example, businesses use population composition data to make marketing decisions

crude density (arithmetic density): the total number of people divided by the total land area

baby boom: the increased number of births in the two decades following World War II

Population Distribution in Canada, 2006

According to Statistics Canada, a Census Metropolitan Area (CMA) is made up of a very large urban area (urban core) and those adjacent urban and rural areas that are highly integrated with that urban core. A CMA is defined as having an urban core population of at least 100 000 in the previous census.

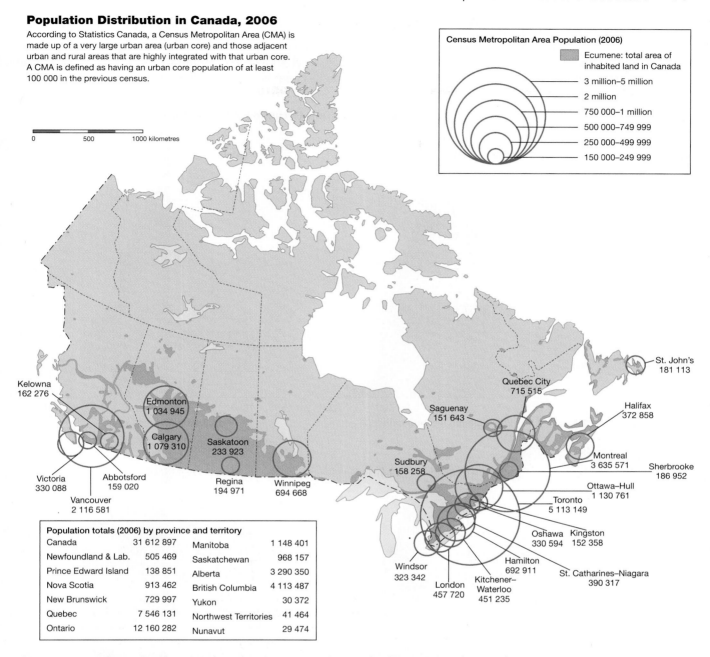

Figure 3.2   Population distribution in Canada, 2006   As can be seen by this map, Canada's population distribution has a number of major characteristics. First, population is extremely dispersed across the country (the area known as the *ecumene* shows the inhabited area of Canada). However, the population density of the ecumene is very low, and the bulk of the country's population is highly concentrated along Canada's southern border (more than 70 percent of the total population live within 150 kilometres of the U.S. border); in the three provinces of British Columbia, Ontario, and Quebec; and in the country's leading urban centres (where almost 80 percent of the total population now lives in towns and cities of more than 1000 people). In fact, despite its large size and relatively small population, Canada has become an urban (even metropolitan) country in terms of where people now live.   (*Sources:* The ecumene is from John Warkentin, *A Regional Geography of Canada,* 2nd ed. Scarborough: Prentice Hall, 2000, p. 71; 2006 Census figures are from Statistics Canada, "Population and Dwelling Counts for Canada, Provinces and Territories, Census Metropolitan Areas and Census Agglomerations, 2006 and 2001 Censuses—100% Data," [**www12.statcan.ca/English/census06**].)

and to decide where to locate their businesses. For many years, businesses used laborious computer models to help target their markets. With the recent development of GIS, however, this process has been greatly simplified. The practice of assessing the location and composition of particular populations is known as **geodemographic analysis.**

geodemographic analysis: the practice of assessing the location and composition of particular populations

Age–Sex Pyramids

age–sex pyramid: a representation of the population based on its composition according to age and sex

The most common way for demographers to graphically represent the composition of the population is to construct an **age–sex pyramid**, which is a representation of the population based on its composition according to age and sex (**Figure 3.3**).

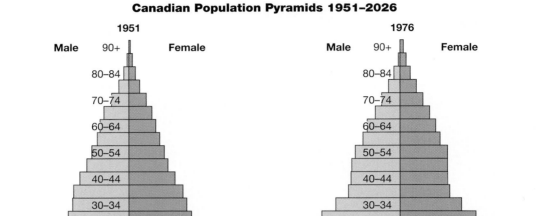

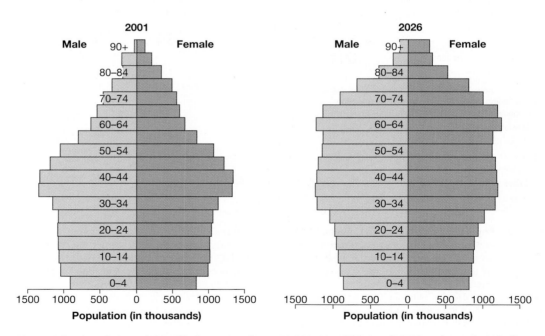

Figure 3.3 Population of Canada, by age and sex, 1951, 1976, 2001, and 2026 The profound effects of the baby boom (1947–1966) on Canada's population structure can be seen in this series of age–sex pyramids. The four pyramids chart the baby boom's initial impact on a population shaped by low fertility rates of the Depression years and show how the baby boom has subsequently become a major factor in the aging of the Canadian population as the relative size of older age groups has increased over time. The decline in fertility rates since the boom has accentuated the impact of aging on the population, since, as the pyramids show, it has led to a relative decline in the size of younger age groups in the population. (*Sources:* "Canadian Population Pyramids," adapted from the Statistics Canada publication *The Daily*, Catalogue 11–001, 16 July 2002, available at **www12.statcan.ca/english/census01/products/Analytic**. A 30-second animated graphic showing how Canada's age–sex pyramids change over time can be seen at www12.statcan.ca/english/census01/Products/Analytic/companion/age/cda01pymd.cfm.)

An age–sex pyramid is actually a bar graph displayed horizontally. Ordinarily, males are portrayed on the left side of the vertical axis and females to the right. Age categories are ordered sequentially from the youngest at the bottom of the pyramid to the oldest at the top. By moving up or down the pyramid, one can compare the opposing horizontal bars to assess differences in frequencies for each age group. Demographers call such population groups *cohorts*. A **cohort** is a group of individuals who share a common *temporal* demographic experience. A cohort is not necessarily based only on age, however. Cohorts may be defined by such criteria as time of marriage or time of graduation.

A critical aspect of the population pyramid is the **dependency ratio**, which is a measure of the economic impact of the young and old on the more economically productive members of the population. Traditionally, to assess this relation of dependency in a particular population, demographers divide the total population into three age cohorts, sometimes further dividing those cohorts by sex. The **youth cohort** consists of those members of the population who are less than 15 years of age and generally considered to be too young to be fully active in the labour force. The **middle cohort** consists of those members of the population aged 15 to 64 who are considered economically active and productive. Finally, the **old-age cohort** consists of those members of the population aged 65 and older who are considered beyond their economically active and productive years. By dividing the population into these three groups, it is possible to obtain a measure of the dependency of the young and old on the economically active and of the impact of the dependent population on the independent.

These various measures of dependency are a useful framework with which to consider Canada's age–sex pyramid (Figure 3.3). In common with many Western countries, Canada's post-war population has been almost entirely shaped by the rise, and then the fall, of the birth rate. In fact, if we look back over a century of population change in this country, we see that there has been a long run (or *secular*) decline in the birth rate since the 1870s (**Figure 3.4**). Before the onset of the decline, the crude birth rate was between 45 and 55 per 1000; by 2001, it stood at 11 per 1000, representing a total fertility rate of 1.4 births per woman. Fewer children being born has had the obvious effect of increasing the proportion of the total population made up of older age groups. In other words, the population as a whole is **aging**. This effect is compounded by the fact that increased life expectancies have meant that people, on average, live longer than they did two or three generations ago. The effect of population aging was temporarily reversed by the baby boom. In Canada's case, the boom years were 1947–1966 (the longest boom recorded in the developed world), and in these years, the crude birth rate increased to almost 30 per 1000. Overall, birth rates have declined since those years, although two periods of increase have occurred. The first was from the mid-1970s to 1990 and is sometimes known as the baby boom "echo" because it represents the children of the large baby boom cohort. We are currently experiencing a second period of increase (the "echo" of the "echo") and Statistics Canada was able to report in the issue of its journal *The Daily* for 28 September 2008 that the total fertility rate in 2006 was 1.59 births per woman, the highest rate since 1996. Overall, 354 617 children were born in 2006, an increase of 3.6 percent over the previous year, and more than double the increase of 1.5 percent reported in 2005. Nevertheless, these rates are far below replacement fertility levels of 2.1.

There are many explanations for the decline of Canada's birth rate and for the baby boom. Most however, are unable to explain both. How can we, for example, explain the increase in births (the baby boom) using the same explanations (such as social change) we are using to explain the longer-lasting decline from 1871? For this reason, we must recognize that there are likely to be several factors—perhaps working differently at different times. That said, nothing should obscure the basic finding of Canadian demography that the underlying cause involves the changing role of women as they have gained greater access to education and paid employment.

cohort: a group of individuals who share a common temporal demographic experience

dependency ratio: the measure of the economic impact of the young and old on the more economically productive members of the population

youth cohort: members of the population who are less than 15 years of age and generally considered to be too young to be fully active in the labour force

middle cohort: members of the population 15 to 64 years of age who are considered economically active and productive

old-age cohort: members of the population 65 years of age and older who are considered beyond their economically active and productive years

aging: a term used to describe the effects of an increasing proportion of older age groups on the population

Crude Birth Rate per 1000 Population, Canada and Quebec,* 1801–1989

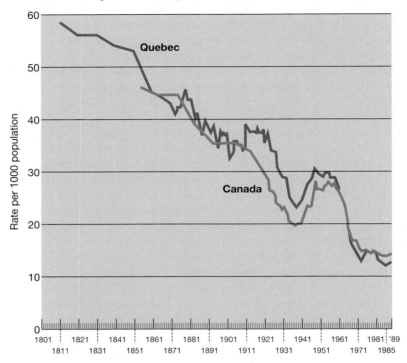

*Crude birth rates from 1801 through 1867 refer to the Catholic population of Quebec.

Figure 3.4   The decline of the birth rate in Canada   This graph shows the decline in the crude birth rate, measured as a rate per 1000 population, for Canada and Quebec from 1801 to 1989.   (*Sources:* Anatole Romaniuc, "Fertility in Canada: Retrospective and Prospective." *Canadian Studies in Population* 18(2), 1991, p. 59. See also Statistics Canada, "Births." *The Daily*, 21 September 2007 and 26 September 2008 [**www.statcan.ca/Daily**].

From their differing perspectives, such economists as David Foot, such sociologists as Roderic Beaujot, and such geographers as John Miron, Mark Rosenberg, and Eric Moore have spent a considerable amount of time analyzing the public-policy implications of Canada's aging population. Let us consider some of these implications as they now affect the three main age groups we used to define the concept of dependency ratios.

The Youth Cohort (0–15 years old)   The relative and absolute decline of this group challenges the Canadian educational system with the problems of enrolment declines and, ultimately, school closures as the numbers of students shrink (especially when compared with the enormous expansion of the baby boom years). Colleges and universities, likely to be similarly affected by the decline in these cohorts, have successfully countered the projected declines by increasing the **participation rate**, that is, the proportion of a cohort attending such institutions.

Indeed, the decline of this cohort affects all organizations that serve this age group. For example, in August 2004, Scouts Canada reported a decline from 300 000 in the 1960s to 130 000 in 2004; Guides Canada noted a similar fall (from 235 000 guides in 1965 to 122 000 in 2004). Both organizations stated that because of such declines, a number of their campsites across Canada would have to be closed.

At the sociocultural level, members of the youth cohort are faced with a country in which, sometime toward the middle of the twenty-first century, there will be more people over 65 years than those under 16 years old. Consumer analysts have already begun to realize that the teenage demand for music, fashion, and recreation that drove the marketplace during the baby boom is being replaced by a much older

participation rate: the proportion of a cohort or group that becomes involved in a specific activity, such as attending an educational institution

demographic. One illustration of this trend is that the radio station CHOM FM 97.7 in Montreal changed its programming in February 2002 from contemporary rock to classic rock. Another example is AM 740, which in the early 2000s switched from rock to "all time favourites" and has now recently switched yet again to appeal to the aging baby boom, defined by the station's owner Moses Znaimer as the "zoomers"—boomers with zip!

The Middle Cohort (16–64 years old)   Demographically speaking, the major factor of change for this group is the baby boom cohort itself. Its oldest members, called "front-end boomers" by David Foot, were born in the late 1940s and will be retiring in the next decade or so. Currently, they occupy the upper ranks of many institutions and corporations. Those born at the end of the boom, in the mid-1960s, are now entering mid-career. In effect, Canada's workforce has had to expand enormously to accommodate the employment aspirations of the baby boomers and will only begin to free up space for younger cohorts when the boomers retire in large numbers, from about 2020 onward.

The 16–64 age group is the one whose behaviour most affects the housing market and, therefore, the form of our cities and towns. The demand for suburban nuclear family housing, small inner-city condos, and rural cottages can all be related to stages in the life cycle. Because of this, demographic analysis has had an important part to play in the real estate industry and in the halls of the Canada Mortgage and Housing Corporation. One prediction currently holds that as this country's population continues to age, the demand for cottages in rural areas will decline as people seek the lifestyle and health care amenities of urban centres.

The Old-Age Cohort (65 years and over)   The policy issues raised by this cohort are primarily those of health care and pension provision, both issues greatly affected by the increased relative and absolute numbers of Canada's elderly. Since this group is made up of larger numbers of women than men (because average female life expectancies are higher), policy problems are also gender-related ones. In terms of average health care expenditures, because an individual over 65 years old costs between two and three times as much as someone under 16 years old, the impacts of an aging society on health care costs are magnified. The policy solutions are being hotly debated at the moment, with a number of provinces, such as Alberta, actively pursuing user fees and a private system to supplement what some see as a struggling universal heath care system.

One main cause of the problems arising from the reliance on hospitals as the primary vehicle of health care delivery is that hospitals are very expensive institutions to run. Moreover, those geographers who have studied this issue point to the basic spatial inequalities produced by delivering health care in this way and have raised issue of access as an ethical issue. Preventive measures are receiving greater attention than in the past because they are often far cheaper than remedies that require drugs and surgery.

Public pensions are also under strain because one of the unforeseen consequences of the aging of baby boomers has been that there will soon be more people receiving these pensions than there are paying into the Canada Pension Plan and Quebec Pension Plan. To cover the shortfall, the federal government has already increased the premiums and will certainly have to do so again before long. Some commentators have suggested a temporary increase in the age of retirement to cope with this problem, but this is not a popular suggestion.

Canadian geographers have examined the spatial distribution of Canada's population and have identified a number of areas that are particularly likely to be affected by the aging of our society. Their work indicates that such cities as Victoria (British Columbia) and Kingston (Ontario) have a higher-than-average population of those aged over 65 because of the in-migration of the elderly to these communities. This situation obviously places increased demands on these cities for such services as the provision of medical facilities, retirement homes, and wheelchair accessible public transit.

Other parts of Canada, such as rural Saskatchewan and Newfoundland and Labrador, are aging not because of in-migration of the elderly but because of the out-migration of the young. Meeting the needs of the elderly in isolated rural communities poses its own problems, especially at a time of rising costs. To what extent people have a right to expect to be cared for in their own communities where they have spent their lives, rather than elsewhere where services can be centrally provided, is a question that geographers have only begun to address. In general terms, we can conclude that the challenge of an aging society is likely to be felt much more in Canada's periphery. The metropolitan core of this country has far more resources to cope with the needs of our growing population of the elderly.

Policy-makers, including a number with geographical training, have put forward a variety of solutions to the problems we have outlined here. Broadly speaking, these can be divided into three types of response.

- *Pronatalism.* If declining birth rates lie at the heart of the problem, some have said that the solution is to try to reverse this trend. The government of Quebec tried to do exactly that in the form of "baby bonus" cheques, which were paid for a few years in the 1990s. More recently, Quebec has turned to a province-wide system of subsidized daycare as an alternative. (Interestingly, this province has, until recently, had the lowest birth rate in Canada, an issue that has concerned those who fear a decline in the number of French speakers in the province.) In reality, as international surveys have shown, no government scheme compensates for the true costs of raising children, and to pose the issue in only economic terms shows a basic misunderstanding of the causes of the decline in the birth rate.

- *Increased economic productivity.* Some economists have argued that the problems of an aging society could all be met by simply having a more productive economy. An economy that produces more can pay higher taxes and health insurance and pension premiums. Moreover, when all of the baby boomers have eventually retired, and Canada's workforce begins to decline in size, the decline need have no impact on the economy if it is countered by rising productivity. In this sense, such agreements as the North America Free Trade Agreement (NAFTA), which have the potential to increase Canada's international markets, may have a long-term beneficial impact. New technologies, many built on the increased use of computers and robotics, offer another possibility.

- *Immigration.* Canada's traditional "policy lever," the one used to people the country and fuel economic growth, is now also promoted by the federal government as a solution to the problems of an aging population. The shortfall in births can be simply replaced by the recruitment of immigrants from overseas. Moreover, unlike many other core nations that have only just begun to contemplate this solution, Canada has the advantages of a trained bureaucracy already in place around the world and a public largely receptive to the policy. However, it should be added that estimates carried out for Health Canada's *Demographic Review* showed that because immigrants themselves age, annual immigration at the levels currently experienced in this country can only postpone the effects of aging by approximately seven years.

POPULATION DYNAMICS AND PROCESSES

To evaluate a different understanding of population growth and change, experts look at two significant factors: fertility and mortality. Birth and death rates, as they are also known, are important indicators of a region's level of development and its place within the world economy.

Birth, or Fertility, Rates

The **crude birth rate** (**CBR**) is the ratio of the number of live births in a single year for every thousand people in the population. The crude birth rate is, indeed, crude because it measures the birth rate in terms of the total population and not with respect to a particular age-specific group or cohort. For example, Canada's crude birth rate in 2007 was 11 per thousand, which compares with 21 per thousand for Mexico in the same year.

Although the level of economic development is a very important factor shaping the CBR, other, often equally important, influences also affect the CBR. In particular, it may be heavily affected by the demographic structure of the population, as graphically suggested by age–sex pyramids. In addition, an area's CBR is influenced by women's educational achievement, religion, social customs, diet, and health, as well as by politics and civil unrest. Most demographers believe that the availability of birth-control methods is also critically important to a country's or region's birth rate. **Figure 3.5** is a world map of the CBR showing high levels of fertility in most of the periphery and low levels of fertility in the core. The highest birth rates occur in Africa, the poorest region in the world.

Fertility is the childbearing performance of individuals, couples, groups, or populations. The crude birth rate is only one indicator of fertility and, in fact, is somewhat limited in its usefulness, telling very little about the potential for future fertility levels. Two other indicators formulated by population experts—the total fertility rate and the doubling time—provide more insight into the potential of a population. The **total fertility rate** (**TFR**) is a measure of the average number of children a woman will have throughout the years that demographers have identified as her childbearing years, approximately ages 15 through 49 (**Table 3.2**). Whereas

crude birth rate (CBR): the ratio of the number of live births in a single year for every thousand people in the population

fertility: the childbearing performance of individuals, couples, groups, or populations

total fertility rate (TFR): the average number of children a woman will have throughout the years that demographers have identified as her childbearing years, approximately ages 15 through 49

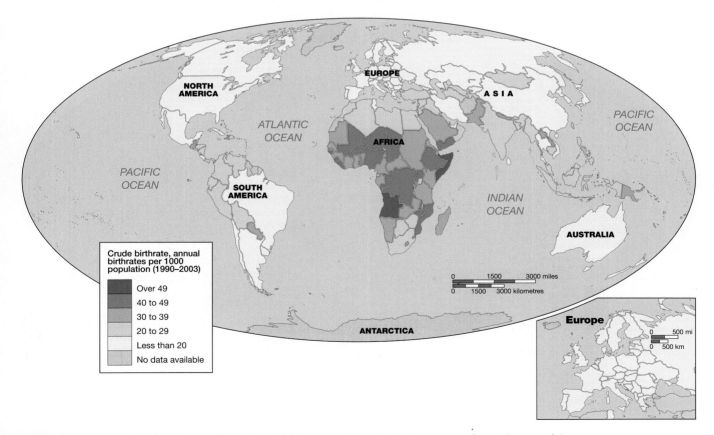

Figure 3.5 World crude birth rates, 2004 Crude birth rates and crude death rates are often indicators of the levels of economic development in individual countries. Compare, for example, Australia, a core country, which offers a stark contrast to statistics for Ethiopia, a very poor and underdeveloped peripheral country. (After World Bank, *World Development Indicators, 2004.* Washington, DC: World Bank.)

TABLE 3.2 Total Fertility Rates for Selected Countries, 2007

Country	Total Fertility Rate (TFR)
Afghanistan	6.8
Canada	1.5
China	1.6
India	2.9
Namibia	3.6
Netherlands	1.7
Russia	1.3
United States	2.1

Source: Population Reference Bureau website, **www.prb.org.**, Mid-2007 World Population tables.

doubling time: the measure of how long it will take the population of an area to grow to twice its current size

crude death rate (CDR): the number of deaths in a single year for every thousand people in the population

the CBR indicates the number of births in a given year, the TFR is a more predictive measure that attempts to portray what birth rates will be among a particular cohort of women over time. A population with a TFR of slightly higher than 2 has achieved replacement-level fertility. This means that birth rates and death rates are approximately balanced and there is stability in the population.

Closely related to the TFR is the doubling time of the population. The **doubling time**, as the name suggests, is a measure of how long it will take the population of an area to grow to twice its current size. For example, a country whose population increases at 1.8 percent per year will have doubled in about 40 years. In fact, world population is currently increasing at this rate. By contrast, a country whose population is increasing 3.18 percent annually will double in only 22 years—the doubling time for Kenya. Birth rates, and the population dynamics we can project from them, however, tell us only part of the story of the potential of the population for growth. We must also know the death, or mortality, rates.

Death, or Mortality, Rates

Countering birth rates and also shaping overall population numbers and composition is the **crude death rate (CDR)**, the ratio of the number of deaths in one year for every thousand people in the population. As with crude birth rates, crude death rates often roughly reflect levels of economic development: countries with low birth rates generally have low death rates (**Figure 3.6**).

Although often associated with economic development, the CDR is also significantly influenced by other factors. A demographic structure with more men and elderly people, for example, usually means higher death rates. Other important influences on mortality include health care availability, social class, occupation, and even place of residence. Poorer groups in the population have higher death rates than

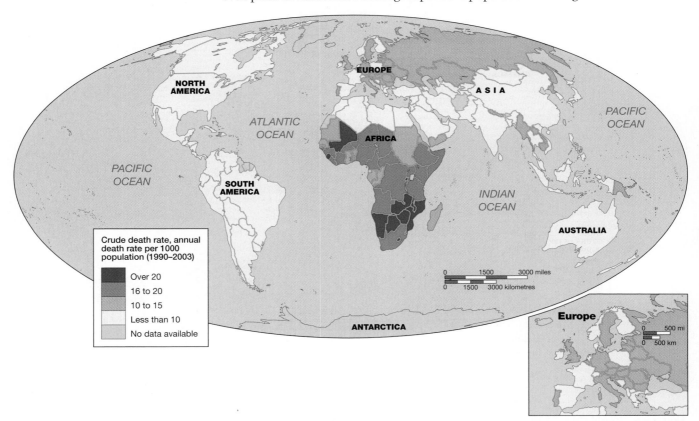

Figure 3.6 World crude death rates, 2004 The global pattern of crude death rates varies from crude birth rates. Most apparent is that the difference between highest and lowest crude death rates is relatively smaller than is the case for crude birth rates, reflecting the impact of factors related to the middle phases of the demographic transition. (After World Bank, *World Development Indicators, 2004.* Washington, DC: World Bank.)

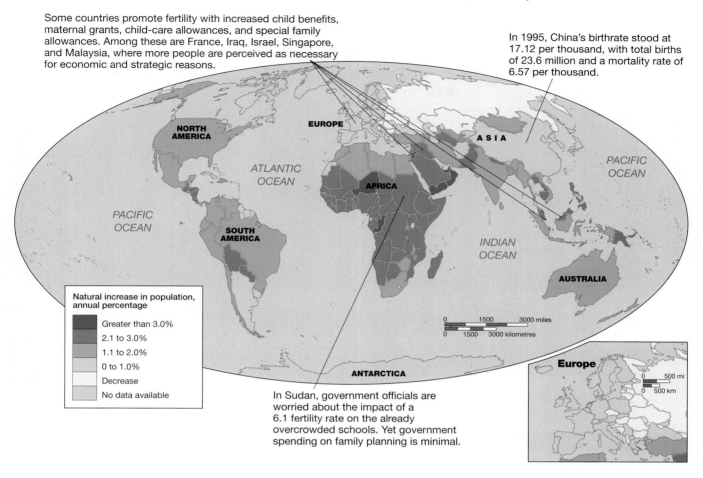

Some countries promote fertility with increased child benefits, maternal grants, child-care allowances, and special family allowances. Among these are France, Iraq, Israel, Singapore, and Malaysia, where more people are perceived as necessary for economic and strategic reasons.

In 1995, China's birthrate stood at 17.12 per thousand, with total births of 23.6 million and a mortality rate of 6.57 per thousand.

Natural increase in population, annual percentage

- Greater than 3.0%
- 2.1 to 3.0%
- 1.1 to 2.0%
- 0 to 1.0%
- Decrease
- No data available

In Sudan, government officials are worried about the impact of a 6.1 fertility rate on the already overcrowded schools. Yet government spending on family planning is minimal.

Figure 3.7   World rates of natural increase, 2004   As the map shows, rates of natural increase are highest in sub-Saharan Africa, the Near East, and parts of Asia, as well as in parts of South and Central America. Europe and the United States and Canada, as well as Australia and parts of central Asia and Russia, have slow to stable rates of natural increase.   (After World Bank, *World Development Indicators, 2004*. Washington, DC: World Bank.)

the middle class. The difference between the CBR and the CDR is the rate of **natural increase**—the surplus of births over deaths—or the rate of **natural decrease**—the deficit of births relative to deaths (**Figure 3.7**).

Death rates can be measured for both sex and age cohorts, and one of the most common measures is the **infant mortality rate**. This figure is the annual number of deaths of infants less than one year of age compared with the total number of live births for that same year. The figure is usually expressed as number of deaths during the first year of life per 1000 live births.

The infant mortality rate has been used by researchers as an important indicator both of a country's health care system and of the general population's access to health care. Global patterns show that although infant mortality rates are high in the peripheral countries of Africa and Asia, they are low in the more developed countries of Europe and North America (**Figure 3.8**). Generally, these patterns reflect adequate maternal nutrition and the wider availability of health care resources and personnel in core regions. When patterns are examined below the global scale, at the level of countries, regions, and cities and regions within countries, infant mortality rates are not uniform. In east central Europe, Bulgaria has a 9.7 per thousand infant mortality rate, while the Czech Republic has a rate of 3.3 per thousand. The point is that global patterns often mask regional and local variations in mortality rates, both for infants and other population cohorts.

A report from the United Nations Children's Fund (UNICEF) released in October 2004 makes use of a related measure, child mortality, to underline its concerns. Child mortality refers to the number of children who die before their

natural increase: the difference between the CBR and the CDR, which is the surplus of births over deaths

natural decrease: the difference between the CDR and the CBR, which is the deficit of births relative to deaths

infant mortality rate: the annual number of deaths of infants under one year of age compared with the total number of live births for that same year

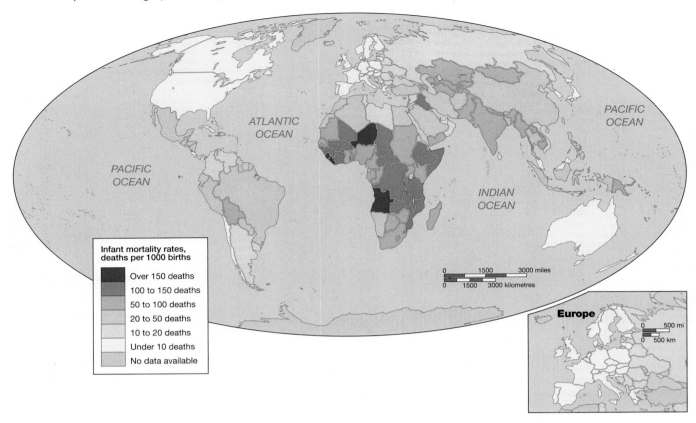

Figure 3.8 World infant mortality rates, 2004 The geography of poverty underlies the patterns shown in this map and allows us to analyze the linkages between population variables and social conditions. Infant mortality rates generally seem to parallel crude death rates, with sub-Saharan Africa generally reporting the highest rates. These rates reflect a number of factors, including inadequate or completely absent maternal health care as well as poor nutrition for infants. (After *Hammond Atlas of the World*. New York: Oxford University Press, 1993. Update from the World Bank, *World Development Indicators, 2004*. Washington, DC: World Bank.)

fifth birthday and is measured in relation to every 1000 live births. In 2002, according to UNICEF, industrialized countries had 7 deaths for every 1000 births, while the poorest nations had an average of 158. (The highest rate, 284 per 1000, was recorded for Sierra Leone.) Despite the goals adopted by world leaders at the UN Millennium Summit in 2000 to reduce child mortality by two-thirds by 2015, the UNICEF report notes "alarmingly slow progress on reducing child deaths." Indeed, in more than one-third of sub-Saharan African countries, child mortality rates had increased or stagnated.

Nevertheless, there is some reason for optimism. A 2005 report shows how advice from Canada's International Development Research Centre (IDRC) has helped reduce child mortality by more than 40 percent in the eastern parts of Tanzania since 2000.[4] Working with the Tanzania Ministry of Health, the IDRC discovered that redesigning the region's health care delivery to meet the needs of local clinics made it possible to properly diagnose illness and to make more efficient use of available financial resources. Given that Tanzania is only able to spend $8 per citizen per year on health care (Canada spends $2700), the IDRC's recommendations should prove invaluable.

life expectancy: the average number of years an individual can expect to live

Related to infant mortality and the crude death rate is **life expectancy**, the average number of years an individual can expect to live. Not surprisingly, life expectancy varies considerably from country to country, region to region, and even

---

[4]Stephanie Nolan, "Canadian Project Halves Tanzania's Child Deaths," *Globe and Mail*, 24 January 2005, pp. A1, A8.

place to place within cities and among different classes and racial and ethnic groups. Canada is no exception in this regard. There are considerable variations in life expectancies across the country and among groups. Aboriginal communities, for example, record some of the lowest average life expectancies in Canada (see "Population, Health, and the Environment" later in this chapter).

Another key factor influencing life expectancy is epidemics, which can quickly and radically alter population numbers and composition. In our times, epidemics can spread rapidly over great distances, largely because people and other disease carriers can now travel from one place to another very rapidly. Also, in countries with well-developed urban systems, diffusion will occur hierarchically, which (as we saw in Chapter 1) is much faster than simple spread, or contagious diffusion. Epidemics can have profound effects at various scales, from the international to the local, and reflect the increasing interdependence of a shrinking globe. They may affect different population groups in different ways and, depending on the quantity and quality of health and nutritional care available, may have a greater or lesser impact on different localities.

One of the most widespread epidemics of modern times is the spread of acquired immune deficiency syndrome (AIDS) and the human immunodeficiency virus (HIV) that is responsible for the disease. According to the *Report on the Global Aids Epidemic 2008* issued by the Joint United Nations Programme on HIV/AIDS (UNAIDS), there was a worldwide total of 33 million people living with HIV/AIDS in 2007, but signs of progress in the battle against the disease were shown by the fact that the number of new HIV infections had declined from 3.0 million in 2001 to 2.7 million in 2007. In other words, to quote the report itself, "the global epidemic is stabilizing, but at an unacceptably high level." By 2007, the annual death rate from the disease had declined from a peak of 2.5 million in 2004 to reach an estimated level of 2.0 million.

Since its beginnings in the early 1980s, probably in parts of Central Africa, HIV/AIDS has spread across most parts of the world, and has usually been able to spread rapidly because it has been able to diffuse hierarchically (see Chapter 1)—especially in countries of the core, with their well-integrated urban systems. Regionally, however, sub-Saharan African nations (those south of the Sahara) have been the hardest affected (**Figure 3.9**). The 2008 UNAIDS report observes that 67 percent

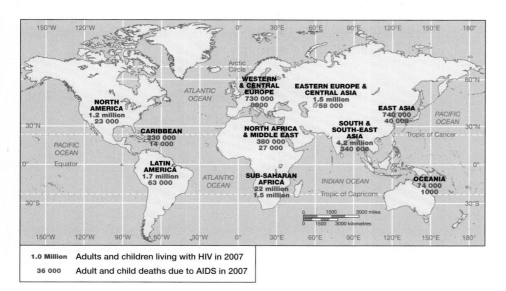

| 1.0 Million | Adults and children living with HIV in 2007 |
| 36 000 | Adult and child deaths due to AIDS in 2007 |

Figure 3.9   Adults and children living with and dying from HIV/AIDS, 2007   HIV/AIDS infections are concentrated in the periphery and semiperiphery, with 86 percent of people with HIV/AIDS living in Asia and sub-Saharan Africa. Compare the number of adults and children living with HIV/AIDS in Africa with those in North America or Europe. Deaths from HIV/AIDS have also been highest in Africa.   (*Source:* Joint United Nations Programme on HIV/AIDS [UNAIDS], "Annex 1," *Report on the Global Aids Epidemic 2008.* Geneva: UNAIDS, 2008, **www.unaids.org/en/ KnowledgeCentre/HIVData/GlobalReport/2008/2008_Global_report.asp**.)

of all people living with HIV/AIDS in 2007 resided in this part of the world, and that this region accounted for 72 percent of all deaths caused by AIDS in 2007.

Although no cure has yet been found, some countries have been successful in slowing the spread of AIDS. Finland, for example, has had significant success in slowing the diffusion of HIV through an intensive public relations campaign and by providing top-notch health services to all its citizens. None of the sub-Saharan African countries, mired in poverty, inadequate health care systems, and political inefficiency and often unrest, can even approach these levels of activity, however. Many Southeast Asian countries may face similar constraints and equally dismal prospects of slowing the diffusion of the disease. Stephen Lewis, a Canadian and until recently the UN secretary-general's special representative on HIV/AIDS in Africa, has compaigned tirelessly for Western countries, such as Canada, to make cheaper drugs available to those affected by this disease.

Demographic Transition Theory

demographic transition: the replacement of high birth and death rates by low birth and death rates

Many demographers believe that fertility and mortality rates are directly tied to the level of economic development of a country, region, or place. Pointing to the history of demographic change in core countries, they state that many of the economic, political, social, and technological transformations associated with industrialization and urbanization lead to a demographic transition. The **demographic transition** is a model of population change when high birth and death rates are replaced by low birth and death rates. Once a society moves from a pre-industrial economic base to an industrial one, population growth slows. According to the demographic transition model, the decrease in population growth is attributable to improved economic production and higher standards of living brought about by changes in medicine, education, and sanitation.

As **Figure 3.10** illustrates, the high birth and death rates of the pre-industrial phase (Phase 1) are replaced by the low birth and death rates of the industrial phase (Phase 4) only after passing through the critical transitional phase (Phase 2) and then more moderate rates (Phase 3) of natural increase and growth. This transitional phase of rapid growth is the direct result of early and steep declines in mortality at the same time that fertility remains at levels characteristic of a place that has not yet been industrialized. Some demographers have observed that many peripheral and semiperipheral countries appear to be stalled in the transitional phase, which has been called a "demographic trap."

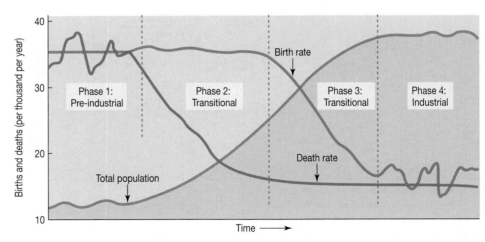

Figure 3.10 Demographic transition model The transition from a stable population based on high birth and death rates to one based on low birth and death rates progresses in clearly defined stages, as illustrated by this graph. With basic information about a country's birth and death rates and total population, it is possible to identify that country's position within the demographic transition process. Population experts disagree about the usefulness of the model, however. Many insist it is applicable only to the demographic history of core countries.

TABLE 3.3 Birth and Death Rates for England and Scotland, 1870–1920

The CBRs and CDRs for England and Scotland between 1870 and 1920 illustrate countries moving between Phase 2 and Phase 3 of the demographic transition, in which death rates are lower than birth rates. England and Scotland are clear examples of the way in which the demographic transition has been theorized to operate in core countries. During the 50-year period covered in the table, both countries were completing their transformation as key industrial regions.

	1870	1880	1890	1900	1910	1920
			Crude Birth Rate			
England	35.2	35.4	32.5	29.9	27.3	22.7
Scotland	35.0	34.8	32.3	30.2	28.4	24.0
			Crude Death Rate			
England	22.5	21.4	19.2	18.2	15.4	14.6
Scotland	22.1	21.6	19.2	18.5	16.6	15.3

Source: M. Anderson and D. Morse, *Scottish Demography* 42, 1993.

The reason for this lag in declining fertility rates relative to mortality rates is that while new and more effective methods for fighting infectious diseases have been advanced, the social attitudes about the desirability of large families have only recently begun to be affected. Historical trends in birth and death rates and natural increase are shown in **Table 3.3** for Scotland and England during their periods of demographic transition. Over a roughly 50-year period, both countries were able to reduce their rates of natural increase by nearly one-third. In the fourth phase of post-industrial development (not shown in the table), birth and death rates have both stabilized at a low level, which means that population growth rates are very slow and birth rates are more likely to oscillate than death rates.

Whereas England and Scotland, early industrializers, passed through the demographic transition over a period of about 150 years beginning in the mid-nineteenth century, most peripheral and semiperipheral countries have yet to complete the transition.

Although the demographic transition model is based on actual birth and death statistics, many population geographers and other population experts increasingly question its generalizability to all places and all times. In fact, although the model adequately describes the history of population change in core countries, it appears less useful for explaining the demographic history of countries and regions in the periphery. Such criticism has led to its declining significance for understanding population geography. Among other criticisms are that industrialization—which, according to the theory, is central to moving from Phase 2 to Phases 3 and 4—is seldom domestically generated in the peripheral countries. Instead, foreign investment seems to drive peripheral industrialization. As a result, the features of demographic change witnessed in core countries, such as higher living standards, where industrialization was largely a result of internal capital investment, have not occurred in many peripheral countries. Other critics of the demographic transition model point to several factors undermining a demographic transition fuelled by economic growth: the shortages of skilled labourers, the absence of advanced educational opportunities for all members of the population (especially women), and limits on technological advances. In other words, while demographic transition may be a characteristic experience of the core regions of the globe, it appears to have limited applicability to the periphery.

POPULATION MOVEMENT AND MIGRATION

In addition to the population dynamics of death and reproduction, the third critical influence is the movement of people from place to place. Individuals may make far-reaching, international or intraregional moves, or they may simply move from one part of a city to another. For the most part, mobility and migration reflect the interdependence of the world-system. For example, global shifts in industrial investment result in local adjustments to those shifts as populations move or remain in place in response to the creation or disappearance of employment opportunities.

Mobility and Migration

mobility: the ability to move, either permanently or temporarily

migration: a long-distance move to a new location

emigration: a movement in which a person *leaves* a country

immigration: a movement in which a person *arrives in* another country

international migration: a move from one country to another

internal migration: a move within a particular country or region

One way to describe such movement is with the term **mobility**, the ability to move from one place to another, either permanently or temporarily. Mobility may be used to describe a wide array of human movement ranging from a journey to work (for example, a daily commute from suburb to city or suburb to suburb) to an ocean-spanning, permanent move.

The second way to describe population movement is in terms of **migration**, a long-distance move to a new location. Migration involves a permanent or temporary change of residence from one place to another. **Emigration** is a movement in which a person *leaves* one country to go to another. **Immigration** describes movement in which a person *arrives* in one country, having left another. Thus, a person from China who moves to Canada *emigrates* from China and *immigrates* to Canada. These types of movement from one country to another are types of **international migration**. Moves may also occur within a particular country or region, in which case they are called **internal migration**. Both permanent and temporary changes of residence may occur for many reasons but most often involve a desire for economic betterment or an escape from adverse political conditions, such as war or oppression.

Interprovincial migration in Canada is one example of the influence of economics on internal migration. Over the five years between the 2001 and 2006 censuses, only three provinces recorded net gains through internal immigration according to data released by Statistics Canada in mid-2008. With its booming economy, it is no surprise to learn that Alberta was the leading destination for those moving across Canada between 2001 and 2006. Over those five years, Alberta gained a total of 88 180 people in this way, a factor that was the principal one responsible for the province's overall increase in population during this intercensal period. British Columbia (22 130) and Prince Edward Island (approximately 600) were the two other provinces benefitting from internal migration over this period; although, as can be seen from these totals, their relative attraction was no match for that of Alberta's. On the other hand, the provinces of Newfoundland and Labrador (–6245), New Brunswick (–10 615) and Saskatchewan (–25 385) lost more people through internal migration than they gained from the net effects of any increases due to births minus deaths and international migration minus emigration. Local and regional economies change, of course, and already there are signs that Saskatchewan's decline, at least, is reversing. Since early 2008, the rise in prices for grain and potash (used for fertilizer) have been substantial, and this turnaround in economic fortunes has begun to translate into the first signs of population growth in the province for several generations.

Governments are concerned about keeping track of migration numbers, migration rates, and the characteristics of the migrant populations because these factors can have profound consequences for political, economic, and cultural conditions at national, regional, and local scales. For example, a peripheral country, such as Cuba, that has experienced substantial out-migration of highly trained professionals may find it difficult to provide needed services, such as health care. Benefiting from lower labour costs are such countries as Canada, the United States, Germany, and France, which have received large numbers of low-skilled in-migrants willing to work for extremely low wages. These countries may also face considerable social stress in times of economic recession when unemployed citizens begin to blame the immigrants for "stealing" their jobs or receiving welfare benefits.

Demographers have developed several calculations of migration rates. Calculation of the in-migration and out-migration rates provides the foundation for discovering gross and net migration rates for an area of study. **Gross migration** refers to the total number of migrants moving into and out of a place, region, or country. **Net migration** refers to the gain or loss in the total population of that area as a result of the migration. Migration is a particularly important concept because the total population of a country, region, or locality is dependent on migration activity as well as on birth and death rates.

Migration rates, however, provide only a small portion of the information needed to understand the dynamics of migration and its effects at all scales of resolution. In general terms, migrants make their decisions to move based on push factors and pull factors. **Push factors** are events and conditions that impel an individual to move away from a location. They include a wide variety of possible motives, from the idiosyncratic (such as an individual migrant's dissatisfaction with the amenities offered at home) to the dramatic (such as war, economic dislocation, or ecological deterioration). **Pull factors** are forces of attraction that influence migrants to move to a particular location. Factors drawing individual migrants to chosen destinations, again, may range from the highly personal (such as a strong desire to live near the sea) to the very structural (such as strong economic growth, and thus relatively lucrative job opportunities).

Usually, the decision to migrate is a combination of both push and pull factors, and most migrations are voluntary. In **voluntary migration**, an individual chooses to move. When migration occurs against the individual's will, push factors can produce **forced migration**. Forced migration (both internal and international) remains a critical problem in the contemporary world. In 2008, the Office of the United Nations High Commissioner for Refugees (UNHCR) reported that the total number of refugees and internally displaced people (IDP) under its care had risen by 2.5 million during the course of 2007, to reach an unprecedented total of 25.1 million people by year's end. The report noted that 11.4 million of this total were refugees (individuals who have crossed international boundaries, and also met criteria discussed below), and 13.7 million were IDPs (individuals who had fled conflict but remained within the borders of their own country). Large as these numbers are, they do not include many of those affected by conflict in the Middle East (because they lie outside UNHCR's mandate) and as many as an additional 12.3 million people in 2007 who were affected by conflict-induced internal displacement in 2007.

According to the 1951 International Convention Related to the Status of Refugees, the term *refugee* has a formal definition. Sometimes known as "political" or "Convention" to clarify their status, they are people who have fled their homelands because they have a well-founded fear of persecution on the grounds of race, religion, nationality, political belief, or social characteristic. People who met these criteria are entitled to the right of non-return to their country of persecution and to the protection of UNHCR. Such international aid is often delivered in refugee camps, and Simon Fraser University geographer Jennifer Hyndman has presented a detailed account of what life is like for those in camps in Kenya in her book *Managing Displacement*.

In recent years, the increasing numbers of refugee claimants asking for protection has led many countries, including Canada, to seek to devise ever more elaborate methods of deciding upon the status of those arriving upon their borders seeking protection. Indeed, fears of increasing numbers or of possible abuse of the system has led many countries of asylum to introduce restrictions on the entry of refugee claimants (such as visas), and on the rights of refugees once they are admitted (such as limited rights to work and the requirement to reside in detention camps). Such a package of restrictions, because they have the effect of denying, or limiting, access, are effectively creating *spaces of exclusion*—an issue that political geographers have begun to address.

Another wider problem has been the effects of environmental change on forced migration. You will have noticed that the definition of *refugee* given above makes no reference to a growing inability to support oneself due to a deterioration

gross migration: the total number of migrants moving into and out of a place, region, or country

net migration: the gain or loss in the total population of a particular area as a result of migration

push factors: events and conditions that impel an individual to move away from a location

pull factors: forces of attraction that influence migrants to move to a particular location

voluntary migration: the movement by an individual based on choice

forced migration: the movement by an individual against his or her will

eco-migration: a population movement caused by the degradation of land and essential natural resources

of the local environment as one of the formal grounds needed to qualify as a refugee. This is because in 1951 the UN was principally concerned with addressing the violations to people's political rights that had occurred during the upheaval of World War II. Nevertheless, many people have suggested that today forced **eco-migration**—population movement caused by the degradation of land and essential natural resources—has created a new category of refugees. In Bangladesh, for example, floodplain settlement that began occurring in the 1960s has led to severe losses of life and property and has forced temporary relocation of huge numbers of people whenever severe flooding occurs. Sea-level increases because of global warming threaten many places. Some Polynesian states may be permanently flooded by mid-century. In Ethiopia, the 1984–1985 famine was attributed not only to drought and pest infestation but also to governmental policies and actions that favoured urban populations and rendered rural populations especially vulnerable to environmental stress. Finally, dams and irrigation projects have annually forced between 1 million and 2 million people worldwide to move. Some experts have used the term *environmental refugees* for this whole category of people. Their plight is, sadly, but one example of the wider impacts of climate change upon human migration discussed in the box **Human Geography and Climate Change 3.1— Population Displacement.**

International Voluntary Migration

Not all migration is forced, however. Indeed, most people who migrate choose to do so (**Figure 3.11**). Canada is a land made up entirely of successive waves of

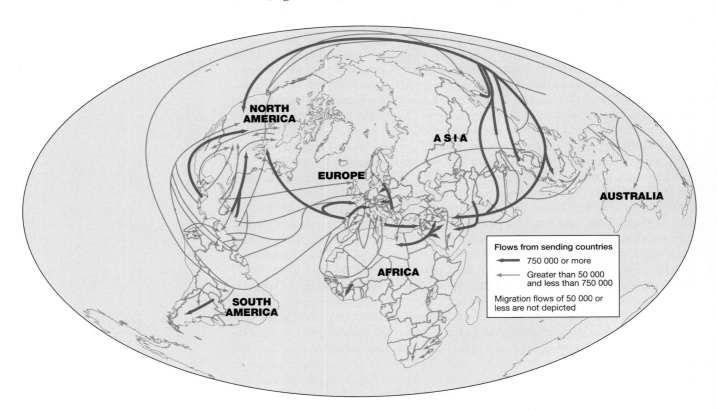

Figure 3.11 Global voluntary migration This map illustrates very complex flows across borders of people who have migrated by choice. Although each of the flows represents a cluster of individual decisions, generally speaking, the flows emanate from the periphery and are moving toward the core. Intracontinental migration, such as that in South America and Africa, represents the apparent pull of economic opportunity for residents of relatively poorer countries.   (*Sources: A. Segal, *An Atlas of International Migration*. New Providence, NJ: Hans Zell Publishers/ Bowker-Saur, 1993, p. 23. Map projection, Buckminster Fuller Institute and Dymaxion Map Design, Santa Barbara, CA. The word *Dymaxion* and the Fuller Projection Dymaxion™ Map design are trademarks of the Buckminster Fuller Institute, Santa Barbara, California, ©1938, 1967, & 1992. All rights reserved.)

Population Displacement

Scientists and policy-makers have largely reached consensus on the causes and certainty of climate change. However, the economic, demographic, and social consequences of this change are far less clear (**Figure 3.1.1**). Released in 2007, the Fourth Assessment Report of the Intergovernmental Panel on Climate Change (IPCC) discussed population displacement as a result of climate change,[5] predicting the displacement of hundreds of millions of people due to climate change by 2080.[6]

A concept that has recently emerged is that of the **environmental refugee**, or people who have been physically displaced from their homes and livelihoods by the effects of climate change. While the term is widely used, governments and the office of the United Nations High Commissioner for Refugees (UNHCR) do not officially recognize these refugees, and their formal legal status remains undecided. Despite this, widespread recognition of these individuals exists, with the New Economics Foundation arguing that international law should "grant refugee status to people driven from [their] homes by a lost or ruined environment."[7]

Climate change will likely have the greatest impact on populations in the developing world where a lack of resources and or a less stable political or economic infrastructure makes it more difficult to deal with its effects.[8]

In a report distributed by the Food and Agriculture Organization of the United Nations, "The capacity to survive and recover from the effects of a natural disaster is the result of two factors: the physical magnitude of the disaster in a given area, and the socioeconomic conditions of individuals or social groups in that area. Altogether, it is estimated that 90 percent of victims and 75 percent of all economic damages accrue to developing countries."[9]

So what might create environmental refugees? Long term, one of the most measurable outcomes associated with climate change is raising sea levels and the disappearance of coastal lands. The IPCC estimates that the average rate of sea level rise is 1–2 mm per year, with sea levels rising by an average of 60 cm by 2100.[10] For coastal communities and island nations, rising seas threaten their economic infrastructure by increasing erosion and flooding that destroys livelihoods and in many instances compromise fresh-water resources. Located in the South Pacific, the Cook Islands are mainly low-lying coral atolls. With climate change, rising sea levels are likely to inundate the coastal areas of these islands where their populations concentrate. The loss of agricultural land will mean people will lose their way of life, and if local governments have limited economic capability to offset these environmental impacts, population displacement will be inevitable.

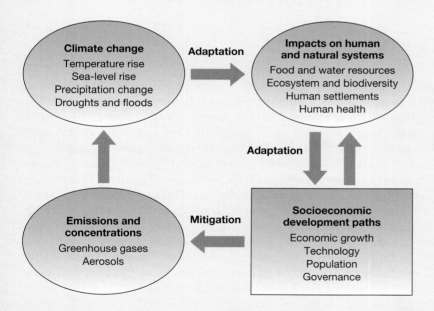

Figure 3.1.1   Climate change: an integrated framework   The expected impacts of climate change are varied and widespread. It is widely expected that climate change will impact human and natural systems through such things as food and water resources, which in turn will affect economic development and personal livelihoods.   (*Source: Climate Change 2001: Synthesis Report.* Contribution of Working Groups I, II and III to the Third Assessment Report of the Intergovernmental Panel on Climate Change. Fig. 8-2 and Fig. 1-1. Cambridge University Press.)

environmental refugee: people who have been physically displaced from their homes and livelihoods by the effects of climate change

[5]*Climate Change 2007*. Intergovernmental Panel on Climate Change, 2007, **www.ipcc.ch**.

[6]Ibid.

[7]M. Conisbee and A. Simms, *Environmental Refugees: The Case for Recognition*. New Economics Foundation: London, 2003, **www.neweconomics.org/gen/uploads/ lpce0g55xjx5eq55mfjxbb5523102003180040.pdf**.

[8]Ibid.

[9]Thouret and D'Ercole 1996: 409, noted in G. Martine and J.M. Guzman, "Population, Poverty and Vulnerability: Mitigating the Effects of Natural Disasters, Part 1." *SD Dimensions*, December 1999, **www.fao.org/sd/wpdirect/wpan0042.htm**.

[10]IPCC, *Climate Change 2007*.

Climate change is also responsible for shifting precipitation patterns and desertification. Africa is extremely vulnerable to climate change and is expected to receive less precipitation than it currently does, a situation made worse by ineffective governments, weak economies, poverty, and an already fragile environment. Shifting precipitation patterns mean that almost half of Africa's land mass is at risk of desertification, where long-term declines in rainfall amounts have already resulted in the southward shift of the Sahelian, Sudanese, and Guinean deserts and resulted in a reduced growing season and decreased water flows on the Niger and Senegal Rivers. Africa's Sahel region, an area that includes Ethiopia, Eritrea, Djibouti, and Somalia, has experienced more intense and frequent droughts in the last 40 years, with rainfall approximately one-third less than the long-run average.[11] Further encroachment of deserts will force population displacement, with the United Nations Food and Agricultural Organization predicting that 135 million people are at risk of displacement due to desertification alone.[12] This influx of environmental refugees into neighbouring countries and regions will likely strain existing infrastructures and social relations.

Extreme weather events such as cyclones can also produce short-term displacement. While we cannot defini-tively attribute particular storms to climate change, the IPCC notes evidence suggesting that cyclones have increased in average intensity, with further increases in their intensity and frequency expected.[13] In 1998, Hurricane Mitch caused flooding and mud slides in Central America, with up to 1.5 million people displaced in Honduras alone. The low lying delta area of Bangladesh is particularly prone to flooding due to cyclones.[14] Cyclone Sidr, which struck Bangladesh in November 2007, resulted in over 2 million displaced.

Climate change is expected to cause massive population displacement. Longer-term concerns focus on rising sea levels, desertification, and changing precipitation patterns. The most vulnerable populations include those in coastal and river flood plains, those whose economies are closely linked with climate-sensitive food and water resources, those in areas prone to extreme weather events, and those whose economic infrastructures are weak and less able to adapt. Climate change will undoubtedly create environmental refugees as people are forced from their homes and livelihoods, straining the coping ability of receiving countries and their governments. For governments, the question remains whether environmental refugees should be officially recognized.

—K.B.N.

[11]IPCC, *Climate Change 2007*.
[12]E. Rosenthal, "Water Is a New Battleground in Spain." *New York Times*, 3 June 2008, p. S1.

[13]Ibid.
[14]IPPC, *Climate Change 2007*.

immigrants, adding their own contributions to the development of this country, progressively inhabiting its spaces, and constructing their own places. In 2007, Canada received a total of almost 240 000 immigrants and refugees—a figure a little lower than the previous year's total of 250 000 but part of a very rich story of migration to this country. The weight of archaeological evidence suggests that Canada was first settled from the west by small bands of hunter-gatherer peoples migrating from Asia at least as early as 11 500 years ago. More than 10 000 years later, the first known migration came from the east. This came in the form of the short-lived Viking settlement in L'Anse aux Meadows in Newfoundland (about A.D. 1000). Another 500 to 600 years were to pass before permanent European immigration to Canada began, led by French ambitions to settle the gulf and lower valley of the St. Lawrence River. Only after the loss of its American colonies after 1783 and the flight of 100 000 Loyalists into Ontario, Quebec, and New Brunswick did Britain show any interest in settling Canada.

For the next century or so, the agricultural lands of Ontario and Quebec attracted a number of different migrant groups. It is estimated that from 1815 to 1865, over 1 million emigrants from the British Isles entered what was then known as British North America, many moving on to the United States. Approximately 60 percent of that flow was made up of migrants from Ireland, prompted to leave by disasters, such as the famine of 1846–1849. By the 1860s, little land remained to be colonized in the east, and Canada began to experience a net emigration. Many of those who stayed in this country chose to move internally, either to Canada's developing cities or to its agricultural frontiers. Indeed, it was in the west that Canada's policy-makers saw the solution to the loss of population growth. The purchase of Rupert's Land, in 1870, and treaty negotiations with the First Nations opened up the Prairies for European settlement. The eradication of the bison and the completion of the transcontinental Canadian Pacific Railroad made it feasible to establish in Canada an economy based on western agriculture.

There followed a 30- to 40-year period of substantial immigration from Eastern and central Europe to Alberta, Saskatchewan, and Manitoba. The twentieth century, with the exception of the war years and the Depression, continued this trend (**Figure 3.12**). Two major changes in the patterns of immigration occurred as the century progressed. First, immigration increasingly focused on urban rather than rural areas as destinations. Second, once a nonracist selection policy was introduced in 1967, the main sources of Canada's immigrants ceased to be European and became, by the century's end, predominantly Asian. In 12 000 years, then, Canada's immigration story has come full circle.

Of course, the full story of Canadian immigration lies buried beneath such statistics and generalizations. For many of us, the hopes and hardships, the memories of countries left behind, and the communities and cultures created in Canada form the real immigration experience. In places all across this country, we can see the indelible effects of that story. Contributions are evident from the Chinese workers brought in to build the railways; the Doukobhors who moved to Verigin in Saskatchewan to flee religious persecution from nineteenth-century Russia; the British gentlemen trying to plant apple orchards at Walkachin in pre–World War I British Columbia; the Czech and Yugoslav miners who, from the 1930s, extracted minerals from the mines of Flin Flon, Manitoba; the waves of post–World War II settlers from Europe who arrived at Pier 21 in Halifax, Nova Scotia, in the 1950s; the Chilean, Ugandan, and Vietnamese refugees who fled persecution in their own countries to settle in Toronto and Montreal in the 1970s; the Central Americans who sought refuge in the 1980s; and the latest wave of migrants from Hong Kong who have become a significant economic presence in late twentieth-century Vancouver. It is impossible to sum up these experiences, but it is obvious that the resulting combined contribution has been to reshape this country. (Two examples of such experiences are provided in **Geography Matters 3.2—Canadian Immigration**.)

Of course, these processes of immigration and settlement are by no means unique to Canada. These processes are major themes of human history and have, to a greater or lesser extent, affected all parts of the globe. Recognizing that we share such common experiences with other countries will greatly enable us to understand other regions.

In some situations, migration does not involve a permanent change of residence. Temporary labour migration has long been an indispensable part of the world economic order and has at times been actively pursued by governments and companies alike. Individuals who migrate temporarily to take jobs in other countries are generally known as **guest workers** (although this is a somewhat inappropriate term, since, strictly speaking, such migrants are not usually treated as "guests"). The temporary migration of Mexican and Caribbean farm labourers to Canada is a good example of this process (see **Geography Matters 3.3—Migrant Farm Workers in Canada**). Sending workers abroad is an important economic strategy for many peripheral and semiperipheral countries; it not only lessens local unemployment but also enables workers to send substantial amounts of money to their families at home. This arrangement helps keep the workers' families afloat and supports the dominance of the core in global economic activities. It is not always an ideal situation, however, since economic downturns in the guest worker's host country may result in a large decrease in remittances received by the home country, thus further aggravating that country's economic situation.

It is important to know the gender of temporary workers and the gender-based differences in the types of work performed. The Philippines, for example, has an Overseas Contract Worker (OCW) program that links foreign demand for workers to Philippine labour supply. The proportion of men and women OCWs is approximately

guest workers: individuals who migrate temporarily to take jobs in other countries

Figure 3.12 Immigration to Canada, 1860–2000 Since 1860, annual immigration totals to Canada have varied considerably, peaking (as the graph shows) between 1910 and 1920, declining through the Depression years until World War II, and then rising in a series of waves from 1950 to 2000. In general terms, these changes have reflected the changing requirements of the Canadian economy. In the early twentieth century, for example, the demand for farm labour fuelled very large annual immigration totals. In more recent years, government policy has been to increase immigration only when the economy is growing. Considerable changes have also occurred in the origins of Canada's immigrants as Canada has altered its immigration policies. If we compare the years 1961–1970 with 1991–1996 (see bar graph), for example, we see that the leading source region has changed over this period from Europe to Asia. A century ago, the majority of Canada's immigrants were headed to the Prairie provinces, but by 1996 (as the map shows), the most important destinations were Canada's major metropolitan centres, especially Toronto, Vancouver, and Montreal. Further information on Canadian immigration is available from Citizenship and Immigration Canada (**www.cic.gc.ca**) and from the Metropolis Project, an inter-university research group on immigration (**http://canada.metropolis.net**). (*Sources:* Citizenship and Immigration Canada, "Facts and Figures 2000: Immigration Overview," available at **www.cic.gc.ca**; "Immigrant Population by Place of Birth," Statistics Canada, 1996 Census: Nation Tables, available at **www.statcan.ca/english/census96/nation.htm**.)

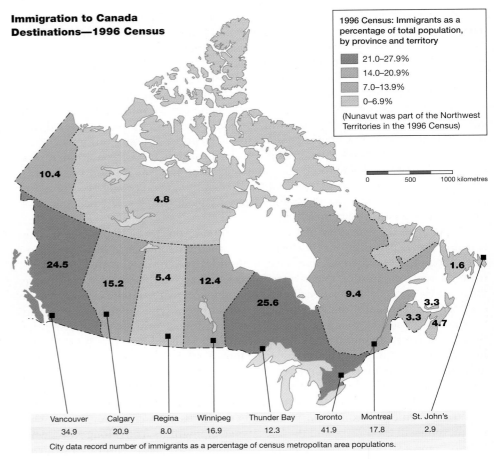

Immigration to Canada Destinations—1996 Census

Vancouver	Calgary	Regina	Winnipeg	Thunder Bay	Toronto	Montreal	St. John's
34.9	20.9	8.0	16.9	12.3	41.9	17.8	2.9

City data record number of immigrants as a percentage of census metropolitan area populations.

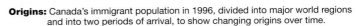
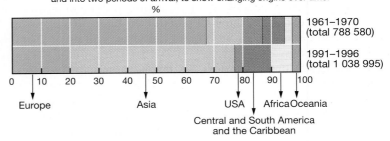

Origins: Canada's immigrant population in 1996, divided into major world regions and into two periods of arrival, to show changing origins over time.

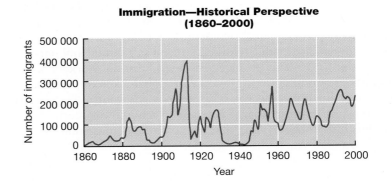

Immigration—Historical Perspective (1860–2000)

Canadian Immigration

It is impossible to convey a full impression of the myriad experiences of the immigrants to this country. However, we can see something of the measure of these experiences by taking as case studies the stories of two very different groups. Though they are widely separated in time and circumstances, we chose them because they illustrate the extraordinary range of backgrounds of Canada's immigrants and the resilience of the individuals and families.

The Petworth Emigration Committee, 1832–1837[15]

Our first example looks at an organized migration of people that occurred in the early part of the nineteenth century, when Canada was still part of the British Empire, and was part of a wider set of colonial policies that sought to encourage settlement overseas. Such policies argued that the increase of population in this way would not only lead to economic growth in the colonies, but also to increased trade between Britain and its empire—both of which developments would increase the value of the periphery to the core.

Surprising as it may at first seem, such early migrations to Canada are by no means forgotten today. They remain the focus of a small but active research community that consists of not just historians and geographers but also of the many descendants of the original migrants interested in their own genealogy. As recently as 2006, Library and Archives Canada (LAC) inaugurated a virtual exhibition called Moving Here, Staying Here: The Canadian Immigrant Experience that provides an introduction to Canada's migration history for the period 1800–1939, and to the documents, many of them now online, that facilitate individual research. The University of Waterloo's Immigrants to Canada website also provides an astonishing amount of material about early migration to this country.[16]

At a smaller scale, the Petworth Emigration Project now uses a website to report on its active investigations into the history of one of the earliest organized efforts to send migrants to this country, and as recently as 2007 published a third volume of its research (concerning the individual who conceived and administered this particular emigration scheme).[17] Indeed, because the amount of material that this particular project has now made available to the public makes this a very useful illustration of some of the experiences that surrounded early emigration to Canada, we will now consider this example in greater detail.

Between 1832 and 1837, about 1800 poor men, women, and children travelled from West Sussex in southern England to Upper Canada. They emigrated under the auspices of a body known as the Petworth Emigration Committee, one of a number of such bodies that existed in England at the time.

The full costs of their passage were paid for by the Earl of Egremont, a wealthy landowner whose estates included Petworth House (see Figure 6.7). His reasons for helping such people, many of whom were paupers from his own estates, were not philanthropic. Rather, he (like many landowners of his day) was inspired, by Malthusian notions and by a fear of rural unrest, to alleviate the pressure a growing population of poor farm labourers placed on local resources by promoting their emigration overseas. (For more on the ideas of Malthus, see later in this chapter.)

Once in Canada, the group of migrants sent by the Petworth Committee received further assistance from the colonial government. Most settled in southwest Ontario (particularly in Adelaide Township west of London and around Guelph), where they were given free or subsidized land on which to establish farms (**Figure 3.2.1**).

From the letters these settlers wrote to their relatives back home in England, we are able to see how they coped with the experiences of migration and how many of these individuals subsequently prospered in their new surroundings.

The sea passage from Portsmouth to Quebec City took between five and a half and seven weeks. "When we came to the banks of Newfoundland," William Voice wrote to his sister in 1834, "we met with lumps of ice as large as your farm floating on the water on the 8th of May, and it was so cold we could not get on deck." Once docked in Quebec City, the dangers did not cease. In 1832, the city was gripped by cholera (Figure 1.25) and immigrants were quarantined at Grosse Île before being allowed to continue their passage up the St. Lawrence. Describing this later to his father, James Rapson wrote that disease "followed us all along the river, about a day behind us."

---

[15]This section is based on Wendy Cameron and Mary McDougall Maude, *Assisting Emigration to Upper Canada: The Petworth Project, 1832–1837*. Montreal and Kingston: McGill-Queen's University Press, 2000; and Wendy Cameron, Sheila Haines, and Mary McDougall Maude, *English Immigrant Voices: Labourers' Letters from Upper Canada in the 1830s*. Montreal and Kingston: McGill-Queen's University Press, 2000. From the latter, a highly informative volume of Petworth emigrants' letters, we include quotations from letters by William Voice (1834, p. 170), James Rapson (1832, p. 70), Edward Longley (1836, p. 203), John and Caroline Dearling (1833, p. 145; 1838, pp. 277 and 278), Harry Harwood (1834, p. 163), and Thomas Adsett (1832, p. 87).

[16]Library and Archives Canada, Moving Here, Staying Here: The Canadian Immigrant Experience, 2006 exhibition, **www.collectionscanada.gc.ca/immigrants/index-e.html**. University of Waterloo, Immigrants to Canada, **http://ist.uwaterloo.ca/~marj/ genealogy/thevoyage.html**.

[17]The Petworth Emigration Project website can be found at **www.petworthemigrations.com**. The first two volumes in their publication series are referenced above; the details of this most recent volume are as follows: Sheila Haines and Leigh Lawson, *Poor Cottages and Proud Palaces: The Life of Thomas Sockett of Petworth 1777–1859*. Hastings, UK: Hastings Press, 2007.

Figure 3.2.1 The lands settled by Petworth emigrants, 1832–1837

(*Source*: Wendy Cameron and Mary McDougall Maude, *Assisting Emigration to Upper Canada: The Petworth Project, 1832–1837*. Montreal and Kingston: McGill-Queen's University Press, 2000.)

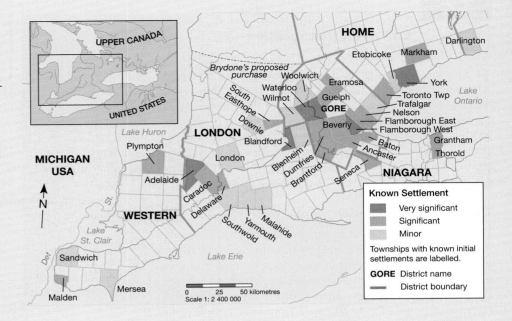

The trip from Quebec City to their destination in southwest Ontario could take another three or four weeks, since it involved negotiating the Lachine Rapids and ensuring a lengthy trip along wagon roads into the interior of Southern Ontario. Once settled there, immigrants faced the arduous task of clearing the wild land that Edward Longley described in a letter in 1836 as "entirely covered with trees, from the huge spreading oak whose diameter is from four to five feet . . . to the smallest sapling, all planted by the hand of nature and so thick that a squirrel may traverse thousands of acres without ever touching the ground."

However, for people who once earned 12 shillings a week as landless labourers, the backbreaking task of tree clearance was well worth the toil. John and Caroline Dearling wrote from Galt to her father in 1833 to tell him, "We have got 50 acres of land, at 3 dollars per acre; we have nothing to pay for 3 years. Our house will be done before long, then we are going to it." Five years later they wrote, "We have 3 acres rye, 3 of oats, 2 of peas, 1 acre of spring wheat, 1 acre of potatoes. . . . We have six hogs and I am hobbing [handrearing] a heifer calf. I have 34 chickens." An 1840 assessment for Waterloo Township recorded that by then the couple had 30 acres (12 hectares) cleared, 70 acres (almost 30 hectares) of wild land, two oxen and three cows. By 1843, when John Dearling died, the farm was valued at 263 pounds sterling.

Other Petworth emigrants quickly found employment outside agriculture. For example, Harry Harwood wrote in 1834, "I have plenty of work at shoe-making, and can earn three shillings and my board a day." He relayed, concerning his three sons, that "Henry is working in a brickyard at three pounds per month. . . . Alfred is in service with Mr Birch for six dollars per month. . . . Richard, I put apprentice to a blacksmith. . . ."

Despite having to leave England and many of their relatives and friends behind, few emigrants would have dis-

agreed with Thomas Adsett's general remark: "I can live better with working one day [in Canada], than in England in seven. . . ." Certainly, Cameron and Maude conclude their recent study of this group by observing "that the bulk of Petworth immigrants were better off in Upper Canada than in England." Their success in southwestern Ontario was due not only to government assistance and the relatively easy access to land but also to their own readiness to embark on careers as farmers and craftspeople. "By contrast with more articulate middle-class immigrants, they integrated so successfully that their contribution to building the province has been largely ignored."[18]

Somali Refugees in Toronto, 1991–2005

Our second case study concerns a very different group of immigrants to Canada, namely, those Somali refugees who have settled in Toronto since 1991. Despite the recentness of their arrival in Canada, this group has already been the focus of a number of studies by geographers and other researchers.[19]

Since the 1991 *coup d'état* that ousted its leader, General Mohamed Siad Barre, Somalia has been torn apart by civil war. Many hundreds of thousands of Somalis have been forced to leave their country for refugee camps in neighbouring countries. By 1996, for example, approximately 150 000 Somali refugees were living in Kenya where, according to Jennifer Hyndman, a geographer at

---

[18]Wendy Cameron and Mary McDougall Maude, *Assisting Emigration to Upper Canada: The Petworth Project, 1832–1837*. Montreal and Kingston: McGill-Queen's University Press, 2000, pp. 194 and 195.

[19]Somali immigrants report their settlement experience on a website funded by Canada's Youth Employment Strategy and produced by the Somali Immigrant Aid Organization. See **http://epe.lac-bac.gc.ca/100/205/301/ic/cdc/somalia/intro.html**.

Figure 3.2.2   Toronto's Somali community

Simon Fraser University who has studied conditions in these camps, refugees were housed in bleak, isolated camps in semi-arid border regions.[20]

Thousands of other Somalis have fled overseas—many to Canada, where they have settled mainly in Toronto. Here, they have formed a rapidly developing Somali community (**Figure 3.2.2**). According to census data, there were more than 17 000 Somalis in Toronto in 1996, but this figure is likely a considerable underestimation of the numbers, since some scholars have placed the total between 35 000 and 40 000 in that year. By 1999, a spokesperson for the Somali Immigrant Aid Organization estimated the size of the Somali community in the Greater Toronto Area at approximately 75 000. (If this estimate is correct, it is another illustration of the problems of accurate census enumeration.)

Robert Murdie and Carlos Teixeira, York University geographers, describing this community, have made these observations:

> When they first arrived in Toronto in the late 1980s, Somalis tended to concentrate in the Dixon Road and Islington Avenue area, also known as Little Somalia. There, large households, together with a tendency to concentrate in order to create a sense of security, have led to overcrowding in apartments that has contributed to cultural clashes and harassment by building managers and property owners.[21]

Certainly, the immigration experience of Somali refugees in Toronto has been a very challenging one, and a number of recent studies have confirmed Opoku-Dapaah's early assessment that they are among the most disadvantaged ethnic minorities in Canada.[22] For example, census analysis conducted by Michael Ornstein of York University's Institute for Social Research in 2000 concluded that more than 62 percent of Somali families in Toronto lived below the poverty line in 1996 and that unemployment rates for people of black, Caribbean, and African origins was 19 percent, or twice the average rate for the city as a whole in that year.[23]

The latest analysis, a 2003 study of multicultural Toronto called *The World in a City,* only confirms this picture. In Chapter 4, an economic examination by geographers Valerie Preston, Lucio Lo, and Shuguang Wang using income tax information shows that recent European immigrants have fared much better in Toronto than recent non-white immigrants from every other continent.[24]

Work based on qualitative methods and interview techniques significantly adds to the picture outlined by statistics. For example, one recent case study, based on interviews concerning the settlement experiences of a group of 21 Somali refugee women who came to Toronto between 1990 and 1997, allows us to clearly see how the refugees themselves view the difficulties they have faced.[25]

The study shows that possessing refugee status is itself the first problem because refugees are denied the full rights accorded Canadians. For example, refugees must pay college or university fees as overseas students, are eligible for only temporary work permits, are not eligible for bank loans, are not eligible for Canadian travel documents, and are unable to sponsor family members to immigrate to Canada. In view of these restrictions, it is hardly surprising that one of those interviewed remarked:

> Before we came to this country, we used to work and manage our lives like any other human beings. Now, we are not allowed to work, to struggle for the well being of our children, to get access to education, and to get loans. Why did they welcome us to their country with open arms only to make life more miserable for us?

[20]Jennifer Hyndman, *Managing Displacement: Refugees and the Politics of Humanitarianism.* Minneapolis: University of Minnesota Press, 2000. Hyndman reports that the bleak conditions of these camps are, in fact, part of a deliberate United Nations High Commission for Refugees' policy of "humane deterrence," an approach that is designed to reduce refugee flows from Somalia by showing potential migrants how unattractive life as a refugee will be (see pp. 23–24).

[21]Robert A. Murdie and Carlos Teixeira, "Towards a Comfortable Neighbourhood and Appropriate Housing: Immigrant Experiences in Toronto." In Paul Anisef and Michael Lanphier (eds.), *The World in a City.* Toronto: University of Toronto Press, 2003, p. 157.

[22]E. Opoku-Dapaah, *Somali Refugees in Toronto: A Profile.* Toronto: York Lanes Press, 1995.

[23]Quoted in Myer Siemiatycki, Tim Rees, Roxanna Ng, and Khan Rahi, "Integrating Community Diversity in Toronto: On Whose Terms?" In Paul Anisef and Michael Lanphier (eds.), *The World in a City.* Toronto: University of Toronto Press, 2003, pp. 418–419.

[24]Valerie Preston, Lucio Lo, and Shuguang Wang, "Immigrants' Economic Status in Toronto: Stories of Triumph and Disappointment." In Paul Anisef and Michael Lanphier (eds.), *The World in a City.* Toronto: University of Toronto Press, 2003, pp. 192–262.

[25]Neita Kay Israelite, Arlene Herman, Faduma Ahmed Alim, Hawa Abdullah Mohamed, and Yasmin Khan, *Settlement Experiences of Somali Refugee Women in Toronto.* Paper presented at the Seventh International Congress of Somali Studies, York University, Toronto, 10 July 1999, available online at **www.ceris.metropolis.net/oldvl/other/israelite2.html**.

A second concern voiced by the women interviewed is about the education of their children. Many do not speak English. As one women says, "Even if the child has a good educational background, with a strong base in math and other subjects, still he wouldn't be able to follow along in class because of the language. Language is the key factor. . . ." Another mother noted student and teacher biases: "When I send my little girl to school wearing our Islamic dress, teachers and students make negative comments about her dress, they are showing intolerance."

A third difficulty concerns access to affordable housing in Toronto. There is a six- to eight-year waiting list for subsidized housing, and with recent declines in social assistance payments in Ontario, the women interviewed said that they spent as much as 80 percent of their monthly income on housing. A more recent study by Ransford Danso reports that access to affordable housing was listed as a significant obstacle to settlement by 16 percent of the 115 Somali and Ethiopian refugees he interviewed in Toronto.[26]

Danso's respondents list two other significant obstacles to settlement. The most important problem (mentioned by 22 percent of those interviewed) was in getting employment. Employers' covert racism, dislike of dealing with those on temporary work permits, and failure to recognize foreign credentials are all cited as impediments that stand in the way of Somali refugee employment. "What is so unique about this 'Canadian experience' every employer is always asking for?" asks one respondent in evident frustration. Another, an individual with a doctoral degree who had been in Toronto for three months, remarked that he was "already facing obstacles finding suitable employment. I am doing odd jobs. It is very difficult to overcome the hidden barriers in Canadian society." When interviewed, he was working as an airport baggage handler.

Most troubling of all is the evidence of discrimination encountered by Somali refugees. Overall, 17 percent of Danso's respondents listed racism as a significant obstacle to settlement, but it is likely that this figure underestimates the problem; the effects of racism cross almost every aspect of the experience in Toronto and so compound the effects of the other difficulties listed above. For example, access to affordable housing is made even more difficult by landlord bias against Somalis. One Somali refugee woman reported, "Sometimes you go to rent an apartment that through the telephone you were assured to be vacant. When they see that you are a Somali, you are told that it has been rented."

We have already seen that Somalis feel a bias against them that affects their employment—what Danso calls a subtle or "courteous" racism. A further illustration is provided by his observation that "many Somalis in Toronto still feel strongly that their community is unfairly targeted by the police and the media."[27]

Danso has argued that for any immigrant group, the movement from "there" to "here" inevitably juxtaposes two kinds of "places" and "identities." In view of what we have seen here, it is hardly surprising that the Somali experience has caused these people to develop a very different approach toward the construction of place and identity from that adopted by many other immigrants groups. Somalis who have sought to participate in the wider Canadian society have generally been rebuffed by the social discrimination and economic inequality that confront them, and their community has therefore had to look inward for its own validation and support. This approach, as one scholar has remarked, "allows them to maintain the identities they established in their homelands rather than accept the racialized identities available to them in Canada."[28]

Recent reports show little overall economic progress. According to a 2008 Statistics Canada study, recent immigrants from African countries have the toughest challenges getting into the Canadian workforce when compared with other immigrant groups. On the basis of 2006 data, the report noted an unemployment rate of 20.8 percent among the 70 000 African immigrants aged between 25 and 54 who had arrived in this country between 2001 and 2006—a rate over four times higher than that found for the Canadian-born population, and twice that for immigrants from either Latin America or Asia (the rate was 8.4 percent for those immigrants from Europe).[29]

In commenting on these statistics in an interview conducted in February 2008, Ahmed Hussein, president of the Canadian Somali Association, observed that he was

[26]Ransford Danso, "From 'There' to 'Here': An Investigation of the Initial Settlement Experiences of Ethiopian and Somali Refugees in Toronto." In Alan Nash (ed.), Geography and Refugees, a special issue of GeoJournal 56(1), 2002, pp. 3–14.

[27]Ibid., p. 9. On this point, see also Myer Siemiatycki, Tim Rees, Roxanna Ng, and Khan Rahi, "Integrating Community Diversity in Toronto: On Whose Terms?" In Paul Anisef and Michael Lanphier (eds.), The World in a City. Toronto: University of Toronto Press, 2003, p. 420.

[28]A.M. Kusow, Migration and Identity Processes among Somali Immigrants in Canada. Unpublished PhD thesis. Wayne State University, Detroit, 1998; quoted in Neita Kay Israelite, Arlene Herman, Faduma Ahmed Alim, Hawa Abdullah Mohamed, and Yasmin Khan, Settlement Experiences of Somali Refugee Women in Toronto. Paper presented at the Seventh International Congress of Somali Studies, York University, Toronto, 10 July 1999, available online at www.ceris.metropolis.net/oldvl/other/israelite2.html.

[29]Statistics Canada, "Study: The 2006 Canadian Immigrant Labour Market: Analysis by Region or Country of Birth." The Daily, 13 February 2008, pp. 5–7, www.statcan.gc.ca/daily-quotidien/080213/dq080213b-eng.htm. The statistics in this report should be studied in conjunction with the fine series of metropolitan maps (showing immigrant arrivals between 2001 and 2006 as a percentage of population in 2006) contained in Robert Murdie, "Diversity and Concentration in Canadian Immigration: Trends in Toronto, Montreal and Vancouver, 1971–2006." University of Toronto, Cities Centre, Research Bulletin 42, March 2008, www.NeighbourhoodChange.ca.

disappointed, but not surprised by the report's findings. He observed that many Somalis experienced a "hard landing" in this country because, finding themselves refugees, they were often unprepared (in terms of language ability or job training, for example) for the conditions found in the country that granted them asylum. Furthermore, he noted, as part of a very recently formed community in this country, Somali immigrants to cities such as Toronto lacked a support network where they might find help—with accommodation, employment, and language skills. "It's a recent community that doesn't have the community support and individual support that might be available for other recent immigrants," he said.[30]

Somewhat more optimistically, the Statistics Canada data show that immigrants from Africa who had been in Canada in 2006 for longer than 10 years have a much lower rate of unemployment (7.6 percent) than that found among those more recently arrived. Known as the "period of residence" effect, and a general result of sufficient time to acquire the necessary language and employment skills, this phenomenon holds the promise of a brighter economic future for those Somalis who have just immigrated to Canada.

Perhaps the last word should be reserved for one Grade 12 student who was born in Somalia but now lives in an area of apartment housing on the corner of Dixon Road and Kipling Avenue. Interviewed in September 2007, she compared her former homeland, where the constant threat of being caught in crossfire made it impossible to wander outside, with her current neighbourhood. "Nobody fights here. It's peaceful," she remarked.[31]

[30]Charles Lewis, "African Immigrants Face Tough Challenges in Canada, Says Report." *Montreal Gazette*, 13 February 2008.

[31]Michele Henry, "4 City Blocks." *Toronto Star*, 6 September 2007, p. L10.

equal, but the jobs they hold are gender biased. Men receive most of the higher-level positions, while women are largely confined to the service and entertainment sectors. Some interesting geographical variations exist as well. Although constituting a small percentage of the total number of women working abroad, a large proportion of the female OCWs who do have professional positions (such as doctors and nurses) work in the United States and Canada. More typical of Filipina OCW experience, however, are the patterns in Hong Kong, Singapore, and Japan. In Hong Kong and Singapore, Filipinas are almost exclusively employed as domestic servants; in Japan, most work in the "entertainment industry," a term often synonymous with prostitution. These women in many ways have been transformed from individuals to commodities—many are even chosen from catalogues. The OCW program has been criticized by feminist groups as well as human rights organizations. Many regard the OCW treatment of women as a contemporary form of slavery.

International Forced Migration

The African slave trade is a classic example of international forced migration. This migration stream was integral to European economic expansion from the seventeenth through the nineteenth century. The huge fortunes made in the sugar trade, for example, were largely earned on the backs of African slaves working the sugar plantations of Brazil, Guyana, and the Caribbean. **Figure 3.13** shows those regions of the world to which slaves from Africa were transported from the seventeenth to the nineteenth century. Other prominent examples of international forced migration include the migration of Jews from Germany and Eastern Europe preceding World War II and the deportation of Armenians out of Eastern Anatolia to other parts of the Ottoman Empire after World War I. **Figure 3.14** shows those countries where residents have been forced from their homes by war, abuse, and fear.

Recently, many European countries, faced with rising numbers of refugees seeking political asylum, have tightened their previously liberal asylum policies. The immigration issue, in the wake of September 11 and other acts of terrorism in Europe, has been reconfigured as a security issue and national governments across Europe have voted to restrict the conditions under which asylum would be granted.

Sudan, however, is in the contrasting position of having displaced several million of its own citizens as a result of civil war while hosting more than 750 000 refugees

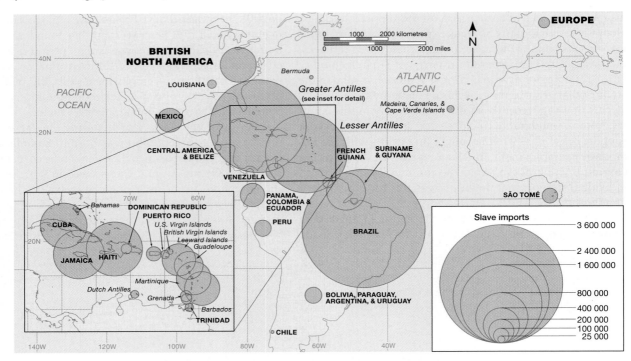

Figure 3.13 African slave trade, seventeenth through nineteenth century This map portrays the numbers of slaves who were imported to Europe and various countries in the New World. Some of the largest importers were Brazil, with 3 647 000 slaves imported, the Greater Antilles, with 2 421 000 imported, and the Lesser Antilles, with 1 619 000 imported, over 200 years. (*Source:* Philip D., Curtin, *The Atlantic Slave Trade,* ©1969. Reprinted by permission of The University of Wisconsin Press.)

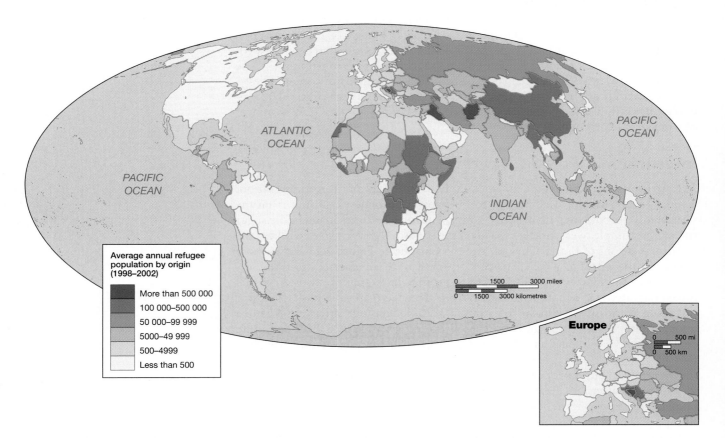

Figure 3.14 Refugee-sending countries, 1998–2002 War is certainly the most compelling factor in forcing refugee migration. Shown are the sending countries, those whose internal situations propelled people to leave. What is perhaps most distressing about this graphic is that refugee populations have increased over the last decade almost exclusively in the periphery. (After **www.unhcr.org/4125cb8c4.html** .)

Migrant Farm Workers in Canada

Migrant labourers, or "guest workers" as they are sometimes called, have played an important part in the economy of many countries. For example, Jonathan Crush, a geographer at Queen's University in Kingston, has written extensively about how South Africa's gold mines have depended on cheap immigrant labour from neighbouring countries. The host countries are not the only beneficiaries of this process, as the example of the Philippines shows. Filipino emigrants working in other countries send a substantial amount of money every year back to the Philippines. Indeed, it is estimated that approximately 15 percent of the entire Philippine population is dependent on overseas sources of income, including money earned overseas and sent home (known as *remittances*).[32]

Nevertheless, the reliance of one country on people recruited temporarily from another country as migrant labour is often seen as a controversial policy. Although the host country benefits from cheaper labour, the migrants themselves are often exploited and their home countries drained of labour and talent.

In view of such controversy, it is perhaps surprising to learn that Canada has long had a migrant labour program, albeit a small and relatively unpublicized one. The program, known as the Seasonal Agricultural Workers Program (SAWP), began in 1966 when 264 men were recruited from Jamaica to work temporarily in Canada. Since then, the number of recruits has grown annually, and in 2004, some 19 000 men and women travelled from the Caribbean and Mexico to work for six weeks to eight months on one of 1600 farms across Canada (**Figure 3.3.1**).

The program certainly has a number of benefits. First, according to Sue Ferguson in a recent *Maclean's* report, 85 percent of SAWP workers go to Ontario, where they form the backbone of that province's $3.6 billion horticultural industry and enable Canadian farmers there to remain competitive.[33]

Second, the localities in Canada where SAWP workers temporarily reside benefit from their presence. One Simcoe, Ontario, farmer involved in the program estimates that the farm output generated by every migrant labourer he employs supports the jobs of three Canadians in related packing and transport activities. He estimates that SAWP migrants spend two-thirds of their income in the area—a "$32 million bounty each year for local shopkeepers, restaurateurs and providers of telephone, banking and other services." A Simcoe discount store manager told researchers from the University of Guelph that the period when SAWP

Figure 3.3.1 Migrant workers in Ontario

migrants are making purchases before they return home is "literally like Christmas in September."

Third, many of the SAWP workers state that the program benefits them economically. Despite the fact that migrant farm workers usually earn only minimum wage in Canada, the economic disparity between the economies of Canada and Mexico or the Caribbean makes the migrant labour program worthwhile. As an example, consider the remarks of Irena Gonzalez, a migrant farm worker who has come from Mexico to pick tomatoes for four months in Ontario every year since 1989:[34]

> In Mexico, we're paid by the day, thirty pesos ($6 to $7 a day). But we have to fill fifteen or twenty pails. The time it takes depends on how fast you move your hands. But in Canada, we're paid by the hour, $7 an hour, and you can work as many hours as you want. If we work eight hours, which is what the contract says, we get $56, which is seven times as much as we get in Mexico.

Not all commentators agree that the program is so beneficial, and some have pointed to several major disadvantages with Canada's guest worker program. First, the dependence on low-wage employment may harm Canadian farmers in the long run by making the industry less efficient and harm Canadian farm workers by depressing the average wages in the agricultural sector. Second, there are consequences for the migrants. "Increasingly," Ferguson writes, "there are concerns about the fairness of the program and the employees' lack of rights." Bound by the program's strict terms of employment and receiving only minimum wage, it is not surprising that workers are left open to abuse.

Under the SAWP, workers do not have the rights of Canadian citizens and are unable to gain permanent

[32]R.T. Jackson, "The Cheque's in the Mail: The Distribution of Dependence on Overseas Sources of Income in the Philippines." *Singapore Journal of Tropical Geography* 11, 1990, pp. 76–86.

[33]Sue Ferguson, "Hard Times in Canadian Fields." *Maclean's*, October 2004, pp. 72–78.

[34]Deborah Barndt, *Tangled Routes: Women, Work and Globalization on the Tomato Trail*. Aurora, Ontario: Garamond Press, 2002, p. 162.

immigrant status in Canada. Assigned a specific employer (who provides accommodation), they can only change jobs if their embassy and both the original and the new employers agree. Although they pay employment insurance in Canada (amounting to $3.4 million per year), workers cannot collect benefits because unemployed SAWP workers are usually repatriated within 24 hours. Workers in the SAWP are not covered by Ontario's health and safety legislation, and they do not have the right to bargain collectively. The effect of what Professor Kerry Preibisch, a University of Guelph sociologist who has examined the program, calls these "extra-economic coercions" is to make workers dependent on the subjective goodwill of their employers.

Some are fortunate. Gustavo Rosales, for example, who has worked on a Simcoe ginseng farm for the last three years, says, "My boss is good." Many try to make their workers feel at home, and one recently provided interest-free loans and $15 000 in cash donations to enable a SAWP employee to rebuild his Jamaican home after Hurricane Ivan in September 2004.

But others are not as lucky, as complaints filed at the Simcoe migrant workers' support centre illustrate: a man who almost lost a leg to an infection he was told to ignore; workers forced to escape their lodgings at night and walk an hour to phone home; sleeping accommodation provided beside massive greenhouse boilers; supervisors berating employees; and so on.

Given these concerns, the fact that many continue to return to Canada year after year cannot be seen as a complete vindication of the program; SAWP workers are simply taking the best of a series of poor options available to them, options that diminish year by year as trade liberalization continues to erode agricultural wages both in this country and abroad.

Nevertheless, as Nelson Ferguson concluded in a recent study published in 2007, the fact remains that the "high number of returning participants and the overall increasing number of farms and participants have been used as evidence of the program's satisfactory nature to both employer and employee."[35] Using data for 2005, a year when over 18 000 migrants participated in the program, Ferguson observes that the SAWP is clearly succeeding in its principal goal of ensuring that Canadian horticulture remains profitable. Its benefits to the countries that send temporary migrants is, however, more elusive. On the basis of interviews with a sample of Mexicans who participated in the SAWP, for example, Ferguson calculates that they were able to save on average approximately $5000 per annual contract, but that the household expenses of their families in Mexico left very little over to invest in the local Mexican economy. On the other hand, Ferguson notes that because other studies report that many

migrant workers use a large share of their earnings to pay for their children's education, there may well be longer-term benefits that have not been considered.

Other recent studies are more critical and allow us to focus on the migrant workers themselves. For a number of years now, the United Food and Commercial Workers Union (UFCW) has issued an annual report on the program and the most recent, entitled *The Status of Migrant Farm Workers in Canada 2006–2007,* repeats many of the comments voiced in Professor Preibisch's 2004 work.[36] In short, despite the many regulations and safeguards under which the program is supposed to operate, the union remains very concerned by the reality of the situation. While it is difficult to measure the full extent of the problem, complaints lodged by SAWP workers at the support centres run by the union indicate that abuses continue to happen. Substandard accommodation and unhealthy conditions are cited in the UFCW report, and—to quote one specific example from a farm in British Columbia— SAWP workers complained that despite a requirement that they be paid an hourly wage, they were required to pick 7 boxes a day and paid $17 per box, whereas non-migrant labour on the same farm only had to fill 3 boxes a day and were paid $50 a box. Such discrepancies in wage rates are obviously a feature that attracts many employers to the scheme, but if farmers come to rely on cheap labour, a level of dependency is introduced into Canadian farming that will ultimately make any attempt to either raise wages or change land uses very difficult.[37]

Ferguson concludes his study with a very perceptive remark, well worth quoting here: "A well-managed and well-designed guest worker program can prove highly beneficial and advantageous to all involved," he notes, "but only by considering the various mitigating factors will we be able to determine what such a program will look like."[38] Difficulties with the SAWP need to be addressed so that the program can act as a model for new schemes, such as the Temporary Low Skilled Worker program (a program introduced in 2002 and designed to recruit workers into the health, services and construction industries, including the Alberta oil sands). From what we have seen here, there are obviously no shortages of suggestions for change, and on the basis of the research reported here, there is no reason for newer programs to repeat past mistakes.

[36]The United Food and Commercial Workers Union (UFCW), *The Status of Migrant Farm Workers in Canada 2006–2007,* www.ufcw.ca/Theme/UFCW/files/PDF2007/StatusReportEN2007.pdf. The union provides 15 recommendations for change on pp. 16–17 of the report, which include, for example, the stipulation that temporary migrant labour should receive the same wage rate as the provincial seasonal average wage.

[37]The problem of creating dependency is made by Sophie Lowe, "*Plus Ça Change*: A Comparative Analysis of the Seasonal Agricultural Workers Program and the Pilot Foreign Worker Program for Farm Workers in Quebec." MA Research Paper, Ryerson University, 2007.

[38]Nelson Ferguson, "The Seasonal Agricultural Workers Program: Considerations for the Future of Farming and the Implications of Managed Migration." *Canadian Issues* 3, Summer 2007, pp. 189–193; the quotation is from p. 193.

[35]Nelson Ferguson, "The Seasonal Agricultural Workers Program: Considerations for the Future of Farming and the Implications of Managed Migration." *Canadian Issues* 3, Summer 2007, pp. 189–193; the quotation is from p. 191.

from neighbouring countries. The situation provides a clear example of the openness of the borders that define many African states. In some cases, refugee populations remain in a host country for long periods. In Jordan and Lebanon, for example, some of the Palestinian refugee camps are multigenerational, dating back to the 1948 Arab–Israeli war. High fertility rates in some of these refugee camps put considerable strain on the humanitarian aid resources of both international organizations and the host countries.

POPULATION DEBATES AND POLICIES

One big question occupies the agenda of population experts studying world population trends today: How many people can Earth sustain without depleting or critically straining its resource base? The relationship between population and resources, which lies at the heart of this question, has been a point of debate among experts since the early nineteenth century.

Population and Resources

The debate about population and resources originated in the work of an English cleric named Thomas Robert Malthus (1766–1834), whose theory of population relative to food supply established resources as the critical limiting condition on population growth. Interestingly, Malthus taught economics at the East India Company's college in London, England. Malthus's theory was published in 1798 in a famous pamphlet called *An Essay on the Principle of Population*. In this tract, Malthus set up two important postulates:

- Food is necessary to the existence of human beings.
- The passion between the sexes is necessary and constant.

It is important to put the work of Malthus into the historical context within which it was written. Revolutionary changes—prompted, in large part, by technological innovations—had occurred in English agriculture and industry and were eliminating traditional forms of employment faster than new ones could be created. This condition led to a fairly widespread belief among wealthy members of English society that a surplus of unnecessary workers existed in the population. The displaced agriculturists began to be a heavy burden on charity, and the so-called Poor Laws were introduced to regulate begging and public behaviour.

In his treatise, Malthus insisted that "the power of the population is indefinitely greater than the power of the earth to produce subsistence." He also believed that if one accepted this premise, then a natural law would follow; that is, the population would inevitably exhaust food supplies.

Malthus was not without his critics, and such influential thinkers as William Godwin, Karl Marx, and Frederich Engels disputed Malthus's premises and propositions. Godwin argued that "there is no evil under which the human species cannot labor, that man is not competent to cure." Marx and Engels were in general agreement and insisted that technological development and an equitable distribution of resources would solve what they saw as a fictitious imbalance between people and food.

Geographers delight in noting that Malthus used data from the work of Alexander von Humboldt (see Chapter 1) to illustrate his case. It is also of interest that Darwin saw in the work of Malthus the key to how evolution worked—the struggle for existence.

Population, Resources, and the Environment

The debate about the relationship between population and resources continues to this day, with provocative and compelling arguments for both positions being continually advanced. Joel Cohen's fascinating account *How Many People Can the*

World Support? illustrates the great range in expert opinion concerning possible global population totals. The geographer David Harvey, for example, has explored the population–resources issue in great detail. He has shown the limitations of Malthus's approach, demonstrating that the adoption of a certain scientific method leads to only one possible outcome—a doomsday conclusion about the limiting effect of resources on population growth. By following Marx's approach, however, Harvey argues that quite different perspectives on, and solutions to, the population–resources issue can be generated. These solutions are based on human creativity and socially generated innovation that, through technological and social change, provide opportunities for people to overcome the limitations of their environment. Certainly, an approach that does not see the increase in resources or food supplies as limited can make a very provocative criticism of Malthus, as the work of Boserup illustrates (see Chapter 8).

Neo-Malthusians—people today who share Malthus's perspective—predict a population doomsday, however. They believe that growing human populations the world over, with their potential to exhaust Earth's resources, pose the most dangerous threat to the environment. Although they point out that the people of core countries consume the vast majority of resources, they and others argue that only strict demographic control everywhere, even if it requires severely coercive tactics, will solve the problem.

A more moderate approach argues that people's behaviours and governmental policies are much more important factors affecting the condition of the environment and the status of natural resources than population size. Proponents of this approach reject casting the population issue as a biological one in which an ever-growing population will create ecological catastrophe. They also reject framing it as an economic issue in which technological innovation and the sensitivities of the market will regulate population increases before a catastrophe can occur. Rather, they see the issue as a political one—one that governments have tended to avoid dealing with because they lack the will to redistribute wealth or the resources to reduce poverty, a condition strongly correlated with high fertility. Conversely, some analysts have recently tried to see the ecological background to political events. Much of the work of Canadian political scientist Thomas Homer-Dixon has examined the background to crises in, for example, Chiapas (Mexico) and Rwanda in terms of ecological crises of food and human security.

The question of whether too many people exist for Earth to sustain bedevilled population policy-makers and political leaders for most of the second half of the twentieth century. This concern led to the formation of international agencies that monitor and often attempt to influence population change. It also led to the organizing of a series of international conferences that have attempted to establish globally applicable population policies. The underlying assumption of much of this policy-making is that countries and regions have a better chance of achieving improvement in the level of development if they can keep their populations from outstripping the supplies of resources and jobs. The environmental challenge provided is forcefully illustrated for each and everyone of us by the concept of the "ecological footprint" (see Chapter 4).

Population Policies and Programs

Contemporary concerns about population—especially whether too many people exist for Earth to sustain—have led to the development of international and national policies and programs. A *population policy* is an official government policy designed to affect any or all of several objectives, including the size, composition, and distribution of population. The implementation of a population policy takes the form of a *population program*. Whereas a policy identifies goals and objectives, a program is an instrument for meeting those goals and objectives.

Most of the international population policies of the last two decades have been directed at reducing the number of births worldwide. The instruments that have been developed to address rising fertility have largely been in the form of family-planning programs. The desire to limit fertility rates by the international population-planning

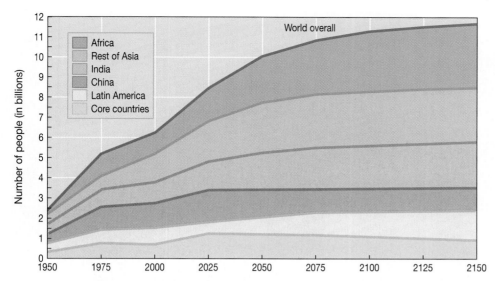

Figure 3.15   World population projection by region   This graph represents a medium-variant projection, one that is in the middle of three possible scenarios, with the other two being higher or lower. In this projection, population continues to expand in the periphery, though in some regions more than in others. Africa is projected to experience the greatest growth, followed by Asia (not including China or India), where growth is expected to level off by 2150. Less dramatic growth is expected to occur in Latin America, while in the core, population numbers remain constant or drop slightly. Though the total number of people in the world will be dramatically greater by 2150, the medium-variant forecast indicates a levelling off of world population. (*Source:* I. Hauchler and P. Kennedy [eds.], *Global Trends: The World Almanac of Development and Peace.* New York: Continuum, 1994, p. 109.)

community is a response to concerns about rapidly increasing global population—an increase that is being experienced significantly more in the periphery and semi-periphery than in core countries. Accompanying this situation of imbalanced population growth between the core and the periphery are gross social and economic inequalities as well as overall environmental degradation and destruction.

Figure 3.15 provides a picture of the recent history and a reasonable projection of the future of world population growth by region. The difference between the core and the periphery is dramatically illustrated. Also striking is the size of growth. In mid-1992, for example, the world contained nearly 5.5 billion people, but by mid-2007, it contained 6.6 billion people (see also Table 3.1). In comparison, over the course of the entire nineteenth century, fewer than one billion people were added to the population. **Figure 3.16** shows a projection of world population in the year 2020.

The geography of projected population growth is noteworthy. Over the next century, population growth is predicted to occur almost exclusively in Africa, Asia, and Latin America, while Europe and North America will experience very low and in some cases zero population growth (as Figure 3.15 shows).

International conferences, sponsored by the United Nations to develop population policy at the global level, have been held on a number of occasions since the first world meeting in Bucharest (1974) and Mexico City (1984). In 1994, the conference took place in Cairo. Called the International Conference on Population and Development, rather than focusing on the increase in global population growth rates, the meeting pointed to the fact that birth rates in almost every country on Earth were dropping—in many cases by significant amounts. Recognizing that a levelling off of the population was possible in the foreseeable future, conference participants from both the core and the periphery were in agreement that efforts to bring down the growth rates must continue so that human numbers will peak sooner rather than later. The policy that emerged from the Cairo conference called for governments not simply to make family-planning programs available to all but also to take deliberate steps to reduce poverty and disease; improve educational opportunities, especially for girls and women; and work toward environmentally sustainable development (**Figure 3.17**).

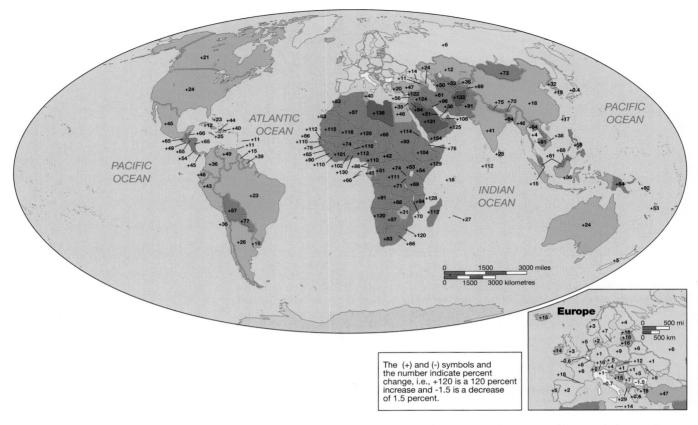

The (+) and (-) symbols and the number indicate percent change, i.e., +120 is a 120 percent increase and -1.5 is a decrease of 1.5 percent.

Figure 3.16   World population, 2020   This map provides a sense of how much the populations of various countries are expected to change by the year 2020. Although the populations of nearly all countries are expected to increase, it is clear that some populations will grow far more dramatically than others. Notice the substantial growth expected in Saudi Arabia and Afghanistan in contrast to the United States and Europe, where little if any population growth will occur. Italy, for example, is expected to lose population, while the Netherlands will grow by only 5 percent.

Figure 3.17   International Conference on Population and Development, 1994   The conference in Cairo had the important effect of insisting on the link between level of development and population growth. At the conference, much discussion ensued about improving the status of women to help control population. However, core and peripheral countries often disagreed about the most appropriate means to halt the present trend of global population expansion.

The goals established at the Cairo meeting have been embraced and extended in the most recent international population conference, which was held at the United Nations in September 2000 as part of the "U.N. Millenium Summit Conference." At that summit, the "Millennium Declaration" adopted by 189 nations made a commitment to achieve eight key "Millennium Development Goals" by 2015. These goals are as follows:

1. Eradicate extreme poverty and hunger.
2. Achieve universal primary education.
3. Promote gender equality and empower women.
4. Reduce child poverty.
5. Improve maternal health.
6. Combat HIV/AIDS, malaria and other diseases.
7. Ensure environmental sustainability.
8. Develop a Global Partnership for Development.[39]

As these goals suggest, enabling more sustainable economic growth worldwide is a way of also shaping population growth and the quality of life for people in the periphery. Certainly, many would agree that it is high time that discussions on population issues recognized their interconnections with economy and the environment. To put it another way, debates on "overpopulation" have not always situated that discussion into a context of poverty, environmental degradation, and diminished human rights. Yet, as the Millennium Development Goals suggest, they all interrelate, and if action is required on one issue (such as population policy), it must inevitably involve progress on almost all of the other goals if change is to be truly effective, sustainable, and fair.

To that end, in 2001 the member nations of the United Nations charged the Secretary-General to report annually on the progress made toward the achievement of the Millennium Development Goals, and in 2005 reaffirmed their commitment to achieve these goals by 2015.

Demographers and policy-makers take care to remind us that controlling fertility is not exclusively a female issue. However, they also stress that a close relationship exists between women's status and fertility. Women who have access to education and employment tend to have fewer children because they have less of a need for the economic security and social recognition that children are thought to provide. In Botswana, for instance, women with no formal education have, on average, 5.9 children, while those with four to six years of school have just 3.1 children. In Senegal, women with no education give birth to an average of 7 children. In contrast, the average number of children born to a woman with 10 years of education drops to 3.6. The numbers are comparable for Asia and South America.

More equality between men and women inside and outside the household is also believed to have a significant impact on reducing fertility. Enabling voluntary constraints that give both men and women a choice, and educating them about the implications of such choices, appears to be an especially successful program for small island populations—such as Bali, Barbados, and Mauritius—with historically high population growth. In Mauritius, in just 24 years (between 1962 and 1986), the introduction of voluntary constraints lowered the total fertility rate from 5.8 to 1.9. It is hardly any wonder, then, that the 1994 population conference in Cairo placed such a clear and well-received emphasis on (1) improving the rights, opportunities, and economic status of girls and women as the most effective way of slowing down global population growth, and (2) rejecting coercive measures, including government sterilization quotas, that force people to violate their personal moral codes.

In implementing the goals of improving women's (and girls') status relative to men's, it is necessary to take a broad view. Respected population experts have provided convincing evidence that an excess of female mortality characterizes much of the periphery. It is estimated that between 60 million and 100 million more females would be alive today were it not for a preference for male children, which results in prenatal choices to abort females, biased health conditions, unequal

[39]United Nations Development Program, "About the Millennium Development Goals," **www.undp.org/mdg/basics.shtml**.

nutritional provision, and female infanticide. In such countries as China, for example, the apparent success of the one-child-per-household policy has been linked to horrifying abuses. The international news media have for years published reports on how the policy has contributed to female infanticide in a culture where male children are highly valued and female children are not.

Success at slowing population growth in the periphery appears to be very much tied to enhancing the possibility for a good quality of life and empowering people, especially women, to make informed choices. But a better quality of life may require altering—even reducing—the consumption practices of populations in the core to make more resources available to the periphery. Only then, with more resources available to them, will women in the periphery have some economic options and thereby become empowered to make choices about their reproductive lives. Whether such an alteration is desirable, or achievable, remains to be seen.

POPULATION, HEALTH, AND THE ENVIRONMENT

medical geography: that part of geography that considers patterns of health and the spread of diseases

The study of the interconnections among population, health, and the environment defines the field of study known as **medical geography**. This broad area of research has traditionally been made up of two quite distinct approaches (the study of the cause and spread of disease and the study of the provision and consumption of heath care), to which modern geographical work adds two more (the study of the social construction of health and the study of the effects of environmental change).

The Study of the Cause and Spread of Disease By mapping patterns of disease, geographical analysis has been able to pinpoint possible causes of illness. The most celebrated early example is the 1850s work of Dr. John Snow. He examined the geographical pattern of cholera cases in London, England, and showed that they were the product of a water supply contaminated by sewage—not, as the rival *miasmic theory* claimed, the result of breathing foul air that had been in contact with putrefied bodies and decaying vegetation. One of the earliest works of medical geography in Canada, *The Medical Topography of Upper Canada,* a work written by John Douglas in 1819, claimed that health in Ontario was the result of such miasmas and such a view was prevalent actoss nineteenth-century Canada (**Figure 3.18**).

epidemiological transition: a theory stating that the prevailing forms of illness changed from infectious to degenerative types as the demographic transition occurred

The connection between disease incidence and geographical patterns continues to be much explored by geographers. The focus is now on the ecology of diseases, their ecological relations with their agents of transmission, known as *vectors* (which have their own environmental constraints), and the environments in which both disease and vector interact with human populations.

These connections have many implications. The importance of these associations from a broader environmental perspective will be considered in Chapter 4. Here, let us briefly note their importance from the perspective of the world-system approach we have been using in this book. In terms of differences between the health experiences of the core and the periphery, medical geographers have drawn attention to the importance of the epidemiological transition as another explanatory tool to use when examining broad patterns of disease incidence (**Figure 3.19**).

Figure 3.18 Nineteenth-century attitudes toward disease This magazine illustration shows that diseases were once thought to be caused by foul or malodorous air (*malaria* literally means "bad air"). Modern medicine, however, stresses the roles of bacteria and viruses in causing contagious diseases.

Humans probably first experienced many infectious and parasitic diseases following the domestication of animals, such as pigs, sheep, and goats, approximately 10 000 years ago. Such illnesses as influenza and small pox are, in this sense, a byproduct of the first agricultural revolution. **Epidemiological transition** is the theory stating that the prevailing forms of illness changed from infectious to degenerative types as the demographic transition occurred. Simply put, one aspect of the demographic transition is a change in the prevailing forms of illness. During the first phases of that transition, it is argued that high death rates are mainly caused by very high rates of infectious and parasitic diseases. This contrasts with the situation after the transition when, according to this theory, mortality is mainly the result of degenerative diseases caused by aging, changing lifestyles, and a deteriorating environment. It will be part of the periphery's challenge to see if it can pass through the demographic transition without bringing on itself these so-called diseases of modernization.

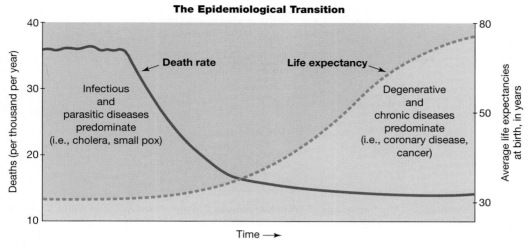

The Epidemiological Transition

Figure 3.19   The epidemiological transition   As societies move through the demographic transition, the prevailing form of illnesses changes from infectious and parasitic diseases to the degenerative diseases caused by modernization and urban life: those of aging, changing lifestyle, and a deteriorating environment.   (*Sources:* Diagram based on a written description in Dhruva Nagnur and Michael Nagrodski, "Epidemiologic Transition in the Context of Demographic Change: The Evolution of Canadian Mortality Patterns." In Frank Trovato and Carl F. Grindstaff [eds.], *Perspectives on Canada's Population: An Introduction to Concepts and Issues.* Toronto: Oxford University Press, 1994, pp. 118–135.)

The connection between disease incidence and spatial pattern is also explored by those medical geographers who examine the diffusion of diseases. We have already seen examples in Chapter 1 of cholera diffusion in nineteenth-century North America and the global spread of the HIV-1 virus in the late twentieth century. A contemporary example is the work of Professor Tinline of Queen's University in Kingston, Ontario. Using advanced diffusion theory, combined with GIS techniques, he has been able to develop computer models that predict the spread of rabies outbreaks in Ontario, thereby aiding the provincial government's attempts to control such outbreaks.

The Study of the Provision and Consumption of Health Care   The examination of the locations of hospitals, physicians, clinics, and nurses across Canada at a variety of scales of analysis has enabled Canadian medical geographers, such as Alun Joseph and Mark Rosenberg, to show how considerable spatial discrepancies in health care provision exist across this country. Simply put, urban areas have a better provision of health care than do rural areas, and richer urban areas have a better provision of services than do poorer urban areas. These discrepancies have prompted analyses of their ultimate causes. They raise questions about the social justice of such spatial inequalities of service provision. They prompt further research into the provision of health care for groups, such as single parents, people with disabilities, and Aboriginal communities, who, because of their disadvantaged position in society, now find themselves further marginalized by where they live. These types of discrepancies also exist at a world scale. For example, the variation in the global distribution of doctors indicates the degree to which inequalities exist between the core and the periphery of the world-system.

The Study of the Social Construction of Health   The work of a number of scholars has shown that *health care* and *medical care* are not the same. Nor are they objective or value-free concepts. In fact, ideas of good health and the nature of illnesses are defined by our social norms. Our medical traditions are themselves an outcome of our views about nature and science. For these reasons, the forces of industrialization and consumption that are embedded in both the world-system and demographic transition models, have fundamentally altered what we consider to be "good health" and our view of how to achieve it.

Environmental Change   An issue of great current concern is the effect of global environmental change on our health and well-being. In a recent paper on this topic

31 October 2001 Human Cases: zero

Distribution of dead birds positively diagnosed with West Nile virus

ONTARIO

UNITED STATES

Migrating birds spreading West Nile virus

0 80 160 kilometres

Figure 3.20   The beginnings of West Nile virus in Canada   West Nile virus (WNV) is carried by mosquitoes and is spread when they bite any of several bird and mammal species. Crows, ravens, blue jays, and magpies are particularly susceptible, as are horses and human beings. In humans, WNV can cause West Nile fever and, in a very few number of cases, develop into fatal inflammations of the brain or spinal cord. WNV was first identified in the West Nile district of Uganda in 1937. Since then, it has slowly spread throughout the Mediterranean and the temperate parts of Europe. The first reported cases in North America occurred in New York City in August 1999. Spread from there by migrating birds, WNV first reached Canada in 2001, when a number of dead birds in Southern Ontario were diagnosed with the disease. The first human cases in this country occurred in Ontario and Quebec in 2002 and six people died that year from the effects of the disease. Most experts suggest that WNV is in Canada to stay because global warming will likely increase the range of infected mosquitoes and birds.   (*Sources:* "Le virus du Nil bientôt terrassé?" *Le Devoir,* 25 April 2005, p. A2; and Helen Branswell, "Summer's Blight, West Nile, Here to Stay." *Globe and Mail,* 13 May 2005, p. A11.)

published in the journal the *Canadian Geographer,* John Eyles and Susan Elliott highlighted the following three aspects as important:[40]

- *Climate change.* If global warming continues as predicted, a wide range of direct and indirect effects will result. Government estimates suggest that annual heat-related deaths could rise from 240 to 1140 in Montreal, from 230 to 1220 in Toronto, and from 80 to 500 in Ottawa. Respiratory-related disorders and increases in waterborne infections could result. It has been suggested that hotter conditions have allowed pathogens, such as the West Nile virus, to gain a foothold in southern Ontario, Manitoba, and Quebec (**Figure 3.20**).

- *Pollution.* Eyles and Elliott stated that air pollution is arguably the major environmental health issue in Canada at this time. Studies in Hamilton, Ontario, for example, suggest that particulate matter in the air result in about 70 cases of premature deaths per year and 300 additional hospital admissions.

- *Psychosocial effects.* We must not overlook the qualitative aspects of environmental change. Our fear of change, the context in which change occurs, and its impacts on our wider community all affect how we are able to deal with environmental changes and the extent to which they will affect our sense of well-being.

Examples from many other parts of Canada can be cited (especially in Arctic Canada where, as Chapter 4 shows, global warming threatens Inuit livelihood). Whatever the example, however, the interconnectedness of the environment means we are *all* affected.

The interrelations between climate change, population, and health are profound, and the growing volume of research being conducted on their interconnections illustrates how important it is to have a basic understanding of the issues involved (see **Human Geography and Climate Change 3.4—Population and Health**).

---

[40]J. Eyles and S.J. Elliott, "Global Environmental Change and Human Health." *Canadian Geographer* 45(1), 2001, pp. 99–104.

Population and Health

The Fourth Assessment Report (*Climate Change 2007*) of the Intergovernmental Panel on Climate Change (IPCC) concludes that global climate change will likely result in significant climatic shifts.[41] Given the close relationship between climate, environment, and health, climate change is expected to have both direct and indirect effects on the health of Canadians.

Direct health effects occur during or soon after an extreme climatic event, and include injuries related to storms and increased risks of gastrointestinal diseases or cholera due to flooding.[42] Direct effects also include increased heat-related stress illnesses and death during extreme heat events.[43] The European heat wave of 2003, which has been attributed to climate change, was directly linked to nearly 15 000 deaths in France alone,[44] with neighbouring European countries experiencing similar increases in mortality at the same time. Most of these deaths were among the old (aged 75 and over). In Canada, a national health impact assessment of climate change points to similar increases in heat-related mortality.[45] Extreme heat events with concurrent poor air quality are also associated with more intense asthma attacks, increased rates of asthma, and cardiovascular disease.[46]

Indirect effects of climate change on human health are often more complex in their origins and relationships and impact health through many avenues including air and water quality and the quality and availability of food.[47] Warmer temperatures are, for example, likely to be associated with increased allergens and air pollution due to more frequent and intense smog episodes, which aggravate asthma and other respiratory conditions. Perhaps the most worrisome impact of climate change on health is associated with changing disease distribution and incidence.[48]

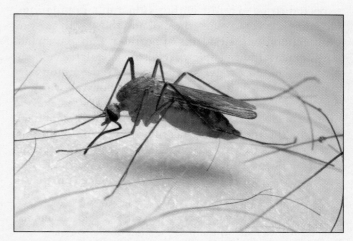

Figure 3.4.1   Mosquitoes as disease carriers   Mosquitoes can transmit West Nile virus, a potentially harmful virus, to humans. Climate change will allow the range of mosquitoes and other disease carrying insects to expand and place humans at risk for a greater length of time.

Warmer climates are expected to allow diseases to move northward and beyond where they are historically located. Mosquitoes or other disease-carrying organisms can also expand their breeding area and the length of time they can survive in a season. Consequently, diseases such as West Nile virus and Eastern and Western Equine Encephalitis (both transmitted by mosquitoes), Lyme disease, and Rocky Mountain Spotted Fever (both transmitted by ticks) will likely be more common in future years, will have a longer season, and be found over an increasingly wide geographical area (**Figure 3.4.1**). For example, as temperature determines the northern limits for the tick responsible for Lyme disease, by 2020 it is expected to spread out of its current reservoirs in southwestern Ontario, British Columbia, and Nova Scotia and extend northwards by approximately 200 km.[49] Tropical diseases including malaria, dengue fever, yellow fever, and encephalitis, which are not typically associated with northern environments, may also emerge with increased regularity.

Given the high likelihood that climate change will result in warmer temperatures and increased precipitation in northern latitudes including Canada,[50] human health and climate change are also linked through water and food-borne diseases. Water-borne diseases such as

[41]Intergovernmental Panel on Climate Change, *Climate Change 2007*, 17 November 2007, **www.ipcc.ch**.

[42]A. Greer, V. Ng, and D. Fisman, "Climate Change and Infectious Diseases in North America: The Road Ahead." *Canadian Medical Association Journal* 178(6), 2008, pp. 715–722, **www.cmaj.ca/cgi/content/full/178/6/715**.

[43]J.M. Balbus and M.L. Wilson, *Human Health and Global Climate Change*. Arlington VA: PEW Center, 2000.

[44]IPCC, *Climate Change 2007*, 17 November 2007, **www.ipcc.ch**.

[45]D. Riedel "Human Health and Well-being." In D. Lemmen and F. Warren (eds.), *Climate Change: Impacts and Adaptation—A Canadian Perspective*. Ottawa, ON: Climate Change Impacts and Adaptation Directorate, Natural Resources Canada, 2004, pp. 151–171.

[46]IPCC, *Climate Change 2007*, 17 November 2007, **www.ipcc.ch**.

[47]A. Greer, V. Ng, and D. Fisman, "Climate Change and Infectious Diseases in North America: The Road Ahead." *Canadian Medical Association Journal* 178(6), 2008, pp. 715–722, **www.cmaj.ca/cgi/content/full/178/6/715**.

[48]J.M. Balbus and M.L. Wilson, *Human Health and Global Climate Change*. Arlington, VA: Pew Center, 2000.

[49]A. Greer, V. Ng, and D. Fisman, "Climate Change and Infectious Diseases in North America: The Road Ahead." *Canadian Medical Association Journal* 178(6), 2008, pp. 715–722, **www.cmaj.ca/cgi/content/full/178/6/715**.

[50]IPCC, *Climate Change 2007*, 17 November 2007, **www.ipcc.ch**.

Legionnaires disease typically increase during warmer, rainy, and humid weather.

The negative health impacts of climate change are expected to be greatest within **vulnerable populations**, including the very young, the old, and those with existing health conditions. Residents of northern Canada, including Canada's Inuit peoples, are also particularly vulnerable to climate change, as Canada's Arctic regions are expected to warm faster than other regions. A warming Arctic will lead to melting permafrost, loss of sea ice, and melting of glaciers, with impacts on animal and plant habitats. For the Inuit, changing environmental conditions, including loss of snow cover and sea ice, means securing traditional food sources may be more difficult and increases risk associated with travel. Changing climate will also impact animal migrations, access to hunting grounds, or the availability of animal food sources. At the same time, plant species and animals from the south will move northward, further disrupting local ecosystems.[51]

With climate change, the increased incidence of disease and illness may place heavy burdens on Canada's health infrastructure due to the increased disease prevalence.[52] The impact of extreme climate events and climate-related natural disasters on the health of Canadians can be minimized with appropriate planning for extreme events. Dealing with indirect effects is less easy and requires long-term planning and adaptation.

—K.B.N.

vulnerable populations: populations that include common characteristics making them more susceptible to health problems and failing to get the health care they need, including the very young, the old, and those with existing health conditions

[51]2006 Canada's Fourth National Report on Climate Change: Actions to Meet Commitments Under the United Nations Framework Convention on Climate Change. Environment Canada, Cat. No.: En4-73/2006E.

[52]A. Greer, V. Ng, and D. Fisman, "Climate Change and Infectious Diseases in North America: The Road Ahead." *Canadian Medical Association Journal* 178(6), 2008, pp. 715–722, **www.cmaj.ca/cgi/content/full/178/6/715**.

The Geography of Canadian Health

Population experts regard life expectancy as one of the basic indicators of the overall health of a population, and one that allows reliable comparisons to be made among places and over time. We should therefore feel extremely pleased that the 1998 United Nations Human Development Report ranked Canada as the top country among its 174 members in terms of human development (as measured in terms of life expectancy, educational attainment, and adjusted income). Canada currently ranks among the top three most developed countries of the world in terms of its life expectancies, self-rated health, and mortality statistics. For example, in 1996, the average life expectancy at birth in Canada was 78.3 years (75.4 for males, 81.2 for females), and in that year, the infant mortality rate fell below six per thousand for the first time.

Yet, Canada's standing drops to tenth place when the Human Poverty Index is applied (this combines measures of literacy, unemployment, percentage of people living below the poverty line, and percentage of people not expected to live past 60 years of age). The UN report comments that this drop is because "Canada has significant problems of poverty and . . . progress in human development has not been evenly distributed."[53]

This statement points us to the single most significant point to be made about the geography of health in Canada (or elsewhere for that matter): people with higher incomes generally live longer than people with lower incomes. In other words, the geography of health is simply one manifestation of the spatial inequalities generated by Canada's economic geography. In 1991, for example, Canadian men in the highest quarter of the income distribution could expect, on average, to live 6.3 years longer and 14.3 more years without disability than those in the lowest quarter (for women, the differences were 3 and 7.6 years, respectively). Experts remark that it is the relative distribution of income in a given society,

[53]The first three paragraphs of this section are based on *Toward a Healthy Future: Second Report of the Health of Canadians*, prepared by the Federal, Provincial, and Territorial Advisory Committee on Population Health for the Meeting of Ministers of Health, Charlottetown, PEI, September 1999. Health Canada: Ottawa, 1999, pp. ix, 14, and 41. Canada's current status can be checked in the latest United Nations Human Development Report, available at **http://hdr.undp.org**.

TABLE 3.4	The Geography of Health in Canada, 1996		
Health Indicators	National Average	Low Regions	High Regions
Total mortality*	668.9	Halton (ON) 585	Nunavut 1082
All cancers*	185.7	Vancouver/ Richmond 154	Nunavut 327
Breast cancer*	28.3	Yukon 16.7	Peace River (BC) 42
All circulatory diseases*	245.8	Northwest (AB) 167	Grenfell (NF) 363
All respiratory diseases*	59.8	Halton (ON) 41.7	Nunavut 209
Average life expectancies (at birth)	78.3	Nunavik (QC) 65.4 Nunavut 69.8	Richmond (BC) 78.3

*Age-standardized rates per 100 000 population

Sources: The Geography of Health in Canada from Health Indicators 1999 from "Health Indicators," October 2002, volume 2002, number 2, Catalogue number 82-221-SIE. (These data can be accessed at **http://secure.cihi.ca/cihiweb/splash.html**. In addition, Statistics Canada publishes periodic reports on special issues, such as the health status of immigrants, the Aboriginal population, and socioeconomic factors. The annual report *How Healthy Are Canadians?* is available at **www.statcan.gc.ca/pub/82-003-S/4060579-eng.htm**.)

rather than the total income, that is the most important determinant of health status. If this is so, then the impacts on marginalized and disadvantaged groups can be profound. For example, the life expectancy of the Status Indian population in 1990 was seven years less than that for the overall Canadian population in 1991.

The geography of Canadian health can be examined at a number of scales. At the countrywide level of analysis, detailed calculations by Statistics Canada enable us to compare directly the mortality data obtained from health districts across the country. (These data were expressed in terms of age-standardized rates per 100 000 population in 1996. Statistics Canada notes that this procedure allows for a more meaningful comparison of rates because it adjusts for variation in population age distributions over time and across geographic areas.) A summary of these data is given in **Table 3.4**. The average total mortality in Canada in 1996 was 669 per 100 000 people. Considerable variation around this average occurred, with the Halton health region in Ontario representing one of the lowest mortality areas of the country, with a figure of 585 per 100 000 people, and Nunavut, one of the highest, with 1082 per 100 000. Overall, in provincial terms, mortality rates in 1996 dropped from east to west, from a high of 753 per 100 000 in Prince Edward Island to a low of 623 per 100 000 in British Columbia, a drop of 21 percent in this indicator of health.

If we consider mortality from the major groups of illnesses, we see, again, considerable variation around the national averages. We also see that the locations of the highs and lows across the country tend to differ by types of illness. The Peace River region of British Columbia has high levels of breast cancer, at 42 per 100 000; the Northwestern health region of Alberta has high levels of mortality from circulatory diseases. Clear patterns are not always easy to identify. Indeed, some of the highest rates of breast cancer deaths in Canada occur next door to some of the lowest rates (the North and South Eastman districts of Manitoba, with rates of 18.7 and 37.1 per 100 000, respectively). Nevertheless, Nunavut's high levels of mortality, from a number of causes, and the Halton (ON) and Richmond (BC) areas' low levels of mortality do indicate some of the major outlines of Canada's medical geography.

Because of this, when we turn to regional patterns of life expectancies for 1996 (**Figure 3.21**), it is not surprising to find Nunavut (with an average life expectancy at birth of 69.8 years) and Richmond (78.3 years) at opposite ends of the spectrum. The variations between parts of Saskatchewan (with above average life expectancies) and parts of the St. Lawrence Valley west and east of Montreal (with below average life expectancies) are also worth noting, since they are indicative of some important underlying patterns. We can sharpen our focus on the geography of health by moving to a smaller scale and examining, as a case study, the city of Montreal.

Figure 3.21 Life expectancy at birth, by health region, 1996
(*Source:* Statistics Canada, *Health Indicators* 1009 [3], December 2001, Catalogue No. 82-221-XTE, available online at **www.statcan.gc.ca**.)

Life Expectancy at Birth, Canada 1996

The health regions of Canada are colour coded according to their statistical difference with the national average life expectancy of 78.32 years.

- Significantly higher than 78.32 years
- Not significantly different from 78.32 years
- Significantly lower than 78.32 years
- Sparsely populated

0   500   1000 kilometres

Data for average life expectancies at birth, calculated for Montreal's Centre local de services communautaires (CLSC) regions, for the years 1994 to 1997, indicate that people on the west of the island can expect to live, on average, almost a decade longer than those in some east-end communities (**Figure 3.22**). This variation, from a life expectancy of 81.3 years in the Lac Saint-Louis CLSC region to one of 70.7 years in the Des Faubourgs CLSC region is one that closely follows patterns of income. In the Lac Saint-Louis area, only 1 percent of all age groups relies on social assistance, while in the Des Faubourgs region, as many as 40 percent receive welfare.

In seeking to explain the existence and persistence of these patterns, medical geographers have generally favoured two types of explanation. The first, a behavioural (or lifestyle) hypothesis, argues that these geographical differences (or spatial inequalities) in health arise because certain groups of people more commonly engage in health-threatening activities (such as smoking) and less commonly participate in health-promoting activities (such as sports or eating a healthful diet) than other groups in the population. As a headline in the 30 May 2001 issue of the *Montreal Gazette* covering this topic bluntly explained it, "Poor people tend to smoke more, eat less healthy food."[54]

The second explanation approaches the pattern of health inequalities from a structuralist perspective and challenges the assumptions of the lifestyle hypothesis. From this perspective, the operation of the economy and society as a whole dictates people's quality of life. For example, less wealthy people, exposed to health hazards where they live or work, may find themselves effectively denied access to high-quality health care facilities simply because such resources tend to be located in more wealthy parts of town. As the medical geographer S. Martin Taylor has observed, "the higher mortality rates for men in the north end of Hamilton, for example, raise questions about exposure to hazards in the local workplace, a heavily industrial area. Equally, they may reflect limits in discretionary time and income as well as limited access to resources and facilities which would support engagement in positive health behaviour."[55]

[54]See also, "Montrealers Die Younger: Life Span among Lowest in Canada." *Montreal Gazette*, 5 July 2002, pp. A1, A4.

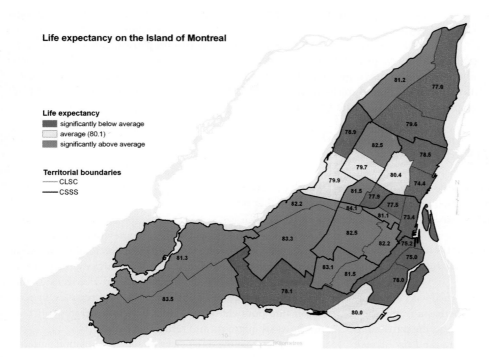

Life expectancy on the Island of Montreal

Life expectancy
■ significantly below average
☐ average (80.1)
■ significantly above average

Territorial boundaries
— CLSC
— CSSS

Figure 3.22 Life expectancies on the island of Montreal This map shows life expectancies at birth, for both sexes combined, using 2001–2005 data for the 29 health districts of the island of Montreal. Considerable variations across the city can be seen, and the 10-year difference between the city centre and the western suburbs is a long-standing feature. (*Source:* The Centre local de services communautaires (CLSC) data are given on "Les CLSC d'un coup d'oeil," Direction de la santé publique de Montreal-Centre at **www.santepub-mtl.qc.ca/Portrait/ Les29/carteesperance.html**.) For more recent information, see the Foundation of Greater Montreal's annual publication *Greater Montreal's Vital Signs: 2006* **http://www.fgmtl.org/en/ VitalSigns/index.htm**.

Certainly, Canadian medical geographers have observed that there are marked discrepancies in the provision of medical services and that a more equitable spatial pattern, across city and country alike, would be one possible public policy solution to Canada's health care problems. The search for the underlying causes of the patterns shown in Canada's medical geography brings us back full circle to the traditional medical geographer's concerns with patterns of spatial association. A provisional list must surely put the various advantages and disadvantages of urban and rural living in the balance, together with the spatial inequalities inherent in the basic differences that are embedded in Canada's economic geography. In this sense, we clearly see the importance of place, this time in our consideration of Canadians' health.

CONCLUSION

The geography of population is directly connected to the complex forces that drive globalization. And, since the fifteenth century, the distribution of the world's population has changed dramatically as the capitalist economy has expanded, bringing new and different peoples into contact with one another and setting into motion additional patterns of national and regional migrations. When capitalism emerged in Europe in the fifteenth century, the world's population was experiencing high birth rates, high death rates, and relatively low levels of migration or mobility. Four hundred years later, birth, death, and migration rates vary—sometimes quite dramatically—from region to region, with core countries experiencing low death and birth rates and peripheral and semiperipheral countries generally experiencing high birth rates and fairly low death rates. Migration rates vary within and outside the core. These variations may be seen to reflect the level and intensity of political, economic, and cultural connectedness between the core and the periphery.

The example of formerly colonized peoples migrating to their ruling countries in search of work provides insights into the dynamic nature of the world economy

---

[55]S.M. Taylor, "The Geography of Urban Health." In L. Bourne and D. Ley (eds.), *The Changing Social Geography of Canadian Cities.* Montreal and Kingston: McGill–Queen's University Press, 1993, pp. 309–325. (The quotation is from p. 317.)

and shows the important role that people play in acting out the dynamics of geographical variety.

In the final analysis, death rates, birth rates, and migration rates are the central variables of population growth and change. These indicators tell us much about transforming regions and places as elements in a larger world-system. Globalization has created many new maps as it has unfolded; the changing geography of population is just one of them.

MAIN POINTS REVISITED

■ **Population geographers depend on a wide array of data sources to assess the geography of populations. Chief among these sources is the census, although other sources include vital records and public health statistics.**

Census collection methods vary from country to country and are often conducted in different years, making it difficult to compare different places.

■ **Population geographers are largely concerned with the same sorts of questions as other population experts study, but they also investigate "the why of where":** *why* **do particular aspects of population growth and change (and problems) occur** *where* **they do, and what are the implications of these factors for the future of places?**

A geographical perspective is sensitive to the important influences of place and sees geographical factors as an important part of an explanation for population growth and change.

■ **Two of the most important factors that make up population dynamics are birth and death. These variables may be examined in simple or complex ways, but in either case, the reasons for the behaviour of these variables are as important as the numbers themselves.**

Birth and death rates are fairly crude measures of population change. Population geographers complicate these rates by looking at such factors as the particular experiences of certain age cohorts or ethnic groups and how those factors influence birth and death rates.

■ **A third crucial force in population change is the movement of populations. The forces that push populations from particular locations, as well as those that pull them to move to new areas, are key to understanding the resulting new settlement patterns. Population migration may not always be a matter of choice.**

Migration is one of the most important factors affecting the distribution of world population today. For some countries whose birth rates are especially low, migration is one way of reversing that trend.

■ **As a generalization, world demographic patterns are easily described within a world-system framework. They are an important aspect of the very different economic and social "spaces" that this model produces. High birth rates and death rates are a feature of today's periphery; low birth rates and death rates a feature of the core. The discrepancy in economic and political terms between them generates substantial flows of migrants and refugees.**

This suggests that the differences we see in population patterns across the globe are the result of the same set of processes that have created the world-system. It also suggests that continued globalization may accentuate these differences rather than remove them.

■ **Perhaps the most pressing issue facing scholars, policy-makers, and other interested individuals is the one articulated at the International Conference on Population and Development, held in Cairo in 1994: how many people can the world adequately accommodate with food, water, clean air, and other basic necessities for the enjoyment of happy, healthy, and satisfying lives?**

Many policies have been advanced to address what some observers feel is an overpopulated world. One important factor that is widely seen to be effective in curbing high birth rates is the education of the female population.

■ **Whether at the world, country, or local scale of analysis, the work of those geographers studying the interactions among population, health, and the environment shows us that the principal explanation for varying spatial patterns of health is variation in income distribution.**

Spatial inequalities are related to differing patterns of disease incidence and affect people's relative access to health care facilities.

Key Terms

administrative record linkage (p. 92)
age–sex pyramid (p. 96)
aging (p. 97)
baby boom (p. 94)
census (p. 91)
cohort (p. 97)
crude birth rate (CBR) (p. 101)
crude death rate (CDR) (p. 102)
crude density (arithmetic
 density) (p. 94)
demographic transition (p. 106)

demography (p. 91)
dependency ratio (p. 97)
doubling time (p. 102)
eco-migration (p. 110)
emigration (p. 108)
environmental refugee (p. 111)
epidemiological transition (p. 128)
family reconstitution (p. 91)
fertility (p. 101)
forced migration (p. 109)
geodemographic analysis (p. 95)

gross migration (p. 109)
guest workers (p. 113)
immigration (p. 108)
infant mortality rate (p. 103)
internal migration (p. 108)
international migration (p. 108)
life expectancy (p. 104)
medical geography (p. 128)
middle cohort (p. 97)
migration (p. 108)
mobility (p. 108)

natural decrease (p. 103)	**participation rate** (p. 98)	**vital records** (p. 91)
natural increase (p. 103)	**pull factors** (p. 109)	**voluntary migration** (p. 109)
net migration (p. 109)	**push factors** (p. 109)	**vulnerable populations** (p. 132)
old-age cohort (p. 97)	**total fertility rate (TFR)** (p. 101)	**youth cohort** (p. 97)

Additional Reading

Beaujot, R. *Population Change in Canada: The Challenges of Policy Adaptation.* Toronto: McClelland and Stewart, 1991.

Bouvier, L., and C. DeVita. "The Baby Boom—Entering Midlife," *Population Bulletin* 46(3), 1991, 2–33.

Castles, S., and M.J. Miller. *The Age of Migration: International Population Movements in the Modern World.* London: Macmillan, 1993.

Eyles, J., and S.J. Elliott. "Global Environmental Change and Human Health," *Canadian Geographer* 45(1), 2001, 99–104.

Foot, D., and D. Stoffman. *Boom, Bust and Echo 2000: Profiting from the Demographic Shift in the New Millennium.* Toronto: Macfarlane Walter and Ross, 1998.

Greer, A. *The People of New France.* Toronto: University of Toronto Press, 1977.

Harris, C. *The Resettlement of British Columbia: Essays on Colonialism and Geographical Change.* Vancouver: UBC Press, 1997.

Mann, C.C. "How Many Is Too Many?" *Atlantic Monthly*, February 1993, 47–67.

Miron, J. *Housing in Postwar Canada: Demographic Change, Household Formation, and Housing Demand.* Kingston and Montreal: McGill–Queen's University Press, 1988.

Nash, A.E. "Environmental Refugees: Consequences and Policies from a Western Perspective," *Discrete Dynamics in Nature and Society* 3, 1999, 227–238.

Nash, A.E. and K. Noonan-Mooney, "Environmental Refugees," *Encyclopaedia of Environment and Society.* Thousand Oaks, CA: Sage Publications, 2007, 590–591.

Statistics Canada. *Report on the Demographic Situation in Canada, 2005 and 2006.* Ottawa: Statistics Canada, 2008.

Taylor, S.M. "The Geography of Urban Health." In L. Bourne and D. Ley (eds.), *The Changing Social Geography of Canadian Cities.* Montreal and Kingston: McGill–Queen's University Press, 1993, 309–325.

Toward a Healthy Future: Second Report of the Health of Canadians, prepared by the Federal, Provincial and Territorial Advisory Committee on Population Health for the Meeting of Ministers of Health, Charlottetown, PEI, September 1999. Ottawa: Health Canada, 1999.

Trovato, F., and C.F. Grindstaff (eds.). *Perspectives on Canada's Population: An Introduction to Concepts and Issues.* Toronto: Oxford University Press, 1994.

Exercises

Here you will find exercises and activities for each chapter. Unplugged exercises help you review chapter discussions, and pose ideas for your own human geography research. On the Companion Website exercises will require you have access to the internet.

Unplugged

1. The distribution of population is a result of many factors, such as employment opportunities, culture, water supply, climate, and other physical environmental characteristics. Look at the distribution of population in your province. Is it evenly distributed, or are the majority of people found in only a few cities? What role do you think these various factors have played in influencing where people live in your province? Can you think of other reasons for this distribution?

2. Immigration is an important factor contributing to the increase in the population of Canada. Chances are your great-grandparents, grandparents, parents, or even you immigrated to, or migrated within, your country of residence. Construct your family's immigration or migration history. What were some of the push and pull factors influencing your family's decision to immigrate to or migrate within your country?

3. Every few years, UNESCO publishes a data book on global refugee statistics indicating both sending and receiving countries among other variables. Use your library's most recent data book to identify one country that has been a large sender of refugees and the matching country that has been the largest receiver of those refugees. The data book provides information not only on the numbers of refugees, but on their age, gender, and other variables. Discuss some of the demographic implications for both countries if the refugee population were not to be allowed to return to the sending country.

On the Companion Website

This book has its own Companion Website where you will find additional resources—maps, photographs, data—as well as exercises and activities that relate to each chapter. To complete the Companion Website exercises, go to **www.pearsoned.ca/knox**. The following is a summary of the types of exercises created for this chapter.

1. The exercises for this chapter use internet websites to help you understand the key concepts. For example, through an interactive map and socioeconomic database, you can view country demographics, economics, geography, and social indicators. Using an animated program, you can illustrate and explain various age–sex pyramids among different countries. There are a number of review questions regarding population movements and migration, along with several map exercises based on population density and composition. A critical-thinking exercise focuses on the impact on our society of the baby boom generation as it reaches maturity. Other exercises help you examine the policies of population and resources.

2. The CBC Video Case, Dying for Doctors—South African Doctors, that accompanies this chapter has been chosen to highlight some of the cultural and economic issues of emigration and immigration discussed in this chapter. You will find a link to the CBC video, the video case, questions, and resources on the Companion Website for this chapter.

4

Nature, Society, and Technology

Some Canadian populations of the American white pelican (*Pelecanus erythrorhynchos*) have greatly diminished in recent years in response to a variety of environmental factors.

Where Have All the Pelicans Gone?" Having once marvelled at the precision of a flock of pelicans flying in tight formation over Manitou Beach in Saskatchewan, this headline in Toronto's *Globe and Mail* could not fail to catch my attention.[1] Apparently, this question was going to be the slogan used on promotional buttons for the September 2004 fair in Medina, North Dakota. This town of only 355 people is located near the Chase Lake National Wildlife Refuge, a lake that until recently was home to the world's largest breeding colony of American white pelicans (*Pelecanus erythrorhynchos*), a migratory species that has been returning to nest there since 1908.

According to the newspaper report, on 20 May 2004, wildlife officials counted 27 000 pelicans at the refuge, but eight days later, only 80 birds remained. The disappearance is still a mystery. Tests conducted on some dead chicks that had been abandoned at the site show no signs of any known toxins, pollutants, or diseases. Since the colony is on a cluster of remote islands in the lake, local biologists have also ruled out human interference or coyote attacks. Perhaps, one research biologist suggested, the pelicans could not find enough food because the salamanders that form part of the birds' diet remained underground during an unusually cold spring and summer. "Really, though," she admitted, "we don't know much. All we can do is twiddle our thumbs and wait for them to come back."

According to the CBC, a mystery also surrounds Canada's most northerly population of pelicans, a flock based on islands in the Slave River rapids near Fort Smith, Northwest Territories. This colony produced 742 chicks in 2000, but only 1 survived to the fall migration of 2003. A local conservation biologist said no one knew the reasons for the decline but speculated that an increase in white water kayaking might have disturbed the birds. Others have blamed film crews on the islands or poor fish habitats.[2]

On first hearing, we might suppose that these two stories are yet more sad examples of human impact on the natural world. Pelicans are particularly vulnerable to environmental change. As a migratory species, the birds are affected by changes in their summer and winter haunts; as a species dependent on fish and amphibians as food, pelicans are affected by the size and health of those populations.[3] However, on reflection, we see that these news items show both

---

[1]Graeme Smith, "Town Wonders: "Where Have All the Pelicans Gone?" *Globe and Mail*, 7 August 2004, p. A7.

[2]CBC, "Bad Breeding Season Imperils Northern Pelicans." *CBC.ca*, 24 December 2003, available online at **www.cbc.ca/health/story/2003/12/23/pelicans031223.html.**

[3]A wonderful visual sense of the life of migratory birds (including Canada geese) can be gained from Jacques Perrin's 89-minute documentary film *Le Peuple Migrateur* (2001), available in English as *Winged Migration* (Sony Classics, 2003). The hazards of life of the Monarch butterfly as it migrates from Ontario to Mexico are ably described in Sue Halpern's *Four Wings and a Prayer: Caught in the Mystery of the Monarch Butterfly*. Vintage Canada: Toronto, 2002.

the complexity of environmental change and the poverty of our understanding. Human interference has undoubtedly been a major problem, as the near extinction of the pelican population in North America in the 1950s demonstrates (through hunting and the effects of DDT, an insecticide). But these effects can be reversed, as the rebound in pelican populations since the 1960s has shown, largely because of conservation measures. These examples also show us that nature itself is constantly undergoing change because of annual migration, much longer cycles of colony abandonment, climate change, or other as-yet-unknown processes. Our ability to detect the magnitude of these changes and the impact of human interference depends on a greater understanding of the environment and a willingness to see it as *our* environment. We are very much a part of the natural world, and the ways we choose to use it to sustain ourselves, in a material sense, and to define the frame of our existence, in a wider sense, will ultimately affect the future.

This relationship between people and the environment is perhaps the most central of all within the discipline of geography. Indeed, the discipline of geography consists of those who study natural systems and those who study human systems. In this chapter, we explore the ways that society has used technology to transform and adapt to nature, together with the human and environmental impact of these technological adaptations.

MAIN POINTS

- Nature, society, and technology constitute a complex relationship. In our view, nature is both a physical realm and a social creation.

- Because we regard nature as a social creation, it is important to understand the many social ideas of nature present in society today and especially the history of those ideas. The most prominent idea of nature in Western culture is derived from the Judeo-Christian tradition, a belief that nature is an entity to be dominated by humans.

- Social relationships with nature have developed over the course of human history, beginning with the early Stone Age. The early history of humankind included people who revered nature as well as those who abused it. Urbanization and industrialization have had extremely degrading impacts on the environment.

- The globalization of the world economy has meant that environmental problems are also global in their scope. Deforestation, acid rain, and global warming affect us all. Many new ways of understanding nature have emerged in the last several decades in response to these serious global crises.

NATURE AS A CONCEPT

As discussed in Chapter 2, a simple model of the nature–society relation is that nature, through its awesome power and subtle expressions, limits or shapes society. This model is known as *environmental determinism*. A second model posits that society also shapes and controls nature, largely through technology and social institutions. This second model, explored in this chapter, emphasizes the complexity of nature–society interactions.

Interest in the relationships among nature, society, and technology has experienced a resurgence over the last two or three decades. The single most dramatic manifestation of this interest occurred in the summer of 1992, when more than 100 world leaders and 30 000 other participants attended the second Earth Summit in Rio de Janeiro (the first Earth Summit was held in Stockholm in 1972). The central focus of the agenda was to ensure a sustainable future for Earth by establishing treaties on global environmental issues, such as climate change and biodiversity. Canada took a very active part in this conference, and one of Ottawa's senior environmental officials, Jim MacNeill, was heavily involved. (He had earlier helped draft the 1987 report *Our Common Future,* that defined sustainable development as meeting the needs of the present without compromising the needs of the future.)

Although dramatic changes have not occurred in the years since then, some very important and significant ones have taken place. One change is the emergence of new international institutions to facilitate and monitor environmental improvements. Under NAFTA in 1992, the North American Commission on Environmental Cooperation was established to monitor the ecological effects of liberalized trade in Canada, the United States, and Mexico. It is based in Montreal, the city where, in 1987, the international Protocol on Substances That Deplete the Ozone Layer was signed. Significant success in reducing ozone depletion has resulted. Real progress has also been achieved on the global phase-out of leaded gasoline.

In addition to formal summits and international actions, an abundance of far less spectacular evidence suggests that concern for the environment has spread from the scientific community to the public and from the core to the periphery. For instance, in 1998, the International Environmental Monitor survey was coordinated by Environics International Ltd. of Toronto. The survey, conducted by associated polling firms in 30 countries, was the largest of its kind. More than 35 000 in-person or telephone interviews (at least 1000 per country) were conducted in March and April 1998. Taken together, the countries surveyed contain two-thirds of the world's population. Majorities in 27 of 30 countries surveyed, ranging from 91 percent in Greece to 54 percent in India, say environmental laws as currently applied in their country "don't go far enough." About two-thirds or more of people surveyed are dissatisfied with environmental laws. Overall concern about the environment was higher than it had been in a similar survey taken in 1992 (**Figure 4.1**).

Why is there such strong and widespread interest in the environment today? To answer that question, it is necessary to recognize that despite repeated attempts to address environmental problems, they persist. Like anyone living close to the land, Canada's First Nations and immigrant farmers were early commentators on human–environment relations. Sir Clifford Sifton, who chaired Canada's Commission of Conservation (1909–1918) was an early advocate of environmental conservation. In 1962, American author Rachel L. Carson in a groundbreaking book, *Silent Spring,* warned of the dangers of agricultural pesticides to ecosystems (**Figure 4.2** and **Figure 4.3**). Yet today the pesticide problem persists and has become a problem for peripheral as well as core countries.

In short, renewed interest in the nature–society relationship is the result of the persistence and large number of environmental crises. This interest has led to attempts to rethink this relationship. In the past, technology has always emerged as the apparent solution to our environmental problems, but now the continued application of technology does not seem to solve them. As a result,

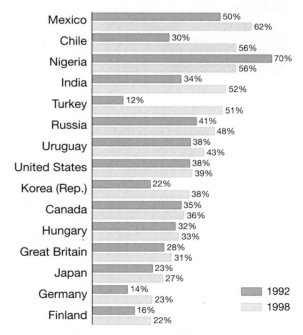

Figure 4.1   Rising levels of environmental concern
In the 1998 International Environmental Monitor survey, there was increased environmental concern in 13 of 15 countries that had been surveyed in 1992. When asked to describe how concerned they were about the environment, the percentages shown in the bar graph answered "a great deal."

Figure 4.2 **Death from DDT** DDT (or dichlorodiphenyltrichloroethane) is a chemical pesticide applied through aerial spraying. It was used widely in agriculture in the United States and other core countries in the middle decades of the twentieth century. It had lethal effects on populations of fish-eating birds, such as osprey, cormorants, brown pelicans, and bald eagles and was banned from use in the United States in 1972. Despite prohibitions against the use of DDT in most core countries, countries in the periphery continue to apply it to improve crop yields.

Figure 4.3 **Rachel L. Carson (1907–1964)** Rachel L. Carson was a professional biologist who worked for the U.S. Fish and Wildlife Service. Her book, *Silent Spring*, was the first piece of critical research published on the environmental effects of pesticides. Many people credit Rachel Carson as a key figure in the emergence of what is now known as the *environmental movement*.

nature: a social creation as well as the physical universe that includes human beings

society: sum of the inventions, institutions, and relationships created and reproduced by human beings across particular places and times

researchers and activists have begun to ask different questions and abandon the assumption that technology is the *only* solution.

Environmental thinkers, including a number of geographers, are beginning to advocate the need to consider nature not as something that sits apart from humans but as inseparable from society. They believe that nature and questions about the environment need to be considered in conjunction with both society and technology because these are the most important influences on how we think about nature and how we identify sources and solutions to environmental problems. Such an approach—uniting nature, society, and technology as interactive components of a complex system—enables us to ask new questions and consider new alternatives to current practices with respect to nature. In Canada, Pierre Dansereau's 1957 book *Biogeography: An Ecological Perspective* struck a similar chord and won an international following. Before asking new questions about nature, we define key terms and look at different approaches to the concept of nature. We then examine how changing conceptions of nature have translated into very different uses of it and adaptations to it.

Nature, Society, and Technology Defined

The central concepts of this chapter—nature, society, and technology—have very specific meanings. Although we discuss the changing conceptions and understandings of nature in some detail, we hold to one encompassing position. **Nature** is a social creation as much as it is the physical universe that includes human beings: understandings of nature are the product of different times and different needs. Nature is not only objects; it is a reflection of society in that philosophies, belief systems, and ideologies shape the way people think about nature and the way they "use" it. The relationship between nature and society is two-way: society shapes people's understandings and uses of nature at the same time that nature shapes society. The amount of shaping by society is dependent to a large extent on the state of technology and the constraints on its use at any given time.

Society is the sum of the inventions, institutions, and relationships created and reproduced by human beings across particular places and times. Nature is just one of the relationships created and reproduced by society, and the social relationship to nature varies from place to place among different social groups. In our scheme, society and nature are interrelated.

The mutual relationship between society and nature is usually mediated through technology. Knowledge, implements, arts, skills, and the sociocultural context all are components of technology. If we accept that all these components are relevant to technology, then we can provide a definition that has three distinguishable, though equally important, aspects. **Technology** is defined as

- physical objects or artifacts (for example, the plow)
- activities or processes (for example, steelmaking)
- knowledge or know-how (for example, biological engineering)

This definition encompasses tools, applications, and understandings and enables recognition of all three as critical components of the processes and outcomes of the human production of technology. The manifestations and impacts of technology can be measured in terms of such concepts as level of industrialization and per capita energy consumption.

The definitions provided in this section reflect current thinking on the relationship between society and nature. For centuries, humankind, in its responses to the constraints of the physical environment, has been as much influenced by prevailing ideas about nature as by the realities of nature. In fact, prevailing ideas about nature have changed over time, as evidence from literature, art, religion, legal systems, and technological innovations makes abundantly clear.

A recent attempt to conceptualize the relationship between social and environmental changes has emerged from concern with global environmental change. Based on the premise that individual societal changes can be both subtly and dramatically related to environmental changes, a formula for distinguishing the sources of social impacts on the environment has been advanced and is now widely used. The formula is known as $I = PAT$, and it relates human population pressures on environmental resources to the level of affluence and access to technology in a society. More specifically, the formula states that $I = PAT$, where I (impact on Earth's resources) is equal to P (population) times A (affluence, as measured by per capita income) times T (a technology factor). For example, the differential impact on the environment of two households' energy use in two different countries would equal the number of people per household times the per capita income of the household times the type of technology used to provide energy for that household (**Figure 4.4**).

technology: physical objects or artifacts, activities or processes, and knowledge or know-how

Figure 4.4   Affluence differences in two households   As the $I = PAT$ formula suggests, the level of affluence of households plays an important role in their impact on the global environment. Pictured here are two families, one from the core and the other from the periphery. Both families are shown outside their homes with all of their possessions displayed around them. The extensive range of possessions shows the Icelandic family, comprising two parents and four children, to be far more affluent than the Guatemalan family, comprising two parents and three children. The Icelandic family possesses two radios, one stereo, two televisions, one VCR, one home computer, two automobiles, and a private airplane. The Guatemalan family possesses one battery-operated radio and no telephone but would like to acquire a television set.

Each variable in the formula—population, affluence, and technology—should be seen as complex; otherwise, some erroneous conclusions can be drawn. For example, with regard to population numbers, it is generally believed that fewer people on the planet will result in fewer direct pressures on resources. Some argue, however, that the increases in world population numbers are quite desirable. The argument is made that a larger population means more labour and more potential for the emergence of innovation to solve present and future resource problems. Clearly, there is no simple answer to the question of how many people are too many people.

It is also the case that the variable affluence cannot simply be assessed in terms of less is better. Certainly, increasing affluence—a measure of per capita consumption multiplied by the number of consumers and the environmental impacts of their technologies—is a drain on Earth's resources and a burden on Earth's ability to absorb waste. Yet, determining how much affluence is too much is difficult. Furthermore, evidence shows that core countries, with high levels of affluence, are more effective than the poor countries of the periphery at protecting their environments. Unfortunately, it is also often the case that core countries protect their own environments by exporting their noxious industrial processes and waste products to peripheral countries. By exporting polluting industries and the jobs that go with them, however, core countries may also be contributing to a rise in the level of affluence of peripheral countries. Given what we know about core countries, such a rise may be sufficient to sustain a set of social values that would foster attitudes and behaviours that would ultimately protect the environment in a new place. It is difficult to identify the moment when an environmental consciousness goes from being a luxury to a being a necessity. The role of affluence in terms of environmental impacts is, like population, difficult to assess.

Not surprisingly, the variable technology is no less complicated than either population or affluence. It is important to recognize that technologies affect the environment in three ways:

- through the harvesting of resources
- through the emission of wastes in the manufacture of goods and services
- through the emission of waste in the consumption of goods and services

Technology is complex because it can work two ways. Technology can sometimes be a solution and sometimes a problem. A technological innovation can shift demand from an existing resource to a newly discovered, more plentiful one. Such is the case with nuclear energy, widely regarded as cleaner and more efficient than coal or oil as an energy source. Producing this energy creates hazards, however, which scientists are still unable to prevent.

It is therefore clear that increases in human numbers, in levels of wealth, and in technological capacity are key components of social and economic progress whose impact on the environment has been extremely complex. In the last 100 years, this complexity has increasingly come to be seen as a triple-barrelled threat to the quality of the natural world and the availability and quality of environmental resources.

ecological footprint: a measure of the biologically productive land area needed to support a country by providing for its needs and absorbing its wastes

An **ecological footprint** provides a measure of the biologically productive land area required to support a city or country by providing for its needs and absorbing its wastes. It allows us to visualize the growth and scale of the impact humans have on Earth in terms of sustainability. Because people use resources from all over the globe, the footprint calculation includes all the cropland and other natural resources required to produce the products consumed by a population, wherever they are located. According to the *Ecological Footprint of Nations Report* for 2004, Canada's footprint is 8.56 hectares per capita, a figure exceeded only by the United Arab Emirates (8.97 hectares) and the United States (9.57 hectares). Such figures are clearly not sustainable, since the report calculates that there are only 1.88 productive acres (0.75 hectares) available for each person on the planet.[4] Such figures also contrast sharply with those for Bangladesh (0.50 hectares) and Mozambique (0.56 hectares), the countries with the smallest footprints in 2004. Before we look more carefully at the specific impacts of populations, affluence, and technology on nature, we need to look first at how differing social attitudes toward nature shape the human behaviours that are a basis for these calculations.

Religious Perspectives on Nature

In a 2003 essay entitled "Engaging Religion in the Quest for a Sustainable World," Garry Gardner argues that all religious traditions involve ideas about nature.[5] Defining religion in the most general terms as "an orientation to the cosmos and to our role in it," Gardner suggests three major ways religious beliefs can affect our attitudes toward the environment.

First, the fundamental worldview of religions shapes beliefs about the natural world and its importance. The proper relationship between humans and the environment and the real value of environmental protection are therefore among the many concepts that may be rooted in particular theologies.

Second, religious rituals in many societies can affect the ways in which natural resources are used. "Before stripping bark from cedar trees, for instance, the Tlingit Indians of the Pacific Northwest perform a ritual apology to the spirits they believe live there, promising to take only what they need," Gardner notes. As another example, some anthropologists suggest that religious injunctions against certain foods may well have their origins in a response the unhealthy effects of eating animals reared in poor environmental conditions.

Third, ethical systems derived from religious beliefs may influence how the environment's resources are used and how they are distributed across society. In this respect, ethical systems whose prime goal is an equitable distribution of resources among people can reduce overconsumption and lead to a more sustainable use of the environment. Dietary practices, such as vegetarianism, also illustrate how ethics can influence our use of animals and plants. Ethical funds, a recent development in the Canadian investment industry, allow investors to support environmentally friendly businesses.

The detailed connections between religious belief and attitudes toward the environment have prompted a number of conferences, including a 1994 Workshop on Environmental Stewardship organized by the University of Winnipeg's Institute of Urban Studies, and the 1996–1998 Harvard Conferences on Religions of the World and Ecology (now continued as the Forum on Religion and Ecology). In a 2003 initiative, the ecumenical patriarch of the Orthodox Church and Roman Catholic, Protestant, and Islamic leaders met with UN officials to discuss the environmental plight of the Adriatic.[6]

Such gatherings have shown not only the importance of understanding the role of the world's religions in environmental matters but also the need to appreciate that religions reflect many different perspectives on human relationships to nature. This appreciation is especially valuable in such a country as Canada, with its great variety of religions and enormous diversity of environments.

---

[4]The full report is available at **www.rprogress.org/publications/index.htm**, a website that also allows you to calculate your own ecological footprint.

[5]Garry Gardner, "Engaging Religion in the Quest for a Sustainable World." In Linda Starke (ed.), *State of the World 2003*. New York: Norton, 2003, pp. 152–175. The quotations are from pp. 153 and 154.

[6]Mary Ann Beavis (ed.), *Environmental Stewardship, History, Theory, Practice*. Institute of Urban Studies, University of Winnipeg, Occasional Paper 32, 1994. The Forum on Religion and Ecology website is a valuable resource and is available at **www.environment.harvard.edu/religion/religion/index.html**. The patriarch's initiatives can be examined at the Religion, Science and the Environment website at **www.rsesymposia.org**.

Taoist perspective on nature: the view that nature should be valued for its own sake, not for how it might be exploited

Buddhist perspective on nature: the view that nothing exists in and of itself and everything is part of a natural, complex, and dynamic totality of mutuality and interdependence

Islamic perspective on nature: the view that the heavens and Earth were made for human purposes

Judeo-Christian perspective on nature: the view that nature was created by God and is subject to God in the same way that a child is subject to parents

animistic perspective on nature: the view that natural phenomena—both animate and inanimate—possess an indwelling spirit or consciousness

The **Taoist perspective on nature**, for example, clearly emphasizes valuing nature for its own sake, not for the utilitarian purposes to which it might be put. An ancient Chinese religion, Taoism emphasizes harmony with nature and views the natural world not as an exploitable resource but as a complex life process to be respected and appreciated.

A **Buddhist perspective on nature** teaches that nothing exists in and of itself, and everything is part of a natural, complex, and dynamic totality of mutuality and interdependence. Humans have a special role in the totality in that they alone are capable of reflection and conscious action. It is up to human beings, therefore, to care for all life, human and nonhuman, and to safeguard the integrity of the universe.

An **Islamic perspective on nature** teaches that authority over nature is given to humans by Allah (God) not as an absolute right but as a test of obedience, loyalty, and gratitude to Allah. Abuse of Earth is opposed to the will of Allah; stewardship of it shows respect and fulfills the will of Allah.

The Judeo-Christian tradition has exerted considerable influence on Western ideas about nature. Generally, the **Judeo-Christian perspective on nature** holds that nature was created by God and is subject to God in the same way that a child is subject to parents. "Man" (by which pre-twentieth-century environmental philosophies meant males *exclusively*) was also created by God but made in God's own image, and so man is separate from nature in this regard.

Indigenous religious traditions in North and South America and Africa also conceptualize nature differently, and there was a widespread system of belief on these three continents before European contact. An **animistic perspective on nature** is the belief that natural phenomena—both animate and inanimate—possess an indwelling spirit or consciousness. For many indigenous peoples (**Figure 4.5**), humans cannot be separated from nature, and the natural cannot be separated from the supernatural. The Cree believe in an unending cycle of reciprocity between humans and animals based on respect. According to this worldview, a hunter is successful because the animal chooses to give itself to the hunter who has behaved with respect toward the animal and its spirit. Through this spirit, the animal may then become part of the hunter, "dissolving any discernable boundary between person and the animal and between the natural and spirit worlds," anthropologist Naomi Adelson writes.[7]

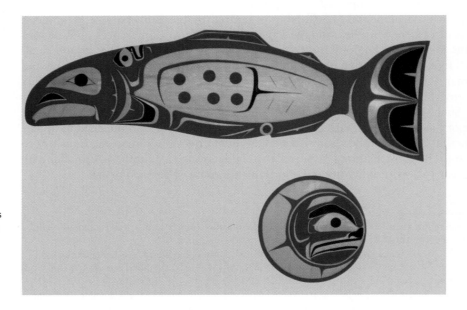

Figure 4.5   Skip Saunders' *Salmon and Egg*   North America's indigenous peoples developed religious traditions that celebrated the connections between people and nature. Many of Canada's Aboriginal artists draw on these traditions in their current work, as these carvings show.

[7]Naomi Adelson, *"Being Alive Well": Health and the Politics of Cree Well-Being.* Toronto: University of Toronto Press, 2000, pp. 67–70. The quotation is from p. 68.

One elder from Whapmagoostui (a Cree community at the mouth of the Great Whale River in northern Quebec) provided this account in a recent interview with Adelson:[8]

> The people would . . . take care of what they had killed very well and handle it with respect so that they did not anger the spirits of the animals. If they handled the killed animals with respect, they would be successful in their hunts and the spirits of the animals would be happy to give food to them. . . . It is said that when someone really angered the animal that he depended on for food, the animal would leave that person for good and starvation resulted.

Zacharius Kunuk's film *Atanarjuat: The Fast Runner* (which won the Camera d'Or at Cannes in 2001) provides another insight into the close connections between the animal realm and the spirit world. The movie draws on the oral tradition to reveal the cultural values and ancient beliefs of the Inuit a thousand years before European contact. The film is spoken in the Inuktitut language, with English subtitles.[9]

The Concept of Nature and the Rise of Science and Technology

In a very influential essay written in 1967, Lynn White argued that the prevalent view in Judeo-Christian thinking that people must dominate nature was one of main causes of the current ecological crisis because it gave humanity free rein to exploit nature for industrial purposes.[10] Many critics now suggest that this view is too simple an interpretation. Their reasons are an important caution to remember when we examine the general connections between people's religious beliefs and their environmental attitudes.

First, a multiplicity of views exists within all religious traditions. The Judeo-Christian tradition, for example, deals not only with domination over nature but also teaches environmental stewardship (as the story of Noah and the Ark illustrates). Second, not all people practise religious beliefs with equal intensity. Third, many people cannot always practise their environmental beliefs (religious or otherwise) because of the pressure of everyday life.

Finally, it is possible that Lynn White was wrong about the date when the separation of humans and nature occurred. Noted geographer Clarence Glacken, in his influential study *Traces on the Rhodian Shore,* a book published in the same year as White's essay, demonstrates that the ancient Greeks were the original source of the idea that nature is separate from humans (**Figure 4.6**). Glacken argues that it was from the Greeks that contemporary society inherited the belief that a fundamental distinction exists between humans and nature, with nature being defined as anything not fabricated by humans.

Whatever the direct connection between religion and environmental crises, an important indirect connection was created in the core European countries in the Middle Ages: the connection between religion and the rise of science and technology.

Francis Bacon (1561–1626) and Thomas Hobbes (1588–1679) were English philosophers, who, as prominent promoters of science and technology, were influential in changing the prevailing organic view of nature. Borrowing from Christian ideology, they advanced a view of nature as something subordinate to humans. Bacon and Hobbes sought to rationalize benevolent nature and the domination of disorderly and chaotic nature.

As feminist environmental historian Carolyn Merchant writes:

> The change in controlling imagery was directly related to changes in human attitudes and behavior toward the earth. Whereas the nurturing earth image can be viewed

---

[8]Ibid. The quotation is from p. 71.

[9]It is worth reading Margaret Atwood's very informative introduction to this film, reprinted in her collection *Moving Targets: Writing with Intent, 1982–2004.* Toronto: House of Anansi Press, 2004, pp. 259–262.

[10]Lynn White Jr., "Historical Roots of Our Ecological Crisis." *Science* 155, 1967, pp. 1203–1207.

Figure 4.6 The Tower of the Winds
The oldest intact building remaining from Greek's Classical Period, it is now believed that this structure in the market place in Athens was probably originally built to house a water clock. It has long been noted for the allegorical images of the four winds shown on its exterior walls.

as a cultural constraint restricting the types of socially and morally sanctioned human actions allowable with respect to the earth, the new images of mastery and domination functioned as cultural sanctions for the denudation of nature.[11]

Merchant shows that before 1500, there existed in Europe a widely held image of Earth as a living entity such that human beings conducted their daily lives in an intimate relationship with the natural order of things. The prevailing metaphor was that of an organism, which emphasized interdependence among human beings and between them and Earth. According to this view, Earth and nature were regarded as female. However, by the sixteenth and seventeenth centuries, the power of science was too great to sustain the organic idea of nature. Subsequently, a view that nature was the instrument of humans became dominant in Western culture.

Environmental Philosophies and Political Views of Nature

Henry David Thoreau (1817–1862), the American naturalist and activist, perhaps best illustrates the Western incorporation of North American Aboriginal conceptions of nature combined with other emerging ecological approaches. Thoreau lived and studied the natural world around the town of his birth, Concord, Massachusetts, during the middle decades of the nineteenth century. He is most famous for his book *Walden,* which chronicles the two years he spent living and observing nature in solitude in a house he built on Walden Pond, 2 kilometres (1.5 miles) from the village green of Concord. Thoreau represents a significant alternative to the "humans-over-nature" approach that characterized his times. Many people credit him as the originator of an ecological philosophy. Others see him as a primary force behind **romanticism**, a philosophy that emphasizes interdependence and relatedness between humans and nature.

romanticism: the philosophy that emphasizes interdependence and relatedness between humans and nature

---

[11]C. Merchant, *The Death of Nature.* San Francisco: Harper and Row, 1979, pp. 2–3.

Early in the twentieth century, writers and politicians drew on the ideas of Thoreau to advocate the wise use of natural resources and the conservation of natural environments. The view that nature should be conserved is one that has persisted to the present. **Conservation** holds that natural resources should be used wisely and that society's actions with respect to the natural world should be actions of stewardship, not exploitation. One example of a group with these views is the Sierra Club, a well-established private institution with chapters throughout Canada and the United States. It possesses an extensive legal division that litigates cases of corporate and individual violation of federal and provincial, territorial, or state environmental regulations.

A more extreme position, **preservation** is an approach to nature advocating that certain habitats, species, and resources should remain off-limits to human use, regardless of whether the use maintains or depletes the resource in question. The philosophy of such groups as the International Fund for Animal Welfare (IFAW) is closely aligned with the preservationist perspective. Whereas the Sierra Club takes its opponents to the courtroom, the IFAW, a Canadian-based group that has taken up the leadership of the anti-seal hunt protest, relies more on active protest and the publicity that generates. Other Canadian preservationist groups employ extralegal tactics—often called *ecoterrorist tactics*—such as driving spikes into trees to discourage logging. Indeed, the anti-sealing Sea Shepherd Conservation Society, under its leader, Canadian environmentalist Paul Watson, actively promotes the use of such tactics. The 2008 arrest of their ship, *The Farley Mowat*, by the Canadian Coastguard off the coast of Newfoundland on charges of endangering the safety of vessels engaged in the seal hunt (by sailing too close to them) is one clear example of what could be considered ecoterrorism. These "quick strike" actions are intended to halt what are regarded as government or corporate environmental abuses (which may, in fact, be perfectly legal though counter to a preservationist philosophy).

Founded in Vancouver in 1979, Greenpeace is an environmental organization global in its reach, meaning that both its membership and its areas of emphasis are international. Focusing on environmental polluters and combining the strategies of both the Sierra Club and the IFAW, Greenpeace utilizes oppositional tactics as well as formal international legal actions. In its membership—with the world headquarters in Amsterdam and regional offices in most major industrial countries—as well as its objectives, halting environmental pollution worldwide, Greenpeace articulates the belief that places are interdependent and that what happens in one part of the globe affects us all.

Such organizations as the IFAW and Greenpeace are practical illustrations of the new approaches to understanding human interactions with nature that have occurred in environmental philosophy since the publication of *Silent Spring* more than 45 years ago. These new approaches—environmental ethics, ecofeminism, and deep ecology—take the view that nature is as much a physical universe as it is a product of social thought. All are new and different ways of understanding how society shapes our ideas about nature. Their combined efforts have led to successes, such as the saving of old-growth forests in British Columbia's Clayoquot Sound (**Figure 4.7**).

- **Environmental ethics** is a philosophical perspective on nature that prescribes moral principles as guidance for our treatment of it. Environmental ethics insists that society has a moral obligation to treat nature according to the rules of moral behaviour that exist for our treatment of one another. An aspect of environmental ethics that has caused a great deal of controversy is the perspective that animals, insects, trees, rocks, and other elements of nature have rights in the same way as humans do. If the moral system of our society insists that humans are to have the right to a safe and happy life, then it is argued that the same rights should also be extended to nonhuman nature.

- **Ecofeminism** shares much of this philosophical perspective. Ecofeminists hold that patriarchy—a system of social ideas that values men more highly than women—is at the centre of our present environmental malaise. As Carolyn Merchant's work (noted above) has suggested, because patriarchy has equated

conservation: the view that natural resources should be used wisely and that society's effects on the natural world should represent stewardship, not exploitation

preservation: an approach to nature advocating that certain habitats, species, and resources should remain off-limits to human use, regardless of whether the use maintains or depletes the resource in question

environmental ethics: a philosophical perspective on nature that prescribes moral principles as guidance for our treatment of it

ecofeminism: the view that patriarchal ideology is at the centre of our present environmental malaise

Figure 4.7 Clayoquot Sound, British Columbia Canadian environmental activists have made the preservation of British Columbia's temperate rain forests a key issue. Aided by powerful European environmental lobbyists who persuaded manufacturers not to use Canadian lumber if it comes from old-growth forests, these Canadian activists have ensured that Canadian forestry companies pay much greater attention to environmental concerns in their forestry practices.

women with nature, it has enabled the subordination and exploitation of both. Not only a movement of the core, ecofeminism has also been widely embraced in the periphery, where women are primarily responsible for the health and welfare of their families in environments that are being rapidly degraded. The unifying objective in all of ecofeminism is to dismantle the patriarchal biases in Western culture and replace them with a perspective that values both cultural and biological diversity.

- **Deep ecology,** which shares many points with ecofeminism, is an approach to nature revolving around two key components: self-realization and biospherical egalitarianism. Deep ecologists believe that there is no absolute division between humanity and everything else and that a complex and diverse set of relationships constitutes the universe. The belief that all things are internally related could enable society to treat the nonhuman world with respect and not simply as a source of raw materials for human use.

deep ecology: an approach to nature revolving around two key components: self-realization and biospherical egalitarianism

Although none of these philosophies is a panacea, each has an important critique to offer. More than anything, however, each serves to remind us that environmental crises are not simple and simple solutions will no longer suffice. All of these approaches attest to a growing concern with the implications of globalization. Global warming, deforestation, the disappearance of species, nuclear accidents, and toxic waste have all been important stimuli for newly emerging philosophies about the preferred relationships between technology and nature within globalizing societies.

THE TRANSFORMATION OF EARTH BY ANCIENT HUMANS

Although the previous discussion might suggest that Earth remained relatively unaffected by human action until well into the early modern period, this section will provide evidence that contemporary humans have inherited an environment that was significantly affected by the practices of even our earliest ancestors.

Paleolithic Impacts

Although humans are thought to have first inhabited Earth approximately six million years ago, almost no evidence exists of how the earliest hominids, as they are called, used the natural world around them to survive. What is known is that their

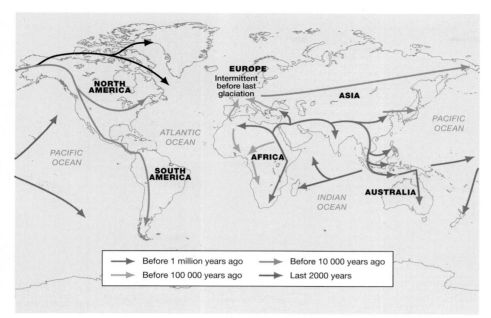

Figure 4.8   The settlement of the world   This map shows the direction and timing of movement of humans. The search for food promoted constant movement. The map represents more than 1 million years of migration. Paleo-eskimos migrated from Alaska across the eastern Arctic about 4000 years ago. They were replaced by the probable ancestors of the Inuit, the Thule, who—from about A.D. 1000—migrated eastward from Alaska to follow the whales they hunted. Within a few generations, the Thule had peopled the Arctic.
(*Source:* C. Ponting, *A Green History of the World.* London: Sinclair-Stevenson, 1991, p. 25. Reprinted with permission of Reed Consumer Books Ltd. *Historical Atlas of Canada,* vol. 1, 1987, plate 11.)

numbers were not large and that they left little behind in the way of technology or art to help us understand their relationship with nature. The earliest evidence about early people–environment relationships comes from the **Paleolithic period** (literally, the "old" [*paleo*] "stone" [*lithic*] age), so called because this was the period when chipped-stone tools first began to be used. According to archaeologists the Paleolithic period runs from 2.5 million to 10 000 years ago—or roughly the same time frame as the geological period known as the Pleistocene.

Living on the land in small groups as hunters and gatherers, early Paleolithic people mainly foraged for wild food and killed animals and fish for their survival. Hunting under these conditions could not support a growing population, however. It is estimated that on the African grassland, only two people could survive on the vegetation and wildlife available within about a 2.5 square kilometre (1.5 square mile) area. To help ensure survival, early Paleolithic people constantly moved over great distances, which ultimately made them a dispersed species (**Figure 4.8**).

Evidence also exists of early Stone Age tools as well as the importance of hunting to existence. The cave paintings of Altamira, Spain, for example, illustrate that hunting was the primary preoccupation of the Paleolithic mind (**Figure 4.9**). Because these early peoples lived in small bands and moved frequently and in wider and wider ranges, it is tempting to conclude that they had very little impact on their environment. It does appear, however, that Paleolithic people frequently used the powerful tool of fire. They used it to attract game, to herd and hunt game, to deflect predators, to provide warmth, and to encourage the growth of vegetation that would attract grazing animals, such as antelope and deer.

We cannot fully re-create the past because conditions and contexts change, but some insights into the hunting behaviour of these small groups can be gained from studies of contemporary hunter-gatherer populations. In one recent study of Inuit hunting practices at Pond Inlet, for example, McGill University geographers David Lee and George Wenzel showed the lengthy periods that narwhale hunters must wait at the floe edge before they sight their prey and how poor visibility (especially fog) means that very few of those sightings result in capture (**Figure 4.10**). Successful hunting demands not only technical sophistication and an awareness of local environmental conditions but also huge reserves of both patience and stamina.

For thousands of years following their settlement of North America, Canada's Aboriginal peoples practised various forms of hunting and gathering adapted to available local resources. On the west coast, for example, abundant fishing resources supported the Haida in villages on the Queen Charlotte Islands. In the North, the

Paleolithic period: the period when chipped-stone tools first began to be used

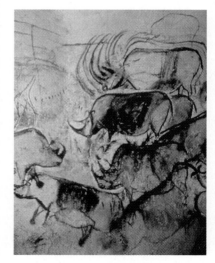

Figure 4.9   Cave paintings   Cave paintings are an important record of the imagination of early hunter-gatherers. Some regard these paintings as clear evidence of the development of forward thinking or anticipation among humans. This cave painting from Vallon-pont-d'Arc in southern France portrays large animals hunted for their meat and skins.

Figure 4.10 Inuit hunting practices
Narwhale hunting is a very difficult activity, even for skilled Inuit hunters, as this example from Pond Inlet shows. Long waiting periods at the floe edge and poor visibility (because of fog) mean that the capture rate is very low. Successful hunting demands not only technical sophistication and individual skill but also considerable patience and stamina.   (*Source:* Map from David S. Lee and George W. Wenzel, "Narwhale Hunting by Pond Inlet: An Analysis of Mode of Foraging in the Floe-Edge Environment," Courtesy of Études/Inuit/Studies, Figure 2, from Lee and Wenzel [2004: 142].)

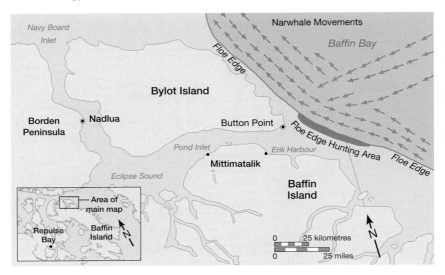

Inuit had developed the sophisticated harpoon technology needed to hunt seals and survive in the Arctic. Across the Prairies, indigenous peoples trapped bison as evidenced by the site at Head-Smashed-In Buffalo Jump (Alberta), which began to be used 5700 years ago and has been designated one of this country's UNESCO World Heritage sites (**Figure 4.11**). Across much of what is now Ontario and Quebec, indigenous peoples supported themselves through a combination of fishing, hunting (of moose and deer), and gathering. On the southern and northeastern coasts of Newfoundland, the Beothuks fished and hunted for seals and other sea mammals and birds.

The worldview of these hunter-gatherers is impossible to generalize, but two points should be recognized by the geographer. First, their very small total population numbers mean that the impact of hunter-gatherers on their environment was insignificant. Recent debate over the part North American Aboriginal peoples played in the extinction of prairie megafauna (such as the mammoth and the giant bison) around 11 000 years ago probably underestimates the importance of environmental change as an independent variable in the demise of such animals and exaggerates the hunting efficiency of these early peoples.[12] Second, it is a great mistake

---

[12]Andrew C. Isenberg, *The Destruction of the Bison: An Environmental History, 1750–1920.* Cambridge: Cambridge University Press, 2000, pp. 63–64.

Figure 4.11   Massive animal kills
Paleolithic hunters appear to have used features of the landscape to aid them in hunting large game. Archaeologists believe that the mounds of skeletal remains of large animals found at various sites (such as at Head-Smashed-In Buffalo Jump, Alberta) are evidence of this. It is not clear whether hunters and their kin were even able to consume all the animal flesh made available through such killing methods. It has been speculated that such gross killing methods may have led to the extinction of some species.   (*Source*: Arthur Lidov/ National Geographic Society Image Collection.)

to believe nomadic hunter-gatherers had no attachment to place. As Hugh Brody has recently shown in his fascinating book *The Other Side of Eden* (2000), such people had to know their landscape and environment in intimate detail if they were to survive.

It used to be assumed that malnutrition, disease, and hardship characterized the lives of early hunter-gatherers. However, modern scholarship challenges this view, and it is worth quoting the conclusions of Mark Nathan Cohen on this matter:[13]

> In summary, a number of lines of evidence from archaeology, from prehistoric skeletons, and from the study of contemporary populations indicate that small, mobile human groups living on wild foods enjoy relatively well-balanced diets and relatively good health. Indeed, the available evidence suggests that hunter-gatherer diets remain well-balanced even when they are low in calories. The data also show that per capita intake of calories and of protein has declined rather than increased in human history for all but the privileged classes. The predominant direction of prehistoric and historic change in human stature has been a decline in size, despite the "secular trend" among some Western populations of the last century. Prehistoric remains of more sedentary and larger groups commonly display an increase in general infection and in specific diseases (such as yaws and tuberculosis), combined with an increase in porotic hypertosis (anemia) and other signs of malnutrition.

Seen in this light, the development of agriculture did not mark a substantial step forward for many hunter-gatherer groups. Indeed, the dependence on a limited range of domesticated crops created dietary deficiencies. Anemia, for example, can result from an inadequate dietary intake of iron, which is often associated with diets high in maize and other cereals. Cereal diets wear down teeth, and it is therefore not surprising that skeletal evidence consistently reveals a higher degree of dental decay among agricultural populations than among hunter-gatherer groups. (Modern standards of dental health are, on average, even lower, having been significantly affected by the introduction of sugar into Western diets beginning in the sixteenth century.)

The domestication of animals also exposed humans to a new range of diseases (many of which, such as influenza and smallpox, jumped the species barrier) and parasites. Hunting-gathering is therefore likely to have been abandoned in favour of settled agriculture only as increasing population pressure forced such technological innovations on to early societies.

---

[13]Mark Nathan Cohen, "History, Diet and Hunter-Gatherers." In Kenneth F. Kiple and Kriemhild Coneè Ornelas (eds.), *The Cambridge World History of Food*, vol. 1. Cambridge: Cambridge University Press, 2000, pp. 63–71. The quotation is from p. 69.

Neolithic Peoples and Domestication

The credit for the development of agriculture—a technological triumph with respect to nature—goes to the Neolithic peoples, also known as the late Stone Age peoples. While the transition between them and the Paleolithic peoples occurred about 10 000 years ago, it is not known exactly when Neolithic peoples shifted from hunting and gathering to cultivating certain plants and taming and herding wild animals. Scholars call this period the First Agricultural Revolution. Climatically, we know that for many regions of the globe, this period coincides with the end of the last Ice Age, which means that spring slowly began to occur in places that had not experienced it for thousands upon thousands of years.

It was just at this time that environmental conditions made possible the domestication of plants and animals, which both enabled and required a sedentary lifestyle based in permanent settlements (**Figure 4.12**). The first domestication successes of the Neolithic peoples were with the most docile animals (herbivores) and the hardiest plants (those with large seeds and a tolerance to drought).

American cultural geographer Carl Sauer (see Chapter 1) is the individual most associated with the geographical study of domestication (see Figure 4.12). In his 1952 series of lectures, published under the title *Agricultural Origins and Dispersals*, Sauer suggested that those areas of the world where domestication first occurred—areas he called hearths of domestication—"are to be sought in areas of marked diversity of plants or animals, where there were varied and good raw materials to experiment with . . . [which] implies well-diversified terrain and perhaps also variety of climate." On this basis, he suggested that domestication probably occurred first in the lands now known as "The Fertile Crescent" approximately 10 000 years ago. In river valleys in what are now part of Iran and Iraq, the slightly wetter conditions than today (probably caused by the end of the last glaciations) allowed wild grasses to grow and feed small groups of people. Having the time to devote to the selection of better yielding grasses, the population was eventually

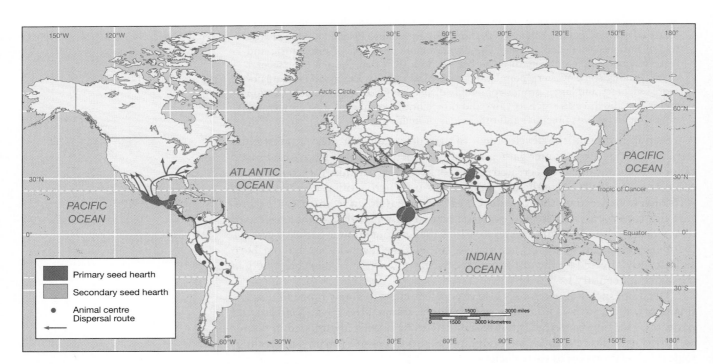

Figure 4.12 Areas of plant and animal domestication Plant and animal domestication did not predominate in any one continent but was spread out across the globe. The origins of plant and animal domestication, however, are not definitively known, and much of what is represented on this map is speculative. Archaeological evidence to date supports the distribution shown here and developed in the mid-twentieth century by Carl Sauer. (After J.M. Rubenstein, *The Cultural Landscape: An Introduction to Human Geography*, 7th ed., Prentice Hall © 2003, p. 319. Adapted from Carl O. Sauer, *Agricultural Origins and Dispersals*, with permission of the American Geographical Society.)

able to domesticate what were to become important grain crops (principally wheat). Indeed, Sauer stressed that domestication could not have been the result of people driven by hunger since they would not have had the time to devote to the careful choice and tending of plants over a considerable period of time. Certainly, one of the key characteristics of domestication (an inability to propagate without human intervention) is very unlikely to have developed without a long period of co-existence between people and the wild forms of those plants and animals that later become domesticated.

More recently, geographer Jared Diamond, in his best-selling work *Guns, Germs and Steel* has suggested that herd animals (such as sheep, cows, and goats) found in the Fertile Crescent were also domesticated at about the same period because of their value for transport and haulage, and as a source of clothing material. While these animals were also eaten, it is unlikely that their value as food was a primary reason for domestication because their early ancestors were relatively small creatures (an increase in size is often a feature of domestication). More important was these animals' docility, and it was this that made them the object of human attention. By contrast, Diamond suggests, in a controversial assertion because it is ultimately geographically deterministic, the ferocity of the large indigenous ungulates in many parts of Africa made them unlikely candidates for domestication, a lack that was to affect the later cultural and economic development of this region.

Certainly, the story from the world's other "hearths of domestication" show the irrelevance of animal size—in the Americas, for example, animals no bigger than the guinea pig were evidently thought worth domesticating as part of a rich complex of New World domesticates that included maize, squash, and beans. In areas of southern China, the domestic pig must have been a diminutive creature as it was easily transported by early peoples in the subsequent colonizing of islands in New Guinea and Polynesia.

Domestication in China and New Guinea is currently thought to have begun a little later than it did the Fertile Crescent—perhaps about 9500 years ago in the case of China, and 9000 years ago in New Guinea, although it should be said that one of the main reasons for this is the fact that early domesticated plant and animals remains simply do not survive well in hotter wetter environments. We should probably expect, therefore that earlier evidence for the beginnings of domestication will be found in China and New Guinea, and that its origins in those regions are likely to be at least as old as its beginnings in the Fertile Crescent.

The emergence of agriculture was an event that changed the course of human history and had important environmental impacts—both negative and positive. One negative impact was the simplification of ecosystems as the multiplicity of wild species began to be replaced by fewer cultivable crops. An **ecosystem** is a community of different species interacting with one another and with the larger physical environment that surrounds them. Along with the vast number of wild species lost, the opportunity to understand their benefit to humans and the wider ecosystem has also gone. More positively, however, increased yields through greater control over available foodstuffs helped to improve human health and eventually increased population growth.

ecosystem: a community of different species interacting with one another and with the larger physical environment that surrounds them

Early Settlements and Their Environmental Impacts

Perhaps the most significant aspect of plant and animal domestication is that it eventually enabled a surplus to be produced. It also permitted the formation of human settlements in which small groups—probably craftspeople and political and religious elites—were able to live off the surplus without being directly involved in its production. Eventually, growing numbers of people, bolstered by increasing surpluses, were able to settle in places where water was available and the land could be cultivated.

The invention of agricultural tools helped further the domestication of plants and animals as well as multiply the early agriculturalists' impact on the landscape.

TABLE 4.1 World Irrigated Area since 1700	
Date (A.D.)	Area (in thousands of square kilometres/square miles)
1700	50/19
1800	80/31
1900	480/185
1949	920/355
1959	1490/575
1980	2000/772
1981	2130/822
1984	2200/849
2000	2740/1057

Source: W. Meyer, *Human Impact on the Earth.* Cambridge: Cambridge University Press, 1990, p. 59. *Original source:* B.G. Rozanov, V. Targulian, and D.S. Orlow, "Soils." In B.L. Turner II, W.L. Clark, R.W. Kates, J.E. Richards, J.T. Matthews, and W.B. Meyer (eds.), *The Earth Transformed by Human Action.* 1990. Cambridge: Cambridge University Press. Updated from FAOSTAT Agricultural Database, 2001. Irrigation. 10 July 2001, **http://apps.fao.org/page/form? collection=Irrigation&Domain=1 and&servlet=1&language=EN&hostname= apps.fao.org&version=default.**

siltation: the buildup of sand and clay in a natural or artificial waterway

deforestation: the removal of trees from a forested area without adequate replanting

Among the early tools that enabled humans a greater measure of control over nature were the sickle for harvesting wheat, the plow for preparing the soil; the yoke for harnessing draft animals (such as oxen) to pull the plows; and the wheel for grinding wheat, creating pottery, and later improving transportation. Among other things, the wheel was also used as a pulley to draw water. In Sumer and Assyria, for example, the wheel enabled the development of large-scale irrigation systems.

Irrigation is one of the most significant ways that humans have been able to alter the limits of their environment. Throughout much of the world, in fact, agriculture could not occur without irrigation (**Table 4.1**). Following the success of the Fertile Crescent, agriculture diffused, and new settlements emerged as a result. The food-producing mini-systems of China, the Mediterranean, Meso-America, the Middle East, and Africa were sustained largely through irrigated agriculture. Yet, despite the existence of a vast irrigation network and a whole social structure bound up with agricultural production and attendant activities, the cities of the Mesopotamian region collapsed around 4000 years ago. Although there is no undisputed explanation for why this occurred, many researchers believe—based on archaeological evidence—that it was due to environmental mismanagement. The irrigation works became clogged with accumulations of salt, resulting in increasingly saline soils. To counteract the effect of salt on production, agriculturalists switched to barley, which is more salt-resistant than wheat; but the ultimate result was a significant drop in yields. **Siltation** (the buildup of sand and clay in a natural or artificial waterway) associated with **deforestation** (the removal of trees from a forested area without adequate replanting) also occurred. Siltation also eventually filled the canals, and the irrigation systems were no longer able to deliver water to the fields.

It was not only the Mesopotamians who made environmental mistakes. Other early urban civilizations, such as the Mayan in Central America (**Figure 4.13**) are also thought to have collapsed because of environmental mismanagement of water.

In the Mediterranean, for example, environmental change is now being seriously considered as a factor in the collapse of Mycenaean civilization that occurred in Greece about 1200 B.C. In a land that we might at first think of as an idyllic and untouched Arcadia (the term itself is an ancient Greek one), this comes as a surprising interpretation. However, the evidence for this view is hardly new, and comes from a great variety of sources. Homer himself, for example, refers in *The Iliad* (a poem dated to the eighth century B.C.) to the clearance of trees outside Troy, prior to its conquest by the Greeks (about 1250 B.C.). Aristotle (384–322 B.C.) writes that "at the time of the Trojan War . . . the land of Mycenae was good and highly

Figure 4.13 The Mayan pyramid at Altun Ha, Belize This temple site was excavated by Dr. David Pendergast of the Royal Ontario Museum. The classic Mayan civilization collapsed suddenly during the century following A.D. 900. At its height, population densities of up to 400 people per square kilometre were supported by a variety of crops and cultivation practices, most important among them being the cultivation of domesticated maize and a form of wetland agriculture involving the construction of raised fields. Some experts blame the collapse on the environmental mismanagement of water; other scholars point to political upheavals as the cause of this sudden decline.

Figure 4.14   The Mycenaean dam at Tiryns   Dating from about 1000 B.C., this dam near the Mycenaean town of Tiryns in Greece's Peloponnese peninsula provides clear evidence of human interference with the environment. Indeed, some archaeologists speculate that the dam was needed to protect the town from flooding by a stream that had greatly increased in volume as a result of land clearance for agriculture.

esteemed. Now, however . . . [it] is dried up and therefore lies idle."[14] In terms of archaeological evidence, it has long been known that a large dam was built outside Tiryns in the fourteenth or thirteenth centuries B.C., probably to divert flood water around the city's citadel (**Figure 4.14**). Recently, however, archaeologists such as Curtis Runnels have speculated that the development of agriculture in the city's vicinity during this period led to an increase of water runoff from the fields—an increase that might easily have resulted in the flooding that the dam was built to prevent.

Other signs of environmental change are perhaps easier to spot and are likely the result of the increased soil erosion that the clearing of land for early agriculture produced. Thus, in the early 1980s, the geographer Claudio Vita-Finzi observed that two layers of ancient soils occurred across much of the Mediterranean basin, each easily recognizable because of its colour (**Figure 4.15**). Concluding that these represented the results of two separate periods of greater soil deposition, Vita-Finzi suggested that these ancient soils had been laid down during wetter interglacial intervals, or at the end of the last glaciation in Europe (about 10 000 years ago). While generally accepting his conclusion as far as the first surface is concerned, work by geoarchaeologists such as Eberhard Zangger and the Argive Plain project increasingly suggest that the second, more recent layer is far more likely to be the result of human-induced erosion.

Our provisional conclusion from this survey must be that an almost unavoidable result of civilization has been environmental degradation.

In the following section, we examine the period of European expansion and globalization. Although many other important cultures and civilizations affected the environment in the intervening period, the impacts of their technological developments were much the same as those we have already described. The period of European colonialism, however, had a profoundly different impact from preceding periods in extent, magnitude, and kind. Furthermore, it set the stage for the kinds of environmental problems contemporary society has inherited, perpetuated, and magnified.

---

[14]Eberhard Zangger, "Prehistoric Coastal Environments in Greece: The Vanished Landscapes of Dimini Bay and Lake Lerna." *Journal of Field Archeology* 18(1), 1991, pp. 1–15. The quotation is from p. 13.

EUROPEAN EXPANSION AND GLOBALIZATION

Europe provides a powerful example of how a society with different environmental attitudes was able to transform nature in ways vastly different from any in previous human history. These new attitudes drew from a newly emerging science and its contribution to technological innovation; the consolidation of the population around cultural and religious beliefs; and, most important, the development of a capitalist political and economic system.

Initially, European expansion was internal, largely contained within its continental boundaries. The most obvious reason for this expansion was population increase: from 36 million in 1000 to more than 45 million in 1100, and more than 60 million in 1200 to about 80 million by 1300 (**Figure 4.16**). As the population continued to increase, more land was brought under cultivation. In addition, more forested land was cleared for agriculture, animals killed for food, and minerals and other resources exploited for a variety of needs. Forests originally covered upward of 90 percent of Western and Central Europe. At the end of the period of internal expansion, however, forested area was reduced to 20 percent.

The continental expansion of Europe ended around 1300. The bubonic plague, also known as the Black Death, had temporarily slowed population growth, while agricultural settlement had by then been extended to take up all readily available land, and then some. In England, Italy, France, and the Netherlands, for example, marshlands were drained, and the sea was pushed back or the water table lowered to reclaim and create new land for agriculture and settlement.

In the fifteenth century, Europe initiated its second phase of expansion. This was a form of external expansion that changed not only the global political map but launched a 500-year period of environmental change that continues to this day. European external expansion, *colonialism,* was the response to several impulses, ranging from self-interest to altruism. Europeans were fast running out of land, and, as we saw in Chapter 2, explorers were being dispatched by monarchs to conquer new territories and enlarge their empires while collecting tax revenues from the monarchs' new subjects. Many of these adventurous individuals were searching for fame and fortune or avoiding religious persecution. Behind European external expansion was also the Christian impulse to missionize and bring new souls into the kingdom of God. Other forces behind European colonialism included the need to expand the emerging system of trade, which ultimately meant increased wealth and power for a new class of people—the merchants—as well as for the aristocracy.

Over the centuries, Europe came to control increasing areas of the globe. Two cases illustrate how the introduction of European people, ideologies, technologies, plant species, pathogens, and animals changed not only the environments into which they were introduced but also the societies they encountered.

Figure 4.15 Ancient soils near Sparta, Greece All round the Mediterranean, evidence of environmental change can be seen in the form of ancient deposits of soils, clearly indicated by their different colours. In the 1980s, scholars such as Dr. Claudio Vita-Finzi suggested that at least two main episodes of such deposition have occurred, each associated with periods of greater than average rainfall. Authorities now suggest that the older episode was likely naturally induced (perhaps during an interglacial period), but the more recent is likely to be associated with increased soil erosion associated with the spread of agriculture between 10 000 to 8000 years ago.

Disease and Depopulation in the Spanish Colonies

Little disagreement exists among historians that the European colonization of the New World was ultimately responsible for the greatest loss of human life in history. There is very little disagreement that the primary factor responsible for that loss was disease. New World populations, including Canada's First Peoples, isolated for millennia from the Old World, possessed immune systems that had never encountered some of the most common European diseases.

Geographer W. George Lovell, of Queen's University in Ontario, has examined the role disease played in the depopulation of some of Spain's New World colonies from the point of initial contact until the early seventeenth century, using several cases to illustrate his point.[15]

In one example, in Central Mexico, Lovell writes of Hernán Cortés's contact with the Aztec capital of Tenochtitlán in the first decades of the sixteenth century, which led to a devastating outbreak of smallpox among the population. An Aztec text provides a graphic description of the disease:

> While the Spaniards were in Tlaxcala, a great plague broke out here in Tenochtitlán. It began to spread during the thirteenth month [30 September–19 October 1520] and lasted for seventy days, striking everywhere in the city and killing a vast number of our people. Sores erupted on our faces, our breasts, our bellies; we were covered with agonizing sores from head to foot. . . .
>
> A great many died from this plague, and many others died of hunger. They could not get up and search for food, and everyone else was too sick to care for them, so they starved to death in their beds.[16]

In another example, Lovell describes the Jesuits' missionizing efforts in northern Mexico during a slightly later period. Because these efforts gathered dispersed groups of the population into single locations, conditions for the outbreak of disease were created. Contact with Spanish conquistadors in advance of the missionaries had already reduced indigenous populations by perhaps 30 percent to 50 percent. When groups were confined to smaller areas oriented around a mission, mortality rates climbed to 90 percent of the total. Ironically, missionizing seems to have killed the Aboriginal inhabitants whose souls it was attempting to save. Eventually, the disease was diffused beyond the initial area of contact as traders carried it across long-distance trade routes to the periphery of the Mayan empire in advance of the Spanish armies and missionaries. The Mayans were not defeated by European technological superiority but by the ravages of a new disease against which they possessed no natural defences (**Figure 4.17**).

Lovell provides similar descriptions of disease impacts in Mayan Guatemala and the Central Andes of South America that led to devastating depopulation. Scholars

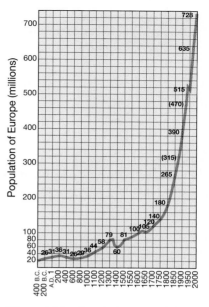

Figure 4.16 Population growth in Europe This graph shows the growth in the European population from 400 B.C. to A.D. 2000. The increase in human numbers at the beginning of the 1500s was an important push to exploration and colonization beyond the confines of the continent. The dip in the graph from 1300 to 1400 is partially explained by the bubonic plague epidemic known as the Black Death, but food shortages also played a significant role in this population decline. (*Source:* Adapted from C. McEvedy and R. Jones, *Atlas of World Population History.* London: Allen Lane, 1978, fig. 1.2, p. 18.)

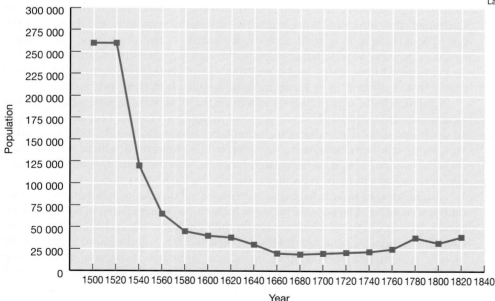

Figure 4.17 The population of the Cuchumatán Highlands, Guatemala, 1520–1825 This graph shows the demographic collapse of northern Guatemala's Aboriginal population after European contact. (*Source:* W. George Lovell, *Conquest and Survival in Colonial Guatemala: A Historical Geography of the Cuchumatán Highlands, 1500–1821.* Montreal and Kingston: McGill-Queen's University Press, 1985, p. 146.)

---

[15] W.G. Lovell, "Heavy Shadows and Black Night: Disease and Depopulation in Colonial Spanish America." *Annals, Association of American Geographers* 82, 1992.

[16] W.G. Lovell, 1992, p. 429, quoting from M. Leòn-Portilla, *The Broken Spears: The Aztec Account of the Conquest of Mexico.* Boston: Beacon Press, 1962, pp. 92–93.

demographic collapse: phenomenon of near genocide of indigenous populations

refer to the phenomenon of near genocide of indigenous populations as **demographic collapse**. The ecological effect of the population decline caused by the high rates of mortality was the transformation of many regions from productive agriculture to abandoned land. Many of the Andean terraces, for example, were abandoned, and dramatic soil erosion ensued. In contrast, large expanses of cleared land eventually returned to forests in some areas, such as the Yucatán, in present-day Mexico.

Old World Plants and Animals in the New World

ecological imperialism: introduction of exotic plants and animals into new ecosystems

Our second illustration concerns the phenomenon known as **ecological imperialism**, or the deliberate introduction of exotic plants and animals into new ecosystems as part of the process of colonization. The interaction between the Old and New Worlds resulted in both the intentional and the unintentional introduction of new crops and animals. Europeans brought from their homelands many plants and animals that were exotics, that is, types unknown to American ecosystems that they might continue to farm using animals and plants with which they were familiar. For example, the Spanish introduced wheat as well as horses, cattle, and pigs.

These introductions altered the environment, particularly as the emphasis on select species led to a reduction in the variety of plants and animals that constituted local ecosystems. Inadvertent introductions of hardy exotic species included rats, weeds, such as the dandelion and thistle, and birds, such as starlings, which crowded out the less-hardy indigenous species. As with the human population, these indigenous populations of plants, birds, and animals had few defences against European plant and animal diseases and were sometimes seriously reduced or made extinct through contact.

Contact between the Old and the New Worlds was, however, an exchange—a two-way process—and New World crops and animals were likewise introduced into the Old World. As part of what environmental historian Alfred Crosby has called "the Columbian Exchange," maize, potatoes, tobacco, cocoa, tomatoes, and cotton were all brought back to Europe, crops that were to have profound benefits for the European population.

The introduction of animals provided the New World not only with additional sources of protein but also with additional animal power. Before the Columbian Exchange, the only important sources of animal energy were the llama and the dog. The introduction of the horse, ox, and donkey created a virtual power revolution in the New World. These animals, through their eventual death or slaughter, also provided fibres, hides, and bones to make various tools, utensils, and coverings. Most significant in its environmental impact, however, was the ox.

Land that had escaped cultivation because the indigenous digging sticks and tools were unable to penetrate the heavy soil and matted root surface became available to an ox-drawn plow. The indigenous form of intensive agricultural production (small area, many labourers) was, therefore, replaced by extensive production (large area, fewer labourers). This transformation, however, was not entirely without negative impacts, such as increased rates of soil destabilization and erosion.

It is important to note here that environmental degradation did not begin with European contact. The popular image of indigenous peoples living in harmony with nature, having only a minimal impact on their environment, has been shown to be flawed. Polynesian contact with Hawaii, for example, had profound effects on the islands' ecosystems. The pigs they introduced ate native flora, and their digging around created pools of water in which insects bred, which subsequently decimated native birds. In reality, different groups had very different impacts, and it is erroneous to conflate the thousands of groups into one romanticized caricature.

In New England, for example, before European contact, groups existed that hunted for wild game and gathered wild foods. More sedentary types also existed, living in permanent and semipermanent villages, clearing and planting small areas of land. Hunter-gatherers were mobile, moving with the seasons to obtain fish, migrating birds, deer, wild berries, and plants. Agriculturalists planted corn, squash, beans, and tobacco and used a wide range of other natural resources. The economy was a fairly simple one based on personal use or on barter (trading corn for fish, for example). The idea of a surplus was foreign here: people cultivated or exploited only the amount of land and resources that they needed to survive. Land and resources were shared in common, without such concept as private property or land ownership. Fire was used to clear land for planting, as well as for hunting. Although vegetation change did occur, it was minimal and reversible.

The Aztecs of Mexico and the Incas of Peru were responsible for dramatic environmental modifications through cultivation techniques that included the irrigation of dry regions and the terracing of steep slopes. As we have seen, irrigation over several centuries will result in the salinization of soils. In the lowland tropics, intensive agricultural practices resulted in widespread deforestation as people cut and set fire to patches of forest, planted crops, and then moved on when soil fertility declined. A surplus was key to the operations of both societies, since tribute by ordinary people to the political and religious elite was required in the form of food, animals, labour, or precious metals. The construction of the sizeable Incan and Aztec empires required the production of large amounts of building materials, specifically wood and mortar. Concentrated populations and the demands of urbanization meant that widespread environmental degradation existed in the Americas before European contact, and the Columbian Exchange.

As the pace of development of the world-system quickened, so did the extent of ecological imperialism increase (**Figure 4.18**). In the earliest stages, flows of plants and animals were mainly toward the core. Much of this movement occurred not because of any utilitarian purpose but because of the attraction of Europe's wealthy to the rare and exotic. For example, European potentates had developed a passion for menageries. During the Middle Ages, one king of Portugal shipped an Indian elephant to the pope, and there are records of live polar bears being sent from Greenland as part of that colony's tribute. Wealthy people could also afford to recruit plant collectors to bring back new species for the botanic gardens they were beginning to establish at this time. Employed by the British crown, John Tradescant and his son visited Russia, North Africa, and the Virginia colonies in the early seventeenth century to bring back specimens. The Dutch fascination with tulips is another example. A native of central Asia, the plant had rapidly spread from Turkey to the Netherlands by 1565. Tulip mania afflicted that country to such an extent during the early seventeenth century that one bulb was worth the price of a townhouse in Amsterdam! It is little wonder, then, that in the 1620s, when the Dutch settled the mouth of the Hudson River at New Amsterdam (New York), they planted tulips in their gardens there.

It is only when the core begins to integrate the periphery into an expanding economic system that we begin to see the far more utilitarian exchange of plants and animals occurring between the Old and New Worlds. What this means is that at this stage, the core directs the diffusion. Because of this, as Alfred Crosby has argued, the most successful exchanges were those that most closely replicated the European environment and its traditional stock-rearing and grain-growing practices. Conversely, European farmers took some time to accept the potato because they were unused to eating tubers.

But the story does not end here. As the core developed colonial empires at a global scale, so were plants and animals moved between colonies and between different parts of the periphery without recourse to the core. One example is the pineapple, carried by both the Portuguese and Spanish across their colonies and spread throughout most of the tropical world by 1600. Another is the breadfruit, which the British moved from Tahiti to St. Vincent to feed their slaves there more efficiently. The ever-increasing grasp and greater sophistication of ecological imperialism had some interesting consequences:

■ Botanic gardens were developed around the world. No longer the playthings of the idle rich, or attempts to re-create the Garden of Eden, botanic gardens were developed so that plants could be collected and acclimatized before the

Movement of Plants

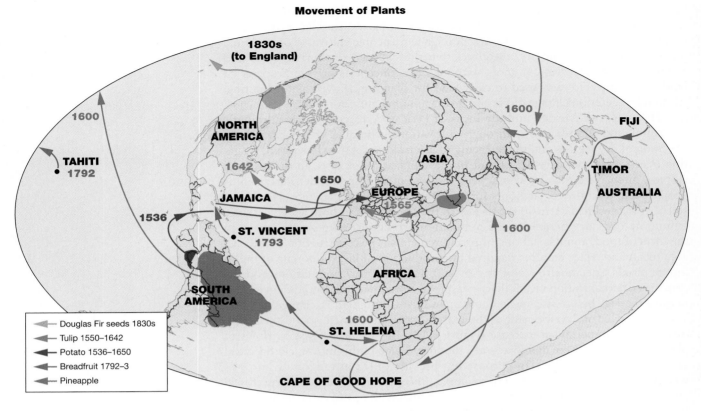

Figure 4.18   Ecological imperialism   The movement of plants occurred on an ever-increasing scale as the core of the world-system extended its grasp into the periphery. The consequences of these movements were often unforeseen, since the introduction of flora into new ecosystems often disturbed the subtle balances of nature. Early transfers, such as the diffusion of the tulip from the foothills of Central Asia to Holland, were affected more by Europe's quest for the exotic than any utilitarian objective. However, as the core developed overseas colonies, plants with agricultural or commercial value (such as the potato) were exchanged between core and periphery. As Europe's colonial empires grew, plant transfers increasingly occurred about the periphery itself: by 1600, the pineapple had been spread across Spanish and Portuguese territories and was virtually ubiquitous across the tropics. By the 1790s, Captain Bligh's transfer of the breadfruit from Tahiti to St. Vincent showed plants could be moved halfway round the world in under a year. Indeed, one of the greatest nineteenth-century collectors, David Douglas, sent the plants he had collected in British Columbia between 1825 and 1834 back to England via the Pacific. The Douglas fir, named after him, was but one of more than 200 species he collected for the Royal Horticultural Society, based at Kew Gardens in England. (*Sources:* Map compiled by author from the following: R.A. Howard, "Captain Bligh and the Breadfruit." *Scientific American* 188[3], March 1953, pp. 88–94; W.H. McNeill, "American Food Crops in the Old World." In H.J. Viola and C. Margolis [eds.], *Seeds of Change*. Washington, DC: Smithsonian, 1991, pp. 43–59; Anna Pavord, *The Tulip*. London: Bloomsbury, 1999; K.F. Kiple and K.C. Ornelas [eds.], *The Cambridge World History of Food*, vol. 2. Cambridge: Cambridge Unversity Press, 2000, p. 1834; J. Grimshaw, *The Gardeners Atlas*. Willowdale, Ontario: Firefly, 1998, p. 11.)

next stage of their transfer. The Dutch East India Company's garden at Cape Town was a vital link in this chain, which included Kew Gardens in England and the botanic gardens on St. Vincent in the Caribbean (the oldest in the Western Hemisphere).

■ The movement of greater numbers of species, in shorter time periods, further and further afield, greatly accelerated the pace of change. After the failure of his first voyage (ended by the famous mutiny on his ship *The Bounty*), Captain William Bligh, on his second expedition, successfully transported more than 2000 breadfruit from Tahiti to the Caribbean and then brought back to England more than 12 000 different plants. These plants had been transported halfway around the world in a voyage of only two years. (Indeed, breadfruit, which only propagate from suckers, had to be transferred speedily.) The governor of the island of St. Helena, on seeing Bligh's ship in December 1792, is said to have described it as "a floating garden transported in luxuriance from one extremity of the world to another."[17] David Douglas, sent out by the Royal Horticultural Society to collect

---

[17]R.A. Howard, "Captain Bligh and the Breadfruit." *Scientific American* 188(3), March 1953, pp. 91–92.

Canadian plants in the 1820s and 1830s, was able to send more than 200 different species back to England via the Pacific.

■ The breaking down of the world's major biogeographic barriers (such as Wallace's Line between Borneo and Sulawesi, which marks the divide between Asian and Australian fauna and flora) in such a concerted manner meant that

– entirely new combinations of plants and animals were being assembled for the first time in environments where natural controls were lacking. The introduction of rabbits to Australia and of starlings to North America were both followed by population explosions of those species.

– many plants we call "weeds" (such as the dandelion) became almost global in distribution. These accidental introductions are ones that have been particularly successful in new ecological areas precisely because the establishment of Western types of agriculture in new settings has re-created the ecological niches (such as open or cleared ground) that such plants favour.

– the flora and fauna of different parts of the world became increasingly homogenized. The tropics now look the same everywhere because they are the product of species assembled from across the equatorial world, but originally they did not. Bananas, royal palm trees, and pineapples seem so much a part of the Hawaiian landscape that it is a shock to discover that these are all introduced species. By the same token, Canadian gardens in the summer are made up almost entirely of introduced species, and yet they are now so familiar to us that we can no longer sense how "out of place" they really are.

As we have seen by the transfer of plants and animals and the subsequent interactions with nature, we have begun to make the world look the same wherever we are: we have, in this sense, homogenized space and created familiar places. This type of place making is therefore directly tied to changing attitudes to nature on the one hand and to the expansion of the world-system on the other hand. (The term *place making* is examined in Chapter 6.)

HUMAN ACTION AND RECENT ENVIRONMENTAL CHANGE

No other transition in human history has had the impact on the natural world that industrialization has. When we couple industrialization with its frequent companion, urbanization, we have the two processes that, more than any others, have revolutionized human life and brought about far-reaching ecological changes. For the first time in history, these changes have moved beyond a local or a regional scale to affect the entire globe. In this section, we explore some of the dramatic contemporary environmental impacts that industrial technology and urbanization have produced. In doing so, we focus on three issues of environmental geography: energy use, land-use change, and the exploitation of natural resources (using the state of the world's fisheries as an example).

The Impact of Energy Needs on the Environment

Certainly the most central and significant technological breakthrough of the Industrial Revolution was the discovery and utilization of fossil fuels—coal, oil, and natural gas. Although the very first factories in Europe and North America relied on water power to drive the machinery, it was hydrocarbon fuels that provided a more constant, dependable, and effective source of power. A steady increase in power production and demand since the beginning of the Industrial Revolution has been parallelled, not surprisingly, by an increase in resource extraction and conversion.

At present, the world's population relies most heavily for its energy needs on nonrenewable energy resources, which include fossil fuels and nuclear ones, as well as renewable resources, such as solar, hydroelectric, wind, and geothermal power. Fossil fuels are derived from organic materials and are burned directly to produce heat. Nuclear energy originates with isotopes, which emit radiation. Most commercial nuclear energy is produced in reactors fuelled by uranium. Renewable sources of energy, such as the sun, wind, water, and steam, are captured in various ways and used to drive pumps, machines, and electricity generators.

According to their publication *Key World Energy Statistics 2008*, the Paris-based International Energy Agency estimates that the largest proportion of the world's current consumption of energy resources, 34 percent, comes from oil; 26 percent from coal (and related materials, such as peat); 21 percent from natural gas; 6 percent from nuclear power; 2 percent from hydroelectricity; and the remainder from a mixture of renewable sources that includes wind, solar, and geothermal sources.[18] The production and consumption of these available resources, however, is geographically uneven, as **Figure 4.19** shows. Fifty percent of the world's oil supplies are from the Middle East, and most of the coal is from the Northern Hemisphere, mainly from the United States, China, and Russia. Nuclear reactors are a phenomenon of the core regions of the world. For example, France generates 90 percent of its electricity from nuclear sources.

The consumption side of energy also varies geographically. It has been estimated that current annual world energy consumption is equal to what it took about 1 million years to produce naturally. In one year, global energy consumption is equal to about 1.3 billion tonnes of coal. This is 4 times what the global population consumed in 1950 and 20 times what it consumed in 1850. And, as the $I = PAT$ formula suggests, the affluent core regions of the world far outstrip the peripheral regions in energy consumption. With nearly four times the population of the core regions, the peripheral regions consume less than one-third of global energy expenditures. Yet, consumption of energy in the peripheral regions is rising quite rapidly as globalization spreads industries, energy-intensive consumer products, such as automobiles, and energy-intensive agricultural practices into regions of the world where they were previously unknown. It has been projected that by the early decades of the twenty-first century, the peripheral regions will become the dominant consumers of energy (**Figure 4.20**).

Rising levels of energy consumption in both the nations of the core and those of the periphery will have serious global implications for climate change unless steps can be taken to reduce the consumption of fossil fuels and practical renewable alternatives can be found. (For a detailed look the impact of energy consumption and the possible solutions available, see **Human Geography and Climate Change 4.1—Energy**).

Most important for our discussion, however, is that every stage of the energy conversion process—from discovery to extraction, processing, and utilization—has an impact on the physical landscape. In the coalfields of the world, from Cape Breton to western Siberia, mining results in a loss of vegetation and topsoil, in erosion and water pollution, and in acid and toxic drainage. It also contributes to cancer and lung disease in coal miners. The burning of coal is associated with relatively high emissions of gases, such as carbon dioxide and sulphur dioxide, which are environmentally harmful in high concentrations.

The burning of home-heating oil, along with the use of petroleum products for fuel in internal combustion engines, launches harmful chemicals into Earth's atmosphere, causing air pollution and related health problems. The production and transport of oil have resulted in oil spills and substantial pollution to water- and ecosystems.

Natural gas is one of the least noxious of the hydrocarbon-based energy resources because it is converted relatively cleanly. Now supplying nearly one-quarter of global commercial energy, natural gas is predicted to be the fastest-growing energy source in the twenty-first century. Significant deposits of natural gas have been discovered in Alberta and off the coast of Nova Scotia. Plans are currently being made to pipe liquefied gas from these sources to the large market for this clean fuel in urban Canada and the eastern United States. Although preferred to oil and coal, natural gas is not produced or consumed without

---

[18]International Energy Agency, *Key World Energy Statistics 2008*. Paris: International Energy Agency, 2008, p. 6 (available at **www.iea.org**).

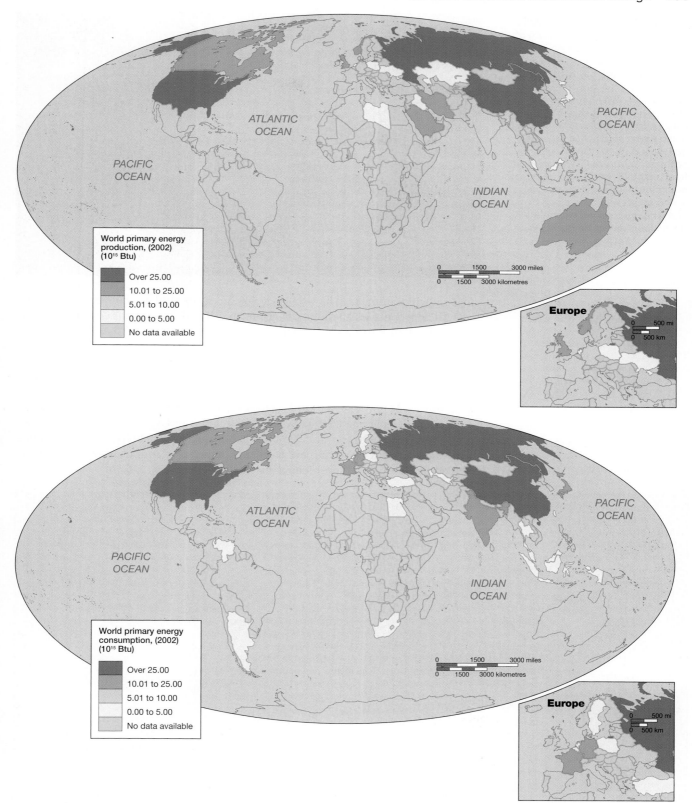

Figure 4.19 World production and consumption of energy, 1993–2002   These paired maps provide a picture of the uneven distribution of the production and consumption of energy resources around the world. The United States is the largest producer and consumer of a range of energy resources. Notice that although the Middle East and North African countries as well as Nigeria are important producers of energy resources, their consumption (as well as that of the rest of the African continent, excluding South Africa) is very low. Japan produces a negligible amount of the total of world energy resources but consumes a relatively high share.   (Top map after *International Energy Annual*, 1999, website: **www.eia.doe.gov/iea**. Data tables "World Primary Energy Production (Btu)" and "World Primary Energy Consumption (Btu)." Bottom map reprinted with permission of Prentice Hall, from E.F. Bergman, *Human Geography. Cultures, Connections, and Landscapes* © 1995, p. 395. Data from the World Resources Institute, World Resources 1994–95. New York: Oxford University Press, 1994, pp. 334–335.)

Figure 4.20 Traffic in Bangkok, Thailand In several of the cities of Southeast Asia, such as Manila, Djkarta, and Hanoi, people spend several hours each day battling traffic. In Bangkok, it can take three to five hours to travel from one section of the city to another because of traffic congestion. An additional outcome of increasing automobile use in the periphery is rising rates of urban air pollution. In Mexico City, air pollution from motor vehicles is so severe that respiratory ailments are increasing, and residents with respiratory problems are routinely warned to stay indoors on hot summer days.

environmental impacts. The risk of explosions at natural gas conversion facilities is significant; leakages and losses of gas from distribution systems contribute to the deterioration of Earth's atmosphere.

At the midpoint of the twentieth century, nuclear energy for civilian use was widely promoted as a clearly preferable alternative to fossil fuels. It was seen as the answer to the expanding energy needs of core countries, especially since the supply of uranium worldwide was thought to be more than adequate for centuries of use (**Figure 4.21**). It was not until serious accidents at nuclear power plants began to occur, such as at the Chernobyl nuclear reactor in Ukraine in 1986, that concerns about reactor safety and the disposal of nuclear waste led to a questioning of the nuclear option. Since these accidents, many core countries have drastically reduced or eliminated their reliance on nuclear energy.

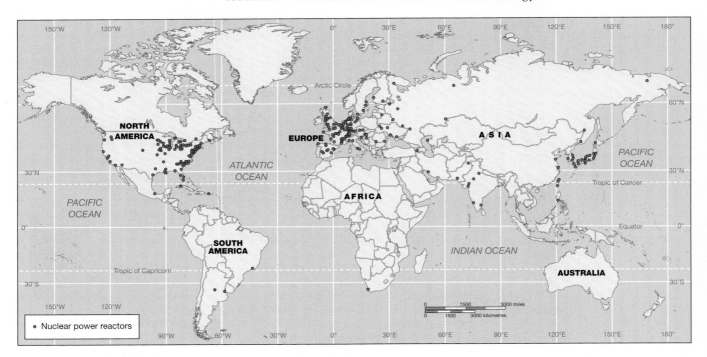

Figure 4.21 World distribution of nuclear reactors, 2000 Most of the dependence on nuclear power is concentrated in core countries. South America and Africa together contain only four nuclear reactors. Whereas some peripheral countries, such as India, are enthusiastic about increasing their nuclear energy production, core countries are phasing out dependence on nuclear power. Australia, where there is a very strong antinuclear movement, is one of the few core countries to have rejected nuclear power altogether.   (After International Nuclear Safety Center website, **www.insc.anl.gov/pwrmaps/map/world_map.php**, "Maps of Nuclear Power Reactors: World Map" 2002, p. 1, retrieved June 15, 2005).

Energy

Energy plays a fundamental role in day-to-day human activity, powering our cars, lights, and entertainment. Since the Industrial Revolution, much of the world relies on fossil fuels such as oil, gas, and coal to meet their energy needs. At the same time, fossil fuels are significant sources of greenhouse gas (GHG) emissions, with their combustion releasing carbon dioxide (CO_2) and nitrous oxide (N_2O) into the atmosphere, two key greenhouse gases. Their use is responsible for approximately 70 percent of greenhouse gas emissions, and 80 percent of all CO_2 emissions, with coal producing proportionately more CO_2 emissions than either oil or gas.[19]

The economies of the developed world are heavily dependent on the use of fossil fuels, having the highest per-capita use. However, the most rapid growth in the use of fossil fuels is occurring in the developing world, driven in part by the economic development of countries including Mexico, India, and China. China's industrialization, for example, is responsible for about one-third of the growth in the world's oil consumption, making it the world's largest source of greenhouse gases.[20] Worldwide, the Intergovernmental Panel on Climate Change (IPCC) estimates that global demand for energy will increase by 65 percent above 2004 levels,[21] largely driven by the increasing energy needs of developing countries. Given the growing demand for energy, greenhouse gas emissions are expected to increase for the foreseeable future.[22]

Like other developed countries, Canada's economy is closely linked to fossil fuels. It has large coal reserves, and its oil reserves are second only to those of Saudi Arabia, enabling the country to be a net exporter of energy.[23] As a source of oil, much of the interest is now focused on northern Alberta's **oil sands**, a mixture of bitumen (a type of oil), sand, clay, and water. The region holds an estimated 174 billion barrels of recoverable oil, and energy companies have rushed to develop their potential, driven by rising crude oil prices, increased concern over the global supply of oil, and increased demand (**Figure 4.1.1**).

Canada's fossil fuel production sector represents 13 percent of Canada's overall GHG emissions. Out of this, oil sands production is a very resource-intensive industry, requiring the energy equivalent of one barrel of oil to produce three barrels of oil from material recovered from the oil sands. On their own, oil sands development accounts for 3 percent of Canada's greenhouse gas emissions, making it the single largest contributor of

Figure 4.1.1 Mining Alberta's oil sands Increased energy demand and limited reserves of easily accessible fossil fuels has led to an expansion of production in Northern Alberta's oil sands.

oil sands: a mixture of bitumen (a type of oil), sand, clay, and water

[19]Intergovernmental Panel on Climate Change, 2007, *Climate Change 2007.* **www.ipcc.ch.**

[20]Paul Krugman, "Dealing with the Dragon." *New York Times,* 4 January 2008, p. A12.

[21]IPCC, *Climate Change 2007.* The projections noted in the IPCC report assume "business as usual," or no significant changes in the efficiency of energy use.

[22]Ibid.

[23]D. Woynillowicz, C. Severson-Baker, and M. Raynolds, *Oil Sands Fever: The Environmental Implications of Canada's Oil Sands Rush.* Drayton Valley, AB: The Pembina Institute, 2005 (**www.pembina.org**).

GHG in Canada.[24] Emissions have increased 25.3 percent since 1990 as production has increased. Even as the intensity of greenhouse gas emissions has been reduced with improved production techniques, new development has undercut these gains. Even under the best-case scenarios, GHG emissions will increase substantially in the coming years as the oil sands industry looks to significantly increase production.[25]

The growth of Alberta's oil sands raises interesting political and economic questions. Ottawa's desire to take action on GHG emissions through carbon taxes, for instance, risks slowing the economy or alienating western provinces. Similarly, who are the emissions attributed to? Alberta becomes the largest source of emissions, but Alberta's production of oil and gas feeds consumption elsewhere. At the same time, California and other jurisdictions have moved to promote cleaner (e.g., lower carbon footprint) sources of energy, meaning that they may not buy Alberta's oil.[26]

Finding energy supplies to match the expected growth in energy demand without increasing greenhouse gases is both difficult and costly. Conventional fossil fuels are not equally distributed across the globe, and new sources are typically costly to develop given their remote location. To date, much of the growth in energy demand has been met with coal-fired power plants, which are comparatively inexpensive and easy to build with existing technology while utilizing a widely available and inexpensive resource, despite increased GHG emissions. Alternative energy sources, including solar, nuclear, wind, or biofuels may provide energy needs in the future. **Biofuels**, or fuels made from plant material including corn, soy, and sugar cane, have been seen as a particularly environmentally friendly alternative to fossil fuels, reducing both greenhouse gas emissions and dependence on foreign oil reserves.

The attraction of biofuels was based on the assumption that they were **carbon-neutral**: any carbon released during their burning was equivalent to the carbon absorbed when the plants grew. Recent research has, however, argued that almost all biofuels are not as "green" as they may seem.[27] In fact, they may release as much or more

greenhouse gases as conventional fuels once the full cost of production is taken into account. These full costs include the destruction of natural ecosystems for planting of biofuel crops such as corn, soy bean, or sugar cane, planting and fertilizing, refining crops into fuel, and their transportation to market. The development of biofuels may also push food prices higher as farmland is used for fuel rather than food production, and they were partially blamed for food riots in several developing nations in early 2008. Biofuels may also result in the destruction of natural ecosystems as new and often marginal lands are cleared for food or fuel production, potentially contributing to soil erosion and longer-term land degradation. Given the often over-stated benefits of biofuels, it may be better to leave land in its natural state or to reforest,[28] as these more natural states typically absorb more carbon than cropland.

In the face of mounting concerns with the use of biofuels, governments must re-think energy policies. European governments have moved to reduce subsidies for biofuels, supporting only those that are environmentally sustainable and that yield a true **carbon benefit**, or the reduction in carbon dioxide emissions for the same quantity of fuel.[29] The greater the carbon benefit, the fewer GHG emissions. At the same time, however, questions emerge as to what alternative energy sources should be supported. Sugar cane, for instance, is transformed much more efficiently into biofuel as compared with corn or soybean. Agricultural or forest industry wastes may also provide more efficient methods of fuel production, and research in this area continues.

Hydroelectric, solar, wind, and nuclear power are among the other energy options that are available and may help to reduce greenhouse gas emissions, but they too come with concerns. Hydroelectric energy, for example, has been criticized because of its land-use impacts. The recently completed Three Gorges Dam in China has resulted in environmental problems including water pollution and landslides, and the displacement of 1.13 million people from their villages and livelihoods.[30] Similar concerns and outcomes were experienced in Northern Quebec with the building of the La Grande hydroelectric system during the 1980s and 1990s. Flooding and river diversion resulted in the loss of traditional Cree lands and

biofuels: fuels made from plant material including corn, soy, and sugar cane

carbon neutral: any carbon released upon burning is equivalent to the carbon absorbed when the plants grew

carbon benefit: the reduction in carbon dioxide emissions for the same quantity of fuel

[24]IPCC, *Climate Change 2007.*

[25]Ibid.

[26]Felicity Barringer, "California Will Offer Plan to Cut Harmful Emissions." *New York Times*, 26 June 2008, p. A8.

[27]T. Searchinger, R. Heimlich, R.A. Houghton, F. Dong, A. Elobeid, J. Fabiosa, S. Tokgoz, D. Hayes, and T. Yu, "Use of US Croplands for Biofuels Increases Greenhouse Gases through Emissions from Land-use Changes." *Science*, 319, 29 February 2008, pp. 1238–1240.

[28]R. Righelato and D.V. Spracklen, "Carbon Mitigation by Biofuels or by Saving and Restoring Forests?" *Science*, 317, 17 August 2007, p. 902.

[29]Elisabeth Rosenthal, "Europe, Cutting Biofuel Subsidies, Redirects Aid to Stress Greenest Options." *New York Times*, 22 January 2008, p. A3. See also J.K. Bourne, "Growing Fuel: The Wrong Way, The Right Way." *National Geographic*, October 2007.

[30]Jim Yardley, "Chinese Dam Projects Criticized for Their Human Costs." *New York Times*, 19 November 2007, p. A4.

population displacement, although more recent hydro-electric projects in the area have been more sustainable.[31]

Renewable energy sources such as solar and wind power are currently small but growing energy providers, but can only provide power when environmental conditions allow either wind production or solar collection. Although research continues to improve the efficiency of solar power technology, current technology means that the true cost of solar power exceeds its returns. Wind generation has been criticized for its visual impacts on the landscape and concerns that migrating birds and bats may be killed by the rotating blades.

Nuclear energy has also been identified as an alternative energy source that is "green." Several jurisdictions, such as Ontario and the United Kingdom, are actively pursuing expansion of nuclear power plants given increased need for energy and the desire to minimize greenhouse emissions. But nuclear energy comes with negative public perceptions and fears, both of security and of the technology, due to events such as the Chernobyl disaster, which released large amounts of radioactive material into the atmosphere when a nuclear reactor exploded. The long-term disposal of radioactive waste, which remains toxic and radioactive for centuries, along with the decommissioning of the reactors themselves, poses additional long-term concerns and questions, and Canada has yet to articulate a policy for dealing with nuclear waste.

While fossil fuels provide the majority of the world's energy supply, government and industry are actively searching for ways to eliminate greenhouse gases through energy conservation and alternative energy sources. The choices, however, are not clear cut, with each energy option having its own implications, and future choices will likely represent a compromise between continued use of conventional energy sources such as oil, gas, and coal, and renewable energy sources such as wind energy or solar power.

—K.B.N.

[31]J.F. Hornig, *Social and Environmental Impacts of the James Bay Hydroelectric Project*. Montreal: McGill-Queen's University Press, 1999.

Interestingly, although the majority of core countries have begun to move away from nuclear energy because of the possibility of environmental disaster in the absence of fail-safe nuclear reactors, the nuclear industry advertises the fact that it does not produce greenhouse gases. India, South Korea, and China have fledgling nuclear energy programs, and Canada is still eager to export its CANDU nuclear reactor technology. So far, no accidents have been associated with nuclear energy production in the periphery.

While nuclear power problems are largely confined to the core, the periphery is not without its energy-related environmental problems. Because a large proportion of populations in the periphery rely on wood for their energy needs, as the populations have grown, so, too, has the demand for fuelwood. One of the most immediate environmental impacts of wood burning is air pollution. But the most alarming environmental problem related to wood burning is the rapid depletion of forest resources. With the other conventional sources of energy (coal, oil, and gas) being too costly or unavailable to most peripheral households, wood is the only alternative. The demand for fuelwood has been so great in many peripheral regions that forest reserves are being rapidly used up (**Figure 4.22**).

Fuelwood depletion is extreme in the highland areas of Nepal as well as in Andean Bolivia and Peru. The clearing of forests for fuelwood in these regions has lead to serious steep-slope soil erosion. In sub-Saharan Africa, where 90 percent of the region's energy needs are met with energy supplied by wood, overcutting of the forests has resulted especially in denuded areas around rapidly growing cities. And although wood gathering is usually associated with rural life, it is not uncommon for city dwellers to use wood to satisfy their household energy needs as well. For example, in Niamey, the capital of Niger, the zone of overcutting is gradually expanding as the city itself expands. It is now estimated that city dwellers in Niamey must travel from 50 to 100 kilometres (30 to 60 miles) to gather wood. The same goes for inhabitants of Ouagadougou in Burkina Faso, where the average haul for wood is also over 50 kilometres.

Hydroelectric power was also once seen as a preferred alternative to the more obviously environmentally polluting fossil fuel sources. It is no exaggeration to state that the wave of dam building that occurred throughout the world over the course of the twentieth century has improved the overall availability, quality, cost,

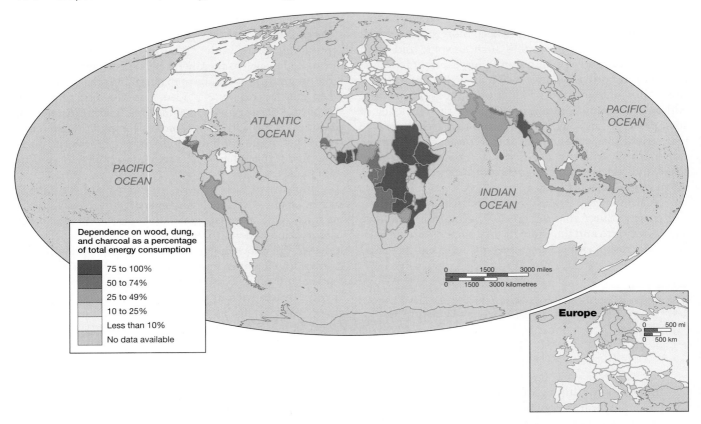

Figure 4.22 Global use of woodfuels, 2001 Firewood, charcoal, and dung are considered traditional fuels, and although their availability is decreasing, dependence on them is increasing. Dependence on traditional sources of fuel is especially high in the periphery where, in Africa, for example, they are the most important energy source for cooking and heating. Wood and charcoal, although renewable sources, are replenished very slowly. Acute scarcity will be a certainty for most African households in the twenty-first century. (After United Nations Development Programme, 2001. *World Resources 2000–2001, People and Ecosystems: The Fraying Web of Life.* Washington, DC: World Resources Institute, p. 98.)

and dependability of energy (**Figure 4.23**). Unfortunately, however, dams built to provide hydroelectric power (as well as water for irrigation, navigation, and drinking) for the burgeoning cities of the core and to encourage economic development in the periphery and semiperiphery have also had profound negative environmental impacts. Among the most significant of these impacts are changes in downstream flow, evaporation, sediment transport and deposition, mineral quality and soil moisture, channelling and bank scouring, aquatic plants and animals, as well as changes in human health. Furthermore, the construction of dams also dramatically alters the surrounding terrain, often with serious consequences. For example, clearance of a forest for dam construction often leads to large-scale flooding. The felled trees are usually left to decay in the impounded waters, which become increasingly acidic. The impounded waters can also incubate mosquitoes, which carry diseases, such as malaria and West Nile virus. The remedies for such problems are difficult to determine, and many argue that new dam projects should not be undertaken without a clear sense of the complex of indirect social and environmental costs. For these reasons, for many years, the James Bay Cree were successfully able to mobilize public opinion against further dam construction. However, an agreement between them and the Quebec government in 2002 allows further damming of James Bay's rivers to proceed. If it is completed, the Great Whale Project will join James Bay I and II as some of the largest hydro developments in Canada (**Figure 4.24**).

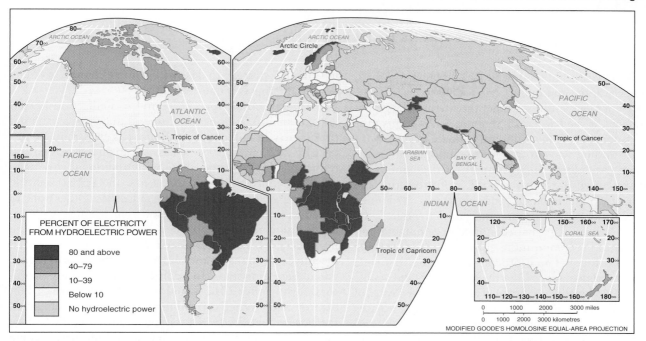

Figure 4.23 World distribution of hydropower, 1999 Although the great dam-building era for core countries is now largely completed, many peripheral countries, in a bid to participate more actively in the world economy, are building dams. Only a few countries are almost exclusively dependent on the hydropower produced from dams. These include Norway, Nepal, Zambia, Ghana, Paraguay, and Costa Rica. Although the power produced by dams is environmentally benign, the construction of large dams can be extremely destructive of the environment and can dislocate large numbers of people.

One of the reasons hydroelectric power continues to be appealing, however, is that it produces few atmospheric pollutants compared with fossil fuels. Indeed, coal and gas power stations as well as factories, automobiles, and other forms of transportation are largely responsible for the increasingly acidic quality of Earth's atmosphere. Although people as well as other organisms naturally produce many gases, including oxygen and carbon dioxide, increasing levels of industrialization and motor vehicle use have destabilized the natural balance of such gases, leading to serious atmospheric pollution (see **Human Geography and Climate Change 4.2—The Kyoto Protocol and Its Legacy**). Increasing the level of acids in the atmosphere are sulphur

Figure 4.24 Dams in Quebec
Using an extensive system of large dams in the James Bay and Great Whale watersheds, Quebec has become an important producer of hydroelectricity. Once considered to be a totally environmentally friendly source of power, the disadvantages of such projects are now becoming apparent. These include the destruction of Aboriginal lands, the disruption of fish stocks and the problems of silt accumulation. Other critics observe that more efficient energy conservation would remove the need for any further dam construction.

The Kyoto Protocol and Its Legacy

Since the 1992 Earth Summit in Rio de Janeiro, Brazil, the international community has sought to ensure economic development without further threatening the global environment. At the Rio Earth Summit, 167 nations ratified the Framework Convention on Climate Change with the aim of finding ways to reduce the amount of greenhouse gases. An additional and equally critical aim of the Summit was to ensure that the burden of protecting the environment would be shared equitably across all nations.

In December 1997, these nations began to address the problem of balancing global economic development and environmental protection more substantively by forging the Kyoto Protocol. The Protocol marked the first time that attempts were made to limit the amount of GHG emissions generated by core countries. The aim of the Protocol was to cut the combined emissions of greenhouse gases from core countries by roughly 5 percent from their 1990 levels by 2012. It also specified the amount each core nation would contribute toward meeting that reduction goal. Nations with the highest carbon dioxide (CO_2) emissions—the United States, Canada, Japan, and most European nations—were expected to reduce emissions by a range of 6 to 8 percent.

Canada ratified the Kyoto Protocol in a vote in the House of Commons on 10 December 2002. However, no method of implementing reductions had been decided, nor had the government indicated how the total burden of emission reduction was to be allocated among government, business, and the public. Disagreements between the federal government and some of the provinces were particularly rancorous. Alberta, for example, was opposed to the implementation of the Protocol owing to fears that its oil-rich economy would be seriously harmed if emission reductions were enforced, the same hurdle faced by the federal government a decade later as it dealt with the growth of Alberta's oil and gas industry. On the other hand, Quebec, with its abundance of hydroelectric power, strongly supported the agreement, believing it would benefit as a provider of "clean" energy to the United States.

Ongoing disagreement between the different levels of government over the implementation of the Kyoto Protocol, and the election of Stephen Harper's Conservative government in January 2006, effectively ended Canada's participation in the agreement. Harper's government cited the 24 percent rise in Canada's greenhouse emissions (between 1990 and 2006), arguing that it was too difficult for the country to meet its Kyoto commitments.[32] Instead, the federal government set out to create a "made

in Canada" strategy to deal with climate change, given its potential impacts (**Figure 4.2.1**).[33]

Announced in April 2007 and formalized in March 2008, Canada's *Turning the Corner* framework committed the country to reducing greenhouse gas emissions 20 percent by 2020 from 2006 levels.[34] It included mandatory reductions for industry, along with additional new measures to address the oil sands and electricity sectors, two key greenhouse gas emitting industries. Other policies to reduce emissions, including new vehicle efficiency standards and consumer appliance standards, would also be introduced. To achieve these reductions, the plan provided incentives for industry and individual Canadians to reduce greenhouse emissions. In addition, new oil sands operators starting after 2012 would be required to have carbon capture and storage capabilities, and the construction of inefficient coal-fired electricity generators would not be allowed. If approved, regulations would ultimately come into force 1 January 2010.

Critics of the policy immediately questioned the new greenhouse targets and the policy's feasibility. It is unclear, for instance, whether the targeted reductions are achievable within ten years, a timeline not all that different than that laid out in the Kyoto Protocol. Others have argued that the targeted reduction levels were too low. On a technical front, it is unclear whether CO_2 capture and storage, whereby carbon emissions are pumped into underground reservoirs rather than released into the atmosphere, is safe, viable, and cost-effective technology.[35] At the same time, construction of coal-fired power plants are experiencing renewed interest given the abundance of coal and its relatively low price in comparison to natural gas, even though they release proportionately more greenhouse gases.[36]

The legacy of Kyoto is limited. The United States never signed the treaty, and both Canada and Australia backed away from commitments to greenhouse gas reductions. Globally, responses to climate change remain mired in political arguments over causes, responsibility, and participation. Kyoto, for instance, placed the burden of reducing global climate change on the core countries most responsible for the buildup of greenhouse gases. At the same time, developing countries, including China and India, were expected to play a role, although Kyoto set no binding limits on their emissions and did not establish a mechanism or timetable for these countries to

---

[32]Jeff Sallot, "Kyoto Plan No Good, Minister Argues: Ambrose Calls for a New Approach to Cutting Emissions." *Globe and Mail*, 8 April 2006, p. A6.

[33]Steve Soloman, "Deep by Shortsighted?" *Globe and Mail*, 14 April 2006, p. A14.

[34]See www.ec.gc.ca.

[35]Elisabeth Rosenthal, "Europe Turns Back to Coal, Raising Climate Fears." *New York Times*, 23 April 2008, p. A6.

[36]Ibid.

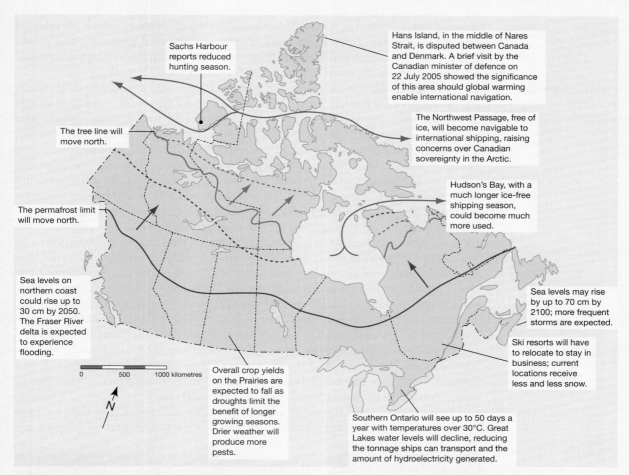

Figure 4.2.1 Impact of climate change in Canada The projected increase in global temperatures associated with the greenhouse effect will have many effects on Canada, some of which are shown on this map. Average temperatures in some regions of the country could rise by as much as 5°–10°C. Even now, evidence suggests that polar bears have suffered from the reduction of winter sea ice on which they hunt. The Inuvialuit community of Sachs Harbour on Banks Island now reports more than a month's reduction in their average winter hunting season. The projected melting of Canada's Arctic ice and permafrost will also affect the global community because it will contribute to a global rise in sea levels. The spread of West Nile virus across southern Canada may be aided by warmer summers, which allow mosquitoes to thrive and transmit the disease. (*Sources:* Geoffrey J. Matthews and Robert Morrow Jr., *Canada and the World: An Atlas Resource*, 2nd ed. Scarborough, Ontario: Prentice Hall, 1995, p. 61; Government of Canada, *Think Climate Change*, Ottawa, 1001 [Catalogue En56-169/2001E]. Further details on regional impacts and on a video about Sachs Harbour [*Sila Alangotok: Inuit Observations on Climate Change*] are available at **www.climatechange.gc.ca/**.)

take on such limits voluntarily. As discussions continued, most developed countries stated that developing nations must sign any new agreement and must participate in emission reductions. Developing countries rejected this condition, however, citing their own need for economic development and their inability to pay for new technology.

Nevertheless, Kyoto initiated new discussions and actions to curb emissions, with Europe largely working to meet Kyoto goals. In Canada, provincial governments charted their own course independent of Ottawa. In 2008, Manitoba became the first provincial government to confirm its commitment to reaching Kyoto targets for

greenhouse-gas emissions by 2012,[37] and Quebec became the first province to introduce a **carbon tax**, which is a tax on emissions of CO_2 and other greenhouse gases.[38]

—K.B.N.

carbon tax: a tax on emissions of CO_2 and other greenhouse gases

[37]Joe Friesen, "Manitoba's Kyoto Bill Will Be a First in Canada." *Globe and Mail*, 12 April 2008, p. A5.

[38]Fannie Olivier, "Gore Praises Quebec's Environmental Record." *Globe and Mail*, 5 April 2008, p. A3.

acid rain: the wet deposition of acids on Earth created by the natural cleansing properties of the atmosphere

dioxide, nitrogen oxides, and hydrocarbons, among other gases, which are released into the atmosphere from motor vehicle exhaust, industrial processes, and power generation (based on fossil fuels). If these gases reach sufficient concentrations and are not effectively dispersed in the atmosphere, acid rain can result.

Acid rain is the wet deposition of acids on Earth created by the natural cleansing properties of the atmosphere. Acid rain occurs as the water droplets in clouds absorb certain gases, which later fall back to Earth as acid precipitation. Also included under the term *acid rain* are acid mists, acid fogs, and smog. The effects of acid rain are widespread. Throughout much of the Northern Hemisphere, for example, forests are being poisoned and killed, and soils are becoming too acidic to support plant life. Lakes are becoming acidic in North America and Scandinavia. As if this were not enough, the Great Lakes that serve much of the population of Ontario have become increasingly polluted with heavy metals and other toxic substances (**Figure 4.25**).

Before giving up all hope that the use of energy can ever be anything but detrimental to the environment, it is important to realize that alternatives to fossil fuels, hydroelectric power, and nuclear energy do exist. Energy derived from the sun, the wind, Earth's interior (geothermal sources), and the tides has been found to be clean, profitable, and dependable. Japan, the United States, and Germany all have solar energy production facilities that have proven to be cheap and nonpolluting. Although contributing only small amounts to the overall energy supply, the production of energy from geothermal and wind sources has also been successful in a few locations around the globe. Iceland, Italy, Germany, the United States, Mexico, New Zealand, Denmark, and the Philippines all derive some of their energy production from either geothermal or wind sources. In southern Alberta, a number of wind farms have been developed on an experimental basis.

Monies to support the development of geothermal, wind, and tidal energies have been scarce, however, because of the lobbying pressures of oil and gas

Figure 4.25 Pollution of Lake Ontario The long-run disposal of industrial waste, municipal drainage, and agricultural runoff into the Great Lakes has contributed to elevated levels of toxic substances (such as dioxins, mercury, and pesticides) in those waters. Although recent environmental legislation has led to a decline in current emissions, it will take many years before the amounts of harmful chemicals already present in the lakes have dissipated to levels that no longer threaten the health of the more than 40 million people that surround and depend on this ecosystem. Despite such measures, however, many problems remain. For example, the continued release of sewerage into the lakes often poses a nuisance for communities downstream—as this photograph of a closed recreational beach in Toronto (south of Woodbine) shows, and until more sustainable solutions are discovered, it is likely that such closures will continue to be an annual event. Photo: © Dick Hemingway

companies, as well as other political factors. Although viable alternatives to traditional energy sources do exist, the further development of these alternatives is likely to hinge on future political and economic factors. The increase in petroleum prices since early 2008 shows signs of hastening such changes in many parts of Europe and North America.

Impacts of Land-Use Change on the Environment

In addition to industrial pollution and steadily increasing demands for energy, the environment is also being dramatically affected by pressures on the land. The clearing of land for fuel, farming, grazing, resource extraction, highway building, energy generation, and war all have significant impacts on land. Land may be classified into five categories: forest, cultivated land, grassland, wetland, and areas of settlement. Geographers understand land-use change as occurring in either of two ways, conversion or modification. *Conversion* is the wholesale transformation of land from one use to another (for example, the conversion of forested land to settlement). *Modification* is an alteration of existing cover (for example, when a grassland is overlaid with railroad tracks or when a forest is thinned and not clear-cut). As human populations have increased and the need for land for settlement and cultivation has also increased, changes to the land have followed.

One of the most dramatic impacts of humans on the environment is loss or alteration of forest cover on the planet caused by the clearing of forests for millennia to make way for cultivation and settlement. Forests are cleared not only to provide land to accommodate increases in human numbers, but they are also exploited for the vast resources they contain. The approximate chronology and estimated extent of the clearing of the world's forests since pre-agricultural times is portrayed in **Table 4.2**. The table shows that the forested area of the world has been reduced by about 8 million square kilometres (about 3 million square miles) since pre-agricultural times, an area equivalent to four-fifths of the territory of Canada. Rapid clearance

TABLE 4.2   Estimated Area Cleared (in thousands of square kilometres)

Region or Country		Pre-1650	1650–1749	1750–1849	1850–1978	Total High Estimate	Total Low Estimate
North America		6	80	380	641	1107	1107
Central America	H	18	30	40	200	288	282
	L	12				——	
Latin America	H	18	100	170	637	925	919
	L	12					
Australia, New Zealand, and the South Pacific	H	6	6	6	362	380	374
	L	2	4	6	362	——	
Former USSR	H	70	180	270	575	1095	997
	L	42	130	250	575	——	
Europe	H	204	66	146	81	497	497
	L	176	54	186	81	——	
Asia	H	974	216	596	1220	3006	2642
	L	640	176	606	1220	——	
Africa	H	226	80	216	469	759	631
	L	96	24	42	469	——	
Total highest		**1522**	**758**	**1592**	**4185**	**8057**	
Total lowest		**986**	**598**	**1680**	**4185**		**7449**

Note: "H" and "L" denote the highest and lowest estimates, respectively, for deforestation in each region or country.

Source: B.L. Turner II, W.C. Clark, R.W. Kates, J.F. Richards, J.T. Mathews, and B. Meyer, *The Earth as Transformed by Human Action: Global and Regional Changes in the Biosphere over the Past 300 Years*. Cambridge: Cambridge University Press, 1990, p. 180.

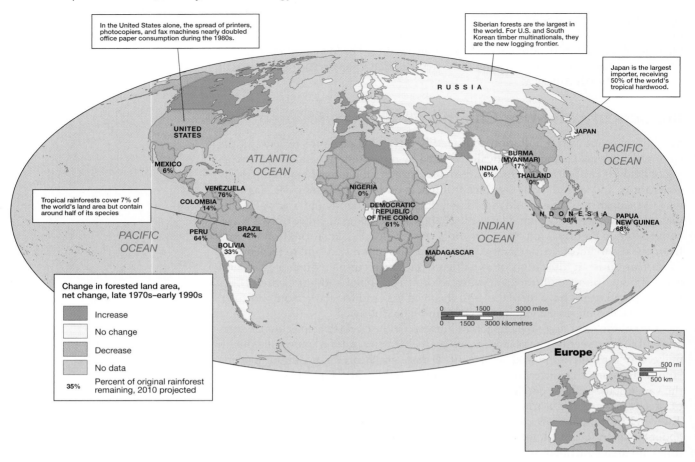

In the United States alone, the spread of printers, photocopiers, and fax machines nearly doubled office paper consumption during the 1980s.

Siberian forests are the largest in the world. For U.S. and South Korean timber multinationals, they are the new logging frontier.

Japan is the largest importer, receiving 50% of the world's tropical hardwood.

Tropical rainforests cover 7% of the world's land area but contain around half of its species

Change in forested land area, net change, late 1970s–early 1990s

- Increase
- No change
- Decrease
- No data
- **35%** Percent of original rainforest remaining, 2010 projected

Figure 4.26 Global deforestation The world's forests are disappearing or being reduced or degraded everywhere, but especially in tropical countries. Whereas forests once occupied about one-third of Earth's surface, they now take up about one-quarter. (*Source:* J. Seager, *The New State of the Earth Atlas*, 2nd ed. New York: Simon & Schuster, 1995, pp. 72–73.)

of the world's forests has occurred either through logging, settlement, and agricultural clearing or through fuelwood cutting around urban areas.

The permanent clearing and destruction of forests, known as *deforestation*, is currently occurring most alarmingly in the world's rain forests. **Figure 4.26** shows the global extent of deforestation. The Food and Agricultural Organization of the United Nations has estimated that rain forests globally are being destroyed at the rate of 0.5 hectare (1 acre) per second.

Today, rain forests cover less than 7 percent of the land surface, half of what they covered only a few thousand years ago. Destruction of the rain forests, however, is not just about the loss of trees, a renewable resource that is being eliminated more quickly than it can be regenerated. It is also about the loss of the biological diversity of an ecosystem, which translates into the potential loss of biological compounds that may have great medical value. The destruction of rain forests is also about destabilizing the oxygen and carbon dioxide cycles of the forests, which may have long-term effects on global climate. Much of the destruction of the South American rain forests is the result of peripheral countries' attempts at economic development. **Figure 4.27** illustrates another aspect of the problem—the clear-cutting of forests in Canada. The question over sustainable forestry practices has dogged this industry, and yet for many parts of Canada's periphery, the harvesting of forests for lumber or pulp and paper is still a crucial economic activity. In Canada, at present, 1 million hectares are harvested (90 percent by clear-cutting) and replanted each year.

Great geographical variability exists with respect to human impacts on the world's forests. For most of the core regions, net clearance of the forests has been

Figure 4.27   Clear-cutting in British Columbia   Views like this one have mobilized groups, such as Greenpeace, against Canadian forestry practices. Although making some concessions and supporting research into more environmentally acceptable methods, the forest industry continues to log large parts of its timber licences in this way.

replaced by regeneration. Yet, for most of the periphery, clearance has accelerated to such an extent that one estimate shows a 50 percent reduction in the amount of forest cover since the early twentieth century.

Cultivation is another important component of global land use, which we deal with extensively in Chapter 8. However, one or two additional points about the environmental impacts of cultivation are pertinent here. During the past 300 years, the land devoted to cultivation has expanded globally by 450 percent. In 1700, the global stock of land in cultivation took up an area about the size of Argentina. Today, it occupies an area roughly the size of the entire continent of South America. Although the most rapid expansion of cropland since the mid-twentieth century has occurred in the peripheral regions, the amount of cropland has either held steady or been reduced in the core regions. The expansion of cropland in the peripheral regions is partly a response to growing populations and rising levels of consumption worldwide. It is also partly due to the globalization of agriculture (see Chapter 8), with some core-region production having been moved to the peripheral regions. The reduction of cropland in some core regions is partly a result of this globalization and partly the result of a more intensive use of cropland—utilizing more fertilizers, pesticides, and farm machinery—and new crop strains.

Grasslands are also used productively the world over, either as rangeland or pasture. In both cases, the land is used for livestock grazing. As **Figure 4.28** shows, most grassland occurs in arid and semi-arid regions that are unsuitable for farming,

Figure 4.28   African grasslands
Shown here is a tropical grassland in Kenya, Africa. Also known as *savannas*, these grasslands include scattered shrubs and isolated small trees as well as extensive herds of hoofed animals, such as gazelles, giraffes, zebras, wildebeasts, and antelopes.

as a result of either lack of water or poor soils. Some grasslands, however, occur in more rainy regions where tropical rain forests have been removed and replaced by grasslands. Approximately 42 million square kilometres (26 million square miles) of land surface is currently taken up by grasslands.

Human impacts on grasslands are largely of two sorts. The first has been the clearing of grasslands for other uses, most frequently settlement. As the global demands on beef production have increased, so has the intensity of use of the world's grasslands. Widespread overgrazing of grasslands has led to acute degradation of the resource. In its most severe form, overgrazing has led to desertification. **Desertification** is the degradation of land cover and damage to the soil and water in grasslands and arid and semi-arid lands. One of the most severe cases of desertification has been occurring in the Sahel region of Africa since the 1970s. The degradation of the grasslands bordering the Sahara Desert, however, has not been a simple case of careless overgrazing by thoughtless herders. Severe drought, land decline, recurrent famine, and the breakdown of traditional systems for coping with disaster have all combined to create increased pressure on fragile resources, resulting in a loss of grass cover and extreme soil degradation. Although the factors behind the human impacts on the Sahelian grasslands are complex, the simple fact remains that the grasslands have been severely degraded, and the potential for their recovery is still unknown (**Figure 4.29**).

Human impacts on wetland environments have also been numerous. The most widespread, however, has been the draining or filling of wetlands and their conversion to other land uses, such as settlement or cultivation. One reliable estimate places the total area of the world's wetlands at about 8.5 million square kilometres (5.0 million square miles) with about 1.5 million square kilometres (0.9 million square miles) having been lost to drainage or filling. In Australia, for example, all of the original 20 000 square kilometres (12 000 square miles) of wetlands have been lost to conversion. For the past 400 years or so, wetlands have been regarded as nuisances, if not sources of disease. In core countries, technological innovation made modification and conversion of wetlands possible and profitable.

The Exploitation of the World's Fisheries

Fishing has always been an important activity, and current statistics show that it remains so on a global scale. For example, data presented in the Food and Agriculture Organization's *The State of the World's Fisheries and Aquaculture* for 2006

desertification: the degradation of land cover and damage to the soil and water in grasslands and arid and semi-arid lands

Figure 4.29 Desertification in sub-Saharan Africa Desertification is a mounting problem in many parts of the world, but especially in sub-Saharan Africa (the portion of Africa between North Africa's Sahara Desert and the five countries that make up southern Africa). This false-colour composite satellite photo shows the belt of desertification stretching from west to east across the widest portion of the continent. The grey areas are where vegetation is absent or dying. The blue-green shades represent areas of shrubs and grasses. The red areas represent mixed and abundant vegetation. Not long ago, the area in this image would have been represented in mostly red tones. Overgrazing on fragile arid and semi-arid rangelands and deforestation without reforestation are thought to be the chief causes of desertification in this part of Africa.
(*Source:* Data available from U.S. Geological Survey, EROS Data Center, Sioux Falls, SD.)

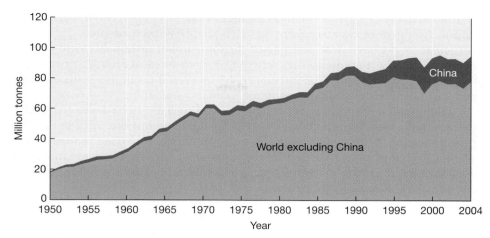

Figure 4.30   The world's rising catch of fish, 1950–2004   The Food and Agricultural Organization's statistics show a rising global volume of fish caught since the 1950s. Note: This graph shows the total for the world's "capture" fisheries (inland and marine). It does not include figures for aquaculture.   (*Source:* Food and Agriculture Organization of the United Nations. "The World's Rising Catch of Fish 1950–2004" from *State of the World's Fisheries and Aquaculture 2006*. Available at **www.fao.org**.)

show that the annual total volume of fish caught in all the world's rivers and oceans has risen consistently every year since the 1950s (**Figure 4.30**). Indeed, the volume for 2004, some 95.0 million tonnes, represented the largest annual amount of fish ever caught, according to the FAO.[39]

According to FAO statistics for 2004, China (16.9 million tonnes) and Peru (9.6 million tonnes) were the top countries, followed by the United States (5.0 million tonnes), and Chile (4.9 million tonnes) (**Figure 4.31**). Canada ranked 19th with a total capture of 1.17 million tonnes in 2004.

Beneath these statistics lies a story that the FAO has been very keen to stress: it appears that the world's fisheries have almost reached the limits of their production, and these very high totals are not sustainable over the long term. Simply put, there is a growing body of evidence that global fish stocks are now being depleted faster than they can replace themselves. For example, in its 2002 report, the FAO observes that only 25 percent of the world's marine fish stocks are "moderately exploited" or "underexploited." The state of the remaining 75 percent makes depressing reading: 47 percent are "fully exploited," 18 percent are "overexploited," and 10 percent are "significantly depleted."

Among the last group are the North Sea herring (whose numbers collapsed in the 1970s), the Atlantic blue fin tuna (which has declined from 250 000 fish in 1975 to 20 000 in recent years), and—of particular concern to Canadian fishers—the North Atlantic cod. Once the most important fish stock in the region, the cod population declined by a factor of 100 between 1990 and 1994. The species

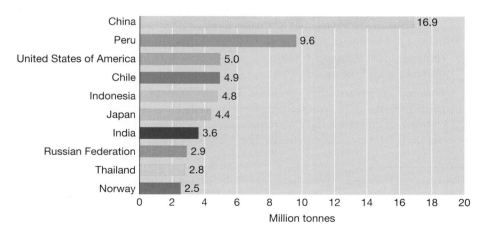

Figure 4.31   Marine and inland capture fisheries: top 10 producer countries in 2004   In a year in which the total catch was 95.0 million tonnes, the leading country (China) caught 16.9 million tonnes. Canada ranked 19th, with a total catch of 1.17 million tonnes. Note: Figures for aquaculture are excluded.   (*Source:* Food and Agriculture Organization of the United Nations. "Leading Fishing Nations by Size of Catch in 2004" from *State of the World's Fisheries and Aquaculture 2006*. Available at **www.fao.org**.)

[39]Data from the Food and Agriculture Organization of the United Nations can be found on the website at **www.fao.org**, where a wealth of other statistics and reports on fisheries can be consulted. Their report, *State of the World's Fisheries and Aquaculture 2006*, can be accessed at **www.fao.org**. The statistics used here are from Part 1 of that report.

maximum sustainable yield (MSY): the equilibrium between a fish population's biological productivity and the level of fishing effort; theoretically, the MSY for a fish stock is the largest number that can be caught while ensuring that enough remain for a productive fishery next year

fishing capacity: the ability of a fleet to catch fish, most easily measured by counting the number of boats in a fishing fleet

is now officially classed as endangered and, as the FAO observes, has failed "to respond to the drastic management measures that have been adopted. . . ." These particular stocks have clearly surpassed their **maximum sustainable yield (MSY)**, a figure defined as the equilibrium between a fish's biological productivity and the level of the fishing effort. The attempt to net more will result in a reduced catch and harm the ability of the species to maintain its population.

How could the world's fisheries have reached such a state? Two very thoughtful reports by the internationally respected Worldwatch Institute suggest that the present situation is the almost inevitable outcome of two competing factors: (1) the world's *overcapacity* to fish, and (2) the *resource depletion* of marine stock.[40] In a nutshell, there are too many fishers chasing a decreasing number of fish. Let us consider each of these factors in turn.

Overcapacity   The FAO defines the term **fishing capacity** as "the ability of a fleet to catch fish" and notes that this capacity can be most easily measured by counting the number of boats in a fishing fleet.[41] Between 1970 and 1992 the size of the world's fishing fleet doubled both in terms of tonnage and in number of vessels. By 1992, there were 3.5 million vessels (a total of 26 million tonnes). Such totals, according to the Worldwatch Institute, mean that the world has twice the fishing capacity it needs to meet present demands—in other words, a large *overcapacity* (or *excess capacity*) exists. This situation, which is both economically and environmentally unsustainable over the long term, is the result of six main factors that have affected the growth of global fishing since the 1950s.

1. *Open access to fisheries.* Historically, beyond 5 kilometres (3 miles) from the coast (the range a cannon could fire), the world's oceans and their fisheries were open to all. Because no one country or person "owned" the fish stocks in these waters, fishers could catch as much as they wanted and had no incentive to conserve stocks. However, the "tragedy of the commons," Garret Hardin's term for the complete exhaustion of a common resource through open access, was not a frequent problem because many fisheries developed informal customs that regulated fishing activities and because fishing vessels were too small to affect fishing stocks and technology was in its infancy. However, traditional practices of open access could not hope to regulate fishing capacity once technology began to change.

2. *Technological change.* The development of the "factory trawler" by European shipbuilders in the 1950s revolutionized fishing. Their enormous stern-mounted trawl nets enabled such ships to catch far more than traditional fishing boats did, and their ability to process and freeze their catch on board meant that they could stay at sea for months (**Figure 4.32**). Modern factory-freezer trawlers are able to track shoals of fish using satellite data and to navigate accurately using Global Positioning Satellite (GPS) technology. Freed from the need to return to port frequently, these huge industrial trawlers are "free to roam the globe in search of profits."[42]

3. *National claims to fishing grounds.* Since 1976, to protect their domestic fleets from the effects of competition from foreign factory trawlers, an increasing number of countries have abandoned the principle of open access by extending their fisheries' jurisdictions. The 1982 UN Convention on the Law of the

---

[40]Peter Weber, "Protecting Oceanic Fisheries and Jobs." In Linda Starke (ed.), *State of the World 1995.* New York: Worldwatch Institute and Norton, 1995, pp. 21–37; Anne Platt McGinn, "Promoting Sustainable Fisheries." In Linda Starke (ed.), *State of the World 1998.* New York: Worldwatch Institute and Norton, 1998, pp. 59–78.

[41]FAO, "Excess Capacity and Illegal Fishing: Challenges to Sustainable Fisheries—What Is Fishing Capacity?" FAO Newsroom, Focus on the Issues, 2004, available online at **www.fao.org/newsroom/en/focus/2004/47127/article_47132en.html**.

[42]Anne Platt McGinn, "Promoting Sustainable Fisheries." In Linda Starke (ed.), *State of the World 1998.* New York: Worldwatch Institute and Norton, 1998, p. 66.

Figure 4.32 Trawler This view of Klaksvik harbour in the Faeroe Islands in the North Atlantic shows a deep-sea trawler moored beside a fish-processing plant. Once a colony of Denmark, the Faeroe Islands are now independent (although Denmark retains responsibility for the islands' defence and overseas relations). In recent years, Faeroese trawlers denied access to ports in Newfoundland and Labrador have been in retaliation for the increasing numbers of Faeroese ships that have been fishing in international waters off Canada's eastern coast. Denmark has been unwilling to respect the Northwest Atlantic Fisheries Organization (NAFO) fishing quotas in that zone.

Sea (UNCLOS) is an international treaty that was formally ratified in November 1994 to support this move. UNCLOS grants coastal nations the right to use and develop fisheries within a 200-nautical-mile Exclusive Economic Zone (EEZ) (**Figure 4.33**). Ironically, perhaps, this development has, in many cases, harmed rather than protected the world's fisheries:

- The oceans *outside* the EEZ now face increased pressures and virtually uncontrolled fishing. FAO statistics do not distinguish between catches made within EEZs and those outside. However, an analysis of those 116 oceanic species that occur principally in the high seas show that catches of oceanic species nearly tripled, from 3 million tonnes in 1976 to 8.5 million tonnes in 2000. Regional agreements do exist for the high seas, but these are unenforceable, as Canada discovered in August 2004, when Denmark

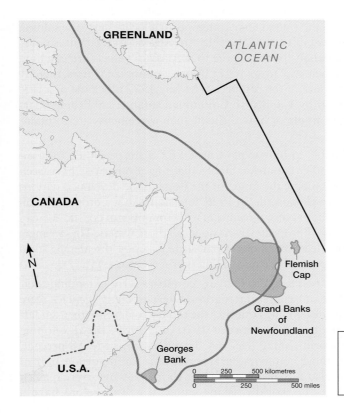

Figure 4.33 Canada's 200-nautical-mile Exclusive Economic Zone (EEZ)
(*Source:* Claude Emery, *The Northern Cod Crisis.* Library of Parliament: Ottawa, 1992, p. 3. It is available online at **http://dsp-psd.tpsgc.gc.ca**. Fisheries and Oceans Canada. Reproduced with the permission of Her Majesty the Queen in Right of Canada, 2006.)

Figure 4.34 Blockade of U.S. ferry in Prince Rupert, July 1997 Angered by the failure of talks over the allocation of fish stocks between the United States and Canada, BC fishers took matters into their own hands and prevented an American ferry from leaving Prince Rupert.

refused to abide by the shrimp quotas allocated by the Northwest Atlantic Fisheries Organization.

■ The exclusion of foreign fleets from the EEZ initially obscured the need to conserve stocks *within* the EEZ. Indeed, freed from the depredations of foreign factory trawlers, many domestic fisheries initially appeared far more sustainable than their stocks actually were, and the need to control domestic fleets through quotas and fleet reductions were thereby sadly delayed by many countries, including Canada.

■ Migratory fish do not observe EEZ boundaries and are therefore very hard stocks to manage successfully. For example, the Pacific Coast Salmon Treaty between Canada and the United States attempts to allocate fairly the salmon catch between fishers in British Columbia and Alaska. Agreement is never easy, however; Canadian fishers charge that Alaskan vessels are catching salmon that are on their way to spawn in British Columbian waters, thereby unduly reducing the size of the resource. The July 1997 blockade of a U.S. ferry in Prince Rupert by 100 British Columbian commercial fishing boats provides a telling example of how difficult such agreements are to maintain (**Figure 4.34**).

■ Those countries unable to fully exploit their EEZ were permitted to grant harvesting rights to other countries. Stocks that might otherwise have been left alone have now become the target of the fleets of the developed nations capable of fishing on a global scale. In 1996, for example, the European Union paid US$250 million for access agreements with a number of coastal African states, and nearly 1000 European vessels now fish those waters. This arrangement often heavily affects traditional small-scale fisheries, threatening local livelihoods in many parts of the developing world (**Figure 4.35**).

4. *Economic development policies.* While many countries were extending their control over their adjacent waters, international development agencies were increasingly lending the developing countries the money to develop their under-exploited fisheries (**Figure 4.36**). Between 1970 and 1989, the developing nations' share of the world fishing fleet rose from 27 percent to 58 percent, and for the first time, those countries became not only an important part of the fishing world but also a major contributor to its growing overcapacity. Any attempts to reduce the world's fishing capacity will therefore have a

Figure 4.35   Traditional fishers in Brazil

disproportionate effect on the poorer countries of the periphery unless such policies are sensitively managed.

5. *Growing demand.* In a 2004 report, the FAO noted that the world's fisheries provide 16 percent of the total animal protein consumed by the world's population. Demand has risen steadily since 1950 because (until recently) fish protein represented a cheaper alternative to meat, and many countries (the former Soviet Union, for example) found it cheaper to feed their population by fishing than by farming. Moreover, because most countries now subsidize their fishers (the FAO estimates that the world fleet is subsidized with US$54 billion per year), the true cost of the fishing industry is not always seen in the price of fish. If food supplies are to remain at the per capita levels they are now, it has been estimated that by 2010, at least 91 million tonnes of fish will be needed for direct human consumption. Since one-third of today's total harvest is used for nonhuman use (mainly animal feed), meeting this target will be a challenge.

Figure 4.36   Fish market, Bequia, St. Vincent   Fishing activity has been promoted in many developing countries by Western development policies. This picture shows a fish market built with Canadian support on the Caribbean island of Bequia (part of St. Vincent and the Grenadines).

6. *Resource depletion.* Although the world's capacity to fish has been increasing, a growing body of evidence suggests that the world's fish stocks have been diminishing. Clearly, this is a matter of concern. If the decline in numbers jeopardizes the critical population that a species needs to ensure breeding, then its future as a sustainable resource is threatened. For some species, experts now suggest that stocks have become so low that they face extinction. The decline of the world's marine and river fishery stocks is due to a series of both direct and indirect causes, the most important of which are the decline of fish stocks through overfishing and the effects of changing environments and pollution on fish populations. Let us briefly consider these factors.

- *Decline.* It seems almost contradictory to suggest that there might be a declining population of fish when the total amount of fish caught in the world's rivers and oceans in recent years has been the highest on record. However, the reason the total catch has been maintained at such high levels is that as the catches of individual species have declined, they have been replaced by other species. In other words, increasing global totals are, in many ways, an illusion that masks a dramatic decline of many species and has prevented many people from realizing the true state of the world's fisheries. The actual evidence for decline is not hard to find. The declining size of fish that are caught and the collapse of particular fisheries are each indicative of a diminishing natural resource.

- *Environmental threats.* Fish numbers can be affected by a range of environmental effects, principally, pollution, habitat destruction, and global warming. Since 60 percent of the world's population now live within 100 kilometres of the sea, it is perhaps hardly surprising to read that marine ecosystems are under increasing threat from the damage that development can cause coastal fish environments and the discharge of human and industrial wastes.

  What is surprising, perhaps, is to see the statement "climate change will have a greater impact on the health of the world's fisheries than overfishing itself."[43] Yet, there are already examples to demonstrate the possibilities of such a future. Off the coast of southern California, sea temperatures have risen by 0.8°C in the past 40 years. This change has led to the decline of zooplankton on which fish feed and the almost total collapse of the anchovy industry. In similar fashion, the most recent *El Niño* had very deleterious effects on the Peruvian anchovetta stock.

Aquaculture has been the most rapidly growing sector of the world fishing industry in the past 20 years (**Figure 4.37**). However, its growth potential may be severely limited by environmental fears. The possibility of fish diseases spreading from farmed stock to wild stock and the damage caused by aquaculture to coastal habitats are but two of the concerns raised by critics of this activity.

Faced with the mounting evidence that the world's fisheries are unsustainable, it is important that we consider what options we have for changing the present situation. Solutions have run the gamut from community-based control of local fisheries (as in the Philippines, for example) to market-based strategies that limit access by privatizing fishing rights (for instance, the individual transferable quota or ITQ). The two most obvious suggestions are that governments should immediately stop subsidizing their fishers and reduce the size of their fishing industries. Yet, few governments in the countries of the core or the periphery have felt able to jeopardize the only means of livelihood in many of their coastal communities. Sadly, many governments have found it cheaper to continue to subsidize fishing in remote regions than to develop economic diversification strategies or to confront the political

---

[43]Anne Platt McGinn, "Promoting Sustainable Fisheries." In Linda Starke (ed.), *State of the World 1998*. New York: Worldwatch Institute and Norton, 1998, p. 63.

Figure 4.37 Aquaculture Aquaculture is a growing industry in Canadian waters.

consequences of closing communities (see **Geography Matters 4.3—Changing Places: The Effects of Resource Depletion and Technological Change on the Geography of Atlantic Canada**). However, as many observers have stated, until we place the needs of the fish populations first, we will not be able to return fish stocks to sustainable levels. For too long, the fishing industry has profited by borrowing at the expense of the environment; if sensitive strategies are not developed soon, the time will come when that debt must be repaid.

The combustion of fossil fuels, the destruction of forest and fishery resources, the damming of watercourses, and the massive change in land-use patterns brought about by the pressures of globalization—industrialization being the most extreme phase—contribute to environmental problems that now reach enormous proportions. It is now customary to speak of the accumulation of environmental problems we, as a human race, experience as global in dimension. Geographers and others use the term **global change** to describe the combination of political, economic, social, historical, and environmental problems with which human beings across Earth must currently contend. Very little, if anything, has escaped the embrace of globalization, least of all the environment.

global change: combination of political, economic, social, historical, and environmental problems at the world scale

In fact, no other period in human history has transformed the natural world as profoundly as have the past 500 years. Although we reap the benefits of a modern way of life, it is critical to recognize that these benefits have not been without cost. Furthermore, it has been argued that in too many cases, the costs have accrued disproportionately to the poor. A growing political consciousness of these costs among the world's poor has resulted in a movement known as environmental justice.

Activists in the **environmental justice** movement consider the pollution of their neighbourhoods through such elements as nearby factories and hazardous waste dumps to be the result of a structured and institutionalized inequality that is pervasive in both the capitalist core and the periphery. They see their struggles as distinct from the more middle-class and mainstream struggles of such groups as the Sierra Club and Greenpeace. These activists have come to conceptualize their struggles as rooted in their economic status. Thus, these struggles are not about quality-of-life issues, such as whether any forests will be left to hike in, but about issues of sheer economic and physical survival. At a time when rising sea levels, among other possible environmental crises, threaten to create a whole new category of migrants— the environmental refugees—issues of human security have increasingly been placed on the agenda of governments around the world (see **Geography Matters 4.4— Disasters**). As a result, the answer to the questions raised by environmental justice activists must be directed toward the redistribution of economic and political resources. Such questions are not easily resolved in a court of law but speak to more

environmental justice: movement reflecting a growing political consciousness, largely among the world's poor, that their immediate environs are far more toxic than those in wealthier neighbourhoods

Changing Places: The Effects of Resource Depletion and Technological Change on the Geography of Atlantic Canada

The effects of changing technology and resource exploitation on altering settlement patterns and people's sense of place are well illustrated by the evolution of the fisheries of Atlantic Canada (**Figure 4.3.1**). Changes in the way that maritime resources have been harvested over the centuries have created a series of differing settlement patterns that have then been re-created to meet the continuing challenges of resource depletion. A brief examination of these particular changes will show how, in more general terms, space and place are profoundly governed by environmental and economic considerations, and how these considerations, in turn, are affected by our approaches to place.

Fishing has been a way of life in Atlantic Canada for centuries, and it began with the Aboriginal fisheries. Archaeological evidence from L'Anse Amour in Labrador and Port au Choix in Newfoundland indicates that a sophisticated technology for catching fish in estuaries using toggling harpoons and nets was in use by 7500 B.C. and supported small, seasonal coastal settlements (**Figure 4.3.1a**).

This pattern of settlement and resource use was slowly undercut by the entry of Europeans into the fisheries. Taking their lead from the Basque exploitation of whales and cod in the Gulf of the St. Lawrence (**Figure 4.3.1b**), Britain and France created a migratory fishery, from the seventeenth century onward, to develop the resources of their new colonies. Under this system, vessels arrived every year to fish and dry their catch for transport back the same year to Europe. Such a system of dependency, articulated by core countries and understandable only in terms of European economic space, resulted in no permanent settlers in Atlantic Canada. (The effects of newly introduced European diseases and brutality on the Aboriginal population also removed many traces of the previous settlement pattern.)

There is evidence that the migratory fisheries in some areas soon showed clear signs of depletion. For example, one early eighteenth-century observer remarked, "Though there be Harbours and conveniences on shoare for the making of Fish there is not fishing ground or can constantly be fish enough for so many Boates as they have kept."[44] Despite such warnings, Europe's increasing population provided a ready market for dried cod and became the impetus for a greater exploitation of the fisheries off Canada's Atlantic coasts. One way to increase yields was to be among the first on the fishery each year; another was to fish the unexploited stocks of the Grand Banks and Labrador. Both methods were greatly facilitated by the development of small permanent settlements on the coasts of Newfoundland and Labrador. In 1675, for example, there were about 1700 overwinterers on the English coast of Newfoundland.

Such settlements, or outports as they would later become known, became the main type of place associated with the exploitation of the fisheries until the 1950s. Small clusters of houses, fish-drying areas, fishing huts, and jetties composed the typical outport (**Figure 4.3.1c**). Built of wood, the impermanence of individual structures (houses were even hauled to new locations) belied the indelible connection such places had with the landscape. With their orientation to the coast, and their lack of any other focus, the geography of such settlements indicates their total reliance on the sea for their support. Ironically, perhaps, despite the fact that the very existence of these communities depended on an increasingly globalized market (dried cod was traded in Europe, Africa, the Caribbean, and the United States), the outports were otherwise almost completely isolated. Often located in remote and inhospitable coves to reach the fisheries, the inhabitants of these communities found themselves isolated from other outports. The lack of roads and the undeveloped state of their hinterlands only added to the self-reliance of such settlements and the development of localized customs and traditions.

By 1864, the Newfoundland fishery was showing signs of decline. The average catch per fisherman had dropped by 25 percent, and many blamed overfishing by the "swarms of French and American ships . . . seen busily employed dragging forth the treasures of the deep."[45] One important result was that most fishers withdrew from the Labrador fishery, which was left to the Newfoundlanders, and began fishing the banks off Nova Scotia and Newfoundland using new fishing methods. In the 1870s, for example, vessels from Lunenburg sailed to the Grand Banks, where their dories collected the cod from mile-long (almost 2 kilometres) baited trawl lines known as "ganglings." The town quickly flourished on the strengths of this new technology and its newly developed rail links to outside markets in New England and central Canada (**Figure 4.3.2**). The fact that the region's outports, not having such links, found themselves increasingly bypassed proved to be an ominous sign of the future.

Twentieth-century changes spelled the end not only of the North Atlantic cod but also of the outports that had so long depended on it. Certainly, nothing could have prepared the Canadian and the Newfoundland and Labrador fishing industry for the shock of the introduction of steam trawlers after 1914, onboard refrigeration units in the

---

[44]Original spelling, punctuation, and grammar are retained. Quoted in C. Grant Head, *Eighteenth Century Newfoundland: A Geographer's Perspective*. Toronto: McClelland and Stewart, 1979, pp. 5–36.

[45]Raymond B. Blake, *From Fishermen to Fish: The Evolution of Canadian Fishery Policy*. Toronto: Irwin Publishing, p. 19.

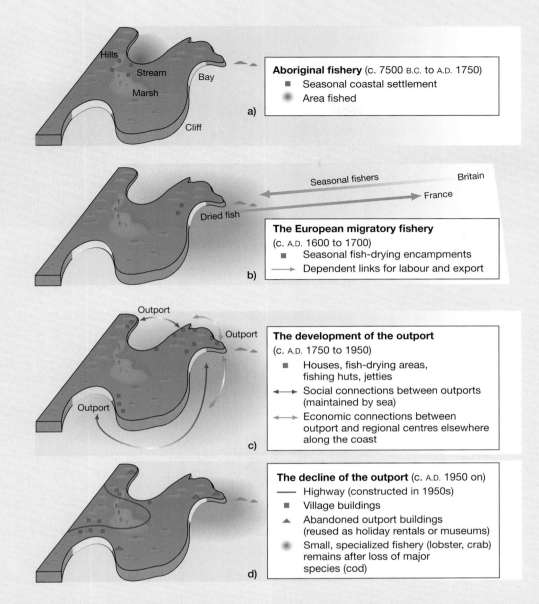

Figure 4.3.1 Changing places: A model of the evolution of the fisheries of Atlantic Canada and its effects on place   This idealized sequence of diagrams shows how changes in the exploitation of Atlantic Canada's fisheries have fundamentally altered that region's meaning of "place" over the centuries. The changes are shown in four simplified stages, (a) to (d). In (a), the early Aboriginal fishery, we find an essentially self-contained, seasonal community located at the head of a bay, based on estuary fishing, and drawing its sense of place from the local environment. That situation is fundamentally altered by European contact. The development of a migratory fishery, (b), creates a series of temporary places that are not homes and that have no connection with their location. Rather they are part of a settlement system that is organized (or "articulated") around British and French ports. They have turned their backs on Canada and draw their meaning as places from their dependency on Europe. The transition from this system to one focused on more regionally based trade, (c), sees the replacement of Europe with the trading hubs of Atlantic Canada (such as Halifax or St. John's) and the growth of permanent settlements or outports. Small and often very remote, these outport communities drew their sense of place from their maritime location. Oriented toward the sea, from which came their livelihood, and located often on rugged peninsulas to reach the expanding fisheries, outports were strung out along the coast and had little connection with the inland interior. Indeed, they maintained social and economic ties with other outports more easily by sea than they did by land. In such a milieu, the classic outport sense of place was developed based on very local social practice and knowledge of the environment. However, as (d) shows, this situation begins to alter by the 1950s. The isolation of the outports was eradicated by the construction of inland highways, and their economic purpose was eliminated by, first, the refocusing of fish processing in larger and larger centres, and, second, by the cod moratoria of the 1990s. In fact, the outports were abandoned; houses were rebuilt along the new highways, and streets now face inland—the source of their new identity. Meanwhile, nostalgia for the past ensures that the meaning of place is once more transformed—in this case, as abandoned outports become "places of memory" for tourists and those who have left.

1930s, and the enormous factory-freezer vessels developed from the 1960s. The greater capacity and speed of these new vessels rapidly shifted the focus from the traditional salt fisheries to new markets in fresh and frozen fish. This shift ended local production by individual fishers and the opened the door to capital-intensive, industrialized

Figure 4.3.2   Lunenburg, Nova Scotia

Figure 4.3.3   The outport as a place of memory   Newfoundland as a place of nostalgia is celebrated in countless photographs such as this view.

processes based on packing and cold storage facilities in a limited number of centres. The fact that most of the European fleets were subsidized by their own governments made it hard for Canadians to compete and especially hard for outport production (which depended on small, labour-intensive production techniques) to reduce costs or become more efficient. Importantly, the shift also hastened the ultimate collapse of the cod fishery by increasing the demands placed on this resource.

As early as the 1950s, following its joining the Confederation, Newfoundland and Labrador endeavoured to move people from outports to larger centres where they could be provided with access to schools, hospitals, and electricity (**Figure 4.3.1d**). The outrage this caused in some circles, however, showed many politicians how important the "attachment to place" could be, and it framed both federal and provincial policy until the cod moratorium of 1992. The outport way of life had by now become the stuff of tradition, a memory hallowed by those who had left to find work elsewhere and celebrated in academic research and literature. In effect, the meaning of place was undergoing another transformation: at the same time that the outport was losing its relevance in economic space, it was beginning to serve as a place of memory with which to combat the processes of modernization sweeping the region (**Figure 4.3.3**).

"It is like coming home to another place and time," writes McGill architect Robert Mellin in his fascinating 2003 study of the small outport of Tilting on Fogo Island, 13 kilometres (8 miles) off the northeastern shore of Newfoundland.[46] Writer E. Annie Proulx used local dialect and customs to convey the uniqueness of such places in her novel *The Shipping News,* while the book's film adaptation, using another approach, relied on use of the distinctive landscapes of the Newfoundland and Labrador coast for the same purpose. A third example, and one which draws directly on geographic concepts, is the work *Places of Presence* by artist Marlene Creates, in which she uses photographs, found objects, and "memory maps" to show how the Newfoundland outport, such as Lewisporte, "is not an abstract physical location, but a *place,* charged with personal significance, shaping the images we have of ourselves."[47]

For the outport to endure as a place with such meaning, fishing had to be defended as a way of life. This meant that despite evidence of a declining fishery (**Figure 4.3.4**) and the clear need to reduce not only the foreign fleets within Canada's 200-nautical-mile limit but also the number of Canadian fishers, reductions to Canada's own exploitation of its fisheries was put off until it was too late. Despite the obvious inefficiencies, the need to preserve jobs in the outports also meant that a greater number of fish plants were supported than were needed, and a rationalization of the industry into fewer major processing centres was delayed. The fact that the decision to protect the social and economic role of the outport had to be one made at the expense of the environment illustrates the insuperable problem facing policy-makers in those years.

With almost no cod to harvest, many of the outports are now redundant. It is estimated that perhaps as many as 1200 such communities across Atlantic Canada are in this position. Their populations are now faced with hard decisions on whether to leave the outport or to retrain for other occupations. Some communities will survive through the development of new fisheries for crab and such, but they will never be the same as they once were: strictly controlled access to scarce fishing quotas will undoubtedly make such communities far more economically polarized than before. But others will disappear, their disappearance warning that unless we learn to protect the needs of the fish populations before we consider our own needs, we can expect further fundamental changes in place.

[46]Robert Mellin, *Tilting: House Launching, Slide Hauling, Potato Trenching, and Other Tales from a Newfoundland Fishing Village.* New York: Princeton Architectural Press, 2003, p. 2.

[47]Marlene Creates, *Places of Presence: Newfoundland Kin and Ancestral Land.* Killick Press: St. John's, Newfoundland, 1997, p. 6.

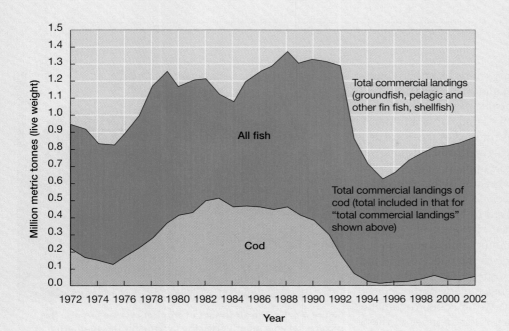

Figure 4.3.4 Canada's declining cod fishery, 1972–2002 This graph shows government data for all commercial landings by live weight (in metric tonnes) in the Atlantic region (Nova Scotia, New Brunswick, Prince Edward Island, and Newfoundland and Labrador) and Quebec. The effects of the decline in cod fishing are clear, as is the growing exploitation of other species (especially shellfish) since the early 1990s.   (*Source:* This graph is based on data from Fisheries and Oceans Canada, Statistical Services, 1972–2002, available online at **www.dfo-mpo.gc.ca/communic/statistics**.)

complex issues, such as the nature of racism, of sexism, and of capitalism as a class-based economic system.

CONCLUSION

The relationship between society and nature is very much mediated by institutions and practices, from technology to religious beliefs. In this chapter, we have seen how the nature–society relationship has changed over time and how the globalization of the capitalist world economy has had more of a widespread impact on attitudes and practices than any cultural or economic system that preceded it.

Ancient humans apparently displayed a reverential attitude toward the natural world, an attitude still evident among indigenous populations in many parts of the New World as well as Africa and Asia. With the emergence of Judaism and, later, Christianity, humans adopted a more dominant attitude about nature. The expansion of European trade, followed by colonization and eventually industrialization, broadcast worldwide the belief that humans should take their place at the apex of the natural world. The Judeo-Christian attitude toward nature as it was taken up by the emergence of the capitalist economic system is the most pervasive shaper of nature–society interactions today.

Besides exploring the history of ideas about nature, this chapter has also shown that society and nature are interdependent and that events in one part of the global environmental system affect conditions in the system elsewhere. The nuclear accident in Chernobyl taught us this lesson when nuclear fallout from Ukraine was spread throughout the globe in the days following the reactor meltdown.

Finally, this chapter has also shown that events that have occurred in the past shape the contemporary state of society and nature. The fallout from Chernobyl has been absorbed not only into the bodies of meltdown survivors but also into the bodies of their children who were born after the disaster.

In short, the environment has been globalized along with the economy. We can now speak of a global environment in which not only the people but also the physical environments in which they live and work are linked in complex and essential ways.

Disasters

On May 2 and 3, 2008, tropical cyclone Nargis hit southern Myanmar (Burma) with almost no warning (**Figure 4.4.1**). As many as 130 000 people were killed. Reports from the United Nations Children's Fund (UNICEF) noted that at least 1.5 million people were affected by the storm and its aftermath. The storm struck towns and farmland along the banks of the Irrawaddy river, and its impacts were probably greater than they might have been because of this area's density of human settlement, and because of the clearance of swamplands that might have served to buffer some of the effects of the wind-driven waves. However, in terms of increasing the cyclone's effects, nothing could compare with Myanmar's own government. Due to the reluctance of the ruling regime in Myanmar to allow outside aid into the country, offers of help were unable to reach many of those most in need. In one telling example, the World Food Programme (potentially the largest emergency relief supplier in these cases) was only able to deliver one-fifth of the 375 tonnes of food a day that it estimated had to be airlifted into the country because its planes were denied access. Simple steps (such as the provision of water purification units), that, if they had been taken quickly, would have enabled more to survive and others to recover more quickly, were not taken, while longer-term emergency measures (including the construction of provisional housing and the re-equipping of farms and fishing boats) were not possible.[48]

Only 10 days later, on 12 May 2008, an extremely powerful earthquake in Sichuan in southwestern China highlighted the differences in response. With as many as 75 000 to 100 000 people killed; many towns and villages virtually levelled around the quake's epicentre; and many of the area's roads rendered impassable, the challenge of providing relief proved challenging. Within three days, however, the government had ordered over 100 000 troops into the areas most affected by the disaster and international relief operations were allowed immediate access. Japan, for example, was able to send an earthquake response team, and funds raised by Canadian charities were quickly dispatched to Sichuan.[49]

The impact of a disaster always raises many questions—why did it happen? What can we do to help? What does the disaster mean? Some of these questions are more immediate than others—certainly, the most urgent would be, how can we best get aid to the victims?[50] Other questions, of a long-term nature, are ultimately more important because in their

Figure 4.4.1   The aftermath of tropical cyclone Nargis. This picture, taken a month after the cyclone hit the southern Irrawaddy delta region of Myanmar on 2–3 May 2008, shows homes damaged in Nyaung Wai village in the township of Kyauktan 49 km (30 miles) south of Yangon.

answers lie the real solutions to how we can successfully deal with such disasters in the future. Such questions concern what the disaster reveals about long-term environmental changes or the nature of society and the distribution of economic wealth, which fundamentally influences how a disaster will affect a population and its ability to recover.

Geography is well situated to deal with both types of questions—those that deal with immediate problems and those that focus on the more long-term or root problems. For example, knowledge of Earth's processes enables physical geographers (or geomorphologists) to understand the conditions of slope formation, soil cohesion, and amounts of rainfall that will lead to catastrophic mudslides in specific hilly regions, such as in Peru or British Columbia.

But above this, an understanding of the economic processes that structure the spaces of the world-system (see Chapter 2) allows geographers to realize that the actual impact of such disasters is related to the ability of the local economy to cope: Peruvian villagers have less financial ability to recover from the loss of their houses and fields than do many who have bought ocean-view properties in Vancouver. In this sense, disasters map the inequalities of the world-system because they point to regions that lack, or are denied, the resources to respond to a crisis.

The reluctance of people to leave areas that are so liable to disaster is itself a phenomenon that modern geography is able to examine. The love of place (or *topophilia*) that we will look at more fully in Chapters 5 and 6 is one that binds people so strongly to areas that they love that even knowledge of almost certain disaster will not prompt evacuation. Examples of this behaviour include the refusal of long-term residents to leave the slopes of Mount St. Helens immediately before the volcanic eruption and the continuing desire

---

[48]United Nations Children's Fund, "UNICEF on the Ground in Myanmar Delivering Life-Saving Supplies." Press release, accessed 18 July 2008 at **www.unicef.ca/portal/SmartDefault.aspx**.

[49]"Days of Disaster: Two Natural Disasters, Two Very Different Responses." *The Economist*, 15 May 2008.

[50]A useful introduction to the provision of aid: Adrian Ward, Raymond Apthorpe, and John Borton (eds.), *Evaluating International Humanitarian Action: Reflections from Practitioners.* London and New York: Zed Books, 2001.

of Winnipeggers to remain in that city despite the obvious threats of Red River floods in the future.[51]

Finally, geographers have come to understand that because the natural environment and the human realm are so intimately connected, disasters are created by how individual societies use and interact with the natural world. Mudslides, according to this interpretation, are as much a result of human activity (building or farming on steep slopes) as they are of natural causes. In this sense, disasters are a direct result of the "political ecology" of an area (a term defined in Chapter 9), the result perhaps of how a particular economic system forces the poor to farm only on land of no commercial value (such as on steep slopes) and, by forcing this to happen, is itself a cause of the deforestation or unsustainable farming that such groups must employ to support themselves. (We will explore ideas of political ecology further in Chapter 5, and we will provide some interesting examples from the work of Canadian scholar Thomas Homer-Dixon concerning his theory of environmental scarcity in Chapter 9).

We have already seen in this chapter how the separation of humans and nature has been seen by scholars as a major cause of our inability to realize how human activity and the natural environment interconnect. The very word *disaster* perpetuates that mindset because it implies that a separate natural force has wreaked untold devastation on a passive and uninvolved population that must now struggle to get back on its feet. In this sense, nature is almost seen as an enemy, a threat that somehow can be "fixed" if we can get the engineering right. But this may be the wrong way to think—the word *disaster* interprets the world from a human point of view; perhaps the phrase *extreme natural event* might be more useful to our understanding.

Certainly, the latest work by disaster scholars suggests that the impact of such an extreme natural event (be it flood or earthquake) only becomes a disaster to the extent that our economy has placed people in the path of that catastrophe, to the extent that our cultures view nature as a separate entity or threat, and to the extent that our own societies are unable to rebuild themselves. In this sense, then, although natural events are out of our hands, disasters are socially constructed.

It is therefore imperative, according to this approach, that we turn our attention to root causes (such as poverty and social inequality) that create or heighten the *socio-economic vulnerability* of the populations who are most at risk. For this reason, the analysis of such types of social or economic vulnerability has engaged the attention of most leading scholars in the field of disaster research since 1983, when Kenneth Hewitt (professor of geography and environmental studies at Wilfrid Laurier University) first developed the concept. More recent work by geographers has contributed to this type of analysis by defining *spaces of vulnerability*—those areas in which socioeconomic circumstances predispose

populations to a crisis.[52] In this approach, disasters are more explainable in terms of the "normal" order of things (that is, the distribution of wealth or power in a society) than in the accidental geophysical features of a place.[53]

With these thoughts as background, let us now consider two other recent disasters as examples of the challenges that such catastrophes place on human society: the 2004 Indonesian tsunami, one of the worst floods in human history, and the 2005 Hurricane Katrina, one of the worst disasters in North American history.

The 2004 Indonesian Tsunami

"On 26 December 2004 an earthquake measuring 9.0 on the Richter Scale struck the far western coast of northern Sumatra, triggering massive tidal waves, or tsunamis, that hit coastal areas in countries all round the Indian Ocean Rim—from Indonesia to Somalia, a total of 226 000 people are presumed to have died in the disaster."[54]

The sheer scale of the disaster caused by the tsunami is hard to grasp. However, reports provided by the International Federation of the Red Cross and Red Crescent Societies (IFRC) in their *World Disasters Report 2005* allow us to begin to see a picture of the tragedy and its aftermath in South Asia (**Figures 4.4.2a and 4.4.2b**).

In Aceh itself, the Indonesian region closest to the epicentre of the earthquake that triggered the tsunami, the devastation was enormous, the result of both quake damage and flooding because of the tidal wave along the coasts. The IFRC reports that on Aceh, the disaster left 164 000 people dead or missing and more than 400 000 homeless. The scale of the disaster meant that settlements scattered along hundreds of kilometres of coast were cut off, and relief workers found it extremely hard to reach survivors in time.

The report observes that because of the extent of this disaster, "it rapidly became the most reported and well-funded disaster in history," a situation that ironically had its own surprising consequences. For example, the unprecedented levels of aid led to what the IFRC report calls a "struggle for beneficiaries" as each of the 200 aid agencies in the region tried to find people to help and to very limited information-sharing among groups as each

---

[51]The cost of Winnipeg's new floodway is estimated at $665 million. Julius Strauss, "Money Flows to Stem the Tide of Winnipeg's Roaring Red." *Globe and Mail*, 15 September 2005, p. A3.

[52]Kenneth Hewitt (ed.), *Interpretations of Calamity*. Winchester, MA: Allen and Unwin, 1983.

[53]An excellent introduction to research on disasters, Anthony Oliver-Smith, "Theorizing Disasters: Nature, Power and Culture." In Susanna M. Hoffman and Anthony Oliver-Smith (eds.), *Catastrophe and Culture: The Anthropology of Disaster*. Santa Fe: School of American Research Press, 2003, pp. 23–47. A more challenging exposition of the ideas in this paragraph is found in the work of the eminent geographer David Harvey, *Justice, Nature and the Geography of Difference*. Cambridge, MA: Blackwell, 1996.

[54]The quotation is taken from an International Federation of the Red Cross and Red Crescent Societies 2005 summary of the interactive map (see **www.ifrc.org/what/disasters/response/tsunamis/map.asp**). The summary concludes that by mid-2005, the Red Cross and Red Crescent had spent more than US$456 million on tsunami relief efforts and that more than 1 million people had received aid. The December 2005 issue of the *Geographical Journal* contains five very valuable analyses by geographers on the effects of the tsunami.

Figure 4.4.2   (a) Before the Indian Ocean tsunami; (b) The aftermath of the Indian Ocean tsunami

"jealously guarded their information to protect their niche." Most agencies flocked to the devastated west coast of Aceh, to the detriment of more than 150 000 people displaced on the east coast, who received far less help.

Interestingly, the IFRC reports that "although international agencies were right in guessing that water, food, and shelter would be survivors' initial needs, they were wrong to assume these needs would not be covered by the Indonesians themselves. Agencies did little to suppress the myth of disaster victims dependent on external aid to survive."[55]

In the wake of the tsunami, Canadians were among the many who responded generously to the crisis. As but one illustration of this, according to a 23 June 2005 report from UNICEF, Canadian individuals, businesses, schools, and other organizations raised a total of C$23 million for UNICEF's tsunami work, a figure that was increased by a further C$15 million from the Canadian International Development Agency, to fulfill the government's pledge to match private donations. In all, it is estimated that the government matched about C$150 million in donations for relief efforts for the tsunami victims.[56]

Canadian efforts did not stop with financial aid. Geography students from the University of Ottawa teamed up with Ottawa-based web-mapping company DM Solutions Group to respond to a request from the Indian government to create a tsunami disaster mapping portal. Constructed within a week, this website aimed to help those involved in tsunami reconstruction and relief work by providing important geographical information, such as road maps, earthquake epicentres, and mortality statistics.[57]

Hurricane Katrina

"It's as if the entire Gulf Coast were obliterated by the worst kind of weapon you can imagine," said U.S. President George W. Bush of the devastation of Hurricane Katrina.[58]

At eight o'clock on the morning of Monday, 29 August 2005, the eye of Hurricane Katrina hit the Mississippi Delta, a few kilometres east of New Orleans on the Louisiana coast, with the force of a category 4 hurricane. With wind speeds of 215 kilometre per hour (135 miles per hour) and a diameter more than 320 kilometres (200 miles) across, meteorologists believe this hurricane was, in fact, the most powerful ever to have hit the United States. The consequences for New Orleans and surrounding states were immediate and severe (**Figures 4.4.3a and 4.4.3b**).

Overall estimates on the economic consequences of the disaster suggest that the total cost of rebuilding the region will be more than US$100 billion dollars, making Hurricane Katrina the most costly disaster in U.S. history and the costliest that insurers have ever faced.[59] The total may well be higher when the full impact is computed. In the New Orleans area alone, 500 000 workers were evacuated and 150 000 properties were damaged. The local tourist industry (worth US$7 billion per year) was destroyed, and local fishing fleets (responsible for 30 percent of the U.S. seafood market) have been largely eliminated. Shipping was interrupted, ports destroyed, and the Gulf's oil and gas installations so badly hit that experts predicted a 30 percent rise in heating oil prices.

The effects of Hurricane Katrina have been enormous. From Louisiana to Florida, an area of more than 145 000 square kilometres (90 000 square miles) was declared a federal disaster area. Within the first two weeks after the hurricane hit, the U.S. federal government approved a total of US$62.3 billion in disaster relief.

But perhaps the last word on the hurricane should go to Pierce Lewis, emeritus professor of geography at Pennsylvania State University, who writes of the power of place in any future rebuilding: "Whether we rebuild

[55]The International Federation of Red Cross and Red Crescent Societies, *World Disasters Report 2005*. Geneva: IFRC, 2005. The quotation is from Chapter 4, "Information Black Hole in Aceh," available online at **www.ifrc.org/publicat/wdr2005/chapter4.asp**.

[56]Jane Taber and Brian Laghi, "Ottawa to Match Quake Aid." *Globe and Mail*, 12 October 2005, p. A1.

[57]The website is **www.dmsolutions.ca/solutions/tsunami.html** and is described more fully in Jan Dutkiewicz, "Map Aid." *Canadian Geographic* 125(2), 2005, p. 30.

[58]Quoted in *National Geographic*'s special issue "Katrina." *National Geographic*, September 2005, p. 43. The paragraphs that follow draw on material in this publication, which contains a very valuable collection of maps, photographs, and analyses of the hurricane.

[59]Insurance estimates are from "Assessing the Damage." *The Economist*, 17 September 2005, p. 73.

**Figure 4.4.3
(a) The gulf coast;
(b) The aftermath of
Hurricane Katrina**

New Orleans or not is an ethical and aesthetic question— one not to be answered glibly by politicians or academic savants. Despite what doomsayers have proclaimed, New Orleans was not destroyed. The community of people called New Orleans has dispersed for a time, and many (if not most) will return to their beloved city."[60]

The Future

In seeking to understand what disasters mean, we can do no better than to continue with the remarks of geographer Pierce Lewis:[61]

> When attention was drawn to the perilousness of New Orleans, those who noted the fact usually shrugged, remarking with enthusiasm on the ability of man to conquer nature. To be sure, people said, the engineers had seemingly "solved" the problem of river flooding. But nobody could divert a hurricane from hitting New Orleans head-on. Scientists at Louisiana State University and elsewhere had warned that New Orleans' luck simply could not hold, but those warnings were taken

with the same kind of optimistic insouciance that had long been among Orleanians' most endearing qualities. Technology had solved the problem in the past. Would it not do so in the future?

In fact, New Orleans was a disaster waiting to happen. Technology and a willful ignorance of the environment had enabled settlement to occur in a low-lying area, and much of that settlement was of poorer people who could only afford to live in areas of the city below sea-level. These people did not have the resources to be able to evacuate when the need arose. In this way, when an extreme natural event in the form of Hurricane Katrina hit the Louisiana coast, its effects were translated into those of a disaster by the circumstances of the economy and the society that it hit. In this sense, any rebuilding of the city is problematic because, as described in *The Economist,* "the more cash that is spent rebuilding New Orleans, the more foolhardy Californians will be about where they build in their earthquake-prone state, confident that the government will bail them out if the 'Big One' strikes."[62]

The tsunami that hit Indonesia and South Asia in December 2004 can be similarly interpreted. There, an extreme natural event, an earthquake, set off a chain of natural events that were turned into a disaster by the many ways in which local socioeconomies in the region have been required to respond to the global economy. For example, experts have commented that the removal of mangrove swamps to engage in shrimp farming had the unforeseen side effect of removing natural coastal defences in many parts of the region—defences that would have dampened and perhaps eliminated the tidal wave's effects on some coastal communities. The over-reliance on local fishing and tourism as economic activities (both encouraged by international aid agencies) had led to increased populations in the most vulnerable areas of the region: the coastal belts. Finally, through urbanization and rural emigration, there had been a substantial increase in the size of the coastal communities in this region. What this all means is that the coastal areas of South Asia support a large number of people with limited economic means— people who are therefore very vulnerable to flood disasters.

Most commentators argue that the number of such disasters is likely to increase in the future, not only because global warming is likely to increase the strength and frequency of natural hazards (such as category 4 and 5 hurricanes, whose frequency has doubled in the last 35 years)[63] but also because the populations living in coastal regions are growing rapidly. In other words, we are creating the "perfect storm" for future catastrophes unless we can address the root causes of social and economic vulnerability that cause disasters.

---

[60]Quoted in "Katrina." Special issue, *National Geographic,* September 2005, p. 101.

[61]Ibid.

[62]"Hurricane Katrina: Whoaaah," *The Economist,* 17 September 2005, p. 14.

[63]See "Frequency and Ferocity of Hurricanes Increasing Dramatically." *Globe and Mail,* 21 September 2005, p. A16. On floods not associated with hurricanes or tsunamis, see S.N. Jonkman, "Global Perspectives on Loss of Human Life Caused by Floods." *Natural Hazards* 34, 2005, pp. 151–175.

In a piece comparing the 2004 tsunami and Hurricane Katrina, Johan Schaar of the International Federation of the Red Cross and Red Crescent Societies wrote:[64]

Whether you are from Banda Aceh or New Orleans, your assets in physical, material and social terms—that is, wealth, insurance and the ability to rely on others—will determine your ability to recover. Resilience is as much a community as an individual quality, and as we can see in Aceh and Louisiana, it is invariably the most vulnerable among us—the poor, the sick, the elderly and the isolated—who fare the worst when disaster strikes. . . . That is why poverty alleviation and disaster reduction are mutually reinforcing and must go hand in hand if we want to ensure safety and security for all.

[64]Johan Schaar, *Hurricane Katrina-Tsunami Recovery Comparisons.* International Federation of Red Cross and Red Crescent Societies, Opinion piece, 13 Sept 2005, available online at www.ifrc.org/docs/News/opinion05/05091301/index.asp.

MAIN POINTS REVISITED

- **Nature, society, and technology constitute a complex relationship. In our view, nature is both a physical realm and a social creation.** Recognizing that nature, society, and technology are interactive requires us also to acknowledge that humans are not separate from nature but are an integral part of it.

- **Because we regard nature as a social creation, it is important to understand the many social ideas of nature present in society today and especially the history of those ideas. The most prominent idea of nature in Western culture is derived from the Judeo-Christian tradition, a belief that nature is an entity to be dominated by humans.**
  Just because the Judeo-Christian tradition is a dominant view of nature does not mean it is the only one nor that it is superior to other views. It does mean, however, that we need to come to terms with how that tradition shapes our views and beliefs about nature if we want to change them.

- **Social relationships with nature have developed over the course of human history, beginning with the early Stone Age. The early history of humankind included people who revered nature as well as those who abused it. Urbanization and industrialization have had extremely degrading impacts on the environment.**

Although other societies have had substantial impacts on nature, the extent and degree of the contemporary core society's impact on the environment is unprecedented. Just as peripheral countries aim to achieve the level of prosperity enjoyed in the core, their economic practices also have similar environmental impacts. The result is that while core countries have begun to limit their negative environmental impacts, peripheral countries, in many ways, are just beginning to produce their own significant environmental problems.

- **The globalization of the world economy has meant that environmental problems are also global in their scope. Deforestation, acid rain, and global warming affect us all. Many new ways of understanding nature have emerged in the last several decades in response to these serious global crises.**
  Some of the most disturbing problems have to do with extensive land-use changes, such as deforestation, as well as with widespread air pollution from the burning of fossil fuels, which many scientists believe are leading to global climate change. In response to these serious global crises, many new ways of understanding nature have emerged in the last several decades, offering insight into our world as a complexly integrated natural system.

Key Terms

acid rain (p. 174)
animistic perspective on nature (p. 146)
biofuels (p. 168)
Buddhist perspective on nature (p. 146)
carbon benefit (p. 168)
carbon neutral (p. 168)
carbon tax (p. 173)
conservation (p. 149)
deep ecology (p. 150)
deforestation (p. 156)
demographic collapse (p. 160)

desertification (p. 178)
ecofeminism (p. 149)
ecological footprint (p. 144)
ecological imperialism (p. 160)
ecosystem (p. 155)
environmental ethics (p. 149)
environmental justice (p. 185)
fishing capacity (p. 180)
global change (p. 185)
Islamic perspective on nature (p. 146)
Judeo-Christian perspective on nature (p. 146)

maximum sustainable yield (MSY) (p. 180)
nature (p. 142)
oil sands (p. 167)
Paleolithic period (p. 151)
preservation (p. 149)
romanticism (p. 148)
siltation (p. 156)
society (p. 142)
Taoist perspective on nature (p. 146)
technology (p. 143)

Additional Reading

Blake, R.B., *From Fishermen to Fish: the Evolution of Canadian Fishery Policy.* Toronto: Irwin, 2000.
Cartwright, J. "Can Canada Afford Its Forest Industry?" *Policy Options* 17(9), November 1996, 5–18.

Chiotti, Q. "An Assessment of the Regional Impacts and Opportunities from Climate Change in Canada," *Canadian Geographer* 42, 1998, 380–393.
Coates, P. *Nature: Western Attitudes Since Ancient Times.* Berkeley: University of California Press, 1998.

Collingwood, R. *The Idea of Nature*. London: Oxford University Press, 1960.

Commission for Environmental Cooperation. *The North American Mosaic: A State of the Environment Report*. Montreal: Commission for Environmental Cooperation, 2001.

Crosby, A.W. *The Columbian Exchange: Biological and Cultural Consequences of 1492*. Westport, CT: Greenwood Press, 1972.

Crosby, A.W. *Ecological Imperialism: The Biological Expansion of Europe, 900–1900*. Cambridge: Cambridge University Press, 1986.

de Villiers, M. *Water: The Fate of Our Most Precious Resource*. Toronto: Stoddart, 1999.

Diamond, I., and G.F. Orenstein. *Reweaving the World: The Emergence of Ecofeminism*. San Francisco: Sierra Club Books, 1990.

Diamond, J. *Guns, Germs and Steel: A Short History of Everybody for the Last 13,000 Years*. London: Jonathan Cape, 1997.

Draper, D. *Our Environment: A Canadian Perspective*, 2nd ed. Scarborough: Nelson, 2002.

Draper, D., and B. Mitchell, "Environmental Justice Considerations in Canada," *Canadian Geographer* 45(1), 2001, 93–98.

Glacken, C. *Traces on the Rhodian Shore*. Berkeley: University of California Press, 1967.

Gould, P. *Fire in the Rain: The Democratic Consequences of Chernobyl*. Cambridge: Polity Press, 1990.

Homer-Dixon, T. (ed.). *Environment, Scarcity and Violence*. Princeton: Princeton University Press, 1993.

Hughes, J.D. *Pan's Travail: Environmental Problems of the Ancient Greeks and Romans*. Baltimore: The Johns Hopkins University Press, 1994.

Lovell, W.G. "Heavy Shadow and Black Night: Disease and Depopulation in Colonial Spanish America." *Annals of the Association of American Geographers* 82(3), 1992, 426–443.

Marsh, G.P. *Man and Nature*. New York: Scribner, 1964.

McKenzie, J.I. *Environmental Politics in Canada*. Toronto: Oxford University Press, 2002.

Merchant, C. *The Death of Nature: Women*. San Francisco: Harper & Row, 1979.

Oelschlager, M. *The Idea of Wilderness: From Prehistory to the Age of Ecology*. New Haven: Yale University Press, 1991.

Peters, R.L., and T.E. Lovejoy. *Global Warming and Biological Diversity*. New Haven: Yale University Press, 1992.

Simmons, I.G. *Environmental History: A Concise Introduction*. Oxford: Blackwell, 1993.

Smith, M., and L. Marx. *Does Technology Drive History? The Dilemma of Technological Determinism*. Cambridge, MA: MIT Press, 1995.

Thomas, W.L. (ed.). *Man's Role in Changing the Face of the Earth*. Chicago: University of Chicago Press, 1956.

Turner, B.L. II, et al. *The Earth Transformed by Human Action: Global and Regional Changes in the Biosphere over the Past 300 Years*. New York: Cambridge University Press, 1990.

Vita-Finzi, C. *The Mediterranean Valleys: Geological Changes in Historical Times*. Cambridge: Cambridge University Press, 1969.

Wilson, A. *The Culture of Nature: North American Landscape from Disney to the Exxon Valdez*. Toronto: Between the Lines, 1991.

Worster, D. *Nature's Economy: A History of Ecological Ideas*. Cambridge, U.K.: Cambridge University Press, 1977.

Exercises

Here you will find exercises and activities for each chapter. Unplugged exercises help you review chapter discussions, and pose ideas for your own human geography research. On the Companion Website exercises will require you have access to the internet.

Unplugged

1. Many communities have begun to produce an index of environmental stress, which is a map of the toxic sites of a city or region. One way to plot a rudimentary map is to use the local phone book as a data source. Use the Yellow Pages to identify the addresses of environmentally harmful and potentially harmful activities, such as dry-cleaning businesses, gas stations, automotive repair and car-care businesses, aerospace and electronic manufacturing companies, agricultural supply stores, where noxious chemicals may be produced or applied. Compile a map of these activities to begin to get a picture of your locale's geography of environmental stress.

2. Locate and read a natural history of the place where your college or university is located. What sorts of plants and animals dominated the landscape there during the Paleolithic period? Do any plants or animals continue to survive in altered form or unaltered from that period?

3. Colleges and universities are large generators of waste, from plain paper waste to biomedical and other sorts of wastes, which can have significant environmental impacts. Identify how your college or university handles this waste stream and how you, as a member of the academic community, contribute to it. Although different constituencies at the university/college are the source of this waste, where does the waste go when it leaves the university/college? Is it locally deposited? Does it go out of the province? Remember to trace the stream of all the types of waste, not just the paper.

On the Companion Website

This book has its own Companion Website where you will find additional resources—maps, photographs, data—as well as exercises and activities that relate to each chapter. To complete the Companion Website exercises, go to **www.pearsoned.ca/knox**. The following is a summary of the types of exercises created for this chapter.

1. The theme of "nature, society, and technology" featured in this chapter is explored online by our critical-thinking essay. It directs you to a website that explores the *nature, society, and technology* of the Incas, an early- and mid-sixteenth century pre-Columbian civilization. You will investigate the Inca's burial customs, deities, economy, transportation system, religion, and origin myth. In a thinking-spatially exercise, you will view and comment on maps demonstrating European expansion,

environmental change, and introduction of new diseases, plants, and animals in the New World. A series of multiple-choice questions, with electronic feedback, will test your understanding of chapter concepts.

2. The Audio Interview, Interview with George Lovell (Part 2), that accompanies this chapter has been conducted to highlight the issue of Old World and New World contacts discussed in this chapter, using the example of the survival and adaptation of the Maya of Central America. In addition, you will hear about some of the challenges geographers face when conducting field work, and the value of a geographical education – or, more importantly perhaps, of having a "geographical imagination". You will find a link to the Audio Interview, interview summary, and questions on the Companion Website for this chapter.

5

Mapping Cultural Identities

A distinctive feature of the cultural landscape of Greece, small wayside shrines (or *kandylakia*), such as the ones shown here in a supplier's yard in Sparta, are usually found along roadsides outside towns and villages, where they have been placed by adherents of the Greek Orthodox church for a variety of reasons. Some *kandylakia* are memorials for those who have died in nearby road accidents, but most have been placed either by the survivors of road accidents to thank their patron saints for their protection, or to commemorate in a more general way the region's patron saints.

The ancient and enduring Asian religion of Jainism had a complex worldview that incorporated the heavens as well as Earth, the human body as well as the wider universes. Much of the ancient religion—and its mapping of the cosmos—is still part of contemporary Jainism's belief system, which recognizes the transmigration of souls in a potentially endless round of birth and rebirth. The vertically stratified universe, with heaven above and hell below Earth, provided a field within which souls could properly locate themselves in their journey toward or away from their ultimate release from the cycle of birth and death (known as *moksa* in Jain but equivalent to *nirvana* in Buddhism). Each heaven and hell had its own specific properties. The figure of a woman or man, standing with arms akimbo, was often used to represent the universe with several graduated widths of hells and netherworlds joining Earth (or *Jamb–udv–ipa*) at the centre to several graduated widths of heaven at the top. As Earth, *Jamb–udv–ipa* consisted of several concentric rings of continents encircled by ring oceans. Each continent and sea was named, and regions (such as India and Pakistan), physical features (such as mountain ranges and rivers), and peoples of the real world were often named on the maps and paintings. The cosmos was often represented in the form of a human being because the Jains believed that the microcosm of the human body and the macrocosm of the universe were inseparable. **Figure 5.1** shows a typical representation of the Jain universe.

Figure 5.1   The Jain universe
This sixteenth-century painting from Gujarat, India, is a typical pictorial representation of the Jain view of the universe. The human figure includes elements representing the heavens, hells, and Earth, the middle world.

The way in which ancient Jains represented their understanding of their universes, their cosmographies, was highly influenced by their local surroundings, their knowledge of the world beyond their immediate region, and their religious beliefs about humans' place in the universe. Ancient maps, such as those drawn by the Jains and other South Asian groups, such as Buddhists and Hindus, provide a window into how religion shaped the way peoples thousands of years ago understood their relationship to their world and the wider universe. Our knowledge of our immediate environment and the larger world and universe of which it is a part is shaped by many knowledge systems, from science to religion.

Culture has been and continues to be a central concept in geography, although our understanding of its meaning and its impact have changed considerably over the last two decades. After providing background on some of the earliest approaches to cultural geography, we examine the many ways that geographers have explored the concept of culture and the insights they have gained from these explorations. We explore the questions: What counts as culture? How do geographers study it? Because of the size of the task, it will take us two chapters fully to answer these questions. In this chapter, we will try to answer these questions by examining how language, religion, and issues of group identity (such as nationalism and multiculturalism) shape and are shaped by cultures and, in the process, are responsible for the creation of cultural regions. In Chapter 6, we will turn our attention to the ways in which individuals have to interpret for themselves the distinct landscapes of these cultural regions.

MAIN POINTS

- Though culture is a central, complex concept in geography, it may be thought of as a way of life involving a particular set of skills, values, and meanings.
- Geographers are particularly concerned about how place and space shape culture and, conversely, how culture shapes place and space. They recognize that culture is dynamic and is contested and altered within larger social, political, and economic contexts.
- Like other fields of contemporary life, culture has been profoundly affected by globalization. However, globalization has not produced a homogenized culture so much as it has produced distinctive impacts and outcomes in different societies and geographical areas as global forces come to be modified by local cultures.
- Contemporary approaches in cultural geography seek to understand the roles played by politics and the economy in establishing and perpetuating cultures, cultural landscapes, and global patterns of cultural traits and cultural complexes.
- Cultural geography has been broadened to include analysis of gender, class, ethnicity, stage in the life cycle, and so on, in recognizing that important differences can exist within as well as between cultures.
- Cultural ecology, an offshoot of cultural geography, focuses on the relationship between a cultural group and its natural environment.
- Political ecologists also focus on human–environment relationships but stress that relationships at all scales, from the local to the global, are intertwined with larger political and economic forces.

CULTURE AS A GEOGRAPHICAL PROCESS

Geographers have long been involved in trying to understand the manifestations and impacts of culture on geography and of geography on culture. While anthropologists are concerned with the ways in which culture is created and maintained by human groups, geographers are interested not only in how place and space shape culture but also the reverse—how culture shapes place and space.

Anthropologists, geographers, and other scholars who study culture, such as historians, sociologists, and political scientists, agree that culture is a complex concept. Over time, our understanding of culture has been changed and enriched. A simple understanding of culture is that it is a particular way of life, such as a set of skilled activities, values, and meanings surrounding a particular type of economic practice. Or, to take a second example, the way of life established by religious belief can also form the basis for culture. Scholars also describe culture in terms of classical standards and aesthetic excellence in, for example, opera, ballet, or literature.

By contrast, the term *culture* has also been used to describe the range of activities that characterize a particular group, such as working-class culture, corporate culture, or teenage culture. Although all these understandings of culture are accurate, for our purposes they are only partial. Broadly speaking, **culture** is a shared set of meanings that are lived through the material and symbolic practices of everyday life (**Figure 5.2**). The "shared set of meanings" can include values, beliefs, practices, and ideas about religion, language, family, gender, sexuality, and other important identities. Culture is often subject to re-evaluation and redefinition, and ultimately altered from both within and outside a particular group.

Culture is a dynamic concept that revolves around complex social, political, economic, and even historical factors. This definition of culture is part of a longer, evolving tradition within geography and other disciplines, such as anthropology and sociology. We will look more closely at the development of the cultural tradition in geography in the following section, in which we discuss the debates surrounding culture within the discipline.

For much of the twentieth century, geographers, like anthropologists, have focused most of their attention on material culture as opposed to its less tangible symbolic or spiritual manifestations. Thus, while geographers have been interested in religion as an object of study, for a long time they have largely confined their work to examining its material basis. For example, they have explored the spatial extent of particular religious practices (for example, the global distribution of Buddhism) and the expression of religiosity (for example, the use of open-air altars in Saskatchewan, **Figure 5.3**). But in the last 20 or so years, the near-exclusive focus on material cultural practices has changed—driven by the larger changes that are occurring in the world around us.

As with agriculture, politics, and urbanization, globalization has also had complex effects on culture. Such terms as *world music* and *international television* are a reflection of the sense that the world has become a very small place, indeed, and people everywhere are sharing aspects of the same culture through the widespread influence of television and other media. Yet, as pointed out in Chapter 2, although powerful homogenizing global forces are certainly at work, the world has not become so uniform that place no longer matters. With respect to culture, just the opposite is true. Place matters more than ever in the negotiation of global forces, as local forces confront globalization and translate it into unique place-specific forms. Nothing perhaps better illustrates this than music, which has both the

culture: a shared set of meanings that are lived through the material and symbolic practices of everyday life

Figure 5.2   Youth culture   The term *culture* has been used to describe a range of practices characterizing a group. Pictured here is a youth culture known as *goth*. Hairstyle, dress, and body adornment, as well as a distinctive philosophy and music, characterize goth culture. Yet, culture is more than just the physical distinguishing aspects of a group. It is also a way in which groups derive meaning and attempt to shape the world around them.

Figure 5.3   Open air places of worship   Most places of worship across Canada are found indoors. Occasionally, however (as with this example of a Roman Catholic site near Forget, Saskatchewan), religious observance occurs in the open air. The purpose of such places is to show respect and devotion; they are also a more public display of religiosity.

formalism to preserve traditional cultural forms and the fluidity to adopt new characteristics. For example, the traditional French lyrics and tunes of the Acadians deported from Nova Scotia were merged in the Cajun music of Louisiana with African and Aboriginal-American rhythms, and played on a variety of instruments—including the French fiddle, the German accordion, and the washboard, a local addition. This distinctive style, with variants, such as zydeco, was altered yet again and became part of "world music" when Paul Simon combined it with the rhythmic pulses of South Africa's Ladysmith Black Mbaza in his 1986 *Graceland* album. International attention has not harmed traditional Cajun music, which, if anything, has enjoyed renewed interest in the last 20 years as Cajuns have sought to re-establish their regional identity as a French-speaking culture in North America. Cajun-inspired music has, not surprisingly, found a ready ear in Quebec, as the popularity of Zachary Richard indicates.

The place-based interactions occurring between culture and global political and economic forces are at the heart of cultural geography today. **Cultural geography** focuses on the ways in which space, place, and landscape shape culture at the same time that culture shapes space, place, and landscape. As such, cultural geography demarcates two important and interrelated parts. Culture is the ongoing process of producing a shared set of meanings, while geography is the dynamic setting in which groups operate to shape those meanings and, in the process, to form an identity and conduct their lives. Geography in this definition can be as small as the micro-space of the body and as large as the macro-space of the globe.

cultural geography: study of the ways in which space, place, and landscape shape culture at the same time that culture shapes space, place, and landscape

To consider how culture and geography interact in these ways, we will examine the geography of religion, the geography of language, and the various ways in which group identity are inscribed on the cultural landscape. Before we do, however, it is necessary to define what geographers mean when they use the terms *cultural landscape* and *cultural region*.

BUILDING CULTURAL COMPLEXES

Geographers have long been interested in the interactions between people and culture, and among space, place, and landscape. One of the most influential individuals in this regard was Carl Sauer, a geographer who taught at the University of California. Sauer was largely responsible for creating the "Berkeley school" of cultural geography (**Figure 5.4**). He was particularly interested in trying to understand the material expressions of culture by focusing on their manifestations in the landscape. This interest came to be embodied in the concept of the **cultural landscape,** a characteristic and tangible outcome of the complex interactions between a human group—with its own practices, preferences, values, and aspirations—and a natural environment. Sauer differentiated the cultural landscape from the natural landscape. He emphasized that the former was a "humanized" version of the latter, such that the activities of humans resulted in an identifiable and understandable alteration of the natural environment. **Figure 5.5** illustrates the idea through a listing of the differences between a natural landscape and a cultural landscape. In making such connections, Sauer was influenced by the work of George Perkins Marsh, whose 1864 book, *Man and Nature,* was one of the first to explore the links between human action and environmental change, and which provided the intellectual transition between the work of environmental determinists such as Edith Churchill Semple and Sauer himself.

Figure 5.4 Carl Sauer (1889–1975) Born in the U.S. Midwest of German-immigrant parents, Carl Sauer spent his career as a geographer at the University of California, Berkeley. He rejected environmental determinism as a way of understanding human geography and emphasized the uniqueness of landscape through the impact of both cultural and physical processes.

cultural landscape: a characteristic and tangible outcome of the complex interactions between a human group and a natural environment

For roughly five decades, interest in culture within geography largely followed Sauer's important work. His approach to the cultural landscape was ecological, and his many published works reflect his interest in trying to understand the myriad ways that humans transformed the surface of Earth. In his own words:

> The cultural landscape is fashioned from a natural landscape by a cultural group. Culture is the agent, the natural area is the medium, the cultural landscape is the result. Under the influence of a given culture, itself changing through time, the landscape undergoes development, passing through phases, and probably reaching

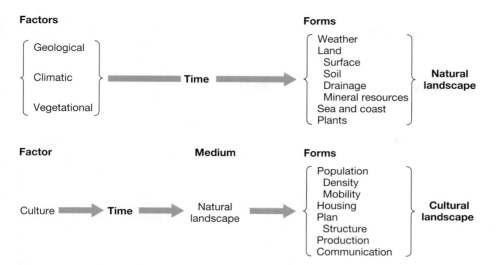

Figure 5.5 Sauer's cultural landscape
This illustration is a graphic representation of the ways in which the natural landscape and cultural landscapes are transformed. Physical features as well as climate factors shape the natural landscape. Cultural practices also have an important impact on it. The results of cultural factors are cultural forms, such as population distributions, patterns, and housing. Over time, people—through culture—reshape the natural landscape to meet their needs. (*Source:* Adapted from C. Sauer, "The Morphology of Landscape." In J. Leighly [ed.], *Land and Life: Selections from the Writings of Carl Ortwin Sauer.* Berkeley, CA: University of California Press. 1964, pp. 315–350.)

ultimately the end of its cycle of development. With the introduction of a different— that is an alien—culture, a rejuvenation of the cultural landscape sets in, or a new landscape is superimposed on remnants of an older one.[1]

In Europe, geographers interested in human interactions with the landscape produced slightly different approaches. For example, in Great Britain, the approach to understanding the human imprint on the landscape was given the term *historical geography*, while in France, it was conceptualized as *genre de vie*. **Historical geography**, very simply defined, is the geography of the past. One of its most famous practitioners was H.C. Darby, who attempted to understand how past geographies changed, or evolved, into more recent geographies (**Figure 5.6**). *Genre de vie*, a key concept in Paul Vidal de la Blache's approach to cultural geography in France, refers to a functionally organized way of life that is seen to be characteristic of a particular cultural group (**Figure 5.7**). *Genre de vie* centres on the livelihood practices of a group, which are seen to shape physical, social, and psychological bonds. Although emphasizing some landscape components over others or giving a larger or smaller role to the physical environment, all of these approaches placed the cultural landscape at the heart of their study of human–environment interactions. The region is still very important as a concept in today's cultural geography.

H.C. Darby most successfully implemented his historical approach to geography by developing a geography of the *Domesday Book*. William the Conqueror ordered the survey that became known as "Domesday" (from the Saxon word *dom*, or "judgment") to be compiled in 1085 so that he could have a list of his spoils of war. The book provides a rich catalogue of the ownership of every tract of land in England and of the conditions and contents of the lands at that time. For geographers like Darby and those scholars influenced by his approach, such data are invaluable for reconstructing past geographies, but they often emphasize economic factors at the expense of a cultural approach to the study of the past.

Vidal de la Blache, conversely, emphasized the need to study small, homogeneous areas to uncover the close relationships that exist between people and their immediate surroundings. He constructed complex descriptions of pre-industrial France that demonstrated how the various *genres de vie* emerged from the possibilities and constraints posed by local physical environments. Subsequently, he wrote about the changes in French regions brought on by industrialization, observing that regional homogeneity was no longer the unifying element. Instead, the increased mobility of people and goods had produced new, more complex

historical geography: the geography of the past

genre de vie: a functionally organized way of life that is seen to be characteristic of a particular cultural group

Figure 5.6 Professor Sir Henry Clifford Darby (1909–1992)
H.C. Darby argued that historical geography is an essential foundation for the study of all human geography. His own studies of past geographies were published in a series of Domesday Geographies of England. (*Source:* Preston. E. James and Geoffrey J. Martin, *All Possible Worlds: A History of Geographical Ideas,* 2nd ed. New York: John Wiley and Sons, 1981, p. 211.)

---

[1]C. Sauer, "The Morphology of Landscape." In J. Leighly (ed.), *Land and Life: Selections from the Writings of Carl Ortwin Sauer.* Berkeley, CA: University of California Press, 1964, pp. 315–350.

Figure 5.7 Paul Vidal de la Blache (1845–1919) Vidal de la Blache was a founder of the *Annales de geographie*, an influential academic journal that fostered the idea of human geography as the study of people–environment relationships. His most long-lasting conceptual contribution was *genre de vie*, which is the lifestyle of a particular region reflecting the economic, social, ideological, and psychological identities imprinted on the landscape. (*Source:* Preston E. James and Geoffrey J. Martin, *All Possible Worlds: A History of Geographical Ideas*, 2nd ed. New York: John Wiley and Sons, 1981, p. 211.)

cultural trait: a single aspect of the complex of routine practices that constitute a particular cultural group

geographies wherein previously isolated *genres de vie* were being integrated into a competitive, industrial economic framework. Anticipating the widespread impacts of globalization, Vidal de la Blache also recognized how people in various places struggled to mediate the big changes that were transforming their lives.

Cultural Traits: Canadian Vernacular Architecture

Geographers have long been interested in understanding specific aspects of culture, ranging from single attributes to complex systems. One simple aspect of culture of interest to geographers is the idea of special traits, which include such things as distinctive styles of dress, dietary habits, and styles of architecture. A **cultural trait** is a single aspect of the complex of routine practices that constitute a particular cultural group. As an illustration, let us pursue the example of *folk* and *vernacular* architecture, since this is a topic beloved by cultural geographers. In one of the most important pieces of work in North American cultural geography, Fred B. Kniffen showed how patterns of folk housing in the United States could be used to distinguish three major American cultural regions on the eastern seaboard and to track the subsequent diffusion of those cultures across the continent.[2] In the years that have followed, a distinguished group of geographers and anthropologists (most notably Terry Jordan and Henry Glassie) have added to the research on this topic.

Following in this tradition, recent research on Canada by Peter Ennals and Deryck Holdsworth has shown us how the single cultural trait of architecture can be studied and how it can contribute to the broader identification of cultural regions in this country (**Figure 5.8**). Their joint work shows that in the areas of Canada first settled by Europeans, migrants built houses that were very similar in style and building technique to those found in the areas of Europe from which they had come. In Newfoundland and Labrador, versions of English and Irish cottages were erected. In Acadia and Quebec, houses were built that copied the regional patterns found in France at the time.

Obviously, having no time to experiment and heavily conditioned by their own images of what a house should look like, these early settlers simply replicated the styles they knew. In this way, at least, Canada was "a simplification of Europe overseas," as some Canadian cultural geographers have described it. Certainly, as we shall see from Chapter 6, these settlers were engaged in their own version of "place making" and re-creating in this country a world they knew.

From about 1750, however, another element is added to the mix—that of fashion. By now, many Canadian settlers had become a little more prosperous and could afford to rebuild their houses. In doing so, they turned to styles affected by new ideals of domestic privacy and by the "polite" architecture of the neo-Georgian houses being built by Canada's elite for themselves. In this way, Ennals and Holdsworth argue that earlier *folk* styles were replaced by what they call *vernacular* architecture. This "everyday" or "common" architecture, developed in Canada, maintains a set of distinct regional styles, ranging from the exuberance of the porches of Lunenburg, Nova Scotia, to the "eyebrow" designs of the nineteenth-century Ontario farmhouse with its distinctive dormer window. The latter has become so quintessentially Ontarian that its design elements are echoed in many subdivisions currently under development across the province (**Figure 5.9**).

Increased immigration and growing urbanization in the nineteenth century did little to erode these patterns. In fact, they added their own distinctive contributions, since the need to adapt vernacular styles to the high-density demands of Canada's cities was met in different ways. In Montreal, for example, the duplex and triplex styles were developed, designs almost unique in North America, possibly inspired by the city's Scottish immigrants with their memories of Glaswegian tenement life.

---

[2]Fred B. Kniffen, "Folk Housing: Key to Diffusion." *Annals of the Association of American Geographers* 55, 1965, pp. 549–577.

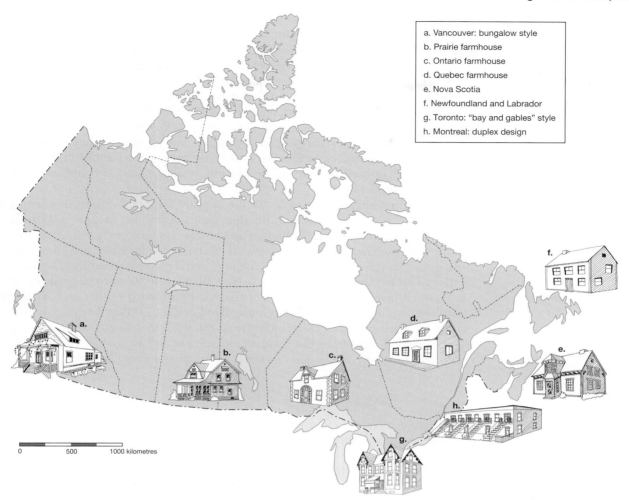

a. Vancouver: bungalow style

b. Prairie farmhouse

c. Ontario farmhouse

d. Quebec farmhouse

e. Nova Scotia

f. Newfoundland and Labrador

g. Toronto: "bay and gables" style

h. Montreal: duplex design

0   500   1000 kilometres

Figure 5.8   Vernacular architectural regions in Canada   Geographers have shown that architectural style is an important characteristic of the cultural region and that differences in architecture are one way of distinguishing different cultural regions. This map shows the major types of *vernacular* (that is, "everyday") domestic architecture found in Canada at the end of the nineteenth century. The pattern reflects the traditional, or "folk," architectural styles of Canada's major European colonizers, adapted to this country's environment and modified over time as more modern ideas about style diffused across Canada.   (*Sources:* Based on redrawings by Karine Arakelian. House types a and c–f based on Peter Ennals and Deryck W. Holdsworth, "The Look of Domestic Building, 1891." In William Dean et al., *Concise Historical Atlas of Canada.* Toronto: University of Toronto Press, 1998, Plate 30; house types b, g, and h from Peter Ennals and Deryck W. Holdsworth, *Homeplace: The Making of the Canadian Dwelling over Three Centuries.* Toronto: University of Toronto Press, 1998, pp. 195–196, 210.)

Figure 5.9   The present preserves the past   These houses in a new Orangeville, Ontario, subdivision echo architectural elements from earlier styles.

In Toronto, the classic farmhouse morphed into the gothic row house. During early twentieth-century expansion in Vancouver, the bungalow, perhaps inspired by immigrants from California, was the leading suburban form of housing.

Meanwhile, out on the Prairies, history was repeating itself with new waves of immigration. By the late nineteenth century, settlers from central Europe were building farmhouses in the styles of that region. From Verigin, Saskatchewan, to Dauphin, Manitoba, the farm architecture of Ukraine, Poland, and Russia was adopted as the design for barns, houses, and churches. Prosperity, when it occurred, was marked this time by the purchase of plans or ready-made houses from the T. Eaton Co. The vernacular architecture of the Prairies became a literally off-the-shelf, central Canadian design made in Toronto that could be seen in countless small towns across the west.

A love of rational planning and the lure of profit from mass production served to suppress regional differences in building styles during the second half of the twentieth century. However, postmodernism's rejection of uniformity (see Chapter 6) and the real estate industry's realization that "difference sells" have been more than sufficient to rejuvenate interest in Canadian regional patterns of vernacular architecture in recent times. This point has been developed by work carried out at McMaster University's geography department by Richard Harris and Nadine Dostrovsky[3] and can be pursued in more detail in their 2008 publication on the revival of historical styles of architecture in the modern suburb—a revival they suggest began in the 1960s in Canadian cities, coincided with inner-city gentrification and, since the 1980s, has favoured Victorian and neo-classical styles.

Cultural Regions

cultural region: the area within which a particular cultural system prevails

A concept key to traditional approaches in cultural geography is the cultural region. Although a **cultural region** may be quite extensive or very narrowly described and even discontinuous in its extension, it is the area within which a particular cultural system prevails. A cultural region is an area where certain cultural practices, beliefs, or values are more or less practised by the majority of the inhabitants.

Illustrations of cultural regions abound in Canada. For example, parts of New Brunswick, Nova Scotia, and Prince Edward Island compose the Acadian cultural region (**Figure 5.10**). The population of the area is made up mainly of a long-settled community of French-speaking, Roman Catholic people who have a series of distinct cultural traits, as we have already seen, for example, in connection with music, folk architecture, and, as we shall see below, language.

To take another example, the Manitoba lowlands (sometimes known as the Manitoba plain or the Agassiz region, after the glacial lake that once covered the area) is an area that was settled by hundreds of thousands of immigrants from continental Europe, who farmed this part of the province in the years before 1914. The settlers' adherence to an agricultural way of life and to their central European traditions serves to define this area as a cultural region. At a finer scale of analysis, this region is, in fact, made up of a great variety of subregions—each the home of a distinctive culture, which gives a specific flavour to a particular community. In their study *The Last Best West*, Yossi Katz and John Lehr provide a detailed analysis of the varied cultural landscapes that were established. They show, for example, how Mennonites, who emigrated from southern Russia in the 1870s, created very distinctive agricultural landscapes around Winkler, Altona, and Steinbach. The European nucleated village form and open-field system of collective farming that they initially reproduced in Manitoba were unusual in an area whose Anglo-American immigrants favoured dispersed settlement on land that was individually farmed. Although abandoned as a way of life in the 1920s, these settlement forms gave a

Figure 5.10   The Acadian region
The Acadian region of Canada preserves its cultural heritage through many visual reminders, as this picture of the Acadian flag at Grand Pré illustrates. The gold star at the top left is the Stella Maris (Star of the Sea). The national park at Grand Pré, Nova Scotia, is a memorial to the deportation of the Acadians in 1755.

[3]Nadine Dostrovsky and Richard Harris, "Style for the Zeitgeist: The Stealthy Revival of Historicist Housing Since the Late 1960s." *Professional Geographer* 60(3), 2008, pp. 314–332.

Figure 5.11   Ukrainian Catholic Church, Dauphin, Manitoba

social cohesion to Mennonite society that has contributed to the retention of their culture in this region of varied cultures. In describing this variety, John Warkentin has written, "Distinctive communities such as Icelanders at Gimli, Mennonites in Southern Manitoba, Ukrainians in the Dauphin area, French in St. Boniface and St. Pierre, Métis in southeast Manitoba, and Ontarians in Portage la Prairie are still visible"[4] (**Figure 5.11**).

To these well-known and established illustrations, we should add examples of ones that are still coalescing around shared cultural values. Around Nelson, in southeast British Columbia, for example, a long countercultural tradition has attracted a considerable number of artists, environmentalists, and community activists in recent years. Their impact on the landscape can be seen in developments as varied as the renovation of old Main Street stores into cooperatively-run stores selling local art and the individually designed houses and organic farms that can be found scattered along the nearby Slocan Valley.[5]

CULTURAL SYSTEMS

Broader than the cultural complex concept is the concept of a **cultural system**, a collection of interacting components that, taken together, shape a group's collective identity. A cultural system includes traits, territorial affiliation, and shared history, as well as other more complex elements, such as language. In a cultural system, it is possible for internal variation to exist in particular elements at the same time that broader similarities lend coherence. For example, Christianity unites all Protestant religions, and yet the practices of particular denominations—Lutherans, Episcopalians, and Quakers—vary. And, while Mexicans, Bolivians, Cubans, and Chileans exhibit variations in pronunciation, pitch, stress, and other aspects of vocal expression, they all speak Spanish. This means they share a key element of a cultural system (which, for these nationalities, also includes Roman Catholicism and a Spanish colonial heritage).

cultural system: a collection of interacting elements that, taken together, shape a group's collective identity

Geography and Religion

Two key components of a cultural system for most of the world's people are religion and language. **Religion** is a belief system and a set of practices that recognize the

religion: belief system and a set of practices that recognize the existence of a power higher than humans

[4]Yossi Katz and John C. Lehr, *The Last Best West: Essays on the Cultural Geography of the Canadian Prairies.* Jerusalem: Magnes Press, 1999; and John Warkentin, *A Regional Geography of Canada: Life, Land and Space,* 2nd ed. Scarborough: Prentice Hall, 2000, p. 403.

[5]See, for example, the Nelson and District Chamber of Commerce website at **www.discovernelson.com**, and click on "Arts and Culture" under "Attractions."

existence of a power higher than humans. Although religious affiliation is perhaps on the decline in some parts of the world's core regions, it still acts as a powerful shaper of daily life, from eating habits and dress codes to coming-of-age rituals and death ceremonies in both the core and the periphery. And, like language, religious beliefs and practices change as new interpretations are advanced or as new spiritual influences are adopted. The most important influence on religious change has been conversion from one set of beliefs to another. From the onset of globalization in the fifteenth century, religious *missionizing*—propagandizing and persuasion— and the conversion of non-Christian souls were key elements of religious change. In the 500 years since the onset of the Columbian Exchange, conversion of all sorts has escalated throughout the globe. In fact, since 1492, traditional religions have become dramatically dislocated from their sites of origin through missionizing and conversion as well as diaspora and emigration. Whereas missionizing and conversion are deliberate efforts to change the religious views of a person or people, diaspora and emigration involve the involuntary and voluntary movement of people who bring their religious beliefs and practices to their new locales.

diaspora: a spatial dispersion of a previously homogeneous group

Diaspora is a spatial dispersion of a previously homogeneous group. The processes of global political and economic changes that led to the massive movement of the world's populations over the last five centuries have also meant the dislodging and spread of the world's many religions from their traditional sites of practice. Religious practices have become so spatially mixed that it is a challenge to present a map of the contemporary global distribution of religion that reveals more than it obscures. This is because the global scale is too gross a level of resolution to portray the wide variation that exists among and within religious practices. **Figure 5.12**

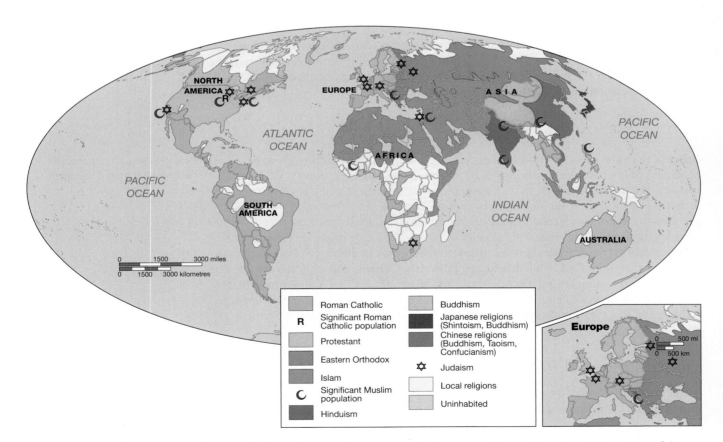

Figure 5.12 World distribution of major religions   The map shows a generalized picture of the world's major religions. Most of the world's peoples are members of one of these religions. Not evident on this map are the local variations in practices, as well as the many other different religions that are practised worldwide. (Although known in the West primarily as philosophies, Taoism and Confucianism both also developed religious traditions and so are included on this map.)

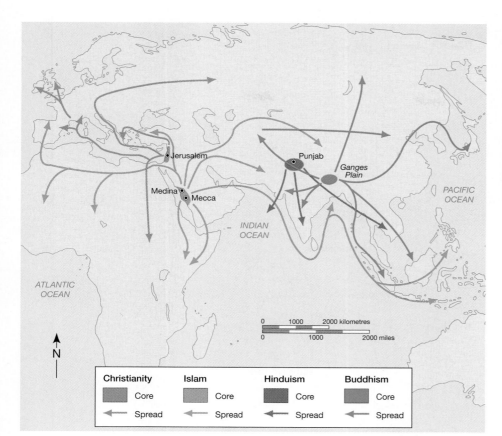

Figure 5.13 Origin areas and diffusion of four major religions
The world's major religions originated in a fairly small region of the world. Judaism and Christianity began in present-day Israel and Jordan. Islam emerged from the western Arabian peninsula (in present-day Saudi Arabia). Buddhism originated in India, and Hinduism in the Indus region of Pakistan. The source areas of the world's major religions are also the cultural hearth areas of agriculture, urbanization, and other key aspects of human development.

identifies the contemporary distribution of what are considered by religious scholars to be the world's major religions because they contain the largest number of practitioners globally. As with other global-scale representations, the map is useful in that it helps present a generalized picture.

Figure 5.13 identifies the source areas of four of the world's major religions and their diffusion from those sites over time. The map illustrates that the world's major religions originated and diffused from two fairly small areas of the globe. The first, where Hinduism and Buddhism (as well as Sikhism) originated, is an area of the lowlands of the subcontinent of India drained by the Indus (Punjab on the map) and Ganges rivers. The second area, where Christianity and Islam (as well as Judaism) originated, is in the deserts of the Middle East.

Hinduism was the first religion to emerge, among the peoples of the Indo-Gangetic Plain, about 4000 years ago. Buddhism and Sikhism evolved from Hinduism as reform religions, with Buddhism appearing around 500 B.C. and Sikhism developing in the fifteenth century. It is not surprising that Hinduism shaped and helped produce new religions because India has long been an important cultural crossroads. As a result, ideas and practices originating in India spread rapidly at the same time that other ideas and practices were being brought to India from far-flung places and then absorbed and translated to reflect Indian needs and values. For example, Buddhism emerged as a branch of Hinduism in an area not far from the Punjab. At first, a very small group of practitioners surrounding Prince Gautama, the founder of the religion, was confined to northern India. Slowly and steadily, however, Buddhism dispersed to other parts of India and was carried by missionaries and traders to China (100 B.C. to A.D. 200), Korea and Japan (A.D. 300–500), Southeast Asia (A.D. 400–600), Tibet (A.D. 700), and Mongolia (A.D. 1500) (**Figure 5.14**). Not surprisingly, as Buddhism spread, it developed

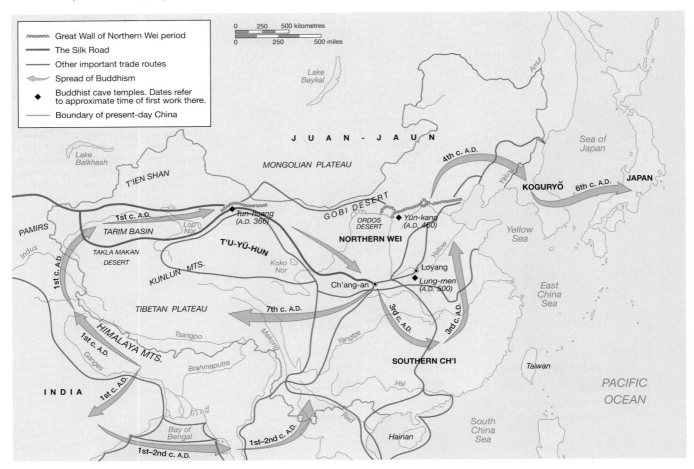

Figure 5.14 Spread of Buddhism This map illustrates the diffusion of Buddhism from its source area in India to China and then from China on to Korea and Japan. Commercial routes, like the Silk Road, were important vectors for the spread of the religion from India to China. Missionaries were responsible for the spread of Buddhism from China to Korea and Japan. (*Source:* C. Schirokauer, *A Brief History of Chinese and Japanese Civilizations.* New York: Harcourt Brace Jovanovich, 1978, p. 84.)

many different regional forms such that Tibetan Buddhism is distinct from Japanese Buddhism.

Christianity, Islam, and Judaism all developed among the Semitic-speaking people of the deserts of the Middle East. Like the Indo-Gangetic religions, these three religions are also related. Although Judaism is the oldest, it is the least widespread. Judaism originated about 4000 years ago, Christianity about 2000 years ago, and Islam about 1300 years ago. Judaism developed out of the cultures and beliefs of Bronze Age peoples and was the first monotheistic (belief in one God) religion. Although the oldest monotheistic religion and one that spread widely and rapidly, Judaism is numerically small because it does not seek new converts. Christianity developed in Jerusalem among the disciples of Jesus; they proclaimed that he was the Messiah expected by the Jews. As it moved east and south from its hearth area, Christianity's diffusion was helped by missionizing and imperial sponsorship. The diffusion of Christianity in Europe is illustrated in **Figure 5.15**.

An excellent illustration of the global forces behind the changing geography of religion is the Columbian contact with the New World. Before Columbus and later Europeans reached the continents of North and South America, the people living there practised, for the most part, various forms of animism and related rituals. They viewed themselves holistically, as one part of the wider world of animate and inanimate nature. They used religious rituals and charms to guide

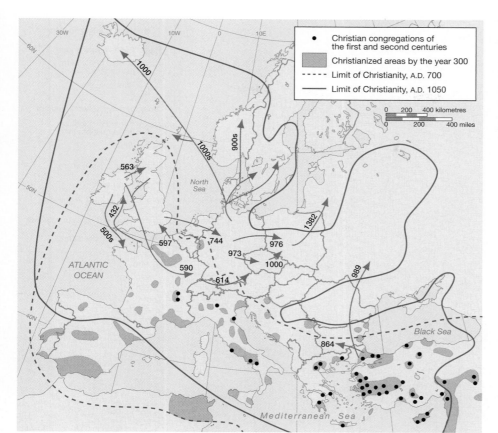

Figure 5.15 Spread of Christianity in Europe Christianity diffused through Europe largely through missionary efforts. Monks and monasteries were especially important as hubs of diffusion in the larger network. The shaded areas indicate those places where Christian converts dominated by the year A.D. 300. (*Source:* C. Park, *Sacred Worlds*. London: Routledge, 1994, p. 107.)

and enhance the activities of everyday life as well as the more extreme situations of warfare. Shamanism, in which spiritually gifted individuals are believed to possess the power to control preternatural forces, is one important aspect of the belief system that existed among Native American populations at the time of European contact (**Figure 5.16**).

European contact with the New World was, from the beginning, accompanied by Christian missionizing efforts directed at changing the belief systems of the Aboriginal peoples and converting them to what the missionizers believed to be "the one true religion" (**Figure 5.17**). Religion, especially for the Spanish colonizing agents, was especially important in integrating the indigenous population into the feudal system.

Perhaps what is most interesting about the present state of the geography of religion is how, during the colonial period, religious missionizing and conversion flowed from the core to the periphery. In the current postcolonial period, however, the opposite is becoming true. For example, the fastest-growing religion in the United States today is Islam, and it is in core countries that Buddhism is making the greatest number of converts. Although Pope John Paul II was the most widely travelled pontiff in Roman Catholic history, the same can be said for the Tibetan Buddhist religious leader, the Dalai Lama, who is also a tireless world traveller for Buddhism. The Papacy's efforts are mostly directed at maintaining Roman Catholic followers and attempting to dissuade their conversion to other religions, such as evangelicalism in the United States and Latin America. We should also note that the bulk of the world's Roman Catholics will be located in Latin America if present population growth trends continue (see Chapter 3). The Dalai Lama is promoting conversion to Buddhism by carrying its message to new places, especially in the core.

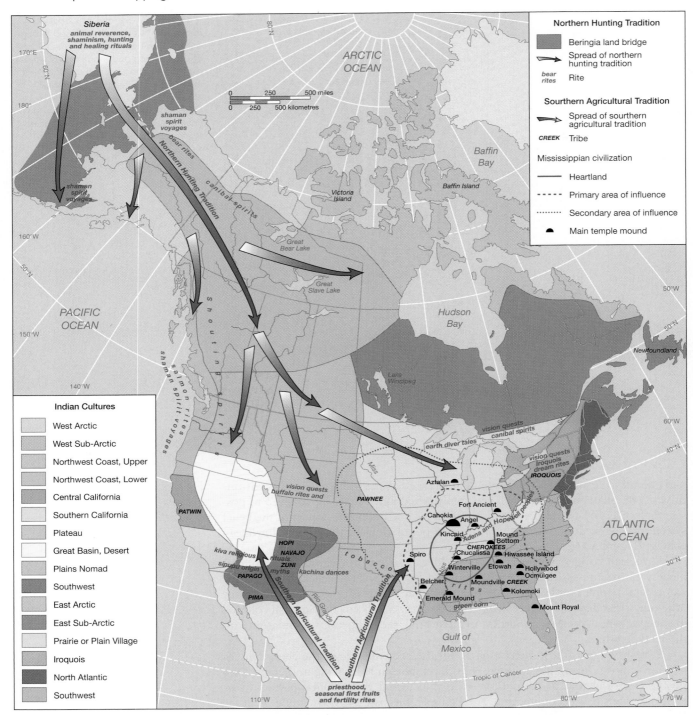

Figure 5.16 Pre-Columbian religions in North America Before European contact, the indigenous populations in North America had developed a range of religious practices. Religious traditions based on agrarian practices diffused from south to north, while those religious traditions based on hunting diffused from north to south. (*Source:* B.E. Carroll, *The Routledge Historical Atlas of Religion in America*. New York: Routledge, 2000, pp. 15–16.)

The Geography of Canada's Religions

The geography of Canada's religions is—as you might expect—a product of this country's history of colonialism and recent immigration (**Figure 5.18**). Following European contact, the original pattern of Aboriginal faiths and belief systems found across Canada were slowly replaced by the dominant Christian faiths of the French

Figure 5.17 Mission at Sainte-Marie-Among-the-Hurons This historically exact re-creation was built in the 1960s on the actual site of a seventeenth-century Jesuit mission to the Hurons, in what is now Midland, Ontario.

and British colonizing powers. Therefore, New France (Quebec and Acadia) was peopled by settlers who brought the Roman Catholic faith of France with them. Conversely, substantial parts of Newfoundland and Labrador were settled by Protestant fishing people from England. When Britain gained control of Canada after 1760, immigrants from Britain and the United States brought with them into Ontario the Protestant denominations of Christianity that they practised (**Figure 5.19**).[6] The legacy of this history can be seen to this day (**Table 5.1**).

Data from Canada's 2006 census concerning religious affiliations will take several years to be processed and published. Fortunately, the 2001 census data has been already extensively analyzed and the results made available on the Statistics Canada website. These show, for example, that when asked to record to which religious group they belong, the majority (70 percent) of the total population of Canada over 15 years old report their religious affiliation as either Roman Catholic or Protestant.[7] The legacy can also be seen at the provincial/territorial level. In Newfoundland and Labrador, 60 percent of people over age 15 record their religious affiliation as Protestant. In Quebec, conversely, 83.2 percent of people over age 15 record their religious affiliation as Roman Catholic. In Ontario, we find that 34 percent are affiliated to Roman Catholicism and 35 percent record a Protestant affiliation.

Since World War II, this pattern has undergone some significant changes, principally because the leading sources of immigration have changed from so-called traditional countries (see Chapter 3). In effect, the abandonment of discriminatory immigration policies in 1966 not only enabled Canada to pursue a multicultural immigration policy, but it also opened up the country to people from a wide variety of religious backgrounds.

Of the 1.8 million new immigrants who came to Canada during the 1990s, 32 percent reported affiliations to religions other than Christianity (15 percent were Muslim, 7 percent Hindu, 5 percent Sikh, and 5 percent Buddhist). The size

---

[6]An excellent introduction is provided in Robert Choquette's study *Canada's Religions*. Ottawa: University of Ottawa Press, 2004. See especially Chapter 18 ("Immigration and Religions," pp. 377–407) and Chapter 19 ("Alternative Religions," pp. 409–430).

[7]When interpreting this data, Statistics Canada cautions that the census asked respondents to report "a specific denomination or group, even if they were not practising members of their group. Consequently, these data indicate only religious affiliation." We cannot, therefore, rely on these data to provide a clear indication about changing levels of faith (religiosity) in the population and must use other information, such as measures of attendance at religious services (provided in Statistics Canada's General Social Survey). The 2001 census data are reported in Statistics Canada, *2001 Census: Analysis Series. Religions in Canada*. Ottawa: Minister of Industry, May 2003, Catalogue No. 96F0030XIE2001015; this report is also available online at **www12.statcan.ca/english/census01/products**.

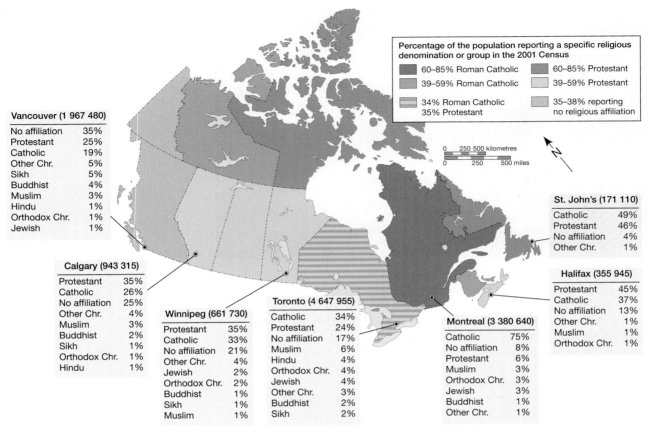

Vancouver (1 967 480)

No affiliation	35%
Protestant	25%
Catholic	19%
Other Chr.	5%
Sikh	5%
Buddhist	4%
Muslim	3%
Hindu	1%
Orthodox Chr.	1%
Jewish	1%

Calgary (943 315)

Protestant	35%
Catholic	26%
No affiliation	25%
Other Chr.	4%
Muslim	3%
Buddhist	2%
Sikh	1%
Orthodox Chr.	1%
Hindu	1%

Winnipeg (661 730)

Protestant	35%
Catholic	33%
No affiliation	21%
Other Chr.	4%
Jewish	2%
Orthodox Chr.	2%
Buddhist	1%
Sikh	1%
Muslim	1%

Toronto (4 647 955)

Catholic	34%
Protestant	24%
No affiliation	17%
Muslim	6%
Hindu	4%
Orthodox Chr.	4%
Jewish	4%
Other Chr.	3%
Buddhist	2%
Sikh	2%

Montreal (3 380 640)

Catholic	75%
No affiliation	8%
Protestant	6%
Muslim	3%
Orthodox Chr.	3%
Jewish	3%
Buddhist	1%
Other Chr.	1%

St. John's (171 110)

Catholic	49%
Protestant	46%
No affiliation	4%
Other Chr.	1%

Halifax (355 945)

Protestant	45%
Catholic	37%
No affiliation	13%
Other Chr.	1%
Muslim	1%
Orthodox Chr.	1%

Percentage of the population reporting a specific religious denomination or group in the 2001 Census

- 60–85% Roman Catholic
- 39–59% Roman Catholic
- 34% Roman Catholic / 35% Protestant
- 60–85% Protestant
- 39–59% Protestant
- 35–38% reporting no religious affiliation

Notes: City data are for Census Metropolitan Areas (CMAs); population totals are from sources cited.
"Catholic" includes Roman Catholic, Eastern Catholic, Polish National Church, and Old Catholic.
"Other Christian" refers to those respondents to the 2001 Census who reported their affiliation as "Christian" without further elaboration.
"No religious affiliation" includes agnostic, atheist, humanist, "no religion," and other responses to the Census, such as Darwinism.
Religious groups or denominations of less than 1 percent of CMA population are not reported.
Totals may not add to 100 percent because of rounding of data.

Figure 5.18   The distribution of religions in Canada, by province and territory, 2001   This map shows the leading religious denomination or group in each province or territory, according to the affiliations expressed by the population in the 2001 census. In broad terms, the map shows that the Roman Catholic and Protestant denominations of Christianity still dominate in most parts of the country, except for British Columbia and Yukon, where those individuals expressing "no religious affiliation" form the largest single group in the population. This pattern is repeated at the city level, although a greater diversity of religious affiliation occurs in cities that have become major centres for recent immigration. Indeed, city diversity is greater than can be shown here because some religious affiliations, such as Baha'i, Jain, Rastafarian, Scientology, and Aboriginal spirituality, are too small to be included in the city data (city data do not show groups with less than 1 percent of the CMA's population). Note that on the 2001 census, individuals were asked to report their affiliation to a specific religious denomination or group, even if they were not practising members of that group. These data can therefore show only broad patterns of religious affiliation and not, for example, the proportion attending religious services or functions in Canada or the degree of devotion across the country.   (*Sources:* Map compiled from provincial and territorial data in Statistics Canada, *2001 Census: Analysis Series. Religions in Canada.* Ottawa: Minister of Industry, May 2003, Catalogue No. 96F0030XIE2001015, available online at **www12.statcan.ca/english/census01/products**; and from city data, including 2001 CMA population sizes adjusted in 2003, in Statistics Canada, *2001 Census: Topic-Based Tabulations: Religions in Canada,* Table 95F0450XCB2001004, available online at **www12.statcan.ca/english/census01/products/standard/themes**.)

of some religious groups in Canada is increasing, while the size of Protestant and Roman Catholic denominations is declining (from 80 percent of the population in 1991 to 72 percent of the population in 2001). Canada's Muslim population, for instance, has seen the largest growth and has doubled from 253 256 in 1991 to 579 640 in 2001. The Orthodox family of Christian churches (479 620 in 2001) reported an increase of 24 percent in its numbers since 1991 because of the arrival of Serbian Orthodox emigrants from the Balkans. Interestingly, this growth compensated for the declines in the size of the Greek Orthodox and Ukrainian Orthodox churches, communities that had earlier grown significantly through immigration flows to this country.

Figure 5.19 Protestant religion in Canada Established by dissident Quakers in Ontario in the early nineteenth century, the small community of Sharon still retains the original Quaker meeting house constructed in what was believed to be the image of Solomon's Temple.

TABLE 5.1	Canada's Religions by Affiliation Numbers for Major Religious Denominations, 1991 and 2001				
Religious Denomination	**2001**	**%**	**1991**	**%**	**% Change 1991–2001**
Roman Catholic	12 793 125	43.2	12 203 625	45.2	4.8
Protestant	8 654 845	29.2	9 427 675	34.9	–8.2
Christian Orthodox	479 620	1.6	387 395	1.4	23.8
Christian*	780 450	2.6	353 040	1.3	121.1
Muslim	579 640	2.0	253 265	0.9	128.9
Jewish	329 995	1.1	318 185	1.2	3.7
Buddhist	300 345	1.0	163 415	0.6	83.8
Hindu	297 200	1.0	157 015	0.6	89.3
Sikh	278 415	0.9	147 440	0.5	88.8
No religion	4 796 325	16.2	3 333 245	12.3	43.9

*Total includes persons who report "Christian" as well as those who report "Apostolic," "Born Again," and "Evangelical."

Source: Statistics Canada, *2001 Census: Analysis Series. Religions in Canada.* Ottawa: Minister of Industry, May 2003, Catalogue No. 96F0030XIE2001015, available online at **www12.statcan.ca/english/census01/products**. 2006 census data will be made available at **www12.statcan.ca/census-recensement/2006/rt-td/index-eng.cfm** in due course.

As might be expected, much of this growth has been the leading destinations for immigration and has focused on Canada's major metropolitan centres. According to 2001 census data, Ontario is now the home to 73 percent of Canada's Hindu population, 61 percent of the Muslim community, and 38 percent of the Sikh population. The majority of Canada's Sikh community is found in British Columbia (**Figure 5.20**).

Canada's religious geography has also been affected by the growing number of people who report to the census that they have no religious affiliation. As Figure 5.18 shows, the majority of the population of both British Columbia and Yukon report that they have "no religious affiliation." Before 1971, less than 1 percent of Canada's total population made such a declaration. However, by 2001, the census noted that 16 percent of Canadians over the age of 15 (4.8 million people) reported that they have no religious affiliation. Another source of Statistics Canada data, the General Social Survey, found that attendance at religious services had fallen from 28 percent of all those aged 15 and over in 1986 to only 20 percent in 2001. There are a variety of reasons for this decline. Statistics Canada observes that many immigrants from China and Taiwan do not claim a religious affiliation.

Figure 5.20 Sikh temple, Surrey, British Columbia

Robert Choquette notes the increase in "new age" religious movements, which may be seen as outside the categories of more traditional religions. Whatever the causes, it is interesting to note that 40 percent of those declaring "no affiliation" in 2001 were under the age of 24.

A declining number of young people report an affiliation with either Protestant or Roman Catholic Christianity, and increases in other faiths because of immigration have combined to mean that the average ages of Canada's religious communities are also changing. The median age of Canada's population in 2001 was 37 years. However, the median age for Canada's Presbyterians in 2001 was 46 years. Canada's Jewish population (329 995 in 2001) is also, as a group, aging—its median age in 2001 was 41.5 years (**Figure 5.21**). Conversely, those faiths

Figure 5.21 Synagogue, Montreal

experiencing growth have much lower medians. For example, in 2001 Canada's Muslim population had a median age of 28 years, the Sikh community had a median age of 30, and the Hindus had a median age of 32 years.

The distribution of religions in Canada is only one aspect of the geographical study of religions in Canada. In recent years, a number of scholars have examined the contribution of religions to the creation of social and cultural geography. For example, the buildings used by religious groups to conduct their worship are a very tangible indicator of that group's presence in the community and contribute to the creation of distinct cultural landscapes. Consider, for example, the part played by Roman Catholic churches in rural Quebec or Sikh *gurdwaras* (temples) in suburban Vancouver in creating a sense of place in those areas.

Other research has focused on the relocation of religious buildings. A recent study by Rosalynn Trigger, for example, examines how the Protestant churches of Montreal moved out from the old city during the nineteenth century to maintain their proximity to their wealthy congregations that were migrating to the suburbs.[8] Interestingly, although population relocations of this sort have meant that older religious buildings become abandoned by their faith community, the buildings often find new purpose in a variety of functions, and many have been preserved by the wider community for their heritage value.

The growing number and diversity of religions have affected this country's geography in another way because they have influenced our ability to appreciate other cultures and their traditions. Robert Choquette, one of the leading authorities on Canada's religions, writes: "The transformation of Canada from a Christian monochrome to a religious kaleidoscope during the second half of the twentieth century meant that a growing number of diverse world views and theologies appeared."[9] In particular, he notes that the teachings of Christianity, Islam, and Judaism (which have a *linear* or historical view of time) contrast greatly with Eastern religions (which see time in *cyclical* terms). The former, he argues, also place more value on this world, which is seen as redeemable, whereas the latter emphasize the need to escape the limitations of this world. We have already seen (in Chapter 4) how these different perspectives affect our view of the environment. Seen in these terms, Canada has been enriched by the variety of insights gained from its growing number of religions. As Choquette concludes,[10]

> Their presence made Canadians become aware that there were other world views competing with their traditional Christian one. When added to the growing secularism of Canadian society during the same period, the result was the transformation of Canada from a Christian bastion to a secular society where all religions became private.

Sacred Spaces

Sacred space includes those areas of the globe recognized by individuals or groups as worthy of special attention because they are the sites of special religious experiences and events. Sacred space does not occur naturally; rather, it is assigned sanctity through the values and belief systems of particular groups or individuals. Geographer Yi-Fu Tuan insists that what defines the sacredness of a space goes beyond the obvious shrines and temples. Sacred spaces are simply those that rise above the commonplace and interrupt ordinary routine.

Religious places can also be read and interpreted. Indeed, most religions designate certain places as sacred, often because a special event occurred there. Sites are often designated as sacred to distinguish them from the rest of the landscape,

sacred space: an area recognized by individuals or groups as worthy of special attention as a site of special religious experiences or events

---

[8]Rosalynn Trigger, *God's Mobile Mansions*. Unpublished PhD thesis, Department of Geography, McGill University, 2005.

[9]Robert Choquette, *Canada's Religions*. Ottawa: University of Ottawa Press, 2004, p. 378.

[10]Ibid., p. 380.

which is considered ordinary or profane. Sacred spaces are special because they are the sites of intense or important mystical or spiritual experiences.

In almost all cases, sacred spaces are segregated, dedicated, and hallowed sites that are maintained as such generation after generation. Believers—including mystics, spiritualists, religious followers, and pilgrims—recognize sacred spaces as being endowed with divine meaning. (**Figure 5.22**).

Often, members of a specific religion are expected to journey to especially important sacred spaces to renew their faith or to demonstrate devotion. A pilgrimage is a journey to a sacred space, and a pilgrim is a person who undertakes such a journey. In India, many of the sacred pilgrimage sites for Hindus are concentrated along the seven sacred rivers: the Ganges, the Yamuna, the Saraswati, the Naramada, the Indus, the Cauvery, and the Godavari. The Ganges is India's holiest river, and many sacred sites are located along its banks (**Figure 5.23**). Hindus visit sacred pilgrimage sites for a variety of reasons, including to seek a cure for sickness, wash away sins, or fulfill a promise to a deity.

Perhaps the most well-known pilgrimage is the *hajj*, the obligatory once-in-a-lifetime journey of Muslims to Mecca. For one month every year, the city of Mecca in Saudi Arabia swells from its base population of 150 000 to more than 1 000 000 as pilgrims from all over the world journey to fulfill their obligation to pray in the city and receive the grace of Allah.

Pilgrimages to sacred sites are made all over the world, and Christian Europe is no exception. The most visited sacred site in Europe is Lourdes, at the base of the Pyrenees in southwest France, not far from the Spanish border (**Figure 5.24**). Another

Figure 5.22 Buddhist temple, central Bhutan This temple is an example of an elaborately constructed and highly maintained sacred site. For Bhutanese Buddhists, these temples are holy places that are the site of worship and important Buddhist rituals.

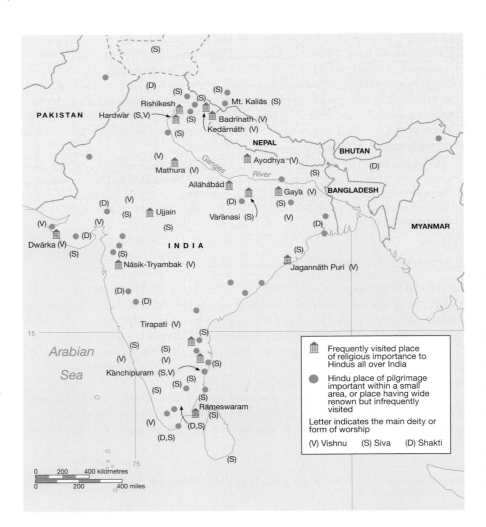

Figure 5.23 Sacred sites of Hindu India India's many rivers are holy places within Hindu religion, and so it is not surprising that sacred sites are located along the country's many riverbanks. Apparently, those shrines closer to the rivers are holier than those farther away. (*Source:* Adapted from Ismail Ragi al Farugi and David E. Sopher, *Historical Atlas of the Religions of the World.* New York: Macmillan, 1974.)

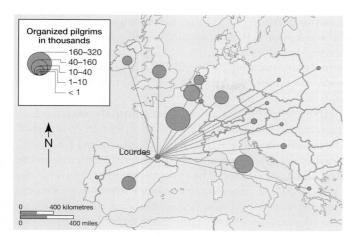

Figure 5.24 Source areas for pilgrims to Lourdes This map shows the points of origin of European, group-organized pilgrims to Lourdes in 1978. These represent only about 30 percent of all pilgrims to Lourdes, most of whom travel to the shrine on their own. Improved transportation (mainly by train) and the availability of organized package trips have contributed to a marked increase in the number of pilgrims visiting. Many of the 5 million pilgrims who visit the town each year do so in the hope of a miraculous cure for medical ills at a grotto where the Virgin Mary is said to have appeared before 14-year-old Bernadette Soubirous in a series of 18 visions in the year 1858. (*Source:* C.C. Park, *Sacred Worlds*. London: Routledge, 1994, p. 284.)

sacred site that attracts pilgrims throughout the world is the city of Jerusalem, and the Holy Land more generally. As is the case with most sacred spaces, the codes that are embedded in the landscape of the Holy Land may be read quite differently by different religious and even secular visitors. Two students of pilgrimage have observed the following:

> Each group brings to Jerusalem their own entrenched understandings of the sacred; nothing unites them save their sequential—and sometimes simultaneous—presence at the same holy sites. For the Greek Orthodox pilgrims, indeed, the precise definition of the site itself is largely irrelevant; it is the icons on display which are the principal focus of attention. For the Roman Catholics, the site is important in that it is illustrative of a particular biblical text relating to the life of Jesus, but it is important only in a historical sense, as confirming the truth of past events. Only for the Christian Zionists does the Holy Land itself carry any present and future significance, and here they find a curious kinship with indigenous Jews.[11]

If we want to make geographical sense of the phenomenon of sacred space, it is useful to consider a very simple model (**Figure 5.25**). In this model, we hypothesize a very early time when almost all of Earth's surface was considered sacred, and contrast this with the present day, when very little of its surface is so considered. In between lies a long period of transition, one affected by many changes in religion and spirituality. We should note that many other changes were occurring during this transition period, including changing attitudes to nature (see Chapter 4) and to material wealth (see Chapter 7).

Let us illustrate our model with some examples from groups we have discussed elsewhere in this book, looking first at the period the whole Earth was

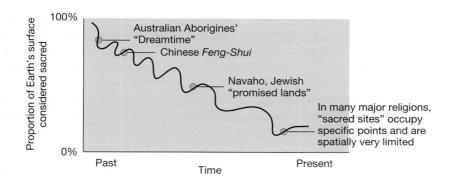

Figure 5.25 A model of sacred space This diagram shows how changes over time may have affected society's changing views of sacred spaces.

---

[11]J. Eade and M. Sallnow (eds.). *Contesting the Sacred*. London: Routledge, 1991, p. 14.

considered sacred. The Australian Aborigine interprets the entire surface of Earth as embodying aspects of the Creation, an event occurring during the Dreamtime. Hills and caves, for example, are where creatures of the Dreamtime have slept or hidden. The Dreamtime can be called to mind by travelling through the landscape on routes known as "Songlines," travels that celebrate the landscape (and creation) in song.

In another manner, Chinese *feng-shui* practitioners recognize the sacredness of the entire Earth's surface as they seek to interpret its energy lines and most propitious landscapes. As we saw in Chapter 1, the early use of the lodestone (a forerunner of the compass) enabled early *feng-shui* geomancers to interpret Earth's magnetic variations as lines of energy across its surface. The topography of that surface can also be interpreted. In a widely quoted paper on this topic, University of Victoria geographer David Lai describes how *feng-shui* was used to locate the first Chinese cemetery in Victoria. In general terms, for example, the close resemblance of a range of hills to the forms of a dragon and a tiger is considered by *feng-shui* interpreters to be an advantage for houses or graves located nearby. This is because these two animals symbolize respectively the yang and yin energies present in nature, and their occurrence together at such locations shows that these two energies will be kept in abundance and harmony.[12]

Other groups believe that they have been given their homeland as a sacred trust, to inhabit as a chosen people. This division of Earth in some way implies that not all space is seen as sacred, at least in the eyes of the group in question. Jewish belief in the "promised land" is one example. Another is the North American Navaho's belief that their appointed territory lies between four sacred mountains. For the Blackfoot, certain locations in the Alberta foothills, where Spirit Beings changed into human form and gave them their sacred ceremonies, are considered special places. As the Blackfoot people explained at a recent exhibition at Calgary's Glenbow Museum that they curated: "These places provide physical evidence that the events really happened and are part of Blackfoot history. Sacred places connect the Blackfoot to our territory, are part of our identity and are the basis of our claim to this territory."[13]

With the development of Islam, Christianity, and Buddhism, ideas of sacred space became more focused into specific locations. Those parts of Earth touched by the deity are more valued than those places that were not. A geography of sacred and profane space begins to unfold. Places of pilgrimage and shrines, as mentioned above, articulate that space and serve to connect us with the sacred. Indeed, it is worth noting that it is necessary *to go* to church, temple, synagogue, or mosque because in some way these are more sacred places than the everyday or profane world in which many of us live.

Various Western "new age" spiritualities seek to bring us full circle by seeing the whole Earth as sacred once more. It is significant that in doing so, many of the traditions of Canada's Aboriginal peoples have been co-opted. Others—perhaps influenced by today's environmental concerns—see nature in spiritual terms. One of Canada's foremost contemplative writers, Sharon Butala, sees the spiritual quality of landscape itself. After some years in Saskatchewan's Cypress Hills, she said, "I began to see not only the visible landscape but the invisible one, a landscape in which history . . . had transmuted itself into an always present spiritual dimension."[14]

The aspect of sacred space that has probably received most attention from cultural geographers has been the cemetery. This work has been mainly focused on

---

[12]Chuen-yan David Lai, "A *Feng Shui* Model as a Location Index," *Annals Association of American Geographers* 64, 1974, pp. 516–513.

[13]*Nitsitapiisinni: The Story of the Blackfoot People.* Toronto: Key Porter, 2001, p. 50.

[14]Sharon Butala, *The Perfection of the Morning: An Apprenticeship in Nature.* Toronto: Harper-Collins, 1994, p. 113.

the regional variations in gravestone design, the diffusion of gravestone iconography across space, and the evolution of cemetery design as a landscape feature. As such, geographers have treated the cemetery as a feature of the cultural landscape and have analyzed it in much the same way as folk or vernacular architecture.

Researchers have shown, for example, that the vernacular designs of the early tombstones in Halifax's Old Cemetery (which incorporate such motifs as crowned skulls and hourglasses) are part of a very distinctive New England tradition that diffused into Nova Scotia in the eighteenth century (**Figure 5.26**). The simple layout of this Halifax cemetery differs from that of Mount Pleasant Cemetery in Toronto or Mount Royal Cemetery in Montreal because by the nineteenth century, a landscape garden design was thought to be one more conducive to contemplation.

Instead of relying on such distinctive local designs, other studies have shown how famous works of art have been adopted for use on tombstones, and how the diffusion of such unique designs can themselves be useful in examining the diffusion of different ways of commemorating the dead (**Figure 5.27**).

More recent geographical work, however, has paid attention to cemeteries as sacred or special places. Having the characteristics of both public and private space, cemeteries also occupy an important boundary between the world of the sacred and the profane—"boundary" or *liminal* space that has the ability to unsettle us, precisely because we cannot decide in which type of place we are. Scholars have also come to recognize that in cemeteries we use place to concretize memory in a way that time cannot. Memories of loved ones are engrained in the space occupied, for example, by the burial plot and its memorial. Cemeteries, therefore, become deeply personal places, with different meanings for each one of us (**Figure 5.28**).

Figure 5.26   Gravestone in Halifax, Nova Scotia   The design of this eighteenth-century gravestone diffused to Nova Scotia from New England.

Copenhagen, Denmark	Diffusion route of *Night*, with cemeteries (by city and country) and dates of grave-stones incorporating *Night*.
•	
1860	

Bertel Thorvaldsen's sculpture *Night* is described as a roundel or tondo that depicts a woman with arms enfolded around two sleeping infants. Widely seen as an allegory (in which the woman represents an angel, and the two babes sleep and death), the sculpture spread as a feature of gravestone iconography across the North Atlantic in the late nineteenth century.

Figure 5.27   Diffusion of sculptural art   The spread of Thorvaldsen's sculpture *Night* from cemeteries in Denmark to other locations shows how iconography can be used to study diffusion and how different ways of commemorating the dead have spread through the cemeteries of Europe and North America. (*Source*: Alan Nash, "Thorvaldsen's 'Night' and Cemeteries: The Diffusion of Gravestone Iconography." New England– St. Lawrence Valley Geographical Society, *Proceedings from 2003 Meeting*.)

Figure 5.28 Gravestone in Montreal
Cemeteries preserve deeply personal memories in place. In this example of a nineteenth-century grave from Montreal, a child's death has been commemorated by the use of a small statue of a lamb.

Geography and Language

Geographers have also been interested in understanding other aspects of cultural systems, such as languages. Language is an important focus for study because it is a central aspect of cultural identity. Without language, cultural accomplishments could not be transmitted from one generation to the next. The distribution and diffusion of languages tells much about the changing history of human geography and the impact of globalization on culture. Before looking more closely at the geography of language and the impacts of globalization on the changing distribution of languages, however, it is necessary to become familiar with some basic vocabulary.

language: a means of communicating ideas or feelings by means of a conventionalized system of signs, gestures, marks, or articulate vocal sounds

dialects: regional variations from standard language, in terms of accent, vocabulary, and grammar

language family: a collection of individual languages believed to be related in their prehistoric origin

language branch: a collection of languages that possess a definite common origin but have split into individual languages

language group: a collection of several individual languages that are part of a language branch, share a common origin, and have similar grammar and vocabulary

Language is a means of communicating ideas or feelings by way of a conventionalized system of signs, gestures, marks, or articulate vocal sounds. In short, communication is symbolic, based on commonly understood meanings of signs or sounds. Within standard languages (also known as *official languages* because they are maintained by offices of government, such as education and the courts), regional variations, known as **dialects**, exist. Dialects emerge and are distinguishable through differences in pronunciation, grammar, and vocabulary that are place-based in nature.

For the purposes of classification, languages are divided into families, branches, and groups. A **language family** is a collection of individual languages believed to be related in their prehistoric origin. About 50 percent of the world's people speak a language that originated from the Indo-European family. A **language branch** is a collection of languages that possess a definite common origin but have split into individual languages. A **language group** is a collection of several individual languages that are part of a language branch, share a common origin in the recent past, and have relatively similar grammar and vocabulary. Spanish, French, Portuguese, Italian, Romanian, and Catalan are a language group, classified under the Romance branch as part of the Indo-European language family.

Language is probably one of our greatest cultural creations and, as we shall see, a creation that is inherently geographical in its place-marking and place-making abilities. Through language, we describe our world in our own words and, by our use of that language, provide others with some indication of where we are from. Regional accents can enable those familiar enough with our language to tell exactly where within a region we were brought up. And, within the vocabulary and structure of our languages, we preserve a faint memory of where our distant ancestors originated. Let us briefly consider the most important aspects of each of these three points.

The Memory of Language   Language is such a sophisticated cultural creation that it retains a memory of its past within its present form. One of the first people to realize this was Sir William Jones, an employee of the British East India Company. In 1786, he recognized the close similarities between Sanskrit (an extinct East Indian language retained for sacred use) and many European languages, both extinct (such as Latin) and extant (such as English or French). If you look at **Table 5.2** you will see the often astonishing similarities in vocabulary among these languages.

Jones asserted, correctly as it turned out, that all of these languages are related to one another (the "Indo-European" language family, **Figure 5.29**) and that they have all descended from a now lost language called "proto-Indo-European." The passage of time and the migration of peoples, who then lost contact with one another, have been sufficient to change proto-Indo-European into the many languages of the Indo-European language family we hear today. (Note that the *present* global distribution of Indo-European languages is much greater than that shown in Figure 5.29, which describes the situation *before* European expansion and globalization carried the languages of the colonizers around the world.)

The obvious questions about where and when proto-Indo-European was originally spoken can also be investigated by again examining the language itself. Scholars of linguistics have been able to reconstruct some of the vocabulary of proto-Indo-European (for some examples, see Table 5.2). On the basis of that vocabulary, they have suggested that it developed between 6500 and 4500 years ago. This is because proto-Indo-European had words for domesticated crops (such as wheat and barley), domesticated animals (horse and goat), and for wheeled

---

TABLE 5.2   Vocabulary Comparisons between Some Indo-European and Non–Indo-European Languages

English	French	Greek	Sanskrit	P-I-E[†]	Japanese
two	deux	duo	dva	*duwo	ni
three	trois	treis	tryas	*treyes	san
four	quatre	tettares	catvaras	*kwetwores	yon
ten	dix	deka	dasa	*dekmt	jyu
cow [ox]	vache	bous	gauh	*kwou	usi
field	champ	agros	ajras	*agras	hatake
water	eau	hudor	udan	*wedor	mizu
father	père	pater	pita	*pater	chichi
god	dieu	theos	devas	*dyeus	kami
wheel	roue	roda	ratha	*roto	sharin
			[chariot]	[wheel, chariot]	

[†]P-I-E: Proto-Indo-European
*denotes a reconstructed word in P-I-E
The proto-Indo-European language may have originated about 6000 years ago in a steppe region somewhere between the Black Sea and the Caspian, or in Anatolian Turkey. Its vocabulary (here shown by the use of an asterisk to denote a reconstructed word) has been reconstructed by linguistic experts on the basis of correspondences between daughter languages (the name given to those languages that are descended from a common original) and known rules of linguistic change over time. P-I-E is believed to be the ancestor of extinct languages (such as Latin and Sanskrit) and many languages of the Indo-European family (such as English, French, and Hindi) currently spoken in the world today. The difference between these languages and those from other language families can be seen in the comparison with Japanese.

Sources: J.P. Mallory, *In Search of the Indo-Europeans.* London: Thames and Hudson, 1989; Colin Renfrew, *Archaeology and Language: The Puzzle of Indo-European Origins.* London: Cape, 1987; T.V. Gamkrelidze and V.V. Ivanov, "The Early History of Indo-European Languages." *Scientific American*, March 1990, pp. 110–116; and P. Tieme, "The Indo-European Language." *Scientific American*, October 1958, pp. 63–74.

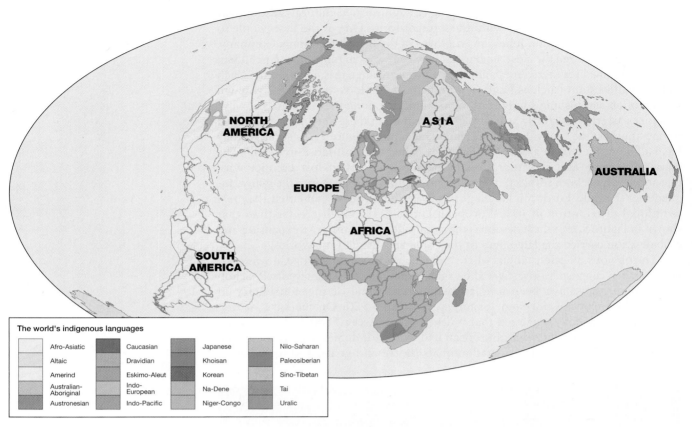

Figure 5.29 World distribution of major languages and major language families Classifying languages by family and mapping their occurrence across the globe provide insights about human geography. For example, we may discover interesting cultural linkages among seemingly disparate cultures widely separated in space and time. We may also begin to understand something about the nature of population movements across broad expanses of time and space. (*Sources:* Reprinted with permission from Prentice Hall, E.F. Bergman, *Human Geography: Cultures, Connections, and Landscapes,* © 1995, p. 240. Western Hemisphere adapted from *Language in the Americas* by Joseph H. Greenberg with the permission of the publishers, Stanford University Press, 1987 by the Board of Trustees of the Leland Stanford Junior University. Eastern Hemisphere adapted with permission from David Crystal, *Encyclopedia of Language.* New York: Cambridge University Press, 1987.)

cultural hearth: the geographical origin or source of innovations, ideas, or ideologies (term coined by geographer Carl Sauer)

vehicles (chariot), but not for iron. In other words, its date of origin is likely to be after the agricultural revolution of the Neolithic Age but before the Iron Age.

Pinpointing a region of origin is much harder. Some scholars, for example, have used references to types of trees (such as beech) or fish (the salmon) in the reconstructed vocabulary as indicators of the original environment in which proto-Indo-European developed. Unfortunately, however, these species are too widely distributed across Eurasia for such environmental information to be of great help. Conversely, the fact that the proto-language contains no words for such plants as the olive, as generally agreed, rules out a Mediterranean origin. (This type of reasoning is called an *argument from silence.*)

These difficulties have not prevented continued speculation about the **cultural hearth** (geographical origins of innovations, ideas, or ideologies) where proto-Indo-European first developed. Using assumptions based on the diffusion of agriculture, the spread of early peoples, and archaeological evidence, a variety of regions have been proposed. These range from Anatolia in Turkey (Professor Renfrew's view) to the steppe land between the Black Sea and the Caspian (Dr. Mallory's suggestion).[15]

---

[15]C. Renfrew, *Archaeology and Language: The Puzzle of Indo-European Origins.* London: Jonathan Cape, 1987; J.P. Mallory, *In Search of the Indo-Europeans: Language, Archaeology and Myth.* London: Thames and Hudson, 1989.

Whichever view ultimately proves correct, it now seems almost certain, in the words of two Russian scholars, that "Europe is seen, therefore, as the destination, rather than the source, of Indo-European migration."[16]

That migration seems to have missed four areas in Europe where Indo-European languages are not indigenous (see Figure 5.29). Finnish, Estonian, and Hungarian are members of the Uralic language family (believed to have originated in the northern Urals around 6000 B.C.). The Basque language of northeastern Spain and southwest France is an **isolate**, a language that has no known relationship with any other and cannot be assigned to a language family. We can gain an impression of how different Basque is from its vocabulary for the numerals 1 through 10, which are *bat, bi, hiru, lau, bost, sei, zazpi, zortzi, beheratzi,* and *hamar*. Recent research by L.L. and F.C. Cavalli-Sforza on European genetics also indicates the distinctiveness of the Basques.[17] Whether they are descended from a pre-Neolithic people who were not completely absorbed by a westward-moving, Indo-European–speaking Neolithic people is an intriguing possibility.

isolate: a language that has no known relationship with any other and cannot be assigned to a language family

The story of Europe's indigenous languages is only one of many that linguists have attempted to unravel. Work on the languages of the Pacific, for example, seems to support the current theories of migration and settlement we examined in Chapter 1. Indeed, it was Captain Cook who first recognized the similarities between Hawaiian and the indigenous languages of the South Pacific islands he knew. Alone among the great navigators of his day, he believed that these apparently "primitive" peoples had the abilities to navigate the great distances involved, and saw that the connection of language supported his view.

Let us now consider Canada. Historical linguists speculate that the thousands of indigenous languages that probably existed in the Americas on the eve of European contact can be divided into just three groups. These are known as the Amerindian, Na-Dene, and Eskimo-Aleut language families. Languages within each of these families can still be found within what is now Canada (see Figure 5.29). Scholars also believe that there may have been three separate phases of migration from Asia to the Americas (see Chapter 4).

Putting these two ideas together has led to speculation that these three language families might be descended from three "proto-languages" brought over at different times by Asian settlers to the New World. Certainly, the fact that Eskimo-Aleut is both the least differentiated of the language families (its only member is the Inuit language, Inuktitut) and the most recent arrival in Canada (moving across the Canadian Arctic about 4000 years ago) is evidence for this claim. Amerindian and Na-Dene, however, were introduced into this continent at least 10 000 years ago and rapidly developed into the hundreds of indigenous languages of the Americas.

Of course, such a model is highly speculative, but if we leave it aside, the fact that Canada's West Coast contains a far greater number of Aboriginal languages than either the Prairies or the Eastern Woodlands is probably indicative of the much greater antiquity of language development in British Columbia than in the rest of this country.

Language and Regional Identity   Because language is spoken by people who occupy space and is an intrinsic part of culture, it is not surprising that language has always been seen as an important characteristic of the cultural region. Many groups speak with pride about their language and will strongly identify with it, using language as part of the means to establish ethnic, regional, and national differences.

Canada is no exception in this regard. Indeed, many see disputes over language as a particularly distressing part of this country's identity. **Figure 5.30** shows the provincial and territorial distribution of the leading languages spoken as a **mother tongue**, or first language learned at home in childhood and still understood, across

mother tongue: the first language learned at home in childhood and still understood by the individual at the time of the census (as defined by Statistics Canada)

---

[16]T.V. Gamkrelidze and V.V. Ivanov, "The Early History of Indo-European Languages." *Scientific American*, March 1990, p. 116.

[17]L.L. and F.C. Cavalli-Sforza, *The Great Human Diasporas: The History of Diversity and Evolution.* Reading, MA: Addison-Wesley, 1995.

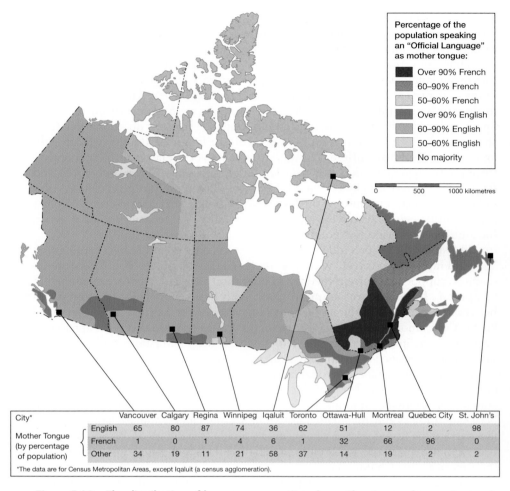

City*		Vancouver	Calgary	Regina	Winnipeg	Iqaluit	Toronto	Ottawa-Hull	Montreal	Quebec City	St. John's
Mother Tongue (by percentage of population)	English	65	80	87	74	36	62	51	12	2	98
	French	1	0	1	4	6	1	32	66	96	0
	Other	34	19	11	21	58	37	14	19	2	2

*The data are for Census Metropolitan Areas, except Iqaluit (a census agglomeration).

Figure 5.30 **The distribution of language across Canada: mother tongue by province and territory** This map shows one way of providing an overview of Canada's language geography. It does this by showing the percentage of people in an area who, in the 1986 census, reported that they used one of the official languages (French or English) as their mother tongue. Using data from small areal units (Statistics Canada's "census divisions"), the map gives a much more detailed picture than is possible from one based on provincial or territorial divisions. The map clearly shows the regions in Canada where these languages predominate (for example, French in southern parts of Quebec and English in Newfoundland). It also allows us to see those areas where neither official language is used as the predominant language by the majority (in Nunavut, northern Saskatchewan, and northeastern Ontario, because of the importance of Aboriginal languages in those regions). In addition, the map shows those regions where the official languages, while in a majority, are less dominant than in other parts of Canada (for example, in northern Alberta and northern Quebec). Such maps, however, cannot show the more detailed patterns that exist within urban communities, places where the many mother tongues of recent immigration make their greatest impact on the pattern of Canada's languages. To do that, data for a selection of cities has been added to show the variation that exists across this country. (*Sources:* David H. Kaplan, "Population and Politics in a Plural Society: The Changing Geography of Canada's Linguistic Groups." *Annals of the Association of American Geographers* 84[1], 1994, pp. 52–53. The material is used permission of Blackwell Publishing Ltd. City data are from Statistics Canada's "1996 Census: Community Profiles," available at **www12.statcan.gc.ca/census-recensement/index-eng.cfm**.)

official languages: languages (in Canada, English and French) in which the government has a legal obligation to conduct its affairs, and in which the public has the right to receive federal services

this country. Canada has two **official languages**, English and French, in which the business of the federal government is conducted. Government policies of "multiculturalism" indicate a tolerance of other languages, but the reality of the workplace shows that a proficiency in English or French is an important determinant of an individual's economic success. As a result, although recent immigrants to this country are not required to learn the official languages, many decide to do so.

According to the 2006 census, 18 million Canadians reported English as their mother tongue, an increase of 3 percent since 2001 and of almost a third since

1971. This English-speaking, or **anglophone**, portion of the population made up about 60 percent of the country's population in 1996 (approximately the same proportion of Canadians it represented in 1971). A considerable range existed around this national average. The highest proportion of anglophones was found in Newfoundland and Labrador (where 98.6 percent of the population recorded their mother tongue as English), the lowest in Quebec (9.2 percent). Provinces with large recent immigrant populations, such as Ontario and British Columbia, recorded anglophone figures of 74.6 percent and 78.9 percent, respectively.

The size of Canada's **francophone**, or French-speaking, population was 6.9 million in 2006. Although this figure has increased in absolute terms since 1971, as a proportion of the total population of Canada, it has fallen from 29 percent in 1951 to 22.1 percent in 2006. (Quebec's low francophone fertility rates and the relatively small number of francophone immigrants to Canada are the main causes of this decline.) According to 1996 census figures, 86 percent of Canada's francophones lived in Quebec (where they represent 82 percent of that province's population).

In Quebec, the use of French is very much seen as an intrinsic part of the "nationalist project" and is also an established part of provincial government policy. Both of the leading provincial political parties (the Liberals and the Parti Québécois) have been conscious of the minority position of the French language in Canada and North America as a whole. Realizing that this position was further weakened by a decline in the provincial birth rate among francophones and an increase in the number of **allophone** immigrants to the province (those whose mother tongue is neither English nor French) who adopted English, both parties have taken legislative steps to encourage the greater use of French in Quebec. Through such legislation as Bill 101, the government has acted to ensure the use of French in government, in public schools, and even on street signs. A provincial agency (Office québécois de la langue française) has the responsibility for monitoring public compliance (**Figure 5.31**). Although initially the target of much opposition, especially from Quebec's large anglophone and allophone communities, which represented 8.8 percent (622 000 people) and 9.7 percent (682 000 people) of Quebec's population in 1996, this policy has now become accepted as a fact of life in the province, one that no political party can afford to oppose (**Figure 5.32**).[18]

Outside of Quebec, the francophone population totals 970 000 and is found mainly in the two provinces of Ontario and New Brunswick, where it is declining in relative size. "Language islands," to use geographer Donald Cartwright's phrase, that historically contained significant numbers of francophones just inside the Ontario border (from Hawkesbury to Cochrane) and anglophones within Quebec (such as the Eastern Townships) have steadily eroded over the years to leave a much starker geographical divide between French-speaking Quebec and the rest of the country.

Bilingualism in English and French, a necessary feature of the language islands, is also the hallmark of a federal government policy to show Quebec that Canada as a whole could also be a home for francophones. The 1996 census records that 17 percent (4.8 million) of the country's population were bilingual in English and French, a figure that had increased from 13 percent in 1971. The highest rates of bilingualism were recorded in Quebec (38 percent of the population) and New Brunswick (33 percent). Urban centres, such as Montreal (50 percent), Ottawa-Hull (44 percent), and Sudbury (40 percent), also have sizeable bilingual populations.

In terms of Canada's allophone population, the 2006 census records that there were 6.3 million people in this country who spoke neither English nor French as their mother tongue. This represents 20.1 percent of the total population, a figure

anglophone: a person whose mother tongue is English

francophone: a person whose mother tongue is French

allophone: a person whose mother tongue is neither English nor French

Figure 5.31 Office québécois de la langue française Quebec's watchdog on language monitors compliance with provincial legislation promoting French. Among the most publicized prosecutions in recent years have been businesses whose store signs do not use French or, if more than one language is used, do not ensure French has the largest font size.

---

[18]A well-received discussion of these issues in English can be found in the recent work of two scholars at Montreal's Institut national de la recherche scientifique. Annick Germain and Damaris Rose, *Montréal: The Quest for a Metropolis.* Chichester: Wiley, 2000, Chapter 7, "Language, Ethnic Groups, and the Shaping of Social Space," especially pp. 230–247.

Figure 5.32 The language divide in Montreal As these maps based on 1991 census data show clearly, the English- and French-speaking populations of Montreal (the anglophone and francophone communities) maintain separate existences. The traditional boundary of St. Laurent Boulevard can still be seen as demarcating these two groups. Bridging the "two solitudes," the allophone communities (made up of people who speak neither English nor French as their mother tongue) have developed language geographies of their own. (*Sources:* L. Lo, and C. Teixeira, "If Quebec Goes . . . The 'Exodus' Impact." *Professional Geographer* 50, 1998, pp. 481–498. The material is used by permission of Blackwell Publishing Ltd. Further information, including mother tongue maps for 1996, can be found in Julie Archambault, Damaris Rose, and Anne-Marie Séguin, *ATLAS: Immigration and Metropolis*, on the website of the Montréal Centre for Interuniversity Research on Immigration, Integration and Urban Dynamics at **http://im.metropolis.net**.

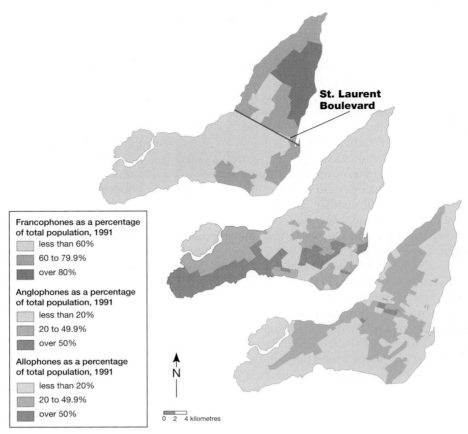

home language: the language most often spoken at home by an individual (as defined by Statistics Canada)

that had risen from 13 percent in 1971, fuelled by Canada's large immigration flows from non–English-, non–French-speaking countries (see Chapter 3). Indeed, as **Table 5.3** shows, there were significant changes. In Canada, in 1971, the leading allophone languages most often spoken at home (the **home language**) were German, Italian, and Ukrainian. In 1996, the top three were Chinese, Italian, and Punjabi.

TABLE 5.3 Canada's Top 10 Home Languages, 1971 and 1996 (Excluding English and French)

1971		1996	
Home Language	Number	Home Language	Number
1. Italian	425 230	1. Chinese	630 520
2. German	213 350	2. Italian	258 050
3. Ukrainian	144 755	3. Punjabi	182 895
4. Greek	86 825	4. Spanish	173 040
5. Chinese	77 890	5. Portuguese	142 975
6. Portuguese	74 760	6. Polish	137 330
7. Polish	70 960	7. German	134 615
8. Hungarian	50 670	8. Arabic	118 605
9. Dutch	36 170	9. Tagalog (Filipino)	111 865
10. Yiddish	26 330	10. Vietnamese	102 905
Aboriginal languages	122 205	Aboriginal languages	146 120

Source: Statistics Canada, *1996 Census Results Teacher's Kit* (**www.statcan.gc.ca/kits-trousses/edu01_0001-eng.htm**). The 1996 results combine single and multiple responses to the question about which language (other than English or French) is spoken most often at home.

By 2006, 1.03 million people (or 3.3 percent of the population) reported a Chinese language as their mother tongue, an increase of almost 162 000 since the 2001 census; Punjabi was the fourth most frequently reported allophone mother tongue in the country; and, Urdu had posted the fastest increase since 2001, rising from 87 000 speakers in 2001 to reach 156 000 in 2006. Overall, by 2006, allophones for the first time represented fully 20 percent of Canada's population.[19]

The discrepancy between mother tongue and home language provides demographers and statisticians with a way of recording the degree of **language shift** that has occurred as newcomers slowly take up one of this country's official languages. The 1996 census data, for example, shows us that 40 percent of allophones spoke English or French at home, a figure somewhat smaller than in 1991, perhaps because of the relative youth of the current immigrant cohorts in this country.

Given the recent pattern of immigration, it is not surprising to see that Toronto has the highest proportion of allophones. According to 2006 census data, in that city, 44 percent of the population has a mother tongue other than English or French. A very similar result (41 percent) is noted for Vancouver. Montreal, however, with 22 percent of its population now allophone, has proportionally less non-French, non-English residents.

Canada's Aboriginal languages are among the most endangered in the world.[20] As of 1996, only 3 of the 50 Aboriginal languages currently spoken in this country can be considered secure, and at least a dozen are on the brink of extinction. Over the years, the numbers of native language speakers has been reduced through slaughter and disease, forced assimilation in residential schools, and the economic and political necessity of learning English or French. The death in 1829 of the last known speaker of the Beothuk language of Newfoundland and Labrador was but the first of a series of Aboriginal language extinctions that continues to this day. For example, the British Columbian languages of Haida (with only 240 speakers left in 1996), Tlingit (145), and Kutenai (120) are almost certain to join that list in the very near future.

The 1996 census records approximately 800 000 Aboriginal people in Canada (a figure which, as Chapter 3 noted, is somewhat incomplete). Of this total, 25 percent reported that they spoke an Aboriginal language as a mother tongue. Of these, the majority spoke Cree (76 475), Ojibway (22 625), or the languages of the Inuktitut language family (26 840). (The 2001 census recorded the sizes of these three language groups as 80 000, 29 700, and 23 500, respectively.) However, when asked about the language most used at home, only 15 percent of the total in 1996 used an Aboriginal language. This statistic gives us an overall indication of the measure of *language shift* into English or French that is occurring.

For a more detailed picture of this shift, experts have derived an *index of continuity*. This index shows, for every 100 people with an Aboriginal mother tongue, the number who used an indigenous language most often at home. An index number below 30 is indicative of a language that is endangered because at that point the language is not being passed on to enough children to enable it to survive. Overall, the index declined from 76 to 65 between 1981 and 1996. Over that period, the index varies from 12 for British Columbia's Salish languages to 65 for Cree and 84 for Inuktitut.

As Mary Jane Norris has recently remarked in a useful study of Canadian Aboriginal languages, the loss of language does not equate with the death of a

language shift: an indicator of the number of people who adopt a new language, usually measured by the difference between mother tongue and home language populations

---

[19]Information from the 2006 census about Canada's language composition and links to more detailed material can be found at **www12.statcan.ca/census-recensement/2006/rt-td/lng-eng.cfm** and in the publication "2006 Census: Immigration, Citizenship, Language, Mobility and Migration." *The Daily*, 4 December 2007 (see **www.statcan.gc.ca/daily-quotidien/071204/dq071204a-eng.htm**).

[20]S.A. Wurm (ed.), *Atlas of the World's Languages in Danger of Disappearing*. Paris: UNESCO Publishing, 1996, p. 23.

TABLE 5.4 Inuit Words for *Snow*	
The language of the Inuit is called *Inuktitut*, and *Inuit* means "the people" in that language.	
anuigaviniq:	very hard, compressed, or frozen snow
apijaq:	snow covered by bad weather
apigiannagaut:	the first snowfall of autumn
katakartanaq:	snow with a hard crust that gives way under footsteps
kavisilaq:	snow roughened by rain or frost
kinirtaq:	compact, damp snow
mannguq:	melting snow
masak:	wet, falling snow
matsaaq:	half-melted snow
natiruvaaq:	drifting snow
pukak:	crystalline snow that breaks down and separates like salt
qannialaaq:	light-falling snow
qiasuqaq:	snow that has thawed and refrozen with an ice surface
qiqumaaq:	snow whose surface has frozen after a light spring thaw

Source: Adapted from R.A. Schroeder, "Gender Vulnerability to Drought: A Case Study of the Hausa Social Environment." NHRAIC Working Paper No. 58, Boulder University of Colorado, 1987.

culture, but it can severely handicap its future.[21] The vocabulary that each language develops is unique, and its loss therefore diminishes a people's ability to describe phenomena in terms most appropriate to it. Perhaps the most famous illustration of this point is the number of words that the Inuit have for *snow* (**Table 5.4**), a range of vocabulary brought about by the importance of snow in their way of life. Given how important language is to a sense of cultural identity, the issue of language extinction has to be a very important one that should concern us—whether it occurs in the global core or in the periphery (**Figure 5.33**).

There are signs of hope. A 1991 survey of Aboriginal peoples noted that 9 out of 10 adults would like to relearn an Aboriginal language they once spoke. Another hopeful sign is the growth of Aboriginal languages as second languages (rather than as mother tongues or languages used most frequently at home) in a number of communities. For example, for every person with Kutenai as their mother tongue, there are two able to speak it. In light of these possibilities, it is not surprising that the Royal Commission on Aboriginal Peoples has recommended that efforts at language retention should be actively pursued. A third hopeful development has been the establishment of the Territory of Nunavut, where the Inuit language of Inuktitut has the best chance of maintaining its vitality (**Figure 5.34**).

Dialects   The use of English and French in Canada provides us with a further insight into the place-making abilities of language. This is because the way in which these languages are now spoken in Canada differs sufficiently from the way they are spoken in England and France that native speakers on either sides of the Atlantic can tell them apart. In fact, both have developed Canadian versions, or dialects, based on distinct accents, vocabulary, and grammar. Similarly, Spanish and Portuguese have developed distinct New World variants. Indeed, we could sum up this phenomenon as "new worlds, old words."

---

[21]The paragraphs on Aboriginal languages are based on M.J. Norris, "Canada's Aboriginal Languages." *Canadian Social Trends*, Statistics Canada, Catalogue No. 11-008, January 13, 1998, pp. 8–16; and Statistics Canada, "1996 Census: Aboriginal Data," *The Daily*, 1998 (**www.statcan.ca/Daily/English/980113/d980113.htm**). The distinctions between Aboriginal languages and language families are from these sources, as are the English spellings used here.

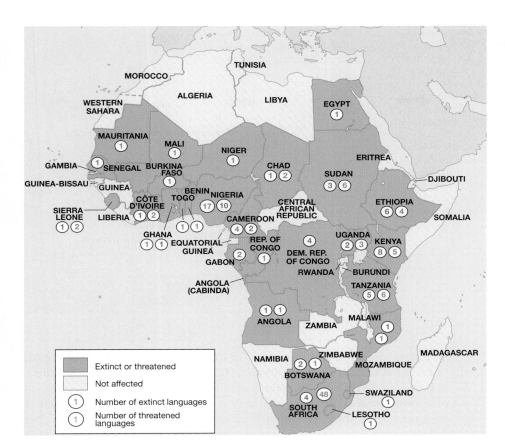

Figure 5.33   Extinct and threatened languages in Africa It is not absolutely certain how many languages are currently being spoken worldwide, but the estimates range between 4200 and 5600. Although some languages are being created through the fusion of an indigenous language with a colonial language, such as English or Portuguese, indigenous languages are mostly dying out. Although only Africa is shown in this map, indigenous languages are dying out throughout the Americas and Asia as well.

Figure 5.34   Office sign in Iqaluit The use of the Inuit language of Inuktitut, written here in syllabics, has received a great boost with the creation of the new Territory of Nunavut, administered from this city. (First developed in 1840 for the Cree language by the Reverend James Evans of Norway House in Manitoba, and based on Pitman's Shorthand, Syllabic orthography was later adapted for the Athapaskan and Inuktitut languages.)

Clearly, these differences must have been caused in some way by the emigration experience. Scholars have identified two general processes, and we can easily see them at work in the Canadian case:

■ *When people move, their language escapes the changes in vocabulary, grammar, or pronunciation that occurs in the region of origin.* The various experiences of the French language in Canada well illustrate this point. The majority of the original French settlers of Quebec came from north of the Loire River in France, a region where a variety of northern French dialects were spoken. The bulk of those who had earlier settled the Acadian regions of Nova Scotia, Prince Edward Island, and New Brunswick came from western France, between the Loire and the Pyrenees, where southern dialects of French were spoken (**Figure 5.35**).

Figure 5.35 The languages of France in 1789 On the eve of the French Revolution, language diversity in France was not so dissimilar from other European regions that were consolidating into states. Whereas a multiplicity of local languages and dialects prevailed before the emergence of a strong central state, many governments created policies to eliminate them. Local languages made it difficult for states to collect taxes, enforce laws, and teach new citizens. (*Source*: D. Bell, "Lingua Populi, Lingua Dei." *American Historical Review*, 1995, p. 1406.)

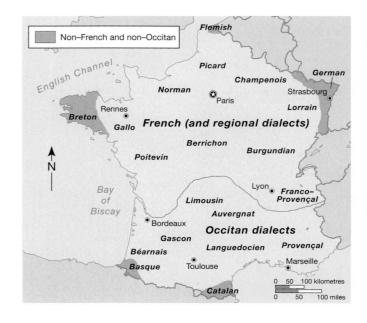

These differences have been preserved in the two regional dialects of French that developed in Canada (for example, Acadian French retains the southern Loire verb *éparer*, meaning "to hang a net out to dry" whereas Quebec French uses the verb *étendre*). Another variant of Acadian French is the Cajun dialect of Louisiana, in the southern United States, where many Acadians settled after their deportation from Nova Scotia. *Ne lache pas la patate* (literally, "Don't drop the potato") is a popular Cajun expression, meaning "Don't give up," which would be expressed as *N'abandonne pas* in France.

At the same time that these dialects were consolidating their position in Canada, they were being made obsolete in France itself. Following the French Revolution of 1789, the central government suppressed the various regional dialects and languages of France in the belief that the use of one language (Parisian French) would unite the country and promote egalitarianism. From 1789 onward, therefore, the French spoken in Canada has preserved older forms of French than found in France itself. The Quebec French verb *gager*, meaning "to bet," has long been replaced by the verb *parier* in France. Sinclair Robinson and Donald Smith's very useful dictionary of Quebec and Acadian French shows how extensive the difference between these long separated forms of French have now become.[22]

Another look, this time with the forms of French spoken on Caribbean islands that were once French colonies (such as Saint Lucia), reveals equally fascinating glimpses of language change. In these cases, versions of French brought by early eighteenth-century colonists merged with African languages spoken by slaves imported to run plantations and with English (when the island switched hands in the 1760s) to create a creole language that, while it follows its own rules, contains a vocabulary that draws on old forms of French.

■ *When people move, their language undergoes considerable changes in vocabulary as people adapt to their new surroundings.* We can illustrate this process by the experience of the English language in Newfoundland and Labrador. Settled from the seventeenth century onward by English-speaking fishing people from southwest England and Ireland, the Newfoundland and Labrador environment was very different from anything these people had experienced before. A great variety of words

[22]Sinclair Robinson and Donald Smith, *Practical Handbook of Quebec and Acadian French*. Toronto: Anansi, 1984.

were needed to describe this particular new world.[23] Many were existing English words, now given new meaning or more use in these new surroundings (*cod* being a very obvious example).

Entirely new words were also created in abundance. As might be expected, many of these were for types of fish (*caplin*) and fish processing (a *water-horse* was a pile of salt cod left to drain after soaking in brine). Others were developed to describe the seal at all stages of its life cycle (a *bedlamer* being an immature seal) and the many forms of ice Newfoundlanders and Labradorians encountered (*ballicatter, clumper, quarr, sish, slob*). Evidence from 1578 even suggests that the word *penguin* was first developed in Newfoundland and Labrador to describe the now extinct Great Auk and may derive from the Welsh *pen gwyn* ("white head").

Newfoundland and Labrador English is spoken with an accent that echoes the pronunciation of Irish and the southwestern parts of England. In terms of grammar, our third requirement for a distinct dialect, *The Dictionary of Newfoundland English* provides a list of 10 unique constructions. These range from the use of "to be after doing (something)," as in "how many times am I after telling you," to the addition of "–en" to adjectives for materials, as in "tinnen cup" and "glassen pole."

We have considered these two processes of dialect formation separately for ease of comprehension, but in reality, of course, both types often worked in unison. In Nova Scotia, for example, the Acadians were confronted with a marshland environment for which they soon developed a new vocabulary (including such words as *aboiteau* to describe the special type of dam built to farm the coastal marshes). And in Newfoundland and Labrador, archaic English words have survived that have long since been abandoned in England itself (words such as *fadge,* "to manage on one's own," or *dwy,* "a gust of wind").

So far, we have considered three distinct dialectical regions in this country. You might have expected that outside of these very obvious regions, we would not be able to find other dialectical areas in Canada. High levels of immigration of non-English, non-French speakers from all over the world and the relatively recent settlement of the rest of this country certainly work against the processes we have discussed above. However, even here we see the effects of the core–periphery model. Only in the metropolitan core of this country are immigration and mobility levels sufficiently high to prevent dialect formation. Outside the cities, in the Canadian periphery, where immigration levels are much lower and the length of residence much longer, it is still reasonable to expect regional accents and dialects to emerge.

Certainly, experts with a keen ear say that it is possible to divide the remainder of English-speaking Canada into additional local dialectical areas: the Maritimes, eastern Ontario (typified by the "Ottawa Valley" accent of Irish origin), western Ontario (with its distinctive pronunciation of such words as "about," pronounced "aboot"), the Prairies (where the presence of large numbers of rural immigrants from all over Europe has had almost a century to exert an influence over the use of English), and British Columbia (where the effects of relative isolation and much more recent immigration may be heard).

CULTURAL NATIONALISM

The protection of regional languages is part of a larger movement in which geographers and other scholars have become interested. The movement, known as **cultural nationalism** is an effort to protect regional and national cultures from the homogenizing impacts of globalization. Cultural nationalism is one manifestation of a much wider set of beliefs known as nationalism. The idea of nationalism (defined

cultural nationalism: an effort to protect regional and national cultures from the homogenizing impacts of globalization

---

[23]G.M. Story, W.J. Kirwin, and J.D.A. Widdowson, *The Dictionary of Newfoundland English.* Toronto: University of Toronto Press, 1982.

Figure 5.36 The United States in Canada This image of a Kentucky Fried Chicken restaurant in Quebec illustrates the influence of U.S. products on Canadian society and culture. Because Canada is the nearest northern neighbour to the United States, it is not surprising that Canada is probably more heavily influenced by U.S. culture than any other country in the world. It should be pointed out, however, that the flow is not one way.

and more fully explored in Chapter 9) holds that individuals have a shared identity with others of the same nation, a group often defined by family ties or geography. In either case, nations endeavour to secure their identities by the promotion of their own distinctiveness, and they use a number of ways to achieve this. Some groups may attempt isolationism as a way of sealing themselves off from undesirable influences. Other groups may attempt to legislate the flow of ideas and values.

Maintaining Cultural Borders: Canada and the United States

Not only the periphery is resisting cultural imperialism. Australia, Britain, France, and Canada also have formally attempted to erect barriers to U.S. cultural products. The most aggressive moves have been made by Canada, which has developed an extensive and very public policy of cultural protection against the onslaught of U.S. music, television, magazines, films, and other art and media forms (**Figure 5.36**).

In early 1995, for example, the Canadian government levied an 80 percent excise tax against Time Inc.'s Canadian version of *Sports Illustrated* magazine because it did not think the version was Canadian enough. The authorities complained that too many of the articles were directed at U.S. sports issues and not enough at Canadian ones.

Other government bodies, such as the National Film Board of Canada and the Canadian Radio-television and Telecommunications Commission (CRTC), are also active in monitoring the media for the incursion of U.S. culture. For example, 30 percent of the music on Canadian radio must be Canadian. Consequently, Nashville-based Country Music TV was discontinued from Canada's cable system in the early 1990s and replaced with a Canadian-owned country music channel.

Besides regulating how much and what type of U.S. culture can travel north across the border, the Canadian government also sponsors a sort of "affirmative action" grant program for this country's own cultural industries. Critically acclaimed television programs are subsidized by the government. The music group Crash Test Dummies produced its first album with the help of a $60 000 grant from the Canadian government. In short, the story surrounding cultural nationalism is that the struggle to control cultural production is an intense one. This is especially true for Canada, which continues to struggle to establish an independent identity beyond the shadow of the United States.

Multiculturalism in Canada One way that Canada has sought to distance itself from U.S. cultural policies has been to develop policies based on the concept of multiculturalism. Such policies enable different cultures to maintain their distinctiveness (as in the Canadian cultural mosaic model), rather than to require them to be assimilated (as in the American melting pot model) into the mainstream French- or English-speaking cultures. This approach has become especially valuable as the number and diversity of immigrants into this country have increased and as the sizes of ethnocultural communities within Canada have grown (see, for one example, Chapter 3 on the experiences of the Somali community in Toronto).

Jean Burnet's concise explanation of multiculturalism in Canada notes that the term *multiculturalism* is used in at least three senses:[24]

1. To refer to a society, such as Canada's, that is characterized by ethnic or cultural heterogeneity

2. To refer to a country's ideal of equality and mutual respect for its minorities

3. To refer to federal government policies proclaimed in 1971 and set out in the Canadian Multiculturalism Act of 1988, which aims "to recognize all Canadians as full and equal participants in Canadian society"

Burnet's reflection on the value of these policies is also worth noting. Multicultural policies since 1971 have not met the needs of all immigrants (especially visible minority groups), since they were tailored much more for the needs of long-established ethnic groups of European background. "Nevertheless," he argues, "the introduction of the term and what has been called 'the multicultural movement' have been important in calling attention to an important type of diversity within society and engendering recognition of it."[25]

Of course, there have been criticisms of this policy over the years. Critics have seen multiculturalism as a way of either distracting Canadians from the implications of official bilingualism, diluting the political clout of francophone Canada, or of "bribing" Canada's ethnic communities with cultural blandishments rather than any real financial aid. Certainly, the experience of groups, such as Toronto's Somali community (see Chapter 3), makes it clear that whatever the effects such policies have had, they have not yet been able to fully combat the social and economic discriminations that many such groups face. The adoption of multicultural hiring goals by many Canadian organizations and institutions serves as another illustration of the challenges that still confront many ethnic communities (**Figure 5.37**).

One important issue that has attracted a lot of attention is the extent to which policies of multiculturalism produce a framework for the creation of minority

Figure 5.37 Canada's multiculturalism Traditional institutions, such as the Royal Canadian Mounted Police, are recognizing that Canada's increasingly multicultural population requires that diversity be recognized in their hiring policies.

---

[24]Jean Burnet, "Multiculturalism." *The Canadian Encyclopedia*, online edition: Historica Foundation, **www.thecanadianencyclopedia.com.**

[25]Ibid.

rights. Authors, such as Neil Bissoondath, have written forceful critiques of these policies, arguing that by empowering minorities, the policies have given them more rights than the majority has. William Kymlicka provides a very well thought out answer to this question in his book *Multicultural Citizenship: A Liberal Theory of Minority Rights.* He suggests that in "multi-nation" or "polyethnic" states, it is necessary to protect ethnocultural minorities from the political and economic power of the majority.[26] This can be done through the use of multicultural policies that either promote the self-government of particular groups (he cites the example of Canada's Aboriginal peoples) or advance the "polyethnic rights" of ethnocultural communities (such as permitting dress codes or minority languages).

A good example of the first type, according to Kymlicka, is those Aboriginal groups that have been accorded rights of self-government (see Chapter 9). Examples of the second include policies that have been developed by provincial and territorial school boards to enable young Sikh males to carry small ceremonial daggers, known as *kirpan.*

Although now abandoned, the 2005 Ontario proposal to recognize *sharia*-based tribunals in family arbitration cases illustrates very clearly some of the dilemmas of multicultural policy.[27] In proposing to recognize differences (the right of the Muslim community to follow its own teachings regarding divorce), the province appeared to disavow universal rights (the rights of women). It is hardly surprising, therefore, that scholars have recognized that countries with significant multicultural communities, such as Canada, must grapple with what are essentially the challenges of the postmodern state (see Chapter 9).

It is important to add here that multicultural policies that promote the self-government of particular groups or advance the rights of ethnocultural communities are, according to Kymlicka, "group-differentiated rights" and not "collective rights" (that is, rights accorded to all individuals who compose the collective). The failure to recognize this distinction is one, he remarks, that has caused some confusion in the past.[28] "It is equally important," he continues, "to stress the limits on such rights." Minority rights "should not allow one group to dominate other groups and they should not allow a group to oppress its own members." It is important that democratic states, such as Canada, ensure that there is equality between groups and freedom and equality within groups. "Within these limits," Kymlicka concludes, "minority rights can play a valuable role within a broader theory of liberal justice."[29]

CULTURE AND IDENTITY

In addition to exploring cultural forms, such as religion and language, and movements, such as cultural nationalism, geographers have increasingly begun to ask questions about other forms of identity. This interest largely has to do with the fact that certain long-established and some more recently self-conscious cultural groups have begun to use their identities as a way of asserting political, economic, social, and cultural claims.

ethnicity: a socially created system of rules about who belongs and who does not belong to a particular group based on actual or perceived commonality

Ethnicity and the Use of Space

Ethnicity is another way in which geographers are exploring cultural identity. **Ethnicity** is a socially created system of rules about who belongs to a particular group based on actual or perceived commonality, such as language or religion.

[26]William Kymlicka, *Multicultural Citizenship: A Liberal Theory of Minority Rights.* Oxford: Oxford University Press, 1995, pp. 3–48.

[27]Karen Howlett, "Islamic-Law Plan Will Respect Rights, Ontario Says." *Globe and Mail,* 7 September 2005, p. A5.

[28]Kymlicka, op. cit., pp. 124–127.

[29]Ibid., p. 194.

A geographic focus on ethnicity is an attempt to understand how it shapes and is shaped by space, and how ethnic groups use space with respect to mainstream culture. For cultural geographers, territory is also a basis for ethnic group cohesion (see Chapter 9 for more on territory). For example, cultural groups—ethnically identified or otherwise—may be spatially segregated from the wider society in ghettos or ethnic enclaves (see Chapter 11). Or these groups may use space to declare their subjective interpretations about the world they live in and their place in it. The use of the city streets by many different cultural groups demonstrates this point (**Figure 5.38**).

Nineteenth-century immigrants to U.S. cities used the streets to broadcast their ideas about life in their adopted country. Ethnic parades in the nineteenth century—such as St. Patrick's Day for the Irish and Columbus Day for the Italians—were often very public declarations about the stresses that existed among classes, cultures, and generations.

At the height of late nineteenth-century immigration, the Irish and many other immigrant groups, such as the Italians, Greeks, Poles, and Slavs, were largely shunned and vilified by the host society and were relegated to low-paying jobs and poor housing. Publicly ridiculed in newspaper and other print venues, these groups took to the streets to re-interpret the city's public spaces, even if only for a day. Released from a strict work routine of 10 to 15 hours a day, participants and spectators could use the parade to promote an alternative reality of pride and festivity, among other things. Participants acquired a degree of power and autonomy that was not possible in their workday lives. Because of their festive and extraordinary nature, nineteenth-century parades temporarily helped to change the world in which they occurred.

The same can be said of cultural parades in the twentieth century. Montreal's St. Jean Baptiste Day parade is a barometer of separatist feelings and is often a highly politically charged event. Irish-American gay and lesbian groups in Boston and New York, with their own interpretations of "Irishness," have been turned away from St. Patrick's Day parades by the more mainstream interpreters of the term. Such a confrontation between ethnicity and sexuality also highlights how difficult it is to separate cultural identity into distinct categories. In different places, for different historical reasons, the complex combinations of cultural identities of race, class, gender, and sexual preference result in unique and sometimes powerful expressions.

Figure 5.38   Parade in Montreal Many ethnic groups use city parades as an opportunity to promote pride and an alternative picture of what it means to belong to an ethnic group. This photo shows members of Montreal's Temple Hare Krishna in their annual *Ratha Yatra* parade along St. Laurent Boulevard. Known as "the Main," this street was traditionally the first place immigrants lived on when they reached the city, and it still constitutes a major divide between Montreal's anglophone and francophone populations.

Race and Place

Prevailing ideas and practices with respect to race have also been used to understand the shaping of places and responses to these forces.[30]

Race is a problematic classification of human beings based on skin colour and other physical characteristics. Biologically speaking, however, no such thing as race exists within the human species. Yet, consider the categories of race and place that correspond to "Chinese" and "Chinatown." Powerful Western ideas about Chinese as a racial category enabled the emergence and perpetuation of Chinatown as a type of landscape found throughout many North American cities (**Figure 5.39**). In this and other cases, the visible characteristics of hair, skin, and bone structure made race into a category of difference that was (and still is) widely accepted and often spatially expressed.

The mainstream approach to neighbourhood is to see it as a spatial setting for systems of affiliation more or less chosen by people with similar skin colour. Recently, cultural geographers have begun to overturn this approach and to see neighbourhoods as spaces that affirm the dominant society's sense of identity. For example, from the perspective of white society, nineteenth-century Chinatowns were the

race: problematic classification of human beings based on skin colour and other physical characteristics

[30]Adapted from K. Anderson, "The Idea of Chinatown: The Power of Place and Institutional Practice in the Making of a Racial Category." *Annals of the Association of American Geographers* 77(4), 1987, pp. 580–598.

Figure 5.39 Chinatowns Chinatowns are features of most major North American cities. (*Source:* Illustration, *Annals of the Association of American Geographers* 77[4], December 1987.)

Chinatown, Vancouver, 1907—The marginalization of the Chinese population of Vancouver, British Columbia, had strong racial and ethnic undercurrents that surfaced in illustrations such as this one, published in 1907. Note how the white settlements are pictured as airy, light, and single-family, whereas the Chinese domiciles are labelled as "warrens" "infested" by thousands of Chinese.

physical expression of what set the Chinese apart from Caucasians. The distinguishing characteristics revolved around the way the Chinese looked, what they ate, their non-Christian religion, their opium consumption, gambling habits, and other "strange" practices. A recent study by Ban Seng Hoe of the history of the Chinese laundry in Canada shows that discrimination against the Chinese often worked at spatial scales much smaller than that of a Chinatown. He shows that many Chinese immigrants established laundries in a large number of communities across Canada during the early part of the twentieth century; however, this way of making a living was almost always fraught with antagonism from the local residents:[31]

> The City of Calgary, for example, stipulated that no Chinese laundries would be allowed to operate on certain streets. In 1905, the Calgary Central Labour Union condemned Chinese laundries as a menace to public health, and *The Calgary Herald* demanded that the Chinese laundries be cleared in order to avoid an epidemic.

Place—Chinatown—maintained and manifested differences between Caucasian and Chinese societies. Furthermore, place continues to be a mechanism for creating and preserving local systems of racial classification within defined geographical confines. The homelands of South Africa, discussed in **Geography Matters 9.1** (Chapter 9), are also an illustration of the interaction of race and place, though at a much larger scale.

gender: category reflecting the social differences between men and women rather than the anatomical differences that are related to sex

Gender

Gender is an identity that has received a great deal of attention by cultural geographers within the last two to three decades. **Gender** is a category reflecting the social

[31]Ban Seng Hoe, *Enduring Hardship: The Chinese Laundry in Canada*. Gatineau: Canadian Museum of Civilization, 2003, p. 55.

differences between men and women. As with other forms of identity, gender implies a socially created difference in power between groups. In the case of gender, the power difference gives males an advantage over females and is socially and culturally created rather than biologically determined. As with other forms of identity, class position can intensify the power differences among and between groups. Furthermore, the implications of these differences are played out differently in different parts of the world.

Among South Asia's poor, for example, women bear the greatest burden and the most suffering. South Asian societies are intensely patriarchal, though the form that patriarchy takes varies by region and class. The common denominator among the poor throughout South Asia is that women not only have the constant responsibilities of motherhood and domestic chores but also have to work long hours in informal-sector occupations (**Figure 5.40**). In many poor communities, 90 percent of all production occurs outside of formal employment, more than half of which is the result of women's efforts. In addition, women's property rights are curtailed, their public behaviour is restricted, and their opportunities for education and participation in the waged labour force are severely limited. Women's subservience to men is deeply ingrained within South Asian cultures, and it is manifest most clearly in the cultural practices attached to family life, such as the custom of providing a dowry to daughters at marriage. The preference for male children is reflected in the widespread (but illegal) practice of selective abortion and female infanticide. Within marriages, many (but by no means all) poor women are routinely neglected and maltreated. More extreme are the cases—usually reported only when they involve middle-class families—of "bride burning," whereby a husband or mother-in-law fakes the accidental death (kitchen fires are favoured) or suicide of a bride whose parents had defaulted in their dowry payments. Several thousand such deaths are reported in India each year, and this is almost certainly only a fraction of the real incidence.

The picture for women in South Asia, as elsewhere, is not entirely negative, however, and one of the most significant developments has been the emergence of women's self-help movements. Perhaps the best-known of these is the Grameen Bank, a grassroots organization formed to provide small loans to the rural poor in Bangladesh. Another is the Self-Employed Women's Association (SEWA) in India, which has made a major contribution to building self-confidence and self-reliance among poor working women by mobilizing and organizing them.

Figure 5.40   Indian women in the informal sector   Many women in South Asia are self-employed as small vendors in the daily markets. Others do home-based work such as weaving and dyeing cloth or embroidering or sewing garments. Nearly all workers in the informal sector, whether male or female, lack any sort of social protection such as health or unemployment insurance.

Figure 5.41 The gendered construction of space This simple model shows the ways in which nineteenth-century and twentieth-century constructions of gender in Western societies affected how those societies created and used landscapes, such as the city. Men, as bread-winners, inhabited a very different social world from that of women, and this affected not only their economic roles but also their geographic experiences in our cities.

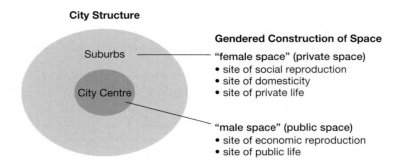

City Structure

Suburbs

City Centre

Gendered Construction of Space

"female space" (private space)
• site of social reproduction
• site of domesticity
• site of private life

"male space" (public space)
• site of economic reproduction
• site of public life

If we turn to examples from the developed world, we can see that geographical studies in Canada have paid special attention to how our city spaces have become gendered and how this has affected our use and appreciation of place. These studies have shown that the suburbs have tended to be seen as "female" space, the downtown and industrial areas as "male" space.[32] This simple dichotomy was created in Canada by nineteenth-century and twentieth-century constructions of gender in which residential space was seen as the site of social reproduction and private life, and commercial and industrial space as the site of economic reproduction and public life. Under gender stereotypes prevalent at the time, the former site became identified as female space; the latter site as male space (**Figure 5.41**).

Although such constructions of gender relations are entirely artificial, their existence has a series of real implications. Scholars have, for example, pointed out that the unquestioning assumption by city planners that the suburbs are still entirely a domestic or female space means that city regulations often forbid the creation of small business in suburban zones. These rules are based on old preconceptions that there is no need for economic activity ("male" work) in residential areas ("female" space). These preconceptions could not envisage the need for people to create paid employment where they live (the mixture of private or domestic and public or economic spheres). Home businesses, for example, are precluded because they are "male" use of "female" space—despite the obvious opportunities for home-based work in the Information Age.

Until recently, the only sub-discipline within geography that concerned itself with the importance of gender in space, place, or environmental concerns was **feminist geography**, a field concerned to examine "the extent to which women and men experience spaces and places differently and to show how these differences themselves are part of the social construction of gender as well as that of place," to quote Linda McDowell's 1999 definition of the field, and it is therefore instructive to consider briefly the evolution of that sub-discipline over the last 30 years or so.

Beginning in the early 1980s in Canada, Britain, and the United States, "Women in Geography" study groups became established and took their place among the more long-standing activities of organizations such as the American Association of Geographers and the Canadian Association of Geographers (where the group is known as the Canadian Women and Geography Group, or CWAG).

Initially concerned with studying how the lives of men and women differed geographically, much of the early work conducted by feminist geographers showed how the gender categories "male" and "female" created different spatial experiences for men and women. Thus, for example, Susan Hanson and Geraldine Pratt's studies of commuting patterns in North American cities such as Worcester, Massachusetts, showed that a clear distinction existed between the travel behaviour of men and women. The former would, as their data showed, take many short trips during

feminist geography: a field that examines the extent to which women and men experience spaces and places differently and to show how these differences themselves are part of the social construction of gender as well as that of place

[32]See, for example, Suzanne Mackenzie, "Restructuring the Relations of Work and Life: Women as Environmental Actors, Feminism as Geographic Analysis." *Gender, Place and Culture* 6(4), 1999, pp. 417–430.

Figure 5.42   Montreal's "Gay Village"   This building, known as the Complexe Bourbon, incorporates a café and a restaurant. It is located on the corner of rue St. Catherine and rue Alexandre de Sève in the heart of Montreal's "Gay Village." The building flies multicoloured flags recalling the rainbow, an emblem of gay culture.

the middle of the day across the city; the latter would take long trips at the beginning and end of the day.

Such studies amply served to show that different geographic opportunities (or "life spaces") existed for men and women in such societies, and many geographers have continued in this research vein. Other feminist geographers have more recently sought to look beyond research that demonstrates the fact that a clear difference exists, to exploring the underlying societal reasons *why* those differences exist and the processes that sustain their continued existence. To take Hanson and Pratt's work again as an example, the commuting pattern they document in Worcester had nothing to do, they suggest, with an intrinsic difference between men and women. Rather, it was caused by the economic and social demands on those whom late twentieth-century North American society had placed the duties of either child care (a female-designated activity) or work in the paid labour force (a male-designated task).

Armed with these insights, a "third wave" of gender-sensitive geographical research is now underway, and is beginning to use the insight that gender is equally as socially constructed as space or place to examine the life spaces of other gender categories.

Gender categories based on gay, lesbian, and other relationships also create their own geographies. In Canada, for example, research has shown how Montreal's Gay Village has created a district in the city where gay men are able to meet and socialize in bars and clubs with less animosity from the general public than elsewhere. The higher-than-average income that many gay Canadian couples enjoy has enabled many gay people who live in the village to embark on an extensive rejuvenation of the area's housing stock and to support an increasingly expensive range of restaurants. In these ways, the urban landscape of the area has been visibly transformed over the past 30 years or so (**Figure 5.42**). Indeed, the city of Montreal has become so accepting of the village that it actively promotes its presence in its tourist literature.

CULTURE AND THE PHYSICAL ENVIRONMENT

Although interest in culture and the built environment has become prominent among geographers over the last several decades, a great deal of attention continues to be paid to culture and the physical environment. As with Sauer's original concept of the cultural landscape, geographers continue to focus their attention on people's relationships to the natural world and how the changing global economy disrupts or shapes those relationships. In this section, we look at two related but distinct ways of understanding the relationship between culture and the natural environment—cultural ecology and political ecology.

Cultural Ecology

cultural ecology: the study of the relationship between a cultural group and its natural environment

cultural adaptation: the use of complex strategies by human groups to live successfully as part of a natural system

Cultural ecology is the study of the relationship between a cultural group and its natural environment. Cultural ecologists study the material practices (food production, shelter provision, levels of biological reproduction) as well as the non-material practices (belief systems, traditions, social institutions) of cultural groups. Their aim is to understand how cultural processes affect adaptation to the environment. Whereas the traditional approach to the cultural landscape focuses on human impacts on the landscape or its form or history, cultural ecologists seek to explain how cultural processes affect adaptation to the environment. **Cultural adaptation** involves the complex strategies human groups use to live successfully as part of a natural system. Cultural ecologists recognize that people are components of complex ecosystems, and that the way they manage and consume resources is shaped by cultural beliefs, practices, values, and traditions as well as by larger institutions and power relationships.

The cultural ecology approach incorporates three key points:

- Cultural groups and the environment are interconnected by systemic inter-relationships. Cultural ecologists must examine how people manage resources through a range of strategies to comprehend how the environment shapes culture, and vice versa.

- Cultural behaviour must be examined as a function of the cultural group's relationship to the environment through both material and nonmaterial cultural elements. Such examinations are conducted through intensive fieldwork.

- Most studies in cultural ecology investigate food production in rural and agricultural settings in the periphery to understand how change affects the relationship between cultural groups and the environment.[33]

These three points illustrate the way in which cultural geographers go about asking questions, collecting data, and deriving conclusions from their research. They also show how cultural ecology is both similar to and different from Sauer's approach to the cultural landscape, described at the beginning of the chapter. Although each point shares an emphasis on culture, in cultural ecology the cultural processes of particular groups, rather than the imprint that culture makes on the landscape, have come to take centre stage. As a result, cultural ecologists look at food production, demographic change and its impacts on ecosystems, and ecological sustainability. Additionally, the scale of analysis is not on cultural areas or cultural regions, but on small groups' adaptive strategies to a particular place or setting.

The impact of Spanish agricultural innovations on the culture of the indigenous people of the Central Andes region of South America (an area encompassing the mountainous portions of Peru, Bolivia, and Ecuador) presents an excellent case study in cultural ecology.[34] The transformation of Andean culture began when Pizarro arrived in Peru from Spain in 1531 and set about vanquishing the politically, technologically, and culturally sophisticated Incan empire. The Spaniards brought with them not only domestic plants and animals (mainly by way of Nicaragua and Mexico) but also knowledge about how to fabricate the tools they needed and a strong sense of what was necessary for a "civilized" life.

---

[33]K. Butzer, "Cultural Ecology." In G.L. Gaile and C.J. Wilmot (eds.), *Geography in America.* Columbus, OH: Merrill Publishing Co., 1989, p. 192.

[34]Adapted from D. Gade, "Landscape, System, and Identity in the Post-Conquest Andes." *Annals of the Association of American Geographers* 82(3), 1992, pp. 461–477.

By 1620, however, the indigenous Andean people had lost 90 percent of their population and had been forced to make significant changes in their subsistence lifestyles (an illustration of demographic collapse as discussed in Chapter 4). The Incan empire, with its large population base, had once engaged in intensive agriculture practices, including building and maintaining irrigation systems, terracing fields, and furrowing hillsides. With the severe drop in population and consequent loss of labour power, the survivors turned to pastoralism because herding requires less labour than intensive agriculture. Ultimately, it was the introduction of Old World domesticated animals that had the greatest impact on the Central Andes (**Figure 5.43**), another example of ecological imperialism (see Chapter 4).

Of the range of animals the peasants could have incorporated into their agricultural practices (including cattle, oxen, horses, donkeys, pigs, sheep, goats, rabbits, and turkeys), only a few animals were widely adopted. Sheep were by far the most important introduction and were kept by Andean peasants as early as 1560. In many areas, sheep herding soon replaced the herding of indigenous animals, such as llamas and alpaca. By the seventeenth century, at elevations below 3500 metres (11 500 feet), sheep herding had been fully integrated into peasant economies and practices.

Adoption of sheep herding was facilitated by several factors. Sheep wool was oilier than that produced by native animals, a quality that made wool clothing more water resistant. Sheep also provided a source of meat, tallow, and manure for farm plots and could become an important source of food to a family in times of flood, frost, or drought. Sheep had a higher fertility level and a lower mortality rate than native herd animals and did not require large inputs of labour to manage. Finally, unlike crops, sheep could be marched to market on their own feet—no small advantage in the rugged terrain of the Andes.

Pigs and goats also proved popular because they fit well into available niches of the peasant economy. Rabbits, however, even though they produced more meat, never replaced the native guinea pigs. Guinea pigs retained a high cultural value as they continued to be a featured food at Aboriginal ceremonies celebrating life-cycle events and curing rites. Likewise cows, though valued by the Spanish colonists, never became important to indigenous ways of life. Cows did not do well at higher altitudes or on steep terrain, and it was difficult to find appropriate fodder for them during the dry season. They also constituted a high risk, for they were an expensive investment and loss or theft created economic hardship for the owner.

The pattern of selective adoption among Central Andean peasants also extended to plants. Of the approximately two dozen crops they could have adopted, Andean peasants adopted only about half of them. Peasants based their planting decisions on usefulness, environmental fit, and competition from other plants. For example, of the various grain crops that were available (rye, barley, oats, and wheat), Andean peasants adopted only wheat and barley. Andean peasants began to cultivate these grains in the highlands as early as the 1540s.

Both wheat and barley found a good ecological "fit" within the Central Andes and could be integrated into the fallow cycles that the peasants had long practised. These crops also had the advantage of supplementing the peasants' array of foods because they complemented—rather than competed with—cultivation of indigenous crops such as maize and potatoes (**Figure 5.44**).

By the 1590s, a "bundle" of Spanish cultural traits had been integrated into the Central Andean rural cultural complex, creating a hybrid rural culture. The hybridized culture—and cultural landscape—combined a much simplified version of Spanish material life with important (though altered) Incan practices of crop growing, herding, agricultural technology, and settlement patterns. That this hybrid cultural complex remains identifiable today, even after four centuries and in the face of contemporary globalizing forces, is due to a combination of factors: the peasants' strong adherence to custom, their geographical isolation, and the poverty of their circumstances.

Figure 5.43 Bolivian herders, Lake Titicaca Though sheep are not indigenous to the Andes, they have been widely adopted in this region since the Columbian Exchange. Sheep are well adapted to the high altitudes and provide wool and meat. Shown here are young girls of the Lake Titicaca region of Bolivia returning at day's end from herding.

Figure 5.44 Andean potatoes in the marketplace The Andean region boasts hundreds of varieties of potatoes. The potato is one of the New World plants that was introduced into Europe following the Columbian Exchange. Forced reliance on the potato in nineteenth-century Irish agriculture led to disaster, however. The Great Potato Famine of the 1840s caused widespread mortality and migration. Many died, and many others migrated to the United States, reducing Ireland's population to levels from which it still has not recovered.

Following the three points outlined earlier, cultural ecologists have been able to understand complex relationships between cultural groups and their environment, showing how choices are shaped by both culture and environmental conditions. Some critics have argued, however, that this conceptual framework of cultural ecology leaves out other intervening influences of the relationship between culture and the environment, namely, the impact of the political and economic institutions and practices.

Political Ecology

During the 1980s, cultural ecologists began moving away from a strict focus on a particular group's interactions with the environment, instead placing that relationship within a wider context. The result is political ecology, the merging of political economy with cultural ecology. **Political ecology** stresses that human–environment relationships can be adequately understood only by reference to the relationship of patterns of resource use to political and economic forces. Just as with the study of agriculture, industrialization, urbanization, and comparable geographical phenomena, this perspective requires an examination of the impact of the State and the market on the ways in which particular groups use their resource base.

Political ecology incorporates the same human–environment components analyzed by cultural ecologists. Yet, because political ecologists frame cultural ecology within the context of political and economic relationships, political ecology is seen to go beyond what cultural ecologists seek to understand.

Two studies of farming on St. Vincent and the Grenadines, an island nation in the Caribbean, illustrate this difference (**Figure 5.45**).[35] You will perhaps remember from Chapter 4 that St. Vincent (its Botanic Gardens, specifically) was the place to which Captain Bligh brought the breadfruit specimens that he had transported

political ecology: an approach to cultural geography that studies human–environment relationships through the relationships of patterns of resource use to political and economic forces

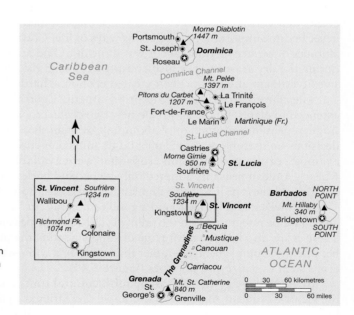

Figure 5.45 St. Vincent and the Grenadines St. Vincent and the Grenadines are part of the island chain of the Lesser Antilles in the Caribbean Sea. The total population is about 116 400, occupying about 240 square kilometres (150 square miles).

---

[35]Adapted from L. Grossman, "Soil Conservation, Political Ecology, and Technological Change on Saint Vincent." *Geographical Review* 87, 1997, p. 353; and L. Grossman, *The Political Ecology of Bananas: Contract Farming, Peasants, and Agrarian Change in the Eastern Caribbean.* Chapel Hill: University of North Carolina Press, 1998.

from the Pacific). The Botanic Gardens remained a centre for agricultural innovation in the islands into the twentieth century, and St. Vincent's leading export crop of the inter-war years—arrowroot—was first grown experimentally there.

Government reports from the 1940s stressed that soil erosion was the leading agricultural problem on St Vincent. Official documents often blamed inappropriate farming methods as the cause. However, Grossman's study of this period shows that more astute commentators realized that the political and economic constraints faced by the island's peasantry contributed to soil loss during this period. Since the best land was owned by large agricultural estates, many of the islanders were forced to farm on slopes too steep for agriculture. Because average holdings were too small to support them, farmers could not afford to leave any land fallow. And because of the constant fear of eviction, farmers could not risk long-term measures needed to conserve the soil.

In recent years, agriculturalists on the main island of St. Vincent have shifted to banana production for export at the same time that local food production has begun to decline (**Figure 5.46**). Without recognizing the impacts of politics and the wider economy, it would be impossible to understand why these two processes are occurring simultaneously. Disincentives and incentives have both played a role. Disincentives to maintain local food production include marketing constraints, crop theft, competition from inexpensive food exports, and inadequate government agricultural extension assistance. Incentives to produce for export include state subsidies to export-oriented agriculture and access to credit for banana producers, as well as a strong British market for Caribbean bananas. As a result, local food production, although faced with the same environmental conditions as banana production, does not enjoy the same political and economic benefits. Because production for export is potentially more lucrative and an economically safer option, and to some extent because of changing dietary practices, local food production is a less attractive option for agriculturalists.

As the St. Vincent case illustrates, the political ecology approach provides a framework for understanding how the processes of the world economy affect local cultures and practices. The St. Vincent case also indicates how State policies and practices and economic demand in the global economy shape local decision making. Furthermore, local cultural practices (especially dietary) are being abandoned as people develop a taste and preference for low-cost and convenient imported agricultural commodities (including flour and rice). Unfortunately, however, production for export also opens up the local economy to the fluctuations of the wider global economy. Recent changes in European Union policy on banana imports, for example, are having negative effects on banana production in St. Vincent. And those policy changes themselves are a response to American demands that Caribbean producers based in Europe's ex-colonies no longer be allowed preferential access to Europe's huge market. St. Vincent's banana industry is therefore but another pawn in the politics of trade that globalization has caused.

Figure 5.46   St. Vincent: banana production

GLOBALIZATION AND CULTURAL CHANGE

The discussion of cultural geography in this chapter raises one central question: how has globalization changed culture? We have seen that it affects different cultural groups differently and that different groups respond in different ways to these changes. With so much change occurring for so long, however, we must still ask ourselves what impact, overall, globalization is having on the multiplicity of cultural groups that inhabit the globe.

Anyone who has ever travelled between major world cities—or, for that matter, anyone who has been attentive to the backdrops of movies, television news stories, and magazine photojournalism—will have noticed the many familiar aspects of contemporary life in settings that, until recently, were thought of as being quite different from one another. Airports, offices, and international hotels have become notoriously alike, and their similarities of architecture and interior design have become reinforced by near-universal dress codes of the people who frequent them. The business suit, especially for males, has become the norm for office workers throughout much of the world. Jeans, T-shirts, and athletic footwear, meanwhile, have become the norm for young people as well as those in lower-wage jobs. The same automobiles can be seen on the streets of cities throughout the world (though sometimes they are given different names by their manufacturers); the same popular music is played on local radio stations; and many of the movies shown in local theatres are the same. Some of the TV programming is also the same—not just the music videos on MTV but also CNN's news, major international sports events, children's series, such as *Sesame Street,* drama series, and comedy series. The same brand names also show up in stores and restaurants: Coca-Cola, Perrier, Carlsberg, Nestlé, Nike, Seiko, Sony, IBM, Nintendo, and Microsoft, to list just a few. Everywhere there is Chinese food, pita bread, pizza, classical music, rock music, and jazz.

It is these commonalities that provide a sense of familiarity among the inhabitants of the "fast world" that we described in Chapter 2. From the point of view of cultural nationalism, the "lowest common denominator" of this familiarity is often seen as the culture of fast food and popular entertainment that emanates from the United States. Popular commentators have observed that cultures around the world are being Americanized, or "McDonaldized," which represents the beginnings of a single global culture that will be based on material consumption, with the English language as its medium (**Figure 5.47**).

There is certainly some evidence to support this point of view, not least in the sheer numbers of people around the world who view *Sesame Street,* drink Coca-Cola, and eat at McDonald's franchises or similar fast-food chains. Meanwhile, U.S. culture is increasingly embraced by local entrepreneurs around the world. Travel writer Pico Iyer, for example, describes finding dishes called "Yes, Sir, Cheese My Baby" and "Ike and Tuna Turner" in a local buffeteria in Guangzhou, China.[36] It seems clear that U.S. products are consumed as much for their symbolism of a particular way of life as for their intrinsic value. McDonald's burgers, along with Coca-Cola, Hollywood movies, rock music, and NFL and NBA insignia, have become associated with a lifestyle package that features luxury, youth, fitness, beauty, and freedom.

Figure 5.47 McDonald's in Poland
The U.S. franchise restaurant McDonald's is becoming a fixture on the landscape of formerly communist Eastern European countries, such as Poland. Although menu prices are quite high by local standards, frequenting places like McDonald's is a sign of status and personal prosperity in Poland and other previously communist countries, such as Romania and the Czech Republic.

[36]P. Iyer, *Video Nights in Kathmandu: Reports from the Not-So-Far East.* London: Black Swan, 1989.

The economic success of the U.S. entertainment industry has helped reinforce the idea of an emerging global culture based on Americanization. In 1996, the entertainment industry was a leading source of foreign income in the United States, with a trade surplus of US$23 billion. Similarly, the United States transmits much more than it receives in sheer volume of cultural products. In 1995, the original versions of more than half of all the books translated in the world (more than 20 000 titles) were written in English. In terms of international flows of everything from mail and phone calls to press-agency reports, television programs, radio shows, and movies, a disproportionately large share originates in the United States.

Neither the widespread consumption of U.S. and U.S.-style products nor the increasing familiarity of people around the world with global media and international brand names, however, adds up to the emergence of a single global culture. Rather, what is happening is that processes of globalization are exposing the inhabitants of both the fast world and the slow world to a common set of products, symbols, myths, memories, events, cult figures, landscapes, and traditions. Although people living in Tokyo, Toronto, Turin, or Timbuktu may be perfectly familiar with these commonalities, they do not necessarily use or respond to them in uniform ways. Equally, it is important to recognize that cultural flows take place in all directions, not just outward from the United States. Think, for example, of European fashions in U.S. stores; of Chinese, Indian, Italian, Mexican, and Thai restaurants in U.S. towns and cities; and of U.S. and European stores selling exotic craft goods from the periphery.

A Global Culture?

The answer to the question "Is there a global culture?" must therefore be no. Although an increasing familiarity exists with a common set of products, symbols, and events (many of which share their origins in a U.S. culture of fast food and popular entertainment), these commonalties become configured in different ways in different places, rather than constituting a single global culture. The local interacts with the global, often producing hybrid cultures. Sometimes traditional, local cultures become the subject of global consumption; sometimes it is the other way around. This is illustrated very well by the case of two suqs (linear bazaars) in the traditional medieval city of Tunis in North Africa. Both suqs radiate from the great Zaytuna Mosque, which was always the geographical focal point of the old city. One suq, which was once *the* suq, leads from the mosque to the gateway that connects the medieval core to the French-built new city, where most tourists tend to stay. The second sets off at right angles to another exit from the formerly walled city.

> The first suq now specializes in Tunisian handicrafts, "traditional" goods, etc. It has kept its exotic architecture and multicoloured colonnades. The plaintive sound of the ancient nose flute and the whining of Arabic music provide background for the European tourists in their shorts and T-shirts, who amble in twos and threes, stopping to look and to buy. Few natives, except for sellers, are to be seen. The second suq, formerly less important, is currently a bustling madhouse. It is packed with partially veiled women and younger Tunisian girls in blouses and skirts, with men in knee-length tunic/toga outfits or in a variety of pants and shirts, with children everywhere. Few foreigners can be seen. The background to the din is blaring rock and roll music, and piled high on the pushcarts that line the way are transistor radios, watches, blue jeans (some prewashed), rayon scarves, Lux face and Omo laundry soaps.[37]

---

[37]J. Abu-Lughod, "Going Beyond Global Babble." In A.D. King (ed.), *Culture, Globalization, and the World-System*. Basingstoke, England: Macmillan, 1991, p. 132.

CONCLUSION

Culture is a complex and exceedingly important concept within the discipline of geography. A number of approaches exist to understand culture. It may be understood through a range of elements and features from single traits to complex systems. Cultural geography recognizes the complexity of culture and emphasizes the roles of space, place, and landscape and the ecological relationships between cultures and their environments. It distinguishes itself from other disciplinary approaches, providing unique insights that reveal how culture shapes the worlds we live in at the same time that the worlds we inhabit shape culture.

Two of the most universal forms of cultural identity are religion and language. Despite the secularization of many people in core countries, religion is still a powerful form of identity, and it has been used to buffer the impacts of globalization. Globalization has caused dramatic changes in the distribution of the world's religions as well as interaction among and between religions. Perhaps most remarkable, religious conversion to religions of the periphery is now underway in the core.

Although a number of languages that exist worldwide are threatened by globalization, some cultures have responded to the threat by providing special protection for regional languages. The 500-year history of globalization has resulted in the steady erosion of many regional languages and heavy contact and change in the languages that persist. However, recently some governments are taking action to protect official and regional languages against the onslaught of globalization. Not only are religion and language at risk from globalization, but other forms of cultural expression, such as art and film, are as well.

Cultural geographers are also interested in understanding how culture shapes groups' adaptations to the natural environment. The aim of cultural ecology is to understand how the availability of resources and technology, as well as value and belief systems, shape the behaviours of cultural groups as active modifiers of, and adapters to, the natural environment. Recently, geographers have begun to pay attention to the role of politics and the wider economy in understanding the relationship between adaptive strategies and the natural world. This approach is known as *political ecology*.

Different groups in different parts of the world have begun to use cultural identities, such as gender, race, ethnicity, and sexuality, as a way of buffering the impacts of globalization on their lives. It is also the case that when the impacts of globalization are examined at the local level, some groups suffer more harm or reap more benefits than others. The unevenness of the impacts of globalization and the variety of responses to it indicate that the possibility of a monolithic global culture wiping out all forms of difference is unlikely.

Finally, it is useful to remember the point made at the beginning of this chapter: it will take us two chapters fully to appreciate the ways in which geography and culture interact. In this chapter, we have considered how language, religion, and issues of group identity (such as nationalism and multiculturalism) shape and are shaped by cultures, and in the process are responsible for the creation of cultural regions. In Chapter 6, we will look at the ways in which individuals have to interpret the distinct landscapes of these cultural regions.

MAIN POINTS REVISITED

- Though culture is a central, complex concept in geography, it may be thought of as a way of life involving a particular set of skills, values, and meanings.

  Culture includes youth styles of dress as well as operatic arias and slang and ecclesiastical languages.

- Geographers are particularly concerned about how place and space shape culture and, conversely, how culture shapes place and space. They recognize that culture is dynamic and is contested and altered within larger social, political, and economic contexts.

  The places in which cultural practices are produced shape cultural production as much as cultural production shapes the places in which it occurs.

- Like other fields of contemporary life, culture has been profoundly affected by globalization. However, globalization has not produced a homogenized culture so much as it has produced distinctive impacts and outcomes in different societies and geographical areas as global forces come to be modified by local cultures.

  Although U.S. culture, especially commercialized culture, is widely exported around the globe, it is important to recognize that foreign cultural practices affect the United States and other parts of the world as well. The French influence on Argentina, for instance, is much more pronounced than is the U.S. influence.

- Contemporary approaches in cultural geography seek to understand the roles played by politics and the economy in establishing and perpetuating cultures, cultural landscapes, and global patterns of cultural traits and cultural complexes.

  For example, the state often facilitates the import or export of cultural practices, such as movies or music, so that economic growth can be enhanced.

- Cultural geography has been broadened to include analysis of gender, class, ethnicity, stage in the life cycle, and so on, in recognizing that important differences can exist within as well as between cultures.

  What geographers find important about these identities are the ways in which they are constructed in spaces and places, and how those particular geographies shape the identities.

- Cultural ecology, an offshoot of cultural geography, focuses on the relationship between a cultural group and its natural environment.

  It recognizes that culture is significantly shaped by the physical environment in which it occurs at the same time that certain cultures shape the ways its participants interact with the environment.

- Political ecologists also focus on human–environment relationships but stress that relationships at all scales, from the local to the global, are intertwined with larger political and economic forces.

  Political ecologists consider the influence of the state in shaping cultural practices since the State plays an increasingly important role in our everyday lives.

Key Terms

allophone (p. 225)
anglophone (p. 225)
cultural adaptation (p. 240)
cultural ecology (p. 240)
cultural geography (p. 200)
cultural hearth (p. 222)
cultural landscape (p. 200)
cultural nationalism (p. 231)
cultural region (p. 204)
cultural system (p. 205)
cultural trait (p. 202)

culture (p. 199)
dialects (p. 220)
diaspora (p. 206)
ethnicity (p. 234)
feminist geography (p. 238)
francophone (p. 225)
gender (p. 236)
genre de vie (p. 201)
historical geography (p. 201)
home language (p. 226)
isolate (p. 223)

language (p. 220)
language branch (p. 220)
language family (p. 220)
language group (p. 220)
language shift (p. 227)
mother tongue (p. 223)
official languages (p. 224)
political ecology (p. 242)
race (p. 235)
religion (p. 205)
sacred space (p. 215)

Additional Reading

Anderson, K. *Vancouver's Chinatown: Racial Discourse in Canada, 1875–1980*. Montreal: McGill–Queens University Press, 1991.

Bebbington, A. "Movements, Modernizations, and Markets: Indigenous Organizations and Agrarian Struggles in Ecuador." In R.P. and M. Watts (eds.), *Liberation Ecologies: Environment, Development, Social Movements*. London: Routledge, 1996.

Cartwright, D.G. "The Divided Continent: Political, Population, Ethnic and Racial Division." In F.W. Boal and S.A. Royle (eds.), *North America: A Geographical Mosaic*. London: Arnold, 1999, 103–122.

Crawford, M. "The World in a Shopping Mall." In M. Sorkin (ed.), *Variations on a Theme Park: The New American City and the End of Public Space*. New York: The Noonday Press, 1992, 3–30.

Cronon, W. *Changes in the Land: Indians, Colonists, and the Ecology of New England*. New York: Hill and Wang, 1983.

Ennals, P., and D.W. Holdsworth. *Homeplace: The Making of the Canadian Dwelling over Three Centuries*. Toronto: University of Toronto Press, 1998.

Ennals, P., and D.W. Holdsworth. "The Look of Domestic Building, 1891." In R.L. Gentilcore (ed.), *Historical Atlas of Canada*, vol. 2. Toronto: University of Toronto Press, 1993, plate 6.

Hiro, D. *Holy Wars: The Rise of Islamic Fundamentalism*. New York: Routledge, 1989.

Ingram, J. *Talk, Talk, Talk*. Toronto: Viking Penguin, 1992.

Ingram, J. *The Talk Show*. (A set of four 60-minute audio cassettes, based on a radio series of that name.) Toronto: CBC Radio, 1993.

Jackson, P. *Maps of Meaning: An Introduction to Cultural Geography*. London: Unwin Hyman, 1989.

Kalman, H. *A Concise History of Canadian Architecture*. Don Mills: Oxford University Press, 2000.

Katz, C., and J. Monk. *Full Circles: Geographies of Women over the Life Course*. London: Routledge, 1993.

Katz, Y., and J. Lehr. *The Last Best West: Essays on the Historical Geography of the Canadian Prairies*. Jerusalem: Magnes Press, 1999.

Lachapelle, R., and J. Henripin. *The Demolinguistic Situation in Canada: Past Trends and Future Prospects*. Montreal: Institute for Research on Public Policy, 1982.

Leyshon, A., D. Matless, and G. Revill (eds.). *The Place of Music*. New York: Guilford Press, 1998.

Moore D. "Contesting Terrain in Zimbabwe's Eastern Highlands: Political Ecology, Ethnography, and Peasant Resource Struggles," *Economic Geography* 69(4), 1993, 380–401.

Rocheleau, D.E., B.P. Thomas-Slayter, and E. Wangari. *Feminist Political Ecology: Global Issues and Local Experiences*. London and New York: Routledge, 1996.

Roy, O. *The Failure of Political Islam*. Cambridge, MA: Harvard University Press, 1994.

Saunders, R. "Kickin' Some Knowledge: Rap and the Construction of Identity in the African-American Ghetto," *Arizona Anthropologist* 10, 1993, 21–40.

Underwood, D. *Oscar Niemeyer and the Architecture of Brazil*. New York: Rizzoli International, 1994.

Ward, P. *A History of Domestic Space: Privacy and the Canadian Home*. Vancouver: UBC Press.

Warkentin, J. "Chapter 6: Interpreting Canadian Landscapes." In *A Regional Geography of Canada: Life. Land and Space*. Scarborough: Prentice Hall, 2000, 144–172.

Women & Geography Study Group. *Geography and Gender: An Introduction to Feminist Geography*. London: Hutchinson, 1984.

Wood, J.D. *Making Ontario: Agricultural Colonization and Landscape Re-creation before the Railway*. Montreal and Kingston: McGill–Queen's University Press, 2000.

Zimmerer, K. "Human Geography and the 'New Ecology': The Prospect and Promise of Integration," *Annals of the Association of American Geography* 84(1), 1994, 108–125.

Exercises

Here you will find exercises and activities for each chapter. Unplugged exercises help you review chapter discussions, and pose ideas for your own human geography research. On the Companion Website exercises will require you have access to the internet.

 Unplugged

1. Using *Billboard Magazine* (the news magazine of the record industry), construct a historical geography of the top 20 singles over the last half century to determine the way in which different regions of the world have risen and fallen in terms of their significance. You should also determine an appropriate interval for sampling—every three to five years is an acceptable one. You may use the hometown of the recording artist or the headquarters of the recording studio as your geographical variable. Once you have organized your data, you should be able to answer the following questions: How has the geography you have documented changed? What might be the reasons for these changes? What do these changes mean for the regions of the world that have increased or decreased in terms of their musical prominence?

2. Ethnic identity is often expressed spatially through the existence of neighbourhoods or business areas dominated by members of a particular group. One way to explore the spatial expression of ethnicity in a place is to look at newspapers over time. In this exercise, you are expected to look at ethnic change in a particular neighbourhood over time. You can do this by using your library's holdings of local or regional newspapers. Examine change over at least a four-decade period. To do this, you must identify an area of the city in which you live or some other city for which your library has an extensive newspaper collection. You should trace the history of an area you know is now occupied by a specific ethnic group. How long has the group occupied that area? What aspects of the group's occupation

of that area have changed over time (for example, school, places of worship, sports activities, the age of the households)? If different groups have occupied the area, what might be the reasons for the changes?

3. College and university campuses generate their own cultural practices and ideas that shape behaviours and attitudes in ways that may not be obvious at first glance. For this exercise, you are asked to observe a particular practice that occurs routinely at your college or university, such as important rituals of college/university life, sports events, and even class discussions. Observe a particular cultural practice that is an ordinary part of your life at college/university. Who are the participants in this practice? What are their levels of importance? Are there gender, age, or status differences in the implementation of this ritual or practice? What are the time and space aspects of the practice? Who controls its production? What are the intended outcomes of the practice? How does the practice or ritual contribute to the maintenance or disruption of order in the larger culture?

4. Using your local library as your source, find a description of a coming-of-age ceremony for any part of the world. Summarize that description and then compare it to one you have either experienced directly or have observed in Canada. What are the differences and similarities between your experience and the one you read about? What might be some of the reasons for these?

On the Companion Website

This book has its own Companion Website where you will find additional resources—maps, photographs, data—as well as exercises and activities that relate to each chapter. To complete the Companion Website exercises, go to **www.pearsoned.ca/knox**. The following is a summary of the types of exercises created for this chapter.

1. The exercises for this chapter will help you not only "see" where various types of **sexualities** are located (place) but answer the question of "why there?" Our review exercise focuses on such topics as race and place, ethnic symbols, gender, and language. The thinking-spatially exercise looks at ethnicity and space, as well as cultural and political ecology, and more. Throughout these drills, you will encounter examples of such concepts as cultural nationalism, cultural imperialism, and cultural borders, to name a few.

2. The CBC Video Case, Inuktitut Survival, that accompanies this chapter, has been chosen to highlight some of the cultural and political issues of language use, decline and retention that have been discussed in this chapter. You will find a link to the CBC video, the video case, questions, and resources on the Companion Website for this chapter.

6

Interpreting Places and Landscapes

The Baroque Italian Garden at Isola Bella shows a very different aesthetic from our own.

To celebrate the millennium, the Royal Bank of Canada produced a 60-minute video entitled *Royal Bank's over Canada*.[1] It consists of stunningly photographed aerial views of this country, carefully edited to take us on a journey from Newfoundland and Labrador to Nunavut to British Columbia. It highlights the enormity of this country and the great differences in physical geography that exist across it. But it also makes evident the great impact on the landscape made by human endeavour, whether it be from roads, railroads, canals, fortifications, farms, villages, or cities. Even the unsettled and supposedly wild or remote areas of Canada have been included in the video. These are all places that have been mapped, named, and appropriated by us as an important part of our image of "Canada."

During the video, viewers realize that human impacts have combined to create distinctive patterns across the landscape. For example, the small, scattered cottages and wharves of Newfoundland and Labrador fishing villages, such as Twillingate, are strung out around small bays, facing the sea, the source of their livelihood. In Manitoba, on the other hand, viewers catch a glimpse of the regimented line of grain elevators along the railroad at Inglis and the small grid-planned town laid out behind them. In the distance stretch hectares of farmland laid out according to vast rectangular surveys, dotted with regularly spaced farmhouses, each surrounded by a windbreak of trees. Such a view contrasts with other agricultural scenes, such as one shown along Quebec's Richelieu River, where the "long lot" field boundaries of the first French colonists still survive in today's landscape.

Geographers suggest that an important reason why these human landscapes are so distinctive is that they have been shaped by different cultures. Cultures may respond differently to the challenges of the physical realm, and different cultural attitudes toward living arrangements or land ownership can have very different impacts on the "look of the land." In short, that "look of the land" is what geographers have called the *cultural landscape*. In this chapter, we explore the relationships among people, landscapes, and places to assess how individuals and groups experience their environments, create places, and find meanings in the cultural landscapes they create.

---

[1]*Royal Bank's over Canada: An Aerial Journey over Canada for the Millennium.* The Jim Pattison Group in association with Gary McCartie Productions and KCTS Television, Royal Bank of Canada, 1999, 60-minute videocassette.

MAIN POINTS

- Landscape serves as a kind of archive of society. It is a reflection of our culture and our experiences. Like a book, landscape is a text that is written by individuals and groups and read by them as well.
- The language in which a landscape is written is a kind of code. The code or codes are signs that direct our attention toward certain features and away from others.
- The written code of landscape is also known as *semiotics*. Codes signify important information about landscapes, such as whether they are accessible or off-limits or are oriented toward work or play.
- In addition to understanding how the environment shapes (and is shaped by) people, geographers seek to identify how it is perceived and understood by people.
- Different cultural identities and status categories influence the ways in which people experience and understand their environments, as well as how they are shaped by—and are able to shape—them.
- The emergence of the most recent phase of globalization has occurred in parallel with a transition from modernism to postmodernism.
- Modernism as a historical period embraced scientific rationality and optimism about progress.
- Postmodernism, the name for the contemporary period, revolves around an orientation toward consumption and emphasizes the importance of multiple perspectives.

LANDSCAPE AS A HUMAN SYSTEM

The foundation for geographers' interest in landscape was Carl Sauer's concept of the cultural landscape, described in Chapter 5. Since 1925, when Sauer advocated the study of the cultural landscape as a uniquely geographical pursuit, new generations of geographers have been expanding the concept. Generally speaking, *landscape* is a term that means different things to different people. For some, the term brings to mind the design of formal gardens and parks, as in landscape architecture. For others, landscape signifies a bucolic countryside or even the organization of plantings around residences and public buildings. For still others, landscape calls to mind the artistic rendering of scenery, as in landscape painting.

What Is Landscape?

In his book *Landscape and Memory*, Simon Schama provides us with a useful answer to the question "what is landscape?" when he recounts the origins of the word itself. He notes that the original English word *landskip* "entered the English language . . . as a Dutch import at the end of the sixteenth century." He adds that the Dutch word *landschap*, like its Germanic root, *Landschaft*, "signified a unit of human occupation." In the Netherlands, "the human design and use of the landscape . . . *was* the story, startlingly sufficient unto itself."[2] This idea of landscape as the sum of human endeavour is one that, as we will see, permeates modern geography's use of the term.

Contemporary geographers think of landscape as a comprehensive product of human action such that every landscape is a complex repository of society. Each

---

[2]Simon Schama, *Landscape and Memory*. Random House: New York, 1996, p. 10.

landscape is a collection of evidence about our character and experience, our struggles and triumphs as humans. To understand better the meaning of landscape, geographers have developed different categories of landscape types based on the elements contained within them.

Ordinary landscapes (or **vernacular landscapes**, as they are sometimes called) are the everyday landscapes that people create in the course of their lives together. From parking lots and trailer parks to tree-shaded suburbs and the patchwork fields of prairie farms, these are landscapes that are lived in and changed and that, in turn, influence and change the perceptions, values, and behaviours of the people who live and work in them.

Symbolic landscapes, by contrast, stand as representations of particular values or aspirations that the builders and financiers of those landscapes want to impart to a larger public. Parliament Hill in Ottawa, for example, with its neo-gothic style of architecture, invokes the British tradition of parliamentary democracy (**Figure 6.1**). In Washington, DC, the neo-classical architecture of the federal government buildings, along with the streets, parks, and monuments of the capital, constitutes a symbolic landscape intended to communicate the power of the American presidential system and also of democracy in its imitation of the Greek city-state (**Figure 6.2**). Geographers also speak about "landscapes of power," such as gated communities, "landscapes of despair," such as homeless encampments, and **derelict landscapes**. The latter are ones that have experienced abandonment, misuse, disinvestment, or vandalism. We may think of such places as part of the "Landscapes of Fear" that Yi-Fu Tuan has described in his 1979 study, places that our culture has taught us to be afraid of. These include, he notes, mountain ranges such as the Alps, which in the Middle Ages were believed to be inhabited by dragons and the devil's minions. Only as a change in aesthetics caused Western society to re-evaluate such landscapes as "sublime" could such places cease to be feared. On a more personal level, we all have places that we find uncongenial—whether they are as bad as Bob Dylan's "Desolation Row," or the noted travel writer, Patrick Leigh Fermor's impressions of one town in the Caribbean, which he described in his 1950 classic *The Traveller's Tree* as having "an absolute charcterness that was so extreme" that this was perhaps its only virtue! For others, a fear of open spaces is a diagnosed condition known as *agoraphobia*—an issue examined by Queen's University scholar Joyce Davidson in her 2003 book, *Phobic Geographies*. (In this regard, it is worth noting the recent work by Canadian geographers such as Allison Williams who have considered the therapeutic role of the experience of landscapes.)

Geographers now recognize that many layers of meaning are embodied in the landscape, meanings that can be expressed and understood differently by different social groups at different times. Put another way, many cultural landscapes exist in any single place. These landscapes reflect the lives of ordinary people as well as the more powerful, and they reflect their dreams and ideas as well as their material lives.

ordinary landscapes (vernacular landscapes): the everyday landscapes that people create in the course of their lives

symbolic landscapes: representations of particular values or aspirations that the builders and financiers of those landscapes want to impart to a larger public

derelict landscapes: landscapes that have experienced abandonment, misuse, disinvestment, or vandalism

Figure 6.1 Parliament Buildings, Ottawa With their neo-gothic style, these buildings were designed to evoke a sense of the British traditions of government. In this way, they represent an example of the use of symbolic space.

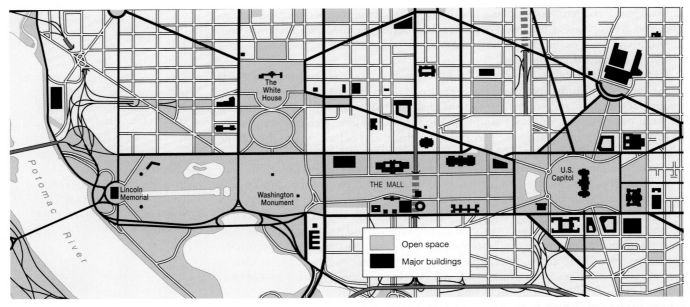

Figure 6.2 Lincoln Memorial and the Mall The Lincoln Memorial, like the other public buildings, monuments, and statuary around the Mall in Washington, DC, is intended to convey a sense of sobriety, authority, and the power of democratic principles. The Mall itself has been designed to communicate pomp and distinction. The wide entry to the Lincoln Memorial and the seated statue of Lincoln inside are meant to inspire awe and appreciation for democratic principles and the wisdom of Lincoln as a democratic leader.

humanistic approach: places the individual—especially individual values, meaning systems, intentions, and conscious acts—at the centre of analysis

One outcome of this shift to individual subjectivity in the study of landscape—also known as the **humanistic approach**—was the emergence of the study of environmental perception, which pointed out that different people comprehend the landscape differently. The humanistic approach in geography is one that places the individual—especially individual values, meaning systems, intentions, and conscious acts—at the centre of analysis. For example, children's perceptions of their worlds are different from those of their parents, and girls see their world differently from boys, even in the same family.

Environmental perception and its close relative, behavioural geography, are interdisciplinary, drawing together geographers, landscape architects, psychologists, architects, and others. Professionals in these disciplines conduct investigations into individuals' preferences in landscapes, how people construct cognitive images of their worlds, and how they find (or fail to find) their way around in various settings. Recall from Chapter 1 that cognitive images are representations of the world that can be called to mind through the imagination. The humanistic approach's focus on the perceptions of individuals is an important counterweight to the tendency to talk about a social group or society more generally. Nevertheless, some critics argue that humanistic research has limited utility because individual attitudes and views do not necessarily add up to the views held by a group or a society.

One alternative to the humanistic approach explores both the role of larger forces, such as culture, gender, and the government, and the ways in which these forces enhance or constrain individuals' lives. Much recent cultural geographical work, therefore, conceptualizes the relationship of people and the environment as interactive, not one-way, and emphasizes the role that landscapes play in shaping and reinforcing human practices. This most recent conceptualization of landscape is more dynamic and complex than the one Carl Sauer advanced, and it encourages geographers to look outside their own discipline—to anthropology, psychology, sociology, and even history—to fully understand its complexity.

Landscape as Text

Such a dynamic and complex approach to understanding landscape is based on the conceptualization of **landscape as text**, by which we mean that, like a book, landscape can be read and written by groups and individuals. This approach departs from traditional attempts to systematize or categorize landscapes based on the different elements they contain. The landscape-as-text view holds that landscapes do not come ready-made with labels on them. Rather, there are "writers" who produce landscapes and give them meaning, and there are "readers" who consume the messages embedded in landscapes. The messages embedded in landscape can be read as signs about values, beliefs, and practices, though not every reader will take the same message from a particular landscape (just as people may differ in their interpretation of a passage from a book). These ideas can be understood by considering how individuals experience or value landscapes. A child sees a park very differently from the way an adult does—the pile of sand in the corner is a playground for the former and a hazard for the latter. Landscapes mean different things to different people. In short, landscapes both produce and communicate meaning, and one of our tasks as geographers is to interpret those meanings. Later in this chapter, in the section "Coded Spaces" we provide an extended example of the "writing" and "reading" of two landscapes: the shopping mall and the capital city of Brazil, Brasilia. First, however, we must establish how places and spaces are given meaning by individuals and by different social and cultural groups.

landscape as text: the idea that landscapes can be read and written by groups and individuals

THE AESTHETICS OF LANDSCAPE

We continually strive to alter, or to improve, landscapes and places we have control over. We improve them according to some received standard of taste, or **aesthetic**, which is itself both culturally and historically determined. Standards of taste are influenced by many things—most importantly, by our changing attitudes to nature (see Chapter 4), our desire to appear *au courant* with the latest styles, and the diffusion of such fashions. As individuals, we have most control over the design of our houses and our gardens. Since we have already looked at vernacular architecture (see Chapter 5), let us look at the garden, a topic that will enable us to consider not only the everyday garden of the average Canadian but also the grand "landscape gardens" of the core's wealthy, whose gardens have so often set the standards of fashions, which the periphery have followed.

aesthetic: culturally determined standard of beauty and good taste

The Evolution of Garden Design

One of the earliest geographical studies of landscape gardens was conducted by Professor Darby (see Chapter 5). He saw that changes in taste were an important example of the "processes of change" that he believed historical geographers should examine. Many cultural geographers have followed Darby's pioneer work and have given us a clear picture of the evolution of the European landscape garden. Their work emphasizes the importance of controlling enough resources to improve a landscape on a large scale, and how the resulting landscape has radically altered over time according to the prevailing garden aesthetic. Such landscapes reflect the elite's ability to control space as they wished and, in doing so, to use the landscape itself to send a visible message of their wealth and power (see "Coded Spaces" later in this chapter). Changes in our attitudes to the landscape also suggest how our attitudes to nature in general are "culturally constructed."

Figure 6.3 Chinese garden, Vancouver

We will take a brief look at how the European landscape garden has evolved because those changes have most influenced Canadian garden aesthetics and still have powerful control over the way we see nature. However, in doing so, we must not overlook the fact that there are several other great gardening traditions in the world (including the Islamic, Japanese, and Chinese traditions). Nor must we fail to appreciate that their influence has begun to spread in Canada as increased immigration to this country has brought with it different cultural attitudes concerning nature (**Figure 6.3**).

Research shows us that the European landscape garden has gone through four basic phases (**Figure 6.4**). Using very approximate dates, they are as follows:

- *The "Italian garden": nature domesticated (the dominant European style from about 1550–1650).* In its small scale and very controlled planting in rectangular beds around the owner's villa, this type reflected a desire to domesticate nature. Fountains and small linear ponds (or "canals") showed water was also controlled. The garden's clear separation from outside indicated the fear that an uncontrolled nature, or wilderness, still existed beyond the walls. Typical examples included many of the mansions of the Italian nobility of the day. The small, controlled design was also used in the new botanic gardens of the period, such as that in Padua (established in 1591), where the many new plant species collected through ecological imperialism were first grown in Europe (**Figure 6.5**).

- *The "French garden": nature subdued (1650–1720).* Gardens, such as those at Versailles, developed by Le Nôtre for Louis XIV, had one message: nature had been "subdued." Beyond the intricate geometric plantings and topiary of the garden around the house, the surrounding landscape was turned into a vast series of endless, straight avenues of trees that radiated out from the house. The wilderness became a park and a very visible metaphor of the Sun King's power across France and its empire. Since imitation was the best (and safest) form of flattery, this design style was soon adopted by the lesser French nobility and spread throughout Europe (**Figure 6.6**).

- *The "English garden": nature triumphant (1720–1850).* Geometric landscapes, especially on a vast scale, did not suit the "romantic" aesthetic that was developing in Britain at this time. Industrialization and urbanization were contributing to a sense of loss and nostalgia for nature. In this set of changing attitudes, nature was no longer feared as wild but loved because, as the antithesis of the industrial world, it was primitive and pure, uncorrupted and closer to God. To show this, garden design turned to a celebration of nature.

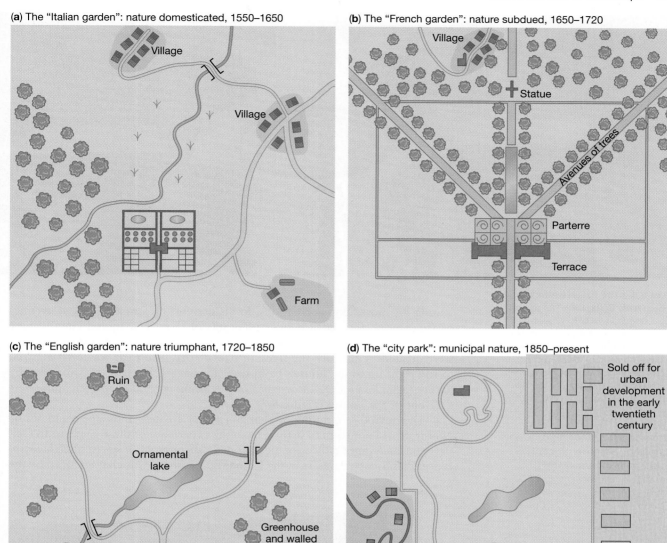

(a) The "Italian garden": nature domesticated, 1550–1650

Village
Village
Farm

(b) The "French garden": nature subdued, 1650–1720

Village
Statue
Avenues of trees
Parterre
Terrace

(c) The "English garden": nature triumphant, 1720–1850

Ruin
Ornamental lake
Greenhouse and walled garden

(d) The "city park": municipal nature, 1850–present

Sold off for urban development in the early twentieth century
1950s Suburban growth
Car parks
Streetcar

Figure 6.4   The evolution of the landscape garden   This sequence of illustrations shows how the design of the landscape garden has changed over 500 years in response to changing aesthetics. Drawn to the same scale, these illustrations show the general elements of redesign that occurred to one idealized garden over the period. A considerable number of gardens in Western Europe underwent many of these transformations, but not all of them experienced all of the changes shown here. Beginning from small, walled gardens in the medieval period (a), landowners expanded and redesigned their properties during the late seventeenth century. Long, straight avenues of trees symbolized their power—a power that stood in the way of design (b). Between 1720 and 1850, more romantic views of nature led to garden relandscaping based on curvilinear paths and lakes, irregular plantings of trees, and vast sweeps of park-like grass (c). Ruins (false or real) were a popular garden feature of the time. By the beginning of the twentieth century, many owners of large properties could no longer afford the upkeep of their estates. Many estates were sold to municipalities, which redeveloped them for housing and city parks, linked by streetcar (and then by car) to the city centre (d).

The leading practitioner of the new design was Lancelot "Capability" Brown, so named because of his expression that he saw "great capability" for improvement in a particular landscape. The gardens at Blenheim Palace are

Figure 6.5 The Italian landscape garden: Isola Bella, Lake Maggiore, Italy Begun in 1632 by Count Borromeo, the gardens of his baroque palace are considered to be a classic of seventeenth-century Italian garden design. (See also the photo that opens this chapter for another view of this garden created from an island in Lake Maggiore.)

picturesque: a landscape design inspired by eighteenth-century landscape painters in the Romantic tradition

among his most famous creations. In his designs, no straight lines of avenues or roads were allowed, irregular plantings of trees in scattered clumps were preferred, and at least one natural-looking lake was *de rigueur*. Small hills were created to enhance the sense of irregularity. The park was even allowed to run right up to the house's front door to suggest that it was surrounded by nature (a sunken fence, known as a *ha-ha*, being used to keep such animals as deer out of the house) (**Figure 6.7**).

The obvious contradiction that an entirely created landscape could not be "natural" did not seem to detract from the experience of these gardens. In fact, the main landscape aesthetic of the period, the **picturesque**, inspired by eighteenth-century landscape painters in the Romantic tradition, was characterized by the

Figure 6.6 The French landscape garden: Versailles Designed for Louis XIV by his gardener, André Le Nôtre, this garden clearly shows how long, straight avenues and perspectives were imposed on the landscape. The intention was not only to produce an aesthetic in which nature was subdued but also to show in a very visible way the power of the French king.

Figure 6.7 The English landscape garden Petworth Park in the south of England was landscaped by Capability Brown and painted by Turner.

celebration of the natural world found in the work of eminent landscape artists, such as Lorrain, Turner, and Constable in England and Thomas Cole and the Hudson Valley School in the United States.

- *The "city park": municipal nature (1850–present)*. The slow decline in the economic fortunes of the core's elite made it too expensive for them to support large houses and gardens. However, nature was to find another champion, this time from those urban reformers who thought its soothing aesthetic effects should be made available to a wider number of people. From the 1850s onward, public interest in the use of city parks as "breathing spaces" led many municipalities to develop public gardens. Design and size varied greatly, with the more formal layouts of earlier generations at least as popular as the more informal. Often, these gardens were connected by streetcar routes to the city centre and became the focus of a fairground of attractions, such as can be found at Copenhagen's famous Tivoli Gardens (**Figure 6.8**).

Canadian Garden Design

Each of the last three of these European landscapes has had an influence on Canadian garden design. The "French school," as might be expected, found early expression

Figure 6.8 Tivoli Gardens, Copenhagen This city centre park combines a garden and amusement park.

Figure 6.9   Louisbourg, Nova Scotia   Gardens within the fortress are inspired by the French landscape garden tradition.

Figure 6.10   Mount Royal Park, Montreal   Landscaped by Frederick Law Olmsted, this park's design is inspired by the English landscape garden tradition.

in Nova Scotia (**Figure 6.9**). For example, in her recent history of Canadian gardening, Carol Martin describes how the "gardens of the leading citizens of Louisbourg . . . had neither the means nor the ability to recreate the magnificent gardens of France but their gardens showed the influence of contemporary French design" in their symmetry and contrasting colour of plantings in the design.[3]

The "English style" was used in the private gardens of some nineteenth-century industrialists, but its main influence in Canada was felt in the growing number of public parks and gardens developed across the country that incorporated its aesthetic. Promoted by such groups as the City Beautiful and Garden City movements (see Chapter 11), a number of these parks were designed by leading landscape architects. For example, in 1877, the architect of New York's Central Park, Frederick Law Olmsted, was hired to design Mount Royal Park in Montreal (**Figure 6.10**). As Martin observes, "drawing heavily on the English landscape tradition, he saw parks as natural landscapes—but natural landscapes improved by design."[4] The main improvements Olmsted made to Mount Royal were to weave curvilinear paths around the hillside to its summit, exploiting the many opportunities for breathtaking views on the way up. Olmsted's influence continued in Canada through the work of his students, Henry Englehart (who designed Mount Pleasant Cemetery in Toronto in 1874) and Frederick Todd (who designed Winnipeg's Assiniboine Park in 1908 and Wascana Park around the Saskatchewan legislative building in 1905).

Of course, there were not ambitious goals or resources for all municipal parks. The majority of parks served the basic purpose of public recreation without the demands of major landscaping projects. By the 1850s, there were city parks in Kingston, Toronto, Hamilton, and Niagara-on-the-Lake, and in 1870 the Halifax Public Gardens were founded. By establishing gardens at strategic points, the Canadian

[3]Carol Martin, *A History of Canadian Gardening*. Toronto: McArthur and Company, 2000, pp. 40–42.
[4]Ibid., p. 79.

Figure 6.11 The suburban lawn
This example from Perth, Ontario, is typical of many lawns in Canada.

Pacific Railroad spread the new idea of beautifying public spaces across the country by the beginning of the twentieth century.

But however modest the garden, the message that these gardens represented "nature improved" was never far from the surface. In a very perceptive essay about the Galt Gardens Park in Lethbridge, a 4-hectare (10-acre) park established in 1885, David Garneau writes that "prairie gardens, especially floral gardens, are acts of will imposed on the wilderness." The park, he notes, has not preserved the Prairies but supports nonindigenous grasses, trees, and flowers—all of which have to be artificially irrigated if they are to grow. Galt Gardens are, he concludes, "an imitation of—or compensation for the lack of—proper, European and Eastern Canadian type, nature/landscape."[5]

It is perhaps surprising to read that this nineteenth-century aesthetic still has a powerful hold over us today, and even more surprising that it should so influence us in Canada, of all countries, where there is wilderness to spare. Yet, our own private gardens, the length and breadth of this country, are a visible testimony that we value landscapes that are "acts of will imposed upon the wilderness." The supreme example, and the most visible part of our garden, is the front lawn. This tract of grass is a mainstay of suburban Canada (**Figure 6.11**). Socially considered as neither public nor private space, it must be kept free of all weeds, mowed to within a few millimetres above ground all summer, and watered every few days during its growing season. Canadians spend millions of dollars in fertilizers and pesticides to keep their lawns looking perfect. And yet nothing further from a natural landscape can be imagined. This manicured front lawn also owes its origins to the English landscape garden and, despite its inappropriateness to our climate, has become a hallmark of the successful garden in Canada.

Many people have argued that the real hallmark of a "Canadian aesthetic" is the ability to appreciate true wilderness or landscapes untouched by people. As a way of valuing Canadian landscapes, this approach is valid and provides its own set of criteria. But it is important to realize that this view is itself a learned ability: the ability to appreciate untouched wilderness is an aesthetic every bit as culturally constructed as the European views we have considered.

---

[5]David Garneau, "Nature Redux: Multiple Natures." In *Nature Redux*. Lethbridge: Southern Alberta Art Gallery, 1996, pp. 52–53.

The Construction of an Aesthetic

In his wonderful book *How the Canyon Became Grand*, Stephen Pyne tells us that the sixteenth-century Spanish explorers who made the first European discovery of the Grand Canyon spent only a few sentences describing it in their report to the Spanish king. Pyne suggests that this is because they did not know what to make of it. They had no cultural frame of reference in which to place it, and so words, literally, failed them. Annie Dillard tells us that in the eighteenth century, "when educated European tourists visited the Alps, they deliberately blindfolded their eyes to shield themselves from the evidence of the earth's horrible irregularity."[6] Yi-Fu Tuan, in his study *Landscapes of Fear,* adds that Europeans feared mountains because they were the realm of ghosts and robbers. On a more prosaic level, Tuan suggests that because mountains were of little use for farming, they were not valued.

How did this view change or become "reconstructed"? The answer lies partly in the Romantic rejection of industrialization we have already discussed and partly in the opening up of the North American frontier. Let us look at each briefly. A number of eighteenth-century writers and artists argued that the ills of industrialization could only be removed by an exposure to nature in its original state. The knowledge that something existed outside human control served to show that industry had its limits, and the fear of nature's elemental power caused people to forget humanity in a contemplation of the infinite. Landscapes that had the power to induce this sense of the **sublime**, or awe, were the ones to be most valued. As a result, *elemental nature,* the nature of windswept coasts, storms, rugged mountains, deserts, glaciers, and snow, became reinterpreted as desirable across Europe by the late eighteenth century. Not for nothing, perhaps, was Franklin's ill-fated search for Canada's Northwest Passage so celebrated—the expedition through the Arctic wasteland was as sublime as anything Coleridge's *Ancient Mariner* could manage. From the 1830s on, Europe's mountains became sought-after destinations, and it was from Switzerland that the Canadian Pacific Railroad recruited the first mountain guides to take their Banff Hotel visitors into the Rockies (**Figure 6.12**).

The sublime was an aesthetic particularly suited to the Canadian landscape, and it is one that has come to dominate in painting, photography, and fiction. It is the sublime landscape that we are taught to value, and it is that which our national parks, from the Rockies to Gros Morne in Newfoundland, seek to preserve.

sublime: a landscape so impressive that it inspires awe or wonder

Figure 6.12 The Canadian Rockies from the highway south of Rogers Pass Mountain views, such as this, are considered to be sublime.

---

[6]Annie Dillard, *Pilgrim at Tinker Creek.* New York: HarperPerennial, 1998, p. 141 [originally published 1974].

The vast Canadian landscape and the challenges its cold and often rugged environment present to those who dare to live there combine to produce the correct mix of beauty and fear that this aesthetic requires. Literary theorists from Margaret Atwood to Northrop Frye have written about the hold that myths of the North have held in the Canadian imagination. From the 1920s, artists, such as Emily Carr and the Group of Seven, repudiated picturesque depictions of landscape to establish a national art "created in the spirit of northern lands" as Lawren Harris, one of the group's founders, said.

It has been said that Canadians have *endured* rather than *conquered* nature in their settlement of this country. South of the border, however, the opposite would be a better generalization of public opinion in the late nineteenth century. Scholars suggest this different attitude resulted in a different evolution of the sublime.

By the time settlement reached the Rockies, Americans were feeling uneasy that wilderness had vanished. In his celebrated "frontier thesis," Frederick Jackson Turner claimed in 1892 that American society had been animated by the "frontier" experience. On the frontier, Turner argued, Americans learned values of hard work and self-reliance. However, the disappearance of the vast tracts of "uninhabited" lands in the west spelled the inevitable end of the frontier. In a recent thought-provoking essay, the environmental historian William Cronon argues that Americans replaced the loss of a real wilderness with an imaginary one in which elemental nature ruled. The energizer of America became preserved in the sublime aesthetic. Landscape painters of this period produced stirring scenes of mountain scenery, the types of views the photographer Ansel Adams was to make iconic in his pictures of the Yosemite Valley. It is significant that the first American national parks are created in this period and that they preserve not the ordinary landscapes, but the spectacular. Yosemite, the Yellowstone Gorge, the Grand Canyon—these are the views Americans are told to value.

Rural Canada provides us with another aesthetic source. In many calendar and postcard views of Prairie farms, we see a vision of a simpler and more traditional life that has largely disappeared (**Figure 6.13**). Why then do we continue to celebrate it?

Geographers point to the importance of pastoral imagery in Western literature that celebrates rural life as more honest and hardworking than the urban realm (**Figure 6.14**). Such utopian visions have inspired many to flee to the countryside, and it is a powerful *trope* (or image) that continues to draw many urban Canadians to the cottage every weekend.

Fictional as this may be, the power of these images is such that they have become an important factor in the revival of rural Canada. Policy analysts and planners are increasingly realizing that as the agricultural value of the countryside diminishes, alternative sources of value in our rural areas must be found. We have seen how environmental stewardship provides one such value. The

Figure 6.13 The rural tradition
Classic scenes like this one celebrate and reinforce our ideas about rural life. This life has largely disappeared, but such ideas continue to frame our views of the countryside and to construct what we could call a "rural aesthetic."

Figure 6.14   The benefits of rural life   The traditional view of rural life draws its vitality from stereotypes, such as the idea that rural living will always refresh the urban dweller.

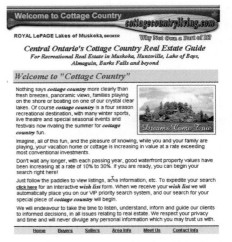

countryside aesthetic provides another—the repository of memory and image in the rural landscape is, in many ways, an untapped resource for Canadian rural development.

PLACE MAKING/PLACE MARKETING

Some social scientists believe that humans, like many other species, have an innate sense of territoriality. The concept of **territoriality** refers to the persistent attachment of individuals or peoples to a specific location or territory. The concept is important to geographers because it can be related to fundamental place-making forces. The specific study of people's sense of territoriality is part of the field of **ethology**, the scientific study of the formation and evolution of human customs and beliefs. The term is also used to refer to the study of the behaviour of animals in their natural environments. According to ethologists, humans carry genetic traits produced by our species' need for territory. Territory provides a source of physical safety and security, a source of stimulation (through border disputes), and a physical expression of identity. These needs add up to a strong territorial urge, which can be seen in the geography of people's behaviour, for example, claims to space in reading rooms or on beaches, and claims made by gangs to neighbourhood turf (**Figure 6.15**). Ethologists argue that the territorial urge can also be observed in cases where people become frustrated because of overcrowding. They become stressed and, in some circumstances, begin to exhibit aggressive or deviant

territoriality: the persistent attachment of individuals or peoples to a specific location or territory

ethology: the scientific study of the formation and evolution of human customs and beliefs

Figure 6.15   Graffiti as territorial markers   Graffiti are used by neighbourhood gangs to establish and proclaim their identity. Some graffiti, such as these, also function as simple territorial markers that help to stake out turf in high-density environments where there exist few other clues about claims to territory.

behaviour. Crowding has been linked by ethologists and environmental psychologists to everything from vandalism and assault to promiscuity, listlessness, and clinical depression.

Although such claims are difficult to substantiate, as is the whole notion that humans have an inborn sense of territoriality, the idea of territoriality as a product of *culturally* established meanings is supported by a large body of scientific evidence. Some of this evidence comes from the field of proxemics. **Proxemics** is the study of the social and cultural meanings that people give to personal space. The increased use of cell phones in recent times destabilizes some of these carefully ordered spaces because larger amounts of personal space are required to keep phone conversations private. As with the proximity we ought to observe at automated banking machines, we have yet to develop the proper customs for the use of space under such technologies.

At larger spatial scales, territoriality is mostly a product of forces that stem from social relationships and cultural systems. This dimension of territoriality underpins a great deal of human geography. All social organizations and the individuals who belong to them are bound at some scale or another by formal or informal territorial limits. Many of them—nations, corporations, unions, clubs—actually claim a specific area of geographical space under their influence or control. In this context, territoriality can be defined as any attempt to assert control over a specific geographical area to achieve some degree of control over other people, resources, or relationships. Territoriality is also defined as any attempt to fulfill socially produced needs for identity, defence, and stimulation. Territoriality covers many different phenomena, from the property rights of individuals and private corporations to the neighbourhood covenants of homeowners' associations; the market areas of commercial businesses; the heartlands of ethnic or cultural groups; the jurisdictions of local, provincial, and national governments; and the reach of transnational corporations and supranational organizations.

Territoriality thus provides a means of fulfilling three social and cultural needs:

- the regulation of social interaction
- the regulation of access to people and resources
- the provision of a focus and symbol of group membership and identity

Territoriality fulfills these needs because, among other things, it facilitates classification, communication, and enforcement. We can classify people and/or resources in terms of their location in space much more easily than we can classify them in relation to personal or social criteria. All that is necessary to communicate territory is a simple marker or sign that constitutes a boundary. This, in turn, makes territory an efficient device for determining whether people are subject to the enforcement of a particular set of rules and conditions.

Territoriality also gives tangible form to power and control but does so in a way that directs attention away from the personal relationships between the controlled and the controllers. In other words, rules and laws become associated with particular spaces and territories rather than with particular individuals or groups. Finally, territoriality allows people to create and maintain a framework through which to experience the world and give it meaning. Bounded territories, for example, make it easier to differentiate "us" from "them."

Sense of Place

The bonds established between people and places through territoriality allow people to derive a pool of shared meanings from their lived experience of everyday routines. People become familiar with one another's vocabulary, speech patterns, gestures, humour, and so on. Often, this carries over into people's attitudes and feelings about themselves and their locality. When this happens, the result is a self-conscious sense of place. The concept of a **sense of place** refers to the feelings evoked among people as a result of the experiences, memories, and symbolism that they associate with a

proxemics: the study of the social and cultural meanings that people give to personal space

sense of place: feelings evoked among people as a result of the experiences and memories that they associate with a place and the symbolism they attach to it

Figure 6.16 Manhattan's financial district This pre–September 11 image of the financial district, which was often portrayed in films and advertising, conveyed a sense of the confidence and authority of American corporate capitalism, as well as the role of the city as the world's financial centre. Since the destruction of the twin towers of the World Trade Center, this image now brings with it a series of other feelings, including patriotism and outrage.

given place. It can also refer to the character of a place as seen by outsiders—its unique or distinctive physical characteristics or its inhabitants.

For *insiders,* this sense of place develops through shared dress codes, speech patterns, public comportment, and so on. It also develops through familiarity with the history and symbolism of particular elements of the physical environment, for example, the birthplace of someone notable, the location of some particularly well-known event, or the expression of community identity through community art. Sometimes, the sense of place is deliberately fostered by the construction of symbolic structures, such as monuments and statues. Often, it is a natural outcome of people's familiarity with one another and their surroundings. Because of this consequent sense of place, insiders feel at home and "in place."

For *outsiders,* such details add up to a sense of place only if they are distinctive enough to evoke a significant common meaning for those with no direct experience of them. Consequently, visits to Niagara Falls, Toronto's CN Tower, Quebec City, or the Canadian Rockies can bring meaning to people who have no direct connection with them because these Canadian places have become familiar to many through television, films, and the promotional activities of the tourist industry. Manhattan, in New York City, is another setting that carries a strong sense of place to outsiders: many people feel a sense of familiarity with the skyline, busy streets, and distinctive commercial districts that together symbolize the heart of the American business world (**Figure 6.16**).

Think for a moment of your own "sense of place"—think about places that you are attached to, and why they are special to you. Going to school, visiting places as a child, your first kiss, a major argument—all of these memories are indelibly associated in our minds with the places where they occurred. In this way, places become engrained with our memories and (because time is fleeting) provide a way to concretize memory. It is because we each have such unique and powerful associations with place that even the least imposing landscapes or locations are valued by someone. It is not the outward appearance, or objective value, that creates a sense of place, but our own personal engagement with such places. We can illustrate this easily enough from our own experience. How many of us have dutifully gone with a friend to see some place that was important to that friend and come away wondering what the fuss was about? As the proverb says, "Beauty (or, in this case, place) is in the eye of the beholder."

It is because place is important to us that its loss can be traumatic. Consider, for example, the damming of the Columbia River in British Columbia, which led to the flooding of 14 communities in the late 1960s. The creation of the Hugh Keenleyside Dam, west of Castlegar, raised the level of the Arrow Lakes and forced the removal of more than 2000 people living in the flooded part of the Columbia Valley (**Figure 6.17**). In total, 615 households and 269 small farmsteads and ranches were affected. At the hearings held to launch the project, many of those to be evicted complained about the loss of livelihood and the inadequate compensation proposed. Significantly, many spoke passionately also about the loss of their community, their home, and their place. One individual observed:

> It is not the financial loss that hurts. What hurts is that you are losing the land on which you had worked, where you know every bit of it, where you get accustomed to it, you know how to farm it. It is full of remembrances, of your failures and successes. It becomes a part of you.[7]

Experience and Meaning

The interactions between people and places raise some fundamental questions about the meanings that people attach to their experiences: How do people process information from external settings? What kind of information do they use? How

[7]Quoted in J. Douglas Porteous and Sandra E. Smith, *Domicide: The Global Destruction of Home.* Montreal and Kingston: McGill–Queen's University Press, 2001, p. 171.

Figure 6.17 Keenleyside Dam, Castlegar, B.C. Retrofitted in 1999 to include a generating chamber, this dam flooded extensive parts of the Arrow Lakes Valley in the southeast interior of British Columbia as part of an extensive flood control scheme begun in the 1960s to regulate the flow of the Columbia River.

do new experiences affect the way they understand their worlds? What meanings do particular environments have for individuals? How do these meanings influence behaviour? Although there are no complete answers to these questions, it is clear that people not only filter information from their environments through neurophysiological processes but also draw on personality and culture to produce cognitive images of their environment, pictures or representations of the world that can be called to mind through the imagination (**Figure 6.18**). Cognitive images are what people see in the mind's eye when they think of a particular place or setting.

Two of the most important attributes of cognitive images are that they both simplify and distort real-world environments. Research on the ways in which people simplify the world through such means has suggested, for example, that many people tend to organize their cognitive images of particular parts of their world in terms of several simple elements (**Figure 6.19**):

Paths: the channels along which they and others move (for example, streets, walkways, transit lines, canals)
Edges: barriers that separate one area from another (for example, shorelines, walls, railroad tracks)
Districts: areas with an identifiable character (physical and/or cultural) that people mentally "enter" and "leave" (for example, a business district, an ethnic neighbourhood)
Nodes: strategic points and foci for travel (for example, street corners, traffic intersections, city squares)
Landmarks: physical reference points (for example, distinctive landforms, buildings, monuments)

Figure 6.18 The formation of cognitive images People form cognitive images as a product of information about the real world experienced directly and indirectly and filtered through their senses, their brain, their personality, and the attitudes and values they have acquired from their cultural background. (*Source:* R.G. Golledge and R.J. Stimpson, *Analytical Behaviour Geography.* Beckenham: Croom Helm, 1987, fig. 3.2, p. 3.)

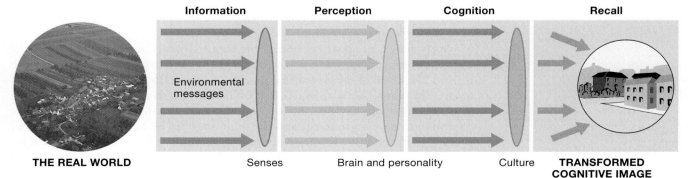

| Information | Perception | Cognition | Recall |

Environmental messages

THE REAL WORLD   Senses   Brain and personality   Culture   **TRANSFORMED COGNITIVE IMAGE**

Figure 6.19 Cognitive image of Boston This map was compiled by Kevin Lynch, one of the pioneer researchers into cognitive images, from interviews with a sample of Boston residents. Lynch found that the residents of Boston tended to structure their cognitive images of the city with the same elements as one another. He produced ingenious maps, such as this one, to demonstrate the collective "mental map" of the city, using symbols of different boldness to indicate the proportion of respondents who had mentioned each element. (*Source:* K. Lynch, *The Image of the City.* Cambridge, MA: M.I.T. Press, 1960, p. 146.)

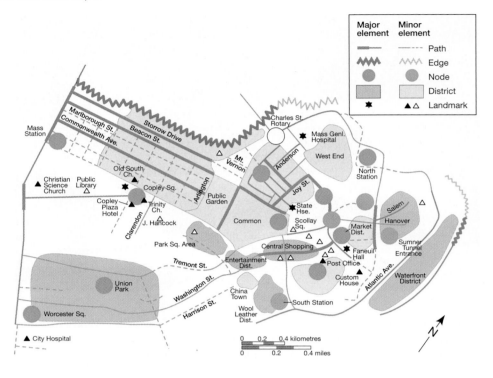

For many people, individual landscape features may function as more than one kind of cognitive element. A highway, for example, may be perceived as both an edge and a path in a person's cognitive image of a city. Similarly, a railroad terminal may be seen as both a landmark and a node.

Distortions in people's cognitive images are partly the result of incomplete information. Once we get beyond our immediate living area, there are few spaces that any of us know in complete detail. Yet, our worlds—especially for those of us in the fast world who are directly tied to global networks of communication and knowledge—are increasingly large in geographical scope. As a result, these worlds must be conceived, or cognized, without many direct stimuli. We have to rely on fragmentary and often biased information from other people and from books, magazines, television, and the internet. Distortions in cognitive images are also partly the result of our own biases. What we remember about places, what we like or dislike, what we think is significant, and what we impute to various aspects of our environments all are a function of our own personalities, our experiences, and the cultural influences to which we have been exposed.

Images and Behaviour

Cognitive images are compiled, in part, through behavioural patterns. Environments are "learned" through experience. Meanwhile, cognitive images, once generated, influence behaviour. In the process of these two-way relationships, cognitive images are constantly changing. Each of us also generates, and draws on, different kinds of cognitive images in different circumstances.

Such elements as districts, nodes, and landmarks are important in the kinds of cognitive images that people use to orient themselves and to navigate within a place or region. The more of these elements an environment contains—and the more distinctive they are—the more legible that environment is to people and the easier it is to get oriented and navigate. In addition, the more first-hand information people have about their environment and the more they are able to draw on secondary sources of information, the more detailed and comprehensive their images will be.

The narrower and more localized people's images are, for example, the less they will tend to venture beyond their home area. Their behaviour becomes circumscribed by their cognitive imagery, in a kind of self-fulfilling prophecy. People's images of places are also important in shaping particular aspects of their behaviour. Research on shopping behaviour in cities, for example, has shown that customers do not necessarily go to the nearest store or the one with the lowest prices; they also are influenced by the configuration of traffic, parking, and pedestrian circulation within their imagery of the retail environment. The significance of this has clearly not been lost on the developers of shopping malls, who always provide extensive space for free parking and multiple entrances and exits.

In addition, shopping behaviour, like many other aspects of behaviour, is influenced by people's values and feelings. A district in a city, for example, may be regarded as attractive or repellent, exciting or relaxing, fearsome or reassuring, or a combination of such feelings. As with all other cognitive imagery, such images are produced through a combination of direct experience and indirect information, all filtered through personal and cultural perspectives. Such images often exert a strong influence on behaviour. Returning to the example of consumer behaviour, one of the strongest influences on shopping patterns relates to the imagery evoked by retail environments—something else that has not escaped the developers of malls, who spend large sums of money to establish the right atmosphere and image for their projects.

Although shopping behaviour is one narrow example of the influence of place imagery on behaviour, other examples can be drawn from every aspect of human geography, and at every spatial scale. An example of the influence of cognitive imagery on people's behaviour is the way that people respond to environmental hazards, such as floods, droughts, earthquakes, storms, and landslides, and come to terms with the associated risks and uncertainties. Some people tend to change the unpredictable into the knowable by imposing order where none really exists (resorting to folk wisdom about weather, for example), while others deny all predictability and take a fatalistic view. Some tend to overestimate both the degree and the intensity of natural hazards, while others tend to underestimate them. These differences point to another important dimension of behaviour—people's attitudes to risk taking.

Finally, one aspect of cognitive imagery is of special importance in modifying people's behaviour, namely, the sentimental and symbolic attributes ascribed to places. Through their daily lives and through the cumulative effects of cultural influences and significant personal events, people build up affective bonds with places. They do this simultaneously at different geographical scales: from the home, to the neighbourhood and locality, to the national country. The tendency for people to do this has been called *topophilia*. **Topophilia** literally means "love of place" and is a term often associated with the work of Yi-Fu Tuan, the geographer who pioneered work on this idea. Geographers use it to describe the complex of emotions and meanings associated with particular places that, for one reason or another, have become significant to individuals. The result is that most people have a home area, hometown, or home region for which they have a special attachment or sense of identity and belonging.

topophilia: the emotions and meanings associated with particular places that have become significant to individuals

Place Marketing

Economic and cultural globalization has meant that places and regions throughout the world are increasingly seeking to influence the ways in which they are perceived by tourists, businesses, media firms, and consumers. As a result, places are increasingly being reinterpreted, re-imagined, designed, packaged, and marketed. Through place marketing, sense of place has become a valuable commodity, and culture has become an important economic activity. Furthermore, culture has become a significant factor in the ability of places to attract and retain other kinds of economic activity. Seeking to be competitive within the globalizing economy, many places have sponsored extensive makeovers of themselves, including the creation of pedestrian plazas, cosmopolitan cultural facilities, festivals, and sports and media events. An increasing number of places have also set up home pages on the internet containing maps, information, photographs, guides, and virtual spaces to promote themselves in the global marketplace for tourism and commerce. Meanwhile, the question of who does the re-imagining and cultural packaging, and on whose terms, can become an important issue for local politics.

Central to place marketing is the deliberate manipulation of material and visual culture in an effort to enhance the appeal of places to key groups. These groups include the upper-level management of large corporations, the higher-skilled and better-educated personnel sought by expanding high-technology industries, wealthy tourists, and the organizers of business and professional conferences and other income-generating events. In part, this manipulation of culture depends on promoting traditions, lifestyles, and arts that are locally rooted; in part, it depends on being able to tap into globalizing culture through new cultural amenities and specially organized events and exhibitions. Some of the most widely adopted strategies for the manipulation and exploitation of culture include funding for facilities for the arts, investment in public spaces, the re-creation and refurbishment of distinctive settings, such as waterfronts and historic districts, the expansion and improvement of museums (especially with blockbuster exhibitions of spectacular cultural products that attract large crowds and can be marketed with commercial tie-ins), and the designation of historic landmarks.

A fascinating example of place marketing is Niagara Falls, Ontario, because as a place it has been marketed in a number of very different ways over the years. Tourism at Niagara began as early as the 1820s, and as a suitably sublime landscape, the Falls were the main attraction (**Figure 6.20**). As one scholar has observed, Niagara was the most-often painted subject in early North American art. There quickly developed, however, additional attractions, such as museums of curiosities and billiard rooms. The boat *Maid of the Mist* (named after a fake legend of Aboriginal sacrifice) began its trips to the base of the Falls as early as the 1840s. In 1859, the great Blondin crossed over them on a tightrope. Many people have gone over them in a barrel. Famous for being famous, Niagara was on every visiting celebrity's itinerary. In short, Niagara was spectacle as well as spectacular.

By the 1930s, the Falls' reputation as a tourist destination, its proximity to large centres of population, and its image as an icon of sublime beauty all combined to turn Niagara into a major destination for honeymooners. Its scenic attractions had even been further enhanced by the addition of a landscaped park, designed by Frederick Law Olmsted, around the top of the Falls.

After the hiatus of the Second World War, Niagara's tourist business developed into a multi-million dollar business, with up to 13 million visitors a year in the 1950s. The 1953 film *Niagara* about a honeymoon (in which, according to

Figure 6.20   Niagara Falls   For 200 years, Niagara has been a tourist attraction. However, the nature of the attraction has changed several times. As a place, Niagara has marketed itself in different ways—from honeymoon destination to casino venue.

the press releases of the time, both the Falls and Marilyn Monroe starred) confirmed the Falls' connection with honeymooners in the public's mind. Niagara's position as the honeymoon capital of North America was seemingly secure.

But by the end of the 1960s, the boom was over. In 1967, the year of Montreal's Expo 67, Niagara motel owners experienced a 50 percent drop in business, a drop from which they never recovered. A 1968 survey revealed that only 3 percent of visitors were honeymooners. Niagara's old image had largely disappeared from popular culture, to be replaced by one it tried not to promote. According to Karen Dubinsky, to many observers at the time, Niagara Falls was in danger of becoming tawdry and cheap, a capital of kitsch that everyone denied visiting.

Yet, by the end of the twentieth-century, Niagara reinvented itself yet again. Its renaissance, this time, was owed to the opening of Casino Niagara in Niagara Falls, which in 1997, its first year of operation, attracted 10 million visitors. However, the prospect that gambling will result in a substantial and long-term revival of tourism in the region seems unlikely on the basis of some preliminary research that suggests gamblers spend little money outside the immediate area of the casino. Karen Dubinsky concludes, "It certainly looks as though the next version of Niagara Falls will owe more to Las Vegas than to Disneyland."[8]

Examples of the re-creation and refurbishment of distinctive settings, such as waterfronts, can be found in many cities. Examples include the development of Vancouver's Expo site (**Figure 6.21**), Toronto's Queens Quay, and the redevelopment of Halifax's waterfront (which includes tourist attractions, such as the Historic Properties, the Maritime Museum of the Atlantic, and Pier 21, the museum of immigration). The largest and most ambitious of all such developments, however, is London's Docklands a development largely begun by the Canadian Reichman family with their Canary Wharf project. The remaking of the Docklands in the 1980s was a deliberate attempt by then prime minister Margaret Thatcher's government not simply to market this part of London to global tourists and investors but to sell the whole idea of the United Kingdom as a rejuvenated, postindustrial economy.

Examples of the re-creation and refurbishment of historic districts and settings are even more widespread—so widespread, in fact, that they have become known as a mainstay of the heritage industry. This industry, based on the commercial exploitation of the histories of peoples and places, is now worldwide,

Figure 6.21   Vancouver's Expo site

---

[8]The paragraphs on Niagara are based on Karen Dubinsky, *The Second Greatest Disappointment: Honeymooning and Tourism at Niagara Falls*. Toronto: Between the Lines, 1999. The quotation is from p. 245.

Figure 6.22 Quebec City One of Canada's leading heritage attractions, Quebec City is on UNESCO's list of world heritage sites.

as evidenced by the involvement of the United Nations Economic, Social, and Cultural Organization (UNESCO) in identifying places for inclusion on world heritage lists. Quebec City, one of Canada's leading heritage attractions (**Figure 6.22**) has joined such places as Jerusalem and Old Havana as a site recognized as culturally and historically significant by UNESCO. In such countries as the United Kingdom, with a high density of historic districts and settings, place marketing relies heavily on the heritage industry.

With over 373 000 buildings of historical interest, almost 20 000 monuments, 1500 parks and gardens, and 17 world heritage sites, this is not surprising. It is difficult, however, to be precise about the number of visitors such sites attract, or the economic impact of such visits. This is because many sites do not charge admission, and many different organizations or bodies are involved in their ownership or operation. (Many nationally important sites, such as Stonehenge, are the responsibility of English Heritage, but this government department is not responsible for sites in Scotland, Wales, or Northern Ireland; nor is it involved with many sites owned by the National Trust, a charitable organization, or the many municipally or privately run sites in England itself.)

Nevertheless, to the extent that it is possible to estimate such numbers, the annual English Heritage audit *Heritage Counts* attempts to give some answers and—by way of its background research papers—provide an essential starting point for the curious. Thus, in its latest edition, *Heritage Counts Report 2008,* we are told that the 791 sites that reported statistics in 2007 received a total of 49.8 million visits. A much larger figure, however, can be found in one of the background reports conducted by the Heritage Lottery Fund for English Heritage, where we are told that "the 1348 visitor attractions in VisitBritain's 2007 English visitor attractions" that took part in the VisitBritain's survey reported that they had received 145 million visits that year.[9]

The economic impact of this level of heritage tourism is perhaps even harder to calculate. The direct benefits include the money that heritage tourists spend on

---

[9]English Heritage, *Heritage Counts Report 2008.* London: English Heritage, 2008, available at **www.english-heritage.org.uk/hc/server/show/nav.10745**. The quotation is taken from a background report for the 2008 English Heritage report, conducted by Heritage Lottery Fund and called *Values and Benefits of Heritage: A Research Review.* London: English Heritage, July 2008, p. 7. (Both documents are most easily accessed by entering "Heritage Counts" in the Advanced Search box on the main site **www.english-heritage.org.uk**, and then clicking on either the relevant headings for annual reports or research reports.)

their admission to historic sites. and any gifts and food they purchase while there. Other less direct impacts, such as the increased revenue brought into the area's hotels, or the money spent on their transport needs, are harder to attribute solely to heritage sites alone—since tourists may have other reasons than simply heritage motives to visit an area.

It is harder still to calculate the so-called "economic multiplier" effects due to heritage tourism. There is no doubt that some of the benefits of heritage tourism "trickle down" through a region's economy, but not all spending will. Hotel stays, for example, may benefit the corporation that owns the hotel rather than the locality, and hotel workers themselves are (on average) less well-paid than many workers outside the tourism industry, so that any spending for which they themselves are responsible is likely to be far less than that which might be supported by a workforce that depended on, for example, automotive manufacture or computer game development. It is for such reasons that tourism is not always a panacea for economic development, or an easy alternative when factories close and their rusting shells are recycled as industrial heritage sites.

Certainly, English Heritage prefers not to indulge in the speculations necessary to arrive at such numbers, and the last time its annual audit *Heritage Counts* gave any indication of the possible sums involved was in its 2002 report, when its authors concluded that the heritage sector generated direct income revenue of between $800 million and $850 million.[10] Since that agency reports little change in overall visitor numbers over the period 2002–2007, we can probably assume that such totals remain a useful guide to the value of heritage tourism in England.

One important aspect of the influence of the heritage industry on spaces, places, and landscapes is the tendency for historic districts and settings to be re-created, imitated, simulated, and even reinvented according to commercial considerations rather than principles of preservation or conservation. As a result, contemporary landscapes contain increasing numbers of inauthentic settings. These are as much the product of contemporary material and visual culture as they are of any cultural heritage.

In Canada, a number of towns have adopted such themes as part of their tourist appeal. The community of Osoyoos in British Columbia has adopted Spanish-American architecture, a style that serves to advertise that this Okanagan valley community enjoys a warmer climate than other parts of the province. Kimberley, also in British Columbia, has developed an Austrian-style town centre, or platz, one evocative of its mountainous location in the southeastern part of the province (**Figure 6.23**).

The intriguing example of Shelburne, Nova Scotia, suggests that we now even value the replica over the real! Settled in 1783, the town still has a considerable number of genuine vernacular buildings of that period to its credit. In fact, partly on the strength of this, in 1994, Shelburne was chosen to be the location for the major film *The Scarlet Letter*, supposedly set in seventeenth-century New England. To fully re-create the appearance of such a place, the filmmakers built a number of additional structures in the style of the period. These buildings were such a success that when shooting was over, the town petitioned the movie company to leave them standing. More than 10 years later, these replica buildings remain and are advertised on the town's website as a major tourist attraction. Using a new meaning of "authentic," the website says, "Why not tour part of the remaining set and experience an authentic historic market square? You can pick up a self-guided tour brochure at the tourist bureau or, for a small fee, participate in a guided tour replete with a myriad of fascinating details."[11]

---

[10]Demos for the Heritage Lottery Fund, "Challenge and Change: HLF and Cultural Values." 2004, p. 38, a background report for the 2004 English Heritage audit, *Heritage Counts*. (The document is most easily accessed by entering "Heritage Counts" in the Advanced Search box on the main site **www.english-heritage.org.uk**, and then clicking on either the relevant headings for annual reports or research reports.)

[11]"Historic Shelburne: Where Canada's History Comes Alive!" **www.historicshelburne.com**.

Figure 6.23 Kimberley, B.C. This community in the interior of British Columbia has adopted an Austrian style of architecture to celebrate its mountain location.

Less specific than place marketing, but just as evocative, is the ability to market a region using some of the many components of the cultural region (see Chapter 5) as selling points. The ability of music, for example, to conjure up an image of a country or region in our minds is well known. In recent years, Cape Breton—densely settled by Highland Scots in the late eighteenth and early nineteenth centuries—has been so successful in promoting the Cape Breton fiddle and old-style piping that it has become internationally recognized as an important homeland for Celtic music. Natalie MacMaster and Ashley MacIsaac have been instrumental in bringing this music to a wider Canadian audience, and the Rankins have established an international reputation with their own brand of Celtic-folk-country-pop music. By 1999, Celtic music and its associated cultural and tourist activities had become the major resource and leading employer on the island, according to a University College of Cape Breton report.

CODED SPACES

As we discussed in an earlier section of this chapter, landscapes are embedded with meaning, which can be interpreted differently by different people and groups. To interpret or read our environment, however, we need to understand the language in which it is written. We must learn how to recognize the signs and symbols that go into the making of landscape. The practice of writing and reading signs is known as **semiotics**.

semiotics: the practice of writing and reading signs

Semiotics in the Landscape

Semiotics proposes the view that innumerable signs are embedded or displayed in landscape, space, and place, sending messages about identity, values, beliefs, and practices. The signs that are constructed may have different meanings for those who produce them and those who read, or interpret, them. Some signs are so subtle as to be recognizable only when pointed out by a knowledgeable observer; others may be more readily available and more ubiquitous in their spatial range. For example, semiotics enables us to recognize that university students, by the way they dress, send messages to one another and the wider world about who they are and what they value. For some of us, certain types, such as the "jock" or the "tree-hugger," are readily identifiable by their clothes, hairstyle, or footwear; by the books they carry; or even by the food they eat. In this section, we will consider two examples of coded spaces to show the importance of this concept: the shopping mall and the city plan.

Figure 6.24 Place Canada Trust mall in downtown Montreal Developers of shopping malls know that consumer behaviour is heavily conditioned by the spatial organization and physical appearance of retail settings. As a result, they find it worthwhile to spend large sums creating what they consider to be the appropriate atmosphere for their projects.

The Shopping Mall as Coded Space Semiotics is not only about the concrete signs that people convey. Messages are also deployed through the landscape and embedded in places and spaces. Consider the very familiar landscape of the shopping mall. Although there is certainly a science to the size, scale, and marketing of a mall based on demographic research as well as environmental and architectural analysis, more exists to a mall than these concrete features. The placement and mix of stores and their interior design, the arrangement of products within stores, the amenities offered to shoppers, and the ambient music all combine to send signals to the consumer about style, taste, and self-image (**Figure 6.24**). Called by some "palaces of consumption," malls are complex semiotic sites, directing important signals not only about what to buy but also about who should shop there and who should not.

As much as we seem to enjoy shopping, there persists for a great many of us an explicit disdain for shopping and the commercialism and materialism that precede and accompany it. Thus, shopping is a complicated activity that is full of ambivalence. It is not surprising, therefore, that developers have promoted shopping as a kind of tourism. The mall is a "pseudoplace" meant to encourage one sort of activity—shopping—by projecting the illusion that something else besides shopping (and spending money) is actually going on. Because of their important and complex function, malls are places with rich semiotic systems expressed through style, themes, and fantasy. Although some malls are intended to convey their messages to particular subsets of the population, such as the very wealthy or teenagers (even within the same mall space), it is possible to send different messages to different consumers. Most malls possess a kind of sociocultural geology, where the lowest level of the mall is a landscape with lower-middle-class semiotics; the more elaborate and pricey upper levels are a landscape more consistent with affluence. Thus, even within one place, different spaces send different messages to different consumers.

However complex the messages that malls send, one message is consistent across class, race, gender, age, ethnicity, and other cultural boundaries: consumption is a predominant aspect of globalization. Indeed, malls are the late twentieth century's spaces of consumption, where just about every aspect of our lives has become a commodity. Consumption—or shopping—defines who we are more than ever before, and what we consume sends signals about who we want to be. Advertising and the mass media tell us what to consume, equating ownership of products with happiness, a good sex life, and success in general. Within the space of the mall, these signals are collected and re-sent. The architecture and design of the mall are an important part of the semiotic system shaping our choices and moulding our preferences. As architectural historian Margaret Crawford writes:

> All the familiar tricks of mall design—limited entrances, escalators placed only at the end of corridors, fountains and benches carefully positioned to entice shoppers into stores—control the flow of consumers through the numbingly repetitive corridors of shops. The orderly rows of goods along endless aisles continuously stimulates the desire to buy. At the same time, other architectural tricks seem to contradict commercial consideration. Dramatic atriums create huge floating spaces for contemplation, multiple levels provide infinite vistas from a variety of vantage points, and reflective surfaces bring near and far together. In the absence of sounds from the outside, these artful visual effects are complemented by the "white noise" of MUZAK and fountains echoing across enormous open courts.[12]

Some of the "tricks" that "seem to contradict commercial consideration" are those of place making. They are needed because we are reluctant to consider malls as real "places" (in Yi-Fu Tuan's sense of "places" as "space filled with meaning"). Rather, we tend to see malls as bland, or mundane, spaces of "placelessness" (to use Toronto geographer Edward Relph's useful term). They are commercial spaces of franchises and chains that could be anywhere. For malls to succeed commercially, we must be persuaded that these drab collections of concrete are not the "machines for consumption" they really are. Only then are we comfortable enough to think about what we might buy there.

Jon Goss has written that to conceal the contradiction in our society between conspicuous consumption and contempt for consumerism, a mall needs us to disconnect from the reality of shopping. We do not want to know about the true circumstances in which the objects we buy were made or distributed, for to do so will diminish the object's value in our eyes, and our own value as discriminating purchasers in the eyes of other people. Malls must therefore mystify the true connection between the ideals and reality of consumption—a "trick" that many successful malls perform by creating a "sense of place."[13] In theory, then, malls should provide an excellent opportunity to see "place making" at work.

What, according to geographers, should we be looking for next time we go to the mall? Goss argues that malls create a sense of place by creating allusions to the following:

- *The traditional "main street" of small town North America.* This entails not only design references (such as the use of cobblestones, awnings, and street signs) but also the creation of a feeling of public space in the mall (such as a bandstand, park benches, or a speakers' corner).

- *Carnivals or open-air markets.* Malls achieve this illusion of more friendly exchange through the use of market handcarts, sidewalk sales, street artists and travelling performers, "quayside" scenes, and even carousels. The sense of fun this conveys is part of the fantasy of consuming, and is seen to its logical excess in the West Edmonton Mall and in Las Vegas.

- *Nature.* To increase people's comfort levels and to disguise the mall's links to consumption, references to nature are made through the use of plants, artificial

---

[12]M. Crawford, "The World in a Shopping Mall." In M. Sorkin (ed.), *Variations on a Theme Park.* New York: Noonday Press, 1992, p. 14.

[13]Jon Goss, "The Magic of the Mall: An Analysis of Form, Function, and Meaning in the Contemporary Retail Built Environment." *Annals of the Association of American Geographers* 83, 1993, pp. 18–47. The quotations that follow are to be found on pp. 19, 27, 22, 33, and 31.

lighting, mirrors, and fountains (see Figure 6.24). A very nice illustration of this lies across the street from Lethbridge's Galt Gardens, where there is a shopping mall called Park Place. Its designers have used such elements as traditional-style park benches and indoor plants to carry over the image of the real park nearby into the interior of this mall.

In a detailed study of the West Edmonton Mall, Jeff Hopkins shows us how to read some of the semiotics embedded in the retail landscape.[14] The stores create in us a sense of place through the following:

- *Their simple allusion to place names.* So, one part of the West Edmonton Mall is called "Bourbon Street." The name alone makes the link with any associations we may have of the real city of New Orleans.

- *Their general allusion to a distant time period*—such as the 1920s—or general type of place—such as "the Wild West"—through statues, other decorative details, or music.

- *The replication of a specific place*—the West Edmonton Mall's "Fantasyland" makes direct reference to Disneyland. Again, this is achieved through architecture and design, colour, lighting, statues, and so on.

At the time of Hopkins's analysis, this mega-mall just outside Edmonton, Alberta, consisted of more than 600 stores, a theme hotel, and recreational facilities (including a wave pool and ice rink). By early 2002, the mall's website stated that it was the "largest shopping centre in the world" (according, it said, to the *Guinness Book of World Records*) and contained over 800 stores on a 49-hectare site, with the world's largest amusement park and the world's largest parking lot.[15] Fortunately or unfortunately, the majority of Canadian malls do not rise to the excesses of the West Edmonton Mall, and do not aspire to be tourist destinations. Nevertheless, for many of us, even the most lacklustre mall is still a place to "hang out."

Depending on our perspective, however, we can each interpret the landscape quite differently, and the mall is no exception in this regard. Not surprisingly, the homeless will be less concerned with how a mall creates a sense of place than with how it can provide warmth and shelter. It would be a mistake, however, to interpret the park benches and open spaces of the mall as an indication of public space in which one can remain. Malls are private space, and security personnel will soon appear to move those people who misinterpret the signals.

In fact, ambiguities about public and private space are deliberately fostered by malls to make us feel at home when we make our purchases. These ambiguities have been strengthened by the recent development in Canada of covered, combined retail and pedestrian spaces, such as the skywalks of Halifax and Calgary, and the "underground cities" of Montreal and Toronto (**Figure 6.25**).

Officially called the "PATH: Downtown Walkway," Toronto's underground city in 1993 comprised 27 kilometres of tunnels beneath the city core, lined with over 1200 stores and services and frequented by over 100 000 pedestrians a day. Montreal's underground city is even more extensive, with more than 30 kilometres of tunnel comprising over 1700 shops and services. Both, by being linked to underground transit systems via a number of stations, have considerable hinterlands, drawing on distant residential districts or nearby office towers. Designed to enable pedestrians to avoid the demands of the Canadian winter and summer, both networks are creating a new environment in which some people never get outdoors. Outside, meanwhile, streets become lifeless—a challenge for retailers and planners alike.

---

[14]Jeffrey S.P. Hopkins, "West Edmonton Mall: Landscape of Myths and Elsewhereness." *Canadian Geographer* 34, 1990, pp. 2–17.

[15]The West Edmonton Mall has a very useful website, at which maps, photos, and information about the mall can be found and its various claims to world record status can be examined (available at **www.westedmall.com/about/wemtrivia.asp**).

Figure 6.25 Toronto's underground city
Underground tunnels and shops are becoming frequent features of such Canadian cities as Toronto, as this diagram shows. They are not only creating new retail opportunities, but new forms of urban spaces as well. (*Source*: City of Toronto Economic Development—Small Business & Local Partnerships Office.)

These forms of retailing present growing difficulties over the use of public and private space. The retailers' desire to attract customers by creating the illusion of a public space is an invitation contradicted by the store owners' rights of exclusion. The tunnels are private property and, as such, are covered by the rights of private property owners against trespass (legislation which, in Ontario, for example, enables "undesirables," such as skateboarders or street people, to be evicted). On the other hand, recent legal decisions have shown that public right can be extended to such private spaces. This is because, in Canadian law, a public space need not be public property, and even in underground cities, individuals have constitutionally guaranteed freedoms of expression and peaceful assembly. In such clearly contested terrain, it is not surprising that the signals the landscape gives are ambiguous and depend heavily on our intentions and who we are.

Malls, condominium developments, neighbourhoods, university campuses, and any number of other possible geographical sites possess codes of meaning. By linking these sites with the forces behind globalization, it is possible to interpret them and understand the implicit messages they contain. And it is certainly not necessary to restrict our focus to sites in the core.

The City Plan as Coded Space Consider Brasilia, the capital city of Brazil. As early as independence from Portugal in 1822, Brazilian politicians began suggesting that a new capital be established on the central plateau in the undeveloped interior of the country. Although authorized in 1899, the establishment of a federal district and a new capital city did not occur until the mid-twentieth century. In 1957, the Brazilian Congress approved the proposed construction of the new capital, and in 1960, the government was officially transferred to Brasilia. A symbol of the taming of the wild interior of the country and the conquest of nature through human ingenuity, Brasilia is also a many-layered system of signs conveying multiple and frequently contradictory messages. Interestingly, Brasilia, intended to symbolize a new age in Brazilian history, was also literally an attempt to construct one. That is why its plan and its architecture are so self-consciously rich with messages meant to transform Brazilian society through a new and radical form of architecture. To launch both the idea and the reality of a "city in the wilderness," the Brazilian government sponsored a design contest hoping to encourage the development of a new vision for the new capital (and by extension a new society). The winner of the contest was engineer Lucio Costa. His original plan, submitted to an international jury, was a simple sketch of a series of three crosses, each more elaborate than the previous one (**Figure 6.26**).

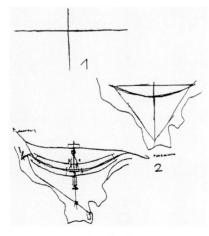

Figure 6.26 Sketch of Lucio Costa's crosses By using a cross to designate the location and orientation of Brasilia, Costa was suggesting a holy origin for Brasilia, the new city in the wilderness. (*Source*: J. Holston, *The Modernist City: An Anthropological Critique of Brasilia.* Chicago: University of Chicago Press, 1989, p. 63.)

In a semiotic reading of Costa's plan as well as of the city, which is now more than 35 years old, the sign-of-the-cross ordering of the plan is an intentional use of a well-known mark. First, in its graphic form, the crossed axes represent the cross of Christianity. This aspect of the sign is important because it suggests that Brasilia was to be built on a sacred site, an important endorsement for the founding of a new capital. The sign of the cross, as the centrepiece of the plan, also makes an important semiotic connection to two ideal types found in both ancient and contemporary city planning and founding. Anthropologist John Holston writes:

> The first is considered one of the earliest pictorial representations of the idea of city: the Egyptian hieroglyph of the cross within the circle, itself an iconic sign standing for "city." . . . The second is the diagram of the templum of ancient Roman augury, a circle quartered by the crossing of two axes. It represents a space in the sky or on earth marked out . . . for the purpose of taking auspices. Hence it signifies a consecrated place, such as a sanctuary, asylum, shrine, or temple.[16]

Many other observers of the plan and the completed city have said that it resembles an airplane. This observation seems especially apt when one looks at the master plan of the city (**Figure 6.27**). The plan shows that the residential districts were to be located along the north and south wings and administrative government offices on the part corresponding with the fuselage. The commercial district was to be constructed at the intersection of the wings and the fuselage, with a cathedral and museum along the monumental axis. Like the sign of the cross, the significance of an airplane is obvious. Politicians and planners envisioned Brasilia as both the engine and the symbol of the rapid modernization of the country. The image of an airplane in flight was an exciting, soaring, uplifting, and speedy means of achieving modernization.

All of Brasilia's major public buildings were designed by the internationally famous Brazilian architect Oscar Niemeyer. The residential axes were designed

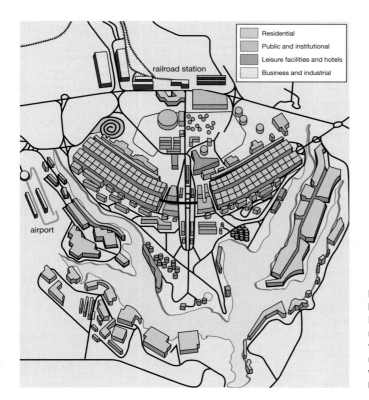

Figure 6.27   Costa's master plan for the new capital of Brasilia In 1957, Lucio Costa submitted his entry to the Master Plan competition for the new capital of Brazil. The more detailed rendition of the plan Costa drew for Brazil's new capital, illustrated here, reveals how he thought the various activities and material forms of city life should be geographically arranged within the city. (*Source:* B. Marshall [ed.], *The Real World.* London: Marshall Editions/Houghton Mifflin, 1991, p. 171.)

---

[16]J. Holston, *The Modernist City: An Anthropological Critique of Brasilia.* Chicago: University of Chicago Press, 1989, p. 71.

Figure 6.28 Palacio de Alvorada, Brasilia The official residence of the president of Brazil combines the homogenized international style of "glass-box" architecture with culturally distinctive artistic elements, such as the sweeping colonnades pictured here.

with clusters of apartment buildings, each cluster surrounding a set of recreational facilities, school buildings, and shopping areas. The University of Brasilia was also part of the early vision of the city, as was the creation of a lake and the official home of the president of the country, the Palacio de Alvorada, or the Palace of Dawn (**Figure 6.28**).

The architecture of Brasilia, like that of other federal capitals—Ottawa in Canada, Canberra in Australia, and Washington, DC, in the United States—contains both subtle and more explicit messages about the strength and purpose of government there. The exclusively modernist architectural style of Brasilia (as opposed to the neo-classical style of Washington, DC, for example) was intended to convey the modernist utopian ideal of technological progress and a democratic and egalitarian society. Niemeyer's architectural designs were conceived to transform colonial Brazilian society by projecting modernism and innovation through bold new urban images. Another message involves the location of the presidential palace. It is far removed from the heart of the city and does not even appear on the plan for the centre of the city shown in Figure 6.27. This spatial distance can be read as a social distance between the ruler and the ruled. It also suggests that the executive branch is elevated over the legislative because the residences of legislators are located within the confines of the city. The name itself, the Palace of Dawn, can be interpreted as suggesting the optimism of a new day for democracy dawning through Brasilia.

Like the city, the palace was intended to reflect the new society it was to inaugurate. In the palace, one can see both the real and the imaginary counterpoised. In its present form, the city itself truly embodies this tension, because egalitarianism was never achieved. The real builders of the city—the migrant workers who came to construct the city and live out their own dreams there—have been relegated to ever-growing *favelas* (or squatter settlements) surrounding the city. Thus although the original plan and architecture were intended to send a message about the aspirations of the new Brazil, the contemporary image of the city contradicts those dreams with the harsh realities of poverty and inequality.

The examples of the shopping mall and the federal district of Brasilia illustrate the way that landscapes can be read, or decoded, by interpreting the signs and symbols they project. Not all the signs are consistent, even when planners and designers have complete control over their projects, because readers do not always interpret signs in ways the creators intended. In both cases, social and political realities can disrupt the plan and insert very different messages.

POSTMODERN SPACES

Since the 1980s, many commentators on cultural change have noted a broad shift in cultural sensibilities that seems to have permeated every sphere of creative activity, including art, architecture, advertising, philosophy, clothing design, interior design, music, cinema, novels, television, and urban design. This shift, broadly characterized as a shift from modernism to postmodernism, has involved both avant-garde and popular culture. It seems to have originated in parts of the world's core countries and is currently spreading throughout the rest of the world. The shift to postmodern cultural sensibilities is of particular importance to cultural geography because of the ways in which changed attitudes and values have begun to influence place making and the creation of landscapes.

Modernism and Postmodernism

Throughout the world, the philosophy of modernism has been one of the major influences on the interdependencies among culture, society, space, place, and landscape for more than a century. **Modernism** is a forward-looking view of the world that emphasizes reason, scientific rationality, creativity, novelty, and progress. Its origins can be traced to the European Renaissance and the emergence of the world-system of competitive capitalism in the sixteenth century, when scientific discovery and commerce began to displace sociocultural views of the world that were backward-looking—views that emphasized mysticism, romanticism, and fatalism. These origins were consolidated into a philosophical movement during the eighteenth century, when the so-called Enlightenment established the widespread belief in universal human progress and the sovereignty of scientific reasoning.

At the beginning of the twentieth century, this philosophy developed into a more widespread intellectual movement. Around the turn of the twentieth century, there occurred a series of sweeping technological and scientific changes that not only triggered a new round of spatial reorganization (see Chapter 2) but also transformed the underpinnings of social and cultural life. These changes included the telegraph, the telephone, the x-ray, cinema, radio, the bicycle, the internal combustion engine, the airplane, the skyscraper, relativity theory, and psychoanalysis. Universal human progress suddenly seemed to be a much more realistic prospect.

Nevertheless, the pace of economic, social, cultural, and geographical changes was unnerving, and the outcomes uncertain. The intellectual response, developed among a cultural avant-garde of painters, architects, novelists, and photographers, was a resolve to promote modernism through radical changes in culture. These ideas were first set out in the "Futurist Manifesto," published in 1909 in the Paris newspaper *Le Figaro* in the form of a letter from the Italian poet Filippo Marinetti. Gradually, the combination of new technologies and radical design contributed to the proliferation of landscapes of modernism. Among the most striking of these were modernist urban landscapes, from Helsinki to Hong Kong and from New York to Nairobi (**Figure 6.29**). Indeed, in a general sense almost all of the place making and landscapes of the early and mid-twentieth century are the products of modernism.

Throughout this period, a confident and forward-looking modernist philosophy remained virtually unquestioned, with the result that places and regions everywhere were heavily shaped by people acting out their notions of rational behaviour and progress. Rural regions, for example, bore the imprint of agricultural modernization. The hedgerows of traditional European field patterns were torn up to make way for landscapes of large, featureless fields in which heavy machinery could operate more

modernism: a forward-looking view of the world that emphasizes reason, scientific rationality, creativity, novelty, and progress

Paris, France: Les Halles

Toronto's downtown landscape

Figure 6.29   Urban landscapes of modernism   These photographs of Paris and Toronto reflect the pervasive influence of modernist architecture on the skylines of the central areas of large cities throughout the world's core regions.

Figure 6.30 Rural landscape of modernism
This photograph of rural East Anglia, Great Britian, shows a landscape that is the product of agricultural modernization. Urban land uses—commuter homes and the cooling towers of a power station, in this case—have encroached into the countryside. In addition, many of the traditional hedgerows in much of East Anglia have been torn out, and small land holdings have been consolidated to create a "prairie" landscape of large fields in which modern agricultural equipment can operate efficiently.

postmodernism: a view of the world that emphasizes an openness to a range of perspectives in social inquiry, artistic expression, and political empowerment

efficiently (**Figure 6.30**). Peripheral areas within the care, and (more generally) within developing countries, sought to remake traditional landscapes through economic modernization. Economic development and social progress were to be achieved through a modern infrastructure of highways, airports, dams, harbours, and industrial parks.

Postmodernism is a view of the world that emphasizes an openness to a range of perspectives in social inquiry, artistic expression, and political empowerment. Postmodernism is often described in terms of cultural impulses that are playful, superficial, populist, pluralistic, and spectacular. Many commentators see it as the result of a reconfiguration of sociocultural values that has taken place in tandem with the reconfiguration of the political economy of the core countries of the world. In this context, postmodernism has been described as the "cultural clothing" of the postindustrial economy.

Postmodernism abandons modernism's emphasis on economic and scientific progress, arguing that modernism's failure to deliver such progress is indicative of its flaws. Because of this, postmodernism also rejects the value of grand universal theories. Instead, postmodernism favours the unique and values difference—both aspects that appeal to geographers and students of "place making." To others, the appeal of postmodernism is its emphasis on living for the moment. Above all, postmodernism is consumption-oriented. This has made for sociocultural environments in which the emphasis is not so much on ownership and consumption as such, but rather on the possession of particular combinations of things and on the style of consumption. Postmodern society has been interpreted as a "society of the spectacle," in which the symbolic properties of places and material possessions have assumed unprecedented importance. The stylistic emphases of postmodernism include eclecticism, decoration, parody, and a heavy use of historical and vernacular motifs—all rendered with a self-conscious stylishness. In architecture, for example, the modernist aphorism "Less is more" is itself parodied: "Less is a bore." Since the mid-1970s, postmodernism has been manifest in many aspects of life, from architecture, art, literature, film, and music to urban design and planning. It has begun to be reflected in the landscapes of some places and regions, especially in more affluent settings. Some of the most striking of these postmodern landscapes are to be found in the redeveloped waterfronts, revitalized downtown shopping districts, and neo-traditional suburbs of major cities (**Figure 6.31**).

Postmodernism has also caused us to re-evaluate how we reflect on "landscapes of dereliction." Canadian artists, such as Edward Burtynsky, have shown us how industrial landscapes, such as quarries and tailing ponds, have their own beauty. In this current rewriting of aesthetics, the value of the landscape is perhaps being reassessed once more. Beauty is being divorced from function or value, and we are thereby returning to an aesthetic appreciation of landscape that celebrates the original Dutch meaning of the term—"a story in itself."

Figure 6.31 Landscape of post-modernism This photograph shows part of Seaside, Florida, a small community that has become famous as an example of neo-traditional planning, whereby designers attempt to reproduce the ambience, appearance, and serenity of small-town neighbourhoods of the past.

Globalization and Postmodernism

As we saw in Chapter 2, economic globalization has brought about a generalization of forms of industrial production, market behaviour, trade, and consumption. This economic interdependence is also tied into several other dimensions of globalization, all of which have reinforced and extended the commonalities among places. Three of these dimensions are especially important. First, mass communications media have created global culture markets in print, film, music, television, and the internet. Indeed, the internet has created an entirely new *kind* of space—cyberspace—with its own "landscape" (or technoscape) and its own embryonic cultures (see the subsection "The Cultural Geography of Cyberspace"). The instantaneous character of contemporary communications has also made possible the creation of a shared, global consciousness from the staging of such global events as LiveAid, the Olympic Games, and the World Cup. Second, mass communications media have diffused certain values and attitudes toward a wide spectrum of socio-cultural issues, including citizenship, human rights, child rearing, social welfare, and self-expression. Third, international legal conventions have increased the degree of standardization and level of harmonization not only of trade and labour practices but also of criminal justice, civil rights, and environmental regulations.

These commonalities have been accompanied by an increased importance of material consumption within many cultures. This is where globalization and postmodernism meet, with each reinforcing the other. People's enjoyment of material goods now depends not only on their physical consumption or use. It is also linked to the role of material culture as a social marker. A person's home, car, clothes, reading, viewing, eating, and drinking preferences, and choice of vacations are all increasingly interpreted as indicators of that person's social distinctiveness and sense of style. This means that there must be a continuous search for new sources of style, and distinctiveness must occur. The wider the range of foods, products, and ideas from around the world—and from past worlds—the greater the possibilities for establishing such style and distinctiveness.

Given that material consumption is so central to the repertoire of symbols, beliefs, and practices of postmodern cultures, the "culture industries"—advertising, publishing, communications media, and popular entertainment—have become important shapers of spaces, places, and landscapes. Because the symbolic meanings of material culture must be advertised (in the broadest sense of the word) to be shared, advertising (in its narrower sense) has become a key component of contemporary culture and place making. In addition to stimulating consumer demand, advertising has always had a role in teaching people how to dress, how to furnish a home, and how to signify status through groupings of possessions.

In the 1970s and 1980s, however, the emphasis in advertising strategies shifted away from presenting products as newer, better, more efficient, and more economical (in keeping with modernist sensibilities) to identifying them as the means to self-awareness, self-actualization, and group stylishness (in keeping with postmodern sensibilities). Increasingly, products are advertised in terms of their association with a particular lifestyle rather than in terms of their intrinsic utility. Many of these advertisements deliberately draw on international or global themes, and some entire advertising campaigns (for Coca-Cola, Benetton, and American Express, for example) have been explicitly based on the theme of cultural globalization. Many others rely on stereotypes of particular places or kinds of places (especially exotic, spectacular, or "cool" places) in creating the appropriate context or setting for their product. Images of places therefore join with images of global food, architecture, pop culture, and consumer goods in the global media marketplace. Advertisements both instruct and influence consumers, not only about products but also about spaces, places, and landscapes.

One result of these trends is that contemporary cultures rely much more than before not only on material consumption but also on *visual* and *experiential* consumption—the purchase of images and the experience of spectacular and distinctive places, physical settings, and landscapes. Visual consumption can take the form of magazines, television, movies, sites on the World Wide Web, tourism, window shopping, people watching, or visits to galleries and museums. The images, signs, and experiences that are consumed may be originals, copies, or simulations.

The significance of the increased importance of visual consumption for place making and the evolution of landscapes is that such settings as theme parks, shopping malls, festival marketplaces, renovated historic districts, museums, and galleries have all become prominent as centres of cultural practices and activities. The number of such settings has proliferated, making a discernible impact on metropolitan landscapes. The design of such settings, however, has had an even greater impact on metropolitan landscapes. Places of material and visual consumption have been in the vanguard of postmodern ideas and values, incorporating eclecticism, decoration, a heavy use of historical and vernacular motifs, and spectacular features in an attempt to create stylish settings that are appropriate to contemporary lifestyles.

Consumption of Place? The Resturant as Cultural Site   One interesting aspect of the increasing trend toward the consumption of experiences is the emergence of restaurants as significant cultural sites. The cultural historian Rebecca Spang has shown how restaurants developed in late eighteenth-century Paris, as eating shifted from a domestic sphere to the public realm, and became increasingly commodified as society industrialized. Restaurants now often represent a synthesis of the global and the local, and they can be powerful cultural and geographical symbols in their own right. This is because restaurants specifically, and food in general, are such powerful place-makers. Spang notes how the use of menus and of specific names for dishes allows restrateurs to "pin down" space and time. In her words, menus become an "atlas." Eminent cultural geographer Yi-Fu Tuan once remarked that a lecture course on "cooking, for instance, will help us to look upon cultures and cultural landscapes with heightened appreciation"[17] The value of Tuan's geographical insight can be seen when we recognize the following points:

■ Dependent, until recently, on the products of the local countryside, and prepared according to traditions sanctioned by the culture of the region, *local cuisines are well able to convey a powerful sense of regional identity*. The Ontario supermarket chain Loblaws capitalized on this not long ago when it began to

[17]Yi-Fu Tuan, "Topophilia: Personal Encounters with the Landscape." In P.W. English and R.C. Mayfield (eds.), *Man, Space and Environment*. New York: Oxford University Press, 1972, p. 538.

market a line of sauces called "Memories of . . ." (for example, "Memories of Singapore").

In this respect, it is significant that quality wines seek to embody region through the *appellation contrôlée* designation. For example, because Champagne is a region *and* a sparkling wine—the two are synonymous—"place" becomes literally monopolized. Indeed, recent legislation in the European Union (EU) has granted a whole series of such place-specific monopolies. Feta cheese, for example, can only be made in Greece (and not, as had been the case, in other parts of the EU, such as Denmark). Formally called *Appellation d'Origine Contrôlée (AOC),* the first non-wine product to be granted an AOC label was Roquefort cheese. In this way, the value of places, as it is embodied in food, is protected. This idea has carried through into the current advertising campaign for Canadian cheeses. For example, we are told that by eating Oka cheese, we can "taste the beauty of the land."

Newfoundland's cods' tongues, Nova Scotian lobster, Quebec's poutine, Ontarian maple syrup and Niagara ice wines, Winnipeg's cinnamon buns, Saskatoon berry pie, Alberta beef, and British Columbia's smoked salmon—such a list conveys regional identities just as powerfully as it stirs up an appetite! And for that reason, most of these items are to be stocked in a new store aimed at the large expatriate Canadian community in London, England.

■ Several other aspects of cuisine are of significance to Canadian cultural geography. As the new London store perhaps illustrates, *food embodies powerful memories of time* as well as images of place or region. We are brought up accustomed by our own culture to eat certain foods, and that familiarity conditions us to a sense of what is "normal." For this reason, of course, comfort foods are often those of our childhood. And, for this reason, immigrants in Canada will strive to preserve as much of their native cuisine as they can. Often, this requires a modification or substitution of ingredients to replace those unavailable in this country or an accommodation with other cultural traditions as unfamiliar foodstuffs are incorporated into the mix.

■ After migrating to Canada, the distinctive cuisines of the immigrant's homeland (often called "ethnic cuisines" because they are identified with particular groups of the population) continue to be cooked. This is not simply because they represent the only way some individuals may know how to prepare food but also—and more importantly—because the cuisines begin to take on a role they did not have before. *They become valued for their memories of "home" and as an important aspect in the retention of group identities in the new country.*

Eventually, new or hybrid cuisines are slowly developed in new surroundings. This serves to remind us of the obvious point that culture does not always merely simplify itself overseas. In fact, it can develop into wholly new forms or, through adaptation with other cultures, develop syncretic or hybrid forms.[18] Certainly, in this case, the superimposition in Canada's metropolitan centres of regional cuisines from all over the world provides a wonderful opportunity for such cuisines to develop. The greater number and variety of cuisines available in metropolitan Canadian centres compared with the rural parts of this country also provide us with yet another illustration of how core–periphery effects play a role in shaping our cultural geographies.

■ Originally developed to serve traditional home cooking from its country of origin to local immigrant groups, the "ethnic restaurant" served as *a clear cultural geographical marker of that group's spatial presence in an area.*

---

[18]As an example, it is interesting to note that one of the "traditional" Aboriginal foods of the North, bannock, is of Scottish origin. Its origins lie in the Orkney Islands, the home of many of the Hudson's Bay Company's employees.

(a)

1951

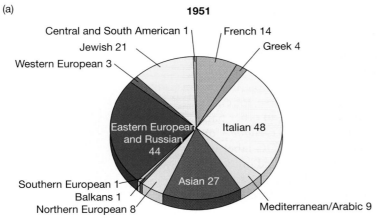

(b)

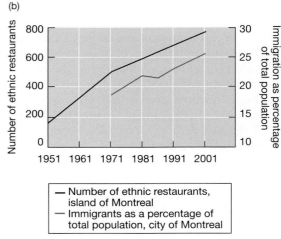

- Number of ethnic restaurants, island of Montreal
- Immigrants as a percentage of total population, city of Montreal

1971

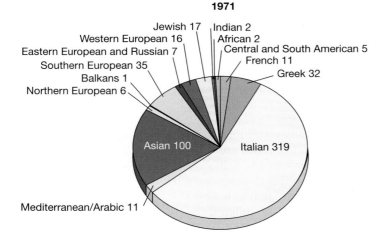

Figure 6.32   Increase in number of ethnic restaurants in Montreal, 1951–2001   These pie charts show the increasing number and diversity of ethnic restaurants on the island of Montreal from 1951 to 2001. What has caused these changes? Some experts believe that increases in immigration over those years are a major factor (see graph (b) above). Other experts suggest that an increasing trend towards diversity (itself an outcome of postmodernism) is a major explanation.   (*Source:* Alan Nash, "From Spaghetti to Sushi: An Investigation of the Growth of Ethnic Restaurants in Montreal, 1951–2001." *Food, Culture and Society* 12 [1], 2009. The author is grateful to Geneviève Aboud, Megan Lewis, and Jake Fogels for their help in this research.)

2001

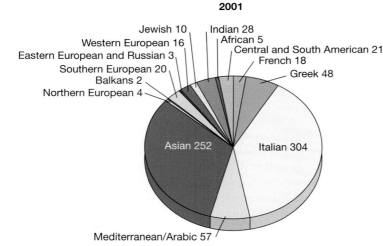

- In recent years, "ethnic cuisines" have become so much sought after by the wider public that "ethnic restaurants" have greatly increased in number (**Figure 6.32**). The "ethnic restaurant" phenomenon has been such a success because it has taken the ability of food to convey place and used it as a marketing device. It has, in other words, *commodified cuisine and place* (**Figure 6.33**). To aid this endeavour, appropriate architectural motifs, styles of writing, music, and folk costume are often used by the restaurant to indicate the place or country it represents (**Figure 6.34**).

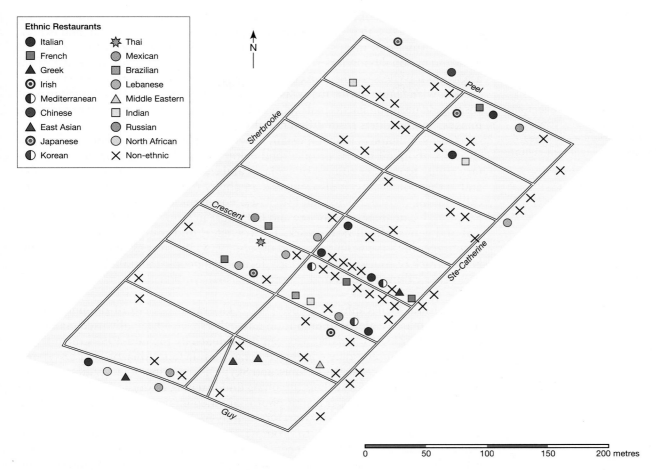

Figure 6.33   Ethnic restaurants   This map of a few blocks of downtown Montreal shows the enormous popularity and variety of ethnic restaurants in Canada's large urban and metropolitan centres.   (*Source:* Marie-Michelle Belanger, Concordia University, B.A. Honours Essay, Department of Geography, April 2002.)

■ Ethnic restaurants have been so successful because they counter the homogenization of the restaurant experience with an emphasis on exotic or unique cuisines from different or unusual places in the world. In other words, *postmodernism's celebration of place is opposed to globalization's erosion of difference.*

Figure 6.34   Ethnic restaurants
This view of ethnic restaurants on Toronto's Queen Street West shows how architectural motifs and sign writing are used to convey a sense of other places.

While the idea of the emergence of a single global culture is too simplistic, we must acknowledge that the postmodern emphasis on material, visual, and experiential consumption means that many aspects of contemporary culture transcend local and national boundaries. Furthermore, many of the residents of the fast world are world travellers—either directly or via the TV in their living room—so that they are knowledgeable about many aspects of others' cultures. This contributes to **cosmopolitanism**, an intellectual and aesthetic openness toward divergent experiences, images, and products from different cultures.

cosmopolitanism: an intellectual and aesthetic openness toward divergent experiences, images, and products from different cultures

Cosmopolitanism is an important geographic phenomenon because it fosters a curiosity about all places, peoples, and cultures, together with at least a rudimentary ability to map, or situate, such places and cultures geographically, historically, and anthropologically. It also suggests an ability to reflect on and judge aesthetically among different places and societies. Furthermore, cosmopolitanism allows people to locate their own society and its culture in terms of a wide-ranging historical and geographical framework. For travellers and tourists, cosmopolitanism encourages both the willingness and the ability to take the risk of exploring off the beaten track of tourist locales. It also develops in people the skills needed to interpret other cultures and to understand the visual symbolism.

The Cultural Geography of Cyberspace The rapid growth of the internet has brought a massive global immigration into cyberspace. Originally used mainly for electronic mailing (or emails) between individuals, by the mid-1990s the internet had developed to embrace commerce (examples include Amazon and eBay) and now, through services such as iTunes and Skype, is replacing other traditional ways of conducting activities such as obtaining and listening to music or making a telephone call. The ability to transmit photos or video images (via Flickr or YouTube for example), to seek information (via search engines such as Google and interactive sources such as wikis), to promote ideas and opinions (through blogs and podcasts), and to engage in social networking (via Facebook or MySpace) or instant messaging (such as Twitter) have all added greatly to the uses of the internet and so have made it an increasingly attractive technology to a very wide range of potential users.

Estimates of its rate of increase and current size vary considerably, and reliable numbers are perhaps even harder to find. However, the Organisation for Economic Co-operation and Development (OECD) has paid close attention to developments in cyberspace, and now issues a series of authoritative reports on information and communication technology on its website. According to one such study, prepared for a meeting of OECD ministers meeting in Seoul in June 2008, there are "about 542 million hosts connected to the Internet worldwide," a total that the report estimates is 13 times larger than the total number connected in 1999.[19]

What is perhaps even more remarkable than the pace of growth is the change that has also been occurring to patterns and types of internet use over the same period. As Susanne Huttner writes in an article in the June 2008 issue of the *OECD Observer,* "Underneath, the network's infrastructure has also fundamentally transformed in the

---

[19]The website for the Organisation for Economic Co-operation and Development (OECD) is **www.oecd.org**. Its reports on "Information and Communication Technologies" can most easily be accessed via that website, and clicking on "topic," and then "innovation" in the menus that appear. The quotation is from OECD, "The Future of the Internet Economy: A Statistical Profile." 17 June 2008, p. 7. (It is worth repeating here the OECD's caution that accompanies these figures: the term *host* is not necessarily a measure of a single individual connected to the internet because a single machine [or host] can have multiple domain names and addresses.) This very useful 43-page report contains a wealth of graphs and statistics; was prepared for the OECD Ministerial Meeting on the Future of the Internet Economy, held in Seoul, South Korea, 17–18 June 2008; and is available at **www.oecd.org/dataoecd/44/56/40827598.pdf**. Another useful source on the history and growth of the internet is the chapter entitled "Internet: Changing the Way We Communicate." *America's Investment in the Future.* Arlington, Virginia: National Science Foundation, 2000, available at **www.nsf.gov/about/history/nsf0050/internet/publicnet.htm**.

last decade. Dial-up Internet access has given way to always-on broadband technology. Moreover, users are accessing the Internet via all manner of wireless devices, from laptops, to mobile phones."[20] One consequence of these changes is that emailing is rapidly becoming obsolete as instant messaging technologies (such as Twitter, which provide continuous access between users) have come to replace it.

Another consequence of this transformation—and one of special interest to geographers—is the announcement in November 2008 by the Ontario-based company POIfriend Inc. that it had developed a means of sharing "points of interest," developed through social networking, via maps that can be downloaded onto mobile global positioning satellite (GPS) units. In this way, people might share maps of their favourite restaurants with their friends, and corporate partners (such as Tim Hortons) provide ready access at their locations anywhere in Canada.[21] These developments are of great significance, for they offer the basis for a massive shift in patterns of social interaction, a seedbed for new forms of human consciousness, and a new medium for cultural change. Culture is fundamentally based on communication. As Canadian cultural theorist Marshall McLuhan (1911–1980) remarked, "the medium is the message," and in cyberspace we have an entirely new form of communication: uncensored, multidirectional, written, visual, and aural. Moreover, because of the decentralized and complex nature of the web of computer hosts that constitute the internet, it is very difficult for the controlling institutions of society to regulate the culture that it carries.

At face value, the internet represents the leading edge of the globalization of culture. In broad terms, the culture propagated by the internet is very much core-oriented. With about 90 percent of all internet communication being conducted in English, the internet portends a global culture based on English as the universal world language. With its origins in affluent Western educational establishments and corporations, the internet also carries a heavy emphasis on core-area cultural values, such as novelty, spectacle, fashionability, material consumption, and leisure. By its very nature, the internet empowers individuals (rather than social groups or institutions), allowing millions of people to say whatever they want to one another, free (for the first time in history) from government control.

It is unlikely, however, that the internet will simply be a new medium through which core-area values and culture are spread. Itself an agent of cultural change, the internet is a unique space with its own landscape of webpages, and multi-user dungeons inhabited by techno-yuppies, chipheads, and info-surfers. A vocabulary of internet slang is already finding its way into everyday usage. Electronic mail is developing its own distinctive syntax and stream-of-consciousness style. A proliferation of electronic magazines includes many that are self-consciously attempting to be in the vanguard of pop culture, while commenting critically on that culture. Although e-zines on narrow or avant-garde subjects can reach large audiences on the internet, they would not be commercially viable in other media. In addition, they offer audio and video clips, instant links to advertisers' home pages, and the opportunity for interactive discussions among authors, editors, and readers. As such, they are potentially important vehicles for the spread of participatory democracy.

Other elements of the landscapes of cyberspace include virtual stores and catalogues, virtual peep shows, teleclinics, and special-interest networks. Internet shopping has begun to change the nature of consumerism: virtual catalogues make price and product comparisons quick and cost-free. Surfing the internet has become an important new form of recreational activity (with voyeurism and cybersex currently heading the list of most frequently visited categories). Internet connectivity is creating virtual communities by drawing together people from different places

---

[20]Susanne Huttner, "The Internet Economy: Towards a Better Future." *OECD Observer* 268, June 2008. Available at **www.oecdobserver.org**.

[21]Matt Hartley, "Mapping Your World." *Globe and Mail*, 6 November 2008, p. B6. The site is **www.POIfriend.com**.

and social and cultural backgrounds into specialized, common-interest chat groups and news groups. Last but not least, the internet has become a vast source of knowledge and information that is both liberating and empowering.

These changes, however, are likely to be highly uneven in their impact because of the digital divide. It is also very possible that these new technologies will actively undermine businesses in the periphery, which have, until now, been protected by their very remoteness. Moreover, the internet allows some new twists on old core–periphery relationships—relationships in which the periphery and its inhabitants are systematically disadvantaged or exploited. Consider, for example, the website that appeared in 1996 on prostitution in Havana, Cuba. This website, operating from a host server in Finland, was perfectly clear about its function as a tourist guide to the re-emerging sex market in Havana. Written in English by Italian correspondents, the site provided detailed information on locations, specializations, and prices, together with tips on how to handle the local police. While undoubtedly something of a boost for Havana's sex industry, the overall result was to intensify the economic and cultural domination of the periphery by the core.

In some places and regions, there is resistance to the cultural globalization associated with cyberspace. The Quebec government, already sensitive about the influence of English-language popular culture, has actively sought ways of allowing francophones to use the internet without submitting to English, the dominant language of websites. The French government has subsidized an all-French alternative to the internet—Minitel, an online videotext terminal that plugs into French telecommunication networks.

In much of Asia, the internet's basic function as an information-exchange medium clashes with local cultures in which information is a closely guarded commodity. Whereas many Canadian and U.S. websites feature lengthy government reports and scientific studies, as well as lively debates about government policy, comparable Asian sites typically offer little beyond public relations materials from government agencies and corporations. In puritanical Singapore, political leaders, worried that the internet will undermine morality, have taken to reading private email as part of an all-out effort to beat back the menace of online pornography. Fearful that the internet will foment political rebellion, Chinese officials have limited the access to it to ensure that the Chinese portion of the internet can easily be severed from the world in the event of political unrest.

The Chinese government's desire to control access to the internet was clearly shown during the 2008 Olympic Games held in Beijing. Despite the commitments China had made to the International Olympic Committee (IOC) that it would allow unfettered access to the internet to the foreign media who had come to Beijing to cover the games, many journalists reported that they had been unable to access websites, including those that discussed Taiwan, Tibet, or the protests in Tiananmen Square; reporters also noted access was denied to the websites of Amnesty International, the British Broadcasting Corporation's Chinese language news, and some Hong Kong-based newspapers.[22] The reluctance of major Asian organizations to put important information on their websites—along with the need for Westerners to use special software to read any local language documents that do exist—has resulted in a largely one-way flow of information, from North America to Asia.

CONCLUSION

Geographers study the interdependence between people and places and are especially interested in how individuals and groups acquire knowledge of their environments, and how this knowledge shapes their attitudes and behaviours. People ascribe meanings to landscapes and places in many ways, and they also derive

---

[22]See, for example, Andrew Jacobs, "China to Limit Web Access During Olympic Games." *New York Times*, 31 July 2008; Edward Cody, "IOC Allows China to Limit Reporters' Access to Internet." *Washington Post*, 31 July 2008.

meanings from the places and landscapes they experience. Different groups of people experience landscape, place, and space differently. For instance, the experience that rural Sudanese children have of their landscape and the way in which they acquire knowledge of their surroundings differ from how middle-class children in a Canadian suburb learn about and function in their landscape. Furthermore, both landscapes elicit a distinctive sense of place that is different for those who live there and those who visit or see the place as outsiders.

As indicated in previous chapters, the concepts of landscape and place are central to geographical inquiry. They are the result of intentional and unintentional human action, and every landscape is a complex reflection of the operations of the larger society. Geographers have developed categories of landscape to help distinguish among the different types that exist. Ordinary landscapes, such as neighbourhoods and drive-in movie theatres, are ones that people create in the course of their everyday lives. By contrast, symbolic landscapes represent the particular values and aspirations that the developers and financiers of those landscapes want to impart to a larger public. An American example is Mount Rushmore in the Black Hills of South Dakota, designed and executed by sculptor Gutzon Borglum. Chiselling the heads of George Washington, Thomas Jefferson, Theodore Roosevelt, and Abraham Lincoln into the granite face of the mountain, Borglum intended to construct an enduring landscape of nationalism in the wilderness. That he did so on part of the Lakota Sioux's sacred mountains is an irony no longer lost on us. (The current effort to complete an enormous sculpture of the famous Sioux chief Crazy Horse in the southern Black Hills demonstrates a recognition of the First Nations' much earlier presence in that landscape.)

More recently, geographers have come to regard landscape as a text, something that can be written and read, rewritten, and reinterpreted. The concept of landscape as text suggests that more than one author of a landscape can exist, and different readers may derive different meanings from what is written there. The idea that landscape can be written and read is further supported by the understanding that the language in which the landscape is written is a code. To understand the significance of the code is to understand semiotics, or the language in which the code is written. The code may be meant to convey many things, including a language of power or of playfulness, a language that elevates one group above another, or a language that encourages imagination or religious devotion and spiritual awe.

The global transition from modernism to postmodernism has altered cultural landscapes, places, and spaces differently as individuals and groups have struggled to negotiate the local impacts of this widespread shift in cultural sensibilities. The shared meanings that insiders derive from their place or landscape have been disrupted by the intrusion of new sights, sounds, and smells as values, ideas, and practices from one part of the globe have been exported to another. The internet and the emergence of cyberspace have resulted in the emergence of new spaces of interaction that have neither distinct historical memory attached to them nor well-established sense of place. Because of this, cyberspace carries with it some unique possibilities for cultural exchange. It remains to be seen, however, whether access to this new space will be truly open—or whether the internet will become another landscape of power and exclusion.

MAIN POINTS REVISITED

- **Landscape serves as a kind of archive of society. It is a reflection of our culture and our experiences. Like a book, landscape is a text that is written by individuals and groups and read by them as well.**
  It is therefore possible to have one landscape convey different meanings for different groups. Landscapes can be constructed

to reflect the everyday worlds of social groups as well as to represent power and the values of a particular society.

- **The language in which a landscape is written is a kind of code. The code or codes are signs that direct our attention toward certain features and away from others.**

To interpret our environment, we must learn how to read the codes that are written into the landscape.

■ **The written code of landscape is also known as** *semiotics*. **Codes signify important information about landscapes, such as whether they are accessible or off-limits or are oriented toward work or play.**
Landscapes as different from each other as shopping malls and national capitals can be understood in terms of their semiotics.

■ **In addition to understanding how the environment shapes (and is shaped by) people, geographers seek to identify how it is perceived and understood by people.**
People not only filter information from their environments through neurophysiological processes but also draw on personality and culture to produce cognitive images of their environment—pictures or representations of the world that can be called to mind through the imagination.

■ **Different cultural identities and status categories influence the ways in which people experience and understand their environments, as well as how they are shaped by—and are able to shape—them.**
Among the most important of these are the cultural identities of class, gender, age, and ethnicity. Often, these identities come together in a group, and their influence in combination becomes central to our understanding of how group identity shapes space and is shaped by it.

■ **The emergence of the most recent phase of globalization has occurred in parallel with a transition from modernism to postmodernism.**
This transition involves a shift in cultural sensibilities that affects every sphere of creative activity, from art and architecture to television and urban design. It seems to have originated in parts of the world's core countries and is currently spreading throughout the rest of the world.

■ **Modernism as a historical period embraced scientific rationality and optimism about progress.**
Modernism has been one of the major influences on culture, society, space, place, and landscape for more than a century.

■ **Postmodernism, the name for the contemporary period, revolves around an orientation toward consumption and emphasizes the importance of multiple perspectives.**
In contrast to modernism's emphasis on economic and scientific progress, postmodern cultural sensibilities focus on living for the moment, emphasizing the *style* of consumption.

Key Terms

aesthetic   (p. 255)
cosmopolitanism   (p. 288)
derelict landscapes   (p. 253)
ethology   (p. 264)
humanistic approach   (p. 254)
landscape as text   (p. 255)

modernism   (p. 281)
ordinary landscapes
   (vernacular landscapes)   (p. 253)
picturesque   (p. 258)
postmodernism   (p. 282)
proxemics   (p. 265)

semiotics   (p. 274)
sense of place   (p. 265)
sublime   (p. 262)
symbolic landscapes   (p. 253)
territoriality   (p. 264)
topophilia   (p. 269)

Additional Reading

Aziz, L. "The Great Canadian Feast: A Celebration of Family Traditions from Canadian Kitchens." In *Canadian Geographic*. Toronto: Key Porter Books, 2002.

Burnett, R. *The Global Jukebox: The International Music Industry*. New York: Routledge, 1996.

Carney, G.O. (ed.). *Fast Food, Stock Cars, and Rock'n' Roll: Place and Space in American Pop Culture*. Lanham, MD: Rowman & Littlefield, 1995.

Cronon, W. "Telling Tales on Canvas: Landscapes of Frontier Change." In J.D. Prown et al., (eds.). *Discovered Lands, Invented Pasts: Transforming Visions of the American West*. New Haven: Yale University Press, 1992, 37–87.

Davidson, J. Phobic *Geographics: The Phenomenology and Spatiality of Identity*. Aldershot, UK: Ashgate, 2003.

Dodge, M., and R. Kitchin. *Atlas of Cyberspace*. London: Pearson, 2001.

Dunlay, K. "The Celtic Revival in Cape Breton." In E. Koskoff (ed.). *The Garland Encyclopedia of World Music, Volume 3: The United States and Canada*. New York: Garland, 2001, 1127–1131.

Gaylor, H. (ed.). *Niagara's Changing Landscapes*. Ottawa: Carleton University Press, 1994.

Gayton, D. *The Wheatgrass Mechanism: Science and Imagination in the Western Canadian Landscape*. Saskatoon: Fifth House Publishers, 1990.

Gold, J.R., and S.V. Ward (eds.). *Place Promotion: The Use of Publicity and Marketing to Sell Towns and Regions*. New York: Wiley and Sons, 1994.

Golledge, R.G., and R.J. Stimpson. *Spatial Behavior. A Geographic Perspective*. New York: Guilford Press, 1996.

Graham, B., G.J. Ashworth, and J.E Tunbridge. *A Geography of Heritage: Power, Culture and Economy*. New York: Oxford University Press, 2000.

Harmon, K. (ed.). *The Pacific Northwest Landscape: A Painted History*. Seattle: Sasquatch Books, 2001.

Hopkins, J. "Excavating Toronto's Underground Streets: In Search of Equitable Rights, Rules, and Revenues." In J. Caulfield and L. Peake (eds.), *City Lives & City Forms: Critical Research and Canadian Urbanism*. Toronto: University of Toronto Press, 1996, 63–81.

Jackson, E., and D. Johnson (eds.). "Feature Issue: The West Edmonton Mall and Mega-malls," *Canadian Geographer* 35(3), 1991.

James, W.C. *Locations of the Sacred: Essays on Religion, Literature and Canadian Culture*. Waterloo, ON: Wilfrid Laurier University Press, 1998.

Kearns, G., and C. Philo (eds.). *Selling Places*. Oxford: Pergamon Press, 1993.

Morley, D., and K. Robins. *Spaces of Identity*. London: Routledge, 1995.

Osborne, B. "Images of People, Place and Nation in Canadian Art." In D. Cosgrove and S. Daniels (eds.). *The Iconography of the Past*. Cambridge: Cambridge University Press, 1988.

Price, J. *Flight Maps: Adventures with Nature in Modern America*. New York: Basic Books, 1999, 167–206.

Pyne, S. *How the Canyon Became Grand*. New York: Penguin, 1998.

Schama, S. *Landscape and Memory*. New York: Vintage Books, 1995.

Shields, R. *Places on the Margin: Alternative Geographies of Modernity*. London and New York: Routledge, 1991.

Shurmer-Smith, P., and K. Hannam. *Worlds of Desire, Realms of Power*. London: Edward Arnold, 1994.

Simpson-Housley, P., and G. Norcliffe (eds.). *A Few Acres of Snow: Literary and Artistic Images of Canada*. Toronto: Dundurn Press, 1992.

Spang, R. *The Invention of the Restaurant: Paris and Modern Gastronomic Culture*. Cambridge, MA: Harvard University Press, 2000.

Tuan, Y.F. *Landscapes of Fear*. Minneapolis: University of Minnesota Press, 1979.

Urry, J. *Consuming Places*. London: Routledge, 1995.

Williams, A. (ed). *Therapeutic Landscapes: The Dynamic between Place and Wellness*. Lanham, MD: University Press of America, 1999.

Zelinsky, W. "The Roving Palate: North America's Ethnic Restaurant Cuisines," *Geoforum* 16, 1985, 51–72.

Zukin, S. *The Cultures of Cities*. Cambridge, MA: Blackwell, 1995.

Exercises

Here you will find exercises and activities for each chapter. Unplugged exercises help you review chapter discussions, and pose ideas for your own human geography research. On the Companion Website exercises will require you have access to the internet.

Unplugged

1. Write a short essay (500 words or two double-spaced, typed pages) that describes, from your personal perspective, the sense of place that you associate with your hometown or province. Write about the places, buildings, sights, and sounds that are especially meaningful to you.

2. Draw up a list of the top 10 places in Canada in which you would like to live and work; then draw up a list of the bottom 10 places in which you would least like to live. How do these lists compare with the lists of your friends and members of your family? Why might your preferences be different from theirs?

3. On a clean sheet of paper and without reference to maps or other materials, sketch a detailed map of the town or city in which you live. When you have finished your sketch, analyze it. Does your sketch contain nodes? Landmarks? Edges? Districts? Paths? How does your sketch compare with the reality shown in a published city map?

4. Using telephone books that can be accessed at your university library and a map of your local area, map the sacred landscape of your locality by identifying the locations of different places of worship. What patterns do you see? How do these patterns fit with your knowledge of particular areas? What other sorts of sacred sites might exist in addition to the institutionalized religious sites?

5. Your campus provides an institutional landscape that has been "written" to convey certain important relationships. "Read" your campus landscape, and discuss the most powerful sites versus the least powerful ones as well as the groups or academic disciplines that occupy them. Map what you think are the most powerful and important places and sites and the least powerful and important ones. Why do different places and sites fit into each category? Are there significant differences in architecture, location (central or on the edges of campus), or accessibility? How might your reading of the campus landscape differ from readings created by other members of the campus community (as well as outsiders)?

On the Companion Website

This book has its own Companion Website where you will find additional resources—maps, photographs, data—as well as exercises and activities that relate to each chapter. To complete the Companion Website exercises, go to **www.pearsoned.ca/knox**. The following is a summary of the types of exercises created for this chapter.

The exercises for this chapter explore in some depth how we recognize the coded spaces of our landscape. Via the internet, we travel to worldwide museums to view Europe's eighteenth-century landscape in classic paintings, as well as the nineteenth-century U.S. landscape as viewed by painters of the Hudson River School, in an effort to decipher the semiotics of these landscapes—how they were written and read. We examine the use of postal codes as identity markers. We also use the internet to examine health concepts, climate, e-commerce, language, and population.

7

The Geography of Economic Development

The Teck Cominco smelter in Trail, British Columbia

Its tall smokestack is visible for kilometres. As shown in the chapter opening photograph, the smelter at Trail, in the southeastern corner of British Columbia, makes a number of clear statements. Its physical presence is indicative of the importance of economic activity in our use of the landscape, of the ways in which that activity has traditionally framed our concerns for the environment, and of the ways in which the development of "place," "space," and "region" are affected by the economy.

A visitor to Trail, contemplating the scene shown in the photograph, inevitably asks some important questions: Why is the smelter here? What does it produce? Who owns it? Where are its markets? What are its effects on the local environment and the local economy? These are also some key questions considered by economic geographers. But economic geographers don't stop there. For example, they would also examine how the site of raw materials, power supplies, and markets dictates the location of industries and the method of transportation of materials between producers and consumers. They would be interested to learn something of the history of the smelter, and probably would be intrigued to discover that production has been occurring here for almost a century, a fact that has led the smelter to become an integral part of the local economy. Other key concerns are how new technologies challenge the role of distance and—especially since the Kyoto Protocol came into effect in February 2005—the effects of industry on environmental sustainability.[1]

A visitor, seeing that the size of the smelter is out of proportion to the small town of Trail (where about 10 000 people live), is also made very aware of the global-regional-local connections that interest geographers. The smelter is clearly part of a much larger economic picture, as this locality alone could not provide sufficient demand for such a large enterprise. Its size hints at an economic system in which long-distance trade is a key component, and at a culture that permits the local economic exploitation of the environment at such a scale to meet far flung demand. The role of global demand in shaping local economies is therefore made evident by this photograph, and that role is a concern of modern economic geographers.

Our visitor to Trail—certainly if he or she has spent some time in the town and bought a coffee or gas—might also make another set of observations. Why has such a large industrial plant not become the foundation for a much larger industrial region than this one? Indeed, the visitor might wonder why the

---

[1]Information about Trail's smelter is available from the website of Teck Cominco at **www.teck.com/**.

downtown boasts more thrift stores than high-end retail establishments. The study of economic geography, through its examination of the processes of regional disparities, provides one answer.

Economic development is always an uneven geographic phenomenon. Explaining how and why these processes occur is an important aspect of human geography.

MAIN POINTS

- The geography of economic development is the cumulative outcome of decisions guided by fundamental principles of land use, commercial and industrial location, and economic interdependence.
- Geographically, the single most important feature of economic development is that it is highly uneven.
- Successive technology systems have rewritten the geography of economic development as they have shifted the balance of advantages among regions.
- Geographical divisions of labour have evolved with the growth of the world-system of trade and politics and with the changing locational logic of successive technology systems.
- Regional cores of economic development are created cumulatively, following some initial advantage, through the operation of several basic principles of spatial organization.
- Spirals of economic development can be arrested in various ways, including the onset of disinvestment and deindustrialization, which follow major shifts in technology systems and in international geopolitics.
- The globalization of the economy has meant that patterns and processes of local and regional economic development are much more open to external influences than before.
- Tourism has increasingly come to represent a major industry at a world scale, and offers the potential for local economic development in forms as various as ecotourism and visits to Aboriginal cultural sites.

WHAT ECONOMIC DEVELOPMENT MEANS

Economic development is often discussed in terms of levels and rates of change in prosperity, as reflected in bottom-line statistical measures of productivity, incomes, purchasing power, and consumption. Increased prosperity is only one aspect of economic development, however. For human geographers and other social scientists, the term *economic development* refers to processes of change involving the nature and composition of the economy of a particular region, as well as to increases in the overall prosperity of a region. We must not overlook the interactions between a prosperous economy and the environment, which we know are intimately linked. These processes can therefore involve four types of changes:

- changes in the structure of the region's economy (for example, a shift from agriculture to manufacturing)
- changes in forms of economic organization within the region (for example, a shift from socialism to free-market capitalism)

- changes in the availability and use of technology within the region

- changes in the region's environment (for example, heightened levels of pollution may diminish the region's overall prosperity; whereas an increase in ecotourism might cause forests previously considered wilderness to now be seen as a valued economic resource)

Economic development is also expected to bring with it some broader changes in the economic well-being of a region. The most important of these changes is the capacity of the region to improve the basic conditions of life (through better housing, health care, social welfare systems, and the provision of public services) and the physical framework, or infrastructure, on which the economy rests. Equally important is that the sustainability of the region's environment is not harmed by these changes and that environmental considerations are made integral to decisions about economic development.

The Unevenness of Economic Development

Geographically, the single most important feature of economic development is that it is *uneven*. At the global scale, this unevenness takes the form of core–periphery contrasts within the evolving world-system (see Chapter 2). These global core–periphery contrasts are the result of a competitive economic system that is heavily influenced by cultural and political factors. The core regions within the world-system—currently, the tripolar core of North America, Europe, and Japan—have the most diversified economies, the most advanced technologies, the highest levels of productivity, and the highest levels of prosperity. They are commonly referred to as *developed regions* (though processes of economic development are, of course, continuous, and no region can ever be regarded as fully developed). Other countries and regions—the periphery and semiperiphery of the world-system—are often referred to as *developing* or *less developed*. Indeed, the nations of the periphery are often referred to as LDCs (less-developed countries). Another popular term for the global periphery, developed as a political label but now synonymous with economic development, is *Third World*. As we saw in Chapter 2, this term had its origins in the early Cold War era of the 1950s and 1960s, when the newly independent countries of the periphery positioned themselves as a distinctive political bloc, aligned neither with the First World of developed, capitalist countries nor with the Second World of the Soviet Union and its satellite countries.

Global Core–Periphery Patterns   At this global scale, levels of economic development are usually measured by economic indicators, such as gross domestic product and gross national product. **Gross domestic product (GDP)** is an estimate of the total value of all materials, foodstuffs, goods, and services that are produced by a country in a particular year. To standardize for countries' varying sizes, the statistic is normally divided by total population, which gives an indicator, *per capita* GDP, that is a good measure of relative levels of economic development. **Gross national product (GNP)** includes the value of income from abroad—flows of profits or losses from overseas investments, for example. In making international comparisons, GDP and GNP can be problematic because they are based on each nation's currency. Recently, it has become possible to compare national currencies based on their **gross national income (GNI)** converted to "international dollars" using a *purchasing power parity* (PPP) conversion factor. According to the Population Reference Bureau, these "international dollars indicate the amount of goods and services one could buy in the United States with a given amount of money."[2] (Gross national income [GNI] is measured as GDP minus the taxes and wages a country

gross domestic product (GDP): an estimate of the total value of all materials, foodstuffs, goods, and services produced by a country in a particular year

gross national product (GNP): similar to GDP, but also includes the value of income from abroad

gross national income (GNI): similar to GDP, but also includes the value of income from abroad and excludes the taxes and wages a country pays to outside interests

[2] A discussion can be found of the concept of PPP (purchasing power parity) and the latest data at Population Reference Bureau website, **www.prb.org**. A definition of gross national income can be found on the OECD's website at **http://stats.oecd.org/glossary**.

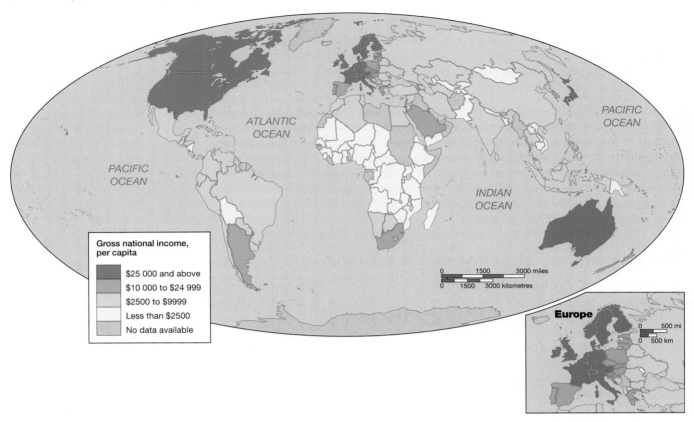

Figure 7.1 **Gross national income (GNI) per capita** GNI per capita is one of the best single measures of economic development. This map, based on 2003 data, shows the tremendous gulf in affluence between the core countries of the world economy—like the United States, Norway, and Switzerland, with annual per capita GNI (in PPP "international dollars") of more than $25 000—and peripheral countries like Angola, Haiti, and Mali, where annual per capita GNI was less than $2500. In semiperipheral countries like South Korea, Brazil, and Mexico, per capita GNI ranged between $5000 and $10 000. (After map projection, Buckminster Fuller Institute and Dymaxion Map Design, Santa Barbara, CA. The word *Dymaxion* and the Fuller Projection Dymaxion™ Map design are trademarks of the Buckminster Fuller Institute, Santa Barbara, CA, © 1938, 1967 & 1992. All rights reserved.)

pays to outside interests, but includes those taxes and wages earned outside its borders by its own businesses or individuals.) In effect, PPP measures how much of a common "market basket" of goods and services each currency can purchase locally, including goods and services that are not traded internationally. Using PPP-based currency values to compare levels of economic prosperity usually produces lower GNP figures in wealthy countries and higher GNP figures in poorer nations, compared with market-based exchange rates. Nevertheless, even with this compression between rich and poor, economic prosperity is very unevenly distributed across nations.

As **Figure 7.1** shows, most of the highest levels of economic development are to be found in northern latitudes (very roughly, north of 30°N), which has given rise to another popular shorthand for the world's economic geography: the division between the "North" (the core) and the "South" (the periphery). Viewed in more detail, the global pattern of per capita GNI (measured in the "international dollars" of PPP) is a direct reflection of the core–semiperiphery–periphery structure of the world-system. In 2006, according to the latest estimates available, in almost all the core countries of North America, northwestern Europe, and Japan, annual per capita GNI (in PPP) exceeds $30 000. For Canada, the equivalent figure in 2006 was $34 610.

In the rest of the world—the periphery—annual per capita GNI (in PPP) typically ranges between $1000 and $7000. The gap between the highest per capita GNIs, $44 260 in the United States and $40 630 in Switzerland) and the lowest ($110 in Burundi) is huge. The gap between the world's rich and poor is also getting

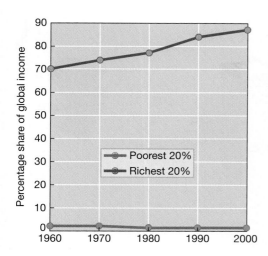

Figure 7.2   Long-term trends in per capita GNI   This graph shows the steady divergence in international economic prosperity between the richest and poorest of the world's population. By 2000, the richest 20 percent of the world's population accounted for 72.1 percent of global income.

wider rather than narrower. In 1970, the average GNI per capita of the 10 poorest countries in the world was just one-fiftieth of the average GNI per capita of the 10 most prosperous countries. By 1990, the relative gap had doubled, and by 2005 the average of the bottom 10 was approaching one two-hundredth of the average of the top 10 (**Figure 7.2**).

Geography of Inequality   Geographic inequality in income is reflected—and reinforced—by many aspects of human well-being. Patterns of infant mortality, a reliable indicator of social well-being, show the same steep core–periphery gradient (refer back to Figure 3.8). For adults in the industrial core countries, life expectancy is high and continues to increase. Life expectancy at birth in North America in 2004 was 78 years. In contrast, life expectancy in the poorest countries is dramatically shorter. In Africa in 2004, it was 52 years. In most African countries, only 60 percent to 75 percent of the population can expect to survive to age 40.

The United Nations Development Programme (UNDP) has devised an overall index of human development based on measures of life expectancy, educational attainment, and personal income. The index is calculated so that a country with the best scores among all countries in the world on all three indicators would have a perfect index score of 1.0, while a country that ranked worst in the world on all three indicators would have an index score of 0.0. **Figure 7.3** shows the international map of human development in 2002. The latest statistics released by the UNDP in 2004 report that in 2002, Norway, Sweden, Australia, and Canada had the highest overall levels of human development (with scores of 0.956, 0.946, 0.946, and 0.943, respectively). The lowest levels in 2002 were recorded by Mali (0.37), Burkina Faso (0.40), Niger (0.35), and Sierra Leone (0.28).[3] The same fundamental pattern is repeated across the entire array of indicators of human development: adult literacy, poverty, malnutrition, access to physicians, public expenditure on higher education, telephone lines, internet users, and so on. Inequality on this scale poses the most pressing, as well as the most intractable, questions of spatial justice.

These questions are underscored by some simple comparisons between the needs of the periphery and the spending patterns in core countries. The UNDP has calculated that the annual cost of providing a basic education for all children in peripheral countries would be in the region of US$6 billion, which is less than the annual sales of cosmetics in the United States. Providing water and sanitation for everyone in peripheral countries is estimated at US$9 billion per year, which is less than Europeans' annual expenditure on ice cream. Providing basic health and nutrition for everyone in the peripheral countries would cost an estimated

---

[3]UNDP data can be acessed online at **www.undp.org**.

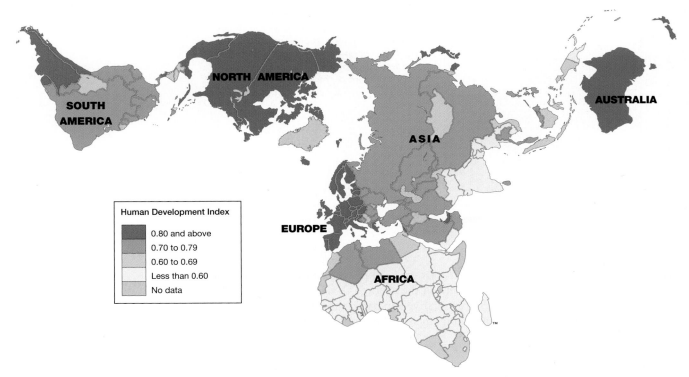

Figure 7.3 An index of human development, 2002 This index, calculated by the United Nations Development Programme, is based on measures of life expectancy, educational attainment, and personal income. A country with the best scores among all countries in the world on all three measures would have a perfect index score of 1.0, while a country that ranked worst in the world on all three indicators would have an index score of zero. Most of the affluent core countries have index scores of 0.9 or more; the worst scores—those less than 0.4—are concentrated in Africa. (After map projection, Buckminster Fuller Institute and Dymaxion Map Design, Santa Barbara, CA. The word *Dymaxion* and the Fuller Projection Dymaxion™ Map design are trademarks of the Buckminster Fuller Institute, Santa Barbara, CA, © 1938, 1967 & 1992. All rights reserved.)

US$13 billion per year, which is less than the annual expenditure on pet foods in Europe and the United States. Reducing the military expenditures of core countries (in the region of US$500 billion per year) by less than 10 percent each year would pay for the costs of basic education, water and sanitation, basic health and nutrition, and reproductive health programs for all people in peripheral countries.

Geography tells us that inequalities exist at levels below that of the global scale. In other words, the sorts of fundamental disparities that we have just seen operating between core and peripheral countries are also operating at regional and local levels. Why is this?

The answer is twofold. First, as we saw in Chapter 2, the operation of the world-system though the interaction of the core and periphery (at global, regional, or local levels) ensures that peripheral regions are kept in a dependent position. A series of processes (economic, political, military, and environmental) work together to support core regions at the expense of peripheral areas and, in so doing, create disparities among those regions.

Second, "space" is, in many important ways, a human construction. In Chapter 1, we saw how the development of a railhead in a previously ignored patch of prairie would begin to "create space." Farmers who found themselves close to the railhead paid much lower costs than other farmers to transport their grain to that shipment point. This simple example (in which people pay for transport and land is privately owned) shows that the effects of distance "create" an economic space—one in which farmers nearest the railhead will make higher profits than those on the periphery. In more general terms, geography tells us that it is through such a *spatial process* that *spatial disparities* are created.

It is precisely because spatial disparities exist and operate at every level of the world-system that they must not only be addressed at each level but also be seen as part of an overall general geographic process. Therefore, any resolution of development problems has to be seen as part of a continuum of activities, which range from the global protests by the World Social Forum, for example, to the local provision of food bank services in many Canadian cities.

Development and Gender Equality   Core–periphery patterns are also reflected in indicators that measure economic development by *gender equality*. The UNDP has established a gender-sensitive development index that adjusts the overall human development index for gender inequality in life expectancy, educational attainment, and income. According to this index, in no country are women better off than men. Perhaps most revealing is the UNDP's Gender Empowerment measure, which is based on measures of women's incomes; their participation in the labour force as administrators, managers, and professional and technical workers; and the percentage of parliamentary seats held by women. As in the overall index of human development, a country with a perfect score (ranked the best in the world on all measures) would score 1.0, with 0.0 representing the worst possible score (ranked worst on all measures). **Figure 7.4** shows the actual index values for 2002. In 2002, the top countries were Norway (0.908) and Sweden (0.854). Canada ranked 10th with 0.787. The lowest were Yemen (0.123), Saudi Arabia (0.207), and Bangladesh (0.218).

Women are, in fact, playing a central and increasing role in processes of development and change in the global economy. In many peripheral countries, women

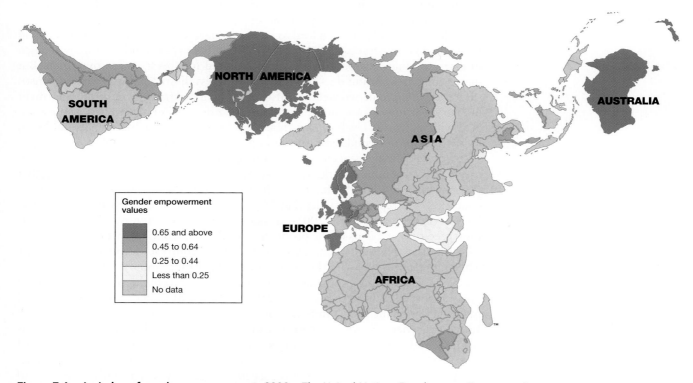

Figure 7.4   An index of gender empowerment, 2002   The United Nations Development Programme's Gender Empowerment measure is based on measures of women's incomes; their participation in the labour force as administrators and managers, and as professional and technical workers; and the percentage of parliamentary seats held by women. As in the overall index of human development (Figure 7.3), a country with a perfect score would score 1.0, with zero representing the worst possible score (ranked worst on all measures). The map reflects a broad core–periphery pattern, though there is by no means a direct correlation between economic prosperity and gender empowerment: creating economic opportunities for women does not necessarily require high levels of economic development.   (After map projection, Buckminster Fuller Institute and Dymaxion Map Design, Santa Barbara, CA. The word *Dymaxion* and the Fuller Projection Dymaxion™ Map design are trademarks of the Buckminster Fuller Institute, Santa Barbara, CA, © 1938, 1967 & 1992. All rights reserved.)

Figure 7.5 Women in development
The changing global economy has placed unprecedented demands on women. Much of the industrialization in peripheral countries depends on female labour because wage rates for women are significantly lower than those for men.

constitute the majority of workers in the manufacturing sector created by the new international division of labour (**Figure 7.5**). In others, it is women who keep households afloat in a world economy that has resulted in localized recession and intensified poverty. On average, women earn 30 percent to 40 percent less than men for the same work. They also tend to work longer hours than men—12 to 13 hours a week more (counting both paid and unpaid work) in Africa and Asia.

Globalization appears to lead to increasing levels of participation by women in the formal labour force. Large firms producing for export tend to employ women in assembly-line jobs because they can be hired for lower wages than men. But increasing participation does not always mean less discrimination. Women constitute a large share of workers in informal subcontracting—often in the garment industry—at low wages and under poor conditions. Globalization is also associated with increasing levels of part-time work. According to a 2007 report published by the European Foundation for the Improvement of Living and Working Conditions (an autonomous agency of the European Union [EU]), "part-time employment is now a common working arrangement in many parts of Europe." Noting that this phenomenon has "dramatically increased over the last 15 years in most EU countries," the report concludes that 18 percent of employed people in the European Union worked part-time in 2005—a figure which rises to almost 33 percent if it is measured only in terms of the proportion of women working part-time.

When considered regionally, some interesting contrasts across Europe appear. Thus, the report notes that the highest rate of part-time employment was found in the Netherlands, where 46 percent of the country's total employees in 2005 worked part-time (measured in terms of gender, 75 percent of women, and 23 percent of men employed in the Dutch labour force worked part-time). In the United Kingdom, where the second-highest rate of part-time employment in the EU was recorded, 25 percent of the country's employees worked part-time (43 percent of employed women, and 10 percent of employed men). At the other end of the scale, the lowest rates in Europe were recorded in Hungary, where only 4 percent of those employed worked part-time (6 percent of employed women, 3 percent of employed men) and in the Czech Republic, where 5 percent of those employed worked part-time (6 percent of employed women, 2 percent of employed men).[4]

---

[4]Colette Fagan et al., *Part-time Work in European Companies: Establishment Survey in Working Time 2004–5*. Dublin: European Foundation for the Improvement of Living and Working Conditions, April 2007, pp. 5–8 and 57 (available at **www.eurofound.europa.eu**). The report is based on a series of labour force surveys of over 21 000 businesses across the EU.

Regional Patterns   Inequality in economic development often has a regional dimension. Initial conditions are a crucial determinant of regional economic performance. Scarce resources, a history of neglect, lack of investment, and concentrations of low-skilled people all combine to explain the lagging performance of certain areas. In some regions, for example, initial disadvantages are so extreme as to constrain the opportunities of individuals born there.

The UNDP noted in its 2005 report that "in many countries regional disparities are a major source of inequality." In Brazil, for example, the northeast of the country spends half as much on health care expenditures as the southeast of the country and, in consequence, experiences twice the infant mortality rate (52 deaths per thousand live births compared with 20 per thousand). In addition, as the UNDP observes, "living in a rural area is, in many countries, a marker for disadvantage." Poverty rates are usually higher, and the provision of public services (such as health care, schools, and citizen support agencies) are far lower. In Ghana, for example, the incidence of poverty is 2 percent in Accra, the capital, but 70 percent in the rural hinterlands, where only one in five residents have access to piped water (compared to four out of five urban residents).[5]

At the regional scale, as at the global scale, levels of economic development often exhibit a fundamental core–periphery structure. As **Figure 7.6** shows, core–periphery contrasts within countries are evident throughout the world: in core countries, such as France, semiperipheral countries, such as South Korea, and peripheral countries, such as China and India.

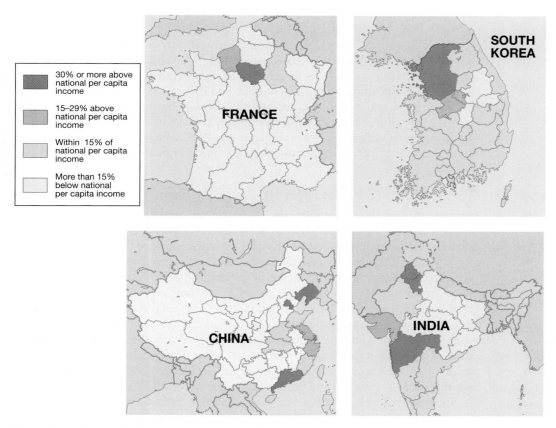

■	30% or more above national per capita income
▨	15–29% above national per capita income
▨	Within 15% of national per capita income
□	More than 15% below national per capita income

Figure 7.6   Regional inequality in incomes   These maps show the extent to which regions within countries vary from the average national income.

---

[5]United Nations Development Programme, *Report 2005*. New York: UNDP, 2006; the quotations are from pp. 2, 59, and 60).

Figure 7.7 Provincial and territorial differences in average earnings: Canada in 2001 (*Source: Average Earnings of the Population [2001 Census]*. Adapted from the Statistics Canada website: **www40.statcan.gc.ca/l01/cst01/labor50a-eng.htm**.)

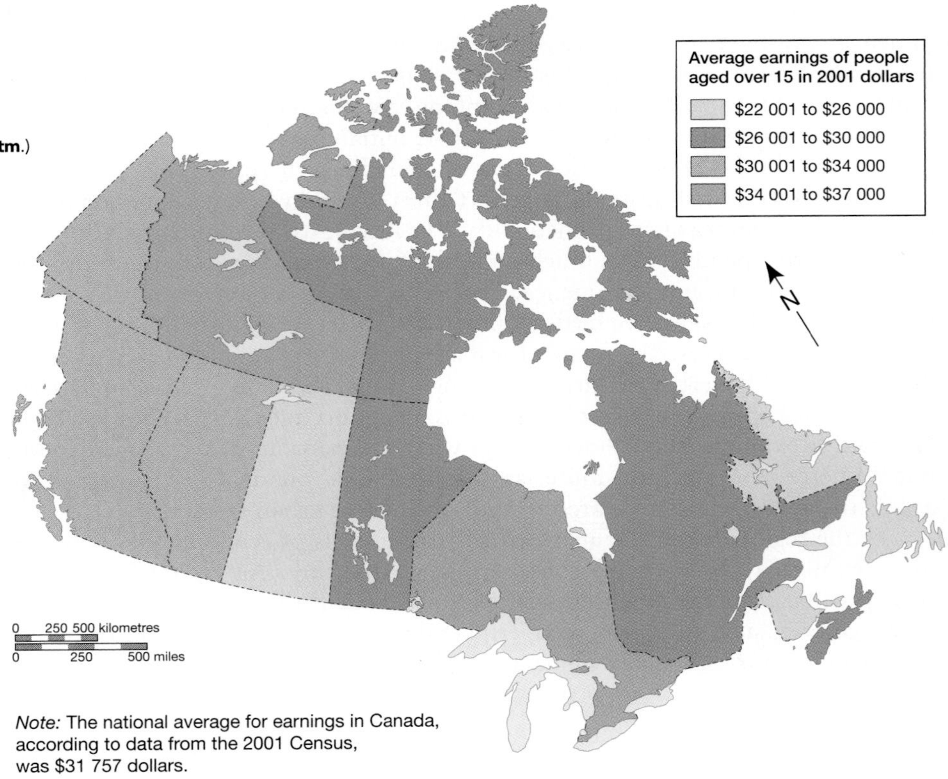

Average earnings of people aged over 15 in 2001 dollars

	$22 001 to $26 000
	$26 001 to $30 000
	$30 001 to $34 000
	$34 001 to $37 000

Note: The national average for earnings in Canada, according to data from the 2001 Census, was $31 757 dollars.

Figure 7.7 shows the provincial and territorial distribution of annual average individual income levels in Canada in 2001. The continuing importance of staple production is shown in the above-national-average income figures for the three northern territories, British Columbia, and Alberta, where resource extraction (based on gold and diamonds, lumber, and oil) has become the mainstay of the regional economy. Although somewhat lower, average individual income levels in Ontario are also above the national average, illustrating the continuing importance of core and periphery relationships in the Canadian economy.

Resources and Technology

It is important at the outset to realize that the concept of "resources" is essentially a cultural and economic construct, constrained by existing technologies, and not one that is mainly determined by physical presence. Perhaps the best way to come to comprehend this is to define the terms *stocks, resources,* and *reserves*.[6]

The entire material components of the environment (including all biological and inert substances, and all of the energy flows) make up the **total stock** of matter and energy on Earth. Despite its abundance, this total stock is mainly inaccessible to us, or in a form we cannot use, so that a stock only becomes a resource when it can be of some use to us as humans. In this way, the stocks of petroleum contained in Alberta's oil sands remain the same as they always have been, but because they are now considered to be "useful" by humans, these stocks are defined as a **resource**.

In a similar vein, **reserves** are defined as that portion of a resource that is exploitable under current technology and economic demand. Much of Newfoundland and Labrador's offshore oil resources have been unexploited, but have come to be

total stock: the entire amount of energy and matter on Earth, much of which is either inaccessible or unusable by humans

resources: that part of the total stock that is considered to be useful to humans in some way

reserves: that part of a resource that is currently exploitable under prevailing technologies and economic demand

---

[6]A useful introduction to this topic is Peter Haggett, *Geography: A Global Synthesis*. (Harlow, UK: Prentice Hall, 2001), Chapter 10 "The Nature of Natural Resources," 305–331, and these paragraphs are based on that account.

part of this country's oil reserves because of recent increases in the price of oil and the development of oilrigs that can function in deeper waters.

It is obviously possible for a reserve to increase or decrease in size as technology or economic or cultural definitions change. Similarly, reassessment, invention, or obsolescence of old technologies change how we value resources. Stocks, however, remain the same.

We should also recall the distinction made in Chapter 4 between *renewable* and *non-renewable* resources (the difference, for example, between wind power and coal as energy sources). Non-renewable resources are finite in supply, but renewable (sometimes called *flow*) resources are recurrent but variable over time. Some geographers make a further distinction between those renewables that can be greatly affected by humans (such as groundwater supplies, which can be overpumped and thereby permanently exhausted) and those that are unaffected (such as tidal energy). Activities such as deforestation lie somewhere between these two poles, since it is can be destructive in the short term, but can be restored (to some extent) by tree-planting over the longer term.

The regional patterns of economic development are the result of many different factors. One of the most important is the availability of key resources, such as cultivable land, energy sources, and valuable minerals. Unevenly distributed across the world, however, are both key resources and—just as importantly—the *combinations* of energy and minerals crucial to economic development (**Table 7.1**). A lack of natural resources can, of course, be remedied through international trade (Japan's success is a prime example of this). For most countries, however, the resource base remains an important determinant of development.

A high proportion of the world's key industrial resources—basic raw materials and sources of energy—are concentrated in Canada, Russia, the United States, South Africa, and Australia. The biggest single exception to the concentration of key resources in these countries is presented by the vast oil fields of the Middle East. It is an exception that has enabled formerly peripheral countries, like Saudi Arabia, to become wealthy, and it has made the region especially important in international politics.

The concentration of known resources in just a few countries is largely a result of geology, but it is also partly a function of countries' political and economic development. Political instability in much of postcolonial Africa, Asia, and Latin America has seriously hindered the exploration and exploitation of resources. On the other hand, the relative affluence and strong political stability of Canada and the United States have led to a much more intensive exploration of resources. We

---

TABLE 7.1 World Energy Resources: Largest Reserves of Coal, Natural Gas, and Crude Oil, 2005

Coal Reserves (millions of tonnes)		Natural Gas Reserves (billions of cubic metres)		Crude Oil Reserves (millions of barrels)	
USA	242 721	Russia	47 820	Saudi Arabia	264 310
Russia	157 010	Iran	26 740	Iran	137 490
China	114 500	Qatar	25 633	Iraq	115 000
Australia	76 600	Saudi Arabia	6 848	Kuwait	101 500
India	56 498	U.A.E.	6 071	U.A.E.	97 800
S. Africa	48 000	USA	5 866	Venezuela	80 012
World	*847 488*	*World*	*176 462*	*World*	*1 215 186*

Note: Coal includes bituminous (including anthracite), sub-bituminous, and lignite deposits; crude oil includes crude oil and natural gas liquids.

U.A.E.: United Arab Emirates.

Source: World Energy Council, *Survey of Energy Resources 2007*, Tables 1.1, 2.1, and 5.1 at **www.worldenergy.org/publications/survey_of_energy_resources_2007/default.asp**. Information on annual production levels can be obtained from the International Energy Agency at **www.iea.org**.)

should bear in mind, therefore, that Table 7.1 reflects only the currently *known* resource base.

We should also recognize, as Chapter 4 has shown, that our attitudes toward science and technology (and hence our view of resources) are a product of our own particular culture. Modern Canadian society, for example, is built on a clear distinction between the human and the natural world, and is founded on a series of economic principles that stress the importance of private ownership, profit maximization, and competition. Such societies will have a very different approach to the sustainable development of global resources than, for example, the Inuit narwhale hunters (also considered in Chapter 4) whose culture frames a very different economic geography—one that is founded on common property, a non-exploitive use of renewable resources, and a respect for nature.

We should also bear in mind that the significance of particular resources is often tied to particular technologies and the state of the environment. As these change, the geography of economic development is "rewritten." One important example of this was the switch in industrial energy sources from coal to oil, gas, and electricity early in the twentieth century. When this happened, coalfield areas in Atlantic Canada found their prospects for economic development on indefinite hold, while oil field areas in Alberta suddenly had potential. More recently, technological improvements and a decline in more easily exploited resources have led to the development of that province's oil sands deposits, despite the huge refining costs involved.

A further fascinating example is discussed in Peter Redfield's book *Space in the Tropics*. In this study of French Guiana, Redfield very ably shows how the value of territory as a resource has changed over time as technology has itself changed. In the nineteenth century, the country was regarded as such an unattractive, disease-ridden wilderness by Europeans; a land fit only for the colonial prison known as Devil's Island. By the late twentieth century, however, that "wilderness" had become reinterpreted as a pristine "jungle," valued for its potential for ecotourists—a wholesale reversal in Western perception of French Guiana aided by the rise of environmental awareness and medical advances that have recast tropical destinations from feared postings to highly desirable holiday venues. In addition, the country's position close to the Equator meant that it became valued as the site for the European Space Agency launch facility.[7]

Regions and countries that are heavily dependent on one particular resource are vulnerable to the consequences of technological change and the collapse of that resource. They are also vulnerable to fluctuations in the price set for their product on the world market. These vulnerabilities are particularly important for a number of Canadian mining industries and Canadian farmers. You will recall from Chapter 2 that the staples thesis lists such vulnerability as one of the challenges of Canadian economic development.

Technology Systems   Technological innovations in power and energy, transportation, and manufacturing processes have been important catalysts for changes in the pattern of economic development. They have allowed a succession of expansions of economic activity in time and space. As a result, many existing industrial regions have grown bigger and more productive. Industrial development has also spread to new regions, whose growth has become interdependent with the fortunes of others through a complex web of production and trade. Each major cluster of technological innovations tends to create new requirements for natural resources as well as labour forces and markets. The result is that each major cluster of technological innovations—called *technology systems*—has tended to favour different regions and different kinds of places. **Technology systems** are clusters of interrelated

technology systems: clusters of interrelated energy, transportation, and production technologies that dominate economic activity for several decades at a time

---

[7]Peter Redfield, *Space in the Tropics: From Convicts to Rockets in French Guiana.* Berkeley: University of California Press, 2000. For further discussion of the themes raised in this book, see the review by Alan Nash in *GeoJournal* (56) 2003, pp. 241–242.

energy, transportation, and production technologies that dominate economic activity for several decades at a time—until a new cluster of improved technologies evolves. Since the beginning of the Industrial Revolution, we can identify five of them:

- **1790–1840:** early mechanization based on water power and steam engines; development of cotton textiles and ironworking; development of river transport systems, canals, and toll roads (known as "turnpike" roads)
- **1840–1890:** exploitation of coal-powered steam engines, steel products, railroads, world shipping, and machine tools
- **1890–1950:** exploitation of the internal combustion engine, oil and plastics, electrical and heavy engineering, aircraft, and radio and telecommunications
- **1950–1990:** exploitation of nuclear power, aerospace, electronics, and petrochemicals; and development of limited-access highways and global air routes
- **1990–present:** exploitation of solar energy, robotics, microelectronics, biotechnology, advanced materials (fine chemicals and thermoplastics, for example), and information technology (digital telecommunications and geographic information systems, for example)

Each of these technology systems has rewritten the geography of economic development as it has shifted the balance of advantages among countries, regions, and places.

It is important to note that these five stages represent only a very broad generalization of an enormous set of changes that occurred: many of them different in detail and certainly different in their location and timing. Certainly, the change from one system to another (the *replacement of technology systems*) did not occur overnight in any area, or, for that matter, was change ever total.

To give but one example, canal transport was a feature of the first technology system as it developed in Britain in the 1790s–1840s, but once transport technology shifted to railroads (during the second stage, 1840–1890), the canal system was not rendered entirely obsolete, although many individual canals were abandoned as they could no longer compete with the much cheaper haulage rates that railroads could provide. Some canals, for example, found new uses as channels for water supply to cities and industry, while the system as a whole remained part of the physical landscape. In an interesting twist to the story, the canal system in countries such as Britain or France has recently seen a substantial revival due to tourism, and much new funding has gone toward the restoration of the locks and lift bridges in those countries.

Our canal example also serves to illustrate one way in which technology systems diffuse. As with other geographic phenomena (see Chapter 2), the spread (or diffusion) of knowledge (in this case, technology) can occur by simple geographic (or contagious) spread, or by hierarchic diffusion (that is, down the urban settlement system). Thus, canals first developed as part of the package of innovations of the early Industrial Revolution in Britain. Knowledge of their use then spread to neighbouring countries such as France and Germany, and then outwards to the United States where they became part of the industrialization of New England and the New York region. Their adoption in Canada then occurred as colonists from Britain brought with them the idea of improving waterways for transportation: examples include the Rideau Canal constructed by Colonel By between Ottawa and Kingston in the 1820s.

This example shows that early technology systems diffused outwards from the core to the periphery. It also shows that by the time a technology had diffused to remoter locations, a newer technology had already supplanted it in the countries of the core, rendering its adoption in the periphery almost outmoded before it was built. Thus, canals were still being built in France and the United States at a time when they were being replaced by railroads in Britain. In this way, a "pulse" of innovation took changes outwards from the core to the periphery, and technology systems became part of broader economic forces that tied the global core and periphery together.

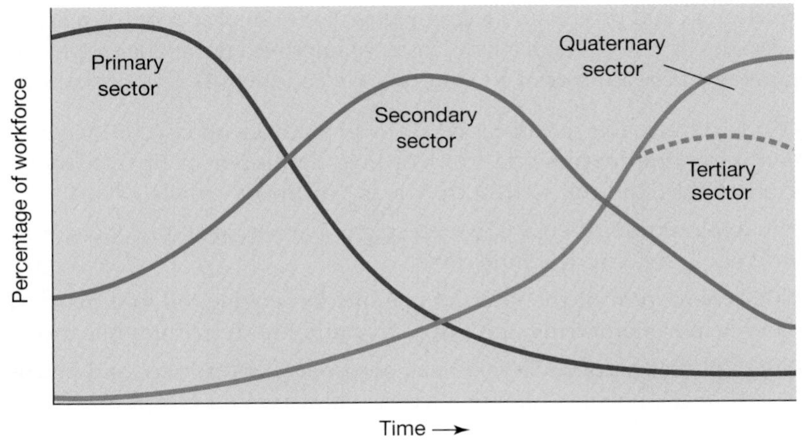

Figure 7.8 A model of the economic transition In very general terms, most "advanced economies" have moved through the same pattern of change in the employment structure of their workforce. Initially, primary sector activities dominate, but over time, these are replaced by secondary and then tertiary categories of employment as the economy matures. In many countries, the present drive for increased productivity, coupled with technological innovation, is now leading to the growth of the quaternary sector.

primary activities: economic activities that are concerned directly with natural resources of any kind

secondary activities: economic activities that process, transform, fabricate, or assemble the raw materials derived from primary activities, or that reassemble, refinish, or package manufactured goods

tertiary activities: economic activities involving the sale and exchange of goods and services

quaternary activities: economic activities that deal with the handling and processing of knowledge and information

Figure 7.9 Home-based business in a downtown Canadian setting By operating out of their home, or using their home as a place of paid employment, many Canadians are redefining the traditional boundaries of "home" and "workplace," and, in so doing, challenging traditional geographical concepts based on their separation.

Current technological change revolves around the use of the cellphone, a phenomenon that Paul Levinson in his 2004 book, *Cellphone,* has called an invention as important as the alphabet. The adoption of cellphones has been remarkable, and projections show that this technology will soon have spread across the entire globe. Already one in every two people has a cellphone. In this case, the spread of technology has not been by a simple geographic (or contagious) spread across space. The short time that has elapsed since the cellphone's invention rules that out as a plausible hypothesis. Rather, its spread has been through the core's world cities, then down through the urban hierarchies of each state, and thus across the global community. Thus, it has been able to "leap frog" older technologies that are still diffusing outwards more slowly from the core, and to render their adoption in the periphery redundant. A clear example of this type of technology diffusion is reported in a 2008 CBC documentary, called *Cell Phone: The Ring Heard Round the World,* and concerns the provision of cellphones by the Grameen phone program in parts of Rwanda, in areas where more traditional telephone service via landlines still has not been provided and now is probably no longer required. A similar process has occurred in many parts of northern and rural Canada, where remote communities or individual homeowners are able to bypass the prohibitive costs of phone installation through more advanced satellite systems.

The Economic Structure of Countries and Regions

The relative share of primary, secondary, tertiary, and quaternary economic activities determines the *economic structure* of a country or region. In general terms, the relative proportions of these sectors in an economy change as shown in **Figure 7.8**. **Primary activities** are those concerned directly with natural resources of any kind; they include agriculture, mining, fishing, and forestry. **Secondary activities** are those that process, transform, fabricate, or assemble the raw materials derived from primary activities, or that reassemble, refinish, or package manufactured goods. Secondary activities include steelmaking, food processing, furniture making, textile manufacturing, automobile assembly, and garment manufacturing. **Tertiary activities** are those involving the sale and exchange of goods and services; they include warehousing; retail stores; personal services, such as hairdressing; commercial services, such as accounting and advertising; and entertainment. **Quaternary activities** are those dealing with the handling and processing of knowledge and information. Examples include data processing, information retrieval, education, and research and development (R&D). These last two types of activities include many that are home-based (such as daycare or computer work). In this way, the traditional divisions between places of home and work are breaking down (**Figure 7.9**).

As **Figure 7.10** shows, the economic structure of much of the world is dominated by the primary sector (that is, primary activities such as agriculture, mining,

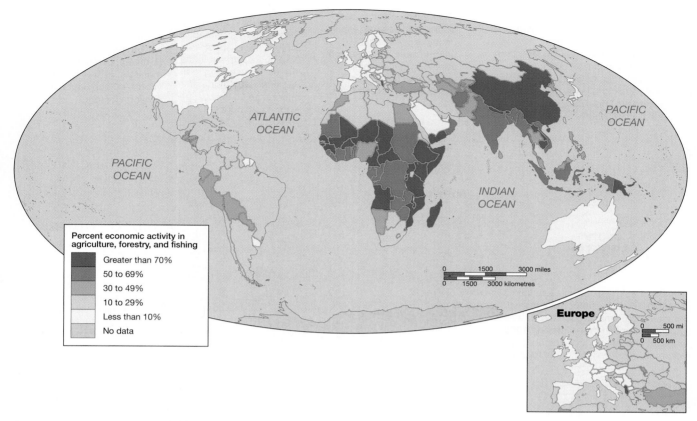

Figure 7.10   The geography of primary economic activities   Primary economic activities are those that are concerned directly with natural resources of any kind. They include agriculture, mining, forestry, and fishing. The vast majority of the world's population, concentrated in China, India, Southeast Asia, and Africa, is engaged in primary economic activities. This map shows the percentage of the labour force in each country that was engaged in primary employment in 2002. In some countries, including China, primary activities account for more than 70 percent of the workforce. In contrast, primary activities always account for less than 10 percent of the labour force in the world's core countries, and often for less than 5 percent.

fishing, and forestry). In much of Africa and Asia, between 50 percent and 75 percent of the labour force is engaged in primary-sector activities. In contrast, the primary sector of the world's core regions is typically small, occupying only 5 percent to 10 percent of the labour force. The secondary sector is much larger in the core countries and in semiperipheral countries, where the world's specialized manufacturing regions are located (**Figure 7.11**). The tertiary and quaternary sectors are significant only in the most affluent countries of the core. In the United States, for example, the primary sector in 1998 accounted for less than 4 percent of the labour force, the secondary sector for about 22 percent, the tertiary sector for just over 50 percent, and the quaternary sector for 22 percent. In Canada, 1991 data show that 6 percent of the labour force was in the primary sector, 21 percent in the secondary sector, and the remainder in the tertiary and quaternary sectors. It is also interesting to look at changes over time. Thus, over 50 years ago, according to the 1951 census, 22 percent of Canada's labour force was in the primary sector, 31 percent in the secondary sector, and 47 percent in the tertiary sector. By 2004, however, only 5 percent of the total labour force of approximately 16.3 million was in the primary sector, 21 percent in the secondary sector, and a total of 74 percent in the tertiary and quaternary sectors.

Stages of Development and Geographical Divisions of Labour

Variations in economic structure—according to primary, secondary, tertiary, or quaternary activities—reflect *geographical divisions of labour*. Geographical

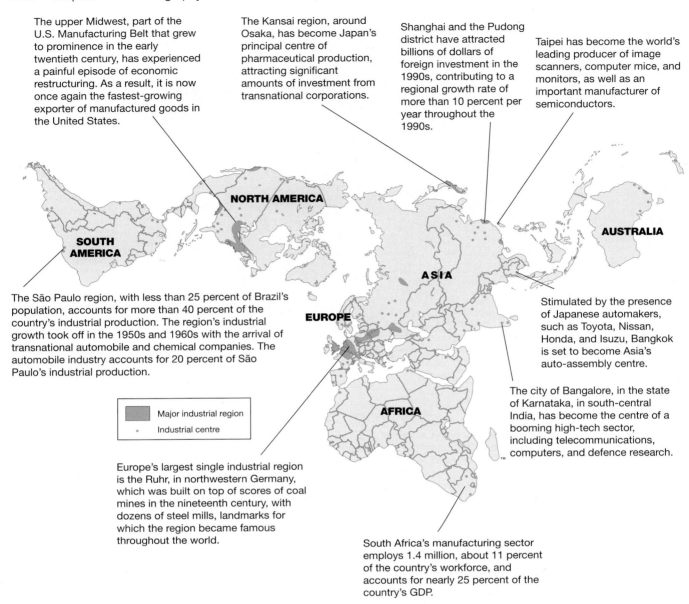

The upper Midwest, part of the U.S. Manufacturing Belt that grew to prominence in the early twentieth century, has experienced a painful episode of economic restructuring. As a result, it is now once again the fastest-growing exporter of manufactured goods in the United States.

The Kansai region, around Osaka, has become Japan's principal centre of pharmaceutical production, attracting significant amounts of investment from transnational corporations.

Shanghai and the Pudong district have attracted billions of dollars of foreign investment in the 1990s, contributing to a regional growth rate of more than 10 percent per year throughout the 1990s.

Taipei has become the world's leading producer of image scanners, computer mice, and monitors, as well as an important manufacturer of semiconductors.

The São Paulo region, with less than 25 percent of Brazil's population, accounts for more than 40 percent of the country's industrial production. The region's industrial growth took off in the 1950s and 1960s with the arrival of transnational automobile and chemical companies. The automobile industry accounts for 20 percent of São Paulo's industrial production.

Stimulated by the presence of Japanese automakers, such as Toyota, Nissan, Honda, and Isuzu, Bangkok is set to become Asia's auto-assembly centre.

The city of Bangalore, in the state of Karnataka, in south-central India, has become the centre of a booming high-tech sector, including telecommunications, computers, and defence research.

Major industrial region

Industrial centre

Europe's largest single industrial region is the Ruhr, in northwestern Germany, which was built on top of scores of coal mines in the nineteenth century, with dozens of steel mills, landmarks for which the region became famous throughout the world.

South Africa's manufacturing sector employs 1.4 million, about 11 percent of the country's workforce, and accounts for nearly 25 percent of the country's GDP.

Figure 7.11   The geography of secondary economic activities   Secondary economic activities are those that process, transform, fabricate, or assemble raw materials, or that reassemble, refinish, or package manufactured goods. As this map shows, the world's largest and most productive manufacturing regions are located in the core regions of Europe, North America, and Japan. Important concentrations of manufacturing industry are located in semiperipheral countries, such as South Korea, Mexico, and Brazil, but the increasing globalization of manufacturing means that patterns are subject to rapid change.   (*Source:* Map projection, Buckminster Fuller Institute and Dymaxion Map Design, Santa Barbara, CA. The word *Dymaxion* and the Fuller Projection Dymaxion™ Map design are trademarks of the Buckminster Fuller Institute, Santa Barbara, California, © 1938, 1967, & 1992. All rights reserved.)

divisions of labour are national, regional, and locally based economic specializations that have evolved with the growth of the world-system of trade and politics (see Chapter 2), the exploitation of environmental resources, and the locational needs of successive technology systems. They represent one of the most important dimensions of economic development. For instance, countries whose economies are dominated by primary-sector activities tend to have a relatively low per capita GDP. As an example, according to 2007–2008 data from the UNDP, the country with the highest proportion of its total labour force in agriculture is Ethiopia, a country with an average per capita income (expressed in terms of GNI PPP) of only $1190 in 2006, according to data from the Population Reference Bureau.

The exceptions to the rule are oil-rich countries, such as Saudi Arabia, Qatar, and Venezuela. Canada provides another exception, since its important primary activities are increasingly replaced by developments in the manufacturing and service sectors. Where the geographical division of labour has produced national economies with a large secondary sector, per capita GDP is much higher (as, for example, in Argentina and Korea). The highest levels of per capita GDP, however, are associated with economies that are *post-industrial*: economies where the tertiary and quaternary sectors have grown to dominate the workforce, with smaller but highly productive secondary sectors. In Canada, for example, as we have seen, the tertiary and quaternary sectors are responsible for a total of 74 percent of the workforce, and, according to data from the Population Reference Bureau, the average per capita income (expressed in terms of GNI PPP) was $34 610 in 2006.

This overall relationship between economic structure and levels of prosperity makes it possible to interpret economic development in terms of distinctive *stages*. Each region or country, in other words, might be thought of as progressing from the early stages of development, with a heavy reliance on primary activities (and relatively low levels of prosperity), through a phase of industrialization, and on to a "mature" stage of postindustrial development (with a diversified economic structure and relatively high levels of prosperity). This, in fact, is a commonly held view of economic development and one that has been conceptualized by a prominent economist, W.W. Rostow (**Figure 7.12**). Rostow's model, like those of most economists, rests on certain simplifying assumptions about the world. As we have seen, however, the real world is highly differentiated, not just in its natural resources but also in its demographics, culture, and politics. The assumptions in Rostow's model

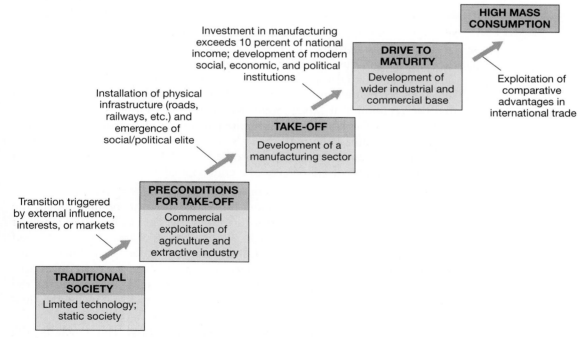

Figure 7.12 Stages of economic development This diagram illustrates a model of economic development based on the idea of successive stages. Each stage is seen as leading to the next, though different regions or countries may take longer than others to make the transition from one stage to the next. According to this view, first put forward by economist W.W. Rostow, places and regions can be seen as following parallel courses within a world that is steadily modernizing. It is, however, too simplistic to be of much help in understanding human geography. The reality is that places and regions are interdependent. The fortunes of any given place are increasingly tied up with those of many others. Rostow's model perpetuates the myth of "developmentalism"—the idea that every country and region will eventually make economic progress toward "high mass consumption" provided that they compete to the best of their ability within the world economy. But the main weakness of developmentalism is that it is simply not fair to compare the prospects of late starters to the experience of those places, regions, and countries that were among the early starters.

fit the experience of some parts of the world but not all. In reality, there are many pathways to development, as well as many different processes and outcomes of development.

Economic Development: War, Peace, and Security

Sadly, warfare appears to be one of the enduring hallmarks of the human condition and while its political effects are more properly treated in Chapter 9, its economic consequences deserve attention here because they are almost inextricably linked with some of the wider issues of economic development and human security that are considered in this chapter. This is because

■ *Poverty is both an outcome and a cause of war or violence.* The circumstances of poverty are fertile grounds for the causes of conflict and it is not surprising to find that according to the UNDP, 7 of the 10 lowest countries in terms of GDP per capita have undergone recent conflict. In its turn, the destruction promoted by armed violence will also cause economic difficulty—the World Bank, for example, has estimated that on average a civil war (such as that in Colombia) reduces the economic growth rate of the affected country by 2.2 percent a year.

■ *Environmental damage can be both an outcome and a cause of war or violence.* Examples of the former include the Iraqi army's deliberate setting fire to Kuwaiti oil wells as it was forced to withdraw from its invasion of that country. Examples of the latter include deforestation and declining soil yields in Chiapas, which, according to the work of Thomas Homer-Dixon, have led to cases of violent unrest in parts of Mexico (see Chapter 9). In a similar vein, William Holden and Daniel Jacobson write in the Winter 2007 issue of the *Canadian Geographer* how the potential environmental effects of mining in the Philippines can drive people into armed groups.

■ *In certain cases, warfare can promote economic development.* The enormous expenditure on arms, military bases, and resources to wage war can have the side-effect of actually promoting economic growth in areas where those resources are manufactured or provided. Richard Stubbs has recently argued that the economies of Japan, South Korea, Taiwan, Hong Kong, Singapore, Malaysia, and Thailand have all benefited in various ways from the long series of wars and conflicts that have beset Southeast Asia since 1945. More localized civil wars can, on average, according to UNDP calculations, result in an increased spending of 1.8 percent of a country's GDP.

■ *In times of war and peace, arms manufacture is used to promote economic development.* Although it is almost too well known to be mentioned, the fact that the world's principal arms manufacturers are to be found amongst the most developed nations (such as the United States, France, United Kingdom, Germany, and Israel) should be noted. Indeed, armament factories and military bases have long been used as tools to promote local economic development. Local debate over the effects of the closure of the Canadian military base in Gagetown, New Brunswick, is an ample illustration of this point. Sadly, it also has to be noted here that much of the advanced technologies that geographers have benefited from (such as GPS and GIS) have their origin in military applications such as the guidance systems for missiles.

Certainly, as geographers, we should also take note that the core–periphery model, which we have used to frame our understanding of many of the fundamental processes that shape our world, also appears to apply here. It is clear, as a generalization at least, that the poorer countries of the periphery experience the negative effects of warfare and civil war to a far greater extent than the richer countries of the core.

An excellent starting point for an analysis of the effects of warfare and general acts of violence is the UNDP's *2005 Human Development Report: International Cooperation at a Crossroads: Aid, Trade and Security in an Unequal World.* According to this document, since 1990, more than 3 million people have died as a direct result of armed conflicts—almost all of which have occurred in developing countries. Indeed, in terms of its Human Development Index (HDI), the UNDP report concludes that 9 of the 10 lowest HDI countries in 2004 had experienced armed conflict at some point since 1990; and 9 of the 18 countries whose HDI declined in the 1990s experienced armed conflict since 1990. In almost all of these countries, life expectancies and per capita incomes also fell. The report goes on to observe that

> The geographical pattern of conflict has changed over time, with a clear shift in security risks towards the poorest countries. During 1946–89 low-income developing countries accounted for just over one-third of all conflicts. Over 1990–2003 low-income countries accounted for more than half of the countries and territories that experienced violent conflict. Nearly 40% of the world's conflicts are in Africa, including several of the bloodiest of the last decade and a half. Meanwhile, even though the number of conflicts is falling, today's wars last longer. As a consequence, their impact on human development is severe.

The indirect effects are even larger. Calling it the "world's worst posthumanitarian disaster," the UNDP estimates, for example, that conflict over the period 1998 to 2004 in the Democratic Republic of the Congo has been responsible for a social and economic upheaval that has resulted in the deaths of 3.8 million more people than would otherwise have occurred in that country. Crude mortality rates are 67 percent higher than when peace was officially declared in 2002, and "nearly 31 000 people still die each month in excess of the average levels for sub-Saharan Africa as a result of disease, malnutrition and violence" the report notes. Children are especially vulnerable and infant mortality rates in the eastern Congo were recorded as 210 deaths per 1000 live births (almost double the sub-Saharan Africa average). Widespread dislocation of the population (an estimated 3.4 million people have become internally displaced, of a total population in 2004 of 51.2 million) has made it impossible for farmers to feed themselves or their families, and production in the eastern parts of the country is a tenth of pre-war levels. As a consequence, three-quarters of the country is malnourished. The conflict has also affected education: UNDP data show that school enrolment rates fell from 94 percent in 1978 to 60 percent in 2001.[8]

Economic Development and the Environment

The environment cannot be overlooked when discussing economic development; certainly, this issue cannot be ignored by geographers, who have argued vociferously for the inclusion of the environment as a major concern in all aspects of our engagement with the world. As we saw in Chapter 4, philosophies of nature may have affected how we have permitted Earth and its species to be exploited for industrial purposes. Because environmental issues profoundly influence social, cultural, *and* economic change, they provide the most valuable overall framework for understanding such changes.

We can encapsulate the importance of such a framework by contrasting the "traditional" approach to economic growth (one that ignores the environment)

---

[8]This section relies on material from the following: The United Nations Development Programme, *2005 Human Development Report: International Cooperation at a Crossroads: Aid, Trade and Security in an Unequal World.* New York: UNDP, 2005, **http://hdr.undp.org**; Richard Stubbs, "War and Economic Development: Export-Oriented Industrialization in East and Southeast Asia." *Comparative Politics* 31(3), 1999, pp. 337–355; William N. Holden and R. Daniel Jacobson, "Mining Amid Armed Conflict: Nonferrous Metals Mining in the Philippines," *Canadian Geographer* 51(40), 2007, pp. 475–500.

with a "new" approach, one that endeavours to achieve economic growth through the goals of sustainable development, in the following manner:

The Traditional Economy	*The New Economy*
– consumes renewable and nonrenewable resources	– recycles, replaces, and reduces its use of renewable and nonrenewable resources
– treats the environment as a "free good"	– prices the use of the environment (through environmental audits)
– uses the environment to absorb pollution	– costs the price of pollution (through emission credits)
– considers any environmental action as a cost	– considers environmental action part of the price of doing business— indeed, "green businesses" have developed as jobs in pollution control and land remediation proliferate and environmentally friendly technologies develop
– regards "place" as simply a location	– regards "place" as a locus of interconnections at the global, regional, and local scales
– regards "space" only in economic terms	– regards "space" as the arena in which those interconnections operate

EVERYTHING IN ITS PLACE: PRINCIPLES OF LOCATION

As geographers have sought to understand and explain local patterns of economic development, they have uncovered some fundamental principles that shape and influence decisions involving the location of economic activities. To the extent that regularity and predictability exist in economic geography, they stem from the logic of these principles. The geography of economic development is the cumulative outcome of decisions guided by fundamental principles of commercial and industrial location and interaction. As location decisions are played out in the real world, distinctive geographical linkages and spatial structures emerge.

Principles of Commercial and Industrial Location

Locational decisions in commercial and industrial life are subject to a number of key factors:

- The relative importance of accessibility to whatever *material inputs* are involved (for example, raw materials, energy).
- The relative importance of the availability of *labour* with particular skills.
- The relative importance of *processing* costs. These include the cost of land and buildings, machinery and hardware, software, maintenance, wages and salaries, utility bills, and taxes.
- The relative pull of the *market* for the product or service, which depends on the importance of being near customers.
- The relative *transfer* costs that would be accrued at alternative locations. Transfer costs involve the costs not only of transporting inputs from various sources and of transporting outputs to markets but also of insuring, storing, unloading, and repacking raw materials and finished products.
- The influence of cultural and institutional factors that channel certain activities away from some locations and toward others. The most important of these

are *government policies* of one kind or another. It is quite common, for example, for local governments to offer tax breaks to companies to attract investments that will result in the creation of new jobs in the area.

■ The influence of *behavioural considerations* that stem from the objectives and constraints affecting individual decision makers.

The importance and influence of these factors varies according to the type of activity involved. In retailing activities, for example, proximity to specific consumer markets is almost always of paramount importance—*almost* always because some retailing occurs through mail order or telemarketing, in which case accessibility to a geographically scattered market becomes even more important. For small retailers, behavioural factors are likely to involve the personal values and priorities of business owners—the owner's attachment to a particular neighbourhood, for example, or the owner's desire to locate his or her business at an upscale or central address. An interesting illustration has been the desire of Toronto-area businesses to have a phone number with a 416 area code (even if this means getting calls rerouted through a purchased 416 area code number) because this will give them the appearance of being a central Toronto business. Large corporate retailers, in contrast, will seek to maximize utility and minimize uncertainty through the extensive use of market research and geographic information systems (GIS; see Chapter 1).

In contrast, decisions on where to locate manufacturing activities depend a great deal on the attributes of the inputs (that is, raw materials or components) and outputs (products) of particular industries. Where heavy, bulky raw materials are used to produce high-value products, it follows that proximity to sources of inputs is likely to be the most important locational factor. Steel production, for example, uses large quantities of iron ore, limestone, coking coal, and water. These basic raw materials lose both bulk and weight as raw steel is produced. When such weight-losing raw materials are involved in production, and when these raw materials are to be found in or near one place, it is most economical to locate the manufacturing plant at that place. Why transport unnecessary weight?

It was this very question that in 1909 prompted Alfred Weber to develop a theory of industrial location. Because of its analytic use of space, geographers overlooked his model until the advent of the *Spatial*, or *Locational* tradition in geography, a period, which, as we have seen in Chapter 1, began in the 1960s and lasted until approximately the 1980s. During that period, Weber's model of industrial location was considered to be an important contribution to the spatial analysis of society, and its approach to the geographic study of economic activity became dominant.

Weber's approach was based on the view that industries attempted to minimize their total transport costs, and that their optimal location would be at the point where this was achieved. A visual example best explains his thinking, and is shown in **Figure 7.13**. If we consider a totally featureless surface—the *isotropic* surface so-loved by locational analysis because it introduces no distortions (such as mountains or rivers) into the discussion—and we consider an industry that requires two raw

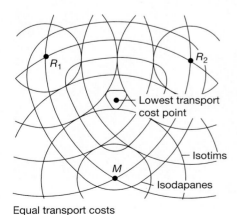

Equal transport costs

(a)

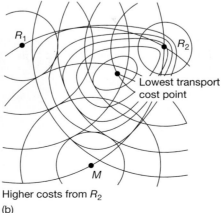

Higher costs from R_2

(b)

Figure 7.13 Weber's model of industrial location This example (see (a)) shows two resources (R_1 and R_2), a single market (M), and assumes a uniform (or isotropic) surface. Lines of equal transport cost (isotims) are shown for R_1, R_2 and M. Lines of total transport cost (isodapanes) indicate where the lowest total transport cost is located. A doubling of transport costs for resource (R_2) shifts that location (see (b)). (*Source:* Peter Haggett, *Geography: A Global Synthesis.* Harlow, UK: Pearson, 2001, p. 471.)

materials (available only at the point sources, R_1 [for resource 1] and R_2 [for resource 2]) to make a product that it then wishes to sell in a market (which also only exists at a point, M), then the optimal location for that industry must lie somewhere between these points.

The exact location can be calculated if we know how much of each raw material (R_1, and R_2) go into the final product (because this tells us something about how much of each must be shipped to the point of manufacture), and we know how much transport costs are for each raw material. For the sake of simplicity, if we assume (as in Figure 7.13(a)) that the same amounts of each of the two raw materials are needed, that they have the same transport costs, and that transport costs are directly proportional to distance, then we can calculate lines of total transport costs (*isodapanes*), which are the sum of the transport costs of assembling each resource (R_1, R_2) and of shipping the finished product to market (M). Such a calculation enables us to find the point of lowest total transport costs, and suggests the most logical place to locate our factory.

Locational analysts were able to develop sophisticated models based on this simple model that they argued came closer and closer to the real world by introducing more realistic assumptions. One of these is shown in Figure 7.13(b), and that is the assumption that one of the raw materials (R_2) costs more to transport than the other. In this case, as the diagram show, the optimal location for its manufacture would lie closer to R_2. Weber, in fact, himself developed some simple rules that indicated where industries would locate; those he called "weight-losing" industries were those based on raw materials, such as coal or iron ore, that lost both bulk and weight as they undergo industrial processing. In such cases, industry tended to locate near the source of the raw materials. The industrial region around Sheffield, England (**Figure 7.14**), for example, was established on exactly this locational logic.

Where the manufacturing process adds significant bulk or weight to a product (as, for example, in brewing), proximity to markets is more likely to be the

Figure 7.14 The Sheffield manufacturing region The growth of Sheffield was largely a result of the locational "pull" of the weight-losing inputs needed for iron and steel manufacturing: limestone, coal, iron ore, and water. Initially, iron ore came from deposits of clayband ironstone found amid nearby coal deposits, water came from the River Sheaf, and magnesian limestone from outcrops a few kilometres to the east. As the steel industry grew, the broad valley of the River Don provided sites for large steelworks, which drew on new coal mines in the extensive coalfield to the east, on high-grade iron-ore deposits that were found in seams 6 to 9 metres (20 to 30 feet) thick near Scunthorpe, and on limestone from the same sources to the east. In Sheffield itself, a multitude of firms sprang up to use high-quality iron and steel in the manufacture of everything from anchors, cutlery, files, and nails to needles, pins, and wire. The photograph shows one of the many ironworks that produced cutlery in Sheffield in the nineteenth century.

overriding factor. Many different inputs to different industries exist, however, each with different attributes (such as weight, bulk, form, perishability, and fragility) and different degrees of availability across geographical space. Some inputs (such as bauxite, sulphur, and zinc) are relatively uncommon and very localized; others (water, for example) are much more generally available.

Critics of Weber's model have tended to use this very complexity (in types of inputs, attributes, and availability) to argue that the model itself should be dismissed. Others have suggested that because it ignores important aspects of industrial production—such as labour costs, government subsidies, or the cachet of a particular location or product—it simply can never capture all of the elements that go into informing an industry's locational decision and should therefore be abandoned as misleading. Certainly, ours is a very different world to that of Alfred Weber's, and he would be stunned to find that water—a resource he considered so generally available that it could not affect industrial location on its own—is now actively traded around the world in the form of mineral waters such as Perrier and Fiji.

A final criticism of Weber's model is that his simple model of industrial location is largely *ahistorical*—by which we mean that the influences of the past are ignored. Of course, to be fair to Weber, discounting history is another simplifying assumption that his model must make if it is to operate. However, to ignore the impact of previous eras of industrial development and their influence on the subsequent location of industry is to argue that locational decisions occur in a temporal vacuum.

An important example of this can be found if we now reconsider the example of Sheffield's industries. While it is true that the presence of iron and steel mills in that city can be explained by the use of Weber's analysis of transport costs, this approach omits the influence of centuries of industrial development in the area, a heritage of innovation in metal work and metallurgical skill that is at least as valuable as the raw materials themselves. In fact, Sheffield began its role as an industrial centre through a process of *proto-industrialization,* a term coined in the early 1980s by historian Hans Medick to describe the earliest phases of industrial development in Europe.[9]

Describing the ways in which many early industries developed before the Industrial Revolution in what was essentially the countryside, Medick's work highlighted the role played by rural-based artisans in the origins of later industrialization. The rural roots of such enterprise often surprises people, but a moment's reflection allows us to see that at a time when the principal motive power was based on water, a location beside a fast-flowing stream provided an ideal spot for a watermill.

Such was certainly Sheffield's experience, and the first records of that area's industrial beginnings are references in Chaucer's *Canterbury Tales* (written c. 1380) to cutlery made there, probably produced in one of the many small forges dotted along the riverbanks of the area (**Figure 7.15**). Slowly, as more artisans spent greater amounts of their time in small-scale manufacturers of this sort, they left their farms and became full-time industrial workers. Over time, the region around the city became so well-known as a centre for cutlery manufacture that many people migrated there to seek work in its small mills and forges (**Figure 7.16**). The many skills required to manufacture cutlery were arguably as important as the location of the raw materials used in iron production, and often were responsible for far more of the "value added" to production.

In other words, a full explanation for the location of industry is often far more nuanced than we might first imagine, and while the dictates of today's spatial economy obviously have to be considered, we must also pay due regard to the part played by the past in shaping present decision making.

[9]Peter Kriedtke, Hans Medick, and Jurgen Schlumbohm, *Industrialization before Industrialization: Rural Industry in the Genesis of Capitalism.* Cambridge: Cambridge University Press, 1981.

Figure 7.15 Old forge Preserved in the city of Sheffield as part of an outdoor heritage site known as the Abbeydale Industrial Hamlet, this forge dates from the eighteenth century and was once one of many in the region.

Figure 7.16 Migration to an early industrial centre: Sheffield, 1650–1861 (*Sources:* Graph prepared by author from data presented in E.J. Buckatzsch, "Places of Origins of a Group of Immigrants into Sheffield, 1624–1799." *Economic History Review*, Second Series 2[3], 1950, pp. 303–306; P. Cromar, "Labour Migration and Suburban Expansion in the North of England: Sheffield in the 1860s and 1870s." In P. White and R.I. Woods [eds.], *The Geographical Impact of Migration*. London: Longman, 1980, pp. 129–151.)

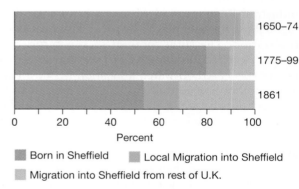

■ Born in Sheffield   ■ Local Migration into Sheffield

■ Migration into Sheffield from rest of U.K.

Note: 1650–74, 1775–99 are based on apprenticeship records: "local migration" is defined as between 5 and 10 miles from Sheffield. 1861 is based on census records for Walkley: "local migration" is defined as within 5 miles of Sheffield.

Economic Interdependence: Agglomeration Effects

We can begin by recognizing that in the real world, the various factors of commercial and industrial location all operate within complex webs of *functional interdependence*. These webs include the relationships among different kinds of industries, different kinds of stores, and different kinds of offices. The webs are based on linkages and relationships that tend to follow certain principles. Among the most important principles to human geography are the principles of agglomeration, which influence the locational patterns of economic activities.

Agglomeration is the clustering together of functionally related activities—for example, the cluster of high-tech firms; the Technology Triangle of Guelph, Cambridge, and Kitchener-Waterloo; and around Ottawa (where such firms as Corel, Mitel, and Nortel have located). Silicon Valley (the area between Santa Clara and San Jose, California). **Agglomeration effects** are the cost advantages that accrue to individual firms because of their locations within such a cluster. These advantages are sometimes known as *external economies*. **External economies** are cost savings resulting from advantages that are derived from circumstances beyond a firm's own organization and methods of production. For example, it pays for a wire-making factory to be located close to a steel mill, not just to save on transporting the steel for the wire but also to save on the cost of reheating the steel and to take advantage of the mill's experienced labour force.

Such situations lead to complex linkages among local economic activities. In relation to any given industry or firm, *backward linkages* are those that develop with suppliers. In our example, the wire-making factory has a backward linkage with the steel mill. The steel mill, in turn, will have backward linkages with its own suppliers—firms that supply raw materials, machinery, specialized maintenance services, and so on. For the steel mill, the wire-making factory is one of a number of *forward linkages* with firms using its output. Others might include can-making firms, tube-making firms, and cutlery firms. In addition, these firms will likely have their own forward linkages. The wire-making factory, for example, will supply local assemblers, finishers, packagers, and distributors. Together, backward and forward linkages often create a threshold of activity large enough to attract ancillary activities. **Ancillary activities** include maintenance, repair, security, and haulage services that serve a variety of industries. **Figure 7.17** summarizes the kinds of linkages that typically develop around a steel production plant.

Where external economies and local economic linkages are limited to firms involved in one particular industry, they are known as **localization economies**. These economies are cost savings that accrue to particular industries as a result of clustering together at a specific location. Examples include sharing a pool of labour with special skills or experience; supporting specialized technical schools; joining

agglomeration effects: cost advantages that accrue to individual firms because of their location among functionally related activities

external economies: cost savings that result from circumstances beyond a firm's own organization and methods of production

ancillary activities: such activities as maintenance, repair, security, and haulage services that serve a variety of industries

localization economies: cost savings that accrue to particular industries as a result of clustering together at a specific location

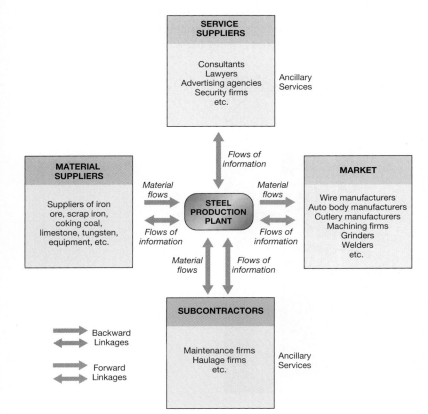

Figure 7.17   Backward and forward linkages This diagram illustrates just a few of the complex webs of economic linkages that exist around a steel production plant. In reality, the number of linkages is much greater. (*Source:* M.J. Healey, *Location and Change: Perspectives on Economic Geography.* Oxford: Oxford University Press, 1990. By Permission of Oxford University Press.)

together to create a marketing organization or a research institute; and drawing on specialized subcontractors, maintenance firms, suppliers, distribution agents, and lawyers. Where such advantages lead to a reputation for high-quality production, agglomeration will be intensified because more producers will want to cash in on the reputation. Among the many examples are the Canadian auto industry (in southern Ontario) and Quebec's aeronautic industry (Montreal).

External economies can be derived in three main ways. The first is through external *economies of scale*. By clustering together, firms can collectively support ancillary activities that can operate efficiently only in settings where there are enough different customers to ensure a continuous demand. Accessibility to these ancillary services, meanwhile, helps make all firms more efficient. An example is the way that specialized engineering, maintenance, and repair firms support—and are sustained by—clusters of manufacturing plants. This occurs in Windsor, Ontario, and in Montreal.

The second source of external economies is through the atmosphere that results from the clustering of functionally related activities. Frequent, easy contact among producers also helps minimize uncertainty. Thus, for example, small firms in industries in which demand is unpredictable (because it is subject to fashion, for example, or to rapidly changing technologies) tend to agglomerate to be able to share information as quickly as possible. Examples include women's clothing in Paris (**Figure 7.18**).

The third source of external economies is the fixed social capital that is generated by clusters of activity. **Fixed social capital** constitutes the **infrastructure** of society, the underlying framework of services and amenities needed to facilitate productive activity. It comes from a mixture of public and private investment, and it includes roads, highways, railroads, schools, hospitals, shopping centres, and recreational and cultural amenities. Agglomeration allows the costs of providing this infrastructure to be shared and more extensive and sophisticated infrastructures to be supported. The more extensive and sophisticated the infrastructure, the more advantages accrue to the producers: more efficient transportation, more specialized education, more attractive environments for key workers, and so on.

Providing firms in many industries with opportunities for external economies are urban settings, with large pools of labour containing a wide range of skills; intensively developed infrastructures; specialized education and training facilities; research institutions; and concentrations of business services. Because of this,

infrastructure (fixed social capital): the underlying framework of services and amenities needed to facilitate productive activity

Figure 7.18 The haute couture garment district in Paris Specialized fashion districts like this one, which is on the Boulevard Saint-Honoré in Paris, just north of the Louvre, provide good examples of external economies based on a narrow community of interest within which close rivalries breed innovation and easy contact among producers helps minimize uncertainty.

external economies are often referred to as **urbanization economies**, those accruing to producers because of the package of infrastructure, ancillary activities, labour, and markets that is typically associated with urban settings.

Interestingly, the study of transport geography has long been an important part of economic geography, in general, and of Canadian geographers, in particular.[10] The current concerns of Canadian municipalities have led to a growing interest in this field, especially in the area of sustainable urban transportation.[11]

urbanization economies: external economies that accrue to producers because of the package of infrastructure, ancillary activities, labour, and markets typically associated with urban settings

PATHWAYS TO DEVELOPMENT

Patterns of economic development are the product of principles of location and economic interdependence, but they are also historical in origin and cumulative in nature. Even though the fundamental principles of spatial organization hold steady over time, societal and technological conditions change. As a result, economic geographies that were shaped by certain principles of spatial organization during one particular period are inevitably modified, later on, as the same principles work their way through new technologies and new actors. Thus, we find different pathways of economic development according to various circumstances of timing and location.

Recognizing this, geographers are interested not only in uncovering the fundamental principles of spatial organization but also in relating them to **geographical path dependence**, the historical relationship between present-day activities in a place and the past experiences of that place. A dynamic relationship exists between past and present geographies. In other words, when spatial structures emerge through the logic of fundamental principles of spatial organization, they do so in ways guided and influenced by pre-existing patterns and relationships. One example is provided by the city of Ottawa. Initially a small and remote lumber town, Ottawa developed into a large administrative employment centre once it was designated as the capital of Canada. Its growing population provided both a market and a labour pool for a host of service and small manufacturing industries that were then able to develop in the area. Most recently, the Ottawa area has added high-tech industries to its activities, industries that developed on the basis of federal government grants.

geographical path dependence: the historical relationship between the present activities associated with a place and the past experiences of that place

These observations lead to an important principle of economic development, the principle of initial advantage. **Initial advantage** highlights the importance of an early start in economic development. It represents a special case of external economies. Other things being equal, new phases of economic development will take hold first in settings that offer external economies: existing labour markets, existing consumer markets, existing frameworks of fixed social capital, and so on. This initial advantage will be consolidated by localization economies and so form the basis for continuing economic growth. This sustained growth, in turn, provides the preconditions for initial advantage in subsequent phases of economic development.

initial advantage: the critical importance of an early start in economic development; a special case of external economies

For places and regions with a substantial initial advantage, therefore, the trajectory of geographical path dependence tends to be one of persistent growth—reinforcing the core–periphery patterns of economic development found in every part of the world and at every spatial scale. That said, geographers recognize there is no single pathway to development. The consequences of initial advantage for both core and peripheral regions can be—and often are—modified. Old core–periphery relationships can be blurred, and new ones can be initiated.

---

[10]For example, Professor Brian Slack's work at Concordia University in Montreal on the Canadian port system has received international recognition and an award from the Association of American Geographers.

[11]The best introduction to this topic is provided by Susan Hanson and Genevieve Giuliano (eds.), *The Geography of Urban Transportation*, 3rd ed. New York and London: The Guilford Press, 2004.

How Regional Economic Cores Are Created

Regional cores of economic development are created cumulatively, following some initial advantage, through the operation of several of the basic principles of economic geography that we have described. These principles centre on external economies, or agglomeration effects, that are associated with various kinds of economic linkages and interdependencies. The trigger for these agglomeration effects can be any kind of economic development—the establishment of a trading port, or the growth of a local industry or any large-scale enterprise. The external economies and economic linkages generated by such developments represent the initial advantage that tends to stimulate a self-propelling process of local economic development.

Given the location of a new economic activity in an area, a number of inter-related effects come into play. *Backward linkages* develop as new firms arrive to provide the growing industry with components, supplies, specialized services, or facilities. *Forward linkages* develop as new firms arrive to take the finished products of the growing industry and use them as inputs to their own processing, assembly, finishing, packaging, or distribution operations. Together with the initial growth, the growth in these linked industries helps to create a threshold of activity large enough to attract *ancillary industries* and activities (maintenance and repair, recycling, security, and business services, for example).

The existence of these interrelated activities establishes a pool of specialized labour with the kinds of skills and experience that make the area attractive to still more firms. Meanwhile, the linkages among all these firms help to promote interaction between professional and technical personnel and allow for the area to support R&D facilities, research institutes, and so on, thus increasing the likelihood of local inventions and innovations that might further stimulate local economic development.

Another part of the spiral of local economic growth is a result of the increase in population represented by the families of employees. Their presence creates a demand for housing, utilities, physical infrastructure, retailing, personal services, and so on—all of which generate additional jobs. This expansion, in turn, helps create populations large enough to attract an even wider variety and more sophisticated kinds of services and amenities. Last, but by no means the least, the overall growth in local employment creates a larger local tax base. The local government can then provide improved public utilities, roads, schools, health services, recreational amenities, and so on, all of which serve to intensify agglomeration economies and so enhance the competitiveness of the area in being able to attract further rounds of investment.

Swedish economist Gunnar Myrdal was the 1974 Nobel Prize winner who first recognized that any significant initial local advantage tends to be reinforced through geographical principles of agglomeration and localization. He called the process **cumulative causation** (**Figure 7.19**), meaning the spiral buildup of advantages that occurs in specific geographical settings as a result of the development of external economies, agglomeration effects, and localization economies. Myrdal also pointed out that this spiral of local growth would tend to attract people—enterprising young people, usually—and investment funds from other areas. According to the basic principles of spatial interaction, these flows tend to be strongest from nearby regions with the lowest wages, fewest job opportunities, or least attractive investment opportunities. In terms of Canadian regional economic development, these processes are embodied in the theories of metropolitanism (see Chapter 10) and the staples thesis (see Chapter 2).

In some regions or places, this outflow of people and resources is sufficient to trigger a cumulative negative spiral of economic disadvantage. With less capital, less innovative energy, and depleted pools of labour, industrial growth in peripheral regions tends to be significantly slower and less innovative than in regions with an initial advantage and an established process of cumulative causation. This, in turn, tends to limit the size of the local tax base so that local governments find it hard to furnish a competitive infrastructure of roads, schools, and recreational amenities. Myrdal called these disadvantages **backwash effects**, the negative impacts on a

cumulative causation: a spiral buildup of advantages that occurs in specific geographical settings as a result of the development of external economies, agglomeration effects, and localization economies

backwash effects: the negative impacts on a region (or regions) of the economic growth of some other region

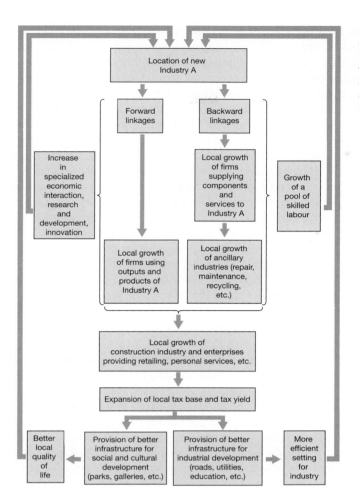

Figure 7.19   Processes of regional economic growth   Once a significant amount of new industry becomes established in an area, it tends to create a self-propelling process of economic growth. As this illustration shows, the initial advantages of industrial growth are reinforced through geographical principles of agglomeration and localization. The overall process is sometimes known as *cumulative causation.*

region (or regions) of the economic growth of some other region. These negative impacts take the form, for example, of out-migration, outflows of investment capital, and the shrinkage of local tax bases. Backwash effects are important because they help explain why regional economic development is so uneven and why core–periphery contrasts in economic development are so common. The processes familiar to Canadian economic geographers as "heartland–hinterland" phenomena (see Chapter 2) are specific types of these general core–periphery processes.

How Core–Periphery Patterns Are Modified

Although very important, cumulative causation and backwash effects are not the only processes affecting the geography of economic development. If they were, the world's economic geography would be even more starkly polarized than it is now and new economic regions could never develop.

Myrdal himself recognized that peripheral regions do sometimes emerge as new growth regions and partially explained them in what he called *spread* (or trickle-down) effects. **Spread effects** are the positive impacts on a region (or regions) of the economic growth of some other region, usually a core region. This growth creates levels of demand for food, consumer products, and other manufactured goods that are so high that local producers cannot satisfy them. This demand gives investors in peripheral regions (or countries) the opportunity to establish a local capacity to meet the demand. Entrepreneurs who attempt this are also able to exploit the advantages of cheaper land and labour in peripheral regions. If strong enough, these spread effects can enable peripheral regions to develop their own spiral of cumulative causation, thus changing the interregional geography of

spread effects: the positive impacts on a region (or regions) of the economic growth of some other region

economic patterns and flows. The economic growth of South Korea, for example, is partly attributable to the spread effects of Japanese economic prosperity.

Another way in which peripheral regions or countries can develop their own spiral of cumulative causation is through a process of *import substitution* (see Chapter 2). In this process, goods and services previously imported from core regions are replaced by locally made goods and locally provided services. Some things are hard to copy, especially in Canada, because of the limitations of climate. However, many products and services *can* be copied by local entrepreneurs, thus capturing local capital, increasing local employment opportunities, intensifying the use of local resources, and generating profits for further local investment.

Core–periphery patterns and relationships can also be modified by changes in the dynamics of core regions—internal changes that can slow or modify the spiral of cumulative causation. The main factor is the development of **agglomeration diseconomies**, the negative economic effects of urbanization and the local concentration of industry. Effects include the higher prices that must be paid by firms competing for land and labour; the costs of delays resulting from traffic congestion and crowded port and railroad facilities; the increasing unit costs of solid waste disposal; and the burden of higher taxes that eventually have to be levied by local governments to support services and amenities previously considered unnecessary—traffic police, city planning, and transit systems, for example.

Deindustrialization and Creative Destruction   The most fundamental cause of change in the relationship between initial advantage and cumulative causation is to be found in the longer-term shifts in technology systems and in the competition among states within the world-system. The innovations associated with successive technology systems generate new industries that are not yet tied down by enormous investments in factories or allied to existing industrial agglomerations. Combined with innovations in transport and communications, this creates *windows of locational opportunity* that can result in new industrial districts, with small towns or cities growing into dominant metropolitan areas through new rounds of cumulative causation. (See **Geography Matters 7.1—A Tale of Two Canadian Towns**.)

Equally important as a factor in how core–periphery patterns are modified are the consequent shifts in the profitability of old, established industries in core regions compared with the profitability of new industries in fast-growing, new industrial districts. As soon as the differential is large enough, some disinvestment will take place within core regions, which, in turn, leads to deindustrialization in formerly prosperous industrial core regions.

Deindustrialization involves a relative decline (and in extreme cases an absolute decline) in industrial employment in core regions as firms scale back their activities in response to lower levels of profitability (**Figure 7.20**). This is what happened to the industrial regions of northern England in the early part of the twentieth century, to the industrial region between Windsor and Quebec City, and to many isolated resource centres in Canada from Powell River (British Columbia) to Corner Brook (Newfoundland) in the 1980s and 1990s, as Canadian industry went through a process of restructuring. Other places, such as Newfoundland's fishing centres, have suffered an economic collapse as fish stocks have dwindled. Wherever restructuring occurs, the plant closures that result from it have serious impacts on their communities and threaten the continued existence of "place," as the slow decline of Newfoundland's outports since the 1950s has all too painfully illustrated (see Chapter 4).

Meanwhile, the capital made available from disinvestment in these core regions becomes available for investment by entrepreneurs in new ventures based on innovative products and innovative production technologies. Old industries—and sometimes entire old industrial regions—have to be dismantled (or at least neglected) to help fund the creation of new centres of profitability and employment. This process is often referred to as **creative destruction**, something that is inherent to the dynamics of capitalism. Creative destruction is a powerful image, helping us to understand the entrepreneur's need to withdraw investments from activities (and regions) yielding low rates of profit to reinvest in new activities (and, often, in new places).

agglomeration diseconomies: the negative economic effects of urbanization and the local concentration of industry

deindustrialization: a relative decline in industrial employment in core regions

creative destruction: the withdrawal of investments from activities (and regions) that yield low rates of profit to reinvest in new activities (and new places)

A Tale of Two Canadian Towns

The 2001 Canadian census reveals in stark form the differences between places that are in areas of economic growth and those that are in areas of decline. We look here at the example of two communities—the towns of Fort McMurray (Alberta), 440 kilometres (275 miles) north of Edmonton, and Trepassey (Newfoundland), 145 kilometres (90 miles) south of St. John's.

Alberta, although not part of the traditional Canadian heartland, is prospering economically and growing demographically. The census shows Alberta grew by 10.3 percent from 1996 to 2001 (to 2.9 million people). The province of Newfoundland and Labrador experienced a 7 percent loss in population over the same period (it now totals 513 000 people). Never part of the Canadian heartland either, this province has supported its population through resource exploitation—in this case, the Atlantic fisheries. The collapse of that resource has meant a downward spiral of disinvestment and deindustrialization for many communities in Newfoundland that were often unable to develop diversified economies. Just as Newfoundland and Labrador struggles to diversify its economy, the message for Alberta must be to do the same.

■ *Fort McMurray.* "It's all fast-paced up here, you're always going, going."

Settled in the 1760s as a fur trading centre, in 1963 Fort McMurray had only 1360 people. However, as the centre for the exploitation of the Athabasca Oil Sands, perhaps development was inevitable (**Figures 7.1.1** and **7.1.2**). Nevertheless, it had to await the growth in demand, the rise in oil prices, and the development of technology to separate oil from sand before any industry here would be worthwhile. During the 1980s and 1990s, these conditions were met. Suncor Energy Inc. (which produced about 220 000 barrels a day in 2002) and Syncrude Canada Ltd. (which produced 81 million barrels in 2001) both now have extensive operations in Fort McMurray to extract oil from the sands. They are soon to be joined by Shell Canada, which plans to invest $3.5 billion in a plant.

The effects of this activity are seen in the fact that population grew from 35 213 in 1996 to 64 441 in 2006, an increase of 83 percent in 10 years. The town is growing so quickly that it is experiencing a severe lack of housing. Many new migrants to Fort McMurray have spent the summer in campgrounds before they have found accommodation. Average house prices, until the fall of the price of oil in late 2008, were commonly reported to be over $600 000. Thus, a report in the *Edmonton Journal* in November 2007 observed that the average cost of a single-family house in Fort McMurray was $624 964—a figure that had tripled since October 2000. By June 2008, according to a Canadian Broadcasting Corporation (CBC) news story, the average had

Figure 7.1.1 Fort McMurray and the oil sands (*Source:* "The Athabasca Oil Sands Story." *Globe and Mail*, 4 April 2005, p. B5. Reprinted with permission from *The Globe and Mail*.)

Figure 7.1.2 Fort McMurray and the oil sands

reached $692 000. According to the same CBC broadcast, the provincial government of Alberta planned to remedy the shortage of affordable housing by releasing enough Crown land in the area to build houses for 40 000 people. The demand by the oil industry for skilled labour is so great that it has been very hard for the town's service sector to keep employees or pay them competitive wages. One measure of this is that although the province's minimum wage was raised to $8.40 an hour in April 2008, few jobs in Fort McMurray start at less than $15 an hour, a situation that puts pressure on small businesses such as restaurants to meet their payroll without passing on increases to their customers.

Growing mainly from in-migration, the town is a young community, with an average age of only 29.4 years. A look at the Chamber of Commerce's website shows the extent to which new schools, libraries, sports facilities, shopping malls, and the like are springing up almost overnight. A significant number of those migrants to Fort McMurray are from Newfoundland and Labrador. (Estimates seem to vary; the *Globe and Mail* quotes a figure of one-third, the Chamber of Commerce 16 percent.)

■ *Trepassey.* "At nighttime, you can look out of the window for an hour, and you won't see a car go by."

Established in the seventeenth century on the basis of fishing (**Figures 7.1.3** and **7.1.4**), Trepassey maintained a viable economy until early 1991 when its fish-processing plant closed down. The cod moratoriums of 1993 and 1994 (closing the Northern and Gulf cod fisheries) were another devastating blow. The sale of the plant's equipment to Tanzania in 1995 marked a realization that a way of life had ended. It was at this point that almost half the workforce of the town left to work in a meat-packing plant in Alberta or in construction jobs in Ontario and British Columbia.

The census tells the story this way: in 1981, there were 1473 people in Trepassey. By 1991, the year the plant closed, there were 1375. In 1996, there were 1084, and in 2006 only 763, a decline of 14 percent in the previous five years alone. The consequences of this loss of population and economic decline are many. Unemployment rates, which stood at 17 percent when the plant was open, increased to 43 percent by 2001. Average income levels in 1996 were only $15 885 according to the census. Sea-view houses, which might be worth at least $100 000 in more prosperous communities, stand empty here. There are not enough young people in the area to form a recreational hockey league, and the elementary school was to close at the end of 2002 for lack of pupils. Ironically, school dropout rates have fallen from 50 percent, when the plant was open and a fishery existed, to almost 0.

Against this backdrop, regional economic development planners strive valiantly. Reports note the possibilities for tourism, aquaculture, agriculture, information technology, marine-related industries, services and crafts, and manufacturing. That not all of this is wishful thinking is shown by the recent development of 30 jobs in the area (in window manufacturing, marine lighting equipment, and a small iceberg water bottling plant for the President's Choice label). It will, however, be a long time before there will be traffic jams again on Trepassey's streets as there were when 500 people used to set off to work for the fish plant.

Sources: Jill Mahoney and Kevin Cox, "Where the Jobs Are: For Many, 'Go West' Still the Best Advice." *Globe and Mail*, 13 March 2002, pp. A6–A7; Charles Mandel, "Vodka on the Rocks: Newfoundland's *Iceberg Harvesting Industry,*" *Canadian Business,* 24 June 2002, *pp. 30–34; Report* for the Trepassey Task Force on Community Economic Development, December 1999; Jane Robinson, "Women and Fish Plant Closure: The Case of Trepassey, Newfoundland." In C. McGrath, B. Neis, and M. Porter [eds.]; *Their Lives and Times; Women in Newfoundland and Labrador: A Collage.* St. John's: Killick Press, 1995, pp. 163–174; The Regional Municipality of Wood Buffalo [Fort McMurray] Community Economic Profile; Syncrude Canada Ltd. [**www.syncrude.com**]. [For Statistics Canada data on Trepassey (and many other communities in Canada), go to **www.statcan.gc.ca**, then click on "Community Profiles" and type "Trepassey (town)" in the search box.] Ron Chambers, "Seasonal Slowdown for House Prices in Fort McMurray." *Edmonton Journal,* 15 November 2007; CBC News, "Alberta Launches Plan to House 40,000 in Fort McMurray," 24 June 2008 [available at **www.cbc.ca/canada/edmonton/story/2008/06/24/edm-fort-land.html?ref=r55**]; "Alta. Youths Picky about Jobs Report." *Edmonton Sun,* 14 June 2007. A fascinating documentary film, originally shown on CBC TV on 13 March 2008, entitled "Tar Sands: The Selling of Alberta" is well worth watching for its glimpse of life in Fort McMurray, and for its interviews with some of the over 10 000 people it notes have now moved there from Newfoundland to find work, albeit on a temporary basis in some cases (**www.cbc.ca/doczone/tarsands/**).

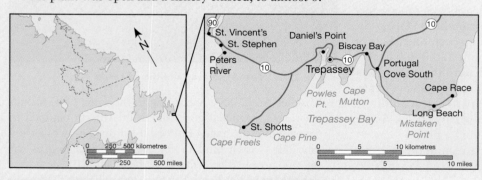

Figure 7.1.3   Trepassey, Newfoundland

Figure 7.1.4   Trepassey, Newfoundland

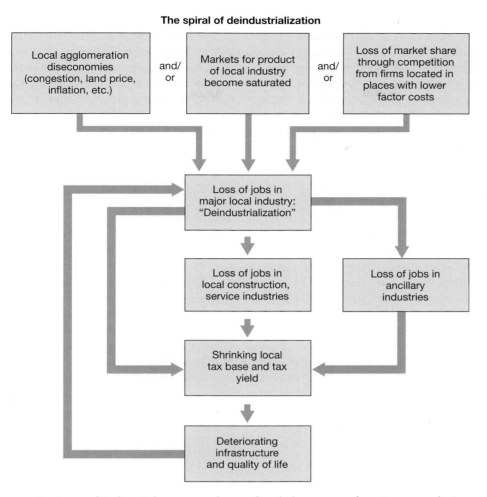

The spiral of deindustrialization

Local agglomeration diseconomies (congestion, land price, inflation, etc.)

and/ or

Markets for product of local industry become saturated

and/ or

Loss of market share through competition from firms located in places with lower factor costs

Loss of jobs in major local industry: "Deindustrialization"

Loss of jobs in local construction, service industries

Loss of jobs in ancillary industries

Shrinking local tax base and tax yield

Deteriorating infrastructure and quality of life

Figure 7.20 **Regional economic decline** When the locational advantages of manufacturing regions are undermined for one reason or another, profitability declines and manufacturing employment falls. This can lead to a downward spiral of economic decline, as experienced by many of the traditional manufacturing regions of Europe during the 1960s, 1970s, and 1980s. (Reprinted with permission of Prentice Hall, from P.L. Knox, *Urbanization*, © 1994, p. 55.)

Antiquated industrial processes have often led to years of toxic accumulations in factory sites, and part of the challenge of creative destruction is generating ways to remediate such properties so that redevelopment of this valuable real estate proceeds. The term **brownfield site** has been used to describe abandoned, idle, or underused industrial and commercial land on which redevelopment is hindered by the effects of contamination (**Figure 7.21**).

brownfield site: abandoned, idle, or underused industrial and commercial land on which redevelopment is hindered by the effects of contamination

Figure 7.21 **Deindustrialization** This derelict steel mill in New Jersey is testament to the downward economic spiral in what was once one of the world's most important heavy manufacturing regions.

According to a 1997 report by the National Round Table on the Environment and the Economy, Canada has some 30 000 brownfield sites, ranging from railway yards, junkyards, and garbage dumps to abandoned factories and refineries. Among the many problems that face developers is the question of who should pay to clean up the land. Is it the responsibility of the original industrialist, the current developer, or one of the levels of government? Confusion over jurisdictions has led to sites remaining untouched for years. In some cases, concerns about the high cost of decontamination and environmental investigation have meant that it is more economical for owners to continue to pay taxes on derelict land rather than to attempt to clean up and sell the property.

How to remediate brownfield sites is a challenge for Canadian geographers and planners. Since so many of the sites are in urban locations and already have a basic infrastructure (roads, water, sewage), their redevelopment offers the intriguing possibility of renewed investment in housing and a substantial amount of inner city and older suburban lands being made available for parks.

As if the problems posed by the redevelopment of brownfield sites are not enough to cope with, many Canadian cities are faced with much wider challenges. This is because the forces that are responsible for the creation of brownfield sites are part of a much wider set of processes of industrial and economic *restructuring* that lead to the *deindustrialization* of old core regions as capital investment moves from developed to less-developed regions—usually in search of cheaper labour or locations in which to set up production, but also increasingly in search of places in which environmental standards for manufacturing are lower.

The case of Montreal can perhaps serve as but one vignette of the effects of deindustrialization and economic restructuring. According to the 2006 census, employment in the metropolitan area of the city grew to 1.83 million jobs, an 8.6 percent increase over 2001. However, such an increase masks a decline in the city's textile industries—which lost 10 200 jobs over the five year period, an average decline of 8.2 percent a year in that sector. Textile manufacturers in Montreal have traditionally relied on immigrant labour to keep their costs down, but even such tactics have failed to allow the industry to compete with manufacturers in developing countries with far cheaper wage rates.

The story is not all gloom, however, because just as these jobs are disappearing, other sectors are growing. Gains of 3400 have occurred in the amusement and recreation sector, for example, many of them in high-tech computer gaming industries such as those established by Ubisoft—ironically, perhaps, in the very same parts of the city that are being vacated by closing textile businesses. Growth has also occurred among independent artists, writers, and performers (an additional 1500 since 2001), and in the performing arts sector (1500 over the period 2001–2006). It is perhaps no accident that Richard Florida, whose 2008 book, *Who's Your City*, describes the role of what he calls the "creative economy" in restoring city fortunes, recently acted as a consultant for the city of Montreal, since the latest changes in the city encapsulate his theories.

The net result of these processes is that the spatial economy and settlement pattern of a country like Canada's are always changing to reflect alterations in economic systems. The survival of towns and regions depends on the extent of their importance to that system.

Government Intervention   In some countries, special government agencies have been established to promote regional economic development and reduce core–periphery contrasts. Among examples are Canada's Department of Regional Economic Expansion (now defunct) and the Atlantic Canada Opportunities Agency (ACOA); the Italian Cassa del Mezzogiorno (Southern Development Agency, replaced in 1987 by several smaller agencies); and the U.S. Economic Development Administration. Some governments have sought to help industries in declining regions by investing in infrastructure and providing subsidies for private investment; others have sought to devise tax breaks that reduce the cost of labour in peripheral regions. Still others have sought to deal with agglomeration diseconomies in core regions through increased taxes and restrictions on land use.

Although each approach has its followers, one of the most widespread governmental approaches to core–periphery patterns involves the exploitation of the principle of cumulative causation through the creation of growth poles. **Growth poles** are places of economic activity deliberately organized around one or more high-growth industries. Economists have noted, however, that not all industries are equal in the extent to which they stimulate economic growth and cumulative causation. The ones that generate the most pronounced effects are known as *propulsive industries,* and they have received a great deal of attention from geographers and economists who are interested in helping to shape strategic policies that might promote regional economic development. In the 1920s, shipbuilding was a propulsive industry. In the 1950s and 1960s, automobile manufacturing was a propulsive industry, and today biotechnology is one. The basic idea is for governments to promote regional economic growth by fostering propulsive industries in favourable locations. These are intended to become growth poles—places that, given an artificial start, develop a self-sustaining spiral of economic prosperity. In practice, governments often fail to invest in the right industries, and they nearly always fail to invest heavily enough to kick-start the process of cumulative causation.

The British Columbia town of Kitimat provides a Canadian example (**Figure 7.22**). Developed in the 1950s around an aluminum smelter that used hydro power created by the diversion of the Kemano River, the townsite was laid out to accommodate

growth poles: economic activities that are deliberately organized around one or more high-growth industries

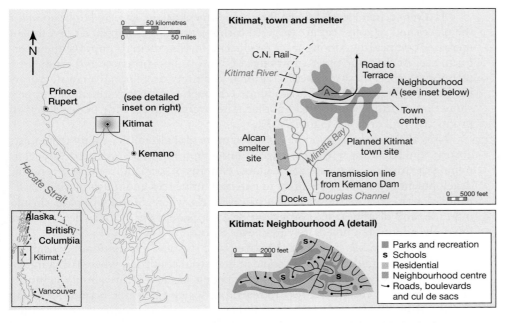

Figure 7.22   Kitimat, British Columbia Originally established in the 1950s as a growth centre based on aluminum smelting, the town of Kitimat, British Columbia, has not seen any significant expansion since. The photo shows the town centre.   (*Source for diagrams:* Based on Ira M. Robinson, *New Industrial Towns on Canada's Frontier.* University of Chicago Research Paper No. 73, 1962. Source for picture: S. Mackenzie.)

substantial population growth. However, the government's projections that this would become one of the province's largest centres have never materialized—perhaps because of its remoteness or perhaps because such large projects are rarely truly propulsive for the local community. In 2007, attempts by the town to require Alcan to pay more for its locally-generated hydro illustrate the community's contention that the full benefits of the project are not kept in the region where they are earned.

GLOBALIZATION AND LOCAL ECONOMIC DEVELOPMENT

As we saw in Chapter 2, the globalization of the world economy involves a new international division of labour in association with the internationalization of finance; the deployment of a new technology system (using robotics, telematics, biotechnology, and other new technologies); and the homogenization of consumer markets.

foreign direct investment: overseas business investments made by private companies

The dynamics of economic globalization rest on the flows of capital, knowledge, goods, and services among countries. In 1998, companies around the world invested more than US$400 billion in business ventures beyond their own shores. This level of **foreign direct investment** is seven times that of the mid-1970s. Approximately 45 percent of this foreign direct investment is targeted at peripheral and semiperipheral countries, the rest going to core countries. These investments are reflected in increased levels of world trade in goods and services. Between the mid-1970s and 1998, world exports of goods and services almost tripled.

At a very general level, foreign direct investment can be expected to be good for the places and regions that are targeted for investment. Foreign direct investment increases competition among local producers, forcing them to improve their performance. At the same time, knowledge of new business practices and production technology spreads through the regional economy as regional manufacturers become suppliers to the enterprises funded through foreign investment and as personnel move from one firm to another. The overall effect is for higher levels of productivity all around (**Figure 7.23**).

Now that the world economy is much more globalized, the ability to acquire, absorb, and communicate knowledge is more important than ever before in determining the fortunes of places and regions. Patterns of local and regional economic development are much more open to external influences and much more interdependent with economic development processes elsewhere. Shrinking space, shrinking time, and disappearing borders are linking people's lives more deeply, more intensely, and more immediately than ever before.

Not everyone has benefited, however, and the new international division of labour has come under attack by some in industrial countries, where rising unemployment and wage inequality are making people feel less secure about the future. Some workers in core countries are fearful of losing their jobs because of cheap exports from lower-cost producers. Others worry about companies relocating abroad in search of low wages, lax labour laws, and weak or poorly enforced

Figure 7.23 Foreign direct investment and regional economic performance Economic globalization has increased levels of foreign direct investment in many semiperipheral and peripheral regions. Other things being equal, this investment tends to lead to improvements in local economic performance because of the increased competition and new forms of organization introduced by the investors. (*Source:* R. Florida, "Regional Creative Destruction: Production Organization, Globalization, and the Economic Transformation of the Midwest." *Economic Geography*, 1996, fig. 1, p. 317.)

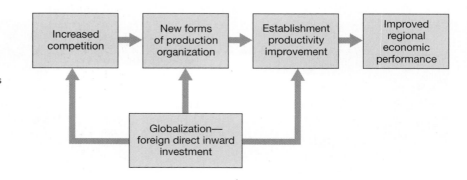

environmental standards. That, certainly, has been one of the fears of some Canadians following this country's accession to the North American Free Trade Agreement (NAFTA). The establishment of the North American Agreement on Environmental Cooperation (NAAEC), through a side-agreement to NAFTA, to act as a watchdog over the three participating countries has been one attempt to allay such fears.[12]

Most of the world's population now lives in countries that are either integrated into world markets for goods and finance or rapidly becoming so. As recently as the late 1970s, only a few peripheral countries had opened their borders to flows of trade and investment capital. About one-third of the world's labour force lived in countries, such as the Soviet Union and China, with centrally planned economies, and at least another third lived in countries insulated from international markets by prohibitive trade barriers and currency controls. Today, with nearly half the world's labour force among them, three giant population blocs—China, the republics of the former Soviet Union, and India—are entering the global market. Many other countries, from Mexico to Thailand, have already become involved in deep linkages. According to World Bank estimates, less than 10 percent of the world's labour force remained isolated from the global economy in the year 2004. (The World Bank, properly called the International Bank for Reconstruction and Development, is a United Nations affiliate established in 1948 to finance productive projects that further the economic development of member nations.)

The Global Assembly Line

In this and the following sections, we examine some specific impacts of three of the principal components of the global economy: the global assembly line, resulting from the operations of transnational manufacturing corporations; the global office, resulting from the internationalization of banking, finance, and business services; and the pleasure periphery, resulting from the proliferation of international tourism.

The globalization of the world economy represents the most recent stage in a long process of internationalization. At the heart of this process has been the emergence of private companies that participate not only in international trade but also in production, manufacturing, and sales operations in several countries. Many of these transnational corporations have grown so large through a series of mergers and acquisitions that their activities now span a diverse range of economic activities. *Transnational corporations* (as defined in Chapter 2) are companies with investments and activities that span international boundaries and with subsidiary companies, factories, offices, or facilities in several countries.

Transnational corporations first began to appear in the nineteenth century, but until the mid-twentieth century there were only a few, most of them U.S.- or European-based transnationals that were concerned with obtaining raw materials, such as oil or minerals, for their domestic manufacturing operations. The majority of Canada's current transnational corporations grew up as domestic mining companies developed operations in other countries to increase market share of world trade in their particular commodity. Examples include Teck Cominico, owner of the Trail lead-zinc smelter and mines in Canada, the United States, and Peru, where it runs another smelter; and Barrick Gold, one of the world's largest producers of that commodity. While not fitting this general pattern, Magna International (an auto parts manufacturer) and Bombardier (manufacturer of subway cars and planes) are also examples of Canadian transnationals.

After World War II, an increasing number of large corporations began to invest in overseas production and manufacturing operations as a means of establishing a foothold in foreign consumer markets. Between 1957 and 1967, 20 percent of

---

[12]The Commission for Economic Cooperation (CEC) in Montreal derives its formal mandate from the NAAEC and seeks to address transboundary environmental concerns in North America. See its website at **www.cec.org**.

all new U.S. machinery plants, 25 percent of all new U.S. chemical plants, and more than 30 percent of all new U.S. transport equipment plants were located abroad. By 1970, almost 75 percent of U.S. imports were transactions between the domestic and foreign subsidiaries of transnational conglomerates. By the end of the 1970s, overseas profits accounted for one-third or more of the overall profits of the 100 largest transnational corporations. By the early 1980s, 40 percent of all world trade was in the form of *intrafirm trade* (that is, trade between different branches and companies of the same transnational conglomerate).

Beginning in the 1970s, a sharp increase occurred in the growth of transnational conglomerates not only in the United States but also in Canada, in Europe, in Japan, and even in semiperipheral countries. By 1998, there were more than 53 000 transnational corporations in the world, fewer than half of which were based in the United States, Japan, and Germany. Of these, the top 300 control approximately one-quarter of the world's productive assets.

The reason for such growth in the number and scale of transnational conglomerate corporations has been that international economic conditions have changed. A recession, triggered by a massive increase in the price of crude oil in 1973, forced companies everywhere to re-examine their strategies. At around the same time, technological developments in transport and communications provided larger companies with the flexibility and global reach to exploit the steep differentials in labour costs that exist between core and peripheral countries. Meanwhile, these same developments in transport and communications made for increased international competition, which forced firms to search more intensely for more efficient and profitable global production and marketing strategies. Concurrently, a homogenization of consumer tastes (also facilitated by new developments in communications technologies) made it possible for companies to cater to global markets.

Transnationals and Globalization   It was the consequent burst of transnational corporate activity that has formed the basis of the recent globalization of the world economy. In effect, the playing field for large-scale businesses of all kinds had been marked out anew. Companies have had to reorganize their operations in a variety of ways, restructuring their activities and redeploying their resources *among different countries, regions, and places*. Local patterns of economic development have been recast time and time again as these processes of restructuring, reorganization, and redeployment have been played out.

As these changes have unfolded, local geographies of economic development have become increasingly interdependent, linked together as part of complex transnational commodity chains. *Commodity chains* are networks of labour and production processes whose end result is the delivery of a finished product. They are, effectively, global assembly lines that are geared to produce global products for global markets.

The advantages to manufacturers of a global assembly line are several. First, a standardized global product for a global market allows them to maximize economies of scale. Second, a global assembly line allows production and assembly to take greater advantage of the full range of geographical variations in costs. Basic wages in manufacturing industries, for example, are between 25 and 75 times higher in core countries than in some peripheral countries. With a global assembly line, labour-intensive work can be done where labour is cheap, raw materials can be processed near their source of supply, final assembly can be done close to major markets, and so on. Third, a global assembly line means that a company is no longer dependent on a single source of supply for a specific component, thus reducing its vulnerability to industrial troubles and other disturbances.

The automobile industry was among the first to develop a global assembly line. In 1976, Ford introduced the Fiesta, a vehicle designed to sell in Europe, South America, and the Asian market as well as North America. The Fiesta was assembled in several different locations from components manufactured in an even greater number of locations.

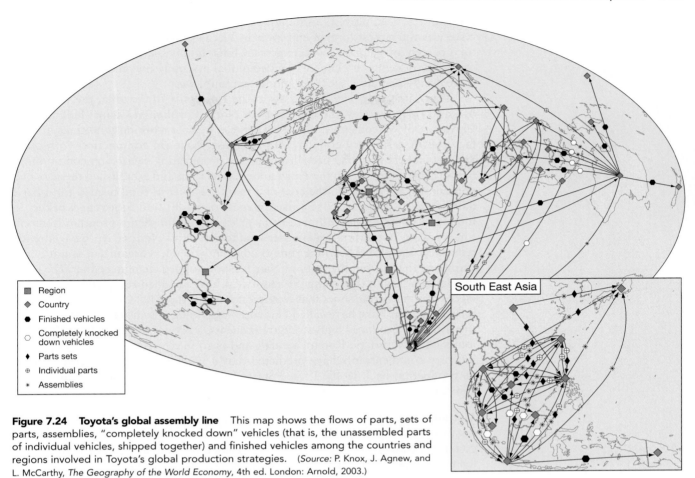

Figure 7.24 Toyota's global assembly line This map shows the flows of parts, sets of parts, assemblies, "completely knocked down" vehicles (that is, the unassembled parts of individual vehicles, shipped together) and finished vehicles among the countries and regions involved in Toyota's global production strategies. (*Source:* P. Knox, J. Agnew, and L. McCarthy, *The Geography of the World Economy*, 4th ed. London: Arnold, 2003.)

Legend:
- ■ Region
- ◆ Country
- ● Finished vehicles
- ○ Completely knocked down vehicles
- ◆ Parts sets
- ⊕ Individual parts
- ∗ Assemblies

South East Asia

Today, most of the 40 million or so vehicles that roll off production lines each year are made by just 10 global corporations (General Motors, Ford, Toyota, Volkswagen, Nissan, Fiat, Peugeot Citroën, Honda, Mitsubishi, and Renault), all of which not only operate global assembly lines (**Figure 7.24**) but also are involved in strategic alliances that intensify economic globalization. The Nestlé food company, for example, has a strategic alliance with the Coca-Cola company in exchanging technologies and in marketing. Nestlé, for example, uses Coca-Cola's distribution network for some products, such as Nescafé instant coffee.

Canada has long benefited from being a "branch plant" for American automotive assembly, first under the Autopact and now under NAFTA. These arrangements have been one reason other automakers, such as Volvo, Toyota, and Honda, have located plants in this country.

The global assembly line is constantly being reorganized as transnational corporations seek to take advantage of geographical differences among countries and regions, and as workers and consumers in specific places and regions react to the consequences of globalization. Nike, the athletic footwear and clothing marketer, provides a good illustration. Nike once had its own manufacturing facilities in both the United States and the United Kingdom. Today, however, all its production is subcontracted to suppliers in South and East Asia. The geography of this subcontracting has evolved over time in response to the changing pattern of labour costs in Asia. The first production of Nike shoes took place in Japan. The company then switched most of its subcontracting to South Korea and Taiwan. As labour costs rose in South Korea and Taiwan, Nike's subcontracting was spread across more and more peripheral countries, in search of low labour costs. By 1997, Nike subcontractors employed more than 500 000 people in more than 30 countries. Nike was the largest foreign employer in Vietnam, where its factories accounted for 5 percent of Vietnam's total exports. China, Indonesia, and Thailand were also major components in Nike's expanded global assembly line because of their low wage costs—around US$50 per month per employee.

That same year, 1997, students at the University of Arizona, the University of California–Berkeley, the University of North Carolina at Chapel Hill, and the University of Wisconsin–Madison led protests against working conditions in Nike factories in peripheral countries. In response, Nike (in conjunction with other apparel makers who had been criticized for propagating sweatshop conditions in overseas factories) set up the Fair Labor Association and established the idea of a minimum wage based on the cost of a market basket of food needed for a basic daily diet. As a result, Nike raised wages for its 80 000 footwear workers in Indonesia by more than 30 percent in 1999 and established a program to monitor working conditions in overseas factories. However, as we have already remarked, the global assembly line is constantly being reorganized, and it is not surprising to hear that the story of Nike has not stopped changing either. The latest developments with that company's footwear have included completely new methods of manufacturing shoes that were pioneered for the 2008 Olympics and involve the use of what Nike have called "Flywire" technology. By using only the thinnest of artificially produced high-strength filaments, a Flywire shoe can be crafted that looks like a futuristic Roman sandal, and is so inexpensive to make that some industry commentators have predicted that it will enable Nike to shift some of its production back to the United States from locations in China (currently the company's current largest source of manufacturing and raw materials).[13]

Maquiladoras **and Export-Processing Zones**   The type of subcontracting carried out by Nike is encouraged by the governments of many peripheral and semiperipheral countries, who see participation in global assembly lines as a pathway to export-led industrialization. They offer incentives, such as tax "holidays" (not having to pay taxes for a specified period), to transnational corporations. In the 1960s, Mexico enacted legislation permitting foreign companies to establish "sister factories"— *maquiladoras*—within 19 kilometres (12 miles) of the border with the United States for the duty-free assembly of products destined for re-export (**Figure 7.25**). By the

Figure 7.25   Principal *maquiladora* **centres on the United States–Mexico border**   Cheap labour and tax breaks for firms manufacturing and assembling goods for re-export have made many Mexican border towns attractive to U.S. companies. Around half a million workers are employed in these maquiladora plants, producing electronic products, textiles, furniture, leather goods, toys, and automotive parts.   (After P. Dicken, *Global Shift*, 4th ed. New York: Guilford, 2003.)

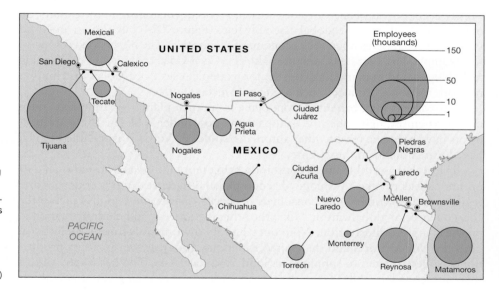

[13]Paul Hochman, "High Tech Gear for Olympic Games." *Fast Company*, July 2008 (issue 127), available at **www.fastcompany.com/magazine/127/innovation-of-olympic-proportions.html**.

late 1990s, more than 2000 such manufacturing and assembly plants had been established, employing more than half a million Mexican workers, most of them women, and accounting for more than 30 percent of Mexico's exports.

Export-processing zones (EPZs) are small areas within which especially favourable investment and trading conditions are created by governments to attract export-oriented industries. These conditions include minimum levels of bureaucracy surrounding importing and exporting, the absence of foreign exchange controls, the availability of factory space and warehousing at subsidized rents, low tax rates, and exemption from tariffs and export duties. In 1985, it was estimated that there were a total of 173 EPZs around the world, which together employed 1.8 million workers. In 1998, the International Labour Organization (ILO) estimated that there were 850 EPZs, employing about 27 million people, 90 percent of whom were women. China alone had 124 EPZs, which together employed 18 million workers. The ILO's report on EPZs[14] criticized these "vehicles of globalization" because very few of them have any meaningful links with the domestic economies around them, and most involve large numbers of people trapped in low-wage, low-skill jobs. By March 2008, the ILO estimated that the number of EPZs had risen still further to reach a total of 3500.

In addition to tax incentives and EPZs, many governments also establish policies that ensure cheap and controllable labour. Sometimes, countries are pressured to participate in global assembly lines by core countries and by the transnational institutions they support. The United States and the World Bank, for example, have backed regimes that support globalized production and have pushed for austerity programs that help make labour cheap in peripheral countries. Countries pursuing export-led industrialization as an economic development strategy do not plan to remain the providers of cheap labour for foreign-based transnational corporations, however. They hope to shift from labour-intensive manufactures to capital-intensive, high-technology goods, following the path of semiperipheral Asian countries, such as Singapore and South Korea.

export-processing zones (EPZs): small areas within which especially favourable investment and trading conditions are created by governments to attract export-oriented industries

The Global Office

The globalization of production and the growth of transnational corporations have brought about another important change in patterns of local economic development. Banking, finance, and business services are now no longer locally oriented ancillary activities but important global industries in their own right. They have developed some specific spatial tendencies of their own—tendencies that have become important shapers of local economic development processes.

A deep-seated restructuring of the world economy has resulted. The effects of this restructuring have altered economic geography at every scale, affecting the lives of people everywhere. Banks and financial corporations with the size and international reach of BankAmerica, Credit Suisse, or Deutsche Bank are able to influence local patterns and processes of economic development throughout the world, as do the major transnational conglomerates involved in the global assembly line.

Electronic Offices: Decentralization versus Concentration   It is clear that an important shift has occurred in the economic structure of the world's core economies, with the rapid growth of banking, financial, and business services contributing to the expansion of the quaternary sector. From a geographical perspective, it is particularly important that this growth has been localized, that is, concentrated in relatively small and distinctive settings within major metropolitan centres. This phenomenon

---

[14]International Labour Organization, *Labour and Social Issues Relating to Export Processing Zones*. Geneva: International Labour Office, 1998; *Report of the InFocus Initiative on Export Processing Zones (EPZs): Latest Trends and Policy Developments in EPZs*. Geneva: International Labour Organization, March 2008, available at **www.ilo.org/global/What_we_do/ Officialmeetings/gb/lang--en/docName--WCMS_090223/index.htm**.

is surprising to some observers, who had expected that new communications technologies would allow for the dispersion of "electronic offices" and, with it, the decentralization of an important catalyst for local economic development.

The reasons for this concentration are to be found in another special case of the geographical agglomeration effects that we discussed earlier in this chapter. Metropolitan areas, such as New York City, London, Paris, Tokyo, and Frankfurt, have acquired the kind of infrastructure—specialized office space, financial exchanges, teleports (office parks equipped with satellite Earth stations and linked to local fibre-optics lines), and communications networks—that is essential for delivering services to clients with a national or international scope of activity. These metropolitan areas have also established a comparative advantage both in the mix of specialized firms and expert professionals on hand, and in the high-order cultural amenities available (both to high-paid workers and to their out-of-town business visitors). Above all, these metro areas have established themselves as centres of authority, with a critical mass of people in the know about market conditions, trends, and innovations—people who can gain one another's trust through frequent face-to-face contact, not just in business settings but also in the informal settings of clubs and office bars. They have become **world cities**, places that, in the globalized world economy, are able not only to generate powerful spirals of local economic development but also to act as pivotal points in the reorganization of global space: control centres for the flows of information, cultural products, and finance that, collectively, sustain the economic and cultural globalization of the world (see Chapter 10 for more details).

An important way that cities act in such economies is as centres for ideas and creators of trends. See the discussion in **Geography Matters 7.2—The Changing Geography of the Clothing Industry.**

A good example of the clustering of business services in major world cities is provided by advertising services in Europe. In the early 1980s, these services were distributed among major European cities, with Paris, London, Amsterdam, and Stockholm accounting for the headquarters of most firms, but with smaller concentrations in Brussels, Düsseldorf, Frankfurt, and Zurich. By 1990, the headquarters of most advertising agencies in Europe had moved to London (**Figure 7.26**), which, along with New York and Tokyo, has become one of the three most dominant world cities in the contemporary world-system.

world cities: cities in which a disproportionate part of the world's most important business—economic, political, and cultural—is conducted

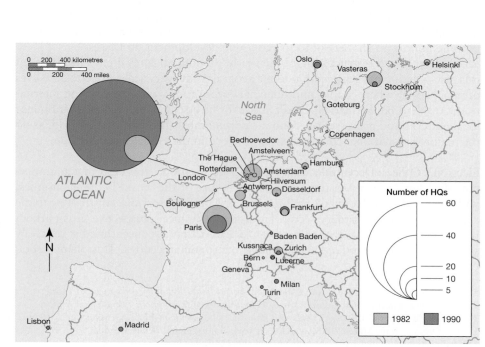

Figure 7.26   The clustering of advertising agencies in European cities
This map shows the changing distribution of the headquarter offices of the top 100 advertising agencies in Europe between 1982 and 1990. Note the striking concentration of agency headquarters in London. (*Source:* P. Daniels, "Services in a Shrinking World." *Geography* 80, 1995, fig. 4, p. 102.)

The Changing Geography of the Clothing Industry

The clothing industry provides a good example of the way that local economic geographies are affected by an industry's response to globalization. In the nineteenth century, the clothing industry developed in the metropolitan areas of core countries, with many small firms using cheap, migrant, or immigrant labour. In the first half of the twentieth century, the industry, like many others, began to modernize. Larger firms emerged, their success based on the exploitation of mass-production techniques for mass markets and on the exploitation of principles of spatial organization within national markets. In the United States, for example, the clothing industry went through a major locational shift as a great deal of production moved out of the workshops of New York to big, new factories in smaller towns in the South, where labour was not only much cheaper but less unionized.

The global textile and apparel industry has undergone several shifts in production since the 1950s. The first was from North America and Western Europe to Japan in the 1950s and early 1960s, when Western textile and clothing production was displaced by a sharp rise in imports from Japan. The second shift was from Japan to Hong Kong, Taiwan, and the Republic of Korea, which dominated global textile and clothing exports in the 1970s and early 1980s. In the late 1980s and the 1990s there was a third migration from these countries to other developing economies. In the 1980s, production moved principally to mainland China, but also to Indonesia, Malaysia, the Philippines, Sri Lanka, and Thailand. In the 1990s, new suppliers included India and Mexico but the largest newcomer in the 1990s was Turkey, whose total of $3.4 billion in clothing exports placed it fifth in world rankings. By 2000, important new clothing-producing countries (with a billion dollars or more of exports) included Bangladesh, the Czech Republic, Hungary, Mauritius, Morocco, Poland, Romania, and Vietnam.

Much of this shifting globalization of production was "buyer-driven" by retailers like Wal-Mart, Sears, and JCPenney, and fashion-oriented apparel companies like Liz Claiborne, Gap, and The Limited. Their cost-reduction strategies led them to retain design and marketing functions but to contract out the production of their apparel to firms in low-wage countries. In effect, they became "manufacturers without factories." In an attempt to protect domestic manufacturers, the United States, Canada, and 13 countries in Europe entered into a trade pact called the Multifiber Arrangement (MFA) in 1974. The MFA used quotas to regulate access to domestic clothing and textile markets, restricting the amount of imports from any one country. Designed to protect MFA signatories from competition from Japan, Hong Kong, Taiwan, and the Republic of Korea, the import quotas ended up working as a kind of affirmative action program for countries that had large workforces and low wage rates—hence the spread of production around the world.

The result was that by 1980 more than half of all apparel purchased in the United States was imported (compared to less than 7 percent in 1960). Leisure wear—jeans, shorts, T-shirts, polo shirts, and so on—was an important component of the homogenization of consumer tastes around the world at that time, and it could be produced most profitably by the cheap labour of young women in the peripheral metropolitan areas of the world. The same holds true today for fashion wear as well as leisure wear. The hourly compensation (including benefits) of apparel workers in the United States is $8–$10 for a 37-hour week, whereas for a 50- or 60-hour week, their counterparts in Hong Kong are paid around US$5 an hour, and in many parts of China the pay rate is US$0.20 an hour for 11–12 hour shift patterns for 6 days a week. Not surprisingly, the retail margin on domestically made clothing sold in Europe and the United States is 70 percent or so, the retail margin on clothing made in workshops in countries like Indonesia and Thailand is 100 to 250 percent.

This globalization of production has resulted in a complex set of commodity chains. Many of the largest clothing companies, such as Liz Claiborne, have most of their products manufactured through arrangements with many different independent suppliers, with no one supplier producing more than a fraction of the company's total output. These manufacturers are scattered throughout the world, making the clothing industry one of the most globalized of all manufacturing activities (**Figure 7.2.1**). In some countries, clothing manufacture is now the primary driver of their economy. Fifty percent of Sri Lanka's export earnings, for example, are derived from clothing, while for Bangladesh, El Salvador, and Mauritius the figure is 63 percent, and for Cambodia it is 76 percent. As we have seen, the actual geography of commodity chains in the clothing industry is rather volatile, with frequent shifts in production and assembly sites as companies and their suppliers continuously seek out new locations with lower costs.

Although cheap leisure wear can be produced most effectively through arrangements with multiple suppliers in peripheral low-wage regions, higher end apparel for the global marketplace requires a different geography of production. These products—women's fashion, outerwear, and lingerie; infants' wear; and men's suits—are based on frequent style changes and high-quality finish. This requires short production runs and greater contact between producers and buyers. The most profitable settings for these products are in the core countries' metropolitan areas—London, Paris, Stuttgart, Milan, New York, and Los Angeles—where, once again, migrant and immigrant labour provides a workforce for "designer" clothing that

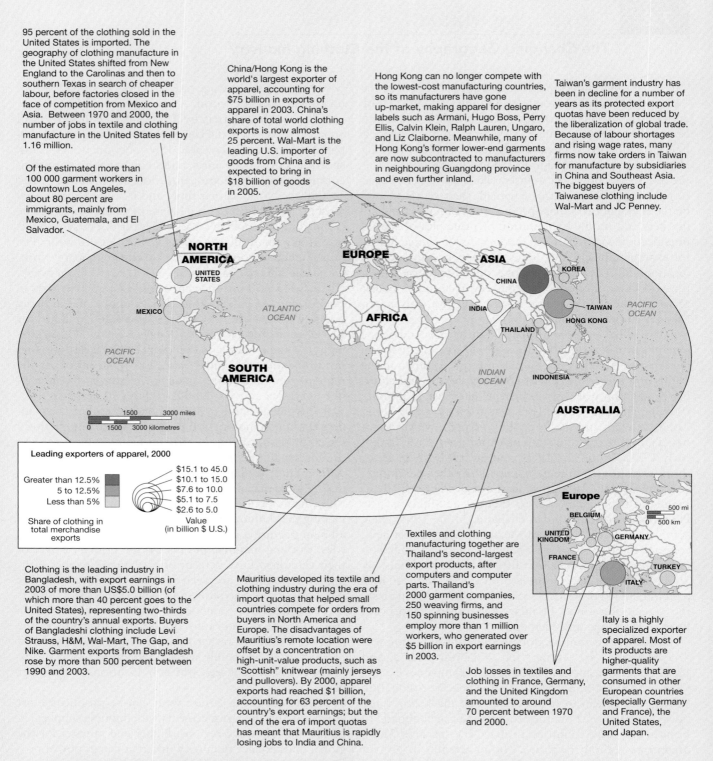

95 percent of the clothing sold in the United States is imported. The geography of clothing manufacture in the United States shifted from New England to the Carolinas and then to southern Texas in search of cheaper labour, before factories closed in the face of competition from Mexico and Asia. Between 1970 and 2000, the number of jobs in textile and clothing manufacture in the United States fell by 1.16 million.

Of the estimated more than 100 000 garment workers in downtown Los Angeles, about 80 percent are immigrants, mainly from Mexico, Guatemala, and El Salvador.

China/Hong Kong is the world's largest exporter of apparel, accounting for $75 billion in exports of apparel in 2003. China's share of total world clothing exports is now almost 25 percent. Wal-Mart is the leading U.S. importer of goods from China and is expected to bring in $18 billion of goods in 2005.

Hong Kong can no longer compete with the lowest-cost manufacturing countries, so its manufacturers have gone up-market, making apparel for designer labels such as Armani, Hugo Boss, Perry Ellis, Calvin Klein, Ralph Lauren, Ungaro, and Liz Claiborne. Meanwhile, many of Hong Kong's former lower-end garments are now subcontracted to manufacturers in neighbouring Guangdong province and even further inland.

Taiwan's garment industry has been in decline for a number of years as its protected export quotas have been reduced by the liberalization of global trade. Because of labour shortages and rising wage rates, many firms now take orders in Taiwan for manufacture by subsidiaries in China and Southeast Asia. The biggest buyers of Taiwanese clothing include Wal-Mart and JC Penney.

Leading exporters of apparel, 2000

Greater than 12.5%
5 to 12.5%
Less than 5%

Share of clothing in total merchandise exports

$15.1 to 45.0
$10.1 to 15.0
$7.6 to 10.0
$5.1 to 7.5
$2.6 to 5.0

Value (in billion $ U.S.)

Clothing is the leading industry in Bangladesh, with export earnings in 2003 of more than US$5.0 billion (of which more than 40 percent goes to the United States), representing two-thirds of the country's annual exports. Buyers of Bangladeshi clothing include Levi Strauss, H&M, Wal-Mart, The Gap, and Nike. Garment exports from Bangladesh rose by more than 500 percent between 1990 and 2003.

Mauritius developed its textile and clothing industry during the era of import quotas that helped small countries compete for orders from buyers in North America and Europe. The disadvantages of Mauritius's remote location were offset by a concentration on high-unit-value products, such as "Scottish" knitwear (mainly jerseys and pullovers). By 2000, apparel exports had reached $1 billion, accounting for 63 percent of the country's export earnings; but the end of the era of import quotas has meant that Mauritius is rapidly losing jobs to India and China.

Textiles and clothing manufacturing together are Thailand's second-largest export products, after computers and computer parts. Thailand's 2000 garment companies, 250 weaving firms, and 150 spinning businesses employ more than 1 million workers, who generated over $5 billion in export earnings in 2003.

Job losses in textiles and clothing in France, Germany, and the United Kingdom amounted to around 70 percent between 1970 and 2000.

Italy is a highly specialized exporter of apparel. Most of its products are higher-quality garments that are consumed in other European countries (especially Germany and France), the United States, and Japan.

Figure 7.2.1   The changing distribution of clothing manufacturing   Most of the world's clothing exports come from just a few countries. However, the geography of clothing manufacturing changes rapidly in response to the changing patterns of costs and opportunities within the world economy.

can be shipped in small batches to upscale stores and shopping malls around the world.

The result is that commodity chains in the clothing industry are quite distinctive for products destined for different segments of the market. Fashion-oriented retailers in the United States who sell "designer" products to upmarket customers obtain most of their goods from manufacturers in a small group of high-value-added countries, including France, Italy, Japan, the United Kingdom, and the United States. Department stores that emphasize "private label" products (that is, store brands, such as Nordstrom) and premium national brands obtain most of their goods from established manufacturers in semi-peripheral East Asian countries. Mass merchandisers who sell lower priced brands buy primarily from a third tier of lower cost, mid-quality manufacturers, while large-volume discount stores like Wal-Mart import most of their goods from low-cost suppliers in peripheral countries like China, Bangladesh, and the Dominican Republic.

Currently, a further realignment of global production is taking place as a result of the phasing out of the MFA's network of quotas, which began in the mid-1990s. The last of the quotas expired on 1 January 2005, prompting what is likely to be one of the largest migrations of production in history as production moves increasingly to China and India, the two countries with the greatest comparative advantage in terms of labour costs, thereby jeopardizing hundreds of thousands of apparel jobs in Bangladesh, Cambodia, E1 Salvador, Lesotho, Mauritius and other countries that had prospered under the quota system.

Offshore Financial Centres   The combination of metropolitan concentration and office decentralization fulfills most, but not all, of the locational needs of the global financial network. There are some needs—secrecy and shelter from taxation and regulation, in particular—that call for a different locational strategy. The result has been the emergence of a series of **offshore financial centres**, islands and micro-states, such as the Bahamas, Bahrain, the Cayman Islands, the Cook Islands, Luxembourg, Liechtenstein, and Vanuatu, that have become specialized nodes in the geography of worldwide financial flows.

offshore financial centres: islands or micro-states that have become specialized nodes in the geography of worldwide financial flows

The chief attraction of these offshore financial centres is simply that they are less regulated than financial centres elsewhere. They provide low-tax or no-tax settings for savings, havens for undeclared income and for "hot" money. They also provide discreet markets in which to deal currencies, bonds, loans, and other financial instruments without coming to the attention of regulating authorities or competitors. For these very reasons, their continued role has been under scrutiny since the events of 11 September 2001, led to the questioning of the wider security issues of such privacy. Overall, about 60 percent of all the world's money now resides offshore.

The Cayman Islands provide the classic example of an offshore financial centre. This small island state in the Caribbean has transformed itself from a poor, underdeveloped colony to a relatively affluent and modern setting for upscale tourism and offshore finance. With a population of just more than 30 000, it has more than 24 000 registered companies, including 350 insurance companies and more than 600 banks from all around the world. These banks account for an estimated US$450 billion in assets.

TOURISM AND ECONOMIC DEVELOPMENT

Many parts of the world, including parts of the world's core regions, do not have much of a primary base (that is, in agriculture, fishing, or mineral extraction), are not currently an important part of the global assembly line, and are not closely tied into the global financial network. For these areas, tourism can offer the otherwise unlikely prospect of economic development. One in every 15 workers, worldwide, is occupied in transporting, feeding, housing, guiding, or amusing tourists; and the global stock of lodging, restaurant, and transportation facilities is estimated to be worth about US$3 trillion. The study of tourism and leisure has become an interdisciplinary venture, to which geographers (with their interests in the movements of peoples, world regions, and the meaning of "place") have become important contributors.

Although most tourists, almost by definition, are relatively affluent people from the more-developed parts of the world, tourism is by no means confined to the less-developed ("unspoiled") peripheral regions. Canada, for example, has long experienced the effects of tourism as a both an origin and a destination for international visitors.

We have already seen how the Canadian Pacific Railway brought mountain guides from Switzerland to the Rockies to promote the growth of Banff as a major tourist

Figure 7.27 The Thousand Islands
Now a federal park, this area along the St. Lawrence River has long been used as a destination for recreation, summer cottages, and vacation camps.

destination and how the grandeur of Niagara Falls became the bedrock for an extensive international tourist trade in that region. An additional interesting example is the discovery of Ontario's Muskoka region by large numbers of American visitors in the years before 1930, many of whom established cottages there. A similar development occurred along the St. Lawrence River in the vicinity of the Thousand Islands (**Figure 7.27**). In both areas, growing tourism demand led to the creation of large resort hotels, the majority of which catered to a wealthy elite who could afford to experience Canada's "wilderness" and "nature"—ideas of place and space increasingly being used by the nascent tourist industry to market this country to the leisured classes. Meanwhile, across Canada, much smaller, domestically oriented tourist destinations grew up to cater to poorer, working-class trippers, seeking to escape from the cities for a day or two. The "sprung" dance floors of Manitou Beach, near Watrous in Saskatchewan, and the amusement parks of Winnipeg Beach in Manitoba catered to visitors from Regina and Saskatoon, and Winnipeg, respectively. Long since declined from their former glory, these destinations defined the tourism experience for many Canadians in the first half of the twentieth century.[15]

Today, people's desire to experience tourism on a much more extensive scale is the product of many of the socioeconomic changes we have discussed earlier in this chapter. Increasing average disposable income and leisure time have made tourism more possible for more people, while cheaper and improved long distance transportation have encouraged the growth of international travel. Finally, we should not forget how place marketing and changing constructions of the meaning of "place" (see Chapter 6) have resulted in travel destinations becoming another commodity that we can consume. In short, Canadians have a greater ability and desire to travel overseas, and Canada, as a destination, has become more accessible to overseas travellers.

In terms of tourism from Canada to countries other than the United States, Statistics Canada reports that "Canadians took more trips abroad than ever before in 2006, spent more money than they ever have while away, and made Mexico their favourite overseas destination."[16] The data show that Canadian residents took a

---

[15]See Geoffrey Wall, "Recreational Lands." In Donald Kerr and Deryck Holdsworth (eds.), *The Historical Atlas of Canada: Volume III. Addressing the Twentieth Century, 1891–1961*. Toronto: University of Toronto Press, 1990, plate 36; Cameron Taylor, *Enchanted Summers: The Grand Hotels of Muskoka*. Toronto: Lynx Images, 1997 (and accompanying video).

[16]The Statistics Canada data reported in these paragraphs comes from the preliminary annual report "Characteristics of International Travellers." *The Daily,* 29 May 2006, available online at **www.statcan.ca/Daily/English/070529/d070529a.htm**. Quarterly updates are also available from the same source.

record number of trips to countries other than the United States (more than 6.7 million) and spent $9.9 billion in the process. The top destinations for Canadians travelling overseas in 2006 were Mexico (842 000 overnight trips) and the United Kingdom (778 000 trips). By 2006, in regional terms, Europe was the most popular destination for Canadians travelling overseas (accounting for nearly 4 million overnight visits). The Caribbean, with 1.6 million visits, ranked second. Despite a rise in the value of the Canadian dollar relative the American dollar, overnight travel by Canadians to the United States increased by 7.6 percent in 2006, to a total of 16 million trips. In that year, Canadians spent $10.2 billion in the United States.

Travel from overseas to Canada in 2006 continued the growth of the previous two years. Statistics Canada reports that the number of overnight trips to Canada from destinations other than the United States totalled more than 4.3 million and that overseas residents spent $5.7 billion in Canada in 2006. The leading overseas sources for tourists to this country in 2006 were the United Kingdom (with more than 842 000 trips), Japan, Germany, France, and Australia. As impressive as they are, such figures are small when compared with the totals for visitors from the United States, who made more than 13.9 million trips to Canada and spent an estimated $7.3 billion here in 2006.

The wider economic impact of tourism on Canada has been substantial. According to a 2002 study based on a detailed analysis of 1996 data, the total number of jobs generated in Canada by tourism was estimated to be 585 000, and the total impact of tourism spending in Canada amounted to an estimated $16.93 billion. This estimate represents 2.3 percent of Canada's GDP—a figure that is larger than the contributions of the agriculture or forestry sectors to the economy in that year.

The regional impact of this spending varied considerably across the country. The economic impact of tourism was highest in Yukon, accounting for 4.8 percent of the territory's GDP and 8 percent (1200) of its total workforce. The impact of tourism spending was also above the national level (2.3 percent) in British Columbia (where it represented 3.5 percent of the province's GDP and 4.7 percent of its workforce), in Prince Edward Island (3.1 percent and 4.6 percent), and in Nova Scotia (2.6 percent and 4.1 percent). The remaining provinces and territories recorded levels of impact close to the national figure. Alberta, for instance, recorded a figure of 2.2 percent of GDP. In Saskatchewan, where the impact of tourism spending was lowest, it was responsible for only 1.8 percent of provincial GDP. Clearly, tourist attractions as varied as the West Edmonton Mall in Edmonton, Anne of Green Gables' house on Prince Edward Island, the "SuperNatural" attractions of British Columbia (to quote the province's vehicle licence plates), and Nova Scotia's heritage attractions (such as Lunenburg and Louisbourg) are as important economically as they are recreationally.

Few places exist anywhere in the developed world, for that matter, that do not encourage tourism as one of the central planks of their economic development strategy. Because tourism requires only a basic infrastructure and no heavy plant and little high-tech equipment, it has been estimated that the cost of creating one new job in tourism is less than one-fifth the cost of creating a job in the manufacturing industry and less than one-fiftieth of the cost of creating a high-tech engineering job. Consequently, as we saw in Chapter 6, place marketing has become an extremely important aspect of local efforts to promote economic development.

The globalization of the world economy has therefore been paralleled by a globalization of the tourist industry. According to the UN's World Tourism Organisation, a total of 898 million international tourist trips took place in 2007, compared with 147 million in 1970 (the total for 2008 will likely be somewhat higher still, increased as it will be by the effects of the 2008 Olympic Games in Beijing, which, according to Chinese statistics, attracted an estimated 389,000 tourists from overseas to that city). Overall, international tourist receipts were estimated to total US$733 billion in 2007. In more specific terms, we will consider core countries such as Canada and the United States later in this section, but to take first a developing country as an example of the impact of tourism, consider Indonesia, which received a total of 4.87 million tourists in 2006 (the majority of whom only visit Bali and Jakarta regions), each of whom spent on average a total of US$913 whilst in Indonesia, a total that was responsible (according to estimates made in 2002) for as much as 5 percent of its total economy. Most striking, though, is not so much the growth in the number of international tourists as the increased range of international tourism. Thanks largely to cheap long-distance flights, a significant proportion of tourism is now transcontinental and transoceanic. Visits to peripheral countries in Africa, Asia, and Latin America now account for one-eighth of the industry. This, of course, has made tourism a central component of economic development in countries with reputations for their wildlife (Kenya, for example), scenery (Nepal), beaches (the Seychelles Islands), shopping (Singapore and Hong Kong), culture (China, India, and Indonesia), or sex (Thailand).

Tourism can provide a basis for economic development in peripheral regions, but it is often a mixed blessing. Although it certainly creates jobs, they often pay very little and are seasonal. Dependence on tourism also makes for a high degree of economic vulnerability. Tourism, like other high-end aspects of consumption, depends very much on matters of style and fashion. As a result, once-thriving tourist destinations can suddenly find themselves struggling for customers. Some places are sought out by tourists because of their remoteness and their "natural," rustic qualities, and these are most vulnerable to shifts of style and fashion. Nepal and New Zealand are recent examples of this phenomenon, but they are now too mainstream as destinations and are consequently having to work hard to continue to attract tourists. Bhutan, Bolivia, Estonia, Patagonia, and Vietnam have been "discovered" and are coping with their first real growth in tourism. China, meanwhile, is likely to become one of the most popular destinations of all by 2010.

It is not only exotic tourist locations that are vulnerable to changing tastes and fashions, however. Canada's own older and established tourist centres have felt the need to "rebrand" themselves to maintain visitor numbers. One of the most controversial developments, perhaps, has been the creation of casinos in many parts of this country (**Figure 7.28**). Supporters of these new attractions note the billions of dollars that have been generated for provincial coffers. Opponents note that the bulk of this money comes from people who live locally and not from tourists.

Tourism in more exotic tourist destinations, meanwhile, is vulnerable in other ways. The tsunami of December 2004 led to a sharp fall in the flow of tourists to Thailand, and New York's hotels were empty immediately after the terrorist attack

Figure 7.28 Casino Niagara
A recent addition to the skyline of Niagara Falls, Ontario, this combined hotel, shopping mall, and casino provides visitors to the Falls with further recreational opportunities in the area.

of 11 September 2001. For ski resorts, warm weather represents the equivalent of a harvest failure for an agricultural region. Moreover, although tourism is a multi-billion-dollar industry, the financial returns for tourist areas are often not as high as might be expected. The greater part of the price of a package vacation, for example, stays with the organizing company and the airline. Typically, only 40 percent is retained by the tourist region itself. If the package involves a foreign-owned hotel, this number may fall to less than 25 percent.

Other new possibilities lie closer to home and concern what has become known as *Aboriginal (or indigenous) tourism.* Defined by Butler and Hinch as "tourism activity in which indigenous people are directly involved either through control and/or having their culture serve as the essence of the attraction," Aboriginal tourism has been described by Industry Canada in a 2006 report as "one of Canada's unique strengths," whose development is a "top priority."

According to government estimates, Aboriginal tourism in 2005 generated $474 million dollars in revenue and employed 16 000 people across the country. In Quebec, to cite just one province, in 2003 there were 199 Aboriginal tourism businesses in operation, and 36 of the 54 Aboriginal communities in the province had developed some heritage-related tourism products (such as a museum or store). A notable example can be found at Wendake, just outside Quebec City, where a five-star hotel-museum in the form of a large tepee is under development. This building aims to recreate the sensation of being in the woods and is described as a "multi-sensory project" because one can smell, see, hear, and feel the Aboriginal culture.

The goals of aboriginal tourism are praiseworthy enough since by using their own culture as an attraction, indigenous peoples in Canada and elsewhere are enabled to foster their own economic development. Indeed, in the often remote areas in which Aboriginal communities are situated, their own communities are—in this way of thinking—a major *local* resource. However, as research has shown, there are some serious disadvantages too. The disruption of life caused by an influx of tourists takes its toll on any community, and Johnston remarks in the 2005 book *Is the Sacred for Sale?: Tourism and Indigenous Peoples,* "globally, no other industry single-handedly endangers the spiritual core of indigenous cultures to such an extent." Others have noted that for many native communities in Canada, the tourist season coincides with the peak of hunting activities and it therefore does not provide employment when it is most needed during the year. Finally, most research has noted that Aboriginal tourism (like many other forms of tourism) tends to be controlled by non-Aboriginal owners who do not re-invest their profits in the local communities where they are generated.

All that being said, however, a note of optimism is sounded in the 2008 work of Andrea Sabelli, who interviewed Aboriginal tourism operators in Wendake and Kahnawake in Quebec. She concludes her investigation of the advantages of Aboriginal tourism with these words: ". . . the social benefits of tourism may outweigh its economic importance. Many participants spoke about the sense of pride that Aboriginal people have in showcasing their culture to tourists. A big finding is the important role tourism can have in building relations between native and non-native people."[17]

The costs and benefits of tourism are not only economic, of course. On the positive side, tourism can help sustain indigenous lifestyles and regional cultures, arts,

[17]The material in this section is based, with thanks, upon the work of Andrea Sabelli, "Aboriginal Tourism as an Economic Development Strategy." Honours Essay, Department of Geography, Planning and Environment, Concordia University, Montreal, 2008. In addition, see *Building a National Tourism Strategy.* Ottawa: Industry Canada, 2006; C. Notzke, "Indigenous Tourism Development in S. Alberta, Canada: Tentative Engagement." *Journal of Sustainable Tourism* 12(1), 2004, pp. 29–54; R. Butler and T. Hinch, *Tourism and Indigenous Peoples.* London: ITP, 1996; A. Johnston, *Is the Sacred for Sale?: Tourism and Indigenous Peoples.* London: Earthscan, 2005; K. Iankova, "Le tourisme et le développement économique des communautés autochtones du Québec." *Recherches Amérindiennes au Québec* 34(1), 2006, pp. 69–78; J. Altman and J. Finlayson, "Aborigines, Tourism and Sustainable Development." *Journal of Tourism Studies* 4(1), 1993, pp. 39–50.

and crafts; and it can provide incentives for wildlife preservation, environmental protection, and the conservation of historic buildings and sites. On the negative side, tourism can adulterate and debase indigenous cultures and bring unsightly development, pollution, and environmental degradation. In the Caribbean, sewage has poisoned mangrove trees and polluted coastal waters, and boats and divers have damaged coral reefs. In Kenya, the Amboselli National Park has been severely degraded by safari vehicles. The large number of visitors to Banff in Alberta have caused tensions between the town (whose businesses thrive on the increasing tourist trade) and Parks Canada, the federal government department responsible for the integrity of the surrounding national park. In the European Alps, where an incredible 40 000 ski runs attract a winter tourist population 10 times greater than the resident population, forests have been ripped up, pastures obliterated, rivers diverted, and scenic valleys and mountainsides covered with chalets, cabins, and hotels.

In a wider sense, tourism can also be a part of the processes of "place making" that have been discussed in Chapters 5 and 6, and those processes, in turn, are often fundamental to creating demand for tourism in an area, as the case of Niagara Falls illustrates. Tourism, like any other human activity, is essentially a social and cultural construct and the "tourist gaze" (a term coined by sociologist John Urry) can be turned on sites and sights as various as natural phenomena (such as Ayers Rock in Australia, or the Grand Canyon), folk housing museums (as in Copenhagen), or the homes of long-dead rock stars (such as Elvis Presley's at Graceland in Memphis). Objectively, what we see is less important than how we see it, and how we use our own biases and frames of reference in that interpretation. In this view, travel does not broaden the mind, it reconfirms what we already know!

Tourism can also involve exploitative relations that debase traditional lifestyles and regional cultural heritages as they become packaged for outsider consumption. In the process, the behaviours and artifacts that are made available to an international market of outsiders can lose much of their original meaning. Traditional ceremonies that formerly had cultural significance for the performers are now enacted only to be watched and photographed. Artifacts, such as masks and weapons, are manufactured not for their original use but as curios, souvenirs, and ornaments. In the process, indigenous cultures are edited, beautified, and altered to suit outsiders' tastes and expectations.

Such problems, coupled with the economic vulnerability occasioned by tourism, have led to the idea of "alternative" tourism as the ideal strategy for economic development in peripheral regions. Alternative tourism emphasizes self-determination, authenticity, social harmony, preservation of the existing environment, small-scale development, and greater use of local techniques, materials, and architectural styles. Costa Rica, for example, despite being a poor country, has won high praise from environmentalists for protecting 30 percent of its territory in biosphere and wildlife preserves. Costa Rica has more bird species (850) than are found in Canada and the United States combined and more varieties of butterflies than in all of Africa. It has 12 distinct ecosystems that among them contain more than 6000 kinds of flowering plants, more than 200 species of mammals, 200 species of reptiles, and more than 35 000 species of insects. The payoff for Costa Rica is the escalating number of tourists who come to visit its active volcanoes, palm-lined beaches, cloud forests, and tropical parks. In 1995, the year Costa Rica received more than 800 000 tourists, tourism exceeded banana exports as the country's main source of foreign exchange. Since 1995, the number of tourists visiting Costa Rica has increased by 10 percent each year.

The advantages and disadvantages of tourism are well illustrated by the example of the cruise ship industry, an industry in which Canada is an important participant. Vancouver has, for example, become an important hub for Alaskan cruises, a market that began in the 1950s and expanded significantly in the 1980s. In their comprehensive report *A Primer on the Canadian Pacific Cruise Ship Industry*, Sue Dobson, Alison Gill (a geographer at Simon Fraser University), and Sam Baird note that this industry "has been increasing in size and complexity over the past

Figure 7.29 Cruise ships Tourism is promoted but the environment threatened—such is the story of the cruise industry, typified in this picture of cruise liners anchored in Skagway, Alaska.

decade with revenue passengers now exceeding 1 million per year."[18] Such a statistic can be seen in context when we realize that in 2004, the worldwide total number of people taking a cruise ship holiday reached 10.85 million—of which over 75 percent were Americans. By 2006, the largest cruise line company, Princess (which merged in 2003 with Carnival) operated 80 ships, and planned to add 15 more to that fleet by 2009. Vance Gulliksen's interesting account of the latest developments (which include the provision of "aqua parks" on board ship) can be seen in the August 2008 issue of *Social Science and Modern Society*.[19]

The attraction of the potential business that such ships may bring to the places in which they berth has been the focus of many port communities from Alaska to the Caribbean and across the Mediterranean. Certainly, when one catches a glimpse of three or four of these luxury behemoths (which nowadays each often carry in excess of 2000 passengers) anchored in places such as Skagway or Antigua, disgorging tourist numbers far greater than the population of the community itself, it is hard not to imagine that there must be economic benefits to such communities from the tourist dollars spent on food, trinkets, and shore excursions by those passengers who choose to disembark for a few hours (**Figure 7.29**).

Reports suggest that such economic effects can, indeed, appear huge: in 2005, for example, the cruise ship industry's impact on the British Columbian economy was estimated to be $1.2 billion annually, of which $660 million was due to the direct spending of the cruise lines, passengers and their crews.[20] Sadly, however, further research has shown that the story is not that simple.

In terms of economic benefits, it is not always apparent, but many of the harbour-side stores and businesses frequented by cruise ship passengers are either owned by the cruise line itself or its local affiliates. In addition, ports are often also obliged to pay the cruise line if they wish the ship to make a stop in their community. Factors such as these mean that much of the revenues apparently earned at port destinations do not, in fact, benefit those communities themselves but flow elsewhere through a process known as "leakage." Other economic drawbacks are that

---

[18]Sue Dobson, Alison Gill, and Sam Baird, *A Primer on the Canadian Pacific Cruise Ship Industry*. May 2002, **www.sfu.ca/cstudies/science/resources/coastalstudies/Cruise_Ship.pdf**, accessed November 2007.

[19]Laura Byrne Paquet, *Wanderlust: A Social History of Travel*. Fredericton: Goose Lane Editions, 2007; Vance Gulliksen, "The Cruise Industry." *Social Science and Modern Society*, 45, 2008, pp. 342–345.

[20]Ross A. Klein, *Playing Off the Ports: BC and the Cruise Tourism Industry*. Vancouver: Canadian Centre for Policy Alternatives, August 2005.

Figure 7.30 Whale watching Following the moratorium on cod fishing and the decline of the Atlantic cod fishery, many fishers turned to alternative sources of employment. Taking tourists to see whales seems a happy fit of environmental tourism and alternative job creation. However, the more whale watchers there are, the greater the threat to the whales (because of engine noise and the boats getting too close), and so this new industry can never make up the shortfall in employment.

ecotourism: an activity which, in addition to following the goals of "sustainable tourism," also (1) contributes to the conservation of an area's natural and cultural heritage; (2) includes local indigenous communities in its planning; (3) interprets the natural and cultural heritage of the destination to the visitor; and (4) is aimed at small-sized groups

the benefits rarely penetrate far beyond the quayside into the wider community, and the disruptive effects an economy based on tourism can have on more traditional livelihoods (such as fishing).

Beyond the economic difficulties, critics have also pointed to the environmental effects of cruise ships. To cite but one example, despite assurances given by the industry to the port of Seattle that Alaska's environmental standards would be obeyed, on 3 May 2003 the cruise ship *Norwegian Sun* "was cited for the illegal discharge of 16 000 gallons of raw sewage into the Strait of Juan de Fuca."[21] Other cases include the alleged discharge of engine oil and ships' garbage, and, in the Caribbean, the potential damage to fragile marine ecosystems such as coral reefs and mangrove swamps. In the final analysis, it may well be that the economic benefits of the cruise ship industry are not ultimately worth the environmental price, but because of the short-term gain to the economy, many communities are not able to take such considered judgments over the choice of economic development strategies.

Ecotourism may offer one way in which this difficult balance can be achieved, but it is important to realize that this activity implies more than simply the concept of "sustainable tourism." In addition to that concept, according to the United Nations Environment Programme (UNEP)'s definition, ecotourism: (1) contributes to the conservation of an area's natural and cultural heritage; (2) includes local indigenous communities in its planning; (3) interprets the natural and cultural heritage of the destination to the visitor; and (4) is aimed at small-sized groups (to minimize their impact).[22]

Ecotourism also provides a fascinating example of how traditional economies have often undervalued the importance of nature. Until very recently, for example, large tracts of rain forest were seen as impediments to any form of development. Now, however, they have been reinterpreted as a key resource to be used to attract tourists eager to experience "untouched places." The current promotion of ecotourism in Canada (**Figure 7.30**) and countries as varying as Belize and Iceland shows how important this changing assessment of the environment has become in reconfiguring the geography of tourism.

CONCLUSION

The growth of alternative tourism in Costa Rica, like the growth of the Cayman Islands as an offshore financial centre, and the decline of Nova Scotia's Cape Breton as a manufacturing region, shows that economic development is not simply a sequential

[21]Ibid., p. 16.

[22]United Nations Environment Programme, "Tourism: About Ecotourism," **www.unep.fr/scp/ tourism/sustain**. Accessed 6 December 2007.

process of modernization and increasing affluence. Various pathways to development exist, each involving different ways of achieving increased economic productivity and higher incomes, together with an increased capacity to improve the basic conditions of life. Economic development means not just using the latest technology to generate higher incomes but also improving the quality of life through better housing, health care, and social welfare systems and enhancing the physical framework, or infrastructure, on which the economy rests.

Local, regional, and international patterns and processes of economic development are of particular importance to geographers. Levels of economic development and local processes of economic change affect many aspects of local well-being and so contribute to many aspects of human geography. Economic development is an important place-making process that underpins much of the diversity among regions and nations. At the same time, it is a reflection and a product of variations from place to place in natural resources, demographic characteristics, political systems, and social customs.

Economic development is always an uneven geographical phenomenon. Regional patterns of economic development are tied to the geographical distribution of resources and to the legacy of the past specializations of places and regions within national economies. As we saw with the examples of France, South Korea, and India, a general tendency exists toward the creation of regional cores with dependent peripheries. Nevertheless, such patterns are not fixed or static. Changing economic conditions can lead to the modification or reversal of core–periphery patterns, such as the stagnation of once-booming northern England and the spectacular growth of Guangdong province in southeast China. Over the long term, core–periphery patterns have most often been modified as a result of the changing locational needs and opportunities of successive technology systems. Today, economic globalization has exposed more places and regions than ever to the ups and downs of episodes of creative destruction—episodes played out ever faster, thanks to the way that new technologies, such as the internet, have shrunk time and space.

At the global scale, the unevenness of economic development takes the form of core–periphery contrasts within the world-system framework. Most striking about these contrasts today are the dynamism and pace of change involved in economic development. The global assembly line, the global office, and global tourism are all making places much more interdependent and faster changing. Parts of Brazil, China, India, Mexico, and South Korea, for example, have developed quickly from rural backwaters into significant industrial regions. The Cayman Islands have been transformed from an insignificant Caribbean colony to an upscale tourist resort and a major offshore financial centre. Countries, such as Ecuador and Costa Rica, with few comparative advantages, suddenly find themselves able to earn significant amounts of foreign exchange through the development of ecotourism. This dynamism has, however, brought with it an expanding gap between rich and poor at every spatial scale—international, regional, and local.

MAIN POINTS REVISITED

- **The geography of economic development is the cumulative outcome of decisions guided by fundamental principles of land use, commercial and industrial location, and economic interdependence.**
  As location decisions are played out in the real world, distinctive geographical linkages and spatial structures emerge.

- **Geographically, the single most important feature of economic development is that it is highly uneven.**
  At the global scale, this unevenness takes the form of core–periphery contrasts. These contrasts raise important

issues of spatial justice that are closely bound up with gender inequality and social justice. Similar core–periphery contrasts—and equally important issues of spatial justice—exist at the regional scale.

- **Successive technology systems have rewritten the geography of economic development as they have shifted the balance of advantages among regions.**
  Technological innovations in power and energy, transportation, and manufacturing processes have been important catalysts for changes in the pattern of economic development, allowing a succession of expansions of economic activity in time and space. Although many existing industrial regions have grown

bigger and more productive, each major cluster of technological innovations tends to create new requirements in terms of natural resources as well as labour forces and markets. As a result, each major cluster of technological innovations has tended to favour different regions and different kinds of places.

■ **Geographical divisions of labour have evolved with the growth of the world-system of trade and politics and with the changing locational logic of successive technology systems.**
Geographical divisions of labour are national, regional, and locally based economic specializations in primary, secondary, tertiary, or quaternary activities. The relationship between changing regional economic specialization and changing levels of prosperity has prompted the interpretation of economic development in distinctive stages. In reality, however, various pathways exist to development, as well as various processes and outcomes of development.

■ **Regional cores of economic development are created cumulatively, following some initial advantage, through the operation of several basic principles of spatial organization.**
Any significant initial local economic advantage—existing labour markets, consumer markets, frameworks of fixed social capital, and so on—tends to be reinforced through a process of cumulative causation, a spiral buildup of advantages that occurs in specific geographical settings as a result of the development of external economies, agglomeration effects, and localization economies.

■ **Spirals of economic development can be arrested in various ways, including the onset of disinvestment and** deindustrialization, which follow major shifts in technology systems and in international geopolitics.
The capital made available from disinvestment in core regions becomes available for investment by entrepreneurs in new ventures based on innovative products and production technologies. Old industries—and sometimes entire old industrial regions—have to be "dismantled" (or at least neglected) to help fund the creation of new centres of profitability and employment. This process is often referred to as *creative destruction*.

■ **The globalization of the economy has meant that patterns and processes of local and regional economic development are much more open to external influences than before.**
The globalization of the world economy involves a new international division of labour in association with the internationalization of finance, the deployment of a new technology system, and the homogenization of consumer markets. This new framework for economic geography has meant that the lives of people in different parts of the world have become increasingly intertwined.

■ **Tourism has increasingly come to represent a major industry at a world scale, and offers the potential for local economic development in forms as various as ecotourism and visits to Aboriginal cultural sites.**
Tourism has many economic benefits (in terms of local employment and the creation of new opportunities), but its negatives (in terms of its impact on the environment, and the fact that much of the economic gains do not stay in the community) often outweigh the advantages.

Key Terms

agglomeration diseconomies   (p. 324)
agglomeration effects   (p. 319)
ancillary activities   (p. 319)
backwash effects   (p. 322)
brownfield site   (p. 327)
creative destruction   (p. 324)
cumulative causation   (p. 322)
deindustrialization   (p. 324)
ecotourism   (p. 346)
export-processing zones
   (EPZs)   (p. 335)
external economies   (p. 319)
foreign direct investment   (p. 330)

geographical path
   dependence   (p. 321)
gross domestic product
   (GDP)   (p. 297)
gross national income
   (GNI)   (p. 297)
gross national product
   (GNP)   (p. 297)
growth poles   (p. 329)
infrastructure (fixed social
   capital)   (p. 320)
initial advantage   (p. 321)
localization economies   (p. 319)

offshore financial centres   (p. 339)
primary activities   (p. 308)
quaternary activities   (p. 308)
reserves   (p. 304)
resources   (p. 304)
secondary activities   (p. 308)
spread effects   (p. 323)
technology systems   (p. 306)
tertiary activities   (p. 308)
total stock   (p. 304)
urbanization economies   (p. 321)
world cities   (p. 336)

Additional Reading

Barnet, R.J., and J. Cavanagh. *Global Dreams*. New York: Simon & Schuster, 1994.

Blake, R.B. *From Fishermen to Fish: The Evolution of Canadian Fishery Policy*. Toronto: Irwin, 2000.

Britton, J.H. (ed.). *Canada and the Global Economy: The Geography of Structural and Technological Change*. Montreal: McGill–Queen's University Press, 1996.

Castells, M. *The Information Age*, vol. 3. Oxford: Blackwell, 1996–1998.

Castells, M., and P. Hall. *Technopoles of the World: The Making of 21st Century Industrial Complexes*. New York: Routledge, 1994.

Cho, G. *Trade, Aid, and Global Interdependence*. London: Routledge, 1995.

Chodos, R., R. Murphy, and E. Hamovitch. *Canada and the Global Economy*. Toronto: Lorimer, 1993.

Dicken, P. *Global Shift*, 3rd ed. New York: Harper & Row, 1997.

Fennel, D.A. *Ecotourism: An Introduction.* London: Routledge, 1999.

Gibb, R., and W. Michalak. *Continental Trading Blocs: The Growth of Regionalism in the World Economy.* New York: Wiley, 1994.

Hayter, R., and P.D. Wilde (eds.). *Industrial Transformation and Challenge in Australia and Canada.* Ottawa: Carleton University Press, 1990.

Howells, J., and M. Wood. *The Globalisation of Production and Technology.* London: Pinter, 1993.

Hugill, P. *Global Communications Since 1844: Geopolitics and Technology.* Baltimore: Johns Hopkins University Press, 1999.

Knox, P.L., and J. Agnew, *The Geography of the World Economy,* 3rd ed. London: Edward Arnold, 1998.

Norcliffe, G. "Canada in a Global Economy," *Canadian Geographer* 45(1), 2001, 14–30.

Potter, R.B., J.A. Binns, J.A. Elliott, and D. Smith. *Geographies of Development.* London: Longman, 1999.

Smith, N. *Uneven Development: Nature, Capital, and the Production of Space,* 2nd ed. Oxford: Blackwell, 1991.

Taylor, P.J. "The Error of Developmentalism in Human Geography." In D. Gregory and R. Walford (eds.), *Horizons in Human Geography.* Totowa, NJ: Barnes and Noble, 1989, 309–319.

Wallace, I. *A Geography of the Canadian Economy.* Toronto: Oxford University Press, 2002.

World Bank. *World Development Report 1995: Workers in an Integrating World.* New York: Oxford University Press, 1995.

Exercises

Here you will find exercises and activities for each chapter. Unplugged exercises help you review chapter discussions, and pose ideas for your own human geography research. On the Companion Website exercises will require you have access to the internet.

Unplugged

1. Although India's per capita income is well below that of Canada (Figure 7.1), India has more people who earn the equivalent of $70 000 a year than Canada does. How can you explain this, and what might be some of the consequences of this from the point of view of economic geography?

2. Figure 7.4 suggests that creating economic opportunities for women does not necessarily require high levels of economic development. Which peripheral countries have a high gender empowerment index score, and which core countries have a relatively low gender empowerment index score? Can you think of explanations for these cases?

3. Write a short essay (500 words, or two double-spaced, typed pages) on any specialized manufacturing region or office district with which you are familiar. Describe the different kinds of firms that are found there, and suggest the kinds of linkages among them that might be considered to be examples of agglomeration effects.

4. Look at the countries advertised as tourist destinations in your daily newspaper. Go to your library, and find copies of that newspaper for 1992 and 2002. What was the pattern of tourist destination ads in those years? What explains the differences you see?

On the Companion Website

This book has its own Companion Website where you will find additional resources—maps, photographs, data—as well as exercises and activities that relate to each chapter. To complete the Companion Website exercises, go to **www.pearsoned.ca/knox**. The following is a summary of the types of exercises created for this chapter.

1. The internet exercises for this chapter compare and contrast the economic success of some capitalist countries that have interpreted capitalism differently. Through the internet, we examine the remarkable success of ecommerce and explore infrastructure development that leapfrogs over certain economic stages through technology. We examine successful and not-so-successful growth poles, and we compare recent economic growth in the United States, Europe, and Japan as well as explore why some highly developed economies flourish, while others stagnated or declined in the decade-long favourable economic cycle that ended in late 2008. We look at a new phenomenon of business-to-business ecommerce and how some transnational companies are exploiting it to the benefit of their employees.

2. The Audio Interview, Interview with Norma Rantisi, that accompanies this chapter has been conducted to highlight the issues of urban economies discussed in this chapter, using the examples of Montreal's fashion and computer gaming industries. In addition, you will hear about the benefits of a geographical training, other courses that combine well with ones in geography, and what to know when conducting interviews. You will find a link to the Audio Interview, interview summary, and questions on the Companion Website for this chapter.

8

Agriculture and Food Production

Market gardens (known as *bostans*) have long been a feature of Istanbul, but their numbers are diminishing as the need for land for housing continues to grow, and as cheaper food becomes available from elsewhere.

The 100-Mile Diet introduced many Canadians to an idea that had already received exposure in the alternative press and on the web for some years before the book's publication in March 2007.[1] The book's authors, Alisa Smith and James MacKinnon, recount their experiences trying to live only on the foods available to them from within a 100-mile radius of where they lived. Since their home was in Vancouver, this project posed more of a challenge than it might otherwise have done, and skeptics and supporters alike had first followed their progress by way of a weekly online newsletter before coverage in *Utne Reader* brought their endeavours to a wider audience.[2]

It is evident from the widespread attention they subsequently received in the national media that their notion struck a chord—perhaps because it provides a response to the following important concerns that lie at the heart of our current agricultural and food production systems.[3]

- First, the focus on locally sourced products meant that the distance foods are transported from producer to consumer can be reduced, and, therefore, the total impact of food production (in terms, say, of carbon dioxide emissions, or "food miles") can be minimized.
- Second, a reliance on locally sourced products often requires a greater knowledge about how food is produced and enables consumers to have more control over what they eat. At a time when many people are paying more attention to food safety and food ethics, an assurance that the foodstuffs are organically and/or sustainably produced has become more important than ever before.
- Third, a reliance on local production is a criticism of large-scale corporate agribusiness, since it often entails a preference for small-scale, individually run operations whose farmers are far less motivated by profit than those who, for example, are contracted to supply large supermarket chains.
- Fourth, a reliance on locally produced food stuff entails a submission to the ebbs and flows of the seasons, which resonates with many environmentalists who suggest that a year-round availability of food has lessened our wonderment at nature's bounty and our sense of its rhythms.

---

[1]Alisa Smith and J.B. MacKinnon, *The 100-Mile Diet: A Year of Local Eating.* Random House Canada: Toronto, 2007. The initial coverage of their endeavour was reported in the British Columbia-based online weekly newspaper *The Tyee* (**www.thetyee.ca**) and updated at **http://thetyee.ca/Life/2006/01/25/Incredible100MileDiet/**. A more general discussion of the issues surrounding local food can be found in Brian Halweil, "Home Grown: The Case for Local Food in a Global Market." Washington DC: Worldwatch Institute, 2002 (Worldwatch Paper 163).

[2]Alisa Smith and J.B. MacKinnon, "The Hundred-Mile Diet: One Couple's Quest to Survive on Locally Grown Foods." *Utne Reader.* November–December 2005, pp. 97–98.

[3]See, for example, Deborah Jones, "100 Mile Diet Spurs Appetite for Local Food." *Globe and Mail*, 18 October 2005, p. A3.

The 100-mile diet's critique of what are essentially some of the major issues of modern agribusiness has not, however, gone unchallenged, and important questions about the diet's practicalities have been raised. Certainly, it is unlikely that we could meet all our own basic food needs in the manner the authors suggest. It would not be possible given the weather in many parts of this country and more problematic for those who live in Canada's urban centres. Luxury commodities such as chocolate or coffee would presumably be completely out of the question. Nor does the notion always make the most sense since economies of scale mean that certain levels of producer specialization and geographies of regional specialization are more efficient than small-scale local operations; mass production may have its faults, but the ability to deliver large amounts of food products quickly and cheaply is something that North American society has come to depend on since at least the 1950s. Finally, to insist on a dependence on local production runs counter to this country's support for multiculturalism; the 100-mile diet would require many of this country's immigrants to forgo imported foodstuffs necessary in many ethnically inspired cuisines.

Clearly, there are many often contradictory issues here, and it is not possible to resolve them all neatly. What is clear, however, is that the 100-mile diet has forced us all to consider closely the many geographical issues embedded in what we eat: Where has it come from? How is it produced? How has the development of industrial agribusiness affected the sustainability of our food systems? These are some of the issues that we shall consider in this chapter.

MAIN POINTS

- Agriculture has been transformed into a globally integrated system; the changes producing this result have occurred at many scales and have originated from many sources.

- Agriculture has proceeded through three revolutionary phases, from the domestication of plants and animals, through the agricultural revolution of the mid-eighteenth century, to the latest developments in biotechnology and industrial innovation.

- The increasing ability to manipulate nature has changed how humans view their environment and think about place.

- The introduction of new technologies, political concerns about food security and self-sufficiency, and changing opportunities for investment and employment are among the many forces that have dramatically shaped agriculture as we know it today.

- The industrialized agricultural system of today's world has developed from— and has largely displaced—older agricultural practices, including shifting cultivation, subsistence agriculture, and pastoralism.

- Canadian agriculture, since European settlement began, has always been affected by international markets—first by those of the colonizing powers and second by those of today's world markets.

- The contemporary agro-commodity system is organized around a chain of agribusiness components that begins at the farm and ends at the retail outlet. Different economic sectors, as well as different corporate forms, have been involved in the globalization process.

- Transformations in agriculture have had dramatic impacts on the environment including soil erosion, desertification, deforestation, and soil and water pollution, as well as the elimination of some plant and animal species.

TRADITIONAL AGRICULTURAL GEOGRAPHY

The study of agriculture has a long tradition in geography. Because of geographers' interest in the relationships between people and land, it is hardly surprising that agriculture has been of primary concern. Research on agriculture is strongly influenced by geography's commitment to viewing the physical and human systems as interactively linked. Such an approach combines an understanding of spatial differentiation, the importance of place, and the fact that such practices as agriculture affect and are affected by processes occurring at different scales. It also provides geographers with a powerful perspective for understanding the dynamics of contemporary agriculture.

One of the most widely recognized and appreciated contributions that geographers have made to the study of agriculture is the mapping of the different factors that shape agriculture. They have mapped soil, temperature, and terrain, as well as the areal distribution of different types of agriculture and the relationships among agriculture, the environment, and society.

The last four decades have been characterized by major changes occurring in agriculture worldwide. One of the most dramatic changes has been the decline in the number of people employed in farming in both the core and the periphery. Meanwhile, farming practices have been significantly intensified through the use of chemical, mechanical, and biotechnological innovations and applications (**Figure 8.1**). Agriculture has become increasingly integrated into wider regional, national, and global economic systems at the same time that it has become more directly linked to other economic sectors, such as manufacturing and finance. These changes have been profound and have had repercussions, ranging from the structure of global finance to the social relations of individual households (**Figure 8.2**).

Through the examination of agricultural practices, geographers have sought to understand the myriad ways in which humans have learned to adapt and domesticate the natural world around them to sustain themselves, their kin, and ultimately the global community. In addition to understanding agricultural systems, geographers have also been interested in investigating the lifestyle and culture of different agricultural communities. They and other social scientists often use the adjective **agrarian** to describe the way of life that is deeply embedded in the demands of agricultural production. *Agrarian* not only defines the culture of distinctive agricultural communities but also refers to the type of tenure (or landholding) system that determines who has access to land and what kind of cultivation practices will be employed there.

Agriculture is considered a science, an art, and a business directed at the cultivation of crops and the raising of livestock for sustenance and profit. The unique and ingenious methods by which humans have learned to transform the land through agriculture are an important reflection of the two-way relationship between people and their environments (**Figure 8.3**). Just as geography shapes our choices and behaviours, we are able to shape the physical landscape.

Although there is no definitive answer as to where agriculture originated, we do know that before humans discovered the advantages of agriculture, they procured their food through hunting (including fishing) and gathering. **Hunting and gathering** characterizes activities whereby people feed themselves through killing

Figure 8.1 Pesticide use In the Cape Verde Islands off the coast of West Africa, an agricultural worker sprays pesticides on irrigated vegetables. Many of the pesticides in use in peripheral countries have been banned in core countries because of human health concerns.

agrarian: referring to the culture of agricultural communities and the type of tenure system that determines access to land and the kind of cultivation practices employed there

agriculture: a science, an art, and a business directed at the cultivation of crops and the raising of livestock for sustenance and profit

hunting and gathering: activities whereby people feed themselves through killing wild animals and fish and gathering fruits, roots, nuts, and other edible plants

Figure 8.2 Human and machine labour In agriculture worldwide, human labour has been increasingly replaced by machines. Here, we see Sudanese women harvesting wheat by hand while modern harvester machines operated by men mow the plants for easier harvesting.

subsistence agriculture: farming for direct consumption by the producers, not for sale

commercial agriculture: farming primarily for sale, not for direct consumption

wild animals and fish and gathering fruits, roots, nuts, and other edible plants. Hunting and gathering are considered subsistence activities in that people who practise them procure only what they need to consume.

As we saw in Chapter 4, subsistence agriculture replaced hunting and gathering activities in many parts of the globe when people came to understand that the domestication of plants and animals could enable them to remain settled in one place over time rather than having to hunt and gather frequently in search of edible wild foods. **Subsistence agriculture** is a system in which agriculturalists consume all they produce. While the practice of subsistence agriculture is declining, it is still practised in many areas of the globe.

During the twentieth century, the dominant agricultural system in the core countries has become **commercial agriculture**, a system in which farmers produce crops and animals primarily for sale rather than for direct consumption by themselves and their families. Worldwide, the practice of subsistence agriculture is diminishing as increasing numbers of places are irresistibly incorporated into a globalized economy with a substantial commercial agricultural sector. Still widely practised in the periphery, however, subsistence activities usually follow one of three dominant forms: shifting cultivation, intensive subsistence agriculture, and pastoralism. Although many people in the global periphery rely on these traditional practices to feed themselves, traditional practices are increasingly being abandoned or modified as peasant farmers convert from a subsistence and barter economy to a cash economy.

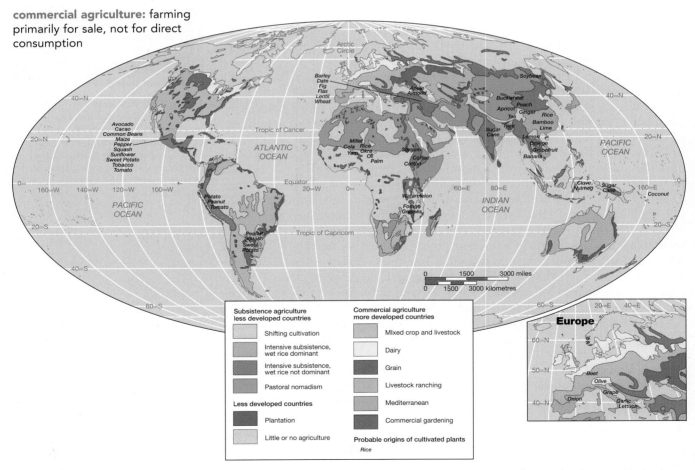

Figure 8.3 Global distribution of agriculture, 2005 The global distribution of agricultural practices is illustrated in this map. Notice the dramatic differences between core and periphery with respect to commercial versus subsistence agriculture. The periphery, though it does contain commercial agriculture, is largely dominated by forms of subsistence, while the core countries contain virtually none. The origins of cultivated plants can also be seen here as they are spread across both the Old World and the New. (After H. Veregin [ed.], *Goode's World Atlas*, 21st ed. Rand McNally, 2005, pp. 38–39.)

Shifting cultivation, a form of agriculture usually found in tropical forests, is a system in which farmers aim to maintain soil fertility by rotating the fields within which cultivation occurs.

Shifting cultivation is globally distributed in the tropics—especially in the rain forests of Central and West Africa; the Amazon in South America; and much of Southeast Asia, including Thailand, Myanmar, Malaysia, and Indonesia—where climate, rainfall, and vegetation combine to produce soils lacking nutrients. The practices involved in shifting cultivation have changed very little over thousands and thousands of years (**Figure 8.4**). As a land rotation system, shifting cultivation requires less expenditure of energy than modern forms of farming, though it can successfully support only low population densities.

The typical method for preparing land for shifting agriculture is through slash-and-burn, in which existing plants are cropped close to the ground, left to dry for a period, and then ignited (**Figure 8.5**). The burning process adds valuable nutrients to the soil, such as potash, which is about the only readily available fertilizer for this form of agricultural practice. Once the land is cleared and ready for cultivation, it is known as **swidden**.

The second dominant form of subsistence activity is **intensive subsistence agriculture**, a practice involving the effective and efficient use of a small parcel of land to maximize crop yield; a considerable expenditure of human labour and application of fertilizer is also usually involved. Unlike shifting cultivation, intensive subsistence cultivation is often able to support large rural populations. Although shifting cultivation is more characteristic of low agricultural densities, intensive subsistence normally reflects high agricultural density. Consequently, intensive subsistence usually occurs in the region of the world with the largest population, namely, Asia, and especially India, China, and Southeast Asia.

While shifting cultivation involves the application of a relatively limited amount of labour and other resources, intensive subsistence agriculture involves fairly constant human labour to achieve high productivity from a small amount of land (**Figure 8.6**). With population pressures fierce and the amount of arable land limited, intensive subsistence agriculture also reflects the inventive ways in which humans confront environmental constraints and reshape the landscape in the process. In fact, the landscape of intensive subsistence agriculture is often a distinctive one including raised fields and hillside farming through terracing.

shifting cultivation: a system in which farmers aim to maintain soil fertility by rotating the fields within which cultivation occurs

swidden: land that is cleared using the slash-and-burn process and is ready for cultivation

intensive subsistence agriculture: practice that involves the effective and efficient use—usually through a considerable expenditure of human labour and application of fertilizer—of a small parcel of land to maximize crop yield

Figure 8.4   Shifting cultivation Shifting cultivation is usually practised in tropical forests. It is a system of agriculture that maintains soil fertility by rotating the fields within which cultivation occurs.

Figure 8.5   Slash-and-burn agriculture Slash-and-burn is a process of preparing low-fertility soils for planting. In this practice, plants are cleared from a site through cutting, and then the remaining stumps are burned. The burning process helps add minerals to the soil and thereby improves the overall fertility. Slash-and-burn is a form of agricultural practice that is most effective when there are low levels of population. This is because the land, once cleared, can sustain enough crops to feed only small numbers of people, and its fertility very quickly diminishes. Therefore, after a few years, people usually move on to new clearings, allowing natural regeneration of the older sites to restore the sites' fertility before they are cleared again.

Figure 8.6 Intensive subsistence agriculture on the Himalayan foothills below Simla, India

pastoralism: subsistence activity that involves the breeding and herding of animals to satisfy the human needs of food, shelter, and clothing

Although not obviously a form of agricultural production, pastoralism is a third, dominant form of subsistence activity associated with a traditional way of life and agricultural practice. **Pastoralism** involves the breeding and herding of animals to satisfy the human needs of food, shelter, and clothing. It is usually practised in the cold and dry climates of deserts, savannas (grasslands), and steppes (lightly wooded, grassy plains) where subsistence agriculture is impracticable (and perhaps, because of this, representing an evolution from subsistence agriculture in such areas). Pastoralism can be either *sedentary* (pastoralists live in settlements and herd animals in nearby pastures) or *nomadic* (they wander with their herds over long distances, never settling in any one place for very long). Although forms of commercial pastoralism (the regularized herding of animals for profitable meat production) exist, for example, among Basque Americans in the basin and range regions of Utah and Nevada and the gauchos of the Argentinean grasslands, we are concerned here with pastoralism as a wandering subsistence activity.

Pastoralism is largely confined to parts of North Africa and the savannas of central and southern Africa, the Middle East, and central Asia. Pastoralists generally graze cattle, sheep, goats, and camels, although reindeer are herded in parts of Eurasia. The type of animal herded is related to the culture of the pastoralists as well as the animals' adaptability to the regional topography and foraging conditions (**Figure 8.7**).

As a subsistence activity, *nomadism* involves the systematic and continuous movement of groups of herders, their families, and their herds in search of forage.

Figure 8.7 Pastoralism This photo shows a Bedouin shepherd and his flock in the Irbid region of Jordan. Bedouins are traditionally nomadic pastoralists. Note the dryness of the landscape. Pastoralism usually occurs where agriculture is not feasible.

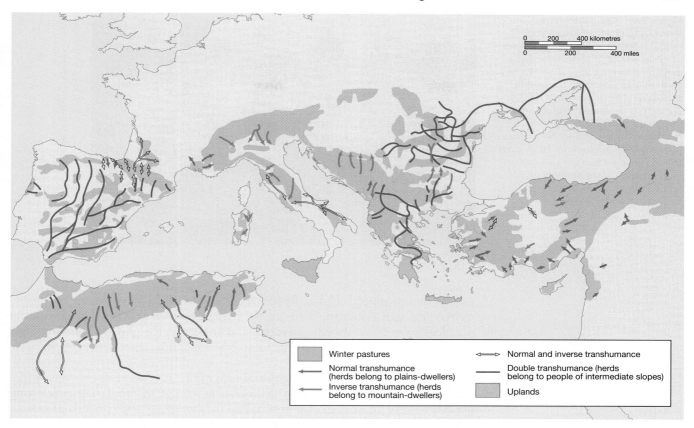

Figure 8.8   Distribution of transhumance routes around the Mediterranean region   Pictured on this map are the seasonal routes taken by herders as animals are moved from summer to winter pastures. As the map shows, transhumance is a well-established practice characterizing an effective adaptation to temporal rhythms. Just as environmental conditions shape herding practices, so do the herding practices shape the landscape through the emplacement of identifiable trails.   (*Source:* "Transhumance" [Figure 7] map from *The Mediterranean and the Mediterranean World in the Age of Philip II, Volume I*, by Fernand Braudel. Copyright © Librairie Armand Colin 1966. English translation copyright © 1972 by Wm. Collins Sons Ltd. and Harper & Row Publishers, Inc. Reprinted by permission of HarperCollins Publisher, Inc.)

This continuous movement, and the different attachment to "place" that it implies, challenges more sedentary societies. As a result, nomadic groups are often persecuted and made to settle down. Most pastoralists practise **transhumance**, the movement of herds according to seasonal rhythms: warmer, lowland areas in the winter and cooler, highland areas in the summer (**Figure 8.8**). Although the herds are occasionally slaughtered and used directly for food, shelter, and clothing, often they are bartered with sedentary farmers for grain and other commodities. Female and younger members of pastoralist groups may also be involved in cultivation.

In such cases, mostly women and children split off from the larger group and plant crops at fixed locations in the spring. They may stay sedentary for the growing season, tending the crops, or they may rejoin the group and return to the fields when the crops are ready for harvesting. The distinguishing characteristic of pastoralists is that they depend on animals, not crops, for their livelihood.

transhumance: the movement of herds according to seasonal rhythms: warmer, lowland areas in the winter and cooler, highland areas in the summer

AGRICULTURAL REVOLUTION AND INDUSTRIALIZATION

Increasingly, geographers and others have come to see world agricultural practices as having proceeded through revolutionary phases, just as manufacturing did. As in manufacturing, practices have not been transformed everywhere at the same time. Consequently, some parts of the world are still largely unaffected by certain

Figure 8.9 **The yoked plow** In this view from a farm near Nagpur in central India, we see how a yoked team of cattle is used in plowing. In many parts of the world, agriculturalists rely on draft animals to prepare land for cultivation. Using animals to assist in agricultural production was an important element in the first agricultural revolution. By expanding the amount of energy applied to production, draft animals enabled humans to increase food supplies. Many contemporary farmers view draft animals as their most valuable possessions.

Figure 8.10 **Present-day agriculture along the Nile** Agriculture along the Nile River dates far back into prehistory. The Nile floodplain was one of the important hearths of domestication, providing the foundation for the growth of complex civilizations in what we now know as Egypt. The Nile floodplain remains a remarkably productive area even today.

aspects of agricultural change. By seeing agriculture in this new light, it is possible to recognize that as in manufacturing, the changes that have occurred in agricultural practices have transformed geography and society as the global community has moved from predominantly subsistence to predominantly capital-intensive, market-oriented practices.

To understand the new agricultural geography, it is necessary to review the history of world agriculture. This history has proceeded in alternating cycles: long periods of very gradual change punctuated by short, explosive periods of radical change. Geographers and others have divided the history of world agriculture into three distinct revolutionary periods.

One very useful way to think about these periods is to use the approach developed by Ester Boserup in her 1965 book *The Conditions of Agricultural Growth: The Economics of Agrarian Change under Population Pressure*. She states that the most important difference among the pre-industrial world's agricultural systems is the frequency of cropping. In other words, the principal difference between shifting cultivation and sedentary agriculture and between patterns of annual cropping and "multicropping" (such as rice paddies) is the frequency with which the land itself is cultivated. The spur to move to increased cropping frequencies, Boserup argues, is independently caused by population pressure requiring agricultural change to feed extra mouths.

Such a theory is directly opposed to the ideas of Malthus, who saw population pressure as the *dependent variable* (a variable whose change is caused by another variable called the *independent variable*). In such situations, population numbers would decline to the level of available resources rather than the other way round (see Chapter 3). Nevertheless, even in Boserup's "model," societies are not free of all limitations. The extra labour needed to sustain ever-increasing frequencies of agriculture is daunting—so daunting that more productive technologies (or "revolutions"), such as irrigation, are often not adopted, even when known, until absolutely required by the pressure of numbers.

As we saw in Chapter 4, the *first agricultural revolution* is commonly recognized as having been founded on the development of agriculture and the use of the plow and draft animals (**Figure 8.9**). This probably occurred about 10 000 to 15 000 years ago, depending on the area of the world we mean. Especially important were floodplains along the Tigris, Euphrates, and Nile rivers, where complex civilizations were built on the fruits of the first agricultural revolution (**Figure 8.10**). Over time, the knowledge and skill underlying seed agriculture and the domestication of plants using other means, such as taking cuttings, diffused outward from these original areas, having a revolutionary impact throughout the world.

It is safe to place the apex of the *second agricultural revolution* historically and geographically alongside the Industrial Revolution in England and Western Europe. Although many important changes in agriculture preceded the Industrial Revolution, none had more of an impact on everyday life than the rise of an industrialized manufacturing sector, the effects of which spread rapidly to agriculture because of the demand for food from a growing urban and industrial population.

On the eve of the Industrial Revolution—in the middle of the eighteenth century—in Western Europe and England, subsistence peasant agriculture was predominant, though partial integration into a market economy was underway. Many peasants were utilizing a crop-rotation system that, in addition to the adoption of fallow crops such as clover (which returns nitrogen to the soil) and the application of natural and semiprocessed fertilizers, improved soil productivity and led to increased crop and livestock yields. Yields were also greatly increased by the adoption of New World crops, such as the potato, in European farming. Additionally, the feudal landholding system was breaking down and yielding to a new agrarian system, based not on service to a lord but on an emerging system of private-property relations. Communal farming practices and common lands were being replaced by enclosed, individually owned land or land worked independently by tenants or renters (**Figure 8.11**). Finally, the addition of new fodder crops, such as the turnip, enabled much larger herds of sheep and cattle to be developed to feed the growing demands of Europe's increasing population.

Such a situation was logical in response to the demands for food production that emerged from the dramatic social and economic changes accompanying the

The Village of Strettington, West Sussex, England

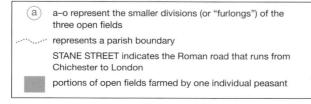

ⓐ a–o represent the smaller divisions (or "furlongs") of the three open fields

⋯⋯ represents a parish boundary

STANE STREET indicates the Roman road that runs from Chichester to London

▓ portions of open fields farmed by one individual peasant

Figure 8.11   Open field farming in England: an example   (*Source:* Author, based on reconstruction presented in Alan Nash, "The Medieval Fields of Strettington, West Sussex, and the Evolution of Land Division." *Geografiska Annaler B,* Volume 64, 1982, pp. 41–49.)

Industrial Revolution. Perhaps most important of all these changes was the development—through the creation of an urban industrial workforce—of a commercial market for food. Many innovations of the Industrial Revolution, such as improvements in transportation technology, had substantial impacts on agriculture. Innovations applied directly to agricultural practices, such as the new types of horse-drawn farm machinery, improved control over—as well as the quantity of—yields.

Another interesting response to the growing demands for food production from an increasingly industrialized and urban population was that the geographical pattern of agricultural land use around cities was often directly and profoundly affected by their proximity to such centres. In one way, this is of course a commonplace observation—it cost more to transport products into market the farther away production occurred—but much agricultural production also put a premium on freshness and therefore the closer to the market the better. Hence, productive agricultural land close to cities was often devoted to high-value, perishable products such as milk or (in the era before cheap airfreight) fruit and tomato production, and producers were prepared to pay high rents to locate in such areas.

The first scholar to spot these spatial patterns of agricultural land was Johann Heinrich von Thünen, a farmer in Mecklenburg, near Rostock in Germany, who first published his findings in 1826 and whose work languished until it was rediscovered by geographers in the 1960s as part of the interest in "locational analysis" (or "spatial analysis") that had then become fashionable in the discipline.

Certainly, von Thünen's model, as it has become known, was an ideal counterpart to the other major models of this approach (such as Weber's model of industrial location discussed in Chapter 7, and the Burgess model of urban land use, introduced in Chapter 11, with which it shares many common characteristics) since it argues that an activity (in this case, agricultural land use) is patterned according to distance from a market. In other words, space and distance are the main determining factors that govern the choice of agricultural production that any farmer chooses to pursue (**Figure 8.12**). However, as might be expected with such a simple model, there are substantial criticisms to be made: its omission of physical factors (such as soil types), government policies (which subsidize land use, or transport), and the assumption that land values are always determined by a rigid economics of space (the kind driven by a market economy), means that the model can now only be of use as a general descriptive tool. However, in showing how Europe's pre-industrial agricultural landscapes were reconfigured by the spatial forces of the Industrial Revolution, it certainly captured the profound changes wrought on many agricultural landscapes by a growing market economy.

By igniting the second agricultural revolution, the Industrial Revolution changed rural life as profoundly as the sedentary requirements of seed agriculture had transformed hunting and gathering societies. As geographer Ian Bowler writes, this revolution moved rapidly from Europe to other parts of the world:

> From its origins in Western Europe, the new commercialized system of farming was diffused by European colonization during the nineteenth and twentieth centuries to other parts of the world. A dominant agrarian model of commercial capitalist farming was established, based on a structure of numerous, relatively small family farms. From this period can be traced both the dependence of agriculture on manufacturing industry for many farm inputs, and the increasing productivity of farm labour, which released large numbers of workers from the land to swell the ranks of factory workers and city dwellers. Moreover, the production of food surplus to domestic demand enabled international patterns of agricultural trade to be established.[4]

As the experience of Canadian agriculture shows, this quotation nicely summarizes the development of farming in this country under colonialism (see **Geography Matters 8.1—Canadian Agriculture**).

---

[4]I. Bowler (ed.), *The Geography of Agriculture in Developed Market Economies*. Harlow, UK: Longman Scientific and Technical, 1992, pp. 10–11.

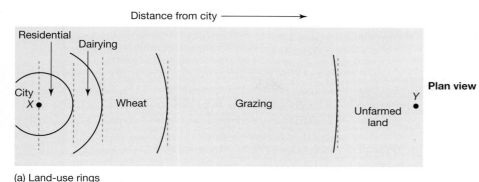

(a) Land-use rings

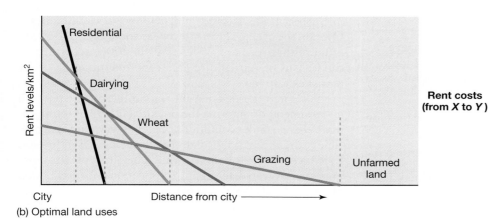

(b) Optimal land uses

Figure 8.12   Von Thünen's model of agricultural location   Von Thünen observed that a concentric pattern of agricultural land uses develop around a city (see (a), where only a segment of the full circle is shown for simplicity's sake). The patterns are caused because certain types of agricultural activity can pay more rent per hectare to locate near a city's market than other types (see (b)).   (*Source:* Peter Haggett, *Geography: A Global Synthesis.* Harlow, UK: Pearson, 2001, p. 463.)

The *third agricultural revolution* is a fairly recent development that, unlike the previous two, emanates mostly from the New World rather than the Old. Scholars identify the third agricultural revolution as beginning in the late nineteenth century and gaining momentum throughout the twentieth century. Each of its three important developmental phases originated in North America. Indeed, the globalization trends framing all our discussions in this text are the very same ones that have shaped the third agricultural revolution. The difference between the second and third agricultural revolutions is mostly a matter of degree; so, by the late twentieth century, technological innovations had virtually industrialized agricultural practices.

The three phases of the third agricultural revolution are mechanization, chemical farming with synthetic fertilizers, and globally widespread food manufacturing. **Mechanization** is the replacement of human farm labour with machines. Tractors, combines, reapers, pickers, and other forms of motorized machines have, since the 1880s and 1890s, progressively replaced human and animal labour inputs to the agricultural production process in Canada and the United States. In Europe, mechanization did not become widespread until after World War II. **Chemical farming** is the application of synthetic fertilizers to the soil and herbicides, fungicides, and pesticides to crops to enhance yields. Becoming widespread in the 1950s in North America, chemical farming diffused to Europe in the 1960s and to peripheral regions of the world in the 1970s.

Food manufacturing also had its origins in late nineteenth-century North America. **Food manufacturing** involves adding economic value to agricultural products through a range of treatments—processing, canning, refining, packing, packaging, refrigeration, and so on—occurring off the farm and before the products reach the market. The first two phases of the third revolution affected inputs to the agricultural production process, whereas the final phase affects agricultural outputs. Although the first two are related to the modernization of farming as an economic practice, the third involves a complication of the relationship of farms to firms in

mechanization: the replacement of human farm labour with machines

chemical farming: the application of synthetic fertilizers to the soil and herbicides, fungicides, and pesticides to crops to enhance yields

food manufacturing: adding value to agricultural products through a range of treatments—such as processing, canning, refining, packing, and packaging—that occur off the farm and before they reach the market

Canadian Agriculture

Some Generalizations

At first sight, two traditional generalizations about Canadian agriculture and its geography would still seem to be reasonable ones to make:

- Canadian agriculture is most affected by the physical environment of the country.
- Agriculture plays an important part in Canadian life.

Yet, to some extent, both these statements are misleading. They indicate either a misunderstanding of the current situation or a desire on our part to believe in a world that either never existed or is long past. Indeed, in terms of generalizations, it is probably more useful now to argue the following:

- Canadian agriculture is now most affected by the globalization of trade.
- Agribusiness plays an important part in Canadian life.

The examination of Canadian agricultural geography therefore involves more than an analysis of local, regional patterns and their erosion in the face of global trends; it must also confront a number of myths—myths that themselves eloquently speak of the space and place we wish agriculture had in Canadian life.

Agriculture in Canada

It must be admitted that the Canadian environment places clear limits on agriculture. Large tracts of mountainous terrain and glacial erosion have severely reduced the potential area available for cultivation. Harsh winters and long periods of below-zero temperatures prohibit most forms of agriculture across northern Canada and restrict the types of farming activity that can be pursued elsewhere in the country. Even those areas blessed with relatively mild climates have only short growing seasons.

It is therefore not surprising that most of Canada's productive agricultural land lies within 200 kilometres (125 miles) of the American border or that the total occupied farmland in Canada, according to 2001 Statistics Canada data, represents only 7 percent (68 million hectares or 168 million acres) of the country's total land area. The greatest part of that occupied land, or *ecumene,* lies in the Prairie provinces (Saskatchewan: 39 percent, Alberta: 31 percent, Manitoba: 11 percent), with only 8 percent in Ontario, 5 percent in Quebec, 4 percent in British Columbia, and fractions of a percent in the Atlantic provinces—percentages that, as we will see below, also have a significance in terms of the regional policies for Canadian farming (**Figure 8.1.1**).

The 2001 Census of Agriculture reported that Canada's total farming area was occupied by a total of 246 923 farms—a number that has declined by 11 percent

since 1996. According to this census, the largest number of farms is found in Ontario (59 728), Alberta (53 652), Saskatchewan (50 598), Quebec (32 139), and Manitoba (21 071). However, in terms of average farm size, the largest farms are found in the Prairies—Saskatchewan (519.1 hectares), Alberta (392.7 hectares), Manitoba (360.8 hectares)—with farms elsewhere in the ecumene averaging much smaller sizes (for example, in British Columbia, the average farm size in 2001 was 127.6 hectares; in Quebec, 106.3 hectares; and. in Ontario, 91.5 hectares).[5] Overall, the average farm size in Canada was 273 hectares, a figure that rose to 295 hectares in 2006, according to the Census of Agriculture data reported in mid-2007 by Statistics Canada.

Although not denying the importance of the physical environment, or ignoring the potential effects of future climate change under conditions of global warming, it is possible to argue that political decisions, themselves influenced by concerns of globalized trade, currently play a more important role in determining the location and distribution of much of today's farming in Canada. Illustrating this point are the recent changes in agriculture in what might once have been considered a classic wheat-growing Prairie environment.

Historical Development of Prairie Agriculture

During the nineteenth century, the Canadian Prairies had been consciously developed by Canadian politicians as an area of farming settlement. Once drought-resistant forms of wheat had been developed and railroads built, an export monoculture developed. Quickly realizing how this dependence made them prone to the vagaries of international markets, Prairie farmers agitated for government-subsidized rail shipment rates (the Crowsnest Pass Agreement, or "Crow Rate," of 1897) and for a collective grain marketing agency to increase their marketing power (the Canadian Wheat Board, established in 1935). These political developments had the effect of sustaining wheat cultivation across the Prairies despite the actual economics of location (that is, if the true costs of transport were considered) and the physical environment, which with its droughts was not an ideal cereal crop area and was worsened by monocultivation, as periodic infestations of grasshoppers illustrated.

---

[5]The first data from the 2001 Census of agriculture was reported in Statistics Canada's *The Daily, 15 May 2002* (**www.statcan.gc.ca/daily-quotidien/020515/dq020515-eng.pdf**). Subsequent releases and updates have been issued by Statistics Canada and are available at **www.statcan.gc.ca/ca-ra2001/index-eng.htm**. Because the full results of that census take some time to compile and analyze, Statistics Canada releases data in stages, and so you should also check its site for future updates. Government policy documents and backgrounders can be found on the website of Agriculture and Agri-Food Canada, the federal government ministry responsible for agriculture, at **www.agr.gc.ca**.

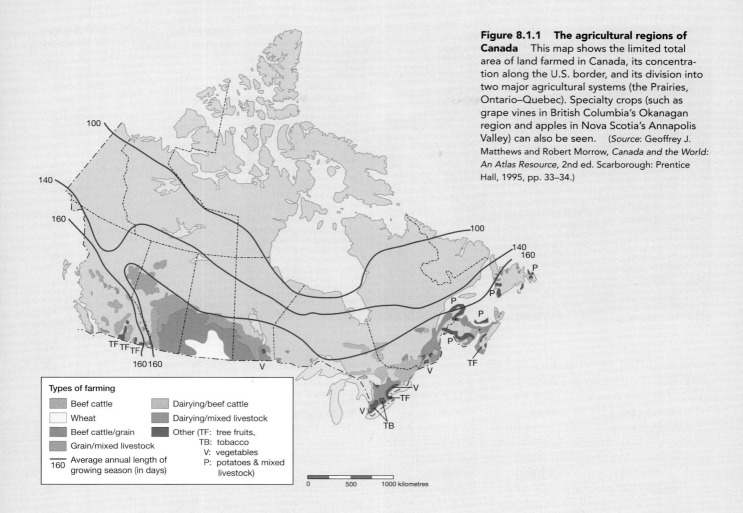

Figure 8.1.1 The agricultural regions of Canada This map shows the limited total area of land farmed in Canada, its concentration along the U.S. border, and its division into two major agricultural systems (the Prairies, Ontario–Quebec). Specialty crops (such as grape vines in British Columbia's Okanagan region and apples in Nova Scotia's Annapolis Valley) can also be seen. (*Source*: Geoffrey J. Matthews and Robert Morrow, *Canada and the World: An Atlas Resource*, 2nd ed. Scarborough: Prentice Hall, 1995, pp. 33–34.)

Types of farming

- Beef cattle
- Wheat
- Beef cattle/grain
- Grain/mixed livestock
- Dairying/beef cattle
- Dairying/mixed livestock
- Other (TF: tree fruits, TB: tobacco, V: vegetables, P: potatoes & mixed livestock)

160 Average annual length of growing season (in days)

0   500   1000 kilometres

Recent Developments in Prairie Agriculture

By the 1990s, however, the federal government felt the need to reduce its overall budget deficit and to begin to eliminate subsidies in agriculture to make that sector more economically competitive in a world of freer trade. Partly as a result of these factors and partly in response to indirect and direct American pressure, the "Crow Rate" was abolished in 1995. This had the effect of doubling the cost to farmers for shipping western grain by rail. For many, wheat production became even more of an economically marginal activity than it had been. To reduce their transport costs, farmers were keen to sell locally, and this sharp reduction in the cost of grain supply spurred an increase in hog and beef cattle production from 1998 onward. In effect, it was now economically more advantageous to feed locally produced grain to animals and to export the animals than it was to export grain itself. As a consequence, hog rearing, especially in Manitoba where several million are now slaughtered each year, and the production of beef cattle, especially in Alberta, have now become fundamental forces restructuring Prairie agriculture.

Consider beef production as an example of these changes. A whole reshaping of the Canadian beef-processing industry into an "agribusiness" has been underway for some time.

Traditionally, cattle raised on ranches of Alberta and British Columbia's interior were shipped live to feedlots in southern Alberta or southwest Ontario for fattening and then were butchered in meat-packing plants in Toronto, Hamilton, and Kitchener-Waterloo. However, from the 1980s onward, the dominance of large supermarkets and the sale of ready-to-use foods encouraged the construction of meat processing in automated nonunion plants in the cattle-rearing areas—a locational change that received a considerable boost with the abolition of the Crow Rate. Statistics Canada data for 1996 show that the average annual throughput of cattle in Albertan and British Columbian meat-processing plants was 220 percent greater than that of Ontario's and that the top four plants accounted for 75 percent of the total beef slaughter in this country. By 2001, the total number of cattle in Alberta had increased to 6.6 million from a figure of 5.9 million in 1996, and many of the additional cattle "serve the voracious market to the United States." However, the discovery of mad cow disease (bovine spongiform encephalopathy, BSE), in 2003 and 2005 in cows in Alberta brought about other changes in this industry, albeit unexpected ones. The impact of the BSE crisis was soon felt at a national level. As early as 2004, for example, Statistics Canada reported in its

Figure 8.1.2 Canadian beef industry in crisis Empty feedlots in Alberta in the wake of the mad cow crisis.

publication *The Daily* that total Canadian farm income in 2003 from beef cattle and calves had declined by 33 percent when compared with the total for 2002. By 2007, when it was possible to compare the results of the 2006 census of agriculture with that of the previous agricultural census in 2001, Statistics Canada was able to add to this picture that "[b]eef farms in Canada have had a tough time in the intercensal period and their numbers reflect that, declining by 10 percent to about 61 000 farms." More specifically, in terms of its impact on Alberta, the Census of Agriculture data showed that the provincial herd had diminished from 6.6 million beef cattle in 2001 to 6.37 million in 2006, a decline which masked the full impact of BSE. (This is because evidence at a national level shows an unexpected *increase* in herd size during these years, caused by the fact that the threat of BSE in older animals made them almost worthless as meat, and cattle farmers therefore preferred instead to slaughter only younger cattle. The total herd became bigger, but its future reproductive capacity—surely a better measure of the viability of the industry declined by 27 percent).[6]

The confirmed case of another incidence of mad cow disease on 17 November 2008 (the fifteenth in Canada), in a dairy cow in British Columbia, showed that the effects of BSE are far from over. In confirming the case, the Canadian Food Inspection Agency assured the public that no part of the animal had entered the human or animal food systems, and that the fact that this case had been discovered by the federal BSE detection team indicated that the protection put in place since the first outbreaks was working. Certainly, the fact that the case did not make headline news, as previous outbreaks had, may indicate a restored public faith in the safety of the food system, or it may suggest a grudging acceptance that BSE will be around for much longer than was first hoped. Either way, BSE is no longer as newsworthy as it once was and in that simple fact must lie some hope for Canadian beef producers.[7]

Agriculture in Canadian Life

The centrality of agriculture in Canadian life was once clear to all. It was not only a mainstay of the nineteenth-century economy but also contributed to the ways in which Canadians shaped, or "constructed," their view of the country and of *space* and *place* within it.

Historical Development

To return to our example of the Prairies, Harold Troper, in his book *Only Farmers Need Apply*, clearly shows how Sir Clifford Sifton (who became federal minister of the interior in 1896) was able to use the needs of the Canadian government to populate the Prairies to justify his focus on the recruitment of farmers from central and Eastern Europe and from the United States. He believed people from the industrial areas and cities of Europe had less useful skills and so excluded them (ostensibly the reason

[6]Statistics Canada, "Study: Potential Impact of Mad Cow Disease on Farm Family Income." *The Daily,* 18 June 2004, **www.statcan.gc.ca /daily-quotidien/040618/dq040618c-eng.htm**. The quotation and the data on changing herd size are taken from Statistics Canada's very informative summary of the 2006 Census of Agriculture, *Snapshot of Canadian Agriculture* (issued in 2007 and available at **www.statcan.gc.ca/ca-ra2006/articles/snapshot-portrait-eng.htm**. For comparisons with the 2001 Census of Agriculture, see Statistics Canada, "Selected Historical Data from the Census of Agriculture: Data Tables," 2007, available at **www.statcan.ca/english/freepub/ 95-632-XIE/2007000/ histmenu-en.htm#i** (data reported to 2006).

[7]CanWest News Service, "Mad Cow Disease Reported in B.C. Farm," 17 November 2008, available at **www.canada.com/topics/news/national/ story.html?id=618c93ac-3d94-478b-854c-f990ad10d532&k=93724**.

Jews and Black Americans were also largely excluded from the Prairies). The perceived needs of rural space, in other words, dictated who could immigrate to Canada and, once they had created rural "places" in the Prairies, it was believed these immigrants would be able to perpetuate Old World agricultural values in a Canadian setting. Sifton was not alone, of course, in believing that a rural farming culture was more honest or moral than an urban or industrial society. Such views have deep roots in Western thinking. He was, unlike many, able to put such ideas into practice and, in so doing, set about creating a farming economy on the Prairies.

That world remains to this day in the many examples of vernacular farm buildings and fences that dot the Prairies, in the now derelict grain elevators, and in the people, folk tales, and literature of the region (for example, Wallace Stegner's *Wolf Willow,* set in East End, Saskatchewan, and W.O. Mitchell's *Who Has Seen the Wind?*). Museums, such as the branches of the Provincial Museum of Saskatchewan, especially that at Yorkton, provide a tangible memory of this world—a place where rural and agricultural values merge.

Recent Developments

However celebrated such an agricultural world is, statistics show that it is now well and truly part of the past. In fact, the available evidence shows that the farming economy has been under attack for the last 50 or 60 years. In 1941, the total number of farms in Canada peaked at an all-time high of 733 000 farms. By 1996, however, that figure had declined by 62 percent to reach 277 000 farms. According to the latest figures from the 2006 census, that number now stands at a total of 229 373 farms. In 1951, 21 percent of the Canadian population was engaged in agriculture, but by 1991, only 3 percent were. More telling perhaps is the observation that farmers now compose only 10 percent of the total rural population itself—the remainder including village dwellers, retirees, and cottagers. Indeed, one leading Canadian agricultural geographer has recently written that "Canadian agriculture is in a precarious state."[8]

Almost symbolic of this state of affairs, grain elevators—to many Canadians an icon of the Prairies and its agriculture—are now themselves a thing of the past. In 1933, there were 5578 grain elevators across the Prairies. This number fell to 3117 by 1981, and in 2002 stood at only 588. The restructuring of rail branch lines across the Prairies has eliminated the need for many small grain elevators. The system has instead become refocused on a limited number of very large inland grain terminals, many with storage capacities 10 times that of the grain elevators of the 1930s (**Figure 8.1.3**).

---

[8]William C. Found, "Agriculture in a World of Subsidies." In John N.H. Britton (ed.), *Canada and the Global Economy: The Geography of Structural and Technological Change.* Montreal and Kingston: McGill–Queen's University Press, 1996, pp. 155–168. The quotation is from p. 155.

(a)

(b)

Figure 8.1.3   The disappearing grain elevator   Grain elevators, such as the one shown in (a) at Lang, Saskatchewan, are fast being replaced by fewer and much larger inland grain terminals, such as the one illustrated in (b) at Shaunavon, Saskatchewan.

What are the causes for these fundamental changes? We can identify a number of major factors:

- *Globalization.* Perhaps the main cause for this decline in the agricultural way of life has been the growing globalization of world trade. Thus, the increasing liberalization of international trade under such treaties as the General Agreement on Tariffs and Trade (GATT—the precursor of the World Trade Organization, or WTO) and the North American Free Trade Agreement (NAFTA) require the elimination of domestic subsidies on a range of products and manufactures as part of a way of promoting fairer competition and more open access to the markets of other countries. Although it is true that Canadian agricultural subsidies have so far been protected from such agreements, their days are surely numbered, as the future round of the World Trade Organization talks indicate, and American protests over NAFTA illustrate. Consequently, Canadian government action, as in the abolition of the Crow Rate, has been proactive in this respect and designed to work toward the elimination of subsidies.

- *Subsidies.* For Canadian farmers, globalization in the form of greater competition has simply meant that the prices of their agricultural products have fallen sharply on the international markets, while globalization in the form of the reduction of subsidies has exacerbated the decline in overall farm income that they might have received. For many Canadian farmers, this situation is made more galling with reports of continued high levels of subsidy to farmers within the European Union (EU), the United States, and Japan. Data from the Organisation for Economic Co-operation and Development (OECD), reported in the *Globe and Mail* on 7 April 2001, noted that in 1999, wheat producers in the United States received 46 percent of their income from subsidies, those in the EU received 58 percent, and those in Canada received only 11 percent. The announcement of substantial increases to American farm subsidies in June 2002 only further heightened the discrepancies between Canadian farmers and their international competitors.

■ *The "cash squeeze."* On the other side of the ledger, farm inputs (such as fertilizers, pesticides, seed, farm machinery, land, labour, and financing) have all increased in cost. To illustrate the "cash squeeze" from 1974 to 1994, total farm operating costs in Canada rose by 40 percent, while the levels of gross revenue (expressed in constant 1986 dollars) remained approximately the same at about $20 billion. Circumstances have now altered somewhat (as noted below), but the challenges of balancing cost and revenue remain.

Average farm statistics show that in 1985, for example, the average total sale of produce per farm in Canada was worth $70 917, and the average level of expenditure was $60 000 per farm, producing an average annual income of only $11 000. By 1996, more than half of all farms in Canada had a net cash income of under $4200 per year, and 39 percent were actually losing money. It is scarcely to be wondered that more than two-thirds of farms at that time reported income from non-farm activities to supplement their incomes.

Many of these non-farm activities were performed by farm women. The income that farm women earn in off-farm employment has become a vital supplement to total farm income and has enabled many families to continue farming. Historically, women's role as unpaid labour on the farm itself was an important one, and in recent years, this role has expanded. No longer confined to traditional domestic duties and lighter farming jobs, farm women are now as likely to be operating heavy farm machinery as they are to be feeding chickens and keeping the farm accounts. As Jocelyn Hainsworth, a farm woman who lives in Redvers, Saskatchewan, has written:

> The role of a farm wife as we begin the 21st century has evolved to where she is a chief, and cheap—make that indispensable—source of labour during the busy seasons. I don't ever remember Mom driving the grain truck or even fuelling up the tractor, yet these are considered specifically my jobs on the farm. And it doesn't stop there; I have cultivated and harrowed with both two- and four-wheel drive tractors, and I've run the swather and the grain auger. I haven't used the airseeder to plant a crop and I'm

a lot more relaxed hauling the grain back to the bins than I am at the helm of a combine, but there are lots of women who do these jobs too, and excel at them.[9]

In many instances, therefore, changes in farming have resulted in a profound reconfiguration of gender roles in the public and private spheres—in effect, making the Prairies a crucible of social change. Certainly, without the unpaid labour of both farm women and men, many small Prairie farms would be unable to survive economically.

■ *Farm polarization.* Polarization has occurred as those farms that are able to compete pull away from the rest of the pack. These are farms that have been able to increase in size, to specialize, or to increase their capital investments to take advantage of the economies of scale of production. Thus, according to 1996 data, 30 percent of the total number of Canadian farms were responsible for more than 83 percent of total farm output; indeed, only 3 percent of farms accounted for over 36 percent of gross farm receipts earned that year. The remainder, 70 percent of the total, was responsible for only 17 percent of farm output. On the basis of the evidence, it is mostly the smaller producers that are dropping out of the industry. Data from the 2006 Census of Agriculture show that 28.6 percent of the farms with less than $25 000 in total revenue reported that they had enough farm income in 2005 to cover their expenses. In contrast, 86 percent of farms with incomes of over $1 million reported enough farm receipts to cover their expenses.

An analysis of farm incomes also allows us to see how Canadian agriculture is currently refocusing its activities in terms of types of agricultural production. Thus, 1991 data show that the four major farm types of beef, dairy, wheat, and other small grains comprised 64 percent of all farms in Canada and accounted for 61 percent of all farm receipts. Such developments are responsible for the increasing division of the country into what economic geographer Iain Wallace has called "two very different sets of production environments."

In the three Prairie provinces, the emphasis is being placed on grain, oilseeds, and beef production, while in the remaining provinces, attention is given mainly to intensive specialty crops (such as the Niagara and Okanagan Valley soft-fruit and wine industries and Prince Edward Island's potato crop) and dairy and poultry production, mainly in Ontario and Quebec, operated under *supply management systems* (methods whereby demand and supply are kept in balance via regulated markets and the use of production quotas). These discrepancies are underlined by differences reported in the 2001 Census of Agriculture. In terms of average farm revenues by type of activity, according to the data, dairy farms spend the least

---

[9] Jocelyn Hainsworth, "My Mother's Farm and Mine" (CBC 2002), available on the website **www.cbc.ca/news/work/wherewework/253.html**.

(75 cents) on operating costs for every dollar of sales, compared with cattle farms, which spend the most (94 cents for every dollar of sales).

The first of these "production environments," the Prairies, Wallace notes, competes in international export markets and is therefore also very vulnerable to their ups and downs. The second is one whose structure of production is not competitive internationally and operates on the basis of protective government regulation. The former is in the Canadian hinterland, the latter in the urbanized heartland—a fact that Iain Wallace suggests gives a clear regional dimension to Canadian agricultural policy.[10]

The Future

As we look forward, it is worth noting that the current situation for many Canadian farmers has completely turned around in the last few years, and—barring total crop failure—the future looks extremely promising for Prairie grain producers, in particular, and Canadian farmers in general. According to Agriculture and Agri-food Canada, net income for the average Canadian farm is expected to rise 16 percent in 2008, and crop receipts that year are projected to be nearly 40 percent higher than they were in 2006.[11] Newspaper accounts are equally rosy, as Joe Friesen's description of Prairie farmers in February 2008 illustrates.

> Farmers are snapping up $300,000 combines and new seeders at a pace not seen in years, Even at twice last year's price, fertilizer dealers are filling orders months in advance of delivery, and nearly everyone seems to be making plans to get the latest global positioning system technology for their tractors. Land is being bought and sold at prices that set the neighbours talking, and that rarest of words, optimism, is a hot topic on coffee row.[12]

The reasons why this has happened and the speed of the turnaround in many farmers' fortunes illustrates the vulnerability of the industry to the forces of the global economy. Forces that for so long have depressed world agricultural prices have now been replaced with a constellation of factors working in the opposite direction, and Canada's farmers clearly stand to benefit.

Four factors are usually identified for the current increase in agricultural prices in Canada:

1. *The increasing demand for grains from India and China.* As living standards rise in Southeast Asia, consumers there are turning to new and more expensive proteins (thereby also permanently changing their diets with higher calorie and more convenience foods).

As but one example from early 2008, the price of yellow peas (a pulse in much demand in India) rose from $400 a tonne to $600 in just two months. With an estimated 50 million people a year joining the middle classes in China and India, the demand for imported agricultural food stuffs seems set to increase—and will affect more than simply grain producers. As Donald Coxe, global portfolio strategist for the Bank of Montreal has noted, "They're adding meat and dairy to their diet and we aren't producing enough feed grains, enough vegetable proteins to supply their needs. Milk is the new oil. Milk demand worldwide is rising faster than oil demand."[13]

2. *The increasing demand from ethanol producers.* Ethanol production now takes up 20 percent of the American corn harvest, and the increasing diversion of such cereals into biofuels in the United States and Canada has created such a competitive market for corn that farmers (who had previously abandoned this crop as not profitable) are eagerly planting additional acreages. Indeed, the price of Saskatchewan farmland, which had been increasing in value by only 1 percent a year over the past 15 years, has increased by 15 percent in some parts of the province as farmland begins to seem a profitable investment once more.

3. *The increasing effects of climate change.* Recent periods of drought have led to reduced production in parts of the Prairies and contribute to increased prices because not enough surplus from previous years is available to meet the demand prompted by either Asia's demands or biofuel's needs.

4. *The rising costs of petroleum.* The increasing cost of gasoline across Canada is being passed straight on to consumers in the form of higher agricultural prices (to pay for the increased costs of transportation and trucking to markets).

However, unlike the other three factors mentioned above, the increasing cost of gasoline is one that will work to farmers' disadvantage since it also greatly increases their costs of production and continues problems of "profit squeeze" discussed above. In this connection, the fact that the price of fertilizers has risen 150 percent during the current period of increasing crop prices will undoubtedly eat into farmers' profits.

In fact, factors like these have led many farmers to treat the present boom with considerable caution. As Keith Gardner, who farms a 1300 acre operation near Virden, Manitoba, remarked about the newfound hope for prosperous times:

> I've been farming since 1977 and we've heard that before. We were told there'd be a shortage of grain to feed the world but it's never really happened. It'd be nice

---

[10]Iain Wallace, *A Geography of the Canadian Economy*. Don Mills: Oxford University Press, 2002. Chapter 3: "Agriculture, Agri-food, and the Rural Economy," pp. 123–139.

[11]These paragraphs are based on Joe Friesen, "Eastern Promises: Asia Is Fuelling a Prairie Agriculture Boom." *Globe and Mail*, 16 February 2008, pp. B1, B4–5.

[12]Ibid., p. B4.

[13]Ibid.

to believe that, but they've been wrong before, haven't they?[14]

Although Canadian agriculture has had a difficult past, it is clear that there are a number of options for the future. However, it is equally clear that these options are only possible if a great deal of effort is expended by the Canadian public. Whether that effort is given or not will provide a measure of how much Canadians really value Canadian agriculture and what value they place on domestic food security. The range of possible options includes the following:

- *Increasing the cost of food*. At present, Canadians spend less than 10 percent of their after-tax income on food purchased in grocery stores. Inexpensive foods are good for the consumer, but they do not help the farmer.

- *Encouraging farmers to develop forms of food processing*. According to 1997 data, the "value added" for farmers represented only one-seventh of what retail sales ultimately realized on the fruits of their labours.

- *Promoting organic or niche forms of farming*. With increasing concern about the environmental damage caused by modern farming, the development of organic farming might represent an alternative in some areas, although, on present evidence, costs to the consumer would likely increase. Other crops, such as ginseng in the British Columbian interior (**Figure 8.1.4**), have proved to be lucrative (as is—although this is not suggested here—the illegal growing of marijuana in that province, which some sources estimate to represent B.C.'s leading crop by value!). Data from the 2001 Census of Agriculture show that the organic sector is more popular than ever, but since it still only represents 1 percent (2230) of all farms, this is a sector that could be developed much further.[15]

- *Promoting alternative uses for agricultural land*. In areas in close proximity to cities, farmers have the option of devoting parts of their land to uses that may be in demand by urban dwellers. In parts of Britain, for example, once-derelict barns have been converted to expensive second homes, or even into office accommodation. Elsewhere, riding stables, "pick your own" fruit and vegetable farms, or even maple-sugar lots offer farmers alternative sources of income.

- *Supporting city-oriented farmers' markets and delivery*. A trend that has become increasingly popular in places such as Toronto and Montreal is for groups of people to contract with individual farmers to purchase produce

Figure 8.1.4   A field of ginseng near Lillooet, British Columbia   One of the new developments in farming is to grow organic or niche-market crops. In this case, the demand for herbal products in Canada and abroad has supported the expansion of ginseng cultivation, a high-value crop particularly suited to the dry conditions of British Columbia's southern interior. The crop is grown under a protective black net.

from them for an entire season. The goods are either delivered by the farmer, or made available for collection at a central location (such as a farmers' market or co-op). The benefits are that consumers know exactly where their food has come from, and under what conditions it has been grown (often, the preference being for organically produced foods); the producers have a sure market and establish connections with people who are committed to supporting local farming.

- *Promoting the production of "exotic" meats*. The discovery of Canada's first case of mad cow disease in Alberta in May 2003, and the subsequent cost to the Canadian beef industry has prompted many consumers and producers alike to turn to the certified organic production of cattle, or of exotic animals (such as emus or bison) that are believed to be unaffected by the disease.[16]

- *Promoting the importance of farmers as "land resource managers"* (to use Iain Wallace's phrase). If Canadians value the rural life as much as their purchase and use of cottages seem to suggest, then it might be possible to maintain those places through the use of a policy that at the same time benefits those few farmers remaining in the area.

In rural Canada, among the most pressing problems, from a policy-maker's perspective, are the decline of the socioeconomic infrastructure in these areas and the emigration of the young—both factors that erode an area's ability to sustain itself.

Fortunately, a great deal of research on solving these problems is underway, some of it by geographers and some

[14]These paragraphs are based on Joe Friesen, "Eastern Promises: Asia Is Fuelling a Prairie Agriculture Boom." *Globe and Mail*, 16 February 2008, pp. B1, B4–5.

[15]A lively debate on this topic followed the initial release of the 2001 Census of Agriculture statistics. See, for example, the remarks of Olds College (Alberta) agrologist Robert Wilson, "Farming Has a Rainbow." *Globe and Mail*, 21 May 2002, p. A17; and Jill Mahoney, "Farmers Take Stock of New Markets." *Globe and Mail*, 16 May 2002, pp. A1, A7.

[16]See also the informative essay on Canada's mad cow disease crisis by Ian MacLachlan, "Betting the Farm: Food Safety and the Beef Commodity Chain." In A. Heintzman and E. Solomon (eds.), *Feeding the Future: From Fat to Famine: How to Solve the World's Food Crises*. Toronto: House of Anansi Press, 2004, pp. 37–69.

of it by Canadians themselves, and we hope that politicians will not wait too long before they implement some of the most useful suggestions. Consider, for example, the work of geographer Sudhir Wanmali. In a series of books and journal articles based on investigations into problems in rural India and Zimbabwe, Dr. Wanmali has suggested that one way that important services (such as libraries, banks, and health care) can continue to be provided in small rural settings is for those services to become mobile. This very interesting geographic solution recognizes that facilities do not always need to be permanently located in one spot. By using mobile branches that can move to different towns on different days, the problem of low demand at any one point is resolved—in effect, by using flexibility in time to resolve problems with space.[17]

The Social Sciences and Humanities Research Council (SSHRC) has funded 15 university researchers who are examining how Canada can rebuild capacity in rural areas (**Figure 8.1.5**). Using 32 research sites, the project (known as the New Rural Economy or NRE) explores how we can develop enhanced political institutions, improve service delivery, better manage natural resources, and increase communications in rural centres.[18] It will be interesting to see what answers are produced, but already three basic lessons are clear. According, to Dr. Bill Reimer, the project's director, these lessons are as follows:[19]

■ Rural Canada is poorly positioned for the new economy, which "requires the ability to extract value from

Figure 8.1.5 Farming near Redvers, Saskatchewan A frequent sight on the Prairies, especially in parts of Saskatchewan, is that of actively farmed land and abandoned buildings. It is a very visible outcome of the processes of farm size increase and consolidation, on the one hand, and the movement and reconcentration of the province's once much more dispersed farming population, on the other hand.

human knowledge, most often acquired through 'global' relationships."

■ The social capital and cohesion found in rural Canada can support economic cohesion. The traditional communal values of rural life are not, at first sight, very appropriate resources in a market-based or bureaucratic-based economy. However, in the right context, these values can still be a valuable resource.

■ A rural–urban alliance is needed. Despite their differences, it is clear that rural and urban Canada share many interests (around, for example, the environment, residential space, recreation, and heritage preservation) that to abandon rural Canada to its own devices makes little sense in terms of the greater good.

---

[17]Sudhir Wanmali, *Periodic Markets and Rural Development in India.* Delhi: BR Publishing Corporation, 1981.
[18]The website for the New Rural Economy (NRE2) project is available at **http://nre.concordia.ca/nre2.htm**.
[19]Bill Reimer, "The New Rural Economy Project: What Have We Learned?" Paper prepared for the Rural Sociological Society, Montreal, July 2003, available online at **http://nre.concordia.ca/nre2.htm**.

the manufacturing sector, which had increasingly expanded into the area of food early in the 1960s (**Figure 8.13**). The third also complicates our relationship with our environment because the increased ability to preserve food distances us from the natural rhythms of the farming year. Considered together, these three developmental phases of the third agricultural revolution constitute the industrialization of agriculture.

The Industrialization of Agriculture

Developed over time, the industrialization of agriculture has largely been determined by advances in science and technology, especially by mechanical as well as chemical and biological innovations. As with industrialization more generally, the industrialization of agriculture has unfolded as the capitalist economic system has become more advanced and widespread. We regard **agricultural industrialization** as the process whereby the farm has moved from being the centrepiece of agricultural production to becoming but one part of an integrated multilevel (or vertically organized) industrial process, including production, storage, processing, distribution,

agricultural industrialization: the process whereby the farm has moved from being the centrepiece of agricultural production to becoming one part of an integrated string of vertically organized industrial processes including production, storage, processing, distribution, marketing, and retailing

Figure 8.13 Food manufacturing
Pictured here are tomatoes being processed through an assembly-line operation. Food processing is one of the ways that economic value is added to agricultural products before they reach the market.

marketing, and retailing. Experts in the study of agriculture have come to see agriculture as clearly linked to industry and the service sector, thus constituting a complex agro-commodity production system.

Geographers have helped demonstrate the changes leading to the transformation of an agricultural product into an industrial food product. This transformation has been accomplished not only through the indirect or direct altering of agricultural outputs, such as tomatoes or wheat, but also through changes in rural economic activities. Agricultural industrialization involves three important developments:

- changes in rural labour activities as machines replace or improve human labour
- the introduction of innovative inputs—fertilizers, hybrid seeds, agrochemicals, and biotechnologies—to supplement, alter, or replace biological outputs
- the development of industrial substitutes for agricultural products (for example, artifical sweeteners instead of sugar, thickeners instead of cornstarch or flour)

Recall, however, that the industrialization of agriculture has not occurred simultaneously throughout the globe. Changes in the global economic system affect different places in different ways as different countries and social groups respond to and shape these changes. For example, the use of fertilizers and high-yielding seeds occurred much earlier in core-region agriculture than in the periphery, where many places still farm without them. Beginning in the late 1960s, however, core countries exported a technological package of fertilizers and high-yielding seeds to regions of the periphery (largely in Asia and Mexico) in an attempt to boost agricultural production. Known as the **Green Revolution**, this package also included new machines and institutions, all diffused from the core to the periphery, designed to increase global agricultural productivity (**Figure 8.14**).

Although the Green Revolution has come under much justified attack over the years, it has focused the world's attention on finding innovative new ways to feed the world's peoples. In the process, the world-system has been expanded into hitherto very remote regions, and important knowledge has been gained about how to conduct science and how to understand the role that agriculture plays at all geographical scales of resolution, from the global to the local.

Green Revolution: the export of a technological package of fertilizers and high-yielding seeds, from the core to the periphery, to increase global agricultural productivity

GLOBAL RESTRUCTURING OF AGRICULTURAL SYSTEMS

When geographers talk about the globalization of agriculture, they are referring to the incorporation of agriculture into the world economic system of capitalism. A useful way to think about the term **globalized agriculture** is to recognize that as both

globalized agriculture: a system of food production increasingly dependent on an economy and a set of regulatory practices that are global in scope and organization

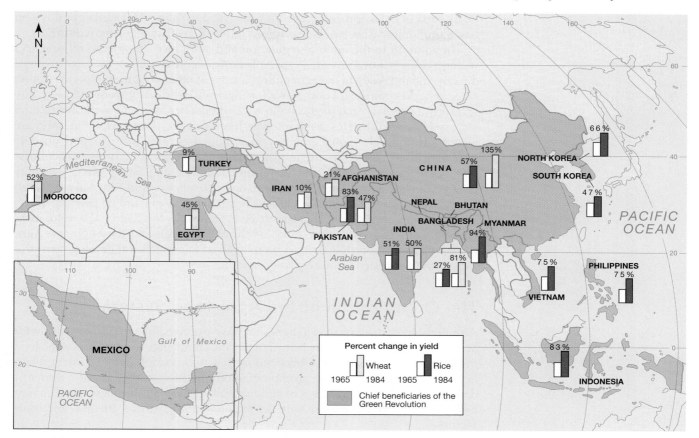

Figure 8.14 Effects of the Green Revolution, 1990 This map illustrates the increases in yields brought about by the Green Revolution in Asia and Mexico. Burgeoning populations in these regions mean that increased yields are critical. Although yields have indeed improved, the costs of implementing the new practices have driven poorer farmers out of agriculture entirely. The abandonment of farming by small-farm workers has led to the concentration of arable land in fewer and fewer hands, similar to trends that have occurred in the core. An additional important effect of the Green Revolution has been the loss of biomass fuel production. Byproducts of more traditional agriculture, wood, crop residues, and dung have been replaced by petroleum as an energy source. (*Source:* F. Shelley and A. Clarke, *Human and Cultural Geography.* Dubuque, IA: William C. Brown, 1994, fig. 7.8, p. 196.)

an economic sector and a geographically distributed activity, modern agriculture is increasingly dependent on an economy and set of regulatory practices that are global in scope and organization.

Forces of Globalization

Three related processes play a role in the globalization of agriculture:

- The forces—technological, economic, political, and so on—that shape agricultural systems are global in their scope.

- The institutions—trade and finance especially—that most dramatically alter agriculture are organized globally.

- The current form of agriculture reflects integrated, globally organized agro-production systems.

The globalization of agriculture has dramatically changed relationships among, between, and within different agricultural production systems. The result is either eventual elimination of some forms of agriculture or the erosion or alteration of systems as they are integrated into the global economy. Two examples include the current decline of traditional agricultural practices, such as shifting cultivation, in many parts of the world and the erosion in Canada of a national agricultural system based on family farms (see **Geography Matters 8.1—Canadian Agriculture**).

In addition to the internal regulation and assistance of agricultural practices within a country, governments—especially those of core countries—are also involved directly and indirectly in the agricultural sectors of other countries, especially those of peripheral countries. Food as well as agricultural development aid are widespread and popularly accepted ways in which core states intervene in the agricultural sector of peripheral states. Such intervention is one way that peripheral states are incorporated into the global economy. In addition to straightforward food aid, core states are also involved in attempting to improve the capacity of the agricultural sector of peripheral states. Unsuccessful agricultural development projects—whether because of poor design, implementation, or some other reason—as well as successful ones illustrate the many ways in which global forces can and do produce different local consequences and reactions from local people. International development organizations and institutions, such as the World Bank and the Food and Agriculture Organization (FAO), have been involved in agricultural development projects in the periphery for nearly five decades.

The Organization of the Agro-food System

Although the history of the changes that have occurred in agriculture worldwide are complex, certain elements help simplify the complexity and serve as important indicators of change. Geographers and other scholars interested in contemporary agriculture have noted three prominent and nested forces that signal a dramatic departure from previous forms of agricultural practice: agribusiness, food chains, and integration of agriculture with the manufacturing, service, finance, and trade sectors.

The concept of agribusiness has received a good deal of attention in the last two decades, and in the popular mind it has come to be associated with large corporations, such as ConAgra or Del Monte. Our definition of agribusiness departs from this popular conceptualization. Although multi- and transnational corporations (TNCs) are certainly involved in agribusiness, the concept is meant to convey more than a corporate form. **Agribusiness** is a system rather than a kind of corporate entity. Indeed, it is a set of economic and political relationships that organizes food production from the development of seeds to the retailing and consumption of the agricultural product. Defining agribusiness as a system, however, is not meant to suggest that corporations are not critically important to the food production process. On the contrary, in the core economies, the transnational corporation is the dominant player operating at numerous strategically important stages of the food production process. TNCs have become dominant for a number of reasons, but mostly because of their ability to negotiate the complexities of production and distribution in many different geographical locations. That capability requires special knowledge of national, regional, and local regulations and pricing factors.

A food chain (a special type of commodity chain) is a way to understand the organizational structure of agribusiness as a complex political and economic system of inputs, processing and manufacturing, and outputs. The **food chain** is composed of five central and connected sectors (inputs, production, processing, distribution, and consumption) with four contextual elements acting as external mediating forces (the state, international trade, the physical environment, and credit and finance). **Figure 8.15** illustrates these linkages and relationships, including how state farm policies shape inputs, product prices, the structure of the farm, and even the physical environment.

The food chain concept illustrates the complex connections among and between producers and consumers and regions and places. For example, there are important linkages that connect cattle production in the Prairies, beef-packing plants in High River, Alberta, and the availability of processed hamburger patties in Toronto. Because of such complex food chains, it is now common to find that traditional

agribusiness: a set of economic and political relationships that organizes agro-food production from the development of seeds to the retailing and consumption of the agricultural product

food chain: five central and connected sectors (inputs, production, product processing, distribution, and consumption) with four contextual elements acting as external mediating forces (the state, international trade, the physical environment, and credit and finance)

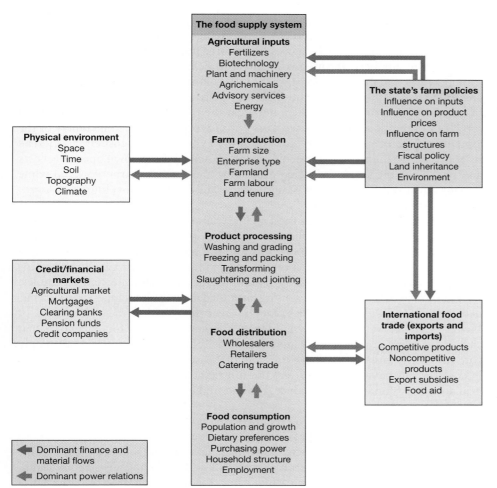

Figure 8.15   The food chain   The production of food has been transformed by industrialization into a complex system that comprises distinctly separate and hierarchically organized sectors. Mediating forces (the state, the structure and processes of international trade, credit and finance arrangements, and the physical environment) influence how the system operates at all scales of social and geographical resolution.   (*Source:* I Bowler [ed.], *The Geography of Agriculture in Developed Market Economies.* New York: J. Wiley & Sons, 1992, p. 12.)

agricultural practices in peripheral regions have been displaced by expensive, capital-intensive practices.

That agriculture is not an independent or unique economic activity is not a particularly new realization. Beginning with the second agricultural revolution, agriculture began slowly, but inexorably, to be transformed by industrial practices. What is different about the current state of the food system is the way in which farming has become just one stage of a complex and multidimensional economic process. This process is as much about distribution and marketing—key elements of the service sector—as it is about the growing and processing of agricultural products in the primary sector.

Food Regimes

A **food regime** is the specific set of links that exist between food production and consumption, as well as capital investment and accumulation opportunities. Like the agricultural revolutions already described, food regimes have developed out of different historical periods, during which different political and economic forces were in operation. Although the food chain describes the complex ways in which specific food items are produced, manufactured, and marketed, the concept also indicates the ways in which a particular type of food item is dominant during a specific temporal period. Although hundreds of different food chains may be in operation at any one time, agricultural researchers believe that only one food regime dominates a particular period.

The decades surrounding the turn of the nineteenth century were the ones in which an independent system of nation-states emerged and colonization expanded

food regime: the specific set of links that exist between food production and consumption, as well as capital investment and accumulation opportunities (see Chapters 2 and 9). At the same time, the industrialization of agriculture began. These two forces of political and economic changes were critical to the fostering of the first food regime, in which colonies became important sources of exportable foodstuffs by supplying the industrializing European states with cheap food in the form of wheat and meat. The expansion of the colonial agriculture sectors, however, created a crisis in production. The crisis was the result of the higher cost-efficiency of colonial food production, which undercut the prices of domestically produced food, put domestic agricultural workers out of work, and forced members of the agricultural sector in Europe to look for new ways to increase cost efficiency. The response was to industrialize agriculture, which helped drive down operating costs and restabilize the sector (reducing even more the need for farm workers) while moving toward the integration of agriculture and industry (also known as *agro-industrialization*).

While a wheat and livestock food regime characterized global agriculture until the 1960s, researchers now believe that a fresh fruit and vegetable regime has emerged. This new pattern of food consumption and production has been called the "postmodern diet" because it represents an important shift away from grains and meats to the more perishable agro-commodities of fresh fruits and vegetables. Integrated networks of food chains, using integrated networks of refrigeration systems, deliver fresh fruits and vegetables from all over the world to the core regions of Western Europe, North America, and Japan. Echoing the former food networks that characterized nineteenth-century imperialism, peripheral production systems supply core consumers with fresh, often exotic and off-season, produce. Indeed, consumers in core regions have come to expect the full range of fruits and vegetables to be available year round in their produce sections, and unusual and exotic produce has become increasingly popular.

This emergence of a new food regime based on fresh fruits and vegetables has been helped by retailers, who provide symbolic cues and incentives to shoppers to consume the more exotic products. Store managers have introduced them by providing associations between the fruit or vegetable and prevailing ideas about health, class attachment, and epicurean eating. Thus, the transformation of agricultural practices at the global level has enabled the emergence of a new food regime, now accompanied by new cultural messages that promote and persuade at the local level. Furthermore, just as traditional agricultural practices worldwide have been affected by globalization trends, so, too, have the mainstream eating habits of consumers in core as well as peripheral regions.

One interesting way of conveying the effects of these changes has been the development of the concept of "food miles"—a measure of the distance travelled by food items from the farm to the consumer. This term first appeared in 1994 in a report written by a British non-governmental group and was designed to draw attention to the growing social and environmental costs of transporting food (in terms of carbon dioxide emissions, air pollution, traffic congestion) in that country. The term's recent popularity lies in its ability to highlight how much we have come to depend on non-local foods—one important indicator of the sustainability of our food production systems.

As an example, consider the 2001 investigation of a team from the Leopold Center for Sustainable Agriculture into food items shipped into Iowa from the Chicago Grain Terminal building.[20] They discovered that food items had travelled *on average* 1518 miles (2429 kms) to get to their Iowa destinations in 1998. This figure is astonishing in itself perhaps, but it is more disturbing to realize that this represents a 22 percent increase over the situation in 1981, a reflection of the increasing globalization of agriculture that had occurred in that period, and was 33 times greater than the "food miles" figure (45 miles) travelled by food items in

---

[20]Rich Pirog, Timothy Van Pelt, Kamyar Enshayan, and Ellen Cook, *Food, Fuel, and Freeways: An Iowa Perspective on How Far Food Travels, Food Usage, and Greenhouse Gas Emissions*. Ames, IA: Leopold Center for Sustainable Agriculture, 2001.

a local farmers-buyers organization in Iowa (a commentary on the impact and sustainability of commercial farming when compared to local systems).

Other work has produced equally compelling results. For example, in her 1995 study "The Well-Travelled Yoghurt Pot,"[21] Stefanie Böge of the Wuppertal Institute in Germany was able to show that the average 150 gram container of yoghurt sold in that country had travelled over 8000 kilometres if we consider all of the materials used in its production (for example, not only the milk but also the plastic for the container and the aluminum for the lid), a figure that meant that for each yoghurt pot sold in southern Germany, the missing ingredient that could be listed on the container was "9.2 metres of lorry [truck] movement." This does not sound like a lot, but recall that it reflects an enormous volume of yoghurt sales.

In similar fashion, 2008 research by Melanie Langlois[22] to establish the food miles required to produce a shepherd's pie in Montreal shows that the average required to assemble all of the ingredients is 4240 kilometres, a figure mainly due to the Alberta-sourced meat, since the rest of the ingredients were locally derived. Transport over such a distance would produce a total of 4.1 tonnes of carbon dioxide emissions if it were solely devoted to the movement of pie ingredients. However, long-distance trucks carry many items, and a better measure of the environmental impact of the food miles required to produce the pie is the actual amount of emission per volume of food shipped, which in the case of a four-serving shepherd's pie produced in Montreal would be 109 grams of carbon dioxide (**Figure 8.16**).

For many people, food miles provide an important indicator of the sustainability of their food, and the fact that British supermarkets are beginning to include them on their food labels is a first step to showing not only where that food has come from, but also showing how consumer choice can be a powerful voice in shaping agriculture and agri-business.

The study of food itself represents a fascinating window on some of the changes this chapter has discussed. Indeed, the geography of food has become a growing research field in recent years. The examination of the origins and diffusion of the world's foodstuffs, the distribution of regional cuisines, and the role of local products have all, for example, shown how a cultural or social perspective greatly adds to our understanding of food production (**Figure 8.17**).

SOCIAL AND TECHNOLOGICAL CHANGE IN GLOBAL AGRICULTURAL RESTRUCTURING

In preceding sections of this chapter, we have tried to show the ways in which the globalization of agriculture has been accomplished through the same kinds of political and economic restructuring that characterized the globalization of industry. Technological change has been of particular importance to agriculture over the last half of the twentieth century as mechanical, chemical, and biological revolutions have altered even the most fundamental of agricultural practices. And, just as restructuring in industry has occurred with innumerable rounds of adjustment and resistance, so has it occurred in agriculture as well.

Besides generating economic competition, the newly restructured agro-commodity production system also fosters conflict and competition within socio-cultural systems. For instance, in both core and peripheral locations, men and women, landowners and peasants, different indigenous groups, corporations, and family farmers struggle to establish or maintain control over production and over ways of life.

---

[21]Stefanie Böge, "The Well-Travelled Yoghurt Pot." *World Transport Policy & Practice* 1(1), 1995, pp. 7–11.

[22]Melanie Langlois, unpublished BA Honours Essay, Department of Geography, Planning and Environment, Concordia University, Montreal, 2008.

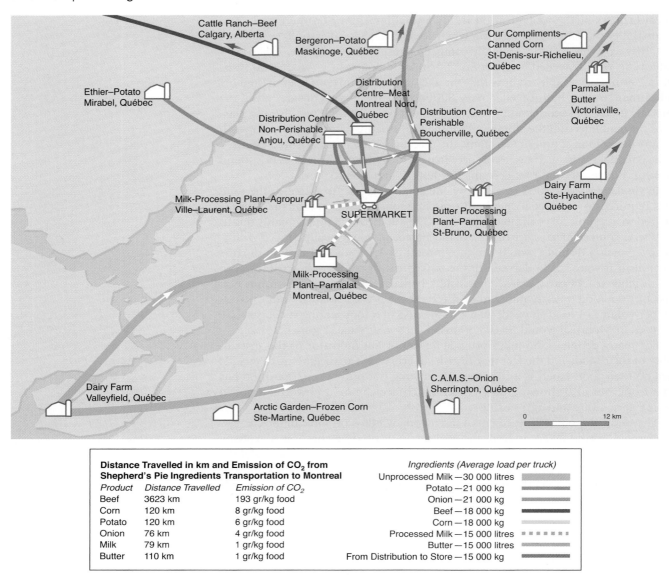

Distance Travelled in km and Emission of CO_2 from Shepherd's Pie Ingredients Transportation to Montreal			Ingredients (Average load per truck)	
Product	Distance Travelled	Emission of CO_2	Unprocessed Milk —30 000 litres	
Beef	3623 km	193 gr/kg food	Potato —21 000 kg	
Corn	120 km	8 gr/kg food	Onion —21 000 kg	
Potato	120 km	6 gr/kg food	Beef —18 000 kg	
Onion	76 km	4 gr/kg food	Corn —18 000 kg	
Milk	79 km	1 gr/kg food	Processed Milk —15 000 litres	
Butter	110 km	1 gr/kg food	Butter —15 000 litres	
			From Distribution to Store —15 000 kg	

Figure 8.16　The environmental impact of food distribution in Montreal: a food miles analysis of shepherd's pie　Many of the meals that we eat in Canada today involve considerable amounts of transportation to assemble the basic ingredients that are needed to prepare them. Such levels of transportation are a significant component of the cost of food in our stores. What is less obvious, perhaps, is that the transportation of food is also associated with a considerable environmental "cost"—one caused, for example, by the emissions of carbon dioxide by trucks into the atmosphere. A very useful way to think about the effects of such long-distance trucking is to calculate the "food miles" required to transport all of the ingredients in a specific dish. If we then multiply this simple measure by the actual amount of carbon dioxide emitted per volume of food shipped, we get an indication of some of the environmental impacts of the amount of transport required to prepare that dish. This diagram provides an illustration of how such calculations are made and, and as an example, assumes that we are purchasing all of the ingredients needed to make a shepherd's pie in a supermarket located on the island of Montreal. As we can see, an amazing web of transport links is needed to bring all of the various products to the supermarket. We also see that although many of the ingredients come from either the vicinity of Montreal (in the case of milk and butter), or from within the province of Quebec (potatoes, corn), the fact that one of the main constituents (beef) is brought from Alberta adds considerably to the dish's total transport costs. In fact, the average total "food miles" needed to assemble all of the ingredients for a shepherd's pie is 4240 kilometres, a figure that would represent over 4.1 tonnes of carbon dioxide emissions if the pie's ingredients were the only articles carried by the trucks involved. However, of course, many other things are transported in these trucks at the same time, and therefore a much better measure of environmental impact is to consider the actual amount of emission per volume of foodstuff shipped, a calculation that gives us a figure of 109 grams of carbon dioxide emitted for a four-serving shepherd's pie. This may not sound like much, but when it is then multiplied by the number of people in the city, or by the number of meals in a year, it begins to provide an indication of the environmental impact of our food systems, and helps us frame discussions about the "real" costs of food, or the benefits of local production. (*Source:* Melanie Langlois, unpublished BA Honours Essay, Department of Geography, Planning and Environment, Concordia University, Montreal, 2008.)

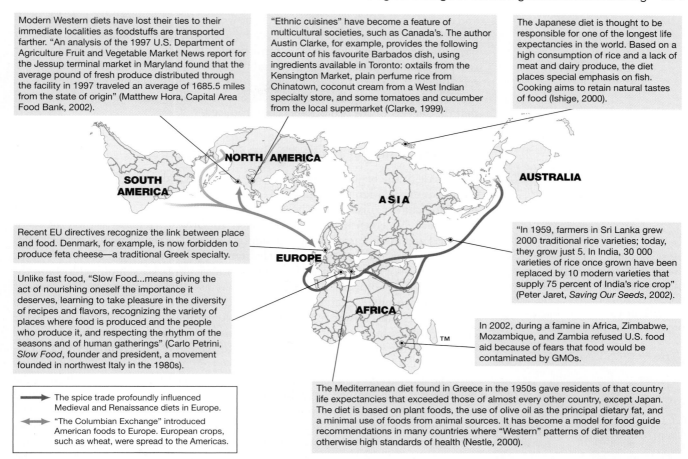

Modern Western diets have lost their ties to their immediate localities as foodstuffs are transported farther. "An analysis of the 1997 U.S. Department of Agriculture Fruit and Vegetable Market News report for the Jessup terminal market in Maryland found that the average pound of fresh produce distributed through the facility in 1997 traveled an average of 1685.5 miles from the state of origin" (Matthew Hora, Capital Area Food Bank, 2002).

"Ethnic cuisines" have become a feature of multicultural societies, such as Canada's. The author Austin Clarke, for example, provides the following account of his favourite Barbados dish, using ingredients available in Toronto: oxtails from the Kensington Market, plain perfume rice from Chinatown, coconut cream from a West Indian specialty store, and some tomatoes and cucumber from the local supermarket (Clarke, 1999).

The Japanese diet is thought to be responsible for one of the longest life expectancies in the world. Based on a high consumption of rice and a lack of meat and dairy produce, the diet places special emphasis on fish. Cooking aims to retain natural tastes of food (Ishige, 2000).

Recent EU directives recognize the link between place and food. Denmark, for example, is now forbidden to produce feta cheese—a traditional Greek specialty.

Unlike fast food, "Slow Food...means giving the act of nourishing oneself the importance it deserves, learning to take pleasure in the diversity of recipes and flavors, recognizing the variety of places where food is produced and the people who produce it, and respecting the rhythm of the seasons and of human gatherings" (Carlo Petrini, *Slow Food*, founder and president, a movement founded in northwest Italy in the 1980s).

"In 1959, farmers in Sri Lanka grew 2000 traditional rice varieties; today, they grow just 5. In India, 30 000 varieties of rice once grown have been replaced by 10 modern varieties that supply 75 percent of India's rice crop" (Peter Jaret, *Saving Our Seeds*, 2002).

In 2002, during a famine in Africa, Zimbabwe, Mozambique, and Zambia refused U.S. food aid because of fears that food would be contaminated by GMOs.

The Mediterranean diet found in Greece in the 1950s gave residents of that country life expectancies that exceeded those of almost every other country, except Japan. The diet is based on plant foods, the use of olive oil as the principal dietary fat, and a minimal use of foods from animal sources. It has become a model for food guide recommendations in many countries where "Western" patterns of diet threaten otherwise high standards of health (Nestle, 2000).

The spice trade profoundly influenced Medieval and Renaissance diets in Europe.

"The Columbian Exchange" introduced American foods to Europe. European crops, such as wheat, were spread to the Americas.

Figure 8.17   A world of food   This diagram is an attempt to show graphically some of the many geographic issues that the study of food raises. Ethnic and regional cuisines embody ideas of place; the movement of spices and other food illustrate diffusion; standards of diet around the globe illustrate regional patterns of inequality; and, lastly, new approaches to bio-engineering reflect some profound changes in our attitudes toward nature.   (*Sources for quotations:* Matthew Hora and Jody Tick, *From Farm to Table: Making the Connection in the Mid-Atlantic Food System.* Washington, DC: Capital Area Food Bank, 2001; Austin Clarke, *Pig Tails 'n Breadfruit: The Rituals of Slave Food, A Culinary Memoir.* Toronto: Random House, 1999; Naomichi Ishige, "Japan." In K.F. Kiple and K.C. Ornelas [eds.], *The Cambridge World History of Food,* vol. 2. Cambridge: Cambridge University Press, 2000, pp. 1175–1183; Peter Jaret, *Saving Our Seeds.* 2002, quoted in Fran McManus and Wendy Rickard [eds.], *Cooking Fresh from the Mid-Atlantic.* Hopewell, NJ: Eating Fresh Publications, 2002; Marion Nestle, *The Mediterranean (Diets and Disease Prevention).* In K.F. Kiple and K.C. Ornelas [eds.], *The Cambridge World History of Food,* vol. 2. Cambridge: Cambridge University Press, 2000, pp. 1193–1203; and Carlo Petrini (William McCuaig, Translator), *Slow Food: The Case For Taste.* New York: Columbia University Press, 2003.)

An Example of Social Change

The impact of a government development scheme to introduce irrigated rice production into the Gambia River Basin illustrates the many ways in which this globalization of agricultural production has affected gender relations among and within households. The Gambian government, with the help of the West African Rice Development Association, launched a program to grow rice along the banks of the Gambia River.[23] The objective of the project was for Gambia to develop its own rice-producing sector and thereby decrease its dependence on imported rice. Through local agents employed by the project, the government distributed a package of high-yielding rice varieties, fertilizers, and pesticides with the hope that 2000 peasant households distributed among 70 villages could attempt a double-cropping rice cultivation program. Husbands and wives were both involved in the project.

The success of the project required a redistribution of labour as well as the restructuring of land and crop rights. Incorrect assumptions about the availability

[23]Adapted from J. Carney, "Converting the Wetlands, Engendering the Environment: The Intersection of Gender with Agrarian Change in the Gambia." *Economic Geography* 69(4), 1993, pp. 329–349.

and cost of women's labour were made, however. These assumptions led to serious problems between spouses when it became apparent that women were not free to work during the season they were most needed to participate in the development scheme. Because of these changes, traditional ways of farming as well as gender relations were significantly challenged. Husbands and wives disagreed to such an extent over who controlled which pieces of land and the crops that were harvested that the success of the project was compromised.

Biotechnology Techniques in Agriculture

As we saw at the beginning of this chapter, ever since the beginnings of plant and animal domestication thousands of years ago, the manipulation and management of biological organisms have been of central importance to the development of agriculture. Nineteenth-century discoveries by Gregor Mendel (of the process of heredity) and Louis Pasteur (of fermentation's secrets), when combined with Charles Darwin's theories on evolution, accelerated the pace of change. The most recent manifestation of the influence of science over agriculture is exemplified by biotechnology. **Biotechnology** is any technique that uses living organisms (or parts of organisms) to make or modify products, to improve plants and animals, or to develop micro-organisms for specific uses. Recombinant DNA techniques, tissue culture, cell fusion, enzyme and fermentation technology, and embryo transfer are some of the most talked-about aspects of the use of biotechnology in agriculture (**Figure 8.18**).

The most common argument for applying biotechnology to agriculture is the belief that it helps reduce agricultural production costs as well as acting as a kind of resource-management technique (where certain natural resources are replaced by manufactured ones). Biotechnology has been hailed as a way to address growing concerns for the rising costs of cash crop production, surpluses and spoilage, environmental degradation from chemical fertilizers and overuse, soil depletion, and other related sorts of challenges now facing profitable agricultural production.

Indeed, biotechnology has provided impressive responses to these and other challenges. For example, biotechnological research is responsible for the development of super plants that produce their own fertilizers and pesticides, can be grown on nutrient-lacking soils, are high-yielding varieties (HYVs), and are resistant to disease or the development of micro-organisms. The potential to develop salt-resistant crops may offer a solution to the increasing salinity of the world's soils—a major threat to agriculture in the near future in many countries. Additionally, biotechnologists have been able to clone, that is, take the cells of tissues from one plant and use them to form new ones. That tissue culture may be no more than one cubic centimetre in size, but it has the potential to produce millions of identical plants. Such a procedure decreases the time needed to grow mature plants ready for reproduction.

Although such technological innovations can be seen as miraculous, there is a downside to biotechnological solutions to agricultural problems. For example, cloned plants are more susceptible to disease than are natural ones, probably because they have not developed tolerances. This susceptibility leads to an increasing need for chemical treatment. And although industry may reap economic benefits from the development and wide use of tissue cultures, farmers may suffer because they lack the capital or the knowledge to participate in biotechnological applications.

It is no understatement that biotechnology has revolutionized the way in which traditional agriculture has been conducted. Its proponents argue that it provides a new pathway to the sustainable production of agricultural commodities. By streamlining the growth process with such innovations as tissue cultures, disease and pest-resistant plants, and fertilizer-independent plants, the optimists believe that the biorevolution can maximize global agricultural production to keep up with global requirements of population and demand.

Just as with the Green Revolution of the 1960s and 1970s (when high yielding varieties of crops such as rice were developed through selective breeding),

biotechnology: a technique that uses living organisms (or parts of organisms) to make or modify products, to improve plants and animals, or to develop micro-organisms for specific uses

Figure 8.18   Biotechnology
Biotechnology laboratories are typically high-technology greenhouses. Biotechnology offers both benefits and costs. Although the benefits include increased yields and more pest-resistant strains, too often the costs of such technology are too high for the world's most needy populations.

Figure 8.19 Coffee plantation in Ethiopia For many peripheral countries, the production of cash crops is a way to boost exports and bring in needed income for the national economy. In Ethiopia, coffee has for decades been a cash crop grown for export. Luxury exports, such as coffee, generate some of the capital needed to import staple foods, such as wheat.

biotechnology may have deleterious effects for peripheral countries (and for poor labourers and small-farm workers in core countries). For example, biotechnology has enabled the development of plants that can be grown outside of their natural or currently most suitable environment. Yet cash crops are critical to economic stability for many peripheral nations—such as bananas in Central America and the Caribbean, sugar in Cuba, and coffee in Colombia and Ethiopia (**Figure 8.19**). These and other export crops are threatened by the development of alternative sites of production. Transformations in agriculture have ripple effects throughout the world system. As an illustration, **Table 8.1** compares the different impacts of the biorevolution and the Green Revolution on various aspects of global agricultural production.

TABLE 8.1 Biorevolution Compared with Green Revolution

Characteristics	Green Revolution	Biorevolution
Crops affected	Wheat, rice, maize	Potentially all crops, including vegetables, fruits, agro-export crops, and specialty crops
Other sectors affected	None	Pesticides, animal products, pharmaceuticals, processed food products, energy, mining, and warfare
Territories affected	Some developing countries	All areas, all nations, all locations, including marginal lands
Development of technology and dissemination	Largely public or quasi-public sector, international agricultural research centres (IARCs), R&D millions of dollars	Largely private sector, especially corporations, R&D billions of dollars
Proprietary considerations	Plant breeders' rights and patents generally not relevant	Genes, cells, plants, and animals patentable as well as the techniques used to produce them
Capital costs of research	Relatively low	Relatively high for some techniques, relatively low for others
Access to information	Restricted because of privatization and proprietary considerations	Relatively easy because of public policy of IARCs
Research skills required	Conventional plant breeding and parallel agricultural sciences	Molecular and cell biology expertise as well as conventional plant-breeding skills
Crop vulnerability	High-yielding varieties relatively uniform; high vulnerability	Tissue culture crop propagation produces exact genetic copies; even more vulnerability
Side effects	Increased monoculture and use of farm chemicals, marginalization of small farmer, ecological degradation; increased foreign debt due to decrease in biomass fuels and the increasing reliance on costly, usually imported, petroleum	Crop substitution replacing Third World exports; herbicide tolerance; increasing use of chemicals; engineered organisms might affect environment; further marginalization of small-farm worker

Sources: Adapted from M. Kenney and F. Buttel, "Biotechnology: Prospects and Dilemmas for Third-World Development." *Development and Change* 16, 1995, p. 70; and H. Hobbelink, *Biotechnology and the Future of World Agriculture: The Fourth Resource.* London: Zed Books, 1991.

In addition, the availability of technology to these peripheral nations is limited because most advances in biotechnology are the property of private companies. For example, patents protect both the process and the end products of biotechnological techniques. Utilizing biotechnological techniques requires paying fees for permission to use them, and the small-farm workers of both the core and the periphery are unlikely to be able to purchase or use the patented processes. Private ownership of biotechnological processes has resulted in control over food production being removed from the farmer and put into the hands of biotechnology firms, as Monsanto's activities in Canada illustrate (see the discussion of the Saskatchewan farmer, Percy Schmeiser, and his court challenge against Monsanto in Chapter 12). Under such circumstances, it becomes possible for world food security to be controlled not by publicly accountable governments, but by privately held biotechnology firms. Finally, with the refinement and specialization of plant and animal species, women who are currently employed in ancillary activities could face the loss of their jobs. For example, if a grower chooses to plant a bioengineered type of wheat that does not require winnowing (the removal of the chaff, a normally labour-intensive process), then those labourers who once were involved in that activity are no longer needed.

The biorevolution in agriculture is so recent that we are just beginning to understand both its negative and positive impacts. At this point, it seems quite clear that these impacts will be distributed unevenly across countries, regions, and locales, and certainly across class, race, and gender lines. It is still too soon to tell what the overall costs and benefits will be. On the one hand, it seems clear that the advantages include the ability to increase production (especially by permitting growth in different environments) and to reduce the level of pesticide use. On the other hand, whether the advantages of temperate farmers being able to grow tropical crops outweighs the tropical producers' loss of their monopoly over those commodities remains to be seen. The commodification of genes and seed stocks raises the concern that farmers will lose control of their own fields to corporate biotechnology interests. A wider social critique of this issue (for example, by Donna Haraway) has suggested that genetic engineering of crops has sparked such public interest because it has reopened issues of "purity," which—because of their racial connotations—we find very troubling.

THE ENVIRONMENT AND AGRICULTURAL INDUSTRIALIZATION

Agriculture always involves the interaction of biophysical as well as human systems. In fact, it is this relationship that makes agriculture distinct from other forms of economic activity that do not depend so directly on the environment to function. It is also this interactive relationship that requires attention regarding how best to manage the environment to enable the continued production of food. Because the relationship between the human system of agriculture and the biophysical system of the environment is highly interactive, it is important to look at the various ways that each shapes the other.

The Impact of the Environment on Agriculture

Management of the environment by farmers has been steadily increasing over the course of the three agricultural revolutions. In fact, the widespread use of fertilizers, irrigation systems, pesticides, herbicides, and industrial greenhouses suggests that agriculture has become an economic practice that can ignore the limitations of the physical environment (**Figure 8.20**). Yet, it is exactly because agriculture is an economic activity that management of the environment in which it occurs becomes critical. As geographer Martin Parry writes:

Soil, terrain, water, weather and pests can be modified and many of the activities through the farming year, such as tillage and spraying, are directed toward this. But

Figure 8.20 Modern irrigation system This photo shows a self-propelling irrigation system that can be electronically programmed to deliver different amounts of water at different times of the day or days of the week. Irrigation is just one way that humans have been able to alter the environment to serve their agricultural needs. In many parts of the core, water prices are heavily subsidized for agricultural users in order to ensure food supplies. For many parts of the periphery, however, access to water is limited to the amount of rain that falls and can be stored behind small dams and in impoundments. (*Source*: Agricultural Research Service, USDA.)

these activities must be cost-effective; the benefits of growing a particular crop, or increasing its yield by fertilizing, must exceed the costs of doing so. Often such practices are simply not economic, with the result that factors such as soil quality, terrain and climate continue to affect agriculture by limiting the range of crops and animals that can profitably be farmed. In this way the physical environment still effectively limits the range of agricultural activities open to the farmer at each location.[24]

Though the impact of the environment on agricultural practices that have become heavily industrialized may not at first seem obvious, the reverse is more readily observable. In fact, there are many contemporary and historical examples of the ways that agriculture destroys, depletes, or degrades the environmental resources on which its existence and profitability depend.

The Impact of Agriculture on the Environment

One of the earliest treatises on the impact of chemical pesticides on the environment is Rachel Carson's *Silent Spring,* which identified the detrimental impact of synthetic chemical pesticides—especially DDT—on the health of human and animal populations. Although the publication of the book and the environmental awareness that it generated led to a ban on the use of many pesticides in most industrialized nations, chemical companies continued to produce and market these pesticides in less-developed countries. Although some of these pesticides were effective in combating malaria and other insect-borne diseases, many were applied to crops that were later sold in the markets of developed countries. Thus, a kind of "circle of poison" was set in motion, encompassing the entire global agricultural system (**Figure 8.21**).

Some of the most pressing issues facing agricultural producers today are soil degradation and denudation, which are occurring at rates more than a thousand times the natural erosion rates. Although we might tend to dismiss soil erosion as a historical problem of the 1930s Dust Bowl, in reality, the effects of agriculture on worldwide soil resources are dramatic. Unfortunately, most forms of agriculture tend to increase natural erosion, and the losses are more severe in peripheral countries.

The loss of topsoil worldwide is a critical problem because it is a fixed resource that cannot be readily replaced. It takes, on average, between 100 and 500 years to generate 10 millimetres (one-half inch) of topsoil, and it is estimated that nearly 50 000 million tonnes (55 000 million tons) of topsoil are lost each year to erosion. The quantity and quality of soil worldwide is thus an important determining factor in the quantity and quality of food that can be produced.

Figure 8.21 Impact of pesticides Pesticides have been shown to have highly damaging impacts on the ecosystem. In addition to fostering pests that are more resistant to chemical suppression, pesticides can kill and cause genetic damage in larger animals, especially birds. One disorder linked to pesticide use is that the shells of bird eggs, such as the one shown here, are not thick enough to remain intact and protect the embryo through the various stages of maturation. The thin shells crack open prematurely, exposing the embryo before it is viable. In the 1960s, many of the most noxious chemicals, such as DDT, were banned in North America. Many peripheral countries, however, continue to allow the sale of such chemicals.

[24]M. Parry, "Agriculture as a Resource System." In I. Bowler (ed.), *The Geography of Agriculture in Developed Market Economies.* Harlow, UK: Longman Scientific and Technical, 1992, p. 208.

Figure 8.22 Desertification Severe and largely permanent loss of vegetation and topsoil may result from human activities, such as overgrazing or excessive deforestation. The ravaged landscapes of desertification are a compelling testimony to the need for humans to consider the implications of their actions more closely—not always an easy thing to do when ill-informed government policies and grinding hunger and poverty are daily facts of life.

Soil erosion because of mismanagement in the semi-arid regions of the world has led to desertification, whereby topsoil and vegetation loss have been extensive and largely permanent. *Desertification* is the spread of desert-like conditions in arid or semi-arid lands resulting from climatic change or human influences. Desertification not only means the loss of topsoil but can also involve the deterioration of grazing lands and the decimation of forests (**Figure 8.22**). In addition to causing soil degradation and denudation problems, agriculture affects water quality and quantity through the overwithdrawal of groundwater and the pollution of the same water through agricultural runoff contaminated with herbicides, pesticides, and fertilizers. Deforestation, discussed in Chapter 4, can also result from poor agricultural practices.

Poor land-use practices and the destruction of complex ecosystems through overuse or misuse led, in the 1980s, to an innovation called a "debt-for-nature swap." In these swaps, a core environmental organization, such as the World Wildlife Fund, retired some part of the foreign debt of a peripheral country. The debt purchase was made contingent on the peripheral country agreeing to implement a conservation program to save ecologically sensitive lands from abuse. This usually meant turning the land into a national park or extending the boundaries of an existing park. Funds generated by the swaps were to be used to administer the parks, train personnel, research habitats, and carry out environmental education.

For much of the 1980s, environmental organizations were extremely optimistic about the possible implications of debt-for-nature swaps for both the affected country and worldwide environmental degradation. It turns out, however, that the swaps were not able to address the fundamental causes of environmental degradation in peripheral regions—including extreme poverty, government subsidies for forest clearing, and insecure land tenure. As a result, the debt-for-nature swaps are seen as mere bandage solutions to extremely complex social, economic, political, and ecological problems.

The nature–society relationship discussed in Chapter 4 is very much at the heart of agricultural practices. Yet, as agriculture has industrialized, the impacts of agriculture on the environment have multiplied and, in some parts of the globe, have reached the crisis stage. Although in some regions the agricultural system leads to overproduction of foodstuffs, in other regions the quantity and quality of water and soil severely limit the ability of a region's people to feed themselves.

Limitations such as these are likely to become even more severe in the future if climate changes as experts predict, although it is possible that not all of the consequences for agriculture will be negative. In some parts of Canada, for example, crop production will probably increase as average temperatures rise; however, because it is also likely that the levels of plant diseases and pests will also increase, the overall effects on agricultural production are difficult to predict (see **Human Geography and Climate Change 8.2—Agriculture**).

Agriculture

Climate is closely associated with agriculture: it defines the length of the growing season, average temperatures, and the amount and timing of precipitation. Not surprisingly, climate change becomes an important factor in the long-run variability of agricultural production in developing and developed countries, and is expected to have profound impacts on agricultural production and crop yields through four key dimensions (**Figure 8.2.1**). First, warming will likely reduce food production due to increased heat stress. Even slight increases in temperature will likely reduce crop yields, particularly in tropical latitudes. Moderate temperature increases (1°C–2°C) in mid- to high-latitude regions, such as Canada and Europe, may initially increase crop yields, but further increases in temperature are likely to reduce crop yields.[25]

Second, changing weather and precipitation patterns will alter agricultural patterns. Higher latitudes and the tropics are expected to see increased precipitation, while mid-latitudes and semi-arid areas will see less. This means that the impact will predominately affect agriculturally marginal and semi-arid regions dependent upon rain for agricultural production.[26] Concurrently, the greater frequency of extreme events such as droughts, cyclones, hailstorms, and floods will negatively affect agriculture and potentially devastate crops through higher risks of floods, landslides, and erosion. Such events cannot be anticipated

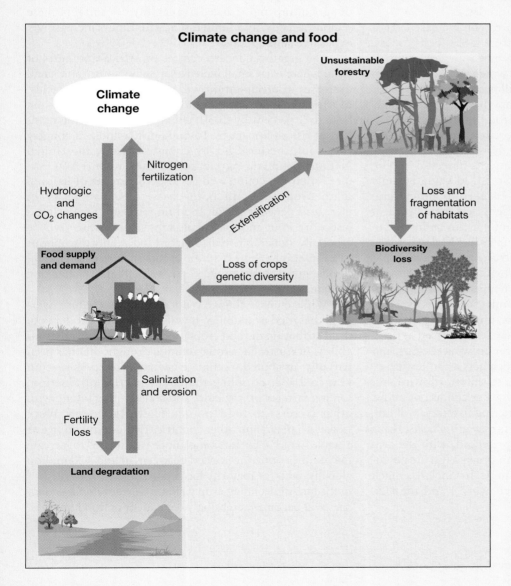

Climate change and food

Climate change

Unsustainable forestry

Nitrogen fertilization

Hydrologic and CO_2 changes

Extensification

Loss and fragmentation of habitats

Food supply and demand

Loss of crops genetic diversity

Biodiversity loss

Salinization and erosion

Fertility loss

Land degradation

Figure 8.2.1   Climate change: an integrated framework   The expected impacts of climate change are varied and widespread. It is widely expected that climate change will impact human and natural systems through such things as food and water resources, which in turn will affect economic development and personal livelihoods.   (*Source: Climate Change 2001: Synthesis Report.* Contribution of Working Groups I, II and III to the Third Assessment Report of the Intergovernmental Panel on Climate Change. Figure 8-2 and Figure 1-1. Cambridge University Press.)

---

[25]Intergovernmental Panel on Climate Change, *Climate Change 2007.* **www.ipcc.ch.**

[26]Ibid.

and prepared for, and may be of even greater risk than climate change itself.[27]

Third, changes in weather patterns and warmer average temperatures are likely to modify pests and diseases relative to crops and livestock, impacting economic activities and livelihoods. Rising temperatures will likely expand the range of many agricultural pests and increase their ability to survive the winter and attack spring crops. Recent warming trends in Canada and the United States have resulted in earlier spring activity of insects and the proliferation of some species, such as the mountain pine beetle, which has decimated British Columbia's forest industry and threatens much of Canada's boreal forest. Rising ocean temperatures may reduce the diversity of species and disrupt fish breeding and feeding patterns, as habitats and ranges are reduced. Increased climate extremes may also promote plant disease and pest outbreaks from the tropics to mid-latitudes.[28]

Finally, increasing temperatures will increase evapotranspiration and lower soil moisture levels. For farmers, this means increased reliance on irrigation for crops. If this is compounded by reduced water availability from rainfall, some cultivated areas will become unsuitable for cropping and some grasslands may become increasingly arid, leading to increased risk of food shortages.

Climatic changes are likely to affect agricultural production worldwide. They will not, however, be felt equally across the globe, with variable patterns observed in both the developed and developing world. In Canada, only 2 percent of the labour force is engaged in agricultural production, and agriculture represents less than 4 percent of the country's economy,[29] meaning it can endure a climatic setback more easily than country like Malawi, where 90 percent of the population lives in rural areas and 40 percent of economy is driven by rain-fed agriculture.

For the developed and largely temperate world (including North America and Europe), climate change is expected to have neutral or mildly positive impacts. Canada and Northern Europe, for instance, may see increased agricultural production as warming, longer growing seasons, and increased CO_2 concentration (which acts as a "fertilizer" for crops) enable crop production to shift northward, but only in those areas where soil and water conditions allow. In addition, the costs of over-wintering livestock will fall, crop yields will improve, and forests may grow faster. Some negative impacts will also be experienced, with the arid southerly portions of the Canadian prairies (an area commonly referred to as Palliser's Triangle that includes much of southern Alberta and Saskatchewan[30]) and the U.S.

plains likely to see decreased agricultural output. Already, drought and annual soil moisture deficits are recurrent problems in this region. More significant increases in temperature (over +2°C) are likely to result in decreased crop yields. The summer 2003 European heatwave, with temperatures approximately 6°C above the long-term mean and reduced precipitation levels, resulted in losses of up to 30 percent for some fruit and grain crops.[31]

The developing world is far more likely to experience the expected negative impacts of climate change. Although higher global temperatures will bring higher rainfall, this will be unevenly distributed, with some areas such as South Asia, northern Latin America, and Africa projected to receive less rainfall than before. The potential loss of farmland due to decreased precipitation and *desertification,* discussed in Chapter 4, will reduce food production. Compounding the problem is the generally lower intensity of agriculture and reduced availability of capital in these regions already, and limited funds to import increasingly expensive staple foods.

The greatest concern centres on Africa and parts of Asia, where even small increases in temperature and small decreases in precipitation will reduce agricultural yields. In Africa, climate change could depress grain production by 2 to 3 percent by 2030, enough to increase the numbers at risk of hunger by 10 million.[32] In India, a country that could be hard hit by climate change, the United Nations Food and Agriculture Organization (FAO) estimates that the country could lose 18 percent of its total grain production. In both cases, this may result in increased dependency on food imports and greater food insecurity. Poor and small-scale subsistence farmers will be especially vulnerable to income or food supply disruptions by crop failure or by extreme events such as drought and floods, given their limited capacity to adapt to changing climate.

While climate change is not expected to reduce overall global food availability, it will impact crop production, the distribution of food crops, and food security and availability. In Australia, a long-running drought that has been partially attributed to climate change entered its seventh year in 2008, crippling the country's rice production, forcing farmers off the land, and contributing (along with other factors) to food riots in Haiti, Indonesia, Ivory Coast, Thailand and other countries that depend on rice as a staple food.[33] Climate change alone is estimated to increase the number of malnourished between 40 and 170 million globally, with the majority located in sub-Saharan Africa.[34] In the face of declining crop yields, many developing countries will become increasingly dependent on food imports.

[27]IPCC, *Climate Change 2007.*
[28]Ibid.
[29]Statistics Canada. Statistics based on 2006 Canadian Census, **www.statcan.gc.ca.**
[30]D.S. Lemmen and F.J. Warren, *Climate Change Impact and Adaptation: A Canadian Perspective.* Ottawa: Climate Change Impacts and Adaptation Directorate, Natural Resources Canada, 2004.

[31]IPCC, *Climate Change 2007.*
[32]Ibid.
[33]Keith Bradsher, "A Drought in Australia, A Global Shortage of Rice." *New York Times,* 17 April 2008, p. A4.
[34]Ibid.

Correspondingly, there will be increased pressure to cultivate marginal land or use unsustainable cultivation practices, which may lead to increased land degradation and reduced biodiversity. Ultimately, changes in crop yields and world food supply patterns raise questions regarding food security. These changes may be more pronounced if other resources such as cropland or water supplies are degraded or depleted. Adaptation of agricultural practices to compensate for climate change will be important.

—K.B.N.

CONCLUSION

Agriculture has become a highly complex, globally integrated system. Although traditional forms of agricultural practices, such as subsistence farming, continue to exist, they have been overshadowed by the global industrialization of agriculture. This industrialization has included not only mechanization and chemical applications but also the linking of the agricultural sector to the manufacturing, service, and finance sectors of the economy. In addition, countries have become important players in the regulation and support of agriculture at all levels, from the local to the global.

The dramatic changes that have occurred in agriculture have affected different places and different social groups. Households in both the core and the periphery have strained to adjust to these changes, often disrupting existing patterns of authority and access to resources. Just as people have been affected by the transformations in global agriculture, so, too, have the land, air, and water.

The geography of agriculture at the turn of the twentieth century is a far cry from the way it was organized 100 or even 50 years ago. As the globalization of the economy has accelerated in the last several decades of the twentieth century, so, too, has the globalization of agriculture. Additionally, unease with genetically engineered foods will affect producers, agricultural research, trade, and a host of other factors that have repercussions throughout the world-system.

MAIN POINTS REVISITED

- **Agriculture has been transformed into a globally integrated system; the changes producing this result have occurred at many scales and have originated from many sources.**
  In addition to the restructuring of entire national farming systems, farming households have been transformed as well in core, peripheral, and semiperipheral regions.

- **Agriculture has proceeded through three revolutionary phases, from the domestication of plants and animals, through the agricultural revolution of the mid-eighteenth century, to the latest developments in biotechnology and industrial innovation.**
  These three revolutionary phases have not occurred simultaneously throughout the globe but have been adopted and adapted to differing degrees based on levels of development, culture, and physical geography.

- **The increasing ability to manipulate nature has changed how humans view their environment and think about place.**
  With the development of agriculture, humans began their first sustained efforts to manipulate their environment as a resource. As agriculture developed, the sedentary life that farming required gave new meaning to the values people attached to place.

- **The introduction of new technologies, political concerns about food security and self-sufficiency, and changing opportunities** for investment and employment are among the many forces that have dramatically shaped agriculture as we know it today. Two of the most important forces behind these transformations in agriculture have been multinational and transnational corporations and states. The World Trade Organization is another important influence.

- **The industrialized agricultural system of today's world has developed from—and has largely displaced—older agricultural practices, including shifting cultivation, subsistence agriculture, and pastoralism.**
  Although these systems no longer dominate agricultural practices on a global scale, they are still practised in many areas of the world, in some cases alongside more mechanized forms.

- **Canadian agriculture, since European settlement began, has always been affected by international markets—first by those of the colonizing powers and second by those of today's world markets.**
  The globalization of trade and the rise of agribusiness is leading to the replacement in Canada of a national farming system based on the family farm, with a system of two production environments based on international exports in the Prairies and supply management elsewhere.

■ The contemporary agro-commodity system is organized around a chain of agribusiness components that begins at the farm and ends at the retail outlet. Different economic sectors, as well as different corporate forms, have been involved in the globalization process.

No longer the centre piece in this chain of agricultural organization, the farm is but one of several important components that includes seed and fertilizer manufacturers, food processors, food distributors, and consumers.

■ Transformations in agriculture have had dramatic impacts on the environment, including soil erosion, desertification, defor-

estation, and soil and water pollution, as well as the elimination of some plant and animal species.

Although most of the core countries have instituted legislation to address some of the problems associated with environmental degradation, these problems exist throughout the global agricultural system to greater and lesser degrees. In peripheral countries, where governments are often too poor to monitor and enforce such legislation, they are being encouraged by international agencies and environmental organizations to limit their degradational practices through relief of part of their national debt.

Key Terms

agrarian (p. 353)
agribusiness (p. 372)
agricultural industrialization (p. 369)
agriculture (p. 353)
biotechnology (p. 378)
chemical farming (p. 361)
commercial agriculture (p. 354)

food chain (p. 372)
food manufacturing (p. 361)
food regime (p. 373)
globalized agriculture (p. 370)
Green Revolution (p. 370)
hunting and gathering (p. 353)
intensive subsistence agriculture (p. 355)

mechanization (p. 361)
pastoralism (p. 356)
shifting cultivation (p. 355)
subsistence agriculture (p. 354)
swidden (p. 355)
transhumance (p. 357)

Additional Reading

Barndt, D. *Tangled Routes: Women, Work and Globalization on the Tomato Trail.* Aurora, ON: Garamond Press, 2002.

Bonanno, A., L. Busch, W.H. Friedland, L. Gouveia, and E. Minzone (eds.). *From Columbus to ConAgra: The Globalization of Agriculture and Food.* Lawrence, KS: University of Kansas Press, 1994.

Boserup, E. *The Conditions of Agricultural Growth: The Economics of Agrarian Change under Population Pressure.* Chicago: Aldine, 1965.

Brody, H. *The Other Side of Eden: Hunters, Farmers and the Shaping of the World.* Vancouver & Toronto: Douglas and McIntyre, 2000.

Found, W.C. "Agriculture in a World of Subsidies." In J.N.H. Britton (ed.), *Canada and the Global Economy: The Geography of Structural and Technological Change.* Montreal and Kingston: McGill–Queen's University Press, 1996, 155–168.

Friesen, G. *The West: Regional Ambitions, National Debates, Global Age.* Toronto: Penguin Canada, 1999.

Goodman, D., and M. Redclift. *The International Farm Crisis.* London: Macmillan, 1989.

Goodman, D., and M. Watts. *Globalising Food: Agrarian Questions and Global Restructuring.* London: Routledge Press, 1997.

Grigg, D.B. *The Agricultural Systems of the World: An Evolutionary Approach.* Cambridge and New York: Cambridge University Press, 1974.

Halweil, B. "Farming in the Public Interest." In C. Flavin, H. French, and G. Gardner (eds.), *State of the World 2002.* New York: W.W. Norton and Company, 2002, 50–74.

Harrison, P. *The Greening of Africa.* London: Paladin Grafton Books, 1987.

Hecht, S., and A. Cockburn. *The Fate of the Forest: Developers, Destroyers and Defenders of the Amazon.* London: Verso, 1989.

Heidenreich, C., and J.V. Wright. "Native Population and Subsistence: Seventeeth Century." In W. Dean, C. Heidenreich, T. McIlwraith, and J. Warkentin (eds.), *Concise Historical Atlas of Canada.* Toronto: University of Toronto Press, 1998, Plate 3.

Heintzman, A., and E. Solomon (eds.). *Feeding the Future: From Fat to Famine: How to Solve the World's Food Crises.* Toronto: House of Anansi Press, 2004.

Hewitt de Alcantara, C. "The Green Revolution as History: The Mexican Experience," *Development and Change* 4(5), 1973, 25–44.

Hobbelink, H. *Biotechnology and the Future of World Agriculture.* London: Zed Books Limited, 1991.

Kloppenburg, J.R., Jr. *First the Seed: The Political Economy of Plant Biotechnology 1492–2000.* Cambridge, England: Cambridge University Press, 1988.

Le Heron, R. *Globalized Agriculture: Political Choice.* Oxford: Pergamon Press, 1993.

McRae, T., C.A.S. Smith, and L.J. Gregorich (eds.). *Environmental Sustainability of Canadian Agriculture: Report of the Agri Environmental Indicator Project. A Summary.* Ottawa: Agriculture and Agri-Food Canada 2000. (Electronic version available at **www. agr.ca/policy/environment/**.)

Momsen, J.H. *Women and Development in the Third World.* London & New York: Routledge, 1991.

Pearson, C., and J. Masby. *The Cultivated Landscape: An Exploration of Art and Agriculture.* Montreal and Kingston McGill-Queen's University Press, 2008.

Persley, G. *Beyond Mendel's Garden: Biotechnology in the Service of World Agriculture.* Wallingford, CT: CAB International, 1990.

Poppendieck, J. *Sweet Charity? Emergency Food and the End of Entitlement.* New York: Viking Press, 1998.

Silversides, B.V. *Prairie Sentinel: The Story of the Canadian Grain Elevator.* Calgary: Fifth House, 1997.

Snow, D.R. "The First Americans and the Differentiation of Hunter-Gatherer Cultures." In B.G. Trigger and W.E. Washburn (eds.), *The Cambridge History of the Native Peoples of the Americas. Volume 1: North America, Part 1.* Cambridge: Cambridge University Press, 1996, 125–199.

Spooner, B. (ed.). *Population Growth: Anthropological Implications.* Cambridge, MA: MIT Press, 1972.

Troper, H. *Only Farmers Need Apply: Official Canadian Government Encouragement of Immigration from the United States, 1896–1911.* Toronto: Griffin House, 1972.

Troughton, M. *Canadian Agriculture.* Budapest: Hungarian Academy of Sciences, 1982.

Vogeler, I. *The Myth of the Family Farm: Agribusiness Dominance of U.S. Agriculture.* Boulder, CO: Westview Press, 1981.

Waithe, D., M. Zafiriou, and D. Niekamp. *Income Inequality in Canada Farm versus Non-Farm Families, 1985–1995.* Ottawa: Agriculture and Agri-Food Canada, 2000.

Wallace, I. *A Geography of the Canadian Economy.* Don Mills, ON: Oxford University Press, 2002.

Exercises

Here you will find exercises and activities for each chapter. Unplugged exercises help you review chapter discussions, and pose ideas for your own human geography research. On the Companion Website exercises will require you have access to the internet.

Unplugged

1. Your neighbourhood grocery store is a perfect location to begin to identify the "global" in the globalization of agriculture. Go to the produce section there, and document the source of at least 10 fruits and vegetables you find. You may need to ask the produce manager where they come from, but once you have established that, illustrate those sources on a world map.

2. The Food and Agriculture Organization (FAO) has been publishing a range of yearbooks containing statistical data on many aspects of global food production since the mid-1950s. Using the *State of Food* and *Agricultural Production* yearbooks, compare the changes that have occurred in agricultural production between the core and the periphery since the mid-twentieth century. You can use just two yearbooks for this exercise, or you may want to use several to get a better sense of when and where the most significant changes have occurred. Once you have identified where the changes have been most significant, try to explain why these changes may have occurred.

3. Your breakfast is the result of the activities of a whole chain of producers, processors, distributors, and retailers whose interactions provide insights into both the globalization of food production and the industrialization of agriculture. Consider the various foods you consume in a typical breakfast, and describe where and by whom they were produced (grown and processed), how they were transported (by whom) from the processing site, and where and by whom they were retailed. Summarize how the various components of your breakfast illustrate the two concepts of globalization and the industrialization of agriculture.

4. The majority of Canadians are, as we have seen, not involved with farming activities. How has this separation from agriculture affected how we think about farming, rural life, and nature? Are we realistic or nostalgic?

On the Companion Website

This book has its own Companion Website where you will find additional resources—maps, photographs, data—as well as exercises and activities that relate to each chapter. To complete the Companion Website exercises, go to **www.pearsoned.ca/knox**. The following is a summary of the types of exercises created for this chapter.

1. The exercises for this chapter focus on the impact of agriculture on the environment. We look at water policies and their effect on agriculture, especially irrigation policies. Using a GIS on sustainable development, we survey chronic undernutrition, dietary patterns, food production growth, and the role of agricultural trade. Exploring the World Agricultural Information Centre website, we appraise human-induced soil degradation, and we provide international time-series data sets for production, trade, chemicals, aid shipments, land use, and more. We also take a backward look (via the internet) at the successes and failures of the Green Revolution. Finally, we examine biotechnology in agriculture and the public's changing attitude about the genetic engineering of our agricultural products.

2. The CBC Video Case, Made in Canada, that accompanies this chapter has been chosen to highlight some of the issues around food's production, safety and environmental impact discussed in this chapter. You will find a link to the CBC video, the video case, questions, and resources on the Companion Website for this chapter.

9

The Politics of Territory and Space

Beginning after the World War II in Europe, the "twinning" of towns and cities provided one way to promote peace and understanding among once-warring countries of that continent. In this example, the small town of Menaggio in northern Italy is twinned with places of equivalent population size in France, Germany, and Brazil, and illustrates how twinning is now becoming a worldwide phenomenon.

Even though globalization has made the world a more interconnected whole, it is important to remember that globalization does not necessarily supersede national interests. Canada, for example, while it has benefited economically from its role as part of the global core and its membership of continental pacts such as the North American Free Trade Agreement (NAFTA), nevertheless has expressed its misgivings over the loss of national sovereignty that such arrangements bring with them. Recent events, post 9/11, have also highlighted these contradictions. On the one hand, Canada may benefit from being part of the United States' global "security umbrella" but, on the other hand, its citizens are thereby subject to a much wider surveillance than before (for example, the new practice of granting American agencies access to Canadian airline passenger lists).

At another scale, at the level of Canadian interests, the possible separation of Quebec has fuelled the growth of federal and provincial political parties dedicated to bring about the independence of that province, and referendums that (in one case) came close to achieving a majority vote for separation from Canada. The desire for independence has not diminished as the world economy has become more integrated. In fact, in some ways, the more obvious presence of that outside world in the day-to-day lives of Quebec's residents could be said to make them more alert to pressures of globalization, and therefore more eager to break up the map of Canada to protect their political identity.

As this chapter demonstrates, globalization continues to create new maps; at the same time, established boundaries persist. Exploration, imperialism, colonization, decolonization, and the Cold War between East and West are powerful forces that have created national boundaries as well as redrawn them. Much of the political strife that currently grips the globe is a local or regional response to the impacts of globalization of the economy, aided by the practices of the state. The complex relationships between politics and geography—both human and physical—are two-way relationships. In addition, political geography is not just about global or international relationships. It is also about the many other geographic scales and political divisions, from the globe to the neighbourhood, from large, far-reaching processes to the familiar sites of our everyday lives.

MAIN POINTS

- A subfield of the discipline of geography, political geography examines complex relationships between politics and geography (both human and physical).
- Political geographers recognize that the relationship between politics and geography is two-way: politics ↔ geography. Political geography can be seen both as the geography of politics and as the politics of geography.
- The relationship between politics and geography is often driven by particular theories and practices of the world's states. Understanding nation-state

imperialism, colonialism, and geopolitical theory is key to comprehending how, within the context of the world-system, geography has influenced politics and how politics has influenced geography.

■ Political geography deals with phenomena occurring at all scales of resolution from the global to the household. Important East–West and North–South divisions dominate international politics, whereas regionalism and similar divisions dominate intra-state politics.

■ Political geography recognizes the importance of the environment. Global change and population growth both make it likely that increased competition for future resources will also involve political conflict.

THE DEVELOPMENT OF POLITICAL GEOGRAPHY

Political geography is a long-established subfield in the wider discipline of geography. Aristotle is often taken to be the first political geographer because his model of the state is based on such factors as climate, terrain, and the ratio between population and territory. Since Aristotle, other important political geographers have existed—from Strabo to Montesquieu—who promoted theories of the state that incorporated elements of landscape and the physical environment, as well as the population characteristics of regions. From about the fourteenth through the nineteenth century, scholars interested in political geography theorized that the state operated cyclically and organically. This meant that states consolidated and fragmented based on complex relationships among and between factors, such as population size and composition, agricultural productivity, land area, and the role of the city.

As these factors indicate, political geography at the end of the nineteenth century was influenced by two important traditions within the wider discipline of geography: the people–land tradition and environmental determinism. Although different theorists placed more or less emphasis on each of these traditions in their own political geographical formulations, the traditions' effects are evident in the factors deemed important to state growth and change. Why these factors were identified as central undoubtedly had much to do with the widespread influence of Charles Darwin on intellectual and social life during this period. Darwin's theory of competition inspired political geographers to conceptualize the state as a kind of biological organism that grew and contracted in response to external factors and forces. It was also during the late nineteenth century that foreign policy as a focus of state activity began to be theorized. This new emphasis came to be called *geopolitics*.

The Geopolitical Model of the State

geopolitics: the state's power to control space or territory and shape the foreign policy of individual states and international political relations

Geopolitics is the state's power to control space or territory and shape the foreign policy of individual states and international political relations. In Germany, geopolitical theory was influenced by Friedrich Ratzel (1844–1904), a German geographer trained in biology and chemistry. Ratzel employed biological metaphors, which he adopted from the work of Charles Darwin, to describe the growth and development of the state as well as seven laws of state growth:

1. The territory of the state grows with the expansion of the population having the same culture.
2. Territorial growth follows other aspects of development.
3. A state grows by absorbing smaller units.
4. The frontier is the peripheral organ of the state that reflects the strength and growth of the state; hence it is not permanent.
5. States in the course of their growth seek to absorb politically valuable territory.

6. The impetus for growth comes to a primitive state from a more highly developed civilization.

7. The trend toward territorial growth is contagious and increases in the process of transmission.[1]

Ratzel's model portrays the state as behaving like a biological organism; thus its growth and change are seen as "natural" and inevitable. Although Ratzel advanced his model of the state at the turn of the nineteenth century, his views have continued to influence state theorizing. What has been most enduring about Ratzel's conceptualization is the conviction that geopolitics stems from the interactions of power and territory.

Although it has evolved since Ratzel first introduced the concept, geopolitics has become one of the cornerstones of twenty-first century political geography and state foreign policy more generally. Although adherence to an organic view of the state has been abandoned, the twin features of power and territory still lie at the heart of political geography. In fact, the changes that have occurred in Europe and the former Soviet Union suggest that Ratzel's most important insights about geopolitics are still being played out.

Figure 9.1 portrays Ratzel's conceptualization of the interaction of power and territory through the changing map of Europe following the end of World War I to the present. In it, we see how the fluidity of maps reflects the instability between power and territory, especially some states' failure to achieve stability. The most recent map of Europe is a reflection of the precariousness of nation-state boundaries in the post–Cold War period. In fact, the 2008 map of Europe has more in common with the 1924 map than with 1989's. Estonia, Latvia, and Lithuania have returned to their sovereign status. Czechoslovakia has dissolved into the Czech Republic and Slovakia. The former Soviet Union is now the Commonwealth of Independent States, with Russia the largest and most powerful. Yugoslavia has dissolved into five states, but not without much civil strife and loss of life. Indeed, the difference between Europe in 1989 and Europe now is, in fact, far more dramatic than any other two maps from the previous 50 years. The maps also illustrate the centrality of territorial boundaries to the operations of the state.

Boundaries

Boundaries are important phenomena because they allow territoriality to be defined and enforced and because they allow conflict and competition to be managed and channelled. The creation of boundaries is, therefore, an important element in place making. It follows from the concept of territoriality that boundaries are normally inclusionary (**Figure 9.2**). That is, they are constructed in order to regulate and control specific sets of people and resources. Encompassed within a clearly defined territory, all sorts of activity can be controlled and regulated—everything, in fact, from birth to death. The delimited area over which a state exercises control and that is recognized by other states is called **territory**. Such an area may include both land and water.

Boundaries can also be exclusionary, however. Again, this often fulfills the function of controlling people and resources. National boundaries, for example, can be used to control the flow of immigrants or the flow of imported goods (**Figure 9.3**). Municipal boundaries and land-use zoning boundaries can be used to regulate access to upscale residential neighbourhoods, field boundaries can be used to regulate access to pasture, and so on (**Figure 9.4**).

Boundaries can be established in many different ways, however, and with differing degrees of permeability. At one extreme are informal, implied boundaries that are set by markers and symbols but never delineated on maps or set down in legal documents. A good example is the turf of a city gang, marked (as we see across

territory: the delimited area over which a state exercises control and that is recognized by other states

---

[1]Adapted from Martin I. Glassner and Harm de Blij, *Systematic Political Geography*, 3rd ed. New York: J. Wiley & Sons, 1980, p. 164.

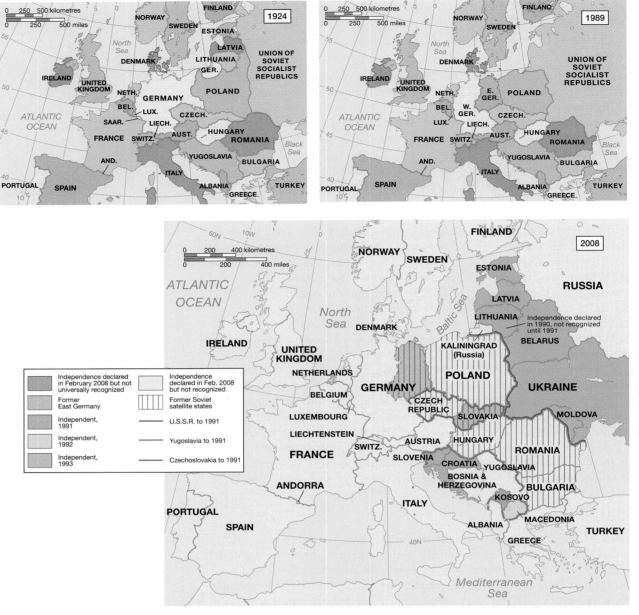

Figure 9.1 The changing map of Europe: 1924, 1989, 2008 The boundaries of the European states have undergone dramatic changes since World War I. The changing map of Europe illustrates the instability of international politics and the resultant dynamism in the geography of the nation-state system. (*Source:* **http://europa.eu/abc/maps/ index_en.htm**. Reprinted with permission from Prentice Hall, from J.M. Rubenstein, *The Cultural Landscape: An Introduction to Human Geography*, 5th ed., © 1996, p. 338.)

Canada) by graffiti on walls and bridges (**Figure 9.5**). At the other extreme are formal boundaries established in international law, delimited on maps, demarcated on the ground, fortified, and aggressively defended—not only against the movement of people but also of goods, money, and even ideas. An extreme example of this sort of boundary is the one between North and South Korea (**Figure 9.6**). In between the two extremes are formal boundaries that have some degree of permeability. The boundaries between the states of the European Union, for example, have become quite permeable because people and goods from member states can now move freely between them, with no customs or passport controls.

Impermeability does not necessarily mean immutability, however. The boundary between East and West Germany, part of the "Iron Curtain" for more than 40 years,

Figure 9.2   Boundary between Canada and the United States
Most boundaries are established to regulate and control specific sets of people and resources within a given territory. Such boundaries need to be clearly identified but do not necessarily need to be fortified. This photograph shows part of the Canada–United States border, a good example of an inclusionary boundary. To an extent, heightened border controls since the events of 11 September 2001, have made the Canada–United States border more like the United States–Mexico border.

Figure 9.3   Boundary between the United States and Mexico
Some boundaries are designed to be exclusionary. The United States–Mexico border provides a striking contrast to the United States–Canada one. The former is heavily patrolled and lined with barbed-wire chain-link fences along the highly urbanized parts. Aerial surveillance is also extensive along the United States–Mexico border. In an effort to stem the flow of illegal immigration from Mexico, the U.S. government increased the Border Patrol from 5176 officers in 1996 to 10 000 in 2000. Numbers have been increased further since the events of 2001 promoted greater American concerns over border security. This photo shows the United States–Mexico border along the Tijuana River estuary, with southern California on the left and Mexico on the right.

Figure 9.4   A stone wall in Derbyshire, England   Some boundaries, such as this stone wall in Derbyshire, England, contribute significantly to the character of places and regions. In a world of modernized agriculture and large-scale agribusiness, traditional field boundaries like these have become potent symbols of regional identity, being visible links with past landscapes and past ways of life.

Figure 9.5   Graffiti on walls   A frequent sight in most cities, graffiti often serves as a territorial marker.

was as aggressively defended as the present boundary between North and South Korea, and yet it was removed in 1989 when Germany was reunified (**Figure 9.7**). Similarly, the boundaries of the former Soviet Union have been entirely redrawn since 1989, allowing states, such as Lithuania and Estonia, to reappear (see Figure 9.1).

Figure 9.6 Border between North and South Korea Some boundaries are virtually impermeable. The border between North and South Korea is highly fortified and heavily patrolled. It was established at the conclusion of the Korean War (1950–1953) between two states that still contest each other's territory. Although occasional talks between the two countries have been held in recent years to declare that war officially over, the announcement in mid-November 2008 that North Korea intended to close its border with South Korea at year's end was a reminder of the difficulties that still confront negotiations.

Figure 9.7 Berlin Wall The boundary between East and West Germany was virtually impermeable for more than 40 years. The photograph here shows the scene on November 12, 1989, when Berliners tore the wall down in celebration of the reunification of Germany.

Boundaries are an important element of geopolitics and of the geography of domestic politics.

Boundary Formation Generally speaking, formal boundaries tend first to follow natural barriers, such as rivers, mountain ranges, and oceans. Good examples of countries with important mountain-range boundaries include France with Spain (the Pyrenees), and Italy with France, Switzerland, and Austria (the Alps). Examples of countries with boundaries formed by rivers include China and North Korea (the Yalu Tumen), Laos and Thailand (the Mekong), and Zambia and Zimbabwe (the Zambezi).

Where no natural features occur, formal boundaries tend to be fixed along the easiest and most practical cartographic device—a straight line. Examples include the western part of the boundary between Canada and the United States (**Figure 9.8**).

Figure 9.8 Straight boundaries A nineteenth-century survey team determined the position of the Canada–U.S. border in southern Manitoba.

Straight-line boundaries are also characteristic of formal boundaries that are established through colonization, which is the outcome of a particular form of territoriality. The reason, once again, is practicality. Straight lines are easy to survey and even easier to delimit on maps of territory that remain to be fully charted, claimed, and settled. Straight-line boundaries were established, for example, in many parts of Africa during European colonization in the nineteenth century. Another example is the pattern of townships employed by early surveyors in the mapping and division of land in Canada. According to the *Historical Atlas of Canada*, the first township survey was for Cataraqui Township, just west of Kingston (Ontario), which was completed on 27 October 1783. The system was used across large parts of Ontario and Quebec, where townships were laid out in a chessboard pattern: a typical township being 16 square kilometres and subdivided into lots and concessions. In western Canada, where settlement occurred later, the township was a square unit of land, 10 kilometres a side, divided into 36 sections—each of which was then divided into four *quarter-sections* of 160 acres each (64 hectares).

In detail, however, formal boundaries often detour from straight lines and natural barriers to accommodate special needs and claims. Colombia's border, for instance, was established to contain the source of the river Orinoco; Democratic Republic of Congo's border was established to provide a corridor of access to the Atlantic Ocean; and Sudan's border detours to include a settlement, Wadi Halfa.

After primary divisions have been established, internal boundaries tend to evolve as smaller, secondary territories are demarcated. In general, the higher the population density, the smaller these secondary units tend to be. Their configuration tends to follow the same generalizations as for larger units, following physical features, accommodating special needs, and following straight lines where there are no appropriate natural features or where colonization has made straight lines expedient (**Figure 9.9**).

Territories delimited by formal boundaries—nation-states, states, counties, municipalities, special districts, and so on—are known as *de jure* spaces or regions. *De jure* simply means "legally recognized." Historically, the world has evolved from a loose patchwork of territories (with few formally defined or delimited boundaries) to nested hierarchies (**Figure 9.10**) and overlapping systems of de jure territories.

These de jure territories are often used as the basic units of analysis in human geography, largely because they are both convenient and significant units of analysis. They are often, in fact, the only areal units for which reliable data are available. They are also important units of analysis in their own right because of their importance as units of governance or administration. A lot of regional analysis and nearly all attempts at regionalization, therefore, are based on a framework of de jure spaces.

Figure 9.9 Rectilinear boundaries
Many of the boundaries between properties and administrative units found across Canada do not follow natural features but are linear and rectangular (that is, "rectilinear"). The consequence of surveying techniques used during colonization, these boundaries impose an ordered look to the landscape. The illustrations show boundaries in (a) Alexandria, Ontario, and (b) the Dirt Hills near Kayville, Saskatchewan.

(a)

(b)

Figure 9.10 Nested hierarchy of de jure territories De jure territories are constructed at various spatial scales, depending on their origin and function. Administrative and governmental territories are often "nested," with one set of territories fitting within the larger framework of another, as in this example of states, districts, and municipalities in India.

Municipalities in Ahmednagar District

Districts in Maharashtra State

States in India

GEOPOLITICS AND THE WORLD ORDER

There is, arguably, no other concept to which political geographers devote more of their attention than the state. The state is one of the most powerful institutions—if not the most powerful institution—cultivating the process of globalization. The state effectively regulates, supports, and legitimates the globalization of the economy.

States and Nations

As described in Chapter 2, the state is an independent political unit with recognized boundaries, even if some of these boundaries are in dispute. In contrast to a state, a **nation** is a group of people often sharing common elements of culture, such as religion or language, or a history or political identity. Members of a nation recognize a common identity, but they need not reside within a common geographical area. For example, the Jewish nation refers to members of the Jewish culture and faith throughout the world regardless of their place of origin. The term **nation-state** is an ideal form consisting of a homogeneous group of people governed by their own state. In a true nation-state, no significant group exists that is not part of the nation. Furthermore, **sovereignty** is the exercise of state power over people and territory, recognized by other states and codified by international law.

The idea of the nation-state as a sovereign body controlling space is actually quite a recent idea. In ancient and medieval history, it was individual rulers, through their own brute force or cunning, who forged kingdoms out of groups of followers who usually were tied to that ruler by gifts of land or treasure in return for their military service. The key point here is that an individual's loyalty was to a *person* not to a physical entity or *space* called the state. From the point of view of political geography, this idea had two important consequences.

- *Kingdoms need not comprise discrete units.* By this we mean that the realm or kingdom over which the ruler held sway did not need to be a unitary whole. It could be made up of a number of discontinuous parts. The best illustration

nation: a group of people often sharing common elements of culture, such as religion or language, or a history or political identity

nation-state: an ideal form consisting of a homogeneous group of people governed by their own state

sovereignty: the exercise of state power over people and territory, recognized by other states and codified by international law

is the Holy Roman Empire, a powerful political entity ruled by the Holy Roman Emperor during the Middle Ages. At its height, the Empire included large parts of present-day Germany, central Europe, and northern Italy. However, there were many enclaves totally surrounded by the Empire that were not part of the Emperor's domain, and there were parts of the Empire that were outliers from the main part of the Empire.

■ *Sovereignty was vested in the ruler's person.* In many medieval countries, the ruler continually travelled around. Wherever he or she was situated, there was the seat of government for the time being. Because, as we have noted, all power flowed from the ruler, or sovereign (the root of the concept of *sovereignty,* of course), the principle developed that power was inherited through royal family lines. Power then became embedded in one or two aristocratic families, not in space and certainly not in the people over whom they ruled.

These ideas were challenged over time but were not radically altered until the **Enlightenment**, which occurred in Europe in the eighteenth century. Two events in particular sparked major changes. The American Declaration of Independence (1776) and the French Revolution (1789) both led to the replacement of the inherent power of the ruler with that of *the people*.

Once power was decoupled from the ruler and vested in the people, a link was soon forged between the area that the people inhabited and the space in which they exercised their sovereign power. How else, we might ask, was the *people's* power to be allocated across Europe or the world? In this way, we see that the two concepts of space (state) and people (nation) began to fuse, and the rise of the *nation-state* as a political force in the nineteenth century began in earnest.

During this period of history, because space (the state) was now the only way of defining those people who had sovereignty (the nation), the nation-state had to achieve as close a correlation as possible between the two concepts of nation and state or lose its legitimacy. What this meant—to suggest (but not insist) on a simple generalization (or model) that may help our understanding—was that the nation-state had two main ways of promoting itself. The first was to ensure, through various means, that all of the people included within the existing boundaries of the state were of one "nation," and to exclude or remove those who were defined as non-members of that particular nation. The second method was to adjust the state's spatial boundaries so that they could encompass all of the people defined as a nation, a process that often led to the break up and reconfiguration of states (**Figure 9.11**).

To use the more technical terms that political geographers have developed, the rulers of the nineteenth-century nation-states promoted a unified nation using **centripetal forces** to hold the state together. Centripetal forces are those that strengthen and unify the state. The alternative was to witness **centrifugal forces** break the state apart. Centrifugal forces are those that divide or tend to pull apart the state. Centripetal forces include cultural, economic, political, and regional factors that can be used to integrate the state. Centrifugal forces employ the same factors but to opposite ends and can lead to the disintegration of the state.

Let us now look more closely at two of the main strategies that the nineteenth-century nation-state used to establish its political dominance—nationalism and territorial manipulation.

Enlightenment: an eighteenth-century European movement that sought to replace ideas of authority or explanation drawn from God with those that individual humans could establish through their own reason

centripetal forces: forces that integrate the state

centrifugal forces: forces that can lead to the disintegration of the state

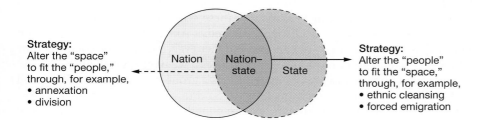

Strategy:
Alter the "space" to fit the "people," through, for example,
• annexation
• division

Strategy:
Alter the "people" to fit the "space," through, for example,
• ethnic cleansing
• forced emigration

Figure 9.11 The nation-state This illustration shows how the nation-state is the product of two different geographical processes. The first attempts to mould the people to the state; the second manipulates the boundaries of the state to fit the space occupied by the people.

Nationalism Despite the fact that concepts of *nation, people, folk, race,* and *ethnic group* are all socially constructed, it was crucial for the proponents of the nation-state to believe that their particular "*nation*" of people developed and grew up as a group in a particular place from which they derived an identity and whose identity they now shaped. **Nationalism** has been coined as a term meaning the feeling of belonging to a nation, as well as the belief that a nation has a natural right to determine its own affairs.

nationalism: the feeling of belonging to a nation as well as the belief that a nation has a natural right to determine its own affairs

To take historic examples, people who lived in eighteenth- and nineteenth-century England (in actuality, a tremendous mixture of races and types) came to see themselves as the "English race." They believed they had a unique set of traditions, customs, history, language, and—at least according to some—some distinctive natural abilities. The French of this period saw themselves as the "French race," defined in similar terms, and both the French and the English agreed they were from different races. Importantly, both also agreed that the indigenous peoples in their colonies were from different races, and nineteenth-century environmental determinism only served to exaggerate such racist views.

Unfortunately, such practices were by no means confined to the early development of the nation-state. In Germany, the Nazi commitment to purge the country of "non-Aryan" peoples led to the killing of millions of Jews and large numbers of other groups (including Roma, Poles, Ukrainians, and homosexuals) as Germany expanded its borders in the 1930s and 1940s. Horrifically, such practices returned to Europe in the 1990s when Serbia, under nationalist leader Slobodan Milosevic, carried out a concerted policy of "ethnic cleansing" against Muslims in Bosnia and ethnic Albanians in Kosovo. In Africa, the genocide of 1994–1995 in Rwanda was an outcome of nineteenth-century colonialism, which originally sowed the seeds of animosity between the Tutsi and the Hutu. In each of these cases, the myth of unique nationhood was perpetuated to justify such atrocities.

It is fascinating—and sometimes deeply disturbing—to see that the means by which many of these myths of nationality were achieved are fundamentally geographical, for they built on the place-making activities we have seen in this book. Indeed, since place making is such a powerful aspect of nationalism, we should, on reflection, not be surprised at its importance.

Regional patterns of vernacular house types, folk customs, songs, languages, cuisine, and accents are all pressed into service by nationalists to stamp a land with a particular identity and to use that identity as indicative of a unique nationality. If we seek to go further, we then deliberately drape the country with national emblems, such as the country's flag, or build elaborate monuments to enshrine ideas of nationhood; for example, Mount Rushmore, a mountain sacred to the Sioux, has been turned into an icon of the nation that has taken its place.

Of course, we should not be surprised to find this in the United States, where the attempt to create one culture has historically been the American approach to forging a country from very disparate immigrant communities. Such a "melting-pot" strategy has been very different from the Canadian response to this issue. In Canada, government policies of multiculturalism and official bilingualism have sought to protect cultural differences among immigrant groups, and, perhaps paradoxically, to make the recognition of differences itself a hallmark of being Canadian.

British historians Eric Hobsbawm and Terence Ranger have shown, in their study of the creation of nineteenth-century nationalism, that it hardly matters that many of the "unique" traditions used to advance the cause of nationalism are, in fact, myths as long as we can all agree that these symbols do work to pull people together as a nation. As political scientist Benedict Anderson has argued, a nation is an **imagined community**—we cannot have met everyone in "our country," nor will we ever likely see all of its space; nevertheless, we have no difficulty conceiving of it as a nation because we can imagine it as a group of people mutually bound by shared symbols. Interestingly, as Edward Said (a scholar known for his writings on cultural studies) has shown, we are equally able to use these powers of

imagined community: a group of people who believe that they share a common bond and thus are part of the same nation

Figure 9.12 Residential schools
Residential schools were established by the federal government to assimilate the Aboriginal population through Western education. Management and control of Blue Quills First Nations College, a former residential school pictured here, were assumed by the Aboriginal people in the region in 1971.

imagination to construct stereotypes of other nations and to believe firmly in the validity of our own inventions.

Fortunately, Canada has been spared the full force of attempts to forge a nation-state within its borders. Yet, we cannot ignore the efforts that were made in the past. The banning of Aboriginal languages and the removal of Aboriginal children to residential schools across the Prairies were part of a deliberate attempt to assimilate Canada's indigenous peoples into the Canadian state that lasted well into the twentieth century (**Figure 9.12**). The deportation of the Acadians from Nova Scotia in the eighteenth century and the internment of Japanese Canadians in British Columbia's interior in the 1940s were both carried out because of questions over loyalty to the Canadian state (**Figure 9.13**). Our immigration policy, until 1967, was based on overt government racism. Only since the abandonment of that policy, and the official commitment to a policy of multiculturalism in the years that followed, can we truly see Canada as a country that has relinquished the concept of the nation-state as a model for its development.

Nor should we think that the use of the place-making tools of nationalism has been neglected in this country. The so-called Sponsorship Scandal, which led to the establishment of the Gomery Inquiry in 2004, has highlighted the federal government's program to promote national unity in Quebec through advertising and the use of the federal flag. And if we look to the other side of this divide, as part of the

Figure 9.13 Japanese internment camp, New Denver, British Columbia
Established during World War II, the internment camp at New Denver was the destination for hundreds of Japanese Canadians who were deported from Vancouver. The Nikkei Internment Memorial Centre now stands on the site.

Figure 9.14 The St. Jean Baptiste parade, Montreal This picture of the annual procession was taken on 25 June 1990. The parade of an estimated 200 000 people was unusually large because many joined the procession to protest the failure of the Meech Lake Accord, which happened earlier that year.

ongoing project of Quebec separation, we see the attempt to create the idea of a Québécois people or "folk" as a "nation" that has inhabited the land of Quebec since the beginning of the seventeenth century. The endeavour to forge a nation-state uses all of the place-making and cultural devices at its disposal—Québécois folk music, architecture, and heritage have all been vigorously promoted, as has the use of the Quebec flag, the *fleur-de-lys*. After the failure of the most recent referendum on Quebec's separation from Canada, the annual St. Jean Baptiste parade was itself a stirring example of how such symbolism could take to the streets (**Figure 9.14**). But of all the means by which the nationalist project is advanced in Quebec, none has been more successful (or disliked by its detractors) than the insistence that French is the official language of the province. French is the language of the schools, of government, and of road and store signs. English-language store signs are the targets of graffiti artists and the *Office Québécois de la langue française*. Increasingly, in fact, the attempt to create a nation has overtly shifted from an exclusionary focus on those descended from the original French settlers of the province to a more broadly based "cultural nationalism" that is aimed at anyone sympathetic to its aims.

Territorial Manipulation The second approach to forging a nation-state has been to adjust the physical boundaries of the state to conform more exactly to the spatial distribution of people thought to comprise the nation. Historical examples include the growth of Germany in the years prior to World War II, as it endeavoured to incorporate all of the lands occupied by German-speaking peoples in central Europe into a greater Germany. That this involved annexing Austria and invading Czechoslovakia, Poland, and parts of France was to lead Europe into conflict. Another example is to be found in the history of Europe's colonization of Africa. Because the nation-state was the model of political geography prevalent at the time when the global core of the world-system was exerting its dominance over the periphery in Africa, the colonizing powers imposed a framework of nation-states on that continent. The problem was that because the imperialists had little understanding of the societies they had subdued and—as we have seen—ideas of "nation" are imaginary, the framework was entirely an artificial one. Once decolonization occurred, the logic of the system fell apart. In fact, the imposed boundaries themselves have become the focus of a large number of conflicts in Africa. Largely being fought in the Democratic Republic of the Congo, the current wars in central Africa that involve the armies of seven states are a direct consequence of the way in which boundaries were imposed on that region.

The manipulation of boundaries to produce nation-states sometimes has resulted in the breakup of larger entities to form smaller units, the division being made on "ethnic" grounds. For example, the breakup of the large Ottoman and

Austrian "multicultural" empires following World War I led to the creation of much of the political geography of today's Middle East and southeastern Europe, with the creation of such countries as Hungary, Romania, Turkey, Syria, Iraq, and Lebanon. The failure of the European powers to accommodate the Kurds, the Jews, and the Palestinians with their own states at that time has led directly to many difficulties. The process of decolonization also brought about division on occasion, the best example being the creation of Pakistan as a separate Islamic state when the Indian subcontinent achieved independence from Britain in 1947. Apartheid's policy of separate development in South Africa led to an attempt to fragment the country into a series of politically independent homelands (see **Geography Matters 9.1—Imperialism, Colonization, and the Dismantling of Apartheid in South Africa**), an attempt that was repudiated by the international community.

The End of the Nation-State?

In reality, of course, the true "nation-state" has never existed, but few would deny the importance of the nation-state *idea* as a model for state formation or that its dominance in recent history has been because it became part of the way in which the global core dominated the world-system. Within the last 20 years, two different views of the nation-state as a model of political geography have developed. The first suggests that the idea of a restricted citizenship that the model promotes may well have an increasing validity in the future. In contrast, the second critique questions the very future of the idea of state sovereignty on which the model depends. Let us consider each of these in turn.

Citizenship   In a recent paper on this topic, Marston and Staeheli tell us that citizenship is *contingent,* that is, "dependent," on both time and space.[2] That it is contingent on time is nicely shown by their summary of Thomas H. Marshall's classic 1950 essay "Citizenship and Social Class," where he argued that the concept of citizenship has parallelled the development of the capitalist state over the last 300 years.

The eighteenth century saw the emergence of the civil and political rights of the citizen as one outcome of the assault on feudal powers and privilege, a development that led to individual freedoms concerning the rights to property, personal liberty, and full and equal justice before the law. The late nineteenth century witnessed the grafting of political rights of citizenship onto the pre-existing civil and legal rights as trade union agitation led to individuals gaining the right to vote and hold elective office. By the mid-twentieth century, according to Marshall, a further set of rights—those of social citizenship—was being developed. These rights included publicly funded universal health care, state pensions, subsidized housing, and unemployment benefits for those that needed them. These new rights were a product of the post-war welfare state, designed to counteract the effects of the free market and to enable each citizen to participate fully in the social life of the country according to society's standards.

In the last 20 years, however, this whole package of rights has increasingly come under pressure across the Western world as the twin forces of domestic economic restructuring and globalization have made the costs of full social citizenship more difficult to meet. Janine Brodie, a Canadian political scientist, in describing Canada's reaction to this situation, sees a "hollowing out" of the welfare state as once universal rights are now only "targeted" to needy individuals (who, as individual members of disadvantaged groups, find themselves stigmatized as "deviants" from the norms of the new citizenship who require "rehabilitation").

In the same way, we find individual regions in this country that once received regional economic development assistance from the federal government increasingly

---

[2]Sallie A. Marston and L.A. Staeheli, "Citizenship, Struggle and Political and Economic Restructuring." *Environment and Planning A* 26, 1994, pp. 840–848.

Geography Matters

Imperialism, Colonization, and the Dismantling of Apartheid in South Africa

Colonial Conquest

The history of imperialism and colonization in South Africa is a long one, dating back to the establishment of a supply station by the Dutch East India Company in Cape Town in 1652. The Dutch, whose settlement developed slowly at first, were segregationists and, from the first, attempted to prevent contact between whites and indigenous peoples. The early settlers included French Huguenots and Germans as well as Dutch free burghers, who were mostly farmers. Over time, as white settlers moved into the dry lands to the east of Cape Town, they pushed into areas already occupied by the native peoples. In this push for land in the western Cape area, the native peoples were decimated in frontier skirmishes as well as by diseases contracted from the white settlers. During these conflicts between the Boers and the native peoples, an Afrikaner (South African Dutch) identity was constructed. As the native peoples were pushed from the land around Cape Town, some survived by migrating north into the Karoo Desert, while others were incorporated as servants into the emerging Boer economy.

By 1806, Britain had established political control over the Cape. Like the Dutch, the British set about expropriating land and setting up defendable boundary lines between the European immigrant settlements and the largely Bantu-speaking Nguni and Sotho people. Conflict between native peoples and whites persisted. Whites claimed increasing control over land and water as indigenous peoples resisted and then retreated south and westward.

An important component of the mid-nineteenth-century colonization of South Africa was the intermittent waging of the "Kaffir Wars" between 1835 and 1879. In contrast to previous conflicts, these wars were not aimed at securing additional lands and resources but at securing a labour supply. Missionaries and traders were especially important in convincing the defeated blacks to work as wage labourers on white farms or in the white urban areas. The previously Boer-established policy of strict racial segregation between blacks and Afrikaners was directly confronted by a British policy of racial commingling, which intentionally exposed blacks to white value systems and institutions.

As British influence came increasingly to undermine Dutch control of native peoples, Boer farmers—in the Great Trek of 1836—moved northward to areas beyond British colonial influence. Known as the *Voortrekkers*, the Boers abandoned the well-established European settlements in and around Cape Town. They did this to preserve their own value system and to protest the abolition of slavery and the repeal of the pass laws designed to control the movements of black labourers.

In their migration east and northward, the Voortrekkers displaced, through direct conflict and expropriation of tribal land, the Sotho and Zulu peoples and founded republics in Natal (renamed KwaZulu-Natal in 1994), the Orange Free State, and the Transvaal. In these areas, the Boers established native reserves while continuing to wrest land from the independent Zulu peoples. Their efforts not only displaced the native peoples but also forced them to participate in a cash economy to obtain money to pay taxes and to purchase particular types of clothes, which they were required to wear when working or travelling in white urban areas.

The British annexed the Republic of Natal as the colony of Natal soon after its establishment by the Voortrekkers. In the other two republics, however, native peoples were incorporated into the economy as servants, squatter tenants, or semifeudal serfs. Ultimately, the Fundamental Law, established in 1852, legally enshrined the inequality between blacks and whites. It had taken about two centuries for white people to colonize and extend their control throughout what was to become the Union of South Africa.

Exploitation of Resources

No history of South Africa would be complete without a discussion of diamond-, gold-, and coal-mining activities, which began with the discovery of diamonds near Kimberley in 1867 and linked white South Africa to the world economy. This discovery spurred investment of British capital in the mines, as well as the construction of the railway network to connect the mines to the ports. Skilled labour, machinery, technology, and capital, as well as the dividends and profits garnered from mining, were the important linkages between South Africa and the world economy. Importantly, this connection to the world economy and the struggle between the British and Dutch colonizers to control South Africa led eventually to the Anglo–Boer War from 1899 to 1902.

The mining of resources was also responsible for the tremendous growth in population in the mining centres and in the ports. By 1911, the major diamond- and gold-mining centres (including Kimberley, Pretoria-Witwatersrand, and Johannesburg) composed 37 percent of the total urban population, with the four ports (Cape Town, Durban, Port Elizabeth, and East London) accounting for an additional 23 percent. This population increase was a result of increased European migration to South Africa, as well as a result of the temporary migration of black males to the mines and urban centres in search of work.

The Era of Territorial Segregation

The first half of the twentieth century witnessed the strengthening and extension of the Boer principles of racial segregation through territorial segregation. Black ownership of land was restricted, as was black settlement activity. In addition, the permanent residence of blacks in white urban areas was prohibited. The Natives (Urban Areas) Act codified this latter restriction, defining blacks as temporary urban residents who were to be repatriated to the tribal reserves if not employed. The act also established that blacks, while within urban areas, were to be physically, socially, and economically separated from the white population.

The intention was for the tribal reserves to operate as independent economies supporting the black population and to be separate from the operations of the white economy. Unfortunately, low wages for black labourers as well as high rates of landlessness among blacks living on the reserves undermined the viability of an independent subsistence economy. The reserves were unable to support the black migrant labour system so necessary to the success of the white economy. In addition, blacks increasingly flowed into the urban areas for work, creating a growing and permanent black population in the white cities. By 1946, blacks were the largest racial group in the urban areas, a direct result of the demand for black labour in the growing urban manufacturing sector. Clearly, territorial segregation was becoming increasingly ineffective as a method of separating the races. By mid-century, the policies of segregation were abandoned and new policies of apartheid were introduced. With the British effectively controlling the politics and economy of South Africa until the mid-1940s, the separation and unequal treatment of races—white, coloured (of mixed race), and black (African)—were ubiquitous practices with a loose set of laws and procedures to uphold them. When the British lost control of national political power in 1946, segregationist practices became more solidly codified. In the wake of their victory, the Afrikaners imposed strict racial separation policies transforming apartheid from practice to rule.

The Era of Apartheid

By 1960, whites were a minority in every South African city. The government introduced the apartheid system to allay the fears of whites who were being crowded out. Apartheid was a system of control of the movement, employment, and residences of blacks. Its main vehicle was the creation of "homelands," a new version of the tribal reserves (**Figure 9.1.1**). The pass system was revived as well, which further restricted the movement of blacks in white urban areas.

For nearly 40 years, apartheid was the method of control of a white minority over a black majority. Through containment of urban blacks, regional decentralization of employment, and the suppression of dissent, Afrikaners attempted to maintain white supremacy while they continued to exploit black labour to fuel a burgeoning economy. Leaving the homeland areas as well as entering the "proclaimed areas"—all urban areas of the country—was strictly controlled by a permission and pass system. Legislation to remove blacks from urban areas was also enacted. Industrial decentralization, though encouraged, was not a successful strategy and instead fostered the settlement of blacks in homeland townships close to white urban areas, such as Soweto near Johannesburg (**Figure 9.1.2**). Protests against apartheid were quickly and ruthlessly repressed, with African National Congress leaders, such as Nelson Mandela, being jailed or killed.

A New South Africa

The late 1980s saw the beginning of the end of apartheid in South Africa: Nelson Mandela was freed from jail, and

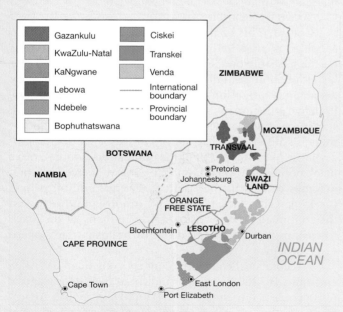

The system of South African "homelands"

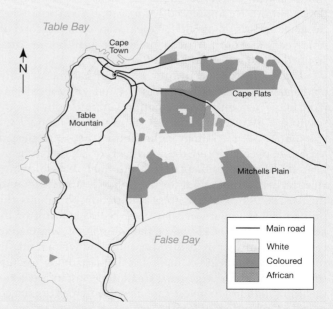

Major residential areas designated for different race groups in the Cape Town metropolitan area (before the dissolution of apartheid in 1994)

Figure 9.1.1   Homelands and post-apartheid South Africa
(*Source:* D.M. Smith [ed.], *Living under Apartheid*. London: Allen & Unwin, 1982; figs. 2.1, 2.3, and 2.5; pp. 26, 34, and 40.)

Figure 9.1.2 Soweto, South Africa: workers' housing

President P.W. Botha agreed to the sharing of political power between blacks and whites. In 1994, South Africa held the first election in its history in which blacks were allowed to vote. Nelson Mandela was elected the first black president there. In 1996, a new South African constitution was signed into law and took effect in early 1997. The constitution includes one of the world's most comprehensive bills of rights and prohibits discrimination based on race, gender, pregnancy, marital status, ethnic or social origin, colour, sexual orientation, age, disability, religion, conscience, belief, culture, language, or birth.

As a result of South Africa's second free general elections held in June 1999, Thabo Mbeki was chosen by the National Assembly as president and replaced Nelson Mandela who had earlier indicated his wish to retire from that position. Re-appointed for a second term following the general election of 2004, Mbeki was to serve a total of nine years as South Africa's president until he, in turn, stepped down in September 2008.

During his period in office, Mbeki has faced many challenges. Domestically, he had to cope with the fall-out from the Truth and Reconciliation Commission, a body set up in 1995 under retired Archbishop Desmond Tutu to examine alleged human rights abuses that were alleged to have happened during the apartheid era. During its hearings, de Klerk (president during the final years of white rule) formally apologised for the policy of apartheid, and the African National Congress admitted responsibility for human rights violations that occurred as a result of its actions in the 1980s. However, the commission was unable to get much further in its investigations and when it finally reported, in March 2003, many felt that it had not lived up to its potential. In large part, this failure lay in the commission's inability to investigate illegal activities organized outside the borders of South Africa.

In terms of foreign policy, Mbeki has aimed to achieve peace and development in the region. He was active in 1999 in brokering a cease-fire between the two sides of the civil war in the Democratic Republic of the Congo. He has widely lobbied for international aid for the region, and his "Millennium African Recovery Plan" became the basis for the "New Partnership for Africa's Development" (NEPAD) initiative that the G-8 countries supported with promises of US$6 billion at their meeting in Alberta in 2002. However, his attempts to use "quiet diplomacy" to attempt to persuade Robert Mugabe, the president of neighbouring Zimbabwe, to deal with international disquiet following his election victory in March 2002, were unsuccessful. In fact, Mbeki's continued support for Mugabe threatened to erode South Africa's wider geopolitical influence in the region, and achieve very little in return. Millions of refugees from Zimbabwe continued to flow into South Africa as recently as 2008—a year when Mugabe was again returned as president of Zimbabwe, in an election widely seen as fraudulent by international observers.

Economically, the International Monetary Fund offered this assessment of the government's record in November 2006: "South Africa has been enjoying its longest economic expansion on record, thanks in large measure to sound macroeconomic management." According to government statistics in June 2007, per head measures of the growth in GDP, which had sometimes been negative in the 1990s, had reached 3.4 percent in 2004, and 3.6 percent in 2005. Government debt (which had stood at 43.5 percent of GDP in 1994) had declined to 31.3 percent in 2007, and was projected to reach 24.3 percent in 2010. In less abstract terms, progress can also be measured by the fact that by 2004, a total of 2 million new houses had been built since 1994; by 2006, 90 percent of the entire country's population had access to the potable water infrastructure, and 74 percent of its households (that is, 9.56 million out of a total of 13 million) had access to electricity.

Considerable challenges remain, however, and when Mbeki was pressured by the African National Congress on the basis of some internal party disputes to announce his resignation from the presidency in September 2008, he left a number of serious issues to be faced by his successors. Principal among these is the continued legacy of apartheid: statistics show that despite the successes reported above, there is still so much left to do. For example, despite representing over 80 percent of the population, South Africa's black population still accounts for only 40 percent of total incomes earned in the country. Twenty million people (or 45 percent of the population) still live in poverty, and the continued lack of basic services in many of the black townships has even led to demonstrations in the Western Cape province.

A second challenge is the country's ongoing HIV/AIDS epidemic. By 2008, statistics indicated that an average of 600 people a day died from HIV/AIDS in South Africa. Losses of this magnitude have placed a severe emotional and economic burden on those who remain. The crisis has been worsened by the unwillingness of many government leaders to advocate more widely-accepted methods of disease prevention, such as the use of retroviral vaccines, since they do not believe HIV to be the cause of AIDS, and seek to promote traditional remedies instead. Be that as it may, the enormous cost of such vaccines has, until recently, placed them out of reach of all but a few, and has rendered any full-scale program against the disease inoperative until circumstances alter.

It will require both international and national efforts to achieve a breakthrough against HIV/AIDS, but the recent history of South Africa is an example in itself to show that such efforts are possible and can succeed.

Sources: J. Browett, "The Evolution of Unequal Development within South Africa: An Overview." In D.M. Smith (ed.), *Living under Apartheid.* London: Allen and Unwin, 1982, pp. 10–23; Linda Van Buren, "South Africa: Economy," and Christopher Saunders, "South Africa: Recent History," In *The Europa World Online.* Routledge: London, retrieved 29 September 2008, from **www.europaworld.com/pub**. (This online version of the highly regarded and authoritative publication *The Europa World Year Book* is not only a very useful source for following world affairs, but also provides extensive and up-to-date "profiles" of each country.)

being denied such assistance. Effectively, as Simon Fraser University geographer Nick Blomley has written, people can no longer expect to live and work where they choose to or, more pointedly, where they were born.

In terms of the more general spatial aspects of citizenship, the rise of the modern welfare state has made it increasingly important for a state to control who it allows as citizens of that country—a right determined in most countries by birth. Consequently, those who have sought permanent entry to a country—whether they are refugees or travellers such as the Roma (traditionally known as Gypsies)—have increasingly found it harder to gain access and have found their rights severely curtailed even if they do gain admittance.

Universalism and Difference   Because we now question the very premise of the idea of "nation" and because the concept of unique spaces called "states" is challenged by the forces of globalization, is it possible to see the end of the "nation-state"?

Paradoxically, the possible end of the nation-state lies in its origins. This is because, as we have seen, the appeal to the rights of the people and to their reason, in the form of the Enlightenment, led to the usurpation of the ruler's power and its replacement with a state whose power was vested in the people. The crucial point is that the appeal was to the universal values and rights that the people have as humans, or their *human rights*. This appeal to universal values, on which the modern state was built, has led to a challenge to the modern state from that very perspective—from *universal* values and rights.

The challenge to the sovereignty of states based on universal standards of human rights meant that it was no longer possible for a country to do what it liked to its citizens. After World War II showed Europe what unfettered sovereignty could do, the move toward international standards gained speed. Canada took a leading role in preparing the 1951 International Convention Regarding the Status of Refugees, and a Canadian, John Humphrey, drafted the first version of the 1948 Universal Declaration of Human Rights. The establishment of the United Nations (UN) itself was part of this effort to limit state sovereignty through the strength of international treaties built on universal values.

The work of modern political geographers has shown that state sovereignty is no longer absolute—a state's activities within its own borders are now limited by these international conventions. Examples include the American-led UN-sanctioned invasion of Iraq in 1991, NATO's campaign against Serbia on the grounds that the human rights of the Kosovars were being attacked, and the arrest in Britain of the dictator Augusto Pinochet on a charge of war crimes committed in Chile. In all cases, an international right (founded on universal principles) has enabled a state's sovereignty to be limited. The establishment of the International Criminal Court in The Hague (in the Netherlands) is a logical extension of this development. The court has the authority under a United Nations' agreement that came into force on 1 July 2002 to try individuals alleged to be guilty of war crimes committed anywhere in the world. (Currently, the United States has refused to sign the agreement to protect its military forces from possible prosecution.)

Treaties, such as the international law of the sea or various environmental protocols, also slowly erode individual states' own sovereignty. Importantly, international bodies, such as the World Trade Organization, and political arrangements, such as the European Economic Community (now the European Union) and the North American Free Trade Agreement (NAFTA) among Canada, the United States, and Mexico, all lead to significant curtailing of individual states' rights.

As but one example, Canada's ability to exploit its own forests is currently under severe threat from American complaints under NAFTA regarding this country's pricing of softwood lumber exports from British Columbia to the United States. It is a complex issue. American business interests regard Canadian producers as benefitting from concealed subsidies because "stumpage" rates (the cost of replanting) are too low. Canadian interests argue that this ignores the costs of "timber licences" that producers must pay to use Crown land. Dispute settlement mechanisms set up under NAFTA have so far found in Canada's favour. But, so far, the United States has shown little sign of complying completely with the settlements. What is also interesting about this dispute is that both sides have accepted that international trade should be governed by international law.

But does this mean that *universalism* goes hand in hand with *globalization*? Is it, as many Islamic and communist states have suggested, merely an excuse for the global core to extend its power by disguising what are really only Western values as universal values? For many theorists in modern political geography, this argument is seen as the *postmodern* challenge to universalism.

This challenge argues that the Enlightenment's idea that universal values are inherent in humanity is really only that—an idea, one that has no better basis supporting it than anything else. Consequently, one cannot insist on the primacy of universal human values (embodied in a UN treaty) over any local set of practices. In other words, differences found in the practices of various cultures toward human rights are no better or worse than anywhere else. There simply is no universal standard from which to criticize them or to moralize.

As an example, the practice of female circumcision (found in parts of Africa) has been severely criticized by Western countries as barbaric and a violation of human rights. Indeed, Canada now defines this practice as persecution against women and has accepted claims to refugee status on this basis. However, some commentators have argued that this practice has to be seen as part of a particular set of practices. They suggest that the Western attempt to criticize is merely an attempt to impose "universal" rules, which have no bearing on the local culture and may, themselves, be biased as they attempt to impose alien values on local practice. As you can see, this is certainly not an easy problem to resolve and is one that has placed many human rights advocates in a quandary.

According to contemporary political geographers, the postmodern appeal to the *local* and the acceptance of *difference* as the new standards of human rights have themselves led to the rise of a number of movements. Consider, for example, the Iranian revolution of the 1970s, in which Western values were replaced by a return to a more fundamentalist Islam, and the 1990s Zapatista movement in the Chiapas region of Mexico, in which the rights of the indigenous peoples were asserted (often over the World Wide Web) against the centralizing powers of Mexico City. Indeed, the general recognition that the force of nationalism, as embodied by the driving force of the metropolitan core, has swept over many smaller "nationalities" and groups has now led to the resurgence of local groups, such as the Basques or the Catalans, for local autonomy within Spain (an autonomy, ironically, that is now easier to achieve under the European Union's umbrella than before).

In Canada, we have seen a measure of political autonomy being given to the Inuit with the formation of the new territory of Nunavut. In the recognition of the rights of Aboriginal self-government accorded the Gitskan of northern British Columbia by the federal and provincial governments in 2001, it is possible that we are seeing a model for the future of the system of reservations that, over the years, the Canadian government has set aside for First Nation peoples (**Figure 9.15**).

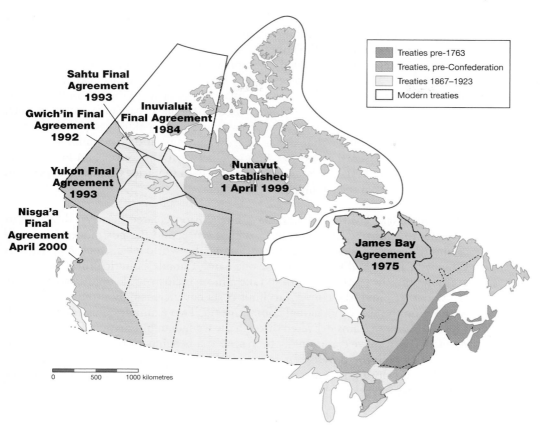

Figure 9.15   First Nations treaties   The earliest treaties between the British government and Canada's Aboriginal peoples were in the Maritimes and were part of a diplomatic arrangement known as the "Covenant Chain." By 1763, a royal proclamation was necessary to protect Aboriginal lands in the St. Lawrence lowlands from European encroachment. During the settlement of Upper Canada (Ontario), treaties set aside reserve lands in exchange for ownership of the province's remaining lands. By the time the Prairies were settled, Aboriginal peoples sought to safeguard their future with treaty provision for agricultural supplies. However, such arrangements were only sporadically honoured. In addition, the poor quality of reserve land meant that many First Nations had to rely on government assistance and quickly lost their independence. Modern treaties between the federal government and a First Nation have taken the form of either specific land-claim agreements or comprehensive agreements. The former attempt to rectify original treaty arrangements; the latter involve First Nations that have never before been covered by a treaty (examples include the Inuit of Nunavut and the Nisga'a of British Columbia).   (*Sources:* Geoffrey J. Matthews and Robert Morrow Jr., *Canada and the World: An Atlas Resource*, 2nd ed. Scarborough, ON: Prentice Hall, 1995, p. 12; Robert M. Bone, *The Regional Geography of Canada*, 2nd ed., Don Mills, ON: Oxford University Press, 2002, maps 3.9 and 3.10, pp. 121–122.)

According to some geographers, it is equally possible that because of their international connections and global movements, Canada's immigrant communities are forging new communities of identity that cross state boundaries and exist only in the interconnections that occur.

The phrase **diasporic community** has become increasingly popular as a term to describe such communities. This phrase has its origins in the word "diaspora," which originally referred to the movement of the Jewish people out of their homeland and across many parts of the world, but has now come to be used more widely to refer to the movement of many other emigrant communities. Present examples would include the Caribbean diaspora of individuals from the countries of the Caribbean seeking work after the World War II in Britain and North America. Although its individual members are physically separated (often by thousands of kilometres), a diasporic community is held to function as an entity in some ways because its individual members maintain their own economic and cultural ties. Some diasporic communities also maintain the political affiliations developed in their homeland, and this has proved to be a problem for host countries, such as Canada, since the struggles of diasporic groups need not correspond with the

diasporic community: a group made up of emigrants from a particular homeland who maintain their cultural, political, and economic ties with each other, despite having been dispersed across many countries

political goals of the Canadian government. Leaving these concerns to one side, it is clear that diasporic communities can provide a strong means of international support for their individual members.

This process is greatly aided by improvements in global transportation and by the World Wide Web. Although they do not occupy a physical space, such **transnational communities** have the potential to develop all of the economic and cultural forces of more traditional entities, such as the state. Canadian geographers, such as Jennifer Hyndman and Catherine Nolin, have written extensively on this issue. They show, for example, that Canada's growing transnational communities are as varied as wealthy entrepreneurs who move between Vancouver and Hong Kong and much poorer Guatemalan refugees in Southern Ontario, who often depend on financial help from their families in Guatemala.

The Ambivalent Position of Canada   The tension created between the goals of the state to control citizenship, in its widest sense, and the postmodern desire to celebrate differences wherever they occur in the world place such countries as Canada in a special dilemma. On the one hand, Canada's multicultural and immigrant heritage urges this country to take a more inclusive role on the world stage. On the other hand, the concern to limit costs has increasingly prompted Canada to question the size of its global commitments. Two examples illustrate this well. Canadian aid programs delivered through the Canadian International Development Agency (CIDA) have traditionally been seen as a benchmark of this country's commitment to help the developing countries. **Figure 9.16** shows the global pattern of CIDA aid during its more well-funded years. However, budget cuts over the last 10 years have steadily eroded the total amount of money available to CIDA,

transnational communities: international communities of peoples across international boundaries

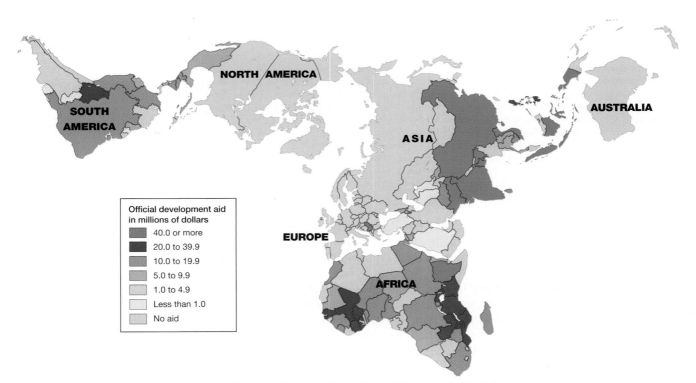

Figure 9.16   The distribution of Canadian foreign aid, 2000–2001   From 2000 to 2001, the Canadian government spent a total of CAN$1694.2 million on Official Development Aid (ODA). Disbursed through the Canadian International Development Agency (CIDA), these ODA funds are spent in the form of direct government-to-government aid, through international multilateral programs (such as the United Nations), or through programs run by non-governmental agencies (NGOs).   (*Source:* CIDA, *Statistical Report on Official Development Assistance Fiscal Year 2000–2001.* Prepared by the Statistical Analysis Section, Policy Planning and Analysis, Information Sources and Management Branch, Canadian International Development Agency, Ottawa, September 2002, Table I, pp. 28–32. This report can be accessed via the publications section of CIDA's website: **www.acdi-cida.gc.ca/cidaweb/acdicida.nsf/En/Home**.)

and today, it is a much more limited endeavour. New CIDA policies, such as aiding only those countries that respect human rights or are in need of debt relief have also brought about a refocusing of support. Our second example is Canada's refugee policy—a policy that has always been seen as either too liberal or too strict, depending on the viewpoint. One minister, Bernard Valcourt, even appealed to a respect for cultural differences as a reason to restrict access to Canada when he said, "I don't think Canada should unilaterally try to impose its values on the rest of the world. Canada cannot go it alone, we just cannot."[3]

This tension is amplified by Canada's ambiguous position as a country in the world-system. As we saw in Chapter 2, Canada is simultaneously in both the global core and the periphery. Canada has, for example, always displayed its core nature in its military alliances with Western Europe and the United States. Canada, while not directly threatened, honoured its commitments with considerable loss of life at Vimy Ridge (in World War I) and in the defence of Hong Kong (during World War II). Most recently, Canadian forces saw action in Afghanistan as part of America's war on terrorism (2002) and have led subsequent peacekeeping duties in that country as part of an international deployment in Afghanistan.

Yet, at the same time, Canada recognizes its peripheral role in global geopolitics. Such policies as this country's support for Cuba and the international treaty against land mines, which Canada has actively promoted, are at variance with American geostrategic concerns. Increasingly, Canada has sought to adopt a "middle power" path, using its special positions in the Commonwealth and la Francophonie (an international organization of French-speaking countries) to add to its credibility as a global intermediary, and compensating for its lack of military clout by sending peacekeepers to the world's trouble spots (**Figure 9.17**). However, the tensions and ambiguity at the heart of Canada's policies and position will always make this country's geopolitical performance, at best, a frustrating one to all observers.

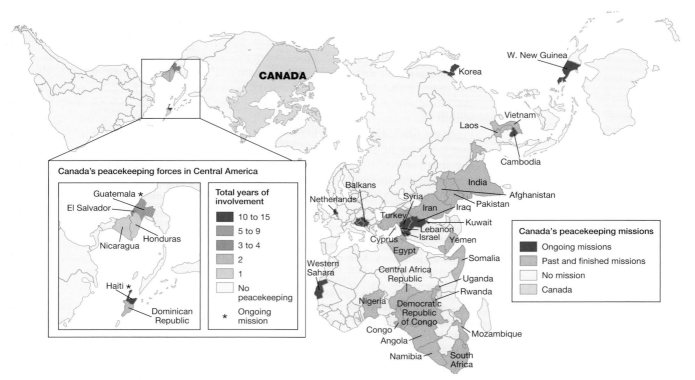

Figure 9.17   The distribution of Canadian peacekeeping forces overseas, 1950–2000
(*Source:* National Defence Centre, Canada 2001.)

[3]Quoted in Margaret Young, *Gender-Related Refugee Claims*. Ottawa: Library of Parliament, Research Branch, 1994, background paper BP 370E, p. 3.

Nothing illustrates this dilemma better than this country's role in the 2003 invasion of Iraq. Despite strong American pressure, Canada did not join the attack. However, it has subsequently become involved in the international effort to rebuild that country. Canada's chief electoral officer, for example, played a key role in the organization of the Iraqi elections of January 2005.

Imperialism, Colonialism, and the North–South Divide

Geopolitics may involve extension of power by one group over another. There are two ways this is achieved. Colonialism, as we have seen, is one way; the other is imperialism. As was discussed in Chapter 1, imperialism is the extension of state authority over the political and economic lives of other territories. As Chapter 2 describes, over the last 500 years, imperialism has resulted in the political, economic, cultural, and even environmental domination of strong core states over the weaker states of the periphery. Imperialism does not necessarily imply formal governmental control over the dominated area. It can also involve a process by which some countries pressure the independent governments of other countries to behave in certain ways. This pressure may take many forms, such as military threat, economic sanctions, ecological imperialism, or cultural domination (described in Chapter 2 and Chapter 5). In its broadest sense, imperialism involves some form of *control* of one state over another.

Generally speaking, in the first phases of imperialism, the core exploits the periphery for raw materials. Later, as the periphery becomes developed, colonization may occur, and cash economies are introduced where none have previously existed. The periphery may also become a market for the manufactured goods of the core. For much of the last 600 years, Africa has been subject to European imperialism (**Figure 9.18**). Eventually, though not always, the periphery—because of the availability of cheap labour, land, and other inputs to production—can become a new arena for large-scale capital investment. In some cases, it is possible for peripheral countries to improve their status, becoming semiperipheral or even core countries.

Colonialism differs from imperialism in that it involves formal establishment and maintenance of rule by a sovereign power over a foreign population through the establishment of settlements. The colony does not have any independent standing within the world-system, but it is considered an adjunct of the colonizing power. From the fifteenth to the early twentieth century, colonization constituted an important component of core expansion. Between 1500 and 1900, the primary colonizing states were Britain, Portugal, Spain, the Netherlands, and France, and these states often competed with each other for control of territory.

Other important states more recently involved in both colonization and imperialist wars include the United States and Japan. Although it is often the case that colonial penetration results in political dominance by the colonizer, such is not always the case. For example, Britain may have succeeded in setting up British colonial communities in China, but it never succeeded in imposing British administrative or legal structures in any widespread way. And at the end of the colonial era, a few colonies, such as Canada, the United States, New Zealand, and Australia, eventually became core states themselves. Others, such as Rwanda, Bolivia, and Cambodia, remain firmly within the periphery. Some former colonies, such as Mexico and Brazil, have come close to, but have not fully attained, core status, and therefore are categorized as being within the semiperiphery. Two examples of the colonization process are the extension of British rule to India and French rule to Algeria.

The substantial British presence in India began with the establishment of the East India Trading Company in the mid-eighteenth century. The British government gave the company the power to establish forts and settlements as well as to maintain an army. The company soon established settlements—including factories—in Mumbai (formerly Bombay), Chennai (formerly Madras), and Calcutta. What began as a small trading and manufacturing operation burgeoned into a major military, administrative, and economic presence by the British government over

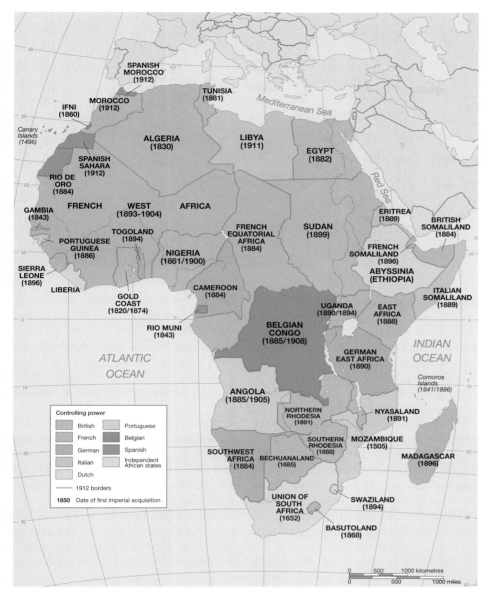

Figure 9.18 **European imperialism in Africa, 1418–1912** The partitioning of the African continent by the colonial powers created a crazy quilt that cross-cut pre-existing affiliations and alliances among the African peoples. Lying directly within easy reach of Europe, Africa was the most likely continent for early European expansion. The Belgian, Italian, French, German, and Portuguese states all laid claim to various parts of Africa and in some cases went to war to protect those claims. (*Source: Harper Atlas of World History.* New York: HarperCollins, 1992, p. 139.)

time, which did not end until Indian independence in 1947 (**Figure 9.19**). During that 200-year period, the Indian population was brutalized, many killed, and their society was transformed by British influence. That influence permeated nearly every institution and practice of daily life—from language and judicial procedure to railroad construction and cultural identity.

The postcolonial history of the Indian subcontinent has included partition and repartition as well as the eruption of regional and ethnic conflicts. In 1947, Pakistan split off from India and became a separate Muslim state. In 1971, Bangladesh, previously part of Pakistan, declared its independence. Regional conflicts include radical movements for independence in the states of Kashmir and Punjab. Ethnic conflicts include decades of physical violence between Muslims and Hindus over religious beliefs and the privileging of Hindus over Muslims in the national culture and economy. It would be misleading, however, to attribute all of India's current strife to colonialism. Caste also plays a significant role in political conflict. The caste system, which distinguishes social classes based on heredity, preceded British colonization and persists to this day. It is a distinctly Hindu institution that perpetuates racism and related discriminatory beliefs and practices. In Hindu society, there are four major social classes: Brahmin, Kshatriya, Vaisya, and Sudra.

Since the turn of the nineteenth century, the effects of colonialism continue to be felt as peoples all over the globe struggle for political and economic independence.

Figure 9.19 **British colonialism in India** The British presence in India affected culture, politics, economy, and the layout of cities, as well as numerous other aspects of everyday life. This painting illustrates the way in which Indian and British cultural practices intermingled, changing both in the process. Importantly, Indian society absorbed and remoulded many British political and cultural practices so that contemporary Indian government, for example, is a hybrid of British and Indian ideals and practices. British society continues to be shaped by its colonial history in India, most obviously through the large numbers of Indians who have migrated to Britain, affecting all aspects of society and culture.

Figure 9.20 Refugees returning to Rwanda
Fleeing civil unrest in their own country, Rwandans from the Hutu tribe increasingly sought refuge in the Democratic Republic of the Congo (formerly Zaire) when the Tutsi-led government assumed power in 1994. Two and a half years later, more than half a million Rwandan refugees in the Democratic Republic of Congo occupied some of the largest refugee camps in the world. In late 1996, refugees began streaming back into Rwanda. Tens of thousands of Rwandans moving on foot jammed the road between eastern Democratic Republic of the Congo and Rwanda for over three days. The Tutsi-led government urged the return of the refugees so that they might help in efforts to rebuild the country. Faced with two difficult alternatives—extremely difficult conditions in the camps or a possible return to violence in Rwanda—the refugees chose to go home.

The civil war in Rwanda in 1994 is a sobering example of the ill effects of colonialism. As occurred in India, where an estimated 1 million Hindus and Muslims died in civil war when the British pulled out, the exit of Belgium from Rwanda left colonially created tribal rivalries unresolved and seething (**Figure 9.20**). Although the Germans were the first to colonize Rwanda, the Belgians, who arrived after World War I, set up what was to become a highly problematic political hierarchy. They established political dominance among the Tutsi by allowing them special access to education and the bureaucracy.

Previously a symbiotic relationship had existed between the Tutsi, who were cattle herders, and the Hutu, who were agriculturists. The Belgians changed that by establishing a stratified society with the Tutsi on top. In effect, colonialism introduced difference into an existing political and social structure that had operated more or less peacefully for centuries. In 1959, the Hutu rebelled, and the Belgians abandoned their Tutsi favourites to side with the Hutu. In 1962, the Belgians ceded independence to Rwanda, leaving behind a volatile political situation that has erupted periodically ever since, most tragically in 1994's civil war. After a year of violence in which over half a million Tutsi were killed, the Hutu were driven across the border to the Democratic Republic of the Congo and a new Tutsi-led Rwandan government was formed. Caught up in this conflict, UN peacekeeping forces were unable to prevent what has now been called a genocide. The Canadian general in charge of UN forces in Rwanda, General Romeo Dallaire, has described in his book *Shake Hands with the Devil* the terrible way in which events unfolded.

The Hutu refugees gathered in refugee camps across the Rwandan border in the Democratic Republic of the Congo. Although run by the United Nations, these camps soon became controlled by armed extremists who used them as bases from which to attack Rwanda.

When Rwanda's new Tutsi-led military took matters into its own hands and, with Uganda's support, invaded Congo to break up the camps, over a million refugees were released. Many of those refugees have since fanned out across Central Africa. The most militant of them are instigating conflict and perpetrating atrocities in Uganda, Congo, and Burundi. Currently, the political situation in Central Africa is one of extreme instability.

North–South divide:
the differentiation made between the colonizing states of the Northern Hemisphere and the formerly colonized states of the Southern Hemisphere

The **North–South divide** is the differentiation made between the colonizing states of the Northern Hemisphere and the formerly colonized states of the Southern Hemisphere. The colonization of Africa, South America, parts of the Pacific, Asia, and smaller territories scattered throughout the Southern Hemisphere resulted in a political geographical division of the world into North and South. In the North—roughly the Northern Hemisphere—were the imperialist states of Europe, the United States, Russia, and Japan. In the South—roughly the Southern Hemisphere—were the colonized. Though the equator has been used as a dividing line, it is clear that some so-called Southern territories, such as Australia and New Zealand, actually are part of the North in an economic sense. In fact, as you will recall from Chapter 1, we are using a relative measure of space when we divide the world up in this way.

The crucial point is that a relationship of dependence was set up of countries in the South, or periphery, on those in the North, or the core, that began with colonization and persists even today. Very few peripheral countries of the South have become prosperous and economically competitive since achieving political autonomy. Political independence is markedly different from economic independence; and the South, even to this day, is very much oriented to the economic demands of the North. An example of this one-way orientation from South to North is the transformation of agricultural practices in Mexico as increasing amounts of production have become directed not toward subsistence for the local peasant populations but toward consumption in North American markets.

Twentieth-Century Decolonization

It can certainly be argued that decolonization has shaped the course of modern world history and geopolitics—and continues to do so. **Decolonization** relates to the acquisition of control by colonized peoples over their own territory. The American Revolution (1776–1783) saw the United States break away from Britain, and laid the foundation for the United States to become a regional and then a global power. From the 1800s, the Spanish and Portuguese colonies in Latin America used European styles of government and warfare if necessary to pressure their imperial rulers to grant independence (Brazil, for example, gaining independence from Portugal in 1822). Between 1918 and 1960, perhaps the most dramatic wave of decolonization occurred when more than 50 countries (with a population of over 800 million at the time) gained independence from European empires (**Figure 9.21**).

For many African and Asian countries, lacking even internal self-government by 1914, the process of decolonization lay less with armed revolt (although these occurred) and more with the development of new local professional elites and in the establishment of political and military organizations. Such organizations not only served to create a "nation" that could subsequently claim independence, but also act as a coherent focus for state-wide resistance (which ranged from peaceful civil disobedience, as in the case of Gandhi's campaign for India's independence in 1947, to sustained civil war, as in the case of Algeria, which achieved independence from France in 1961). As an ongoing coda to this story, since the 1990s, the breakup of the former Soviet Union's "empire" of satellite states has radically altered European and wider international relations, leaving the United States as the only remaining global superpower.

Writing in 2008 about these historic trends in a very useful entry in *The International Encyclopedia of the Social Sciences,* Karl Hack has suggested that scholars identify three types of cause for decolonization. These are "metrocentric," "peripheral," and "international," and they suggest that the reasons for decolonization lie in the imperial power, the colonized territory, and the wider world, respectively. We can illustrate the operation of each of these types of cause in the case of one historical example, the decolonization of the Portuguese empire. In Portugal's case, metrocentric causes were clearly rooted in the change of that country's rulers in 1974 from a dictatorship to a left-wing, democratically-elected government completely opposed to ideas of empire. Colonies such as Mozambique and Angola were quickly granted independence by the new regime. Peripheral causes are also important and augmented the decolonization of Angola, for example, where armed local rebellion against Portuguese rule began as early as 1961. Finally, international causes can be seen in the Portuguese case on a number of occasions. For example, in the early nineteenth century the Portuguese hold on Brazil was affected by the Napoleonic Wars, which significantly weakened Portugal's military and political power in Europe, and therefore its global reach. By the 1970s, both American

decolonization: the acquisition of control by colonized peoples over their own territory

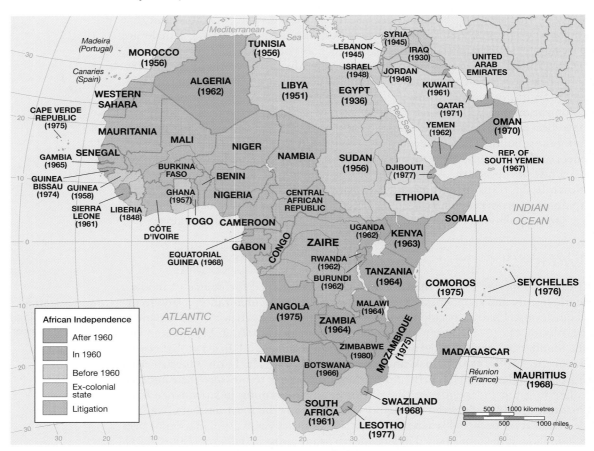

Figure 9.21   Decolonization of Africa, before and after 1960   Britain, France, and Belgium—the dominant European presences in African colonization—were also the first to divest themselves of their colonies. Britain began the process in 1957, when Ghana was granted its independence. France granted independence to its African colonies soon after Britain made the first move. Belgium's and Britain's withdrawal from the remainder of their colonial holdings did not go at all smoothly, with civil wars breaking out. Portugal did not relinquish its possession of Guinea Bissau, Mozambique, and Angola until 1974.   (*Source: The Harper Atlas of World History*, rev. ed., Librairie Hachette, p. 285. Copyright © 1992 by HarperCollins Publishers, Inc. Reprinted by permission of HarperCollins Publishers, Inc.)

and European rhetoric championed the cause of self-determination, and Portugal was increasingly pressured by world leaders and human rights activists to see its remaining empire as more of a stigma than a sign of status on the world stage.

In our discussion so far, decolonization has been seen as only a political step—the formal act of separation. But it is possible to argue that "full" decolonization must involve far more than simply a transfer of sovereignty. This is especially so if the achievement of independence marks little more than the transfer of political power from one elite to another, leaving all the ties of dependence in place between the former colony and colonial power. We have already seen in Chapter 2 how the core maintains its hegemony over the periphery in the world-system by a variety of means, one of which (according to subaltern theory) is by the maintenance of cultural dominance over the periphery. Considered in terms of a full decolonization, however, the former colony may need to re-assess its language of government and education, since these are often inherited from the former colonial power, and to seek to restore its former pre-colonial cultural traditions. We have already mentioned the work of Franz Fanon in Chapter 2, and an important part of his critique of the "mental hegemony" of imperialism was that it affected both the colonized and the colonizer, an important aspect of what has come to be called *postcolonial studies.*

Certainly, the colonized and the colonizers are tied together in a series of dependent relationships that are not as easy to end as formal decolonization would suggest. Indeed, in more than one case, formal or legal decolonization has merely served as a cloak for business interests in core countries to continue their domination over former colonies using informal means, for economic or political purposes, in a way that does not bring with it either the opprobrium of old-style imperialism or its costs.

For example, in 2007, the British supermarket chain, Sainsburys, signed a contract with the government of Saint Lucia to buy this Caribbean island's entire banana crop at a "fair trade" price (one that allows growers to benefit from their labours), on condition that the island move toward organic cultivation over the next few years. Such a deal ensures the British retailer a guaranteed supply of produce that meets its specifications and provides the islanders with a secure demand for their crop. At a time when "fair trade" practices are becoming fashionable among consumers in core nations, deals such as this one also serve to ensure that Sainsburys maintains an ethical edge over its competitors in the fierce retail environment of the British high street and shopping mall. Closer markets for Saint Lucia in North America are closed to Saint Lucia's producers because of long-standing trade disputes between the United States and the European Union over the marketing of bananas.[4] A recent agreement between the European Union and a group of African, Caribbean, and Pacific states, the Cotonou Agreement, has encouraged European consumers to continue to import their bananas from countries in the Caribbean that were once part of their overseas colonies, rather than to open their markets to cheaper products from American-owned producers (for example, the United Fruit Company, an American firm that issues contracts for banana production in places such as the Central American country of Honduras), as the United States has long tried to insist under World Trade Organization rules.

Indeed, in the case of the United States (which has never had an overseas empire or colonies as such), the processes of *neo-colonialism* (as shown in Chapter 2) have enabled that country to extend its global reach in a variety of ways, without the formal or overt act of formally colonizing other states. Principal among these has been the U.S. promotion of private enterprise wherever possible. Thus, for example, American-funded international development projects, in countries as various as Nicaragua and Nepal, have sought in recent years to replace traditional methods of landholding in favour of the creation of individual title (a process that has often involved the detailed mapping of the countryside). The ensuing creation of a market in land (and the "creation" of a source of equity for those holding land) are some of the hallmarks of such "neo-liberal" development policies, and may well offer economic development, but at the price of becoming part of an American-led value system. The re-casting of many American values as "universal" or "global ideals" is clearly to the United States' advantage, but it is a step that, not surprisingly, has led to a series of anti-globalization movements across the world, as peoples seek to turn back what they see as the rising tide of American neo-imperialism. Nevertheless, such values, in an almost unconscious way, serve to underpin American foreign policy in its dealings with other states and international bodies, such as the United Nations.

The spread of a capitalist world order has had the undeniable impact of "modernizing" traditional societies through education, health care, and other factors. It is also the case that this world order, based on imperialism and colonialism, has been financed with a great deal of bloodshed and numerous human lives. An example is the imperial historical geography of South Africa, a country still labouring under the burdens of colonization (see **Geography Matters 9.1—Imperialism, Colonization, and the Dismantling of Apartheid in South Africa**). South Africa and other formerly colonized locations around the globe, such as Egypt and Indonesia, provide examples of how the global processes of imperialism and colonialism have unfolded locally.

---

[4]Gordon Myers, *Banana Wars: The Price of Free Trade*. London and New York: Zed Books, 2004.

Geographers have historically played very central roles in the imperialist efforts of European states. Imperialism usually begins with exploration. Most, if not all, of the early geographical expeditions undertaken by Europeans were intended to evaluate the possibilities for resource extraction, colonization, and the expansion of empire. In fact, organizations like the royal geographical societies in England and Scotland were explicitly formed to aid in the expansionary efforts of their home countries.

Geographers have also played a part in developing geopolitical theories that justified the continued domination of the world by the colonial powers. One interesting example is the "heartland theory" of Sir Halford Mackinder, himself a member of the Royal Geographical Society and first professor of geography at Oxford University. When Mackinder presented this theory in 1904 (**Figure 9.22**), Russia controlled a large part of the Eurasian land mass, and had, he believed, the potential to control more. In particular, he feared that with a further development of railroads, Russia's armies would be able to dominate Western Europe itself, and thereby perhaps the entire world.

As it turned out, Mackinder had ignored the importance of new technologies in his geopolitical assessment, especially the importance of aircraft, which completely altered the vulnerability of places to attack by distant aggressors. Nevertheless, by

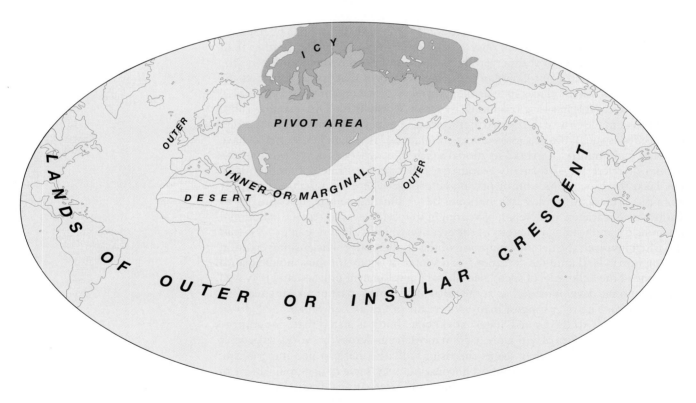

Figure 9.22   Inner and outer crescent of Mackinder's heartland   A quintessential geographical conceptualization of world politics, Mackinder's heartland theory has formed the basis for important geopolitical strategies throughout the decades since its inception. Although the pivot area of Eurasia is wholly continental, the outer crescent is wholly oceanic and the inner crescent part continental and part oceanic. It is interesting to compare the Mercator map projection, which Mackinder used to promote his geostrategic theory, with the Dymaxion projection used in this text. This is a classic example of how maps can be used for ideological purposes. The Mercator projection decreases the importance of the northern and southern oceans, which are vast and significant natural barriers. The spatial distortions inherent in the Mercator projection overemphasize the importance of Asia. And the splitting of North and South America so that they appear on both sides of the map adds even more exaggerated emphasis to the centrality of Asia. The Dymaxion projection, as a northern polar representation, de-emphasizes the centrality of any one land mass but exaggerates distances between continents (see Chapter 1). Mackinder's worldview map provides a good example of how cartographic representations can be employed to support ideological arguments.   (*Source*: M.I. Glassner and H. de Blij, *Systematic Political Geography*, 3rd ed. New York: J. Wiley & Sons, 1980, p. 291.)

pointing to the important general observation that "space is power" (or more precisely, that "location confers a strategic advantage dependent on the available technology"), Mackinder's approach paved the way for later geopolitical theories such as the "domino theory," and modern efforts to achieve a "balance of power" between geopolitical power blocs.

Exploration and colonization did not cease at the midpoint of the twentieth century, however. In fact, exploration and, to a lesser extent, colonization continued to occur in Antarctica. This iced land mass is therefore a somewhat exceptional example of ongoing imperialism, where strong states exert power in an area of land where no people and, therefore, no indigenous state power have existed. At present, although no one country exclusively "owns" the continent, 15 countries lay claim to territory and/or have established research stations in Antarctica. More disturbing examples, perhaps, include attempts to control interplanetary space, the virtual realm of the internet, and the deep ocean floors.

The East–West Divide and Domino Theory

In addition to a North–South divide based on imperialism and colonization, the world order of states can also be seen to cluster along an East–West split. The **East–West divide** refers to communist and noncommunist countries, respectively. Though the Cold War appears to have ended, the East–West divide played a significant role in global politics since at least the end of World War II in 1945 and perhaps, more accurately, since the Russian Revolution in 1917. By the second decade of the twentieth century, the major world powers had backed away from colonization. Still, many were reluctant to accelerate decolonization for fear that independent countries in Africa and elsewhere would choose communist political and economic systems instead of some form of Western-style capitalism.

East–West divide: communist and noncommunist countries, respectively

The end of World War II marked the rise of the United States to a dominant position among countries of the core. Following the war, the tension that arose between East and West translated into a U.S. foreign policy that pitched the United States against the former Soviet Union. Geopolitics in this era was based on an approach that came to be known as the **domino theory**. The domino theory was the source of American foreign policy that included economic, political, and military objectives directed at undermining the possibility for Soviet world domination. The domino theory held that if one country in a region chose or was forced to accept a communist political and economic system, then neighbouring countries would be irresistibly susceptible to falling to communism as well. The concept behind the domino theory was that one falling domino in a line of dominoes causes all the others in its path to fall. The antidote to preventing the domino-like spread of communism was often military aggression.

domino theory: the belief that if one country in a region chose or was forced to accept a communist political and economic system, then neighbouring countries would be irresistibly susceptible to falling to communism

Adherence to the domino theory began in 1947, when the post-war United States feared communism would spread from Greece to Turkey to Europe. It culminated in the more recent events of U.S. wars in Korea, Vietnam, Nicaragua, El Salvador, and the Persian Gulf. Yet, preventing the domino effect was not just based on military aggression. Cooperation was also emphasized, such as in the 1949 establishment of NATO (North Atlantic Treaty Organization), in which the United States, Canada, and most of the countries of Western Europe allied themselves against Soviet aggression in Europe. Following the end of World War II, core countries set up a range of foreign aid, trade, and banking organizations, such as the World Bank and the International Monetary Fund (IMF). All were intended to open up foreign markets and bring peripheral countries into the global capitalist economic system. The strategy not only improved productivity in core countries but was also seen as a way of strengthening the position of the West in its Cold-War confrontation with the East.

The collapse of the Soviet Union in 1989 and the consequent end of the Cold War effectively left the United States as the only superpower. This reconfiguration has also led to a reframing of world geopolitics, as old views are made redundant. Some theorists, such as Canada's Gwyn Dyer, have speculated that a "war on terror" will provide the West with a new rationale for its approach to other states. If so, the strategic value of countries will be altered to take account of this "new reality" as, for example, the heightened value the United States now gives its relations with Pakistan, Bulgaria, and Turkey. Spaces, such as Guantanamo Bay (a U.S. base in Cuba), take on new value as places where such a war on terror can escape the sanctions of universal human rights that otherwise limit its reach. An alternative vision, however, places its hopes on a new role for the world's international bodies as a counterbalance to American hegemony.

International and Supranational Organizations

Just as states are seen as key players in political geography, so, too, have international and supranational organizations become important participants in the world-system in the last century. These organizations have become increasingly important in dealing with situations in which international boundaries stand in the way of specific goals. These goals include, among other things, the freer flow of goods and information and more cooperative management of shared resources, such as water.

international organization: a group that includes two or more states seeking political or economic cooperation with each other

An **international organization** is one that includes two or more states seeking political or economic cooperation with each other. One well-known example of an international organization operating today is the United Nations (UN) (**Figure 9.23**). Other examples of international organizations include the Organisation for Economic Co-operation and Development (OECD), the Organization of Petroleum

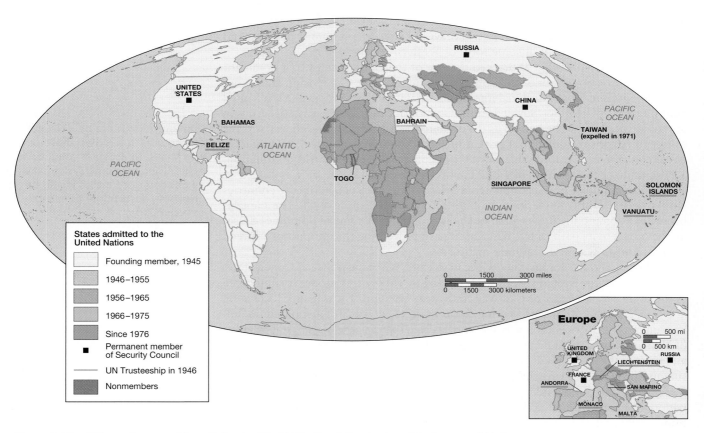

States admitted to the United Nations

- Founding member, 1945
- 1946–1955
- 1956–1965
- 1966–1975
- Since 1976
- ■ Permanent member of Security Council
- — UN Trusteeship in 1946
- Nonmembers

Figure 9.23   UN member countries   Following World War II and the demise of the League of Nations, renewed effort was made to establish an international organization aimed at instituting a system of international peace and security. The UN Charter was approved by the U.S. Senate in July 1945, raising hopes for a more long-lived organization than the ineffective League of Nations. Located in New York City, the United Nations is composed of a Security Council, which includes the permanent members of the United States, Britain, China, France, and Russia; and a General Assembly, which includes all of those countries identified on the map.

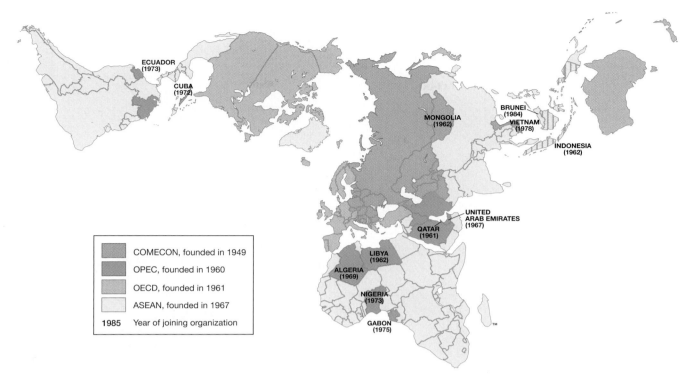

Figure 9.24 International economic groups   OPEC (Organization of Petroleum Exporting Countries) states joined together to foster cooperation in the setting of world oil prices in 1960. ASEAN (Association of South-East Asian Nations), founded in 1967, exists to further economic development in Southeast Asia. The OECD (Organisation for Economic Co-operation and Development), founded by the United States, Canada, and 18 European states in 1961, aims to increase world trade through the provision of financial security. Groupings such as these suggest that the independent state has lost effectiveness in promoting its own and other states' economic progress and stability. Founded in 1949, COMECON (the Council for Mutual Economic Assistance) was the grouping organized to promote trade among former communist and socialist states. It is no longer functioning.   (*Source*: Map projection, Buckminster Fuller Institute and Dymaxion Map Design, Santa Barbara, CA. The word *Dymaxion* and the Fuller Projection Dymaxion™ Map design are trademarks of the Buckminster Fuller Institute, Santa Barbara, California, ©1938, 1967, & 1992. All rights reserved.)

Exporting Countries (OPEC), the Association of South-East Asian Nations (ASEAN), and the now-disbanded Council for Mutual Economic Assistance (COMECON), as well as the League of Nations, discussed earlier. Though these organizations were formed to accomplish very different ends, they all aim to achieve cooperation while maintaining full sovereignty of the individual states. The countries involved in these organizations are shown in **Figure 9.24**.

The post-war period has seen the rise and growth not only of large international organizations but also of new regional arrangements. These arrangements vary from the highly specific, such as the Swiss–French cooperative management of Basel–Mulhouse airport, to the more general, such as the North American Free Trade Agreement (NAFTA), which joins Canada, the United States, and Mexico into a single trade region. Regional organizations and arrangements now exist to address a wide array of issues, including the management of international watersheds and river basins (such as the International Joint Commission, through which Canada and the United States control the Great Lakes).

Unlike international organizations, **supranational organizations** reduce the centrality of individual states. Through organizing and regulating designated operations of the individual member states, these organizations diminish, to some extent, individual state sovereignty in favour of the collective interests of the large membership. The European Union (EU) is perhaps the best example of a supranational organization.

As far back as the end of World War II, European leaders realized that Europe's fragmented state system was insufficient to meet the demands and levels of

supranational organizations: collections of individual states with a common goal that may be economic and/or political in nature; such organizations diminish, to some extent, individual state sovereignty in favour of the group interests of the membership

Figure 9.25   Map of membership in the European Union   The goal of the European Union is to increase economic integration and cooperation among the member states. The EU was established on 1 November 1993, when the Maastricht Treaty was ratified by the 12 members of the European Economic Community (Belgium, Denmark, France, Germany, the United Kingdom, Greece, Ireland, Italy, Luxembourg, the Netherlands, Portugal, and Spain). The European Economic Community (EEC) had been created in 1967. Upon ratification of the treaty, the countries of the EEC became members of the EU, and the EEC became the policy-making body of the EU. The Maastricht Treaty established European citizenship for citizens of each member state, enhanced EEC customs and immigration agreements, and allowed for the establishment of a common currency—the euro—which is currently in circulation among all of the original 12 members except for Denmark and the United Kingdom, as well as more recent members Slovenia, Cyprus, and Malta. The remainder have yet to meet the conditions for adopting the single currency, although some also use the euro in addition to their own currencies (further information on the European Union can be obtained from its website **http://europa.eu/index_en.htm**). The EU is governed through both supranational European institutions (the European Commission and the European Parliament, both administered by the EU) and the governments of the member states, which send representatives to the Council of Ministers (the main law-making body of the EU). Membership in the EU is much sought after, and numerous European countries have applied and are on the waiting list for admission. The largest expansion in its history occurred in 2004, when the EU admitted 10 new members: Cyprus, the Czech Republic, Estonia, Hungary, Latvia, Lithuania, Malta, Poland, Slovakia, and Slovenia.

competition coalescing within the world political and economic systems. They endeavoured to create an entity that would preserve important features of state sovereignty and identity. They have also intended to create a more efficient intra-European marketing system and a more competitive entity in global transactions. **Figure 9.25** shows the progression of integration of European countries into the European Union—a direct descendant of the European Economic Community—since 1957.

The EU holds elections, has its own Parliament and court system, and decides whether and when to allow new members to join. Generally speaking, the EU aims to create a common geographical space within Europe in which goods, services, people, and information move freely and in which a single monetary currency will prevail. Whether an EU foreign policy will ever be accomplished remains to be seen, but a common European currency—the *euro*—is now in circulation. However, other indicators of nationalism within the individual member countries continue to be strong. For example, just as the European system of states is on the threshold of dissolving into the larger EU organizational form, national and regional movements (see Chapter 5) have become potent forces operating against full integration.

THE TWO-WAY STREET OF POLITICS AND GEOGRAPHY

Political geography can be seen to proceed according to two contrasting orientations. The first orientation sees political geography as being about the *politics of geography*. This perspective emphasizes that *geography*—or the areal distribution/differentiation of people and objects in space—has a very real and measurable impact on politics. Regionalism, discussed later in this section, provides examples of how geography shapes politics. The politics-of-geography orientation is also a reminder that politics occurs at all levels of the human experience, from the international order down to the scale of the neighbourhood and household.

The second orientation sees political geography as being about the *geography of politics*. In contrast to the first orientation, this approach analyzes how *politics*—the tactics or operations of the state—shapes geography. Examination of a series of maps of Palestine/Israel since 1947 reveals how the changing geography of this area is a response to changing international, national, regional, and local politics (**Figure 9.26**).

The Politics of Geography

Territory is often regarded as a space to which a particular group attaches its identity. Related to this concept of territory is the notion of **self-determination**, which refers to the right of a group with a distinctive politico-territorial identity to determine its own destiny, at least in part, through the control of its own territory.

self-determination: the right of a group with a distinctive politico-territorial identity to determine its own destiny, at least in part, through the control of its own territory

Regionalism   As we have already seen, it is sometimes the case that different groups with different identities—religious or ethnic—coexist within the same state boundaries. At times, discordance between legal and political boundaries and the distribution of populations with distinct identities becomes manifested as a movement to claim particular territories. These movements, whether conflictual or peaceful in their claim to territory, are known as *regional movements*. **Regionalism** is a feeling of collective identity based on a population's politico-territorial identification within a state or across state boundaries.

Regionalism often involves ethnic groups whose aims include autonomy from an interventionist state and the development of their own political power. For example, in the spring of 1993, several leading Basque guerrillas were arrested in France, raising hopes for an end to Basque terrorism in Europe. For more than 25 years, the French, Spanish, and more recently the Basque regional police have attempted to undermine the Basque Homeland and Freedom movement through arrests and imprisonments. "Basquism" represents a regional movement that has roots back to industrialization and modernization beginning at the turn of the nineteenth century. The Basque people feared that *cultural forces* accompanying industrialization would undermine Basque pre-industrial traditions. Because of this, the Basque provinces of northern Spain and southern France have sought autonomy from those states for most of the twentieth century. Since the 1950s, agitation for political independence has occurred—especially for the Basques in Spain—through terrorist acts. Not even the Spanish move to parliamentary democracy and the

regionalism: a feeling of collective identity based on a population's politico-territorial identification within a state or across state boundaries

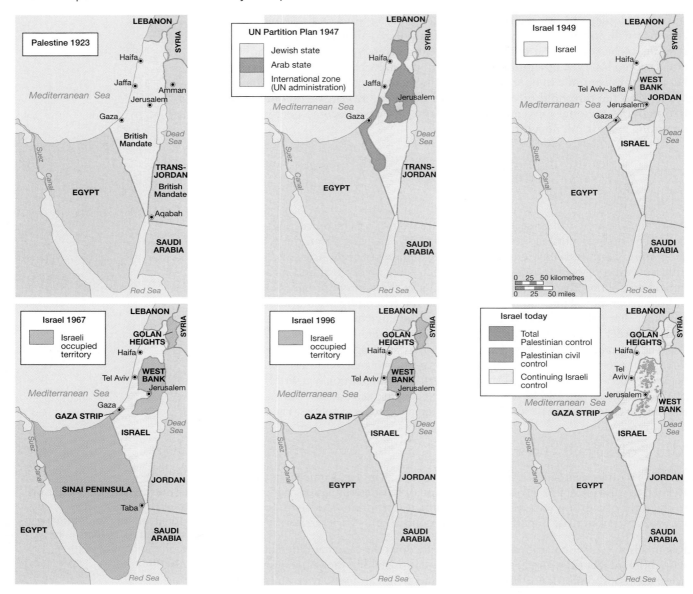

Figure 9.26 Changing geography of Israel/Palestine, 1923–2005 Since the creation of Israel from the former Palestine in 1947, the geography of the region has undergone significant modifications. A series of wars between Israelis and Arabs and a number of political decisions regarding how to cope with both resident Palestinians and large volumes of Jewish people immigrating to Israel from around the world have produced the changing geographies we see here. (*Source:* Reprinted with permission from Prentice Hall, from J.M. Rubenstein, *The Cultural Landscape: An Introduction to Human Geography,* 5th ed., © 1996, p. 233.)

granting of autonomy to the Basque provinces, however, could quench the thirst for self-determination among the Basques in Spain (**Figure 9.27**). Meanwhile, on the French side of the Pyrenees, although a Basque separatist movement does exist, it is neither as violent nor as active as the movement in Spain.

We need only look at the long list of territorially based conflicts that have emerged in the post–Cold War world to realize the extent to which territorially based ethnicity remains a potent force in the politics of geography. For example, the Kurds continue to fight for their own state separate from Turkey and Iraq. As we have noted earlier, a significant proportion of Quebec's French-speaking population, already accorded substantial autonomy, persists in advocating complete independence from Canada. Consider also the former Yugoslavia, whose geography has fractured along the lines of ethnicity (**Figure 9.28**). Regionalism also underlies efforts to sever Scotland from the United Kingdom.

The politics of geography, in terms of regionalism, also finds strong focus today in rural versus urban politics. In France, for example, attitudes about birth control (and birth rates themselves) are significantly different between the urbanized north of the country and the more rural south. Throughout the EU, farmers have fought against removal of farm subsidies and tariff arrangements, advocated by urban-based policymakers, which have long protected agricultural productivity. Here, the dispute pits the politics of local farmers against an international organization.

In Canada, outside Quebec, regional discontent with Ottawa has led to the creation of political parties, such as the Alliance Party (based in the west) or New Brunswick's CORE party. Provincially, urban-rural differences in the Prairies can be seen in the fact that the New Democratic Party (NDP) receives more urban votes. In New Brunswick, tradition plays an important role in which party a region supports.

In Mexico, the contest is between local and national levels. Chiapan peasants have forced the federal government in Mexico City to address the profound problems of rural poverty. These rural problems are seen to have been aggravated by the government's largely urban (and industrial agriculture) orientation. Likewise, rural-to-urban migration throughout the periphery (grossly inflating the populations of cities, such as Lima, Peru; Nairobi, Kenya; and Jakarta, Indonesia) has generated enormous social and political pressures and poses overwhelming challenges. Policy-makers must ask themselves difficult questions: How much of the country's scarce resources should be devoted to slowing (or reversing) rural out-migration through development projects? What level of resources should be devoted to accommodating the throngs of new urban dwellers, most of whom have worse living conditions in the city than they did in the countryside?

The Geography of Politics

An obvious way to show how politics shapes geography is to show how systems of political representation are geographically anchored.

Figure 9.27 Basque independence poster   This independence poster is plastered over the door of a shop in Donostia (San Sebastian) in one of the Basque provinces of Spain. The poster is a sign of the passionate opposition the Basques have adopted toward the central government in Madrid. Acts of terrorism continue to occur throughout Spain as the Basques maintain their desire for independence. What is most interesting about the sign is that it is written in neither Castillian Spanish (the national language) nor Euskadi (the Basque language). It appears as if this and declarations like it are directed at the tourists who have made Donostia a popular destination.

Figure 9.28 Map of the former Yugoslavia Today, the former Yugoslavia consists of six nations: Slovenia, Croatia, Bosnia and Herzegovina, the new Yugoslavia (made up of Serbia and Montenegro), the former Yugoslav Republic of Macedonia and the newly separated state of Kosovo. For the most part, the boundaries of the Yugoslav states were laid out only in the twentieth century, across segments of the Austro-Hungarian and Ottoman empires that had acquired a complex mixture of ethnic groups. The history of these boundaries has also been the history of ethnic conflict revolving around claims to territory as well as intolerance for religious differences. As this map shows, with the exception of Slovenia, the new states are home to a mix of nationalities. (*Source:* Redrawn with permission from Prentice Hall, from J.M. Rubenstein, *The Cultural Landscape: An Introduction to Human Geography*, 6th ed., © 1999, p. 260.)

democratic rule: a system in which public policies and officials are directly chosen by popular vote

territorial organization: a system of government formally structured by area, not by social groups

unitary state: a form of government in which power is concentrated in the central government

confederation: a grouping of independent jurisdictions, such as provinces, into a larger unit that is given separate powers

federal state: a form of government in which powers are divided between the federal government and smaller units of government (such as provinces) within the country

reapportionment: the process of allocating electoral seats to geographical areas

redistricting: the defining and redefining of territorial district boundaries

Geographical Systems of Representation In a country such as Canada, **democratic rule** ensures that our representatives are chosen by popular vote. **Territorial organization**, a system of government formally structured by area and not by wealth or social group, ensures that we vote where we live. In this way, geography and politics—space and power—are intimately connected.

Canada has inherited this system from Britain and shares this approach to voting and elections with many other countries. But unlike Britain, a **unitary state** (a form of government in which power is concentrated in the central government), Canada is a **confederation** (a grouping of independent jurisdictions, such as provinces, into a larger unit that is given separate powers), a **federal state** in which powers are divided between the federal government and the provinces and territories. (Municipal government is under provincial jurisdiction, and the territories are ultimately a federal responsibility.)

As a consequence, Canada is made up of a nested hierarchy of jurisdictions (municipal, provincial and territorial, and federal), each represented by its own spatial unit of representation (*boroughs* or *wards* at a city level, *ridings* at the provincial or territorial and federal level) and its own elected representatives (such as councillors, members of the legislative or national assembly [MLAs or MNAs] and, at the federal level, members of Parliament [MPs]).

At Confederation in 1867, the British North America Act established that the four provinces (Ontario, Quebec, New Brunswick, and Nova Scotia) that composed Canada at the time should have a Parliament compring two houses. The upper house, the Senate, was to consist of non-elected members, appointed to represent their regions. The lower house, the House of Commons, was to be elected by the people. For the purposes of electing the members of the House of Commons (the MPs), the general principle of representation by population was adopted, and the provinces were to be divided into ridings (or seats) for that purpose.

From the very start, the historical compromises at the root of Canadian confederation meant that this general principle has been subject to the need to recognize Canada's diversity, Quebec's status, and the position of the smaller provinces and territories as Canada grew in population size and geographical extent (**Figure 9.29**). The current formula used to determine the **reapportionment** (or allocation) of seats is set out in the Representation Act, 1985. The formula is as follows: the three territories (Yukon, the Northwest Territories, and Nunavut) are allocated one seat each. The population of Canada, as established by the latest decennial census, is then divided by 279 (the number of seats when the act came into force) to produce what is called the *electoral quotient*. The population of each province, when divided by this quotient, produces the total number of seats per province (subject to the provisions that no province can have fewer MPs than it has members of the Senate or than it had when the act came into force). For example, as a result of the population growth recorded in the 2001 census, 7 new seats (3 in Ontario, 2 in Alberta, and 2 in British Columbia) were created in 2004, increasing the total number in the House of Commons from 301 seats to 308 in the general election held in that year. (**Figure 9.30**).

Once the allocation of seats per province is determined, the actual **redistricting** (or drawing) of federal riding boundaries is the responsibility of each province's independent boundary commission. If additional seats have been created since the last election, a considerable redrawing of boundaries may be required to accommodate the extra ridings. The commissions must take into account such issues as the historical development of the riding and the strength to which areas within it identify with particular communities. In more sparsely populated rural or northern regions, a manageable geographical size is also a criterion, for this contributes to the riding's sense of identity and the MP's ability to travel around in it. In addition, ridings should be of equal population size. Because this is extremely hard to achieve in practice, a variation of plus or minus 25 percent of the electoral quotient for that province is permitted. The task of redrawing is not an easy

Yukon. Became a separate territory in 1898.

Northwest Territories. The North-western Territory and Rupert's land were transferred to Canada in 1870 and divided into the Northwest Territories and Manitoba. The subsequent growth of other provinces and territories has greatly reduced its size.

Nunavut. Canada's newest territory was created on 1 April 1999 with its capital at Iqaluit.

Newfoundland and Labrador. Joined Confederation in 1949.

British Columbia. Reached its present boundaries in 1866 and joined Confederation in 1871.

Alberta and Saskatchewan. Were added to the Dominion in 1905.

Manitoba. Reached its present boundaries in 1912 (having been first created as a much smaller province in 1870.)

Prince Edward Island. Joined Confederation in 1873.

Nova Scotia, New Brunswick, Quebec, and Ontario. Formed the Dominion of Canada at Confederation in 1867. (Ontario and Quebec reached their present boundaries in 1912.)

0   500   1000 kilometres

Figure 9.29   Canada's political geography: provinces and territories   (*Source:* Geoffrey J. Matthews and Robert Morrow, *Canada and the World: An Atlas Resource*, 2nd ed. Scarborough, ON: Prentice Hall, 1995, pp. 5–6. See also the National Atlas of Canada's website at **http://atlas.gc.ca/site** where a sequence of maps on the territorial evolution of Canada can be found.)

one, and geographers have often been asked to help in the work of the provincial commissions.

The same procedures we have described here for federal elections are used at the provincial and territorial level to elect provincial and territorial governments and, with some modifications, at municipal levels to vote for metropolitan or urban administrations. At every level, the process is designed to be as objective and non-partisan as possible.

Before independent boundary commissions were established, the redrawing of boundaries in Canada was often deliberately influenced by political parties to further their own partisan ends. For example, by drawing boundaries that excluded areas that did not vote for a particular party and included those areas that did, it was possible to manipulate the boundaries of a riding to achieve the election of a particular party's candidate. The most celebrated example of this type of behaviour dates from a U.S. election of 1812, in which Massachusetts Governor Elbridge Gerry sought to maximize the number of Republican-Democrats elected at the expense of the Federalist Party. His tactics have given us the word **gerrymandering** to describe such types of manipulation (**Figure 9.31**).

gerrymandering: the practice of redistricting for partisan purposes

Politics and the Environment

In a recent chapter in the Worldwatch Institute's *State of the World* report, Michael Renner observed that "about a quarter of the 49 wars and armed conflicts waged during 2000 had a strong resource dimension—in the sense that legal or illegal

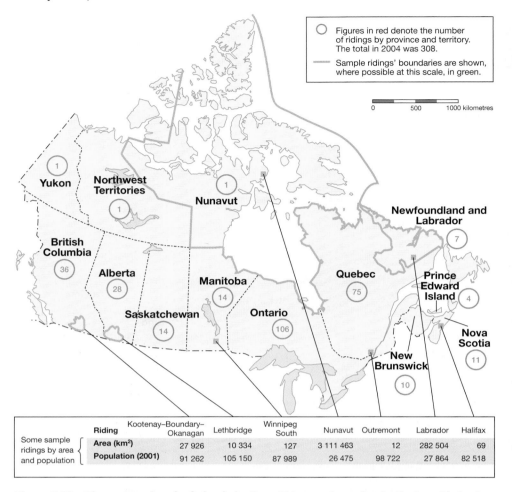

	Riding	Kootenay–Boundary–Okanagan	Lethbridge	Winnipeg South	Nunavut	Outremont	Labrador	Halifax
Some sample ridings by area and population	Area (km²)	27 926	10 334	127	3 111 463	12	282 504	69
	Population (2001)	91 262	105 150	87 989	26 475	98 722	27 864	82 518

Figure 9.30   The geography of a federal election   This map shows the distribution of federal *ridings* (election districts) in the general election of 28 June 2004 by province and territory. Canada's vast territorial expanse and very uneven population distribution pose difficulties for the creation of ridings that are equal in terms of population. Low population densities in rural and northern areas make it very difficult for ridings to reach national averages for population before they become physically too large for one person (the MP) to represent adequately. For example, the entire territory of Nunavut comprises only one federal riding. It is more than 3 million square kilometres but has a population of only 26 475. The much higher population densities of urban and southern regions mean that there are more ridings in these areas and, all other things being equal, that their interests predominate in the House of Commons. Of the examples shown on the map, the small inner Montreal district of Outremont is the smallest, with an area of only 12 square kilometres, but with a population of 98 722. The challenges of balancing competing spatial interests lies at the heart of electoral geography.   (*Source:* Number of electoral districts and district boundaries are taken from the Elections Canada website at **www.elections.ca**.)

resource exploitation helped trigger or exacerbate violent conflict or financed its contribution."[5] Examples of resources range from so-called "blood diamonds" in Africa (**Figure 9.32**) to land availability in Chiapas.

In 1991, the Revolutionary United Front (RUF) invaded Sierra Leone and took control of the Kono diamond fields. Renner notes that "although the RUF professed to act on unresolved grievances [against the government of Sierra Leone], its principal aim was to gain control over the country's mineral wealth." In the course of this takeover, the RUF's rebellion was responsible for the deaths of 75 000 people, the creation of 500 000 refugees, and the displacement of half of Sierra Leone's

---

[5]Michael Renner, "Breaking the Link between Resources and Repression." In Worldwatch Institute, *State of the World 2002*. New York: W.W. Norton, 2002, pp. 148–173. The quotation is from p. 149.

Figure 9.31   Gerrymandering salamander, 1812   This strange beast was the result of political shenanigans that used the geography of U.S. electoral district boundaries to concentrate Federalist votes within a single "sacrifice" district to avert the possibility of Federalist supporters influencing elections in the other districts. Today, laws attempt to prevent such blatant manipulations of the geography of voting.   (*Source: Boston Gazette*, 26 March 1812.)

population of 4.5 million people. Using the proceeds of the diamond fields (operated by forced labour), the RUF was able to create an annual income estimated as at least US$25 million (some estimates go as high as US$125 million) to purchase the arms it needed to continue its control.

A UN investigation in December 2000 found that RUF diamonds had entered the world market as Liberian, Guinean, and Gambian diamonds. Embarrassed by the ease with which such "conflict diamonds" passed into world trade, steps were taken to track their true origins. Since 2001, the governments of 38 countries (including the largest consumer, the United States) and the world diamond industry (led by the main producer of finished diamonds, De Beers) have taken steps to monitor the source of supply. Canada has been active in promoting this initiative, known as the Kimberley Process, but since Canada is a leading producer of non-conflict diamonds and stands to benefit from the global certification, these efforts cannot be seen as entirely altruistic.

Canadian political scientist Thomas Homer-Dixon has more formally explored the complex links among the environment, environmental change, and political conflict in a series of studies on environmental scarcity and the causes of civil violence.[6] **Environmental scarcity** is a scarcity of renewable natural resources that, if

environmental scarcity: a scarcity of renewable natural resources that, if not addressed by technological, social, or economic means, may cause social disruption or violent conflict

Figure 9.32   Blood diamonds   A number of conflicts in Africa are partially caused by a desire to control important resources, such as diamonds. To prevent the proceeds of the diamond business from inadvertently fuelling military endeavours, the international community has begun to develop certification procedures so that such "blood diamonds" are no longer sold on the world market. (Canada's own diamond industry has benefited from these concerns because its sources can be easily verified.)

---

[6]Thomas Homer-Dixon, *Environment, Scarcity, and Violence*. Princeton: Princeton University Press, 1999.

not addressed by technological, social, or economic means, may cause social disruption or violent conflict.

Consider, for example, the 1994 Zapatista uprising in the Mexican state of Chiapas.[7] Based on their research of this case study, Howard and Homer-Dixon conclude that the *Ejército Zapatista de Liberación Nacional* (EZLN), or the Zapatista National Liberation Army, was prompted into rebellion by the maldistribution of natural resources, a problem exacerbated, in turn, by problems of land degradation and population growth. In fact, each of these problems illustrates one of the main three types of environmental scarcity that Homer-Dixon suggests can occur:

1. *Demand-induced scarcity because of population growth or increasing per capita consumption.* In Chiapas, the population rose from 1.57 million in 1970 to 3.2 million by 1998. In the Lacandón Rain Forest area of that state, the population grew from 12 000 to 300 000 over that period through population growth, in-migration from elsewhere in Mexico, and immigration from Guatemala as people searched for new cultivable lands.

2. *Supply-induced scarcity because of the degradation or depletion of natural resources.* It is estimated that 500 years of deforestation have reduced the Lacandón Rain Forest from 1.5 million hectares (3.7 million acres) to approximately 500 000 hectares (1.2 million acres) and that much of this clearance has occurred since 1970. This deforestation has led to a shortage of firewood on which highland Maya communities depend and to severe soil erosion of the cleared land. (Howard and Homer-Dixon estimate that soil erosion in this area could lead to as much as an 8 percent loss in the land's agricultural yield after 1 year and 20 percent after 20 years.)

3. *Structural scarcity because of an unbalanced distribution of resources that affects less powerful groups in society.* In Chiapas, the average landholding for subsistence is only 2 hectares (5 acres), but for commercial production, it is 20 hectares (50 acres). In describing this situation, Howard and Homer-Dixon observe that "this structural scarcity of land for poorer farmers arises from the domination and manipulation of land-tenure arrangements by a wealthy elite of agricultural producers. It is reinforced by the political hegemony of this elite, by the economies of scale and commercial success of large agricultural producers, and by corrupt and inequitable credit and social-spending programs managed by the state."[8]

According to Homer-Dixon, these three types of scarcity "often occur simultaneously and can interact."[9] Two patterns of interaction are especially common:

1. *Resource capture,* which occurs when both supply-induced and demand-induced scarcities work in conjunction to produce structural scarcity. In this case, powerful groups in society may act to shift resource distribution in their favour, thus creating shortages for other members of the population.

2. *Ecological marginalization,* which occurs when demand-induced scarcities and structural scarcity interact to cause supply-induced scarcity. Thus, for example, a lack of access to resources, caused by their unequal distribution, may cause a growing population to migrate from areas where resources are scarce to regions that are ecologically vulnerable.

---

[7]This paragraph is based on Philip Howard and Thomas Homer-Dixon, "The Case of Chiapas, Mexico." In Thomas Homer-Dixon and Jessica Blitt (eds.), *Ecoviolence: Links among Environment, Population, and Security.* Lanham, MD: Rowman and Littlefield, 1998, pp. 19–65.

[8]Philip Howard and Thomas Homer-Dixon, "The Case of Chiapas, Mexico." In Thomas Homer-Dixon and Jessica Blitt (eds.), *Ecoviolence: Links among Environment, Population, and Security.* Lanham, MD: Rowman and Littlefield, 1998, p. 35.

[9]Thomas Homer-Dixon, "Introduction: A Theoretical Overview." In Thomas Homer-Dixon and Jessica Blitt (eds.), *Ecoviolence: Links among Environment, Population, and Security.* Lanham, MD: Rowman and Littlefield, 1998, p. 6.

Both types of interaction are found in the Chiapas case. There, squatters who had cleared forest land for crops and firewood found themselves evicted to increasingly marginal lands by wealthier farmers. As Howard and Homer-Dixon write,[10]

> The history of Chiapas is a chain of multiple yet discrete instances of resource capture and ecological marginalization. . . . As pressures have mounted on agricultural land in Chiapas, elites and wealthy farmers have often taken control of the best land and have perverted land reform and redistribution policies. Many peasants affected by these degradations have migrated to the periphery of the Lacandón Rain Forest. There they have cleared new land, only to be forced—either by the quick depletion of soil nutrients or by more land seizures by wealthy farmers—to move into the vulnerable forest.

Land pressures on the Maya peasant farmers in Chiapas finally caused Subcommandante Marcos to lead the EZLN in revolt against the Mexican government. However, it is important to stress here that the friction caused by environmental scarcity need not lead to violence (or, of course, that violence—when it does occur—is the result only of environmental scarcity). Homer-Dixon himself has recently pointed out that societies can surmount environmental scarcity through technical and social ingenuity.[11] And even if ingenuity is prevented by either the economic inability to finance change (because of, say, market failure or poor capital availability) or the political inability to countenance reform, societies may respond peacefully. Economies may become more constrained, and societies may become more fragmented into richer and poorer classes. Certainly, as we saw in Chapter 3, migration (i.e., leaving the stressed environment) is an option in such circumstances. However, if all avenues are closed, "severe environmental scarcities often contribute to major civil violence."[12]

Of course, even if environmental scarcity does not always directly cause conflict, it can still be a major factor behind the worsening of social and economic conditions that trigger violence, as another of Homer-Dixon's case studies—that of water shortage in the Gaza Strip—illustrates. With an area of only 365 square kilometres (140 square miles) and a population of some 800 000, this region faces a crisis. Simply put, more water is being consumed from Gaza's wells (100 million to 140 million cubic metres per year) than their annual rate of recharge allows on a long-term basis (65 million cubic metres per year). This unsustainable situation is the result of population pressure, intensive agriculture, and—most importantly—a highly inequitable distribution of resources.

To hear that population stress is a factor is hardly surprising. Despite its small area, the Gaza Strip has had to accommodate large numbers of Palestinian refugees, often in such places as the Jabalya camp. It is estimated that more than 70 percent of the people living there are descended from refugees who fled the 1948 Arab-Israeli conflict. As large as the water consumption is (in terms of present water supplies), it will increase further because Gaza's population is increasing at a rate of between 5.2 percent and 6.9 percent per year.

Gaza's economy relies on agriculture, but its focus on intensive citrus fruit cultivation provides a second unsustainable factor. Currently, citrus tree groves occupy 55 percent of the total irrigated land in Gaza, and they use about half the region's agricultural water supply. However, these crops are unlikely to be cultivated for much longer. The continual pumping of water to meet the demands of irrigation has caused Mediterranean sea water to infiltrate into the region's underlying aquifer. The citrus trees cannot tolerate the increased levels of salinity.

---

[10]Philip Howard and Thomas Homer-Dixon, "The Case of Chiapas, Mexico." In Thomas Homer-Dixon and Jessica Blitt (eds.), *Ecoviolence: Links among Environment, Population, and Security.* Lanham, MD: Rowman and Littlefield, 1998, p. 39.

[11]Thomas Homer-Dixon, *The Ingenuity Gap.* Toronto: Vintage Canada, 2001.

[12]Thomas Homer-Dixon, "Introduction: A Theoretical Overview." In Thomas Homer-Dixon and Jessica Blitt (eds.), *Ecoviolence: Links among Environment, Population, and Security.* Lanham, MD: Rowman and Littlefield, 1998, p. 15.

The third factor, inequity, arises from the Gaza Strip's political circumstances. In 1967, Israel declared all water resources in the Gaza Strip and West Bank to be state owned and under military control. Palestinian water consumption was limited by orders that prohibited the drilling of new wells without a permit and measures that authorized the uprooting of thousands of citrus trees. Israeli settlers in the Gaza Strip, conversely, faced far fewer restrictions and much greater subsidies on their water supplies. On average, according to one estimate, Israeli settlers consume 10 times more water than does the Palestinian population. "The net effect of Israel's policies in Gaza," write Kelly and Homer-Dixon, "is to buffer Israelis from the effects of declining levels of water quality and quantity, while Palestinians bear the brunt of water scarcity." They conclude that the effects of this structural scarcity "generate serious friction between these communities."[13]

Unfortunately, the water problems in the Gaza Strip's are only a small part of those facing the whole Middle East, the region "of the most concentrated water scarcity in the world," according to Sandra Postel, where 9 out of 14 countries face serious water shortages.[14] Canadian author Marq de Villiers, in his recent award-winning book *Water: The Fate of Our Most Precious Resource,* says that "the Middle East has always been the place where water wars are most probable. Indeed, Israel did have a shooting war with Syria over water, and it is now widely accepted that the 1967 Arab–Israeli war had its roots in water politics as much as it did in national territorialism."[15]

With only one major river in the region, the River Jordan, and only three major groundwater supplies, it is not hard to see why water supplies have been added to the geopolitics of the area. For example, Israel now diverts most of the River Jordan to supply its own needs through a large pipeline. Yet, Jordan itself, now faced with a seven-eighths reduction in the flow of that river, has had to institute occasional water rationing in Amman and pump increasing amounts of water from underlying aquifers. Water rationing is also practised in Lebanon, where the breakdown of civil authority between 1976 and 1990 left farmers chronically short of water despite the abundance of the Litani River.

Israel itself will face water rationing if future projections hold. By 2010, if water continues to be consumed at its current rate, Israel will have a deficit of 360 million cubic metres a year. Such considerations are believed to be one of the reasons Israel continues to occupy the Golan Heights, which it took from Syria in 1967. Its control of this territory not only has strategic value but also confers control of the water resources of the Dan and Banyias rivers, which flow into the Jordan above Lake Tiberias—an increasingly precious resource in this troubled region.

The political implications of how Canada handles its own water resources provide our final example, and they are the subject of an interesting chapter in the book by Marq de Villiers. He refers, as many do when consideration of this issue is raised, to the concern that Canada's water resources may become a tradeable commodity under the terms of Chapter 11 of the NAFTA agreement. Environmental activists (such as CELA, the Canadian Environmental Law Association) have expressed fears that if this happens, Canada will lose control over an important resource. Canadian nationalists (such as the Council for Canadians) have pointed to the problems for this country's sovereignty if the United States is able to gain access to Canadian water supplies.

Matters were brought to a head in 1998 when a company called the Nova Group received a permit to export 600 million litres (132 million gallons) of Great Lakes water to Asia. How they were to achieve this was never disclosed; the Ontario

---

[13]Kimberley Kelly and Thomas Homer-Dixon, "The Case of Gaza." In Thomas Homer-Dixon and Jessica Blitt (eds.), *Ecoviolence: Links among Environment, Population, and Security.* Lanham, MD: Rowman and Littlefield, 1998, pp. 67–107. The quotation is from p. 77.

[14]Sandra Postel, *The Last Oasis: Facing Water Scarcity.* London: Earthscan Publications, 1992, p. 29.

[15]Marq de Villiers, *The Fate of Our Most Precious Resource.* New York: Houghton Mifflin/Mariner, 2001, p. 190.

environment minister cancelled the permit after its issuance unleashed a storm of public protest. However, as de Villiers concludes, if we believe that this is the end of the issue, then we fundamentally misunderstand some important points: Canadians misuse their own water supplies through pollution and waste, and Canada already exports more water overseas (in the guise of beer and mineral water) than would ever be feasible by a tanker trade in fresh water. As an editorial in Toronto's *Globe and Mail* very forcefully commented, "We say that [water] is priceless, but act as if it were absurdly cheap."

Canada's most northern waters also look set to become the focus of renewed political debate over issues of Arctic sovereignty. As we saw in Chapter 4, one of the results of global warming will be to make the Northwest Passage navigable for commercial shipping and, if that route is interpreted as an "international water-way," to become used freely by the world's fleets. A greater ease of access to the Arctic combined with a growing pressure on fossil fuel reserves has also meant that almost all of the countries with Arctic coastlines (including Russia, Norway, the United States, and Denmark) now vie with Canada to stake out legal title to the Arctic seabed—a process long delayed because of its difficulty in arduous conditions and (until recently) the lack of interest in the results. Now, however, Arctic sovereignty has become a geopolitical issue, and one that Canada is being forced to address. As recently as August 2008, the federal government announced that it was funding an initiative to find the remains of the Franklin expedition (see Chapter 1), an endeavour that if it were to succeed would establish a prior claim to those Arctic islands and waters. Certainly it shows how environmental change can force a reassessment of the geopolitical value of space.

CONCLUSION

The globalization of the economy has been largely facilitated by the actions of states extending their spheres of influence and paving the way for the smooth functioning of markets and industries. Political geography is as much about what happens at the global level as it is about what happens at other levels of spatial resolution, from the region to the neighbourhood to the household and the individual.

Theories of the state have been one of geography's most important contributions to understanding politics. Ratzel's emphasis on the relationship between power and territory and Mackinder's model of the geographical pivot remind us that space and territory shape the actions of states in both dramatic and mundane ways. Time as well as space shape politics, and events distant in time and space—such as colonialism—continue to have impacts long after decolonization. The civil war in Northern Ireland, instigated by English colonial practices now centuries old, has only recently shown credible signs of ceasing. The impacts of English colonization have been felt in countries throughout the Northern Hemisphere, as well as by neighbours living unhappily for several generations side by side in cities, such as Belfast.

Continuing strife is also the case with the enduring North–South divide that pits core countries against peripheral, mostly formerly colonial, countries. Perhaps the most surprising political geographical transformation of the twentieth century was the near dissolution of the East–West divide. Although it is too soon to tell whether communism has truly been superseded by capitalism, it is certainly the case that the distinctions between them are more blurred than clear.

The pairing of the terms *politics* and *geography* serves to remind us that politics is clearly geographical at the same time that geography is unavoidably political. The simple divisions of area into states, counties, cities, towns, and special districts means that where we live shapes our politics, and vice versa. Geography is politics just as politics is geography. And geographical systems of representation, as well as identity politics based on regional histories, confirm these interactive relationships.

Today—and for the future—access to increasingly scarce resources, such as water, will require nations and state to negotiate conflicts and cooperate if they are to survive.

MAIN POINTS REVISITED

■ **A subfield of the discipline of geography, political geography examines complex relationships between politics and geography (both human and physical).**

As societies are organized around territorial units, geography and access to it are often at the centre of political conflicts and can also enable the resolution of conflicts.

■ **Political geographers recognize that the relationship between politics and geography is two-way: politics ↔ geography. Political geography can be seen both as the geography of politics and the politics of geography.**

The geography-of-politics approach recognizes that systems of political representation are geographically anchored and shape the opportunities of the people who live within them.

■ **The relationship between politics and geography is often driven by particular theories and practices of the world's states. Understanding nation-state, imperialism, colonialism, and geopolitical theory is key to comprehending how, within the context of the world-system, geography has influenced politics and how politics has influenced geography.**

At the present moment, theories about globalization and the interconnectedness of places are particularly important, whereas the domino theory and heartland theory have waned in their intellectual and popular appeal.

■ **Political geography deals with phenomena occurring at all scales of resolution from the global to the household. Important East–West and North–South divisions dominate international politics, whereas regionalism and similar divisions dominate intra-state politics.**

No one scale necessarily dominates any other, and changes emanating from a locality may have international impacts and vice versa.

■ **Political geography recognizes the importance of the environment. Global change and population growth both make it likely that increased competition for future resources will also involve political conflict.**

As limited resources, such as water, become much more scarce, issues of human security will require us to reframe traditional concepts of sovereignty to cooperate in the use of resources.

Key Terms

centrifugal forces (p. 397)
centripetal forces (p. 397)
confederation (p. 424)
decolonization (p. 413)
democratic rule (p. 424)
diasporic community (p. 407)
domino theory (p. 417)
East–West divide (p. 417)
Enlightenment (p. 397)
environmental scarcity (p. 427)

federal state (p. 424)
geopolitics (p. 390)
gerrymandering (p. 425)
imagined community (p. 398)
international organization (p. 418)
nation (p. 396)
nation-state (p. 396)
nationalism (p. 398)
North–South divide (p. 412)
reapportionment (p. 424)

redistricting (p. 424)
regionalism (p. 421)
self-determination (p. 421)
sovereignty (p. 396)
supranational organizations (p. 419)
territorial organization (p. 424)
territory (p. 391)
transnational communities (p. 408)
unitary state (p. 424)

Additional Reading

Alia, R., and L. Lifschultz. *Why Bosnia? Writings on the Balkan War.* Stony Creek, CT: The Pamphleteer's Press, Inc., 1993.

Anderson, B. *Imagined Communities: Reflections on the Origin and Spread of Nationalism.* London: Verso, 1983.

Anderson, J., C. Brook, and A. Cochrane (eds.). *A Global World? Re-ordering Political Space.* Oxford: Oxford University Press, 1995.

Bradshaw, Y.W., and M. Wallace. *Global Inequalities.* Thousand Oaks, CA: Pine Forge Press, 1996.

Brockway, L.H. *Science and Colonial Expansion: The Role of the British Royal Botanic Gardens.* New York: Academic Press, 1979.

Brodie, J. "Restructuring and the New Citizenship." In Isabella Bakker (ed.), *Rethinking Restructuring: Gender and Change in Canada.* Toronto: University of Toronto Press, 1996, 126–140.

De Leeuw, S. "Intimate Colonialisms: The Material and Experienced Places of British Columbia's Residential Schools," *Canadian Geographer* 3, 2007, 339–359.

Dodds, K. *Geopolitics: A Very Short Introduction.* New York: Oxford University Press, 2007.

Dodds, K. *Geopolitics in a Changing World.* Harlow, UK: Prentice Hall, 2000.

Dyer, G. *War: The New Edition.* Toronto: Random House of Canada, 2004.

Enloe, C. *Bananas, Beaches and Bases: Making Feminist Sense of International Politics.* Berkeley: University of California Press, 1989.

Gould, K.A., A. Schnaiberg, and A.S. Weinberg. *Local Environmental Struggles: Citizen Activism in the Treadmill of Production.* New York: Cambridge University Press, 1996.

Hampson, F. Osler, M. Hart, and M. Rudner (eds.). *A Big League Player? Canada among Nations 1999.* Don Mills, ON: Oxford University Press, 1999.

Hobsbawm, E., and T. Ranger (eds.). *The Invention of Tradition.* Cambridge: Cambridge University Press, 1983.

Juergensmeyer, M. *The New Cold War? Religious Nationalism Confronts the State.* Berkeley: University of California Press, 1993.

Knight, D.B. "People Together, Yet Apart: Rethinking Territory, Sovereignty, and Identities." In G.J. Demko and W.B. Wood, *Reordering the World: Geopolitical Perspectives on the 21st Century.* Boulder: Westview Press, 1994, 71–86.

McRae, D.M. "Arctic Sovereignty: Loss by Dereliction?" In W.C. Wonders (ed.) *Canada's Changing North,* 2nd ed. Montreal and Kingston: McGill-Queen's University Press, 2003, 427–440.

Nash, A. "The Handwriting Is on the Berlin Wall," *Policy Options* 11(5), 1990, 26–27.

Pratt, C. "The Impact of Ethical Issues on Canadian Foreign Aid Policy," *Canadian Foreign Policy* 9(1), 2001.

Riesebrodt, M. *Pious Passion: The Emergence of Modern Fundamentalism in the United States and Iran*. Translated from the German *Fundamentalismus als patriarchalische Protestbewegung* by Don Reneau. Berkeley: University of California Press, 1993.

Smith, S. "Immigration and Nation-Building in Canada and the United Kingdom." In Peter Jackson and Jan Penrose (eds.), *Constructions of Race, Place and Nation*. Minneapolis: University of Minnesota Press, 1994, 50–77.

Stoett, P. *Human and Global Security: An Exploration of Terms*. Toronto: University of Toronto Press, 1999.

Thurow, L. *The Future of Capitalism*. New York: Morrow, 1996.

Exercises

Here you will find exercises and activities for each chapter. Unplugged exercises help you review chapter discussions, and pose ideas for your own human geography research. On the Companion Website exercises will require you have access to the internet.

Unplugged

1. International boundaries are a prominent feature of the political geography of the contemporary world. In this exercise, you are asked to explore the impact of a boundary on nationalist attitudes and behaviours. You will need to use your university or college library's collection of Canadian newspapers (such as the *Globe and Mail*) and magazines (such as *Maclean's*) to complete this assignment. Using the United States–Canada border as your theme, describe the range of issues that derive from this juxtaposition of two different countries. You should concentrate on a five-year period and explain the issues that grew in importance, the issues that declined, and the issues that continued to have a consistent news profile throughout the period.

2. Using two maps of Europe (up to but not including Russia and the former Soviet Union), one from 1930 and one from 2000, compare the differences in them and provide explanations for the changes. How do issues of ethnicity, religion, and political system help explain these changes? Identify any areas on the map that you feel may be the sites of future border changes, and explain why.

On the Companion Website

This book has its own Companion Website where you will find additional resources—maps, photographs, data—as well as exercises and activities that relate to each chapter. To complete the Companion Website exercises, go to **www.pearsoned.ca/knox**. The following is a summary of the types of exercises created for this chapter.

The exercises for this chapter will help you to better understand political geography. We focus on such issues as the expansion of NATO membership, the reintegration of Hong Kong into China, the separation of East Timor from Indonesia, the increasing powers of the European Union, and the threatened breakup of such countries as Canada, Spain, Russia, Indonesia, and the United Kingdom as a result of separatist movements. All these issues combine issues of the organization of power with those of geographical definition. These and other issues will be considered using a number of geopolitical maps found in our thinking-spatially exercise, a concept review exercise that revisits chapter ideas on the geopolitics of the world order including nationalism, imperialism, and colonization.

10

Urbanization

São Paulo, Brazil

"We are on the verge of a historic transition," heralded the Worldwatch Institute, "at some point in 2008, more than half of all people will live in urban areas."[1]

Quoting United Nations' estimates, Kai N. Lee noted that "By 2005, the world's urban population of 3.18 billion constituted 49 percent of the total population of 6.46 billion. Very soon, and for the first time in the history of our species, more humans will live in urban than rural places." This increase is due to rapid urban growth in China, and (according to UN projections) will be driven over the next generation largely by urban growth in low- and medium-income countries. Asia and Africa, in particular, are projected to double their urban populations to about 3.4 billion people by 2030.[2]

Such rapid increases pose huge problems. Discussing the plight of the current population of the world's urban dwellers, the United Nations Human Settlements Programme (UN-HABITAT), in a 2007 report, highlighted three issues of special concern: urban violence, the vulnerability of cities to climate changes, and the increasing number living in slums, noting that "the most insecure residents are the world's 1 billion poor people living in slums"; informal settlements that often lack clean drinking water, sanitation, decent housing, and secure tenure (**Figure 10.1**). UN-HABITAT estimates that at least 2 million people a year are forced to leave their homes through "incidents of forced eviction [which] are often linked to bulldozing of slums, and informal enterprises in developing countries, as well as to processes of gentrification, public infrastructure development, and urban redevelopment and beautification projects." Such evictions mainly affect those living in the worst housing conditions, particularly disadvantaged groups including

Figure 10.1 Slum housing in peripheral cities
Throughout much of the world, the scale and speed of urbanization, combined with the scarcity of formal employment, have resulted in very high proportions of slum housing, much of it erected by squatters. (a) In Nairobi, Kenya, 40 percent of the city's population live in unauthorized settlements. The largest—the Mathere Valley squatters area—grew from 4000 inhabitants in 1964 to 90 000 in 1979 and over 300 000 in 2004.

[1]Linda Starke (ed.), *State of the World 2007: Our Urban Future*. Washington, DC: Worldwatch Institute; the quotation is taken from the book's back cover.

[2]Kai N. Lee, "An Urbanizing World." in Linda Starke (ed.) *State of the World 2007: Our Urban Future*. Washington, DC: Worldwatch Institute, pp. 3–21; the quotation is from p. 4.

women and children. As Ban Ki-moon, Secretary of the United Nations, wrote in his introduction to the UN-HABITAT report, "the resulting social exclusion swells the army of the poor and the angry."[3]

The excluded are not only to be found in the developing world since the processes and challenges of urbanization are also well-known in the developed countries of the core. For example, artist Stan Douglas's 2001 photomontage *Every Building on 100 West Hastings* shows a part of Vancouver's Downtown Eastside, an area that has a reputation across Canada as a "problem" inner-city neighbourhood, the haunt of drug-dealers, prostitutes, and the down-and-out. When it was first exhibited in the Contemporary Art Gallery in Vancouver, Reid Shier remarked that the picture

> shows a row of buildings in evident disrepair. Many of them are boarded up and appear on the verge of demolition. Paradoxically, there's a stark contrast between the buildings in Douglas' panoramic image and ones directly around the corner and down the street. Save for an area to its east, the architecture of the 100 block stands yards from buildings that are, economically and socially, worlds apart. Three blocks west the heart of the downtown core begins, and with it the start of the most expensive commercial real estate in Vancouver. Two blocks north along Water Street in Gastown, buildings in every way similar to the dilapidated Edwardian structures of Hastings are renovated into loft apartments and tourist shops. To the south along False Creek, sparkling condominium towers rise in one of the most comprehensively planned inner city redevelopment schemes in North America. Within this enfolding sphere of civic entitlement and reimagination, the 100 block stands out in stunning relief.[4]

As Shier remarks, "this conjunction of ruin and renovation isn't an oddity brought on by the vagaries of Vancouver's redevelopment." It marks, as he notes later in his essay on the picture, a "pattern of withdrawal from a city's problem area [that] is a common narrative, and is allusive of the familiar exodus from urban cores that has plagued many North American cities in the post-war years." One reason has been the movement of jobs by transnational industries to cheaper and less regulated countries in the periphery; another has been a process of gentrification, which has become "part of a meticulously planned global phenomenon."[5]

Clearly, urbanization is one of the most important geographical processes in today's world, and to give the topic the attention it deserves will require the considered examination of two chapters. In this chapter, we describe the extent

---

[3]United Nations, *Global Report on Human Settlements 2007: Enhancing Urban Safety and Security.* New York: United Nations Center for Human Settlements, 2007, pp. 1–2.

[4]Reid Shier, "Introduction." In Stan Douglas, *Every Building on 100 West Hastings.* Vancouver: Contemporary Art Gallery, Arsenal Press, pp. 10–17; the quotation is from p. 10. Of interest also is Timothy Taylor, "A Neighbourhood Speaks and Hears Its Own Voice." *Globe and Mail*, 21 April 2008, p. L2, a review of *Hope in Shadows*, a forthcoming collection of photographs taken and stories told by residents of Vancouver's Downtown Eastside.

[5]Reid Shier, "Introduction." In Stan Douglas, *Every Building on 100 West Hastings.* Vancouver: Contemporary Art Gallery, Arsenal Press, pp. 10–17; the quotations are from p. 12. In their essays in this book, geographers Nick Blomley and Neil Smith expand on these wider processes of urban growth and change.

and pattern of urbanization across the world, explaining its causes and the resultant changes brought in people and places. The next chapter, Chapter 11, will then consider the processes responsible for the internal shaping of cities and urban areas.

MAIN POINTS

- The urban areas of the world are the lynchpins of human geographies at the local, regional, and global scales.
- The earliest urbanization developed independently in the various hearth areas of the first agricultural revolution.
- The expansion of trade around the world, associated with colonialism and imperialism, established numerous gateway cities.
- The Industrial Revolution generated new kinds of cities and many more of them.
- Today, the single most important aspect of world urbanization from a geographical perspective is the striking difference in trends and projections between the core regions and the peripheral regions.
- Cities form linked networks, known as *urban systems,* which determine the importance of component cities of the system and organize these cities into their various functional niches within an economy.
- Canada's urban system is a product of processes that operate in both core and peripheral regions.
- A small number of "world cities," most of them located within the core regions of the world-system, occupy key roles in the organization of global economics and culture.
- The populations of many of the largest cities in the periphery have a doubling time of only 10 to 15 years.
- Many of the megacities of the periphery are primate and exhibit a high degree of centrality within their urban systems.

URBAN GEOGRAPHY AND URBANIZATION

From small market towns and fishing ports to megacities with millions of people, the urban areas of the world are the lynchpins of human geographies. Since the beginning of European contact, urban centres have been the focus of Canada's economic transformation and have become the places where the great majority of Canadians live. They have always been a crucial element in spatial organization and the evolution of societies, but today they are more important than ever. Between 1980 and 2000, the number of city dwellers worldwide rose by 1.1 billion. Cities now account for almost half the world's population. Much of the developed world has become almost completely urbanized (**Figure 10.2**), while in many peripheral and semiperipheral regions the current *rate* of urbanization is without precedent (**Figure 10.3**). In 1996, the United Nations held a major conference on human settlement in Istanbul. Statistics prepared for the conference report that some 5 billion urban dwellers will exist by the year 2025, of which 80 percent will be in peripheral and semiperipheral countries. Urbanization on this scale is a remarkable geographical phenomenon—one of the most important groups of processes shaping the world's landscapes.

Towns and cities are engines of economic development and centres of cultural innovation, social transformation, and political change. Although they often pose

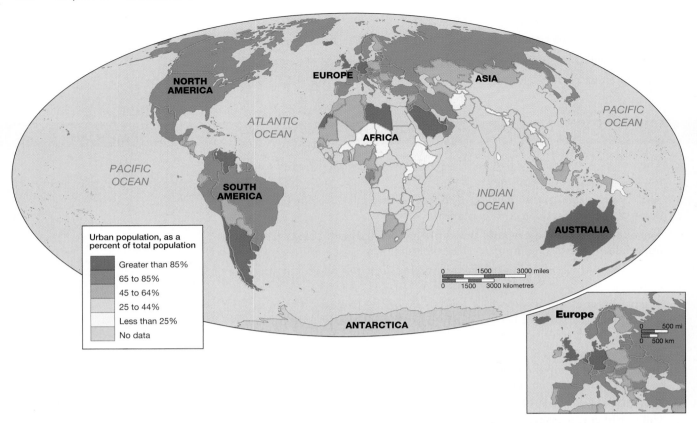

Figure 10.2   Percentage of each country's population living in urban settlements, 2003   The lowest levels of urbanization—less than 25 percent—are found in Central Africa and South and Southeast Asia. Most of the core countries are highly urbanized, with between 65 and 95 percent of their populations living in urban settlements.   (*Source:* Data from United Nations Department of Economic and Social Affairs, Population Division, *World Urbanization Prospects: The 2003 Revision,* 2004, pp. 25–29.)

social and environmental problems, they are essential elements in human economic and social organization. Experts on urbanization point to four fundamental aspects of the role of towns and cities in human economic and social organization:

- The *mobilizing function* of urban settlement. Cities provide efficient and effective environments for organizing labour, capital, and raw materials, and for distributing finished products.

- The *decision-making capacity* of urban settlement. Because urban settings bring together the decision-making machinery of public and private institutions and organizations, they become concentrations of political and economic powers.

- The *generative functions* of urban settlement. The concentration of people in urban settings makes for much greater interaction and competition, which facilitate the generation of innovation, knowledge, and information.

- The *transformative capacity* of urban settlement. The size, density, and variety of urban populations allow people to escape the rigidities of traditional rural society and to participate in a variety of lifestyles and behaviours.

Urban geographers are concerned with the development of towns and cities around the world, particularly with the similarities and differences both *among* and *within* urban places. What attributes make towns and cities distinctive? How did these distinctive identities evolve? What are the relationships and interdependencies between particular sets of towns, cities, and their surrounding territories? Do significant regularities exist in the spatial organization of land use within cities, in the patterning of neighbourhood populations, or in the layout and landscapes of particular kinds of cities?

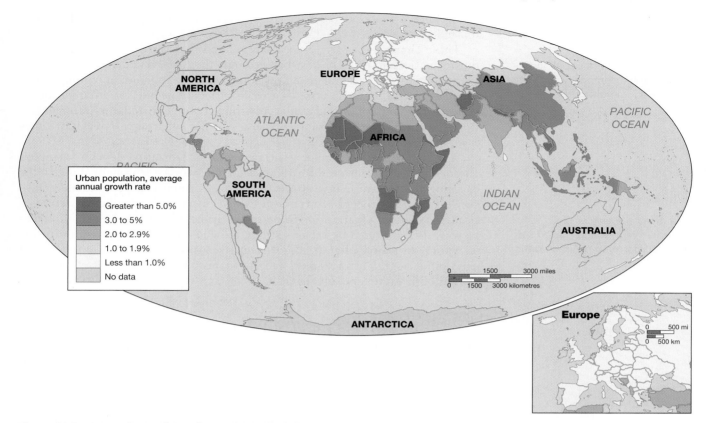

Figure 10.3 Rates of growth in urbanization, 2000–2005 This map shows the annual average growth rate between 2000 and 2005 in the proportion of people in each country living in urban settlements. Core countries, already highly urbanized, grew quite slowly. The urban populations of peripheral countries such as Angola, Afghanistan, Burundi, Liberia, Rwanda, and Somalia, on the other hand, grew by more than 5 percent each year, creating tremendous pressure on cities' capacity to provide jobs, housing, and public services. (*Source:* Data from United Nations Department of Economic and Social Affairs, Population Division, *World Urbanization Prospects: The 2003 Revision*, 2004, pp. 70–78.)

Urban geographers also want to know about the causes of the patterns and regularities they find. How, for example, do specialized urban subdistricts evolve? Why did urban growth occur in a particular region at a particular time? Why did urban growth exhibit a distinctive physical form during a certain period? In pursuing such questions, urban geographers have learned that the answers can be found in the wider context of economic, social, cultural, and political life. In other words, towns and cities must be viewed as part of the economies and societies that maintain them.

Urbanization, therefore, is not simply a process of the demographic growth of towns and cities. It also involves many other changes, both quantitative and qualitative. From the geographer's perspective, these changes can be conceptualized in several different ways. One of the most important of these is by examining the attributes and dynamics of urban systems. An **urban system**, or city system, is any interdependent set of urban settlements within a given region. For example, we can speak of the Canadian urban system, the African urban system, or even the global urban system. As urbanization takes place, the attributes of urban systems will, of course, reflect the fact that increasing numbers of people are living in ever-larger towns and cities. They will also reflect other important changes, such as changes in the relative size of cities, in their functional relationships with one another, and in their employment base and population composition.

Another important aspect of change associated with urbanization processes concerns **urban form**—the physical structure and organization of cities in their land use, layout, and built environment. As urbanization takes place, not only do towns and cities grow bigger physically, extending upward and outward, but they

urban system: an interdependent set of urban settlements within a specified region

urban form: the physical structure and organization of cities

also become reorganized, redeveloped, and redesigned in response to changing circumstances.

These changes, in turn, are closely related to a third aspect of change—transformations in patterns of **urban ecology**, the social and demographic composition of city districts and neighbourhoods. Urbanization not only brings more people to cities, but it also brings a greater variety of people. As different social, economic, demographic, and ethnic subgroups become sorted into different territories, distinctive urban ecologies emerge. As new subgroups arrive or old ones leave, these ecologies change.

A fourth aspect of change associated with urbanization concerns people's attitudes and behaviour. New forms of social interaction are brought about by the liberating and transformative effects of urban environments. These changes have given rise to the concept of urbanism, which refers to the distinctive nature of social and cultural organization in particular urban settings. **Urbanism** describes the way of life fostered by urban settings, in which the number, physical density, and variety of people often result in distinctive attitudes, values, and patterns of behaviour. Geographers are interested in urbanism because of the ways in which it varies both within and among cities.

urban ecology: the social and demographic composition of city districts and neighbourhoods

urbanism: the way of life, attitudes, values, and patterns of behaviour fostered by urban settings

URBAN ORIGINS

It is important to put the geographical study of towns and cities in historical context. After all, many of the world's cities are the product of a long period of development. We can understand a city, old or young, only if we know something about the reasons behind its growth, the rate at which it has grown, and the processes that have contributed to its growth.

In broad terms, the earliest urbanization developed independently in the various hearth areas of the first agricultural revolution. The very first region of independent urbanism was in the Middle East, in the valleys of the Tigris and Euphrates (in Mesopotamia) and in the Nile Valley from around 3500 B.C. (see Chapter 8). Together, these intensively cultivated river valleys formed the so-called Fertile Crescent. By 2500 B.C. cities had appeared in the Indus Valley, and by 1800 B.C., they were established in northern China. Other areas of independent urbanism include Mesoamerica (from around 100 B.C.) and Andean America (from around A.D. 800). Meanwhile, the original Middle Eastern urban hearth continued to produce successive generations of urbanized world-empires, including those of Greece (**Figure 10.4**), Rome, and Byzantium.

Experts differ in their explanations of these first transitions from subsistence mini-systems to city-based world-empires. The classical archaeological interpretation emphasizes the availability of an agricultural surplus large enough to allow the emergence of specialized, nonagricultural workers.

Changes in social organization were an important precondition for urbanization. Specifically, urbanization required the emergence of groups that were able to exact tributes, impose taxes, and control labour power, usually through some form of religious persuasion or military coercion. Once established, this elite group provided the stimulus for urban development by using its wealth to build palaces, arenas, and monuments to show off its power and status. This activity not only created the basis for the physical core of ancient cities (**Figure 10.5**) but also required an increased degree of specialization in nonagricultural activities—construction, crafts, administration, the priesthood, soldiery, and so on—which could be organized effectively only in an urban setting. By A.D. 1000, city-based world-empires had emerged in Europe, the Middle East, and China, including a dozen major cities with populations of 100 000 or more (**Figure 10.6**).

The urbanized economies of world-empires were a precarious phenomenon, however, and many of them lapsed into ruralism before being revived or recolonized. In a number of cases, the decline of world-empires was a result of demographic setbacks associated with wars or epidemics. Such disasters left too few people to maintain the social and economic infrastructure necessary for urbanization. This lack of labour

Corinth began to develop as a commercial centre in the eighth century B.C., though its site had been inhabited since before 3000 B.C. This photograph shows the ruins of the Temple of Apollo.

Ancient Athens was at its peak in the fifth century B.C., when, as the largest and wealthiest *polis* (city-state), it became the cultural and intellectual centre of the classical Greek world. The Parthenon, built on top of the Acropolis, dates from this time.

Figure 10.4 Greek colonization The Greeks traded and colonized throughout the Aegean from the eighth century B.C. onward. Later, they extended their activities to the central Mediterranean and Black Sea, where their settlements formed important nuclei for subsequent urbanization. The shaded area on the map shows the extent of the *polis*, the Greek ideal of a democratic city-state. (*Source for map*: J. Rich and A. Wallace-Hadrill (eds.), *City and Country in the Ancient World*. London: Routledge, 1991, fig. 1b.)

power seems to have been a major contributing factor to the eventual collapse of the Mesopotamian Empire. Similarly, the population of the Roman Empire began to decline in the second century A.D., giving rise to labour shortages, abandoned fields, and depopulated towns and allowing the infiltration of "barbarian" settlers and tribes from the German lands of east-central Europe. Conversely, the abandonment of much of the Mayan Empire more than 500 years before the arrival of the Spanish may have more to do with social upheaval or environmental change.

The Roots of European Urban Expansion

In Europe, the urban system introduced by the Greeks and re-established by the Romans almost collapsed during the Dark Ages of early medieval Europe (A.D. 476–1000). During this period, feudalism gave rise to a fragmented landscape of inflexible and inward-looking world-empires. *Feudalism* was a rigid, rurally oriented form of economic and social organization based on the communal chiefdoms of Germanic tribes who had invaded the disintegrating Roman Empire. Essentially, these rulers held all the lands in a chiefdom but allowed them to be farmed by the local population of peasants in return for rents, taxes, and military

Figure 10.5 Ancient Troy Situated on the southern side of the Dardanelles, where it could easily control all seaborne trade between the Aegean and the Black Sea, the remains of the ancient city of Troy can still be easily found only a short drive from the town of Çanakkale in present-day Turkey. Declared a World Heritage site in 1998, and identified as the most likely site of the legendary Trojan War (which, if it actually took place, has been dated to approximately 1250 B.C.), these ruins have long attracted the attention of archaeologists eager to explore the city evoked in Homer's poem *The Iliad* (which itself dates from about 700 B.C.). First excavated in the late nineteenth century by Heinrich Schliemann, and currently the focus of an archaeological team led since 1988 by Manfred Korfmann, it is now becoming clear that most of the surviving walls and buildings found on the site are not part of the exterior walls of the city, but originally formed part of a citadel and palace buildings located *within* Troy. Outside the citadel lay the houses of Troy's various working and trading groups, but these structures (being built of less durable materials, such as wood) have left little physical evidence of their presence in the city. It is also becoming clear that the city is much older than legend might suggest: the walls shown in the photograph, for example, are believed to date from approximately 1650 B.C., and excavations now suggest that the city's origins date from almost 3000 B.C.

Figure 10.6 Kyoto The ancient city of Kyoto had a population of 180 000 in A.D. 1000.

services. From this unlikely beginning, an elaborate urban system developed, its largest centres eventually growing into what would become the nodal centres of a global world-system.

Early medieval Europe, divided into a patchwork of feudal kingdoms and estates, was mostly rural. Each feudal estate was more or less self-sufficient regarding foodstuffs, and each kingdom or principality was more or less self-sufficient

Figure 10.7 Towns of early medieval Europe Urbino, Italy, on a classic hilltop defensive site, had been settled by Etruscans and Romans before coming under church rule in the ninth century. It then became the centre of the dukedom of the Montefeltro family and by the late medieval period had become a hub of artistic and literary activity.

regarding the raw materials needed to craft simple products. Most regions, however, did support at least a few small towns (**Figure 10.7**). The existence of these towns depended mainly on their role:

- *Ecclesiastical or university centres*—Examples include Rheims and Chartres in France; Bremen in Germany; and Lund in Sweden.

- *Defensive strongholds*—Examples include the hilltop towns of central Italy, such as Urbino, and the *bastide,* or fortress, towns of southwestern France, such as Aigues-Mortes.

- *Administrative centres*—for the upper tiers of the feudal hierarchy. Examples include Köln, Mainz, and Magdeburg in Germany.

From the eleventh century onward, however, the feudal system faltered and disintegrated in the face of successive demographic, economic, and political crises, which were caused by steady population growth in conjunction with only modest technological improvements and limited amounts of cultivable land. To bolster their incomes and raise armies against one another, the feudal nobility began to levy increasingly higher taxes. The rural peasants were consequently obliged to sell more of their produce for cash on the market. As a result, a more extensive money economy developed, along with the beginnings of a pattern of trade in basic agricultural produce and craft manufactures. Some long-distance trade even began in luxury goods, such as spices, furs, silks, fruit, and wine. Towns began to increase in size and vitality on the basis of this trade. Indeed, the role of such trade in rejuvenating Europe's cities cannot be overemphasized.

The regional specializations and trading patterns that emerged provided the foundations for a new phase of urbanization based on merchant capitalism (**Figure 10.8**). Beginning with networks established by the merchants of Venice, Pisa, Genoa, and Florence (in northern Italy) and the trading partners of the Hanseatic League (a federation of city-states around the North Sea and Baltic coasts), a trading system of immense complexity soon came to span Europe from Bergen to Athens and from Lisbon to Vienna. By 1400, long-distance trading was well established, based not on the luxury goods of the pioneer merchants but on bulky staples, such as grains, wine, salt, wool, cloth, and metals. The populations of Milan, Genoa, Venice, and Bruges had all grown to 100 000 or more. Paris was the dominant European city, with a population of about 275 000. This was the Europe that stood poised to extend its grasp to a global scale.

Between the fifteenth and seventeenth centuries, a series of changes occurred that transformed not only the cities and city systems of Europe but also the entire world economy. Merchant capitalism increased in scale and sophistication; economic and social reorganization was stimulated by the Protestant Reformation and the scientific revolution. Meanwhile, aggressive overseas colonization made Europeans the leaders, persuaders, and shapers of the rest of the world's economies and societies. Spanish and Portuguese colonists were the first to extend the European urban system into the world's peripheral regions. They established the basis of a Latin American urban system in just 60 years, between 1520 and 1580. Spanish colonists founded their cities on the sites of native American cities (in Oaxaca and Mexico

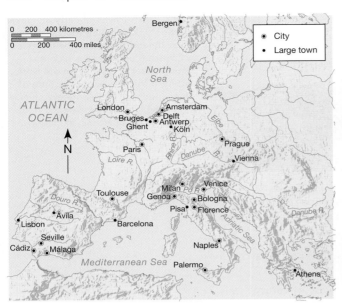

Bergen, Norway

Avila, Spain

Ghent, Belgium

Florence, Italy

Figure 10.8   The towns and cities of Europe, c. 1350   Cities with more than 10 000 residents were uncommon in medieval Europe except in northern Italy and Flanders, where the spread of cloth production and the growth of trade permitted relatively intense urbanization. Elsewhere, large size was associated with a complex of administrative, religious, educational, and economic functions. By 1350, many of the bigger towns (for example, Barcelona, Köln, Prague) supported universities as well as a variety of religious institutions. Most urban systems, reflecting the economic and political realities of the time, were relatively small in extent.   (*Source for map:* P.M. Hohenberg and L.H. Lees, *The Making of Urban Europe 1000–1950.* Cambridge, MA: Harvard University Press, 1985, fig. 2.1.)

City, Mexico; Cajamarca and Cuzco, Peru; and Quito, Ecuador) or in regions of dense indigenous populations (in Puebla and Guadalajara, Mexico; and Arequipa and Lima, Peru). These colonial towns were established mainly as administrative and military centres from which the Spanish Crown could occupy and exploit the New World. Portuguese colonists, in contrast, situated their cities—Recife, Salvador, São Paulo, and Rio de Janeiro—with commercial rather than administrative considerations in mind. They, too, were motivated by exploitation, but their strategy was to establish colonial towns in locations best suited to organizing the collection and export of the products of their mines and plantations.

In Europe, Renaissance reorganization saw the centralization of political power and the formation of national states, the beginnings of industrialization, and the funnelling of plunder and produce from distant colonies. In this new context, the port cities of the North Sea and Atlantic coasts enjoyed a decisive locational advantage. By 1700, London's population had grown to 500 000, while Lisbon's and Amsterdam's populations had each grown to about 175 000. The cities of continental and Mediterranean Europe expanded at a more modest rate. By 1700, Venice had added only 30 000 inhabitants to its 1400 population of 110 000, and Milan's population did not grow at all between 1400 and 1700.

The most important aspect of urbanization during this period, however, was the establishment of gateway cities around the rest of the world (**Figure 10.9**). A **gateway city** is one that serves as a link between one country or region and others because of its physical situation. It is a control centre that commands entrance to and

gateway city: a city that serves as a link between one country or region and others because of its physical situation

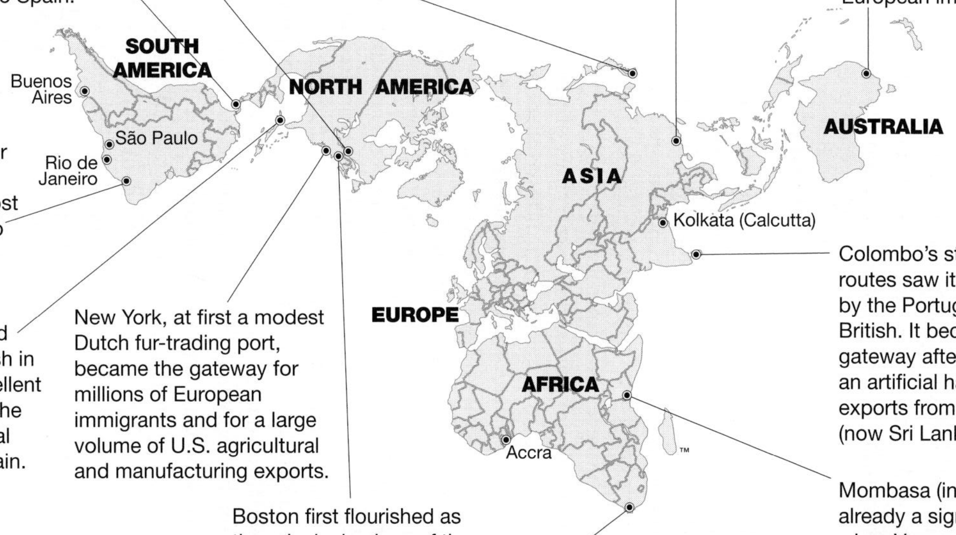

Montreal, the gateway to Canada for Europe and a leading rail centre, became Canada's principal city until it was eclipsed by Toronto's growth.

Panama City, founded by the Spanish in 1519, became the gateway for gold and silver on its way by galleon to Spain.

Salvador, Brazil, was the landfall of the Portuguese in 1500. The Portuguese established plantations that were worked by slave labour from West Africa. Salvador became the gateway for most of the 3.5 million slaves who were shipped to Brazil between 1526 and 1870.

Havana was founded and developed by the Spanish in 1515 because of its excellent harbour. It was used as the annual assembly point for annual convoys returning to Spain.

New York, at first a modest Dutch fur-trading port, became the gateway for millions of European immigrants and for a large volume of U.S. agricultural and manufacturing exports.

Boston first flourished as the principal colony of the Massachusetts Bay Company, exporting furs and fish and importing slaves from West Africa, hardwoods from Central America, molasses from the Caribbean, manufactured goods from Europe, and tea (via Europe) from South Asia.

Cape Town was founded in 1652 as a provisioning station for ships of the Dutch East India Company. Later, under British rule, it developed into an import-export gateway for South Africa.

Nagasaki was the only port that feudal Japanese leaders allowed open to European traders, and for more than 200 years Dutch merchants held a monopoly of the import-export business through the city.

Guangzhou was the first Chinese port to be in regular contact with European traders—first Portuguese in the sixteenth century and then British in the seventeenth century.

Sydney, Australia, was not settled until the late eighteenth century, and even then many of the settlers were convicts who had been forcibly transported from Britain. It soon became the gateway for agricultural and mineral exports (mostly to Britain) and for imports of manufactured goods and European immigrants.

Colombo's strategic situation on trade routes saw it occupied successively by the Portuguese, the Dutch, and the British. It became an important gateway after the British constructed an artificial harbour to handle the exports from tea plantations in Ceylon (now Sri Lanka).

Mombasa (in present-day Kenya) was already a significant Arab trading port when Vasco da Gama visited it in 1498 on his first voyage to India. The Portuguese used it as a trading station until it was recaptured by the Arabs in 1698. It did not become an important gateway port until it fell under British imperial rule in the nineteenth century, when railroad development opened up the interior of Kenya, along with Rwanda, Uganda, and northern Tanzania.

Kolkata (Calcutta)

Accra

NORTH AMERICA

SOUTH AMERICA

Buenos Aires

São Paulo

Rio de Janeiro

ASIA

AUSTRALIA

EUROPE

AFRICA

Figure 10.9 Gateway cities in the world-system periphery Many of the world's most important cities grew to prominence as gateway cities because they commanded routes into and out of developing colonies. Gateway cities are control centres that command entrance to and exit from their particular country or region. (*Source:* Map projection, Buckminster Fuller Institute and Dymaxion Map Design, Santa Barbara, CA. The word *Dymaxion and the Fuller Projection Dymaxion*™ Map design are trademarks of the Buckminster Fuller Institute, Santa Barbara, California, © 1938, 1967, & 1992. All rights reserved.)

exit from its particular country or region. European powers founded or developed literally thousands of towns as they extended their trading networks and established their colonies. The great majority of them were ports. Protected by fortifications and European naval power, they began as trading posts and colonial administrative centres. Before long, they developed manufacturing of their own to supply the pioneers' needs, along with more extensive commercial and financial services.

As colonies were developed and trading networks expanded, some of these ports grew rapidly, acting as gateways for colonial expansion into continental interiors. Into their harbours came waves of European settlers; through their docks were funnelled the produce of continental interiors. Rio de Janeiro (Brazil) grew on the basis of gold mining; Accra (Ghana) grew on the basis of cocoa; Buenos Aires (Argentina) on the basis of mutton, wool, and cereals; Kolkata (formerly Calcutta, India) on the basis of jute, cotton, and textiles; São Paulo (Brazil) on the basis of coffee; and so on. As they grew into major population centres, these cities became important markets for imported European manufactured goods, adding even more to their functions as gateways for international transport and trade.

Industrialization and Urbanization

It was not until the late eighteenth century that urbanization came to be an important dimension of the world-system in its own right. In 1800, less than 5 percent of the world's 980 million people lived in towns and cities. By 1950, however, 16 percent of the world's population was urban, and more than 900 cities with 100 000 or more inhabitants existed around the world. The Industrial Revolution and European imperialism had created unprecedented concentrations of humanity that were intimately linked in networks and hierarchies of interdependence.

Cities were synonymous with industrialization. Industrial economies could be organized only through the large pools of labour; the transportation networks; the physical infrastructure of factories, warehouses, stores, and offices; and the consumer markets provided by cities. As industrialization spread throughout Europe in the first half of the nineteenth century and then to other parts of the world, urbanization increased—at a faster pace. The higher wages and greater variety of opportunities in urban labour markets attracted migrants from surrounding areas. The countryside began to empty. In Europe, the *demographic transition* caused a rapid growth in population as death rates dropped dramatically (see Chapter 3). This growth in population provided a massive increase in the labour supply throughout the nineteenth century, further boosting the rate of urbanization, not only within Europe itself but also in Australia, Canada, New Zealand, South Africa, and the United States, as emigration spread industrialization and urbanization to the frontiers of the world-system.

shock city: a city that is seen as the embodiment of surprising and disturbing changes in economic, social, and cultural lives

The shock city of nineteenth-century European industrialization was Manchester, England, which grew from a small town of 15 000 in 1750 to a city of 70 000 in 1801, a metropolis of 500 000 in 1861, and a world city of 2.3 million by 1911. A **shock city** is one that is seen at the time as the embodiment of surprising and disturbing changes in economic, social, and cultural lives. As industrialization took hold in North America, the shock city was Chicago, which grew from fewer than 30 000 in 1850 to 500 000 in 1880, 1.7 million in 1900, and 3.3 million in 1930. Both Manchester and Chicago were archetypal forms of an entirely new kind of city—the *industrial city*—whose fundamental reason for existence was not, as in earlier generations of cities, to fulfill military, political, ecclesiastical, or trading functions. Rather, it existed simply to assemble raw materials and to fabricate, assemble, and distribute manufactured goods. Both Manchester and Chicago had to cope, however, with unprecedented rates of growth and the unprecedented economic, social, and political problems that were a consequence of their growth (see **Visualizing Geography 10.1—Shock Cities: Manchester and Chicago**). Both were also *world cities*, cities in which a disproportionate part of the world's most important business—economic, political, and cultural—is conducted. At the top of a global urban system, these cities experience growth largely as a result of their role as key nodes in the world economy.

Shock Cities: Manchester and Chicago

"One day I walked with one of these middle-class gentlemen into Manchester. I spoke to him about the disgraceful unhealthy slums and drew his attention to the disgusting condition of that part of the town in which the factory worker lived. I declared that I had never seen so badly built a town in my life. He listened patiently and at the corner of the street he remarked: 'And yet there is a great deal of money to be made here. Good morning, Sir!'"

Friedrich Engels, *The Condition of the Working Class in England in 1844*

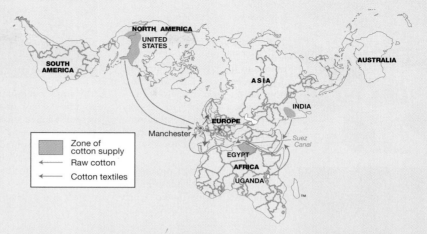

Zone of cotton supply
Raw cotton
Cotton textiles

Manchester City Hall, a classic example of Victorian Gothic architecture, was built to show the world that the city had arrived. Manchester in the nineteenth century was a city of enormous vitality, not only in its economic life but also in its political, cultural, and intellectual lives.

In the mid-nineteenth century, the United States produced more than 80 percent of the world's raw cotton, much of it from plantations like this one in Georgia. Manchester was the chief consumer of this cotton, and it, in turn, became the world's chief exporter of cotton textiles.

The opening of the Suez Canal in 1869 halved the travelling time between Britain and India. It ruined the Indian domestic cotton textile industry, but it allowed India to export its raw cotton to Manchester. Around the same time, British colonialists established cotton plantations in Egypt and Uganda, providing another source of supply.

The Manchester Ship Canal (1894), a joint undertaking of the municipality and private enterprise, connected Manchester with the Irish Sea and world markets beyond. The canal revived the city's trade and made possible the development of a concentration of heavy industry in nearby Trafford Park Estate.

Manchester's first cotton mill was built in the early 1780s, and by 1830 there were 99 cotton-spinning mills. As the city grew, it spilled out into the surrounding countryside, bringing its characteristic landscape of red-brick terrace housing and "Dark Satanic Mills" with their tall brick chimneys.

In the late nineteenth century, working-class housing was built to conform with local building codes—but only just. Much of it has now been replaced, but a good deal still remains.

Migrants from Ireland and northern England contributed to Manchester's rapid growth from the mid-nineteenth century.

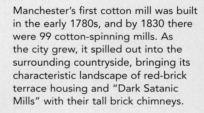

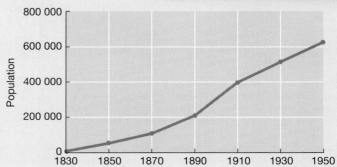

When Chicago was first incorporated as a city in 1837, its population was only 4200. Its growth followed the arrival of the railroads, which made the city a major transportation hub. By the 1860s, lake vessels were carrying iron ore from the Upper Michigan ranges to the city's blast furnaces, and railroads were hauling cattle, hogs, and sheep to the city for slaughtering and packing. The city's prime geographical situation also made it the nation's major lumber-distributing centre by the 1880s.

Chicago announced its prosperity through elaborate skyscrapers and towers. The Tribune Tower, shown here, was built in Gothic Revival style and based on the winning entry in an international design competition organized by the *Chicago Tribune* in 1922. The city has regarded itself ever since as a sponsor of landmark architecture.

Chicago's immigrant and African-American neighbourhoods were an entirely new urban phenomenon—highly segregated and with very distinctive social and cultural attributes. The 1880 and 1890 censuses showed that more than three-quarters of Chicago's population was made up of foreign-born immigrants and their children. These photographs of ethnic neighbourhoods in Chicago's Southside were taken in 1941.

Hog-butcher for the World,
Tool Maker, Stacker of Wheat
Player with Railroads and the Nation's
Freight Handler;
Stormy, husky, brawling,
City of the Big Shoulders.
                    Carl Sandburg, 1916

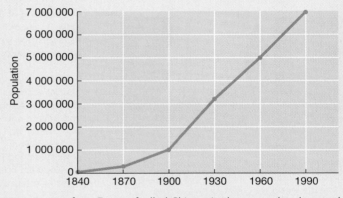

Immigrants from Europe fuelled Chicago's phenomenal early growth.

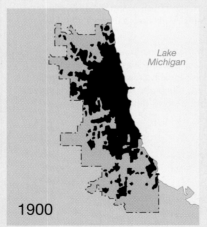

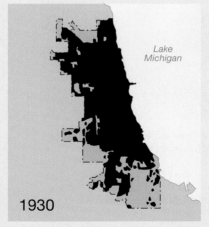

In 1870, when Manchester was already a thriving metropolis, Chicago was at the beginning of a period of explosive growth. A year later, 9 square kilometres (3.5 square miles) of the city, including the business district, were destroyed by fire. They were rebuilt rapidly, with prosperous industrialists taking the opportunity to build impressive new structures in the downtown area. The city's economic and social elite colonized the Lake Michigan shore, while heavy industry, warehouses, and railyards crowded the banks of the Chicago River, stretching northwestward from the city centre. To the south of the city centre were the Union Stockyards and a pocket of heavy industry where the Calumet River met Lake Michigan. All around were the homes of working families, in neighbourhoods that spread rapidly outward as wave after wave of immigrants arrived in the city.

Throughout the nineteenth century, European imperialism gave a significant impetus to urbanization in the world's peripheral regions. New gateway cities were founded, and, as Europeans raced to establish economic and political control over continental interiors, colonial cities were established as centres of administration, political control, and commerce. **Colonial cities** are those that were deliberately established or developed as administrative or commercial centres by colonial or imperial powers. In fact, geographers often distinguish between two distinct types of colonial city. One, the pure colonial city, was usually established, or "planted," by colonial administrations in a location where no significant urban settlement had previously existed. Such cities were laid out expressly to fulfill colonial functions, with ceremonial spaces, offices, and depots for colonial traders, plantation representatives, and government officials; barracks for a garrison of soldiers; and housing for colonists. Subsequently, as these cities grew, they added housing and commercial land uses for local peoples drawn by the opportunity to obtain such jobs as servants, clerks, or porters. Examples of such "pure" colonial cities are Mumbai (formerly Bombay), Kolkata (formerly Calcutta), Ho Chi Minh City (formerly Saigon), Hong Kong, Jakarta, Manila, and Nairobi.

In the other type of colonial city, colonial functions were grafted onto an existing settlement, taking advantage of a good site and a ready supply of labour. Examples include Delhi, Mexico City, Shanghai, and Tunis. In these cities, the colonial imprint is most visible in and around the city centre in the formal squares and public spaces, the layout of avenues, and the presence of colonial architecture and monuments. This architecture includes churches, city halls, and railway stations (**Figure 10.10**); the palaces of governors and archbishops; and the houses of wealthy traders, colonial administrators, and landowners.

The colonial legacy can also be read in the building and planning regulations of many of these cities. Often, colonial planning regulations were copied from those that had been established in the colonizing country. Because these regulations were based on Western concepts, many of them turned out to be inappropriate to colonial settings. Most colonial building codes, for example, were based on Western models of family and work, with a small family living in a residential area that was some distance from the adults' places of work. This is at odds with the needs of large, extended families whose members are involved in a busy domestic economy and with family businesses that are traditionally integrated with the residential setting. With its gridiron street layouts, zoning regulations that did not allow for a mixture of land uses, and building codes designed for European climates, colonial planning ignored the specific needs of local communities and misunderstood their cultural preferences. The contrast between New Delhi, built by the British, and Delhi, the pre-colonial city that it adjoins, well illustrates this point.

colonial cities: cities that were deliberately established or developed as administrative or commercial centres by colonial or imperial powers

Victoria Station, Mumbai, India

Figure 10.10 Colonial architecture and urban design Cities in the periphery of the world-system have grown very rapidly since the colonial era, but the legacy of the colonial period can still be seen in the architecture, monuments, and urban design of the period.

WORLD URBANIZATION TODAY

It is difficult to say just how urbanized the world has become. In many parts of the world, urban growth is taking place at such a pace and under such chaotic conditions that it is impossible even for experts to do more than provide informed estimates. The most comprehensive source of statistics is the United Nations, whose data suggest that almost half of the world's population is now urban. These data incorporate the very different definitions of *urban* used by different countries. Some countries (Australia and Canada, for example) count any settlement of 1000 people or more as urban; others (including Italy and Jordan) use 10 000 as the minimum for an urban settlement; and Japan uses 50 000 as the cut-off. This tells us something about the nature of urbanization itself: it is a *relative* phenomenon. In such countries as Peru, where population is thin and scattered, a settlement of 2000 represents a significant centre. In such countries as Japan, however, with greater numbers, higher densities, and a tradition of centralized rather than scattered agricultural settlement, a much larger concentration of people is required to count as "urban."

TABLE 10.1	Urbanization by Major World Regions, 2003		
	Percent of Total Population in Urban Areas	**Percent of Urban Population in Cities of Less Than 500 000**	**Percent of Urban Population in Cities of 5 Million or More**
Africa	39.7	58.9	7.9
Asia	39.9	49.7	17.2
Latin America	77.6	48.0	20.6
North America	80.8	37.5	20.5
Europe	73.3	63.3	8.5
Oceania	73.3	41.7	0.0
World	**49.2**	**51.7**	**15.3**

Source: Data, United Nations, *World Urbanization Prospects: The 2003 Revision.* New York: UN Department of Economic and Social Affairs, 2004.

Taking the definitions used in individual countries, almost one-half of the world's population is now urbanized. As **Table 10.1** shows, North America is the most urbanized continent in the world, with more than 80 percent of its population living in urban areas. In contrast, Africa and Asia are less than 40 percent urban.

To put these figures in perspective, only 29.7 percent of the world's population was urbanized in 1950, using the same definitions of urban settlements. In that year, there were only 83 metropolitan areas with a million or more people, and only 8 cities with 5 million or more people existed; in 2000, there were approximately 372 metropolitan areas with a million or more people and 45 with over 5 million. Looking ahead, population projections for 2010 suggest that more than 52 percent of the world's population will be living in urban areas, and there will be around 475 cities with a population of a million or more, including about 55 cities of 5 million or more.

Regional Trends and Projections

The single most important aspect of world urbanization, from a geographical perspective, is the striking difference in trends and projections between the core regions and the semiperipheral and peripheral regions. In 1950, two-thirds of the world's urban population was concentrated in the more developed countries of the core economies. Since then, the world's urban population has increased three-fold, the bulk of the growth having taken place in the less-developed countries of the periphery (**Figure 10.11**). In 1950, 3 of the world's largest 10 metropolitan areas were located in core countries—By 2010, all but 2 of the 10 largest metropolitan areas are expected to be located in peripheral and semiperipheral regions (**Table 10.2**).

Asia provides some of the most dramatic examples of this trend. From a region of villages, Asia is fast becoming a region of cities and towns. Between 1950 and 1985, for example, its urban population rose nearly fourfold to 480 million people. By 2020, about two-thirds of Asia's population will be living in urban areas. Nowhere is the trend toward rapid urbanization more pronounced than in China, where for decades the communist government imposed strict controls on where people were allowed to live, fearing the transformative and liberating effects of cities. By tying people's jobs, school admission, and even the right to buy food to the places where people were registered to live, the government made it almost impossible for rural residents to migrate to towns or cities. As a result, more than 70 percent of China's 1 billion people still lived in the countryside in 1985. In recent years, the Chinese government, having decided that towns and cities can be engines of economic growth within a communist system, has not only relaxed residency laws but also drawn up plans to establish more than 430 new cities. Between 1981 and 2003, the number of people living in cities in China more than tripled, from

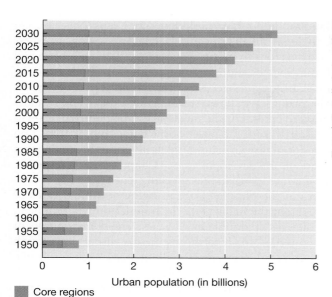

Figure 10.11 Urban population growth, 1950–2030 Although the metropolitan areas of the world's core countries have continued to grow, most of them have been overtaken by the startling growth of the "unintended" metropolises of peripheral and semiperipheral countries. (*Source:* Data from United Nations, *World Urbanization Prospects.* New York: UN Department of Economic and Social Affairs, 1998.)

TABLE 10.2   The World's 10 Largest Metropolitan Areas, Ranked by Population Size, 1950, 1980, and 2010 (in millions)

1950	Population	1980	Population	2010	Population
New York	12.3	Tokyo	28.5	Tokyo	35.8
London	8.7	New York	15.6	Mumbai	20.4
Tokyo	6.9	Mexico City	13.0	Mexico City	19.8
Paris	5.4	São Paulo	12.1	São Paulo	19.3
Moscow	5.4	Shanghai	11.7	New York	19.1
Shanghai	5.3	Osaka	10.0	Delhi	18.2
Essen	5.3	Buenos Aires	9.9	Jakarta	15.5
Buenos Aires	5.0	Los Angeles	9.5	Kolkata	15.5
Chicago	4.9	Kolkata	9.0	Dhaka	15.2
Kolkata	4.4	Beijing	9.0	Lagos	14.0

Source: Data, United Nations, *World Urbanization Prospects.* New York: UN Department of Economic and Social Affairs, 2003, pp. 120–123.

162 million to 504 million, and the number of cities with a population of half a million or more increased from 16 to 97.

In the world's core countries, levels of urbanization are high and have been so for some time. According to their own national definitions, the populations of Belgium, the Netherlands, and the United Kingdom are more than 90 percent urbanized, while those of Australia, Canada, Denmark, France, Germany, Japan, New Zealand, Spain, Sweden, and the United States are all more than 75 percent urbanized. In these core countries, however, *rates* of urbanization are relatively low, just as their overall rate of population growth is slow (see Chapter 3).

Levels of urbanization are also very high in many of the world's semiperipheral countries. Brazil, Mexico, Taiwan, Singapore, and South Korea, for example, are all at least 75 percent urbanized. Unlike the core countries, however, their rate of urban growth has been high. In peripheral countries, the contrast is even greater.

Whatever the current level of urbanization in peripheral countries, almost all are experiencing high rates of urbanization, with growth forecasts of unprecedented speed and unmatched size. Karachi, Pakistan, a metropolis of 1.03 million in 1950, had reached 8.5 million in 1995 and is expected to reach 16.2 million by 2015. Likewise, Cairo, Egypt, grew from 2.41 million to 9.7 million between 1950 and 1995, and is expected to reach 13 million by

2015. Mumbai (formerly Bombay, India), Jakarta (Indonesia), Lagos (Nigeria), São Paulo (Brazil), and Shanghai (China) are all projected to have populations in excess of 17 million by 2015. The reasons for this urban growth vary. Wars in Liberia and Sierra Leone have pushed hundreds of thousands of people into their capitals, Monrovia and Freetown. In Mauritania, Niger, and other countries bordering the Sahara, deforestation and overgrazing have allowed the desert to expand and swallow up villages, forcing people toward cities. For the most part, though, urban growth in peripheral countries has resulted from the onset of the demographic transition (see Chapter 3), which has produced fast-growing rural populations in regions that face increasing problems of agricultural development (see Chapter 8). As a response, many people in these regions migrate to urban areas seeking a better life.

Many of the largest cities in the periphery are growing at annual rates of between 4 percent and 7 percent; at the higher rate the population will double in 10 years, while at the lower rate, it will double in 17 years. The *doubling time* of a city's population is the time needed for it to double in size at current growth rates. To put the situation in numerical terms, metropolitan areas, such as Mexico City and São Paulo, are adding half a million people to their population each year—nearly 10 000 every week, even after making up for deaths and out-migrants. It took London 190 years to grow from half a million to 10 million; it took New York 140 years. By contrast, Mexico City, São Paulo, Buenos Aires, Kolkata (formerly Calcutta), Rio de Janeiro, Seoul, and Mumbai (formerly Bombay) all took less than 75 years to grow from half a million to 10 million inhabitants.

Urban Systems

Every town and city is part of one of the interlocking urban systems that link regional-, national-, and international-scale human geographies in a complex web of interdependence. These urban systems organize space through hierarchies of cities of different sizes and functions. Many of these hierarchical urban systems exhibit certain common attributes and features, particularly in the relative size and spacing of individual towns and cities.

central places: settlements in which certain products and services are available to consumers

Central Places Geographers have long recognized the tendency for the functions of towns and cities as market centres to result in a hierarchical system of **central places**—settlements in which certain types of products and services are available to consumers. The tendency for central places to be organized in hierarchical systems was first explored by Walter Christaller, a German geographer, in the 1930s. Christaller's ideas gave rise to the ideas that subsequently were to become part of the *locational analysis* tradition of geography, when these ideas became "rediscovered" by geographers in the late 1950s and 1960s who were interested in the notion of geography as a spatial science (as we saw in Chapter 1).

central place theory: a theory that seeks to explain the relative size and spacing of towns and cities as a function of people's shopping behaviours

In the same way that Weber's theory of industrial location (Chapter 7), von Thünen's theory of agricultural location (Chapter 8), and Burgess's theory of urban residential patterns (Chapter 11), offered insight into the operation of a variety of geographic processes across space, so Christaller's work on the location of towns and cities offered an explanation for urban geographers that could be expressed in the almost geometric, abstract language of locational analysis. His findings gave rise to **central place theory**, which seeks to explain the relative size and geographical spacing of towns and cities as a function of people's shopping behaviours. Christaller had noticed that southern Germany had quite a number of smaller places, each offering a limited assortment of stores, services, and amenities for its residents and the residents of nearby areas. He noticed that these places tended to be located at relatively short and consistent distances from one another. Large towns and cities, on the other hand, were fewer and farther between but offered a much greater variety of stores, services, and amenities, many of them catering to customers and clients from quite distant towns and intermediate rural areas. In between were intermediate-sized places serving intermediate-sized markets with middling collections of stores, services, and amenities.

Christaller called these collections of stores, services, and amenities "central place functions." Towns and cities serve different-sized territories and populations. To explain the observed tendency for a hierarchy of central places, Christaller drew on principles concerning the range and threshold of central place functions. The **range** of a product or service is the maximum distance that consumers will normally travel to obtain it. "High-order" goods and services are those that are relatively costly and generally required infrequently (specialized equipment, professional sports, and specialized medical care, for example). They have the greatest range—100 or more kilometres is not unusual. At the other extreme, "low-order" goods and services are those that are relatively inexpensive and required at frequent intervals (bakery products, dairy products, and groceries, for example). They have a very short range, perhaps as low as 500 metres.

The **threshold** of a good or service can be thought of as the minimum market area with enough potential buyers to make the enterprise profitable. High-order services, such as hospitals, have thresholds in the tens of thousands of people. Low-order services, such as small grocery stores, can have thresholds of between 200 and 300 people.

It follows that, in any given region, a need will exist for only a limited number of large central places in which all the higher-order goods and services are provided. It is logical that these communities will also provide the entire spectrum of central place functions. The number and spacing of other smaller central places will depend on the combination of different-sized ranges and thresholds. Using a series of different starting assumptions, Christaller was able to demonstrate that, under ideal circumstances (on flat plains with good transportation in every direction), towns and cities tend to be arranged in clear hierarchies, with hexagonal-shaped market areas of different sizes arranged around different-sized areas (**Figure 10.12**). Although such circumstances are never found in real life, geographers did subsequently find many instances where hierarchies of central places existed, with a high degree of regularity in their size and spacing. The distribution of settlement across the Canadian Prairies has been seen as one example, and a similar environment (that of Iowa) became a classic example of central place theory. Today, in fact, relatively few regions exist where the functions of most towns and cities are still dominated by local markets and shopping. Nevertheless, the urban systems of most regions do exhibit a clear hierarchical structure. This is partly a legacy of past eras, when towns and cities did function mainly as market centres for surrounding agricultural areas. **Figure 10.13** shows a typical example: the Spanish urban system, with smaller towns and cities functioning interdependently with

range: the maximum distance that consumers will normally travel to obtain a particular product or service

threshold: the minimum market size required to make the sale of a particular product or service profitable

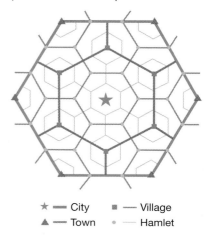

★ — City   ■ — Village
▲ — Town   • — Hamlet

Figure 10.12 Central places and locational hierarchies This illustration shows Walter Christaller's basic concept of a hierarchy of settlements (central places) of different sizes, with successively larger settlements offering a greater variety of goods and services, thus commanding a broader market territory. The hexagonal market areas were hypothetical, allowing Christaller to avoid gaps or overlapping market areas.

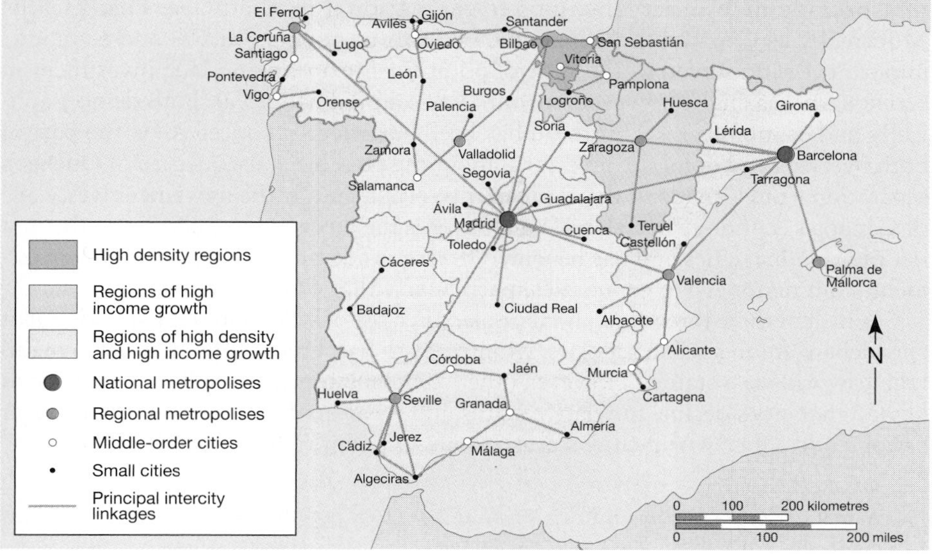

Figure 10.13 The Spanish urban system Note how the smaller cities tend to be linked to middle-order cities, while these, in turn, are linked to regional metropolises, which are linked to the national metropolises, Madrid and Barcelona. These linkages represent the major flows of capital, information, and goods within the Spanish urban system. (*Source:* L. Bourne, R. Sinclair, M. Ferrer, and A. d'Entremont (eds.), *The Changing Geography of Urban Systems.* Department of Human Geography. Navarra, Spain: Universidad de Navarra, 1989, fig. 2, p. 46.)

High density regions

Regions of high income growth

Regions of high density and high income growth

● National metropolises

● Regional metropolises

○ Middle-order cities

• Small cities

— Principal intercity linkages

El Ferrol, La Coruña, Santiago, Pontevedra, Vigo, Orense, Lugo, Avilés, Gijón, Oviedo, Santander, Bilbao, San Sebastián, Vitoria, Pamplona, León, Burgos, Logroño, Huesca, Girona, Palencia, Soria, Lérida, Zamora, Valladolid, Zaragoza, Barcelona, Segovia, Salamanca, Tarragona, Ávila, Guadalajara, Madrid, Cuenca, Teruel, Toledo, Castellón, Cáceres, Valencia, Palma de Mallorca, Badajoz, Ciudad Real, Albacete, Córdoba, Jaén, Murcia, Alicante, Huelva, Seville, Granada, Cartagena, Cádiz, Jerez, Almería, Málaga, Algeciras

0 100 200 kilometres
0 100 200 miles

N

Figure 10.14 Canada's urban hierarchy This illustration shows the structure and composition of the top levels of this country's urban system.

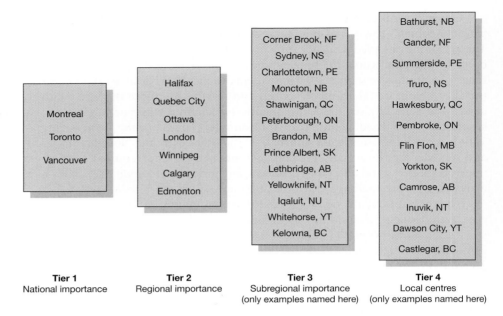

Tier 1	Tier 2	Tier 3	Tier 4
National importance	Regional importance	Subregional importance (only examples named here)	Local centres (only examples named here)

successively larger ones, the whole system dominated by one or two metropolitan areas whose linkages are national in scope.

Urban systems also exhibit clear *functional* differences within such hierarchies, yet another reflection of the interdependence of places. The geographical division of labour resulting from such processes of economic development (Chapter 7) means that many medium- and larger-sized cities perform quite specialized economic functions and so acquire quite distinctive characters. Thus, for example, there are steel towns (for example, Sydney, Nova Scotia; Sheffield, England), textile towns (for example, Lowell, Massachusetts; Manchester, England), and auto-manufacturing towns (for example, Windsor, Ontario; Oxford, England; Turin, Italy; Toyota City, Japan). Some towns and cities, of course, do evolve as general-purpose urban centres, providing an evenly balanced range of functions for their own particular sphere of influence.

Canada's urban system provides an excellent example of the development of such a hierarchy (**Figure 10.14**) as the extensive work by Larry Bourne, a geographer at the University of Toronto and one of the world's foremost authorities on urban systems, has shown. His work and that of other Canadian geographers enable us to identify the elements of this country's urban system and to appreciate how it operates. The top tier of cities consists of Toronto, Montreal, and Vancouver—cities that provide high-order functions to the national marketplace. Historically, Montreal was Canada's principal city, in terms of population size and economic importance, and served as the control point for European and U.S. investment in Canada. Increasingly, however, Toronto has eclipsed Montreal, both demographically and economically. This trend has been hastened by concerns, on the part of both overseas and domestic investors, about the possible consequences of Quebec's separation from Canada, if that were ever to occur, and by the movement westward of Canada's economic heartland. Vancouver is the most recent addition to the first tier of Canadian cities and has benefited from considerable immigration and investment from major Asian economies, particularly that of Hong Kong.

Which of these three cities merits a place in a list of world cities is a question that stirs debate among urban scholars. Montreal still has fervent supporters who maintain its world-class status.[6] However, other commentators are mindful of the reasons behind that city's decline in relative status and regard only Toronto and Vancouver as contenders for "world-city" status, if only of junior rank (**Figure 10.15**).

---

[6]See Annick Germain and Damaris Rose, *Montréal: The Quest for a Metropolis*, World Cities Series. Chichester, UK: Wiley, 2000, pp. ix–xii.

Top-Tier World Cities
London
New York
Tokyo

2nd-Tier World Cities
Brussels   São Paulo
Chicago   Singapore
Frankfurt   Washington, DC
Los Angeles   Zürich
Paris

3rd-Tier World Cities
Amsterdam   Johannesburg   Milan   Seoul
Bangkok   Madrid   Mumbai (Bombay)   Sydney
Berlin   Manila   Osaka   Taipei
Buenos Aires Mexico City   Rio de Janeiro   Toronto
Hong Kong   Miami   San Francisco   Vancouver
Houston

● Top-Tier world city
● 2nd-Tier world city
● 3rd-Tier world city

Brussels qualifies as a world city because it is the administrative centre of the European Union and because it has attracted a large number of non-governmental organizations that are transnational in scope.

Milan has global status in terms of cultural influence (especially fashion and design) and is an important regional financial centre, but it is relatively dependent in terms of corporate control and information-processing activities.

London, New York, and Tokyo are major world cities because of their major financial markets, their transnational corporate headquarters, and their concentrations of financial services. Because of their geographical locations in different time zones, office hours in each city overlap just enough to allow 24-hour trading and decision making.

London

Tokyo

New York

Figure 10.15 World cities World cities are not simply the world's largest and economically most important cities. Rather, they are the control centres of the world economy, places where critical decision making and interaction take place with regard to global economic, cultural, and political issues. (*Source*: Map projection, Buckminster Fuller Institute and Dymaxion Map Design, Santa Barbara, CA. The word *Dymaxion* and the Fuller Projection Dymaxion™ Map design are trademarks of the Buckminster Fuller Institute, Santa Barbara, California, © 1938, 1967, & 1992. All rights reserved.)

The second tier of Canadian cities consists of Halifax, Quebec City, Ottawa-Hull, London (Ontario), Winnipeg, Calgary, and Edmonton. These can be described as general-purpose cities with diverse functions but only regional importance.

The third tier is made up of more specialized centres of subregional importance. Smaller provincial capitals, such as Regina or Charlottetown; northern cities, such as Yellowknife, Whitehorse, and Iqaluit; important centres, such as the rapidly growing city of Kelowna, British Columbia; the university and agricultural service cities of Brandon, Manitoba, and Lethbridge, Alberta; and industrial centres such as Corner Brook, Newfoundland, all provide examples of third-order functions.

The fourth functional tier in the Canadian urban hierarchy comprises those centres that have only local importance—such towns as Castlegar, British Columbia, or Bathurst, New Brunswick, for example, which can provide their populations with little more than a basic range of shopping and service needs.

In total, the Canadian urban system consists of only approximately 750 communities, ranging in size from small resource towns to our three metropolitan centres, of which approximately 140 are cities with more than 10 000 people. As a number of Canadian geographers have observed, this urban system, for most practical purposes, *is* Canada. The relationships between the cities of this system define the major geographical regions of our country.

Certainly, the present urban hierarchy, dominated by the cities of the Quebec City–Windsor "corridor," embodies the dichotomy between core and periphery, heartland and hinterland, that lies at the root of so much of our country's geographical patterns. The importance of this corridor was first brought to geography's attention by Maurice Yeates of Queen's University. Some geographers (as discussed below) have seen this dichotomy as the driving force for the development of Canada's urban system itself.

City-Size Distributions, Primacy, and Centrality   The functional interdependency between places within urban systems tends to result in a distinctive relationship between the population size of cities and their rank within the overall hierarchy. This relationship is known as the **rank-size rule**, which describes a certain statistical regularity in the city-size distributions of countries and regions. The relationship is such that the *n*th largest city in a country or region is $1/n$ the size of the largest city in that country or region. If the largest city in a particular system has a population of 1 million, the fifth-largest city should have a population one-fifth as big (that is, 200 000); the hundredth-ranked city should have a population one-hundredth as big (that is, 10 000); and so on. Plotting this relationship on a graph with a logarithmic scale for population sizes would produce a perfectly straight line. The actual rank-size relationship for the U.S. urban system has always come close to this (**Figure 10.16**). Over time, the slope has moved to the right on the graph, reflecting the growth of towns and cities at every level in the urban hierarchy.

In some urban systems, the top of the rank-size distribution is distorted as a result of the disproportionate size of the largest (and sometimes also the second-largest) city (**Figure 10.17**). Geographers call this **primacy**, a condition occurring when the population of the largest city in an urban system is disproportionately large in relation to the second- and third-largest cities in that system. Such cities are called *primate cities*.

Primacy is not simply a matter of sheer size. Some of the largest metropolitan areas in the world—Karachi, New York, and Mumbai (formerly Bombay)—are not primate. Further, as the examples in Figure 10.17 show, primacy is a condition that is found in both the core and the periphery of the world-system. This suggests that primacy is a result of the roles played by particular cities within their own national urban systems. A relationship does exist to the world economy, however. Primacy in peripheral countries is usually a consequence of primate cities' early roles as gateway cities. In core countries, it is usually a consequence of primate cities' roles as imperial capitals and centres of administration, politics, and trade for a much wider urban system than their own domestic system.

rank-size rule: a statistical regularity in city-size distributions of countries and regions

primacy: a condition in which the population of the largest city in an urban system is disproportionately large in relation to the second- and third-largest cities in that system

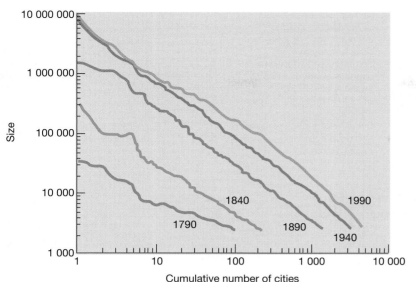

Figure 10.16   The rank-size distribution of cities in the U.S. urban system, 1790–1990 This graph shows that the U.S. urban system has conformed fairly consistently to the rank-size rule. As urbanization brought increased populations to cities at every level in the urban hierarchy, the rank-size graph has moved to the right. Meanwhile, the growth of some cities (for example, San Diego) has sent them from the lower end of the hierarchy to the very top, while other cities (for example, Savannah, Georgia) have declined, at least in relative terms, so that they have fallen down the hierarchy.   (*Source*: Reprinted with permission of Prentice Hall from P.L. Knox, *Urbanization*, © 1994, p. 32.)

When cities' economic, political, and cultural functions are disproportionate to their population, the condition is known as **centrality**, or the functional dominance of cities within an urban system. Cities that account for a disproportionately high share of economic, political, and cultural activities have a high degree of centrality within their urban system. Very often, primate cities exhibit this characteristic, but cities do not necessarily have to be primate to be functionally dominant within their urban system. **Figure 10.18** shows some examples of centrality, revealing the overwhelming dominance of some cities within the world-system periphery. Bangkok, for instance, with around 10 percent of the Thai population, accounts for approximately 38 percent of the country's overall gross domestic product (GDP); over 85 percent of the country's GDP in banking, insurance, and real estate; and 75 percent of its manufacturing.

centrality: the functional dominance of cities within an urban system

World Cities   Ever since the evolution of a world-system in the sixteenth century, certain cities known as *world cities* (sometimes referred to as *global cities*) have played key roles in organizing space beyond their own national boundaries. In the

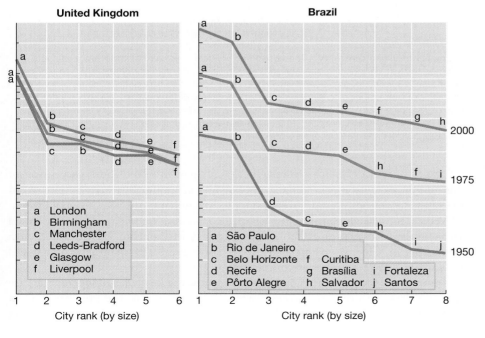

Figure 10.17   Rank-size distributions of city systems   Some urban systems are dominated by *primate cities* whose populations are much larger than would be expected according to the rank-size rule. These rank-size graphs show two examples, each for 1950, 1975, and 2000. In the United Kingdom, London has always been disproportionately large. Brazil has two primate cities: São Paulo and Rio de Janeiro. Note how the rank-size curves for Brazil are spaced farther apart than in the United Kingdom's example, reflecting rapid population growth throughout its urban system.
(*Source*: After S. Brunn and J.F. Williams, *Cities of the World*, 2nd ed. New York: HarperCollins, 1993, fig. 1.11, p. 24. Reprinted by permission of Addison-Wesley Educational Publishers Inc.)

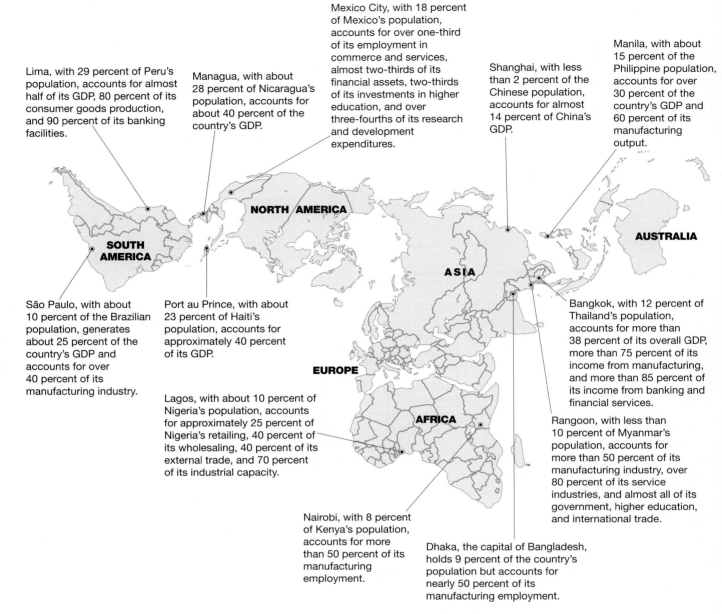

Lima, with 29 percent of Peru's population, accounts for almost half of its GDP, 80 percent of its consumer goods production, and 90 percent of its banking facilities.

Managua, with about 28 percent of Nicaragua's population, accounts for about 40 percent of the country's GDP.

Mexico City, with 18 percent of Mexico's population, accounts for over one-third of its employment in commerce and services, almost two-thirds of its financial assets, two-thirds of its investments in higher education, and over three-fourths of its research and development expenditures.

Shanghai, with less than 2 percent of the Chinese population, accounts for almost 14 percent of China's GDP.

Manila, with about 15 percent of the Philippine population, accounts for over 30 percent of the country's GDP and 60 percent of its manufacturing output.

São Paulo, with about 10 percent of the Brazilian population, generates about 25 percent of the country's GDP and accounts for over 40 percent of its manufacturing industry.

Port au Prince, with about 23 percent of Haiti's population, accounts for approximately 40 percent of its GDP.

Lagos, with about 10 percent of Nigeria's population, accounts for approximately 25 percent of Nigeria's retailing, 40 percent of its wholesaling, 40 percent of its external trade, and 70 percent of its industrial capacity.

Bangkok, with 12 percent of Thailand's population, accounts for more than 38 percent of its overall GDP, more than 75 percent of its income from manufacturing, and more than 85 percent of its income from banking and financial services.

Rangoon, with less than 10 percent of Myanmar's population, accounts for more than 50 percent of its manufacturing industry, over 80 percent of its service industries, and almost all of its government, higher education, and international trade.

Nairobi, with 8 percent of Kenya's population, accounts for more than 50 percent of its manufacturing employment.

Dhaka, the capital of Bangladesh, holds 9 percent of the country's population but accounts for nearly 50 percent of its manufacturing employment.

Figure 10.18 Examples of urban centrality The economic, political, and cultural importance of some cities is disproportionate to their population size, making them "central" to their economies. This is a reflection of core–periphery differentials within countries and often becomes a political issue because of the economic disparities. The centrality of these cities also leads to localized problems of congestion, land price inflation, and pollution. (*Source:* Map projection, Buckminster Fuller Institute and Dymaxion Map Design, Santa Barbara, CA. The word *Dymaxion* and the Fuller Projection Dymaxion™ Map design are trademarks of the Buckminster Fuller Institute, Santa Barbara, California, © 1938, 1967, & 1992. All rights reserved.)

first stages of world-system growth, these key roles involved the organization of trade and the execution of colonial, imperial, and geopolitical strategies. The world cities of the seventeenth century were London, Amsterdam, Antwerp, Genoa, Lisbon, and Venice. In the eighteenth century, Paris, Rome, and Vienna also became world cities, while Antwerp and Genoa became less influential. In the nineteenth century, Berlin, Chicago, Manchester, New York, and St. Petersburg became world cities, while Venice became less influential.

Today, with the globalization of the economy, the key roles of world cities are concerned less with the deployment of imperial power and the orchestration of trade and more with transnational corporate organization, international banking and finance, supranational government, and the work of international agencies. World cities have become the control centres for the flows of information, cultural products, and finance that collectively sustain the economic and cultural globalization of the world.

World cities also provide an interface between the global and the local. They contain the economic, cultural, and institutional apparatuses that channel national and provincial or territorial resources into the global economy and that transmits the impulses of globalization back to national and provincial centres. As such, world cities possess several functional characteristics:

- They are the sites of most of the leading global markets for commodities, commodity futures, investment capital, foreign exchange, equities, and bonds.
- They are the sites of clusters of specialized, high-order business services, especially those that are international in scope and attached to finance, accounting, advertising, property development, and law.
- They are the sites of concentrations of corporate headquarters—not just of transnational corporations but also of major national firms and large foreign firms.
- They are the sites of concentrations of national and international headquarters of trade and professional associations.
- They are the sites of most of the leading non-governmental organizations (NGOs) and intergovernmental organizations (IGOs) that are international in scope.
- They are the sites of the most powerful and internationally influential media organizations.

A great deal of synergy exists among these various functional components. A city, for example New York, attracts transnational corporations because it is a centre of culture and communications. It attracts specialized business services because it is a centre of corporate headquarters and of global markets, and so on. These interdependencies represent a special case of the geographical *agglomeration effects* that we discussed in Chapter 7. Agglomeration is the clustering of functionally related activities. In the case of New York City, corporate headquarters and specialized legal, financial, and business services cluster together because of the mutual cost savings and advantages of being close to one another. At the same time, different world cities fulfill different roles within the world-system, making for different emphases and combinations (that is, differences in the nature of their world-city functions), as well as for differences in the absolute and relative localization of particular world-city functions (that is, differences in their degree of importance as world cities).

Today, the global urban system is dominated by three world cities whose influence is truly global: London, New York, and Tokyo (see Figure 10.15). The second tier of the system consists of world cities with influence over large regions of the world-system. These include, for example, Brussels, Frankfurt, Los Angeles, Paris, Singapore, and Zürich. A third tier consists of important international cities with more limited or more specialized international functions (including Amsterdam, Madrid, Miami, Mexico City, Seoul, Sydney, Toronto, and Vancouver). A fourth tier exists of cities of national importance and with some transnational functions (including Barcelona, Dallas, Manchester, Munich, Melbourne, and Philadelphia).

Megacities Megacities are not necessarily world cities, as described earlier, though some of them are (London and Tokyo, for example). **Megacities** are very large cities characterized by a high degree of centrality within their national economy. Their most important common denominator is their sheer size—most of them number 10 million or more in population. This, together with their functional centrality, means that in many ways they have more in common with one another than with the smaller metropolitan areas and cities within their own countries.

megacities: very large cities characterized by high centrality within their national economy

Examples of such megacities include Beijing, Cairo, Lagos, Manila, Mexico City, São Paulo, Shanghai, and Tehran. Each one of these has more inhabitants than 100 of the member countries of the United Nations. Although most of them do not function as world cities, they do provide important intermediate roles between the upper tiers of the system of world cities and the provincial towns and villages of large regions of the world. They not only link local and provincial economies with the global economy but also provide a point of contact between the traditional and the modern, and between formal and informal economic sectors. The **informal sector** of an economy involves a wide variety of economic activities whose common feature is that they take place beyond official record and are not subject to formalized systems of regulation or remuneration.

informal sector: economic activities that take place beyond official record and are not subject to formalized systems of regulation or remuneration

URBAN GROWTH PROCESSES

The large-scale urbanization triggered in the world's core countries by the evolution of a world-system, and later reinforced by the Industrial Revolution, was based on growth processes that were self-sustaining. Cities themselves were the engines of economic growth, and this growth, in turn, attracted the migrants, settlers, and immigrants that made for rapid population growth. In this urbanization process, a close and positive relationship existed between rural and urban development (**Figure 10.19**). The appropriation of new land for agriculture, together with mechanization and the innovative techniques that urbanization allowed, resulted in increased agricultural productivity. This extra productivity released rural labour to work in the growing manufacturing sector in towns and cities. At the same time, it provided the additional produce needed to feed growing urban populations. The whole process was further reinforced by the capacity of urban labour forces to produce agricultural tools, machinery, fertilizer, and other products that made for still greater increases in agricultural productivity.

Urbanization and Economic Development

In this self-sustaining process of urbanization, the actual rate and amount of a city's growth depends on the size of its economic base. A city's **economic base**

economic base: set of manufacturing, processing, trading, or service activities that serve markets beyond the city

Figure 10.19 The urbanization process in the world's core regions
Urbanization was stimulated by advances in farm productivity that (1) provided the extra food to support the increased numbers of townspeople, and (2) made many farmers and farm labourers redundant, prompting them to migrate to cities. Labour displaced in this way ended up consuming food rather than producing it, but this was more than compensated for by the increases in agricultural productivity and the increased capacity of enlarged urban labour forces to produce agricultural tools, machinery, fertilizers, and so on, that contributed further to agricultural productivity.

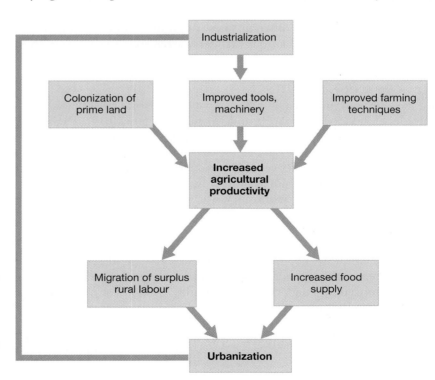

consists of those economic functions that involve the manufacturing, processing, or trading of goods or the provision of services for markets beyond the city itself. Activities that provide income-generating "exports" for a city are termed **basic functions**. In contrast, **nonbasic functions** are those that cater to the city's own population and so do not generate profit from "outside" customers. Examples of nonbasic activities include local newspapers, local bakeries and restaurants, schools, and local government.

The fundamental determinant of cities' growth in population, employment, and income in the world's core countries is the percentage of their economies that is devoted to basic activities. The prosperity generated by basic economic activities leads to increased employment in nonbasic activities to satisfy the demand for housing, utilities, retailing, personal services, and other services. The incomes generated by the combination of basic and nonbasic economic activities allow for higher potential tax yields, which can be used to improve public utilities, roads, schools, health services, recreational amenities, and other infrastructures. These activities are also nonbasic, but they all serve to improve the efficiency and attractiveness of the city for further rounds of investment in basic economic activities. The whole process is one of cumulative causation (Chapter 7), in which a spiral buildup of advantages is enjoyed by a particular place as a result of the development of external economies, agglomeration effects, and localization economies.

This process is by no means uniform across space, even in the core countries. Canada, with an urban system that has developed according to a process called **metropolitanism**, provides an interesting illustration of this. According to this explanation, the cities that have been able to dominate the Canadian urban hierarchy have done so because of their ability to control the economy of the heartland. Cities in this favoured position, such as Toronto, have been able to develop into manufacturing and service centres of national dominance through the upward spiral of cumulative forces described in Figure 10.19. However, those centres of the periphery may never be able to develop beyond their initial function as resource centres designed to exploit the staples of this country's hinterland (**Figure 10.20**). This is because the economic investment that they would need to do this is channelled to the metropolitan centres of the heartland instead.

Certainly, cities in the periphery have responded to the pulse of global demand for their resources and have been the focus of inward investment to exploit such

basic functions: economic activities that provide income from sales to customers beyond city limits

nonbasic functions: economic activities that serve a city's own population

metropolitanism: the process by which the economic growth of a city enables it to attain a position of national dominance and, in so doing, creates the geographical structure of a metropolis and hinterland

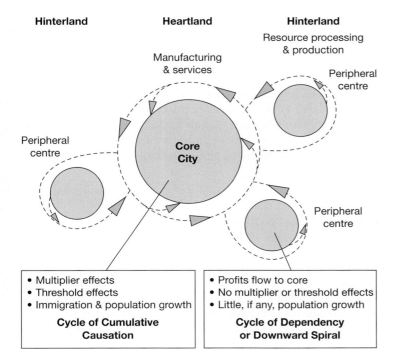

Figure 10.20 Metropolitanism
Urban growth in Canada's heartland cities has occurred through a process of upward cumulative causation. It has also benefited from the resources of the hinterland. In fact, as this illustration shows, the ability of the heartland cities to profit from the economic surpluses of the hinterland centres has prevented the latter from ever reaching self-sustained growth.

materials. However, the profits of those investments have seldom remained in the periphery, and population—unless directly working in resource extraction—is not attracted to the limited economic potential of single-industry towns. In this manner, the spiral of cumulative causation rarely begins, and Canada's resource towns remain tributary to those of the heartland. Therefore, the core continually creates the peripheral spaces of Canada and maintains the relative size and function of Canada's urban places.

Of course, this model is too simple to be an entirely adequate explanation of the differential growth of Canadian cities and their economies. The growth of Vancouver, a peripheral resource town in its early years, attests to the ability of some peripheral centres to take off economically. A greater understanding of the underlying causes of such growth would be an undoubted asset to Canadian economic and urban policy-makers.

Deindustrialization and Decentralization

The logic of economic development does not always work uniformly in the direction of population concentration and urban growth. The forces of cumulative causation are refocused from time to time as new technologies, new resources, and new opportunities alter the balance of comparative advantages enjoyed by particular places within the world's core and semiperipheral countries. New rounds of urbanization are initiated in the places most suited to the new circumstances, while those least suited are likely to suffer a spiral of *deindustrialization* and urban decline. Deindustrialization involves a decline in industrial employment in core regions as firms scale back their activities in response to lower levels of profitability (see Chapter 7). Such adversity particularly affected such cities as Pittsburgh and Cleveland (United States), Sheffield and Liverpool (United Kingdom), Lille (France), and Liège (Belgium)—places where heavy manufacturing constituted a key economic sector. Cities like these suffered substantial reductions in employment throughout the 1970s and 1980s. During the same period, better and more flexible transport and communications networks allowed many industries to choose from a broader range of potential locations. The result has been a *decentralization* of jobs and people from larger to smaller cities within the urban systems of core countries. In some cases, routine production activities relocated to smaller metropolitan areas or to rural areas with low labour costs and more hospitable business climates. In other cases, these activities moved overseas—as part of the new international division of labour (see Chapter 2)—or were eliminated entirely.

These trends toward deindustrialization and decentralization have been intensified by the dampening effects of *agglomeration diseconomies* (Chapter 7) on the growth of larger metropolitan areas. The negative effects of urban size and density, agglomeration diseconomies include noise, air pollution, increased crime, commuting costs, the costs of inflated land and housing prices, traffic congestion, and crowded port and railroad facilities. They also include higher taxes levied to rebuild decaying infrastructure and to support services and amenities previously considered unnecessary—traffic police, city planners, and homeless shelters, for example.

Counterurbanization

counterurbanization: the net loss of population from cities to smaller towns and rural areas

The combination of deindustrialization in core manufacturing regions, agglomeration diseconomies in major metropolitan areas, and the improved accessibility of smaller towns and rural areas can give rise to the phenomenon of counterurbanization. **Counterurbanization** occurs when cities experience a net loss of population to smaller towns and rural areas. This process results in the deconcentration of population within an urban system. This is, in fact, what happened in Canada, the United States, Britain, Japan, and many other developed countries in the 1970s and early 1980s. Metropolitan growth slowed dramatically, while the growth rates of small- and medium-sized towns and of some rural areas increased.

In Canada, urban growth also shifted from the industrial heartland of southern Ontario and Quebec to the western provinces. Overall, the effect of counterurbanization was for population to be redistributed down the urban hierarchy. However, it was a short-lived phenomenon, coming to an abrupt end with the severe recession that hit Canada in the 1980s. One of the features of the subsequent economic recovery was a renewed growth in the major centres of the urban hierarchy.

Counterurbanization was a major reversal of long-standing trends, but it seems to have been a temporary adjustment rather than a permanent change. The globalization of the economy and the growth of postindustrial activities in revamped and expanded metropolitan settings have restored the trend toward the concentration of population within urban systems. Most of the cities that were declining fast in the 1970s are now either recovering (for example, New York and London) or bottoming out (for example, Paris and Chicago). Most of those that were growing only slowly (such as Tokyo and Barcelona) are now expanding more quickly, though counterurbanization is still underway in a few cities (such as Madrid, Milan, and Rome).

The Unintended Metropolis

Urban growth processes in the world's peripheral regions have been entirely different from those in core regions. In contrast to the self-sustaining urban growth of the world's core regions, the urbanization of peripheral regions has been a consequence of demographic growth that has preceded economic development. Although the demographic transition is a fairly recent phenomenon in the peripheral regions of the world (see Chapter 3), it generated large increases in population well in advance of any significant levels of industrialization or of rural economic development.

For the mainly rural populations of peripheral countries, the result was more and more of worse and worse. Problems of agricultural development (see Chapter 8) meant that fast-growing rural populations faced an apparently hopeless future of drudgery and poverty. Emigration provided one potential safety valve, but as the frontiers of the world-system closed out, the more affluent core countries put up barriers to immigration. The only option for the growing numbers of impoverished rural residents was—and still is—to move to the larger towns and cities, where at least there is the hope of employment and the prospect of access to schools, health clinics, piped water, and the kinds of public facilities and services that are often unavailable in rural regions. Cities also have the lure of modernization and the appeal of consumer goods—attractions that are now directly beamed into rural areas through satellite TV. Overall, the metropolises of the periphery have absorbed four out of five of the 1.2 billion city dwellers added to the world's population since 1970.

Rural migrants have poured into cities out of desperation and hope, rather than being drawn by jobs and opportunities. Because these migration streams have consisted disproportionately of teenagers and young adults, an important additional component of urban growth has followed—exceptionally high rates of natural population increase. In most peripheral countries, the rate of natural increase of the population in cities exceeds that of net in-migration. On average, about 60 percent of urban population growth in peripheral countries is attributable to natural increase.

The consequence of all this urban population growth has been described as **overurbanization**, which occurs when cities grow more rapidly than the jobs and housing they can sustain. In such circumstances, urban growth produces instant slums—shacks set on unpaved streets, often with open sewers and no basic utilities. The shacks are constructed out of any material that comes to hand, such as planks, cardboard, tarpaper, thatch, mud, and corrugated iron. Such is the pressure of in-migration that many of these instant slums are squatter settlements, built illegally by families who are desperate for shelter. **Squatter settlements** are residential

overurbanization: a condition in which cities grow more rapidly than the jobs and housing they can sustain

squatter settlements: residential developments on land that is neither owned nor rented by its occupants

developments on land that is neither owned nor rented by its occupants. Squatter settlements are not always slums, but many of them are.

Collectively, it is these slums and squatter settlements that have to absorb the unprecedented rates of urbanization in the megacities of the periphery. As we shall see in the next chapter, this often leads to severe problems of social disorganization and environmental degradation. Nevertheless, many neighbourhoods are able to develop self-help networks and organizations that form the basis of community amid dauntingly poor and crowded cities.

Frontier Urbanization

Urban growth in the periphery is not all channelled into megacities and older urban centres. Urbanization can be a consequence of the commercial exploitation of regions that are only just becoming incorporated, selectively, into the world-system. Historically, many parts of Canada's periphery were first developed by frontier boomtowns, such as Barkerville, British Columbia (**Figure 10.21**). These centres grew up almost overnight on the site of newly discovered resources and are now largely abandoned and forgotten. The best contemporary example is the urbanization of the Amazon rain forest, where global economic forces have created frontier towns and cities to organize the local exploitation of gold, hardwood, rubber, and land. Here is an extract from the logbook of John Browder, an American researcher, who gives a graphic impression of this frontier urbanization:[7]

> No map in my possession showed a town called Rolim de Moura in the Federal Territory of Rondônia. Yet I was assured . . . by several prominent mahogany exporters in Curitiba, São Paulo and Rio de Janeiro that, although *meia precária* (primitive), this town did indeed exist. . . . [This was] the last 65-kilometer leg of a 3,000 kilometer journey from Belém, at the mouth of the Amazon River, to the frontier town of Rolim de Moura, *capital mundial de mogno* ("world capital of mahogany").

Since 1950, the population of northern Brazil has increased from fewer than 2 million to nearly 10 million. Over the same period, the urban population of the region has increased from just over 30 percent of the total population to just under 60 percent. In 1960, the region had only 22 towns of 5000 inhabitants or more, only 2 of which were larger than 100 000. By 1991, 133 towns existed of 5000 or more inhabitants, including 8 towns of at least 100 000 and 2 towns of 1 million

Figure 10.21 Frontier urbanization Established when gold was discovered in the mountains in the nineteenth century, the frontier town of Barkerville, British Columbia, now lies abandoned.

[7]John Browder and Brian J. Godfrey, *Rainforest Cities*. New York: Columbia University Press, 1996.

or more. The growth rate of some of these towns has been phenomenal. Porto Velho, for example, the capital of the land-rush state of Rondônia, grew from just 48 839 in 1970 to 229 410 in 1991, an annual growth rate of over 7.5 percent. Remote Boa Vista, capital of gold-rich Roraima, grew by almost 10 percent a year.

The main function of this region of Brazil has always been to provide raw materials and new markets for national, and sometimes global, economic expansion. The Brazilian government has encouraged frontier urbanization through the construction of major infrastructure projects, such as the Trans-Amazon highway, and through the creation of free-trade zones in frontier cities, such as Manaus. More recently, state corporations have created planned company towns as part of their resource extraction megadevelopments for which the Brazilian Amazon is famous. Other towns have appeared spontaneously as smaller businesses based on extractive forest industries, crop processing, regional commerce, auto repair, banking, and other services have been established throughout the frontier region.

As with the unintended metropolises of the periphery, the population growth of these frontier towns is fuelled mainly by poor migrants. Drawn to frontier towns and cities by the prospects of economic opportunities, they number so many that up to one-third or one-half wind up having to survive through informal-sector activities. As a result, frontier urbanization is characterized by the same problems of shanty and squatter housing as elsewhere in the periphery. Official statistics for Belém, for example, show that about 15 percent of the city's dwellings in 1991 consisted of squatter housing. Unofficial statistics, compiled by researchers and journalists, suggest that about 60 percent of the housing in the city, accommodating about 450 000 people, is a product of spontaneous, unregulated settlement in low-lying shantytowns that are subject to frequent flooding. Not surprisingly, frontier urbanization is also characterized by acute but widespread problems of disease.

CONCLUSION

Urbanization is one of the most important geographical phenomena. Cities can be seedbeds of economic development and cultural innovation. Cities and groups of cities also organize space—not just the territory immediately around them but, in some cases, national and even international spaces. The causes and consequences of urbanization are very different in different parts of the world. For example, the urban experience of the world's peripheral regions stands in sharp contrast to that of the developed core regions. This contrast is a reflection of some of the demographic, economic, and political factors that we have explored in previous chapters.

Much of the developed world has become almost completely urbanized, with highly organized systems of cities. Today, levels of urbanization are high throughout the world's core countries, while rates of urbanization are relatively low. At the top of the urban hierarchies of the world's core regions are world cities, such as London, New York, Tokyo, Paris, and Zürich, which have become control centres for the flows of information, cultural products, and finance that collectively sustain the economic and cultural globalization of the world. In doing so, they help to consolidate the hegemony of the world's core regions.

Few of the metropolises of the periphery, however, are world cities that occupy key roles in the organization of global economics and culture. Rather, they operate as connecting links between provincial towns and villages and the world economy. They have innumerable economic, social, and cultural linkages to their provinces on one side and to major world cities on the other. Almost all peripheral countries, meanwhile, are experiencing high rates of urbanization, with forecast growth of unprecedented speed and unmatched size. In many peripheral and semiperipheral regions, current rates of urbanization have given rise to unintended metropolises and fears of "uncontrollable urbanization," with urban "danger zones" where "work" means anything that contributes to survival. The result, as we shall see in Chapter 11, is that these unintended metropolises are quite different from the cities of the core as places in which to live and work.

MAIN POINTS REVISITED

- **The urban areas of the world are the lynchpins of human geographies at the local, regional, and global scales.**
  Towns and cities are engines of economic development and centres of cultural innovation, social transformation, and political change. They now account for almost half the world's population.

- **The earliest urbanization developed independently in the various hearth areas of the first agricultural revolution.**
  The very first region of independent urbanism, in the Middle East, produced successive generations of urbanized world-empires, including those of Greece, Rome, and Byzantium.

- **The expansion of trade around the world, associated with colonialism and imperialism, established numerous gateway cities.**
  European powers founded or developed literally thousands of towns as they extended their trading networks and established their colonies. The great majority of the towns were ports that served as control centres commanding entrance to, and exit from, their particular country or region.

- **The Industrial Revolution generated new kinds of cities and many more of them.**
  Industrial economies could be organized only with the large pools of labour; the transportation networks; the physical infrastructure of factories, warehouses, stores, and offices; and the consumer markets provided by cities. As industrialization spread throughout Europe in the first half of the nineteenth century and then to other parts of the world, urbanization increased at a faster pace.

- **Today, the single most important aspect of world urbanization from a geographical perspective is the striking difference in trends and projections between the core regions and the peripheral regions.**
  In 1950, two-thirds of the world's urban population was concentrated in the more developed countries of the core economies. Since then, the world's urban population has increased threefold, the bulk of the growth having taken place in the less developed countries of the periphery.

- **Cities form linked networks, known as *urban systems,* which determine the importance of component cities of the system and organize these cities into their various functional niches within an economy.**
  A hallmark of the integrated spatial economies found in the developed countries of the core, an urban system is a network of cities in which each city serves the needs of its immediate region and larger cities (defined in terms of their functions) also meet the more specialized demands of a wider area.

- **Canada's urban system is the product of processes that operate in both core and peripheral regions.**
  The development of this country's urban system is the result of metropolitanism, a process in which the cities of Canada's heartland have been able to grow at the expense of cities in the hinterland (or, as it is sometimes called, the periphery).

- **A small number of "world cities," most of them located within the core regions of the world-system, occupy key roles in the organization of global economics and culture.**
  At the top of a global urban system, these cities experience growth largely as a result of their role as key nodes in the world economy. World cities have become the control centres for the flows of information, cultural products, and finance that collectively sustain the economic and cultural globalization of the world.

- **The populations of many of the largest cities in the periphery have a doubling time of only 10 to 15 years.**
  The doubling time of a city's population is the time needed for it to double in size at current growth rates.

- **Many of the megacities of the periphery are primate and exhibit a high degree of centrality within their urban systems.**
  Primacy occurs when the population of the largest city in an urban system is disproportionately large in relation to the second- and third-largest cities in that system. *Centrality* refers to the functional dominance of cities within an urban system. Cities that account for a disproportionately high share of economic, political, and cultural activities have a high degree of centrality within their urban system.

Key Terms

basic functions   (p. 461)
central place theory   (p. 452)
central places   (p. 452)
centrality   (p. 457)
colonial cities   (p. 447)
counterurbanization   (p. 462)
economic base   (p. 460)
gateway city   (p. 444)

informal sector   (p. 460)
megacities   (p. 459)
metropolitanism   (p. 461)
nonbasic functions   (p. 461)
overurbanization   (p. 463)
primacy   (p. 456)
range   (p. 453)
rank-size rule   (p. 456)

shock city   (p. 446)
squatter settlements   (p. 463)
threshold   (p. 453)
urban ecology   (p. 440)
urban form   (p. 439)
urban system   (p. 439)
urbanism   (p. 440)

Additional Reading

Abrahamsun, M. *Global Cities.* New York: Oxford University Press, 2004.

Angotti, T. *Metropolis 2000.* New York: Routledge, 1993.

Bourne, L.S., and D.F. Ley (eds.). *The Changing Social Geography of Canadian Cities.* Montreal and Kingston: McGill–Queen's University Press, 1993.

Brunn, S., and J.F. Williams (eds.). *Cities of the World,* 2nd ed. New York: Harper Collins, 1993.

Bunting, T., and P. Filion (eds.). *Canadian Cities in Transition: The Twenty-First Century,* 2nd ed. Toronto: Oxford University Press, 2000.

Chandler, T. *Four Thousand Years of Urban Growth: An Historical Census*. Washington, DC: Worldwatch Institute, 1987.

Gugler, J. (ed.). *Cities in the Developing World: Issues, Theory, and Policy*. Oxford: Oxford University Press, 1997.

Hall, P. *Cities of Tomorrow*. New York: Blackwell, 1988.

King, A.D. *Urbanism, Colonialism, and the World Economy: Cultural and Spatial Foundations of the World Urban System*. New York: Routledge, 1991.

Knox, P.L. *Urbanization: An Introduction to Urban Geography*. Englewood Cliffs, NJ: Prentice Hall, 1994.

Knox, P.L., and P.J. Taylor (eds.). *World Cities in a World-System*. Cambridge: Cambridge University Press, 1995.

Merrifield, A. *Metromarxism*. London: Routledge, 2002.

Potter, R.B., and S. Lloyd-Evans. *The City in the Developing World*. Harlow, UK: Addison Wesley Longman, 1998.

Sassen, S. *Cities in a World Economy*. Thousand Oaks, CA: Pine Forge Press, 2000.

Short, J.R., and Y.H. Kim. *Globalization and the City*. New York: Addison Wesley Longman, 1999.

United Nations Centre for Human Settlements (HABITAT). *An Urbanizing World: Global Report on Human Settlements, 1996*. Oxford: Oxford University Press, 1996.

World Resources Institute. *World Resources 1996–97: The Urban Environment*. New York: Oxford University Press, 1996.

Exercises

Here you will find exercises and activities for each chapter. Unplugged exercises help you review chapter discussions, and pose ideas for your own human geography research. On the Companion Website exercises will require you have access to the internet.

Unplugged

1. Canada, like most core countries, is already highly urbanized and has a relatively low rate of urbanization. Nevertheless, some Canadian cities have been growing much faster than others. Which have been the fastest-growing Canadian cities in recent times, and what reasons can you suggest for their relatively rapid growth? *Hint:* Look at the census published by Statistics Canada (**www.statcan.ca**).

2. From census volumes in your library, find out the population of the town or city you know best. Do the same for every census year, going back from 1991 to 1981, 1971, and so on, all the way back to 1851. Then, plot these populations on a simple graph. What explanations can you offer for the pattern that the graph reveals? Now, draw a larger version of the same graph, annotating it to show the landmark events that might have influenced the city's growth (or decline).

3. The following cities all have populations in excess of 2 million. How many of them could you locate on a world map? Their size reflects a certain degree of importance, at least within their regional economy. What can you find out about each? Compile for each a 50-word description that explains its chief industries and a little of its history.

Poona	Ibadan	Recife
Bangalore	Turin	Ankara

4. "Were you ever in Quebec, Stowing timber on the deck. . . ." So run the lines of an old sea shanty, referring, in this verse, to Quebec City, a colonial gateway city on the St. Lawrence. Find out about the commodities and manufactured goods that it imported and exported in the nineteenth century and about the origin and destination of these imports and exports. Which geographical concepts do you consider to be useful in explaining these facts?

On the Companion Website

This book has its own Companion Website where you will find additional resources—maps, photographs, data—as well as exercises and activities that relate to each chapter. To complete the Companion Website exercises, go to **www.pearsoned.ca/knox**. The following is a summary of the types of exercises created for this chapter.

1. The exercises for this chapter will help you to better understand the forces of urbanization. Using the internet, we examine some major world cities, such as Paris, London, and Washington, DC. City development was not carefully controlled but instead was driven by the desire for land and by the hunger of the huge markets that arose in that quest. U.S. cities are, perhaps to a greater extent than anywhere else in the world, the products of unrestrained capitalism. In this light, we examine the growth of Los Angeles and Atlanta. We also compare and contrast regional growth during different time frames, we survey how American cities tend to distinguish themselves from their peers, we investigate counterurbanization, and we explore frontier urbanization in the United States.

2. The Audio Interview, Interview with Carlos Teixeira, that accompanies this chapter has been conducted to highlight the contribution of Canadian scholars to the study of urban geography, and to the importance of immigration as part of the growth of cities and urban ecology discussed in this chapter. In addition, you will hear about the fascination of geography, and the insights into real world problems that geography provides. You will find a link to the Audio Interview, interview summary, and questions on the Companion Website for this chapter.

City Spaces:
Urban Structure

Urban sprawl in Winnipeg, Manitoba

The neighborhood shopping street is at the end of the block. It is a narrow lane, barely wide enough for one car to pass, and is lined on both sides with small shops whose fronts open widely to the street . . . and invite customers in. There are more and more boutiques and other new arrivals on the street, including an extremely busy supermarket, but there are still quite a few of the older establishments left as well: fishmongers, rice sellers, a noodle maker, a cracker bakery, a cubby-hole that sells only buttons, a glazier's shop, and countless other, small places for the local market. Tucked away to the side is the neighborhood's Buddhist temple. It is a new building but designed in a traditional style, and has a welcome open space for community fairs and other gatherings in front, and a lovely Japanese garden at the back. The garden is such a contrast to the harsh lines and bustling activity of the surrounding city that at times it seems to me to be the most secluded and contemplative place in the world.[1]

We can recognize in this description of a Tokyo neighbourhood several elements that are fairly common in central cities throughout the world's core regions: the mixture of old stores, new boutiques, and local supermarket, for example. However, some elements are unique: the noodle maker and the Buddhist temple with its Japanese garden. In this chapter, we turn our attention to the internal dynamics of cities, looking at the ways in which patterns and processes tend to vary according to the type of city and its history. In many ways, the most striking contrasts are to be found between the cities of the core regions and those of the periphery. The evolution of the unintended metropolis of the periphery has been very different from the evolution of metropolitan areas in the world's core regions. The problems they face are also very different.

MAIN POINTS

- The typical North American city is structured around a central business district (CBD); a transitional zone; suburbs; secondary business districts and commercial strips; industrial districts; and, in larger metropolitan areas, edge cities.
- The overall structure of North American cities is shaped primarily by competition for territory and location. In general, all categories of land users—commercial and industrial, as well as residential—compete for the most convenient and accessible locations within the city.
- Cities experiencing high rates of in-migration tend to become structured into a series of concentric zones of neighbourhoods of different ethnicity, demographic composition, and social status through processes of invasion and succession.

[1]Roman Cybriwsky, *Tokyo*. London: Belhaven Press, 1991, p. 3.

- In cities where growth has been less dominated by successive waves of immigrant ethnic groups, neighbourhood patterns tend to be structured around the development of industrial corridors and high-class residential corridors.

- Urban structure varies a good deal from one region of the world to another because of the influence of history, culture, and the different roles that cities have played within the world-system.

- Geographers are interested in the distinctive physical features of urban landscapes because they can be read as multi-layered texts that show how cities have developed, how they are changing, and how people's values and intentions take expression in urban form.

- The most acute problems of the postindustrial cities of the world's core regions are localized in the central city areas, which have borne the brunt of restructuring from an industrial to a postindustrial economy.

- Canadian cities are different from U.S. cities.

- The problems of the cities of the periphery stem from the way in which their demographic growth has outstripped their economic growth.

- Cities are created as "places" and can become "place makers."

URBAN STRUCTURE AND LAND USE

The internal organization of cities reflects the way that they function, both to bring people and activities together and to sort them out into neighbourhoods and functional subareas. The simple stereotype of the North American city, for example, is based on several main elements of land use. Traditionally, the very centre of the city has been the principal hub of shops and offices, together with some of the major institutional land uses, such as the city hall, libraries, and museums. This centre, known as the **central business district**, or **CBD** (**Figure 11.1**), is a city's nucleus of commercial land uses. It always contains the densest concentration of shops, offices, and warehouses and the tallest group of nonresidential buildings in the city. It usually develops at the nodal point of transportation routes so that it also contains bus stations, railway terminals, and hotels. The CBD typically is surrounded by a zone of mixed land uses: warehouses, small factories and workshops, specialized stores, apartment buildings, and older residential neighbourhoods (**Figure 11.2**). This zone is often referred to as the **zone in transition** because of its mixture of

central business district (CBD): the central nucleus of commercial land uses in a city

zone in transition: area of mixed commercial and residential land uses surrounding the CBD

Figure 11.1   Downtown Edmonton from the air   This photograph of Edmonton's central business district (CBD) shows the concentration of high-rise buildings that is typical of CBDs in North America. In Edmonton, as in other major cities, the CBD originally grew up around the point of maximum accessibility: near railway stations and the intersection of the city's principal road and water transportation routes.

Figure 11.2   The zone in transition
This photograph of stores along the western end of Queen Street in Toronto shows part of the zone in transition. In many North American cities, the CBD is surrounded by such a zone, which consists of older neighbourhoods with mixed land uses, parts of which are in long-term decline and parts of which are undergoing redevelopment.

growth, change, and decline. Beyond this zone are residential neighbourhoods, suburbs of various ages and different social and ethnic compositions.

As cities have grown larger and become more complex, this simple stereotype has had to accommodate additional elements. *Secondary business districts* and *commercial strips* have emerged in the suburbs to cater to neighbourhood shopping and service needs. *Industrial districts* have developed around large factories and airports, and in larger metropolitan areas, edge cities have emerged as new suburban hubs of shops and offices that overshadow the old CBD. **Edge cities** are nodal concentrations of shopping and office space that are situated on the outer fringes of metropolitan areas, typically near major highway intersections. Meanwhile, other changes have occurred in more central locations as older buildings and neighbourhoods have been restructured to meet new needs. One of the most striking of these changes has been the gentrification of older, centrally located, working-class communities (**Figure 11.3**).

Gentrification occurs when higher-income households, seeking the character and convenience of less expensive and centrally located residences, move into neighbourhoods previously occupied by working-class, lower-income households. While gentrification can displace original occupants, it can also result in the physical renovation and upgrading of housing.

edge cities: nodal concentrations of shopping and office space that are situated on the outer fringes of metropolitan areas, typically near major highway intersections

gentrification: the movement into older, centrally located working-class neighbourhoods by higher-income households seeking the character and convenience of less-expensive and well-located residences

Figure 11.3   Gentrification   A newly-renovated row of townhouses in Halifax, Nova Scotia, where the process of gentrification has redeveloped an older neighbourhood that had previously been occupied by lower-income households.

congregation: the territorial and residential clustering of specific groups or subgroups of people

minority groups: population subgroups that are seen—or that see themselves—as somehow different from the general population

segregation: the spatial separation of specific population subgroups within a wider population

Figure 11.4   Congregation and separation—Chinatown, Montreal
In most larger cities, there is a patchwork of distinctive neighbourhoods that results from processes of congregation and segregation. Most distinctive of all are neighbourhoods of ethnic minorities, such as the Chinatowns and Little Italys, found in a number of Canadian cities.

Figure 11.5   Separation and congregation—Loyalist neighbourhood Belfast, Northern Ireland
Congregation is an important placemaking activity. It enables group identity to be established and preserved in relation to "other" people and places.

Territoriality, Congregation, and Segregation

In cities, as at other geographical scales, territoriality provides a means of establishing and preserving group membership and identity. The first step in forming group identity is to define "others" in an exclusionary and stereotypical way. **Congregation**—the territorial and residential clustering of specific groups or subgroups of people—enables group identity to be consolidated in relation to people and places outside the group. Congregation is thus a place-making activity and an important basis for urban structure and land use. It is particularly important in situations in which there are one or more distinctive minority groups. Defined in relation to a general population or host community, **minority groups** are population subgroups that are seen—or that see themselves—as somehow different from the general population. Their defining characteristics can be based on race, language, religion, nationality, caste, sexual orientation, or lifestyle.

Several specific advantages of congregation exist for minority groups:

- Congregation provides a means of cultural preservation. It allows religious and cultural practices to be maintained and strengthens group identity through daily involvement in particular routines and ways of life. Particularly important in this regard is the way that clustering fosters within-group marriage and kinship networks.

- Congregation helps minimize conflict and provides defence against "outsiders."

- Congregation provides a place where mutual support can be established through minority institutions, businesses, social networks, and welfare organizations.

- Congregation helps establish a power base in relation to the host society. This power base can be democratic, organized through local elections, or it can take the form of a territorial heartland for insurrectionary groups.

Congregation is not always voluntary, of course. Host populations are also impelled by territoriality, and they may respond to social and cultural differences by *discrimination* against minority groups (**Figure 11.4**). Discrimination can also have a strong territorial basis, the objective being to restrict the territory of minority groups and to resist their assimilation into the host society. This resistance can take a variety of forms. Social hostility and the voicing of "keep out" attitudes are probably the most widespread, although other forms of discrimination can have more pronounced spatial effects. These effects include exclusion and prejudice in local labour markets, the manipulation of private land and housing markets, the steering of capital investment away from minority areas, and the institutionalization of discrimination through the practices and spatial policies of public agencies.

The combined result of congregation and discrimination is **segregation**, the spatial separation of specific subgroups within a wider population. Segregation varies a great deal, both in intensity and in form, depending on the relative degree and combination of congregation and discrimination (**Figure 11.5**). Geographers and demographers have developed indexes of segregation that measure the relative spatial concentration of population subgroups. Comparisons are often problematic, however, because of the influence of spatial scale on the computation and construction of such indexes. In terms of form, geographers have identified three principal situations:

- *Enclaves,* in which tendencies toward congregation and discrimination are longstanding but dominated by internal cohesion and identity. The Jewish districts of many of today's cities in Europe and the eastern United States are examples of enclaves.

- *Ghettos,* which are also long-standing but are more the product of discrimination than of congregation. Examples are the segregation of African Americans and Hispanics in U.S. cities.

- *Colonies,* which may result from congregation, discrimination, or both but in relatively weak and short-lasting ways. Their persistence over time therefore depends on the continuing arrival of new minority-group members. For example, in the nineteenth century, Canadian cities contained distinctive colonies of Irish immigrants, which have now all but disappeared.

Competing for Space in North American Cities

The overall structure of North American cities is shaped primarily by competition for territory and location. Individual households and population groups compete for the most socially desirable residences and neighbourhoods, while all categories of land users—commercial and industrial, as well as residential—compete for the most convenient and accessible locations within the city. Geographers draw on several different perspectives in looking at these aspects of competition among urban land users.

Four are particularly useful:

- an economic perspective based on the concept of accessibility
- an economic perspective that emphasizes the functional links between types of land uses
- a sociocultural perspective that examines the congregation and segregation of groups of people
- a historical perspective that emphasizes the influence of transport corridors

We will now consider each of these four perspectives in turn, but before we do, it is also worth noting that each of them owes their intellectual origins to the approach to geographical study known as *locational analysis* (sometimes also known as *spatial analysis*) that was developed in the 1960s (as we saw in Chapter 1), as part of what was then know as the "New geography." In the same way that we saw with both industrial location (Chapter 7) and agricultural land use (Chapter 8), many distinguished geographers have endeavoured to study urban structure and land use using locational theories that state that the use of space is shaped by economic or social activities.

What this also means, of course, is that when the economy or society changes, then the rationale for a particular use of space changes. In economies or societies where people compete in some way for resources (whether they be tangible, such as food, or intangible, such as accessibility), then the use of space becomes allocated according to some principle that flows from that type of economy or society (whether it be by price competition in a free market economy, or by government policy). In other words, as we have seen in Chapter 1, our economies and societies create "space"—and urban structures provide another example of that finding. Certainly, these four perspectives, as we shall see, provide important illustrations of how changes in the relative importance of various activities can affect urban structures.

Accessibility and Land Use   Most urban land users want to maximize the *utility* that they derive from a particular location. The utility of a specific place or location refers to its usefulness to particular persons or groups. The price they are prepared to pay for different locations—the bid-rent—will be a reflection of this utility. In general, utility will be a function of *accessibility*. Commercial land users want to be accessible to one another, to markets, and to workers; private residents want to be accessible to jobs, amenities, and friends; public institutions want to be accessible to their clients. In an idealized city built on an isotropic surface, the point of maximum accessibility is the city centre. An **isotropic surface** is a hypothetical, uniform plane—flat and with no variations in its physical attributes. Under these conditions, accessibility falls off steadily with distance from the city centre. Likewise, utility falls off, but at different rates for different land users. The result is a tendency for concentric zones of different mixes of land use (**Figure 11.6**).

One counterintuitive implication of this model is that the poorest households will end up occupying the periphery of the city. Although this is true in some parts

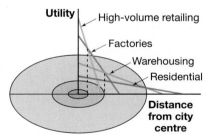

Figure 11.6   Accessibility, bid-rent, and urban structure   Competition for accessible sites near the city centre is an important determinant of land-use patterns. Different land users are prepared to pay different amounts—the bid-rent—for locations at various distances from the city centre. The result is a tendency for a concentric pattern of land uses.   (*Source:* Reprinted with permission of Prentice Hall, from P. Knox, *Urbanization*, © 1994, p. 99.)

isotropic surface: a hypothetical, uniform plane—flat and with no variations in its physical attributes

of the world, we know that in core countries, the farthest suburbs are the territory of wealthier households, while the poor occupy more accessible locations closer to city centres. Some modification of the assumptions is clearly required. In this case, we must assume that wealthier households trade off the convenience of accessibility for the greater utility of larger amounts of (relatively cheap) suburban space. Poorer households, unable to afford the recurrent costs of transportation, must trade off living space for accessibility to jobs so that they end up in high-density areas, at expensive locations near their low-wage jobs. Because of the presumed trade-off between accessibility and living space, this urban land-use model is often referred to as a *trade-off model*.

Functional Clustering: Multiple Nuclei   The multiple-nuclei model of urban land use is based on the observation that some activities attract one another, while others repel one another. Without denying the concentric patterns that result from principles of distance, accessibility, and utility, geographers recognize that certain categories of land use are drawn together into functional clusters, or nuclei, while others tend to repel one another. At the broadest scale, economic relationships draw manufacturing, transportation, and warehousing together. These activities need to be in proximity to one another so that each can function as effectively and efficiently as possible. Similarly, functional relationships exist between these land uses and blue-collar housing, which tends to result in their mutual attraction. Conversely, upper-middle-class housing is repelled by industrial and working-class districts.

We can see the same principles operating at a more detailed scale. Within the sphere of commercial land use in downtown areas, for example, fashion clothing and shoe stores are drawn together near larger department stores, all seeking to exploit the same pool of potential shoppers. All these high-end retail land uses are compatible with the large commercial hotels and professional office buildings that also seek busy and accessible locations. However, they all tend to be repelled by certain other commercial land uses, such as meat and vegetable markets, budget stores, and X-rated businesses. The result is that urban land use becomes spatially segregated, with nodes or nuclei of different groupings of land users (**Figure 11.7**).

Social and Ethnic Clustering: Social Ecology   Just as different categories of land use attract and repel one another, so do different social and ethnic groups. The third model of land use is based on an ecological perspective developed by Chicago School sociologists Park and Burgess to explain this phenomenon, with special reference to cities in the United States whose rapid growth has been fuelled by streams of migrants and immigrants with very different backgrounds. It is based on the idea of city neighbourhoods being structured by the "invasion" of successive waves of migrants and immigrants.

When immigrants first arrive in the city looking for work and a place to live, they will have little choice but to cluster in the cheapest accommodation, typically to be found in the zone in transition around the CBD. The classic example is provided by Chicago in the 1920s and 1930s. Immigrants from Scandinavia, Germany, Italy, Ireland, Poland, Bohemia (now part of the Czech Republic), and Lithuania established themselves in Chicago's low-rent areas, the only places they could afford. By congregating together in these areas, however, immigrants accomplished several things: they were able to establish a sense of security; to continue speaking their native language; to have familiar churches or synagogues, restaurants, bakeries, butcher shops, and taverns; and to support their own community newspapers and clubs. These immigrants were joined in the city's zone in transition by African-American migrants from the South, who also established their own neighbourhoods and communities. In Chicago, as in other U.S. cities of the period, the various ethnic groups formed a patchwork or mosaic of communities encircling the CBD.

These ethnic communities lasted from one to three generations, after which they started to break up. Many of the younger, city-born individuals did not feel the need for the security and familiarity of ethnic neighbourhoods. Gradually, increasing

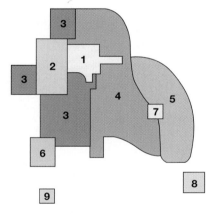

1. Central business district
2. Wholesale light manufacturing
3. Low-income residential
4. Medium-income residential
5. High-income residential
6. Heavy manufacturing
7. Outlying business district
8. Residential suburb
9. Industrial suburb

Figure 11.7   Multiple-nuclei model of urban land use   When cities reach a certain size, the traditional downtown (1) is no longer sufficient to serve the commercial needs of the whole city, and so additional nodes of shops and offices emerge in outlying districts (7). Functional groupings of related activities of other kinds—manufacturing (2, 6), wholesaling (2), and so on—also tend to develop, creating multiple nuclei of economic activities around which the city is organized. (*Source*: C.D. Harris and E.L. Ullman, "The Nature of Cities." *Annals of the American Academy of Political and Social Science* 242(1), 1945, fig. 5.)

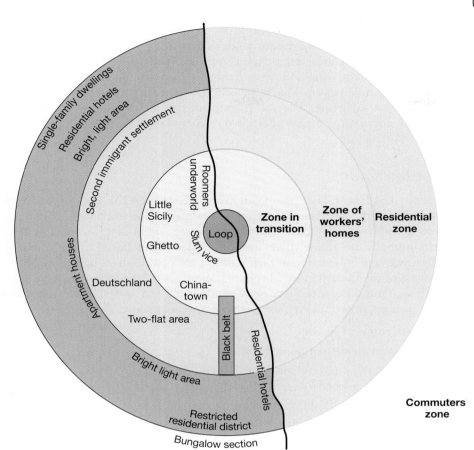

Little
Sicily

Ghetto

Deutschland

Two-flat area

Roomers
underworld

Slum vice

Chinatown

Loop

Zone in
transition

Black belt

Residential hotels

Zone of
workers'
homes

Residential
zone

Single-family dwellings

Residential hotels

Bright, light area

Second immigrant settlement

Apartment houses

Bright light area

Restricted
residential district

Bungalow section

**Commuters
zone**

**Figure 11.8   The ecological model of
urban land use: Chicago in the 1920s**
Competition between members of different migrant and immigrant groups for
residential space in the city often results
in distinctive neighbourhoods that have
their own social "ecology." The classic
example, shown in this illustration, is
Chicago of the 1920s, which had developed a series of concentric zones of distinctive neighbourhoods as successive
waves of immigrants established themselves. Over time, most immigrant
groups made their way from low-rent,
inner-city districts surrounding the CBD
(known in Chicago as the Loop) to more
attractive and expensive districts farther
out.   (*Source:* R.E. Park, E.W. Burgess, and
R.D. McKenzie, *The City.* Chicago: University
of Chicago Press, 1925, p. 53.)

numbers of them were able to establish themselves in better jobs and move out into
newer, better housing. As the original immigrants and their families moved out, their
place in the transitional zone was taken by a new wave of migrants and immigrants. In this way, Chicago became structured into a series of *concentric zones* of
neighbourhoods of varying ethnicity and status (**Figure 11.8**). The same situation
can occur in other cities, where rapid growth is fuelled by streams of migrants and
immigrants from very different backgrounds.

Throughout this process of invasion and succession, people of the same background tend to stick together—partly because of the advantages of residential clustering and partly because of discrimination. **Invasion and succession** is a process
of neighbourhood change whereby one social or ethnic group succeeds another in
a residential area. The displaced group, in turn, invades other areas, creating over
time a rippling process of change throughout the city. The result is that within
each concentric zone, there exists a mosaic of distinctive neighbourhoods. Classic
examples include the Chinatowns found in many North American cities. Such neighbourhoods can be thought of as *ecological niches* within the overall metropolis—
settings where a particular mix of people have come to dominate a particular territory and a particular physical environment, or habitat.

invasion and succession: a
process of neighbourhood change
whereby one social or ethnic
group succeeds another

Corridors and Sectors   The fourth model of land use is a historical one. It is generally known as the Hoyt "sector" model. In cities where growth has been less dominated by successive waves of different immigrant ethnic groups, neighbourhood
patterns are often structured around the development of two different types of district: industrial districts and high-class residential districts. Over time, both tend to
grow outward from the centre of the city, but for different reasons and in different directions. Industry tends to follow transportation corridors along low-lying,
flat land where space exists for large factories, warehouses, and railway marshalling

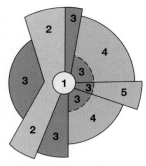

1. Central business district
2. Industrial area
3. Working-class residential district
4. Middle-class development
5. High-income residential district

Figure 11.9 Corridors and sectors
Cities that have not been dominated by successive waves of migrant or immigrant ethnic groups tend to be organized around the linear development of two main features that grow outward from the CBD (1): corridors of industrial development (2) and sectors of high-status residential development (5). Sectors of working-class residential districts (3) surround the industrial corridors, while sectors of middle-class residential districts (4) surround the high-status developments.
(*Source:* C.D. Harris and E.L. Ullman, "The Nature of Cities." *Annals of the American Academy of Political and Social Science* 242(1), 1945, fig. 5.)

yards. Working-class residential areas grow up around these corridors, following them out in sector-shaped neighbourhoods as they grow (**Figure 11.9**).

High-status residential districts, converseley, tend to grow outward from a different side of town, often following a ridge of high ground (free from flooding and with panoramic views). This outward growth creates another sectoral component of urban structure. The social status of this sector attracts middle-class housing, which, in turn, creates additional sectors of growth, thus completing the city's overall structure.

Canadian Cities

Difference   Until the publication of Goldberg and Mercer's *The Myth of the North American City,*[2] the patterns and *processes* outlined in the previous section were believed to apply equally across North America (a region that, in urban geography, traditionally includes Canada and the United States but excludes Mexico). However, with the publication of their study in 1986, a case was made for the distinctiveness of the Canadian city. From that date, a variety of scholars have highlighted important differences between Canadian and U.S. cities. When compared with the average American city, for example, Canadian cities

■ are more compact in size

■ have a higher density of population

■ have far fewer inner city zones of poverty ("urban blight") and contain far lower levels of poverty overall

■ have greater levels of public transit provision and use

■ have greater levels of public investment in infrastructure and facilities

■ have more dispersed immigrant populations

■ have more powerful and less-fragmented municipal governments

■ in total, represent an even larger share of the country's population than that found in the United States

History and politics contribute significantly to the contrasts between Canada's and the United States' urban centres. Historically, the Canadian city developed as part of a colonial economy that was dependent and export-driven. The American urban system grew from a locally run economy, producing food and manufactured goods for its own needs. As a result, Canada required only a handful of administrative and port centres, which continue to predominate in our country and its urban systems (**Table 11.1**).

Political differences contribute most significantly to the differences between urban settlements in the two countries. In Canada, the government and public sector have always been deeply involved in urban affairs. In contrast, the United States favours fragmented and less powerful municipal administrations because Americans place a high value on individual rights and freedoms, and local autonomy.

Canada's more expansive social welfare net has meant that far fewer people experience poverty and homelessness than in the United States. This is reflected in the relative lack of inner-city "urban blight" areas in this country, an unfortunate hallmark of American cities and one that had fuelled an exodus to the suburbs. The relative lack of large areas of poor or dilapidated inner-city housing in Canada has also reduced the opportunities for the large-scale urban redevelopment or "gentrification" of such areas and thereby kept house prices or rents within the reach of the existing inhabitants of these neighbourhoods. The existence of fewer

[2]M.A. Goldberg and J. Mercer, *The Myth of the North American City: Continentalism Challenged.* Vancouver: University of British Columbia Press, 1986. (The title of this book is a conscious echo of *The North American City,* a book by Canadian geographer Maurice Yeates and one very influential in its day.)

TABLE 11.1   The Urban Transformation of Canada: Urban Population Distributions, 1901–2001

Year	Total Population (000s)	Urban* Population (000s)	(%)
1901	5 371	2 014	37.5
1921	8 788	4 352	49.5
1941	11 507	6 271	54.5
1961	18 232	12 700	69.6
1981	24 343	18 436	75.7
1991	27 296	21 008	77.0
2001	30 007	23 908	79.7

Sources: Census of Canada, various years.

*Definitions of urban populations from 1901 to 1941 were not the same as those from the 1951 census to the present.

and less-fragmented municipalities in this country (often containing the inner city and suburbs in one unit, with much larger tax bases than their American counterparts) makes local government a much more effective agent in the battle against pockets of deprivation. Canada's universal health care system and provincial and territorial commitments to education also result in more equitable distributions of institutions and schools throughout our cities.

The provision of government-subsidized public transit systems has encouraged large numbers of people to live close within the confines of the Canadian city. This feature, when coupled with the more extensive zoning and land-use controls available in this country, has meant that Canadian cities are generally more dense and compact than their American counterparts, where controls are seen as restrictions on individual property rights and public spending as inhibiting free competition.

The net result, according to many commentators, is that when compared with the United States, Canada has been able to create far more "livable" cities. In its approach to urban life, Canada is in many ways much closer to Europe than to the United States. Canadian cities are therefore perhaps best described as representing an "intermediate" urban form.

Ironically, just as Canadian urban geographers are beginning to document the distinct qualities of the Canadian city, they are also beginning to see signs of its disappearance. This is because the increasing cutbacks in government spending that occurred in Canada in the 1980s and 1990s and the growing implications of the NAFTA have begun to remove the causes of the differences between Canadian and U.S. cities. Troubling trends, such as the growth of food banks and an increasing incidence of poverty across Canadian cities, may indicate that in the futures, our cities may more closely resemble those of the current United States.

Certainly, we need to be wary of stereotyping the Canadian city and not to overlook the possibility that American cities may offer useful examples. In February 2008, for example, Nancy Taylor, a senior adviser on intergovernmental and strategic initiatives for the City of Victoria, noted in an interview that "on any given night in Victoria's downtown, you cannot go a block without coming across folks who are huddled in doorways sleeping," a situation she contrasted with a recent visit she undertook as part of a delegation to Portland (Oregon), where "I did not see a see a single individual. I saw individuals with blankets. I did not see them sleeping in the streets. They were in transition from one place to another with blankets or pillows or whatever."[3]

---

[3]Ian Bailey, "Can Portland Provide Answers?" *Globe and Mail*, 16 February 2008, p. A7.

Since January 2005, Portland (a city of 600 000) has implemented a strategy to combat homelessness that has been able to place 1200 people into permanent housing and, as a result, homelessness statistics have fallen in that city by 39 percent. The strategy uses three principles: a focus on the most chronically homeless; streamlined access to city services that prevent homelessness; and a concentration on programs that deliver measurable results. According to Nancy Taylor, Victoria could learn from Portland about the value of coordination, setting targets, and focusing on a "housing first approach," the key to its strategy. The fact that delegations from Calgary and Ottawa have also recently visited Portland certainly indicates the potential value of American experience to Canada's cities.

It is also sadly true that the plight of the homeless has become politicized to such an extent that different jurisdictions in Canada (federal, provincial, and municipal) have sought to embarrass each other by giving attention to the perceived mishandling of this issue by other levels of government. In a similar vein, others have suggested that the relative attention paid to the problem of homelessness in different cities is less a reflection of the true scale of the problem than of the relative ability of interest groups to attract political attention to this issue. Seen from such a perspective, the Portland example may say less about the success of any policy toward homelessness than it does about the skills of local activists, an observation that would certainly place other cities in a more attractive light in the media than has been the case.

Change   Having considered these differences, we can now turn our attention to the Canadian city in its own right and examine the changes it has experienced in recent years. In such a consideration, economic and demographic forces must be seen as paramount, but the influences of social and cultural change cannot be downplayed.

The twin forces of the baby boom (which lasted in Canada from 1947 to 1966) and the post–World War II economic boom spurred the development of the Canadian suburbs to their present position as the place where the majority of Canadians live. The growth in both the number and the size of households, the ability of Canadians to purchase new homes, and the desire for a lifestyle that was both modern and healthy, created an urban form that has scarcely abated since the 1950s. Indeed, the greater availability of space and the relative cheapness of land at the city's periphery have maintained this form's attraction for young families, and suburbia has increased its own attractions for many Canadians. Recent developments have included the creation of "suburban downtowns," such as in Scarborough (a borough of Toronto featured in **Visualizing Geography 11.1—The Development of Urban Planning in Canada**), the growth of ever-larger suburban shopping malls, and, as the most recent stage in the evolution of retailing, the large, stand-alone "big-box stores" (exemplified by Wal-Mart) set within their own giant parking lots.

Critics have observed that increasing suburban sprawl has created its own environmental and social problems. The loss of surrounding agricultural land and the high amounts of energy consumption necessitated by long commutes to areas of low population density mean that the environmental impact of the suburbs is large. Others have noted that the physical separation of work and home, in the shape of the city and its suburbs (often enforced by zoning regulations), was based on a 1950s set of social relations that saw "work" as a man's space—a public domain—and "home" as a woman's place—a domestic, private space. This literal concretizing of gender relations in space has made it far harder, this criticism argues, for the city to accommodate current social changes.

More recent economic and demographic change has had its own profound effects on the Canadian inner city. The massive loss of manufacturing jobs that occurred as part of the economic restructuring of the 1980s and 1990s might have led to an abandonment of the inner city, had it not been for the almost simultaneous development there of quaternary industry (that is, the professional and

Visualizing Geography

The Development of Urban Planning in Canada

Although obviously the result of deliberate intent, the small urban settlements developed by the European colonial powers in Canada were not the first settlements in this country, nor were their layouts planned. The winding streets of Quebec City, founded by the French in 1608, continue European traditions of the medieval city, in which streets were allowed to follow the topography as economic and social need dictated—for "form" to follow "function," in other words (**Figure 11.1.1**).

Function followed form in eighteenth-century Canada with the Enlightenment's emphasis on rationality and scientific thought. The massive fortress of Louisbourg (Nova Scotia) and the streets of Charlottetown (Prince Edward Island) (**Figure 11.1.2**) were deliberately laid out to conform to the aesthetics of geometry, not to the lay of the land or the desires of the locals.

This approach continued into the nineteenth century (**Figure 11.1.3**). Indeed, the grid plan's efficient and economic layout became the preferred design for the thousands of settlements that were coming into existence as the Canadian Prairies were developed by European immigration. Because its layout imposed a very visible order and authority across the landscape, the grid plan itself became eloquent of a worldview that celebrated economic growth and the subduing of a disorderly nature in the creation of urban places.

By the late nineteenth century, Canadian cities had become victims of their own success. Urbanism in Canada was proceeding swiftly and beginning to cause problems of overcrowding and poor sanitation—especially in the larger cities—that urban government could not ignore. Primarily as a health measure, municipal authorities began to introduce planning controls. These measures were aimed at the reduction of urban disease and included the introduction of water and sewer lines. On a more abstract level, the coincidence of immigration and poverty in central city locations was interpreted in one of two ways. Some people saw it as telling evidence that "race" determined behaviour and

Planners work on the design of Ottawa These assistants were photographed in 1949 as they prepared a model of Jacques Greber's 1937 plan for the National Capital Region. The plan guided federal development for the capital for more than a generation. The section in the foreground contains the Parliament Hill area; Hull is at the lower left.

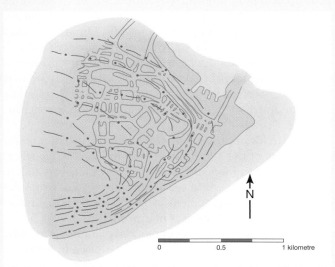

Figure 11.1.1   Quebec City   Founded by the French in 1608, this city illustrates an organic street layout that connected places of industry and trade with places people lived, and reflected the city's topography.   (*Source*: J. Grant, "Planning Canadian Cities: Context, Continuity, and Change." In T. Bunting and P. Filion [eds.], *Canadian Cities in Transition: The Twenty-First Century*, 2nd ed. Toronto: Oxford University Press, 2000, pp. 443–461, fig. 19.1 p. 443.)

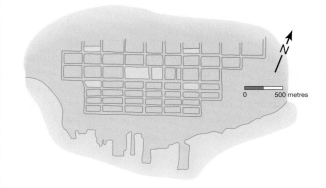

Figure 11.1.2   Charlottetown   Laid out by British soldiers in 1768, the design for this town shows the simplicity of geometry, narrow blocks, and a central square.   (*Source*: J. Grant, "Planning Canadian Cities: Context, Continuity, and Change." In T. Bunting and P. Filion [eds.], *Canadian Cities in Transition: The Twenty-First Century*, 2nd ed. Toronto: Oxford University Press, 2000, pp. 443–461, Figure 19.2, p. 444.)

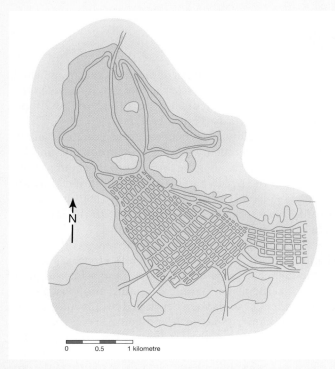

Figure 11.1.3   Vancouver The rigidity of the survey grid is evident in the design of this city, which was first settled in 1862. (*Source:* J. Grant, "Planning Canadian Cities: Context, Continuity, and Change." In T. Bunting and P. Filion [eds.], *Canadian Cities in Transition: The Twenty-First Century,* 2nd ed. Toronto: Oxford University Press, 2000, pp. 443–461, fig. 19.3, p. 444.)

thereby shaped the characteristics of "place" (a belief that led many to construct ideas of "Chinatowns" or ghettos). Other people saw it as a demonstration of the very opposite, that it was the environment that determined behaviour.

Fortunately, the latter view came to dominate the nascent Canadian urban reform movement, and from 1890 to 1930, two different approaches to city planning were used. Spurred on by city boosters, improvement first took the form advocated by the American City Beautiful movement. The **City Beautiful movement** was a Progressive Era (c. 1890–1920) attempt to remake cities in ways that would reflect the higher values of society, using neo-classical architecture, grandiose street plans, parks, and inspirational monuments and statues.

Increasingly, however, the more profound vision offered by the **Garden City movement**, established in England in 1899 by Sir Ebenezer Howard, found favour in Canadian circles. In fact, the future Canadian prime minister,

City Beautiful movement: an attempt to remake cities in ways that would reflect the higher values of society, using neo-classical architecture, grandiose street plans, parks, and inspirational monuments and statues

Garden City movement: an attempt to plan cities in ways that combined the benefits of urban living with the spaciousness and environmental quality of rural life

W.L. Mackenzie King, strongly endorsed the movement's ideas in his 1918 book *Industry and Humanity.* Howard believed that people should be able to combine the benefits of urban living with a more healthy rural way of life. To achieve this, he stressed the importance of overall planning and particularly emphasized the need for spaciousness and environmental quality in the urban context.

The ideal "garden city," Howard believed, should be built on land that was owned by the community to prevent land speculation and enable efficient planning. It should be relatively small (about 30 000 people) and should contain separate residential and industrial areas. In its design, it should feature wide boulevards (often curvilinear, or "organic" in plan); low-density, good-quality housing; and public parks and be surrounded by a greenbelt. The success of Letchworth and Welwyn garden cities, both built near London, England, following these principles, demonstrated the value of the movement's utopian vision.

Howard's ideas were soon transferred to Canada with the appointment in 1914 of Howard's talented assistant Thomas Adams as Town Planning Advisor to the Commission of Conservation, on the recommendation of its chair Sir Clifford Sifton. Indeed, Adams lost little time. By the time he departed Canada in 1923, he had an extensive legacy in the form of town plans (for parts of Halifax and Ottawa, and for the cities of Prince Rupert and Corner Brook, for example), legislation, and propaganda—all designed to promote the garden city concept.

Unfortunately, the Depression and World War II virtually eliminated any energy or funds for urban planning. It was only in the guise of zoning regulations and land-use plans that city planning continued its existence through the period up to the 1950s. By this date, however, the pent-up demand for housing and the desire to create forms worthy of the modern post-war era led to the development, best shown by the example of Don Mills, Ontario, of what was to become the classic form of the modern suburb (**Figure 11.1.4**). Its design merged garden city principles with the "neighbourhood concept" to create a layout that was both adapted to the increasing use of the automobile and the desire of people for a healthier, more spacious lifestyle.

Desire for improvement also led to the urban renewal movements of the 1960s and 1970s in which large tracts of poor quality inner-city housing were demolished and, in their place, large tracts of social housing created. Examples include la Cité development in Montreal (**Figure 11.1.5**) and the Regent Park project in Toronto.

Initially, these examples of modern planning, with their emphasis on efficiency and order, were praised by residents and planners alike. However, the fashion for such grandiose pieces of social engineering was abandoned by the mid-1970s as it came to be realized that such developments had no "soul" and lacked character when compared with the communities that had been uprooted. At the same time, noted commentators of urban life, such as Jane Jacobs, began to promote older forms of urban existence,

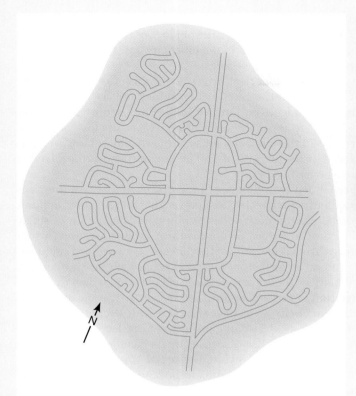

Figure 11.1.4 Don Mills Based on garden city precepts and the neighbourhood unit, this Toronto suburb was developed by Macklin Hancock in the 1950s. Stripped down to its fundamentals (wide lots, winding streets, and retail strips), the form was repeated across Canada and came to represent suburbia. (*Source:* J.Grant, "Planning Canadian Cities: Context, Continuity, and Change." In T. Bunting and P. Filion [eds.], *Canadian Cities in Transition: The Twenty-First Century,* 2nd ed. Oxford University Press, 2000, pp. 443–461, Figure 19.3, p. 444.)

Figure 11.1.5 La Cité development, Montreal The original late-1960s plan for this development called for the demolition of 255 houses as part of a slum clearance program. However, the project was greatly amended by community action. Only one-third of the houses were demolished and a greatly scaled down complex (consisting of 1350 apartments in three towers) constructed in the late 1970s. The remaining homes (some 600 housing units) became integrated into cooperative and non-profit housing associations.

such as had been found in the inner city, as more conducive to successful and safe urban living.

The conjunction of these ideas with the growing trend toward gentrification in Canadian cities during the late 1980s and 1990s has led to a rediscovery of older urban forms as a postmodern expression of the differences of urban living (**Figure 11.1.6**).

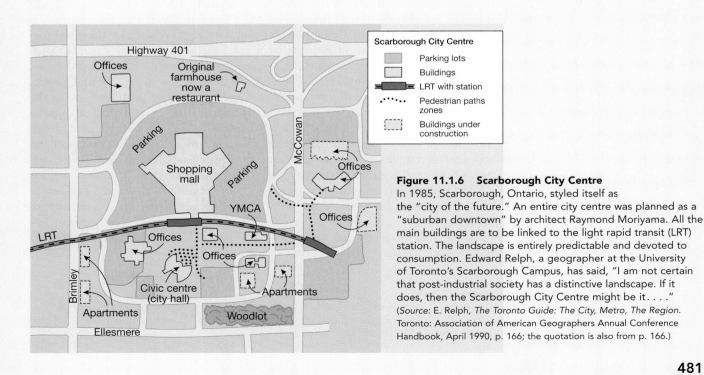

Figure 11.1.6 Scarborough City Centre
In 1985, Scarborough, Ontario, styled itself as the "city of the future." An entire city centre was planned as a "suburban downtown" by architect Raymond Moriyama. All the main buildings are to be linked to the light rapid transit (LRT) station. The landscape is entirely predictable and devoted to consumption. Edward Relph, a geographer at the University of Toronto's Scarborough Campus, has said, "I am not certain that post-industrial society has a distinctive landscape. If it does, then the Scarborough City Centre might be it. . . ." (*Source:* E. Relph, *The Toronto Guide: The City, Metro, The Region.* Toronto: Association of American Geographers Annual Conference Handbook, April 1990, p. 166; the quotation is also from p. 166.)

information sector) and the easing of municipal restrictions on condominium development and loft conversions. Significantly, a large number of the people employed in these new occupations also chose to live in the inner city and so initiated a considerable amount of gentrification in these areas.

Research by Professor David Ley of the University of British Columbia into the processes of change in Canadian inner cities has examined the six metropolitan areas of Toronto, Montreal, Vancouver, Ottawa-Hull, Edmonton, and Halifax over the period 1971–1991.[4] In those 20 years, there was a net loss of almost 230 000 nonquaternary jobs in the inner-city areas of the six cities. However, this decline was almost replaced by the net gain of 160 000 quaternary sector jobs that occurred in the same areas over this period.

This process has been aided by a number of factors, such as city authorities encouraging the conversion of rental properties and vacant lots to condominiums, the attractiveness of smaller accommodations for households made up of single people, and the trendiness of inner-city living resulting from postmodernism's emphasis on heritage and a carnival-like atmosphere. In effect, an upward spiral has been created in which a number of factors mutually reinforce one another and ensure the continued viability of these areas as desirable places in which to live.

An important illustration of this is that until very recently, average household income levels in Canadian inner-city areas have seen very little decline when compared with equivalent U.S. statistics. Also, the problem of displaced poorer families is not as evident. With respect to the 460 census tracts included in his study of the six inner cities, Ley concludes that "while the social status of a few tracts declined over the twenty-year period, the dominant movement was upwards, and some tracts rose markedly."[5]

This very broad description cannot hope to capture all of the differences and complexities of Canadian urban life. At a fundamental level, each city is a unique place with its own character. Similarly, there is considerable variety within each of the urban zones we have discussed. For example, Ley points to the range of types within the inner city: the pockets of poverty, the areas of affluence, the heritage zones, and the "ethnic" villages. Indeed, the latter provide another telling difference from U.S. cities. This is because overseas immigration flows into our cities, while proportionately much larger than those to U.S. cities, have been much more dispersed.

Finally, no examination of urban geography should overlook Canada's small towns. Defined as having fewer than approximately 10 000 people, these communities fall outside of the hinterlands of Canada's urban centres and comprise a very small percentage of Canada's total population. Nevertheless, their place in the Canadian imagination is secure, for they are seen as a repository of old-fashioned values and neighbourliness—even if they are only for weekend visits, for example, to buy antiques in St. Jacob's, Ontario, or jam in Knowlton, Quebec.

In reality, of course, these small centres face an array of problems—from the loss of their business to larger centres, the collapse of resource industries, and the decline of Canadian agriculture. Such problems of decline are sometimes met with imaginative local responses that attempt to find other activities to support the economy. Examples include tourism development based on heritage (Lunenburg, Nova Scotia), dinosaurs (Drumheller, Alberta), and murals (Chemainus, British Columbia); the creation of ski resorts (Mont Tremblant, Quebec); and, more specialized activities, such as documentary film festivals (Yorkton, Saskatchewan). If the "new economy," based on the internet, really can conquer the "tyranny" of distance, then it is likely that many more activities than call centres will be located in our small towns.

---

[4]David Ley, "The New Middle Class in Canadian Central Cities." In J. Caulfield and L. Peake (eds.), *City Lives & City Forms: Critical Research & Canadian Urbanism.* Toronto: University of Toronto Press, 1996, pp. 15–32.

[5]Ibid., p. 19.

Sense in the City: An Alternate Approach to Urbanism

As we have already seen in Chapter 5, there are many different ways of viewing space, and in that chapter we examined the processes by which space can be differently structured depending on factors such as ethnicity or gender—using, as an example of the first, the Chinatowns that are found in many Canadian cities, and as an illustration of the second, downtown Montreal's Gay Village. A recent exhibition at the Canadian Centre for Architecture in Montreal, entitled *Sense in the City: An Alternate Approach to Urbanism,* provides yet another way of looking at the city.[6] In addition, by focusing on our own personal and subjective experiences, it signals some very different approaches than the ones we have considered so far in this chapter (which have tended to emphasize the objective, quantifiable and often economically-driven aspects of city life).

Divided into five sections, the exhibition (which ran from 26 October 2005 to 10 September 2006) presented ways in which sight, smell, sound, touch, and perception of temperature are experienced in urban settings. For example:

- *Sight.* The exhibition very clearly showed how planners, architects, and urban theorists in general consider sight to be the most important sense that people use in experiencing the city; the "look" of the city, the design of its buildings, and its overall aesthetics are usually evaluated solely in visual terms. As the exhibition showed, for example, darkness forces us to experience the city in wholly new ways and to open up unused parts of our perception to the full range of urban experience as noted below. (This finding is an obvious one to the blind, as Braille and tactile city maps, included in the exhibition, tried to indicate.) City lighting is often promoted on the grounds of public safety, but the excessive levels of "light pollution" now found in many Canadian cities could be interpreted as an attempt to turn night into day because that is the urban environment in which we are conditioned to feel most comfortable. Many years ago, cultural geographer Yi-Fu Tuan remarked how different pre-industrial cities must have seemed because an absence of electric lighting meant that work could only be pursued during hours of daylight.

- *Smell.* In our current urban settings, we have become unaccustomed to many types of smell, and strong smells in general are often associated with a rural and not an urban world, yet it is quite apparent that in both the cities of the pre-industrial core and in today's developing world that a whole realm of odours and perfumes are to be encountered—whether they be from the open sewers of medieval Rome or the noxious garbage heaps of Phnom Penh. We are conditioned perhaps to find powerful smells a warning of the decay and germs that urban health programs have fought long to prevent. However, the dulling of our sensorial realm, in this respect, while symptomatic of an urban lifestyle, perhaps denies us a richer experience of living.

- *Sound.* In contradistinction to smell, perhaps, the noise of many modern Western urban environments has conditioned us to accept a cacophony of sound as typical of our everyday life in the city. If it is too quiet (especially, in restaurants, or stores), the concern is that nothing is happening, and personal iPods step in to amplify the individual's auditory stimulation. The noises of construction crews, delivery trucks, air conditioners and heating systems, cellphones, and people constantly on the move are now considered part of the urban experience. Indeed, Canadian composer R. Murray Schafer endeavoured to record the "soundscape" of Vancouver in 1973, and the Montreal exhibition invited visitors to compare that city's sound with those of cities elsewhere.

---

[6]For a longer review of this exhibition, see Alan Nash, "Making Sense of the City." *Senses & Society* 1(2), 2006, pp. 283–286. The lavishly illustrated exhibition catalogue contains a useful collection of essays on the topic: see Mirko Zardini (ed.), *Sense of the City: An Alternate Approach to Urbanism.* Montreal: Canadian Centre for Architecture, 2005.

A more apparent comparison perhaps, is between urban and rural settings, and in this respect consider the following remarks quoted from the field notes of one of the authors of this textbook:

> I well recall how early one morning, on a recent stay in a small village in southern Greece, I could hear a donkey clip-clopping down the street, the noise of cicadas in the olive groves beyond, and even the chug-chug of the distant ferry far out to sea. The sounds are exotic in themselves, but their main importance, I think, lies in the fact that they formed part of an almost perfect silence that pervaded the area. To me, it was a little unnerving, and definitely a sign I was in a different place; to the locals, it was as unquestioned a characteristic of that village as the Mediterranean sunshine that beamed on us all that day.[7]

■ *Touch.* In its broadest sense, the "tactile" environment is engaged when we experience the various textures of the surfaces of the city, which can range from the steel frames of office door handles to the softer surfaces of lawns in urban parks. In a very interesting example, the Montreal exhibition used the widespread adoption and use of asphalt to show how our cities have simply become covered over with that material during the course of the last 100 years. The dusty, wooden boardwalks and rutted muddy roads that typified Canadian cities have now become smoothed over and covered with blacktop to create what many have portrayed as a an anodyne world of neat parking lots—a world that appeals to many as one that is ordered, tidy, rational, and functional. Such a view is challenged by works such as Jeff Koons' 1992 playful representation of a puppy made from living flowers planted in a wire mesh, a favourite among visitors to the Guggenheim Museum in Bilbao, Spain (**Figure 11.10**). Such works, by challenging the permanence and formality of stone

Figure 11.10   Smell the view!
Jeff Koons' playful organic sculpture of a puppy outside the Guggenheim Museum in Bilbao, Spain, challenges us to experience a city's landscape with more than just our sense of sight.

---

[7]Alan Nash, unpublished field notes, "Greece 2007."

monuments, not only deliberately contrast our ideas of "nature" with those we have about the city, but also urge us to use senses such as smell and touch in our engagement with the urban landscape.

■ *Ability to sense temperature.* Called "the seasonal city," the final set of displays at the Canadian Centre for Architecture dealt with our perception of temperature in the city, and illustrated this with the effects of heat in the summer and snow in the winter. Air conditioning, for example, represents an extreme form of trying to combat both nature and our ability to sense it. We have become socialized not to sweat in the urban office, or to notice that it is summer outside. Regarding winter, photographs of skaters and ice palaces contrasted with video clips of snow removal show that the challenges of snow removal in an urban milieu are balanced by the joy of different recreational activities made possible by winter. Interestingly the way in which snow dampens noise levels and increases the reflection of city lights also nicely illustrates how a range of our senses, rather than only one, can be engaged by the various phenomena of the urban "sensorium."

   Again, however, it is worth noting that the whole approach of city living (even in Canada, where we perhaps should know better) is to try to ignore or to eliminate the effects of the seasons. Even as late as the 1950s, many people put their cars away for the winter and accepted the limitations of the season. We now, however, expect to be able to continue to drive to work throughout the winter, and expect the streets to be plowed to enable us to do so (**Figure 11.11**). Perhaps there is no better example of how we have allowed modern urban life almost completely to erase our experiences, and thereby to dull our senses!

   We have seen already (in Chapter 6) how our appreciation of the senses is itself a cultural construction, and it is therefore not surprising that the inhabitants of a modern urban environment should act in the ways described here. Since the period of the Enlightenment, the senses have been tacitly prioritized such that those most associated with primary labour (smell, touch) are "below" sight and sound—senses that are more associated with aesthetic sensibility (the reason why art galleries and symphony orchestras are mainstays of the urban cultural elite). We have been slowly conditioned to place the strongest emphasis on sight in our evaluation of experience: we "read" an urban landscape, we do not "experience" it in its totality.

Figure 11.11   Snow plowing in downtown Montreal   This typical scene reflects our growing refusal to allow winter weather to impede our ability to drive around the city at any time of year.

Gradually, however, such approaches are being challenged, and modern urban geographers have reminded us that not everybody experiences the city in such neutral or unquestioning terms. For example, the *flaneur* who had the time to simply walk and observe crowds in nineteenth-century Paris has many equivalents today, whether they be sitting in Starbucks or playing dominoes on the street corner. The city is much richer as a place than we have imagined, and we need all of our senses to experience the full nuances of its urban structure.

Comparative Urban Structure

Certain fundamental forces—economic competition for space and accessibility, social and ethnic discrimination and congregation, functional agglomeration, and residential search behaviour—can be traced in many of the world's cities, particularly in affluent core regions where economic, social, and cultural forces are broadly similar. Nevertheless, urban structure varies considerably because of the influence of history, culture, and the different roles that cities have played within the world-system.

Cities reflect these place-making influences in their buildings and layouts, and these "built forms" can become potent place-making factors in their own right as they, in turn, shape our behaviour and our memories as urban dwellers. In this sense, just as our cultures create cities, so do those cities create their own culture, or "place." Thus, world cities, such as Paris, New York, and Berlin, have a unique and defining sense of place that is immediately recognizable. For example, movie producers and novelists turn to that sense of place as shorthand to set the scene, whether it is romance in Paris or intrigue in Berlin, trapping the real city in our own images of it.

European Cities European cities are typically the product of several major epochs of urban development. As we saw in Chapter 2, because many of today's most important cities were founded during the period of the Roman Empire, it is not uncommon for the outlines of Roman and medieval urban development to be preserved in these cities' street plans (**Figure 11.12**). Many of the distinctive features of European cities derive from their long history and include complex street patterns, plazas or squares, and a long tradition of high-density urban living in tenements and apartment houses (**Figure 11.13**).

Figure 11.12 Towns of medieval Europe The towns of medieval Europe were typically small, with compact outlines defined by defensive walls. In addition to their defensive function, these walls were status symbols, signs of wealth and power. At their gates, tolls were collected and goods checked. They enclosed a separate administrative area in which residents were free and usually self-governing. Within the walls, towns were typically organized around a fortress, or *cité*, though the focuses of activity and sources of growth were more likely to be religious institutions, market squares, and merchants' quarters. The example depicted here, Arras, in northeastern France, shows the "organic" pattern of irregular-shaped blocks with narrow, winding streets, which is typical of many of the medieval towns of Europe. Its growth was focused successively on three elements: (a) the *cité*, or fortress, (b) the monastery, and (c) two market squares. (*Source*: P.M. Hohlenberg and L.H. Lees, *The Making of Urban Europe 1000–1950*. Cambridge, MA: Harvard University Press, 1985, p. 32. Photo © Yann Arthus-Bertrand/Altitude/Photo Researchers.)

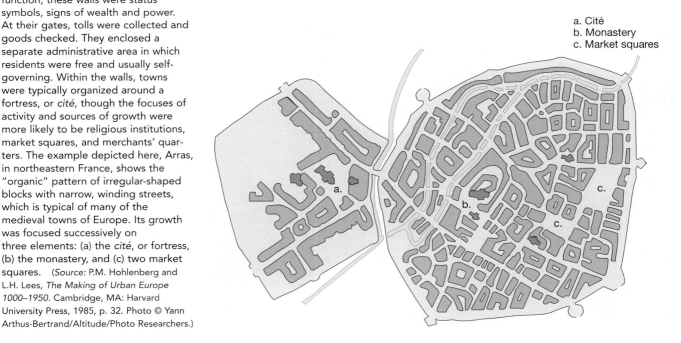

a. Cité
b. Monastery
c. Market squares

Figure 11.13   Distinctive characteristics of European cities   Florence, Italy—This photograph shows the city's compact form and high density that are a legacy of pre-automobile urban development.

Putting all this together, we can produce a composite model of the Western European city (**Figure 11.14**). We should note, however, that the richness of European history and the diversity of its geography mean that several variations on this theme do exist.

One of the most interesting is the Eastern European city, in which the legacy of an interlude of 44 years of socialism (1945–1989) was grafted onto cities that had already developed mature patterns of land use and social differentiation. Major examples include Budapest (Hungary), Prague (Czech Republic), and Warsaw (Poland). State control of land and housing meant that huge public housing estates and industrial zones were created in outlying districts. Public ownership of land meant that the economics of land-use competition (see Figure 11.6) could be ignored, and cities could therefore be planned on a more centralized basis. (The Utopian visionary Sir Ebenezer Howard saw the competition for space as a problem and, as we shall see below, sought to eliminate its effects.) The structure of the older city was little altered, however, apart from the addition of socialist monuments and the renaming of streets.

Colonial Cities   Colonial cities are those that were deliberately established or developed as administrative or commercial centres by colonial or imperial powers. Examples are Accra (Ghana), Hanoi (Vietnam), Macau (China), Nairobi (Kenya), and New Delhi (India). The stereotypical colonial city reflects a fundamental division among three original functional components: colonial administration and commerce, military security, and indigenous commerce and residence. Usually located on a coastal site or a navigable river, the form and structure of colonial cities were dictated by European models of urban design, with a gridiron pattern of town planning and deliberate racial segregation (**Figure 11.15**).

Cities of the Periphery   The cities of the world-system periphery, often still referred to as Third World cities, are numerous and varied. What they have in common is the experience of unprecedented rates of growth driven by rural "push"—overpopulation and the lack of employment opportunities in rural areas—rather than the "pull" of prospective jobs in towns and cities. Most of them have also grown a great deal in a relatively short period of time. São Paulo, Brazil, provides a good example (**Figure 11.16**). In 1930, the urban area of São Paulo was approximately 150 square kilometres (60 square miles), and the population was 1 million. By 1962, the city had grown to 750 square kilometres (290 square miles)

CBD, Vienna

Low-density Villa Belt, Vienna

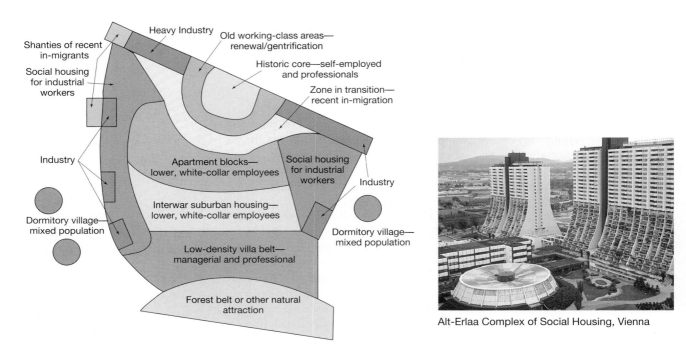

Figure 11.14 **Urban structure in continental Western Europe** In the typical continental Western European city, the historic core has a more dominant role in commercial and social life than in North American cities. This illustration depicts land-use patterns in the generic Western European city. The density of residential development is also high, with large amounts of nineteenth-century housing—including stable, high-status neighbourhoods close to the city centre—and significant amounts of social housing. (*Source:* P. White, *The West European City.* London: Longman, 1984, fig. 7.6, p. 188. Reprinted by permission of Addison Wesley Longman Ltd.)

with a population of 4 million. In 1980, the area was 1400 square kilometres (540 square miles), and the population was 12.1 million. By 1995, the city covered 2400 square kilometres (925 square miles) with a population of 15 million. By 2007, São Paulo's population had reached 18.8 million and, according to UN projections made that year, is predicted to reach a total of 20.5 million by 2015.[8]

---

[8]United Nations Department of Economic and Social Affairs, Population Division, "World Urbanization Prospects: The 2007 Revision." New York: United Nations Department of Economic and Social Affairs, Population Division, 2008. Available via their website at **www.un.org/esa/population/unpop.htm**. Some very useful maps showing the latest growth of the city and the impacts of its spreading suburbs can be seen in the draft paper prepared for a 2005 World Bank conference by Harold Torres, Humberto Alves, and Maria Aparecida de Oliveira, "São Paulo. Peri-Urban Dynamics: Some Social Causes and Environmental Consequences." **www.worldbank.org/urban/symposium2005/papers/torres.pdf**.

Fort

European quarter bungalow

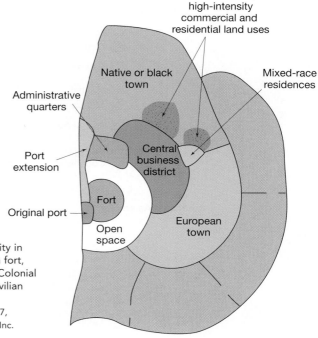

Figure 11.15   Urban structure in colonial cities   The typical colonial city in South Asia was developed around a port facility and often protected by a fort, which would have had an open space around it to provide a field of fire. Colonial administrative offices were nearby, with military barracks and European civilian residences set apart from "native" residential areas.   (*Source:* S. Brunn and J. Williams [eds.], *Cities of the World*, 2nd ed. New York: HarperCollins, 1993, fig. 9.7, p. 360. © 1993. Reprinted by permission of Addison-Wesley Educational Publishers Inc. Top left photo © John Elk/Stock Boston/PNI.)

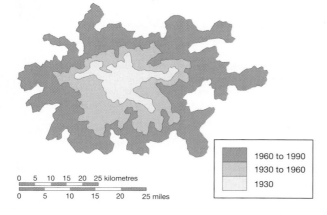

	1960 to 1990
	1930 to 1960
	1930

0   5   10   15   20   25 kilometres

0   5   10   15   20   25 miles

Figure 11.16   The growth of São Paulo   Since 1930, the city has grown 16-fold in extent, though the bulk of this growth has taken place since 1960. (*Source: Urban Transport.* Washington, DC: The World Bank, 1986, fig. 3, p. 5.)

The structure of peripheral cities varies according to three factors:

- relative levels of economic development, and the degree to which they have become industrialized and modernized

- regional cultural values as, for example, in the traditional layout and design of Islamic cities

- whether society is organized more strongly on class or ethnic divisions

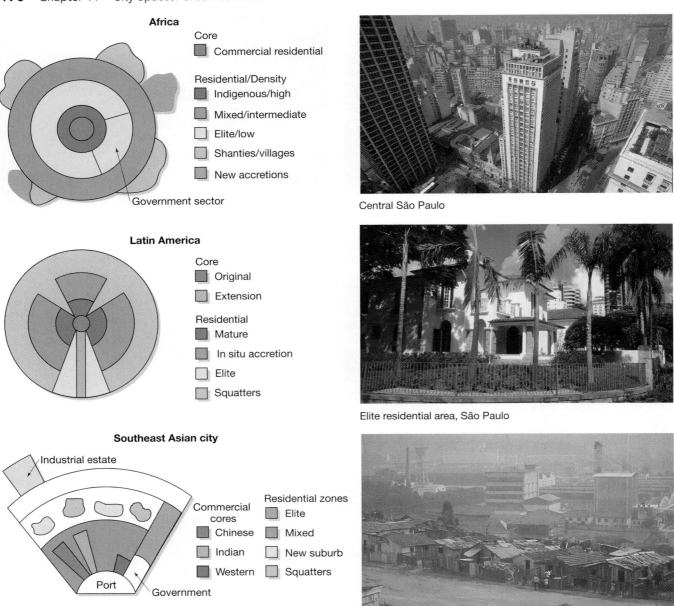

Figure 11.17 Urban structure in peripheral cities The most distinctive feature of cities in the world's periphery is their dualism with, on the one hand, a core of modern commerce, retailing, and industry and its associated residential areas; and on the other, an informal economy with extensive areas of makeshift shanty housing. (*Source:* S. Lowder, *Inside Third World Cities.* London: Croom Helm, 1986, figs 7.1 and 7.2, pp. 211 and 214.)

In many cities, however, once-distinctive patterns of spatial organization and land use have disappeared as a result of the congestion and overcrowding caused by overurbanization. To the extent that it is possible to generalize about the urban structure of the cities of the periphery (**Figure 11.17**), we can identify three important, common elements:

■ a central concentration of modern commerce, retailing, and industry

■ a distinctive zone or sector of elite residential neighbourhoods

■ shanty or squatter neighbourhoods that fill in every available space between and around them

Later in this chapter, we will see how prominent this third element has come to be in the landscapes and affairs of the unintended metropolises of the periphery.

URBAN FORM AND DESIGN

Within the framework provided by the overall organization of land uses and activities, cities acquire a distinctiveness that comes from their physical characteristics: the layout of streets, the presence of monumental and symbolic structures, and the building types and architectural styles that fill out their built environment. The resulting urban landscapes are a reflection of a city's history, its physical environment, and its people's social and cultural values.

Geographers are interested in urban landscapes because, like other landscapes (Chapter 6), they can be read as multi-layered texts that show how cities have developed, how they are changing, and how people's values and intentions take expression in urban form. The built environment, whether it is planned or unplanned, is what gives expression, meaning, and identity to the various forces involved in urbanization. It becomes a biography of urban change. At the same time, the built environment provides people with cues and contexts for behaviour, with landmarks for orientation and with symbols that reinforce collective values, such as civic pride and a sense of identity.

Symbolic Landscapes

Some individual buildings and structures are so powerfully symbolic that they come to stand for entire cities: the Peace Tower in Ottawa, the Opera House and Harbour Bridge in Sydney, the Forbidden City in Beijing, and the Houses of Parliament in London, for example. It is the generic urban landscapes of different kinds of cities that are most interesting to geographers, however. Some generic urban landscapes come to symbolize entire nations or cultures. These are ordinary cityscapes that are powerfully evocative because they are understood as being a particular *kind* of place.

Geographer D.W. Meinig identified three types of symbolic cityscapes. The stereotypical New England townscape, for example (**Figure 11.18**), which Meinig described as being "marked by a steeple rising gracefully above a white wooden church which faces on a village green around which are arrayed large white clapboard houses which, like the church, show a simple elegance in form and trim,"[9] is widely taken to symbolize not just a certain type of regional architecture but the best that Americans have known "of an intimate, family-centred, God-fearing, morally conscious, industrious, thrifty, democratic *community*."

Another ordinary townscape with powerful symbolic connotations is what Meinig called Main Street of Middle America (see Figure 11.18). It is "middle" in several respects: it is between the frontier to the west and the cosmopolitan seaports to the east, between agricultural regions and industrial metropolises, and between affluence and poverty. It represents a landscape of property-minded, law-abiding citizens devoted to free enterprise and a certain kind of social morality.

A third symbolic cityscape identified by Meinig is suburbia, or, more specifically, California suburbia (see Figure 11.18). The commonplace landscape of single-family dwellings standing on broad lots and fronted by open green lawns is widely attached to an image of a particular lifestyle for middle-class, nuclear families: individualistic, private, informal, and recreation- and consumption-oriented. First developed in California, this kind of suburb has diffused throughout North America (and, indeed, beyond), and has come to symbolize the "American dream" of an affluent, independent lifestyle.

---

[9]D.W. Meinig, "Symbolic Landscapes." In D.W. Meinig et al. (eds.), *The Interpretation of Ordinary Landscapes*. New York: Oxford University Press, 1979, p. 165.

The New England townscape symbolizes for many a particular kind of community: intimate, family-centred, industrious, thrifty, democratic, and morally aware.

Main Street of Middle America has come to be associated with the ideal of a "balanced" community in terms of income and class, with shared values of free enterprise, conservative morality, and commonsensical practicality.

California suburbia is symbolic of the modern "American Dream" of a consumption- and leisure-oriented lifestyle.

Figure 11.18 Ordinary landscapes Some ordinary cityscapes are powerfully symbolic of particular kinds of places. The New England village, the Main Street of Middle America, and California suburbia are in this category, so much so that they have been taken as symbolizing the United States itself, part of the "iconography of nationhood," the symbolic landscapes that give the country a sense of identity, both at home and abroad.

Planned Urban Design

City planning and design have a long history. As we have seen, many ancient Greek and Roman settlements were deliberately laid out on grid systems, within which the location of key buildings and the relationship of neighbourhoods to one another were carefully thought out. In ancient China, cities were laid out with strict regard to Taoist ideas about the natural order of the universe; with different quarters representing the four seasons of the year; and with the placement of major streets and the interior layout of buildings designed to be in harmony with cosmic energy. (Distinguished geographer Paul Wheatley has described such cities in his landmark book on Chinese urbanism *The Pivot of the Four Quarters*.) This kind of mystical interpretation of nature is known as *geomancy,* and its application to design is known as *feng-shui*. It has always been important in Eastern cultures and continues to influence many aspects of urban planning and design in the Far East because many people believe that creating a positive energy flow through a home or place of business brings good luck and fortune. In Hong Kong, the GIS database for the 1990 Land Information System included a *feng-shui* layer that recorded areas subject to development restrictions based on *feng-shui* principles. Meanwhile, globalization has brought *feng-shui* to the rest of the world. East Asian immigrants have long practised *feng-shui* within the Chinatowns of North American cities. Recent waves of more affluent East Asian immigrants to Pacific Rim cities, such as Los Angeles, Vancouver, Sydney, and Auckland, have required developers, architects, and

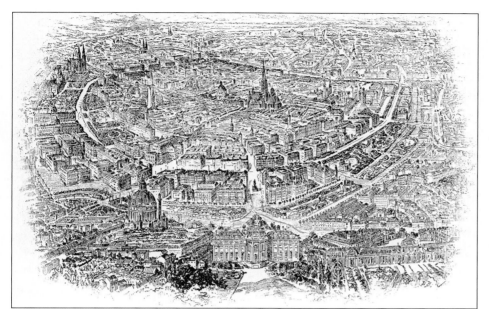

Figure 11.19 **The Ringstrasse in Vienna** Developed by the Emperor Franz Joseph in the mid-nineteenth century on the site of derelict fortifications around the medieval Altstadt, or old town, the Ringstrasse is 3.2 kilometres (2 miles) long and 61 metres (200 feet) wide. Along this broad, semicircular boulevard, Franz Joseph arrayed a series of major public buildings, including the national parliament, the city hall, the university, museums, the theatre, and the opera house. This lithograph, viewing the city from the southwest, was published in 1873, soon after the completion of the Ringstrasse and still shows how the medieval fortifications fixed the city's layout well into the nineteenth century.

interior designers to use *feng-shui* principles in the construction of new suburbs. At the same time, some speculative East Asian investors in the real estate markets of such world cities as New York and London have insisted on the use of *feng-shui* in the design of skyscrapers and commercial developments.

The roots of modern Western urban planning and design can be traced to the Renaissance and Baroque periods (between the fifteenth and seventeenth centuries) in Europe, when rich and powerful regimes used urban design to produce extravagant symbolizations of wealth, power, and destiny. Dramatic advances in military ordnance (cannon and artillery) brought a surge of planned redevelopment that featured impressive fortifications, geometric-shaped redoubts, or strongholds, and an extensive *glacis militaire* (a sloping, clear zone of fire) (**Figure 11.19**). These developments were often of such a scale that they effectively fixed the layout of cities well into the eighteenth century and even into the nineteenth century, when walls and/or glacis eventually made way for urban redevelopment in the form of parks, railway lines, or beltways.

As societies and economies became more complex with the transition to industrial capitalism, national rulers and city leaders looked to urban design to impose order, safety, and efficiency, as well as to symbolize the new seats of power and authority. One of the most important early precedents was set in Paris by Napoleon III, who presided over a comprehensive program of urban redevelopment and monumental urban design. The work was carried out by Baron Georges Haussmann between 1853 and 1870. Haussmann demolished large sections of old Paris to make way for broad, new, tree-lined avenues, with numerous public open spaces and monuments. In doing so, he not only made the city more efficient (wide boulevards meant better flows of traffic) and a better place to live (parks and gardens allowed more fresh air and sunlight in a crowded city and were held to be a "civilizing" influence), but he also made it safer from revolutionary politics (wide boulevards were hard to barricade; monuments and statues helped to instill a sense of pride and identity) (**Figure 11.20**).

The preferred architectural style for these new designs was the **Beaux Arts** style, which takes its name from l'École des Beaux Arts in Paris. In this school, architects were trained to draw on Classical, Renaissance, and Baroque styles, synthesizing them in designs for new buildings for the industrial age. The idea was that the new buildings would blend artfully with the older palaces, cathedrals, and civic buildings that dominated European city centres. Haussmann's ideas were widely influential and extensively copied.

Beaux Arts: a style of urban design that sought to combine the best elements of all of the classic architectural styles

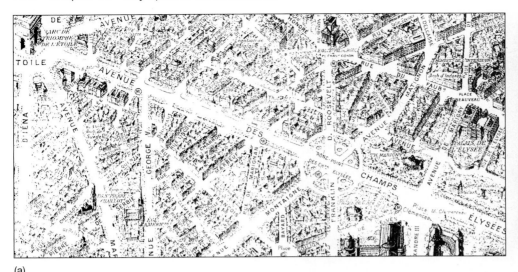

(a)

(b) The Champs-Élysées was laid out in the 1660s to provide a processional route appropriate to the king.

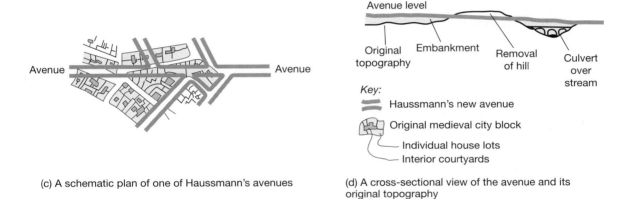

(c) A schematic plan of one of Haussmann's avenues

(d) A cross-sectional view of the avenue and its original topography

Figure 11.20   Haussmann's Paris   Between 1853 and 1870, the city of Paris in France was extensively redesigned to include wide boulevards and spaces.

In the United States, the City Beautiful movement, which began in the late nineteenth century, drew heavily on Haussmann's ideas and Beaux Arts designs. This movement was an attempt to remake cities in ways that would reflect the higher values of society, using neo-classical architecture, grandiose street plans, parks, and inspirational monuments and statues. The idea, again, was to deliberately exploit urban design as an uplifting and civilizing influence while emphasizing civic pride and power. Daniel Burnham's 1909 Chicago Plan (**Figure 11.21**) provides a good example. During the same period, European imperial powers imposed similar designs on their colonial capitals and administrative centres. Examples include New Delhi (India), Rangoon (Burma, now Myanmar), Saigon (Vietnam), and Windhoek (Namibia).

Early in the twentieth century, there emerged a different intellectual and artistic reaction to the pressures of industrialization and urbanization. This was the **modern movement**, which was based on the idea that buildings and cities should be designed and run as machines are. Equally important to the modernists was that urban design not reflect dominant social and cultural values but rather help create a new moral and social order. The movement's best-known

modern movement: the idea that buildings and cities should be designed and run as machines are

Figure 11.21   The Chicago Plan, 1909
Daniel Burnham's Chicago Plan of 1909 was based on aesthetic means toward social objectives. By giving the city a strong visual and aesthetic order, Burnham wanted to create the physical preconditions for the emergence of a harmonious social climate and strong moral order. These were popular sentiments in the Progressive Era, and much of Burnham's ambitious plan was actually carried out.   (*Source:* R. Burnham and E. Bennett, *Plan of Chicago.* New York: Princeton Architectural Press, 1993, plate CXXXII, p. 112. Jules Guerin [American, 1866–1946], pencil and watercolour on paper, 1908, 75.5 cm × 105.5 cm. On permanent loan to The Art Institute of Chicago, 28.148.1966.)

advocate was Le Corbusier, a Paris-based Swiss who provided the inspiration for technocratic urban design. Modernist buildings sought to dramatize technology, exploit industrial production techniques, and use modern materials and unembellished, functional design. Le Corbusier's ideal city (*La Ville Radieuse*—**Figure 11.22**) featured linear clusters of high-density, medium-rise apartment blocks, elevated on stilts and segregated from industrial districts; high-rise tower office blocks; and transportation routes—all separated by broad expanses of public open space.

After World War II, this concept of urban design became pervasive, part of what became known as the International Style: boxlike steel-frame buildings with concrete and glass façades. The International Style was avant-garde yet respectable and, above all, comparatively inexpensive to build. Toronto's TD Bank towers, designed by Mies van der Rohe, are one example. It has been this tradition of urban design that has, more than anything else, imposed a measure of uniformity and globalization has brought the appearance of International Style buildings to big cities in every part of the world. Furthermore, the International Style has often been the preferred basis for large-scale urban design projects around the world. One of the best examples of this is Brasilia, the capital of Brazil, founded in 1956 in an attempt to shift the country's political, economic, and psychological focus away from the past; differentiate it from the former colonial cities on the coast; and orient the country toward the future and the interior (see Chapter 6).

Modern urban design has had many critics, mainly on the grounds that it tends to take away the natural life and vitality of cities, replacing varied and human-scale environments with monotonous and austere settings. In response to this, historic preservation has become an important element of urban planning in every city that can afford it. In addition, postmodern urban design has brought a return to traditional and decorative motifs and introduced a variety of deliberately "playful" and "interesting" architectural styles in place of the functional designs of modernism (**Figure 11.23**). **Postmodern urban design** is characterized by a diversity of architectural styles and elements, often combined in the same building or project. It makes heavy use of symbolism, colour, and decoration. It is no coincidence that postmodern design has flourished in the most recent phase of globalization. Having emerged as a deliberate reaction to the perceived shortcomings of modern design, its emphasis on decoration and self-conscious stylishness has made it a very convenient form of packaging for the new global consumer culture. It is geared to a cosmopolitan market, and it draws quite deliberately on a mixture of elements from different places and times. In many ways, it has become the transnational style for the more affluent communities of the world's cities.

postmodern urban design: a style characterized by a diversity of architectural styles and elements, often combined in the same building or project

Figure 11.22 *La Ville Radieuse*
The modern era and the advent of new transportation and construction technologies encouraged the Utopian idea that cities could be built as efficient and equitable "machines" for industrial production and progressive lifestyles. One of the most famous and influential examples was *La Ville Radieuse* (1933), a visionary design by Swiss architect Le Corbusier. His vision was for the creation of open spaces through collectivized, high-density residential areas, strictly segregated from industrial areas and highways through a geometric physical plan. (*Source*: Le Corbusier, *La Ville Radieuse*. Paris: Éditions de l'Architecture d'Aujourd'hui, p. 170.)

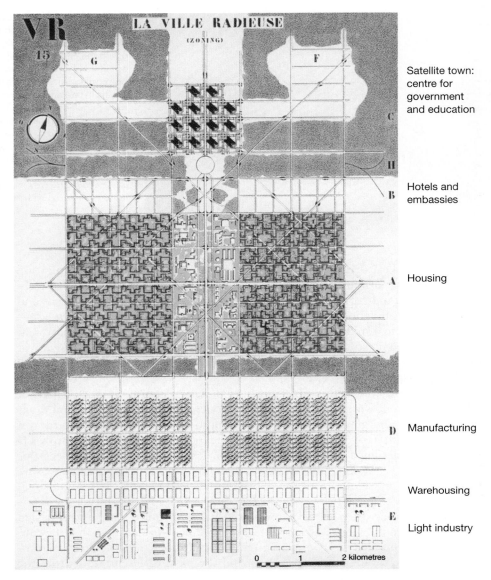

Satellite town: centre for government and education

Hotels and embassies

Housing

Manufacturing

Warehousing

Light industry

Figure 11.23 Postmodern architecture: Park Place mall, Lethbridge
Postmodern architecture is characterized by an almost playful diversity of different architectural styles from previous times, often combined in the same building. This example from Lethbridge, Alberta, shows a recently completed mall that is designed to be reminiscent of a nineteenth-century downtown, complete with its clock tower and use of patterned brick. The mall's name and interior use of park benches make reference to Galt Gardens, which is immediately adjacent.

URBAN TRENDS AND PROBLEMS

Differences in urban growth processes between the world's core regions and the underdeveloped periphery are mirrored in patterns and processes of urban change. In the core regions, urban change is dominated by the consequences of an economic transformation to a postindustrial economy. Together with the continuing revolution in communications and information-processing technologies and the increasing dominance of transnational corporate organizations, this transformation has made for a fundamental restructuring of metropolitan areas. Traditional manufacturing and related activities have been moved out of inner-city areas, leaving deteriorating neighbourhoods and a population of elderly and socially and economically marginalized people. New commercial activities have meanwhile begun to cluster in redeveloped CBDs and in edge cities around metropolitan fringes. The logic of agglomeration economies has created *100-mile cities*— metropolitan areas that are literally 100 miles (160 kilometres) or so across— consisting of a series of cities and urban districts that are bound together through urban freeways. One example is the area around Chicago. In Canada, economic change has been less aggressive than in the United States, but agglomeration effects can be seen in the "corridor" between Quebec City and Windsor.

In contrast, the basic trend affecting the cities of the world's periphery is demographic—the phenomenal rates of natural increase and in-migration that have given rise to overurbanization. This trend is reflected in an ever-growing informal sector of the economy in which people seek economic survival.

At the same time, however, these cities under stress represent local and regional concentrations of investment, manufacturing, modernization, and political power. As we have seen, the typical peripheral metropolis plays a key role in international economic flows, linking provincial regions with the hierarchy of world cities and, thus, with the global economy. Within peripheral metropolises, this role results in a pronounced **dualism**, or juxtaposition in geographical space of the formal and informal sectors of the economy. It is among these peripheral metropolises— Mexico City (Mexico), Lagos (Nigeria), and Manila (the Philippines) are examples—that we can find contenders for the title of the shock city of the late twentieth century—the city that is the embodiment of the most remarkable and disturbing changes in economic, social, and cultural life (see **Visualizing Geography 11.2**—"Shock City": Lagos, Nigeria).

dualism: the juxtaposition in geographical space of the formal and informal sectors of the economy

Problems of Postindustrial Cities

For all their relative prosperity, the postindustrial cities of the world's core regions have their share of problems. The most acute are localized in the central city areas that have borne the brunt of restructuring from an industrial to a postindustrial economy. These areas are experiencing several interrelated problems: fiscal problems; infrastructure problems; and localized spirals of neighbourhood decay, cycles of poverty, and homelessness. A discussion of each condition follows.

Fiscal Problems   Economic restructuring and metropolitan decentralization have meant that central cities have been left since the mid-1970s with a chronic problem that geographers call "fiscal squeeze." The squeeze comes from increasing limitations on revenues and increasing demands for expenditure. The revenue-generating potential of central cities has steadily fallen as metropolitan areas have decentralized, losing both residential and commercial taxpayers to suburban jurisdictions. However, central city governments are still responsible for services and amenities used by the entire metropolitan population: municipal galleries and museums, sports facilities, parks, traffic police, and public transport, for example.

In Canada, these problems are far less acute than in many U.S. cities. This is because our central cities have lost far less revenues, our cities are more compact, and our municipal governments cover much wider areas than do cities in the

"Shock City": Lagos, Nigeria

A Day in the Life of Kate Adikiwe

Kate Adikiwe lives in the suburban district of Olaleye, Lagos (**Figure 11.2.1**), once a small village whose residents grew herbs, fruits, and vegetables; fished; trapped; made palm wine; and processed palm oil. The village grew rapidly when a railway line was constructed through it and as Lagos grew outward after independence. In the mid-1960s, Olaleye had about 2500 residents; today, there are about 25 000 (**Figure 11.2.2**). Within its small site of some 35 hectares (86 acres) is an enormous range of economic activities—a large market, beer parlours, nightclubs, brothels, a makeshift movie theatre, tailors, shoemakers, blacksmiths, tinkers, watch repairers, knife sharpeners, mechanics, battery chargers, and itinerant barbers and beauticians. Many of the women produce and sell a great variety of cooked foodstuffs, while many of the men work outside the district in factories or offices.

Kate is one of six children. Her father is a clerical worker in one of the city's department stores. Her mother is a seamstress, working from the house. The house itself contains 12 families, each having a single room and sharing the one kitchen, toilet, and bathroom in the building. One of Kate's jobs is to draw water from the nearby well each morning before school. The water is stored in plastic buckets in the living room until needed. After school, Kate has to complete her homework and help her mother prepare food for the family. Most of the cooking is done on kerosene stoves in the passageway. After the meal, Kate and her older sister help their mother with sewing. They do not expect to be able to get jobs after school, and so they are learning to sew to become seamstresses.

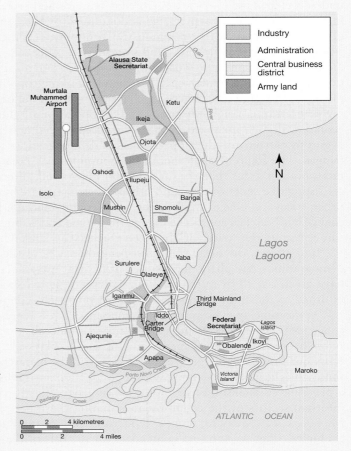

Figure 11.2.1 Layout of Lagos Lagos developed from an initial settlement at Iddo on the northern shore of Lagos Island. Ikoyi, on Lagos Island, was laid out in 1918 as a government residential estate to house colonial officials. Most of the city's growth, however, has been unplanned and irregular, with swamps, coves, and canals impeding efficient development. (*Source:* M. Peil, *Lagos*. London: Belhaven Press, 1991, p. 23.)

Lagos, like most metropolises in the world's periphery, grew relatively slowly until quite recently. The combination of the demographic transition, political independence, and an economic boom stimulated by the discovery of oil reserves in southeastern Nigeria triggered an explosive growth in population. Because of its difficult site on sand spits and lagoons, this growth has resulted in an irregular sprawl and, in the central area, a density of population higher than that of Manhattan Island in New York.

The cityscape on Lagos Island reflects both residential congestion and the postcolonial development of the city as a peripheral metropolis with important corporate functions.

For many people, life in the unintended metropolis is a matter of survival. This leads to a tremendous variety of informal economic activities, from street vending to home-brewed beer, and from prostitution to drug peddling. This photograph shows the most common form of informal activity: street trading, which takes place on almost every unoccupied sidewalk, street, or unclaimed space.

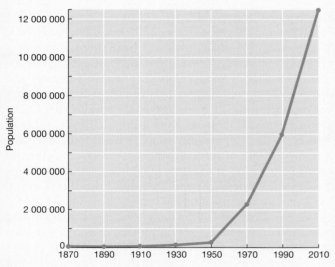

Figure 11.2.2   The growth of the city   Population growth has far outstripped the city's capacity to deal with the daily movement of people, a problem that is worsened because the central city is trapped on an island site, with limited access by road bridges.

Overwhelmed by an unprecedented rate of urbanization, an economy that cannot provide regularly paid employment for a significant proportion of its residents, and a municipal government that has neither the financial resources nor the personnel to deal with the problems, Lagos has become emblematic of the problems of overurbanization. Shanty housing is a direct consequence of widespread poverty; open sewers are a consequence of limited or nonexistent municipal resources.

Kate's story is typical of many of those who have either been brought up or migrated to Lagos, a city that according to statistics from the United Nations Human Settlements Programme (UN-HABITAT) currently has a population of about 15 million, and is projected to reach 20.2 million by 2010 and perhaps 23 million by 2015. Such numbers would place it third behind Tokyo and Mumbai in terms of the world's largest cities (see Chapter 10).

The recent population growth of Lagos has been phenomenal by any standards. Owing its origins to the Portuguese who, from 1472 onwards traded with what was once a small coastal Yoruba village, the settlement became known from the lakes (or *lagos* in Portuguese) that surrounded it, and developed as a centre for the slave trade until 1861 when Britain captured the city and abolished the activity. From 1914, Lagos served as the capital of Nigeria and grew at a sedate pace. In 1950, for example, it contained no more than 300 000 people, a total that rose to 5.09 million by 1976, when the purpose-built city of Abuja replaced it as the national capital.

By 1980, the city's population had at least doubled and was beginning to show the problems of unplanned growth. For example, by 2003, 42 slums (covering 1622 hectares) were officially acknowledged to form part of the city's make-up—a total that has risen to 62 in 1995, and 100 in 2003. In more general terms, by 2003, it is estimated that 65 percent of the city's population was living below the poverty line. With an estimated 600 000 people a year migrating from rural west Africa into Lagos each year, the growing size of the city demonstrates the "urbanisation of poverty," to use the words of a city official quoted by UN-HABITAT.[10]

Getting work in such a city of slums and deprivation becomes increasingly difficult, and its residents are driven to whatever means they can to survive. Consider, for example, George Packer's account of a visit he took to the city's main garbage dump in 2006:

> Hundreds of pickers were trudging across an undulating landscape of garbage. Every minute, another dump tuck backed and released its load . . . the pickers rushed over it, swarming dangerously close to the vehicles. Bent under their sacks, they worked quickly and with focus, knowing what they were looking for. Some pickers wanted only copper; others specialized in printer cartridges . . .

For many of the pickers, the dump not only provided their livelihood, but also their home. "Across the floor of the pit," Packer writes, "are hundreds of hovels, a sizable shantytown of dwellings made of plastic sheeting and scrap metal bound together with baling wire." They have, he adds, even built a mosque and a church, which they decorate at Christmas.[11]

The image of this garbage pit may serve as emblematic of the present situation of Lagos, but it is also seen by a number of urban theorists as key to the city's role as a "shock city," and to the role of similar cities now and in the future. The garbage pickers may be part of the extreme poverty of Lagos, but according to this interpretation, their ability to make a living out of almost nothing, and the ingenuity they show in doing it, represents opportunities. Rem Koolhaas, a professor at the Harvard Graduate School of Design, has described his experience flying over the same garbage dump in these terms: "What seemed, on ground level, an accumulation of dysfunctional movements, seemed from above an impressive performance, evidence of how well Lagos might perform if it were the third largest city in the world."

Writing of his ideas in his 2007 book *Lagos: How It Works,* Rem Koolhaas observes how there is almost a mutual dependency between the areas of extreme deprivation and those of development within the city, and describes how the interplay between them creates continual opportunities for improvising employment. The garbage pit pickers are but one example of this process. Another is the way in which massive traffic jams instantly become the site of informal markets as traders seize an opportunity to sell to suddenly immobile population. Lagos is not "a kind of backward situation," Koolhaas notes, but "an announcement of the future."[12]

As the shock city of the future, such an announcement may also be a warning. Certainly, to make a go of it in such an environment requires constant work. As one person told George Packer, "If you sit down, you will die of hunger." Others have seen such megacities as simply too big to provide the necessary economic niches for everyone—however creative they may be. "The really disturbing thing about Lagos's pickers and venders" Packer concludes, "is that their lives have essentially nothing to do with ours. They scavenge an existence beyond the margins of macroeconomics. They are, in the harsh terms of globalization, superfluous."

As geographers, we recognize that this is, in fact, a description of another type of space, and it is therefore going to be important over the coming years to see to what extent, if at all, shock cities play their role as its portal, and to what extent these spaces can at least become "places of hope" in the eyes of their residents.

[10]"A Tale of Two Cities: Lagos and Rio de Janeiro." *UN-Habitat Feature/Backgrounder.* World Urban Forum III: An International UN-Habitat Event on Sustainability, Vancouver 2006, available at **www.unhabitat.org.**

[11]George Packer, "The Megacity: Decoding the Chaos of Lagos." *New Yorker.* 13 November 2006, pp. 62–75; the quotations are from pp. 64–65.

[12]Rem Koolhaas, *Lagos: How It Works.* Baden, Switzerland: Lars Müller Publishing, 2007.

United States. The reorganizations of Toronto, Montreal, Ottawa, Hull, Winnipeg, Quebec City, and Halifax are as much an attempt by the provinces to win greater efficiencies from local government as they are responses to the growing status of Canadian suburbs.

These recent municipal mergers have provoked great debate. Critics mourn the loss of local identity and control over their own affairs. Proponents argue that the advantages of merger include a greater municipal tax base and the end to fragmented local planning jurisdictions that make integrated city planning impossible.

Infrastructure Problems   The continued growth of cities in the core countries has often ignored the need to renew original infrastructure (such as drains) built many years ago. Many cities still use water-cleaning technology dating from World War I. About one-third of all towns and cities in the United States have contaminated water supplies. Canada has its own examples where provincial cutbacks have been blamed for jeopardizing the health of many urban dwellers. A much-publicized example occurred in Walkerton, Ontario, in the spring of 2000, when the town's water supply was contaminated by *E. coli*. The outbreak contributed to seven deaths and illness in approximately 2300 people.

A number of coastal cities (such as Halifax, Dartmouth, and Victoria) still discharge untreated sewage into the sea and therefore need to have expensive treatment systems built. It is estimated that almost 50 percent of all waste-water treatment systems in North America are operating at 80 percent or more of their capacity, the level at which the federal government prohibits further industrial hookups in a community.

Poverty and Neighbourhood Decay   As we have seen, the relative lack of urban decay in Canadian cities has been one of the major differences between our urban geography and that of the United States. In U.S. cities, inner-city poverty and neighbourhood decay have become increasingly pronounced since the 1960s, as manufacturing, warehousing, and retailing jobs have moved out to suburban and edge-city locations and as many of the more prosperous households have moved out to be near these jobs. The spiral of neighbourhood decay begins with substandard housing occupied by low-income households that can afford to rent only a minimal amount of space. The consequent overcrowding not only causes greater wear and tear on the housing itself but also puts pressure on the neighbourhood infrastructure of streets, parks, schools, and playgrounds. The need for maintenance and repair increases quickly but is rarely met. Individual households cannot afford it, and landlords have no incentive to do so because they have a captive market. Public authorities face a fiscal squeeze and are, in any case, often indifferent to the needs of such neighbourhoods that have a relative lack of political power (**Figure 11.24**).

There is, meanwhile, a dismal cycle of poverty that intersects with these localized spirals of decay. The **cycle of poverty** involves the transmission of poverty and deprivation from one generation to another through a combination of domestic circumstances and local neighbourhood conditions. This cycle begins with a localized absence of employment opportunities and, in turn, a concentration of low incomes, poor housing, and overcrowded conditions. Such conditions are unhealthy. Overcrowding makes people vulnerable to poor health, which is compounded by poor diets. This, in turn, contributes to absenteeism from work, which results in decreased income. Similarly, absenteeism from school through illness contributes to the cycle of poverty by constraining educational achievement and occupational skills, thus leading to low wages. Crowding also produces psychological stress, which contributes to social disorganization and a variety of pathological behaviours, including crime and vandalism. Such conditions not only affect people's educational achievement and employment opportunities but can also lead to the *labelling* of the neighbourhood, whereby all residents may find their employment opportunities affected by the poor image of their neighbourhood.

cycle of poverty: transmission of poverty and deprivation from one generation to another through a combination of domestic circumstances and local neighbourhood conditions

Figure 11.24   Urban decay Urban decay is especially pronounced in the United States. Landlords of older inner-city apartments have little incentive to invest in maintenance or repair because they have a captive market of low-income households who have no other source of shelter. Equally, the low incomes of tenants mean that rents must be kept relatively low, leaving many landlords with small profit margins that leave nothing to spare for upkeep or improvement. Faced with rising property taxes and with profit margins that are unacceptably low, some landlords simply write off their property by abandoning it to long-term vacancy. This photograph shows crumbling residential housing in the Bronx, New York.

underclass: a subset of the poor, isolated from mainstream values and the formal labour market

Social trends have compounded the problems of these areas in many instances. Increased divorce rates and a high incidence of teen pregnancy have led to far greater numbers of single-parent families and a feminization of poverty. These families have been portrayed in much American writing on this topic as the core of a geographically, socially, and economically isolated underclass. The idea of an **underclass** refers to a group of individuals who experience a form of poverty from which it is very difficult to escape because of their isolation from mainstream values and the formal labour market. Isolated from the formal labour force and the social values and behavioural patterns of the rest of society, the underclass has been perceived as being subject to an increase in social disorganization and deviant behaviour. In cities in the United States, localized inner-city poverty is now characterized by senseless and unprovoked violence, premeditated and predatory violence, domestic violence, the organized violence of street gangs, and epidemic levels of AIDS and other communicable diseases—all closely associated with drug use and drug dealing.

Homelessness   One consequence of extreme poverty is *homelessness*. Chronic, long-term homelessness means not having customary and regular access to a conventional dwelling. This includes people who have to sleep in shelters, flophouse cubicles, and emergency dormitories and missions, as well as those sleeping in doorways, bus stations, cars, tents, temporary shacks, and cardboard boxes and on park benches and steam grates.

The number of homeless persons in the world's more affluent cities rose sharply in the mid-1970s. This was mainly a consequence of the increased poverty and the economic and social dislocation caused by economic restructuring and the transition to a globalized, postindustrial economy. Homelessness was intensified by the fiscal squeeze confronting central cities and by the trend for governments to cut back on welfare programs of all kinds. It was also intensified by the adoption of revolving-door policies of mental-health hospitals, which released large numbers of patients who had formerly been institutionalized. As a result, the homeless are now very visible throughout the major cities of the developed world, for example, in the subterranean world of the Paris Métro, under Budapest's bridges

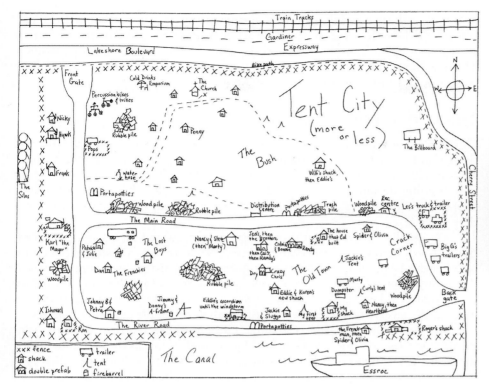

Figure 11.25   The new homeless
Tent City, Toronto   (*Source of Map: Down to This: Squalor and Splendour in a Big-City Shantytown* by Shaughnessy Bishop-Stall. Copyright © 2004 Shaughnessy Bishop-Stall. Reproduced by permission of Random House Canada.)

and in Warsaw's parks, in cardboard boxes close by glass office towers in downtown Tokyo, and near abandoned factories in Sydney and Melbourne. In Canada, although the most widely known example disappeared when the residents of Toronto's "Tent City" (**Figure 11.25**) were evicted in 2002, the homeless have now become an enduring feature of many Canadian towns and cities.

The Canadian Council for Social Development estimated in 1987 that there were between 130 000 and 250 000 homeless people in Canada. The federal government disputes the method used to reach this estimate and says that the true number is, almost by definition, unknowable. Consequently, Canada has no official statistics on the homeless.[13] Estimates of the number of homeless people in U.S. cities in the late 1990s varied a good deal. The estimate of the National Coalition for the Homeless is between 1.5 million and 3 million. Germany, with more than 1 million, has the most homeless in Europe, followed by Britain's 700 000 and France's 600 000. In the former Soviet Union, the "shock therapy" of free markets has brought homelessness to cities that had not experienced it for decades. In Moscow alone, almost 100 000 people became homeless during the 1990s.

What makes contemporary homelessness such a striking problem is not just the scale of the problem but also the nature of it. Whereas homelessness had previously involved white, adult males, relatively few of whom actually had to sleep outdoors, the new homeless are of all ethnic groups and include significant numbers

---

[13]This topic is the focus of continued debate. The Homelessness Partnership Strategy, a federal government initiative set up in 2006 to research and propose solutions to the problems of homelessness, discusses the difficulties of gathering data in its background document "Understanding Homelessness." Human Resources and Social Development Canada, Homelessness Partnership Strategy, 2008, available at **www.hrsdc.gc.ca/en/homelessness/general_information/understanding_homelessness.shtml**. In terms of individual cities, very useful material and statistics for Toronto can be found in the City of Toronto's *Housing and Homelessness Report Card, 2003*. Toronto: City of Toronto, 2003, at **www.toronto.ca/homelessness/**. The situation in Ottawa has been the subject of considerable work by a research team led by Carleton University geographer Fran Klodawsky; see, for example, her study "Landscapes on the Margins: Gender and Homelessness." *Gender, Place and Culture* 13(4), 2006, pp. 365–388.

of women, children, and the elderly. In Europe, estimates suggest that up to 70 percent of the homeless are under 20 years old, and official statistics show that more than 40 percent of the people receiving services for the homeless are women. The new homeless are much less likely to find shelter indoors, and so they have become a very visible feature of the public spaces of many cities.

The Urban Environment

Obviously, the Canadian environment places great stress on urban centres and those that live there. Most Canadian cities devote large sums to snow clearance, and our cities must accommodate the rigours of winter in plans for street layout and building design. It is even said that one reason for the success of indoor shopping malls in this country has been the sheltered retail environment that they provide.

It is equally apparent that Canadian cities, because of their large concentrations of people, pose a considerable environmental threat to their surroundings, whether this be in the form of city garbage trucked to distant abandoned mines or the construction of large dams to provide hydroelectricity for urban use. The debate on the utility of the "sustainable city" is therefore one that continues and takes into account the levels of consumption that Canadian urban life currently requires.

Less apparently, perhaps, Canadian cities have created their own environments, and these are not always as healthy or comfortable as those found outside the city. The examples of urban climate and urban health well illustrate this contention. We have already considered questions of urban health (see Chapter 3). Here, we consider the issue of urban climate.

It is well known that a city acts to create an **urban heat island** (**Figure 11.26**). This is not only because bricks and concrete absorb and radiate solar radiation but also because the range of activities that take place in a city (industry, domestic heating, etc.) create heat. Thus, on average, a city may be up to 3°C warmer than its surroundings. Research, published in 2008, by geographers at the University of Montreal showed absolute variations are far higher—the bare asphalt surface of downtown city parking lots can be several degrees above the city average.

The configuration of buildings, especially tower blocks, also can modify weather conditions as vortices are created and wind is funnelled along urban canyons. The example of Bloor Street in Toronto is particularly telling, for at certain times of the year, pedestrians are in grave danger of being blown over (**Figure 11.27**).

Through a combination of urban heat island, wind, and local topographic effects, cities act to concentrate the pollution that results from much of their own

urban heat island: an effect resulting from the absorption and radiation of thermal energy by buildings and roads, together with the heat generated by urban living, which causes the average city to be warmer than its surrounding countryside

Figure 11.26 The urban heat island: a general model The urban heat island effect results from the absorption and radiation of thermal energy by buildings and roads, together with the heat generated by urban living. The average annual temperatures in cities can be 0.3°C to 3°C higher than the surrounding countryside; average humidity can be 6 percent lower; average summer cloud cover is increased by 30 percent and average snowfalls reduced by 5 percent to 10 percent. (*Source:* W.M. Marsh, *Landscape Planning: Environmental Applications,* 2nd ed., 1991, p. 231. This material is used by permission of John Wiley & Sons, Inc.)

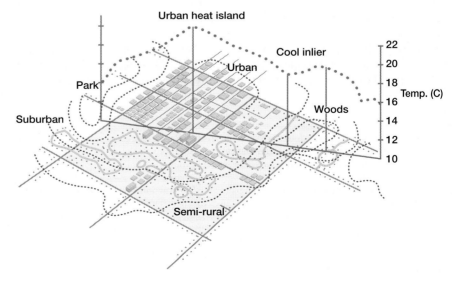

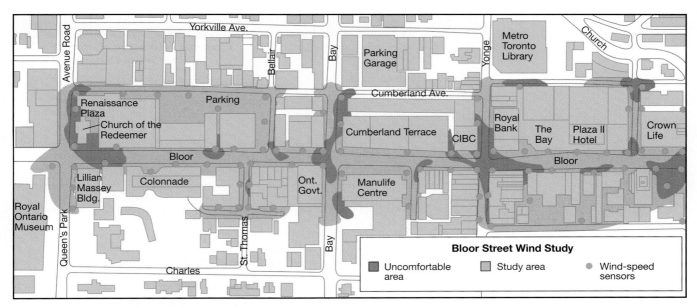

Figure 11.27   Wind speeds on Bloor Street, Toronto   The darker shading indicates areas that are uncomfortable for any pedestrian activity. Along parts of Bloor, a modest wind of 13 km/h (8 mph) can be accelerated to 19 km/h (12 mph) by the funnel effects of the street's buildings, a speed that will drive rain laterally. If the average wind speed is stronger than 32 km/h (20 mph; which it can be in the winter), occasional gusts of up to 48 km/h (30 mph) will be accelerated to more than 71 km/h (44 mph), a speed accepted as the limit for people's safety. At the foot of the Toronto Dominion Plaza (an office block not shown on this map), it has been necessary to string ropes for handholds.   (*Source: Canadian Geographic*, vol. 107, no. 1, February/March 1987. Rowan Williams Davies & Irwin and *Canadian Geographic*.)

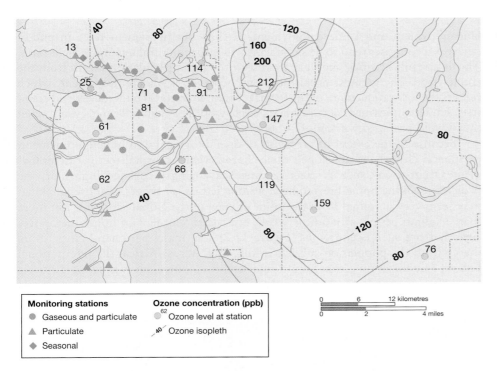

Figure 11.28   Ozone concentrations in Vancouver   The map shows the distribution of air-quality monitoring stations across the greater Vancouver Regional District. The numbers and isopleths show ozone concentrations in the lower atmosphere (in parts per billion [ppb]) at 4:00 p.m. on 3 September 1988 during a particularly severe period of air pollution. (*Note:* Lower level atmospheric ozone is harmful to humans if its concentrations pass certain levels. Federal government guidelines stipulate that 0 to 50 ppb/h is "desirable"; 50 to 80 ppb/h "acceptable"; and 80 to 150 ppb/h "tolerable," a level that needs abatement immediately to prevent damage to human health. It should be noted that the highest reading on this map is 212 ppb/h.) (*Source:* Reprinted with permission of the Publisher from *Vancouver and Its Region*, edited by Graeme Wynn and Timothy Oke. © University of British Columbia Press 1992. All rights reserved by the publisher.)

industrial and transportation activities. Smog has become an increasing problem of larger Canadian centres (**Figure 11.28**) and is a phenomenon that poses considerable health risks to some people, including the elderly and asthmatics.

The significance of these phenomena, especially when combined with increasing global warming, is that urban living will become much more stressful than it already is.

TABLE 11.2 Informal Employment in Selected Cities, 1998	
	Estimated Percentage of Population in Informal-Sector Occupations
Chennai (Madras), India	64.8
Delhi, India	65.7
Guayaquil, Ecuador	53.0
Lahore, Pakistan	50.7
Rio de Janeiro, Brazil	40.1
Yaoundé, Cameroon	46.0

Source: United Nations Human Settlements Programme, Global Urban Indicators Version 2 Database 2001. Available online at **http://ww2.unhabitat.org/programmes/guo/guo_indicators.asp.**

Problems of Unintended Metropolises

The problems of the dependent cities of the periphery stem from the way in which their demographic growth has outstripped their economic growth. High rates of long-term unemployment and underemployment mean that a significant proportion of the population of peripheral cities is forced to seek survival through the informal sector (**Table 11.2**). The low and unreliable wages of informal-sector jobs lead directly to further problems—chronic poverty and slum housing. On top of all this, the combination of rapid population growth and economic underdevelopment gives rise to transport and infrastructure problems and to problems of environmental degradation. Together, these problems are so severe that they pose almost impossible tasks for metropolitan governance and management.

Unemployment and Underemployment   Urban unemployment rates in underdeveloped countries tend to be significantly higher than rural unemployment rates. This is a result of cities' inability to absorb the rapid population influx from the countryside. The greatest urban problem, however, is underemployment, which reflects the low productivity of the formal economic sector in underdeveloped countries. **Underemployment** occurs when people work less than full time, even though they would prefer to work more hours.

Because of the extent of problems of unemployment and underemployment, peripheral cities have developed their characteristic informal sector of employment. Occupations, such as street vending, scavenging at garbage dumps, driving pedicabs, making home-brewed beer, writing letters for others, and dressmaking, may seem very marginal from the point of view of the global economy, but more than 1 billion people around the world must feed, clothe, and house themselves entirely from such occupations (**Figure 11.29**). In many peripheral cities, more than half of the population subsists in this way. Across Africa, the International Labour Organization estimates informal-sector employment is growing 10 times faster than formal-sector employment.

underemployment: the state of working less than full time, even though the people concerned would prefer to work more hours

Figure 11.29   Informal economic activities   In cities where jobs are scarce, people have to cope through the informal sector of the economy, which includes a very broad variety of activities.

Garbage scavenging, Manila, Philippines

Street market, Surabaja, Indonesia

Despite this side of the picture, the informal sector also has a few positive aspects. Pedicabs, for example, provide an affordable, nonpolluting means of transportation in crowded metropolitan settings. Garbage picking, while it may seem desperate and degrading in Western eyes, provides an important means of recycling and can provide a considerable, indirect subsidy to production—a subsidy often passed on to consumers in the core regions in the form of lower prices for goods and consumer products made in the periphery.

Consider, for example, the case of child garbage pickers in Phnom Penh, Cambodia. Orphaned by the atrocities of Pol Pot and the Khmer Rouge, a whole generation of children, who have no other means to support themselves, now find work as daily scavengers in dumps on the outskirts of the city. This situation, scandalous in the eyes of Canadian news reporters (who commented on this story on CBC as recently as April 2008), is tolerated and even condoned by city authorities, who claim that to prevent the children gaining access to the dump would be the equivalent of depriving them of the means to support themselves. Be that as it may, such explanations ignore the health consequences of such work, a problem perhaps best illustrated on film by a documentary on the work of eminent Canadian photographer Edward Burtynsky. Entitled *Manufactured Landscapes*, this 2006 film shows the often literally breathtaking scenes of garbage pickers collecting recyclable metals from the still-burning plastic shells of huge piles of obsolete computer equipment, discarded in countries such as Canada, and shipped to China where labour costs are much cheaper, and health standards are low enough to enable such work to continue. Arrangements such as these illustrate how abstract notions of core–periphery relations affect places and individuals.

Slums of Hope, Slums of Despair Unemployment, underemployment, and poverty mean overcrowding. In situations where urban growth has swamped the available stock of cheap housing and outstripped the capacity of builders to create affordable new housing, the inevitable outcome is makeshift, shanty housing that offers, at best, precarious shelter. Such housing has to be constructed on the cheapest and least desirable sites. Often, this means building on bare rock, over ravines, on derelict land, on swamps, or on steep slopes. Nearly always, it means building without any basic infrastructure of streets or utilities. Sometimes, it means adapting to the most extreme ecological niches, as in Lima, where garbage pickers actually live on the waste dumps, or in Cairo, where for generations, the poor have adapted catacombs and cemeteries into living spaces. In many cities, more than half of the housing is substandard. The United Nations estimated in 1999 that more than 1 billion people worldwide live in inadequate housing.

Faced with the growth of these slums, the first response of many governments has been to eradicate them. However, the thinking now is that informal-sector housing should be seen as a rational response to poverty. Shanty and squatter neighbourhoods provide affordable shelter and function as important reception areas for migrants to the city, with supportive communal organizations and informal employment opportunities that help them to adjust to city life. They can, in other words, be "slums of hope." City authorities, recognizing the positive functions of informal housing and self-help improvements, are now increasingly disposed to be tolerant and even helpful toward squatters, rather than sending in police and municipal workers with bulldozers (**Figure 11.30**).

Nevertheless, there are many shanty and squatter neighbourhoods where self-help and community organization do not emerge. Instead, grim and desperately miserable conditions prevail. These are "slums of despair." Consider, for example, the squatter settlement of Chheetpur in the city of Allahabad, India. The settlement's site is subject to flooding in the rainy season, and a lack of drainage leads to stagnant pools for much of the year. Two standpipes (outdoor taps) serve the entire population of 500, and there is no public provision for sanitation or the removal of household wastes. In this community, most people have food intakes of less than the recommended minimum of 1500 calories a day; 90 percent of all infants and

Self-help housing, Ndola, Zambia

Sites-and-services housing, Lusaka, Zambia

Figure 11.30 Self-help as a solution to housing problems Self-help is often the only solution to housing problems because migrants' wages are so low and so scarce that builders cannot construct even the most inexpensive new housing and make a profit and because municipalities cannot afford to build sufficient quantities of subsidized housing. One of the most successful ways of encouraging self-help housing is for municipal authorities to create the preconditions by clearing sites, putting in the footings for small dwellings, and installing a basic framework of water and sewage utilities. This "sites-and-services" approach has become the mainstay of urban housing policies in many peripheral countries.

children under the age of 4 years have less than the minimum calories needed for a healthy diet. More than half of the children and almost half of the adults have intestinal worm infections. Infant and child mortality is high—though nobody knows just how high—with malaria, tetanus, diarrhea, dysentery, and cholera being the principal causes of death among those under 5 years old.

Transport and Infrastructure Problems Even though the governments of peripheral cities typically spend nearly all of their budgets on transport and infrastructure in their race to keep up with population growth, conditions are bad and rapidly getting worse (**Figure 11.31**). In many of the world's peripheral and semiperipheral metropolises, sharp increases have occurred in the availability and use of automobiles. Some of the worst traffic tales come from Mexico City—where traffic backups total more than 90 kilometres (55 miles) each day, on average—and Bangkok, where the 24-kilometre (15-mile) trip into town from Don Muang Airport can take three hours. In São Paulo, gridlock can span 160 kilometres (100 miles), rush-hour traffic jams average 85 kilometres (53 miles) in length, and 15-hour traffic jams are not unusual.

Figure 11.31 Urban transportation Creative responses to the problem of transportation come in many forms, but their success is limited by the sheer congestion of overurbanization.

Outdoor standpipe, Ankara, Turkey   Street water pump, Raipur, India

Figure 11.32 Water supply problems
Many peripheral cities have grown so quickly, and under such difficult conditions, that large sections of the population do not have access to supplies of clean water. Where a public supply exists—a well or an outdoor standpipe—water consumption is limited by the time and energy required to collect water and carry it home. It is not rare for 500 or more people to have to share a single tap. Because low-income people work very long hours, the time spent waiting in line for water and then transporting buckets to homes is time that could have been used in earning an income. Limited quantities of water mean inadequate supplies for personal hygiene and for washing food, cooking utensils, and clothes. Where public agencies provide no water supply—as is common in squatter settlements—the poor often obtain water from private vendors and can pay 20 to 30 times the cost per litre paid by households with piped supplies. Water vendors probably supply about one-quarter of the population of peripheral metropolises.

Water supplies and sewerage also present acute problems for many cities. The World Bank estimates that worldwide, only about 70 percent of urban residents in less-developed countries have access to a satisfactory water source, and only about 40 percent are connected to sewers (90 percent of which discharge their waste untreated into a river, lake, or sea). Hundreds of millions of urban dwellers have no alternative but to use contaminated water—or at least water whose quality is not guaranteed (**Figure 11.32**).

In many cities, including Bangkok, Bogotá, Dar-es-Salaam, Jakarta, Karachi, and São Paulo, only one-quarter or one-third of all garbage and solid waste is collected and removed. The rest is partially recycled informally, tipped into gullies, canals, or rivers, or simply left to rot. Sewage services are just as bad. São Paulo has more than 1600 kilometres (1000 miles) of open sewers, and raw sewage from the city's slums drains into the Billings Reservoir, a major source of the city's drinking water.

Again, these problems provide opportunities for the informal sector. In many Asian cities, for example, human waste is removed overnight by handcart operators. Unfortunately, the waste is rarely disposed of properly and often ends up polluting the rivers or lakes from which the urban poor draw their water.

Environmental Degradation   With pressing problems of poverty, slum housing, and inadequate infrastructure, it is not surprising that peripheral cities are unable to devote many resources to environmental problems. Because of the speed of population growth, these problems are escalating rapidly. Industrial and human wastes pile up in lakes and lagoons, polluting long stretches of rivers, estuaries, and coastal zones. Groundwater is polluted through the leaching of chemicals from uncontrolled dumping sites, and the forests around many cities are being denuded by the demand of cities for timber and domestic fuels. This environmental degradation is, of course, directly linked to human health. People living in such environments have much higher rates of respiratory infections, tuberculosis, and diarrhea and much shorter life expectancies than people living in surrounding rural communities. Children in squatter settlements may be 50 times as likely to die before the age of 5 years than those born in affluent core countries.

In addition, air pollution has escalated to very harmful levels in many cities. With the development of a modern industrial sector and the growth of automobile ownership, but without enforceable regulations on pollution and vehicle

Figure 11.33 Cubatao, Brazil
Cubatao contains a high concentration of heavy industry—including a Union Carbide fertilizer factory and Brazilian oil, chemical, and steel factories—that was developed in the 1960s under a military government with little or no attempt to control pollution.

emissions, tonnes of lead, sulphur oxides, fluorides, carbon monoxide, nitrogen oxides, petrochemical oxidants, and other toxic chemicals are pumped into the atmosphere every day in large cities. The burning of charcoal, wood, and kerosene for fuel and cooking in low-income neighbourhoods also contributes significantly to dirty air. In cities where sewerage systems are deficient, the problem is compounded by the presence of airborne dried fecal matter. Worldwide, according to United Nations data, more than 1.1 billion people live in urban areas where air pollution exceeds acceptable levels.

Amid these generally dangerous and unpleasant environments, some places stand out as being particularly appalling. The city of Cubatao, Brazil, for example (**Figure 11.33**), has acquired a reputation in the neighbouring cities of São Paulo and Santos as the "Valley of Death." Most of the city's housing is of extremely poor quality, with many industrial workers living in shantytowns built on stilts above swamps. Toxic industrial wastes have been dumped in the surrounding forests and are contaminating the city's water supplies. Vegetation in and around the city has suffered substantially from air pollution, and because dying vegetation can no longer retain the soil on steeper slopes, landslides have become a danger to shanty dwellers. In 1984, hundreds of inhabitants were killed after a gasoline pipeline leaked into a swamp under one shanty and caught fire. As a result, the government of the state of São Paulo developed an extensive pollution-control program for Cubatao. The program has been successful in reducing levels of pollution, but Cubatao remains a deadly environment. The Cubatao River, once an important source of fish, now supports only a few eels and some hardy crabs that are too toxic for humans to eat. Local hospitals routinely accept young children to breathe medicated air; but infant mortality rates—along with the incidence of stillborn and deformed babies, and rates of death from tuberculosis, pneumonia, leukopenia, bronchitis, emphysema, and asthma—remain high.

Governance and Management The governments of towns and cities in the world's periphery are faced with tremendous problems. Just keeping up with the rate of physical and demographic growth presents an enormous challenge. Typical growth rates mean that cities' physical infrastructure of roads, bridges, and utilities needs to be tripled every 10 years. Meanwhile, most city governments find it nearly impossible to take care of the daily upkeep of their existing infrastructure because of the wear and tear that is caused by overurbanization. Somehow, basic services have to be provided to populations that cannot afford to pay more than a fraction of their costs.

The governance of most peripheral countries tends to be highly centralized, with relatively little political power allocated to city or metropolitan governments. In addition, city and metropolitan governments are typically fragmented—both geographically and functionally—as well as being understaffed and underfinanced.

Although many of the individuals involved do the best they can, metropolitan governance and management seem doomed to be ineffective and inefficient until some way can be devised to improve the institutional framework (in both geographical and democratic terms) and reduce the financial constraints faced by municipal governments. This last point, regarding financial constraints, brings us back to local–global interdependencies once again, for the financial predicament of peripheral cities is ultimately tied to their dependent role in the global economic system.

CONCLUSION

Patterns of land use and the functional organization of economic and social subareas in cities are partly a product of the economic, political, and technological conditions at the time of the city's growth and partly a product of regional cultural values. Geographers can draw on four particularly useful perspectives in looking at patterns of land use within North American cities: an economic perspective that emphasizes competition for space, an economic perspective that emphasizes functional linkages between land uses, a sociocultural perspective that emphasizes ethnic congregation and segregation, and a historical perspective that emphasizes the influence of transportation technology and infrastructure investment.

In many ways, the most striking contrasts in urban structure are to be found between the cities of the core regions and those of the periphery. The evolution of the unintended metropolis of the periphery has been very different from the evolution of metropolitan areas in the world's core regions. Similarly, the problems they face are very different. In the core regions, urban change is dominated by the consequences of an economic transformation to a postindustrial economy. Traditional manufacturing and related activities have been moved out of central cities. New postindustrial activities have begun to cluster in redeveloped CBDs and in edge cities around metropolitan fringes.

In other parts of the world, patterns of land use and the functional organization of economic and social subareas are quite different, reflecting different historical legacies and different environmental and cultural influences. The basic trend affecting the cities of the world's periphery is demographic—the phenomenal rates of natural increase and in-migration that have given rise to overurbanization. The example of Lagos provides some sobering insights into the human consequences of overurbanization. An ever-growing informal sector of the economy, in which people seek economic survival, is reflected in extensive areas of shanty housing. High rates of unemployment, underemployment, and poverty generate acute social problems, which are overwhelming for city governments that are understaffed and underfunded. If present trends continue, such problems are likely to characterize increasing numbers of the world's largest settlements. In the next chapter, we consider this question as part of a broader discussion of future geographies.

MAIN POINTS REVISITED

- **The typical North American city is structured around a central business district (CBD); a transitional zone; suburbs; secondary business districts and commercial strips; industrial districts; and, in larger metropolitan areas, edge cities.**
  This internal organization of cities reflects the way that they function, both to bring certain people and activities together and to sort them out into neighbourhoods and functional sub-areas.

- **The overall structure of North American cities is shaped primarily by competition for territory and location. In general, all categories of land users—commercial and industrial, as well as residential—compete for the most convenient and accessible locations within the city.**

An important exception is that wealthier households tend to trade off the convenience of accessibility for larger amounts of (relatively cheap) suburban space. Poorer households, unable to afford the recurrent costs of transportation, are forced to trade off living space for accessibility to jobs so that they end up in high-density areas at expensive locations near their low-wage jobs.

- **Cities experiencing high rates of in-migration tend to become structured into a series of concentric zones of neighbourhoods of different ethnicity, demographic composition, and social status through processes of invasion and succession.**

Within each concentric zone, a mosaic of distinctive neighbourhoods tends to develop—ecological niches where particular mixes of people have come to dominate a particular territory or geographical setting.

■ **In cities where growth has been less dominated by successive waves of immigrant ethnic groups, neighbourhood patterns tend to be structured around the development of industrial corridors and high-class residential corridors.**
Industry tends to follow transportation corridors along low-lying, flat land where space exists for large factories, warehouses, and railway marshalling yards. Working-class residential areas grow up around these corridors, following them out in sector-shaped neighbourhoods as they grow. High-status residential districts, in contrast, tend to grow outward from a different side of town, often following a ridge of high ground (free from flooding and with panoramic views).

■ **Urban structure varies a good deal from one region of the world to another because of the influence of history, culture, and the different roles that cities have played within the world-system.**
European cities have evolved under circumstances very different from those faced by North American cities; consequently, European cities exhibit some distinctive characteristics in urban form. European urban ideals have influenced many colonial cities, while the new cities of the world's peripheral regions are distinctive because of their explosive growth.

■ **Geographers are interested in the distinctive physical features of urban landscapes because they can be read as multi-layered texts that show how cities have developed, how they are changing, and how people's values and intentions take expression in the urban form.**
The built environment is what gives expression, meaning, and identity to the various forces involved in urbanization. It becomes a biography of urban change, offering people cues and contexts for behaviour, landmarks for orientation, and symbols that reinforce collective values.

■ **The most acute problems of the postindustrial cities of the world's core regions are localized in the central city areas, which have borne the brunt of restructuring from an industrial to a postindustrial economy.**
In these areas, there are several interrelated problems: fiscal problems, infrastructure problems, and localized spirals of neighbourhood decay, cycles of poverty, and homelessness.

■ **Canadian cities are different from U.S. cities.**
Unlike U.S. cities, Canadian cities have avoided inner-city decline, have experienced far greater levels of gentrification, are more compact in form, and have experienced greater government involvement in their management and planning.

■ **The problems of the cities of the periphery stem from the way in which their demographic growth has outstripped their economic growth.**
The result is high rates of long-term unemployment and underemployment; low and unreliable wages of informal-sector jobs; chronic poverty; and slum housing. The low rates of economic growth of these peripheral cities reflect their dependent position in the global economy.

■ **Cities are created as "places" and can become "place makers."**
The physical form of a city (its buildings and layout) reflects the culture that built it. In turn, that form comes to shape our image of the city.

Key Terms

Beaux Arts (p. 493)	**edge cities** (p. 471)	**postmodern urban**
central business district	**Garden City movement** (p. 480)	**design** (p. 495)
(CBD) (p. 470)	**gentrification** (p. 471)	**segregation** (p. 472)
City Beautiful movement (p. 480)	**invasion and succession** (p. 475)	**underclass** (p. 502)
congregation (p. 472)	**isotropic surface** (p. 473)	**underemployment** (p. 506)
cycle of poverty (p. 501)	**minority groups** (p. 472)	**urban heat island** (p. 504)
dualism (p. 497)	**modern movement** (p. 494)	**zone in transition** (p. 470)

Additional Reading

Angotti, T. *Metropolis 2000*. New York: Routledge, 1993.

Artibise, A.F.J., and G.A. Stetler (eds.). *The Usable Past: Planning and Politics in the Modern Canadian City*. Toronto: Macmillan, 1979.

Bourne, L.S., and D.F. Ley (eds.). *The Changing Social Geography of Canadian Cities*. Montreal and Kingston: McGill–Queen's University Press, 1993.

Bradbury, B., and T. Myers (eds.) *Negotiating Identities in 18th and 20th-Century Montreal*. Vancouver: UBC Press, 2005.

Brunn, S., and J.F. Williams (eds.). *Cities of the World*, 2nd ed. New York: Harper Collins, 1993.

Bunting, T., and P. Filion (eds.). *Canadian Cities in Transition: The Twenty-First Century*, 2nd ed. Toronto: Oxford University Press, 2000.

Caulfield, J., and L. Peake (eds.). *City Lives & City Forms: Critical Research & Canadian Urbanism*. Toronto: University of Toronto Press, 1996.

Florida, R. *Cities and the Creative Class*. New York: Routledge, 2005.

Florida, R. *Who's Your City? How the Creative Economy Is Making Where You Live the Most Important Decision of Your Life*. Toronto: Random House of Canada, 2008.

Germain, A., and D. Rose. *Montreal: The Quest for a Metropolis*. Chichester: John Wiley, 2000.

Goldberg, M.A., and J. Mercer. *The Myth of the North American City: Continentalism Challenged*. Vancouver: University of British Columbia, 1986.

Gugler, J. (ed.). *Cities in the Developing World: Issues, Theory, and Policy*. New York: Oxford University Press, 1997.

Hall, P. *Cities in Civilization*. New York: Pantheon, 1998.

Hall, P. *Cities of Tomorrow*. New York: Blackwell, 1988.

Knox, P.L. *Urbanization: An Introduction to Urban Geography*. Englewood Cliffs, NJ: Prentice Hall, 1994.

Knox, P.L., and S. Pinch. *Urban Social Geography*, 4th ed. London: Longman Scientific, 2000.

Lemon, J. *Toronto Since 1918: An Illustrated History*. Toronto: James Lorimer; Ottawa: National Museum of Civilization, 1985.

Musterd, S., W. Ostendorf, and M. Breebaart. *Multi-Ethnic Metropolis: Patterns and Policies*. Boston: Kluwer Academic, 1998.

Potter, R.B., and S. Lloyd-Evans. *The City in the Developing World*. Harlow, UK: Addison Wesley Longman, 1998.

Simpson, M. *Thomas Adams and the Modern Planning Movement: Britain, Canada and the United States, 1900–1940*. London: Mansell, 1984.

Sloan, J. (ed.) *Urban Enigmas: Montreal, Toronto, and the Problem of Comparing Cities*. Montreal and Kingston: McGill-Queen's University Press, 2007.

Smith, D.A. *Third World Cities in Global Perspective*. Boulder, CO: Westview Press, 1996.

Taylor, J.H. *Ottawa: An Illustrated History*. Toronto: James Lorimer; Ottawa: National Museum of Civilization, 1986.

Taylor, Z., and J. van Nostrand. *Shaping the Toronto Region, Past, Present and Future*. Toronto: The Neptis Foundation, 2008.

U.S. Congress, Office of Technology Assessment. *The Technological Reshaping of Metropolitan America*. OTA-ETI-643. Washington, DC: U.S. Government Printing Office, 1995.

U.S. Department of Housing and Urban Development. *The State of the Cities 1999*. Washington, DC: U.S. Department of Housing and Urban Development, 1999.

Vance, J.E. Jr. *The Continuing City: Urban Morphology in Western Civilization*. Baltimore: Johns Hopkins University Press, 1990.

Wynn G., and T. Oke (eds.). *Vancouver and Its Region*. Vancouver: University of British Columbia, 1992.

Exercises

Here you will find exercises and activities for each chapter. Unplugged exercises help you review chapter discussions, and pose ideas for your own human geography research. On the Companion Website exercises will require you have access to the internet.

Unplugged

1. Collect a week's worth of local newspapers, and review the coverage of urban problems. What kinds of problems are covered and for what kinds of cities? Compile a list of such categories, and then carefully analyze the content of the week's coverage, calculating the amount of space devoted to each category of problems.

2. On a tracing-paper overlay of a street map of your town or city, plot the distribution of houses and apartments for sale or rent in different cost brackets. (You can obtain the information from the real estate pages of your city's local newspaper; in smaller cities, you may have to gather data from several different issues of the paper a week or more apart in order for a pattern to emerge. Your local library will likely have back issues.) What can you say about the spatial distribution that is revealed?

3. What famous buildings, landmarks, or cityscapes are associated with the following cities: Amsterdam, Athens, Moscow, Ottawa, San Francisco, Rio de Janeiro? What is the significance for these cities of having such symbolic locales?

4. Most cities consist of "ordinary" cityscapes that are strongly evocative because they are widely understood as being a particular kind of place. Write a brief essay (500 words, or two double-spaced, typed pages) describing an "ordinary" cityscape with which you are familiar. What are its principal features, and why might it be considered typical of a particular kind of place?

On the Companion Website

This book has its own Companion Website where you will find additional resources—maps, photographs, data—as well as exercises and activities that relate to each chapter. To complete the Companion Website exercises, go to **www.pearsoned.ca/knox**. The following is a summary of the types of exercises created for this chapter.

1. The exercises for this chapter focus on the diversity of urban areas and their importance in spatial organization and the evolution of societies. One observer described cities as "a place of our meeting with the other," while another critic observed that urban dwellers are always "people in the presence of otherness." Diversity is one certainty in urban geographies, from the energy of everyday life in the cities to alienation and a loss of community. In describing the urban structure of contemporary cities, there are many realities that can be revealed through the internet.

2. The CBC Video Case, Big Thirst, that accompanies this chapter has been chosen to highlight some of the challenges of environmental change for cities discussed in this chapter, particularly how the predicted decline of water supplies in the Prairies will affect both the urban and rural inhabitants of that region within the next 20 years. You will find a link to the CBC video, the video case, questions, and resources on the Companion Website for this chapter.

Future Geographies

The Sharp Centre for Design at Ontario's College of Art and Design   Instead of building on land next to the existing college, architect Will Alsop's 2004 two-storey extension stands 26 metres on 12 legs *above* the existing buildings of the college. The design conserves urban space and represents a type of thinking "outside the box" that may be a hallmark of the future.

According to a news item in the *Vancouver Sun* on 8 April 2008, Google Earth is now able to show close-up views of United Nations' refugee camps and aid projects. The search engine's mapping platform, used by an estimated 350 million people (mainly to view three-dimensional satellite images of holiday destinations) has been adapted to show browsable, high-definition pictures of humanitarian crisis zones. Rebecca Moore, head of Earth Outreach for Google, told experts at the Office of the United Nations High Commissioner for Refugees that they could add video interviews of refugees, photographs of displacement crises and educational text to Google's satellite backdrop to inform casual users about ongoing or potential crises. "Use Google Earth to tell your story," she urged.[1]

In this way a technology such as Google offers us the chance to learn more about the effects of change across parts of the world we may never visit, and to be made very aware of our abilities to affect solutions. Such "Future Geographies" combine the results of changing technologies with the fundamental geographical processes we have considered throughout this book to produce new worlds—worlds in which many new geographical questions can be posed.

Will the internet bring about new patterns of human interaction? Will globalization bring an end to distinctive regional cultures? Will we be able to cope with the environmental stresses that increasing industrialization and rapid population growth will bring to many parts of the world? Will more countries move up from peripheral status to join the semiperiphery and core of the future world-system? What kind of problems will the future bring for local, regional, and international development? What new technologies are likely to have the most impact in reshaping human geographies? These are just a few of the many questions that spring from the key themes in human geography that we have examined in Chapters 5 through 11. This chapter examines some scenarios for future geographies, drawing on the principles and concepts established in Chapters 1 through 4.

MAIN POINTS

- In some ways, the future is already here, embedded in the world's institutional structures and in the dynamics of its populations.
- New and emerging technologies that are likely to have the most impact in reshaping human geographies include advanced transportation technologies, biotechnology, materials technologies, and information technologies.

---

[1] Laura MacInnis, "Search Engine's Platform a 'Significant Tool,' " *Vancouver Sun*, 8 April 2008.

- We must not underestimate the scope and impact of future environmental change in shaping future geographies.
- The changes involved in shaping future geographies will inevitably bring some critical issues, conflicts, and threats, including important geographical issues that centre on scale, boundaries, and territories; on cultural dissonance; and on the sustainability of development.

MAPPING OUR FUTURE

It is important to be able to envisage the future. We have to live in the world for a while, and we naturally want to leave it in good shape for future generations. Canada, with its vast territory and growing population drawn from all parts of the globe, has the human and physical resources to shape its future, not just react to current pressures. We need, therefore, to be able to identify the changes that the future might bring so that we can begin to work toward the most desirable outcomes. The problem is that predicting the future can be a risky business. The uncertainties of geopolitical change, the unexpectedness of technological breakthroughs, and the complexity of environmental change all compound one another to make our future seem, at first glance, highly unpredictable.

Nevertheless, there is no shortage of visionary projections (**Figure 12.1**). Broadly speaking, these can be divided into two sorts of scenarios—optimistic and pessimistic. Optimistic futurists stress the potential for technological innovations to discover and harness new resources, to provide faster and more effective means of transportation and communication, and to enable new ways of living. This sort of futurism is characterized by science-fiction cities with towering skyscrapers and spaceship-style living pods, by ecological harmony, and by unprecedented social and cultural progress through the information highways of cyberspace. It projects a world that will be stabilized and homogenized by supranational or even "world" governments. The sort of geography implied by such scenarios is rarely spelled out. Space and place, we are led to believe, will be transcended by technological fixes.

Pessimistic futurists, however, stress the finite limitations of Earth's resources, the fragility of its environment, and population growth rates that exceed the capacity of the peripheral regions to sustain them. This sort of doomsday forecasting is characterized by scenarios that include irretrievable environmental degradation, increasing social and economic polarization, and the breakdown of law and order. The sort of geography associated with these scenarios is rarely explicit, but it usually involves the probability of a sharp polarization between the haves and have-nots at every geographical scale.

Fortunately, we don't have to choose between these two extreme scenarios— between visions of utopia and dystopia. Using what we have learned from the study of human geography, we can suggest a more grounded outline of future geographies. To do so, we must first glance back at the past. Then, looking at present trends and using what we know about processes of geographical change and principles of spatial organization, we can begin to map out the kinds of geographies that the future most probably holds.

Looking back at the way that the geography of the world-system has unfolded, we can see now that a fairly coherent period of economic and geopolitical development occurred between the outbreak of World War I (in 1914) and the collapse of the Soviet Union (in 1989). Some historians refer to this period as the "short twentieth century." It was a period when the modern world system developed its triadic core of the United States, Western Europe, and Japan; when geopolitics was based on an East–West divide; and when geoeconomics was based on a North–South divide. This was a time when the geographies of specific places and regions within these larger frameworks were shaped by the needs and opportunities of technology systems that were based on the internal combustion engine, oil

Scenario 1—The world becomes populated by consumers rather than citizens. Technology breeds unlimited, customized choices. Computers do increasing amounts of white-collar work. Real leisure increases. Governments become virtual corporations and come to rely on electronic voting. Southeast Asia and the coast of China manufacture most of the world's goods and consume almost half themselves. Latin America is their branch office. Japan gets richer and unhappier. Russia exports trouble in the form of neo-religious cultists and mafioso. The United States and Europe become large theme parks.

Scenario 2—The world becomes dominated by a new international division of labour, based on an intensive use of networked communications. Technology dominates global culture, which turns inward toward personal spaces. Old public spaces crumble, and ethnic subcultures give way to a patchwork of unbridled individual variety. Europe is wracked by civil strife as its collectively oriented civilization unravels. Russia rebounds, while Japan lags. China and the developing countries become huge flea markets where anything goes.

Scenario 3—Economic development is slowed in reaction to earlier decades of high crime and chaos. Europe experiences a second renaissance, becoming a moral beacon. Communitarian values become stronger, and governments undertake large-scale public works directed at environmental improvement. Dirty technologies are tightly regulated, and this increases the income gap between the core and peripheral regions. Asia and Latin America become refuges for the young and restless of the core regions who find environmentalism and communitarianism too dogmatic; they settle in "free economic zones" where their education and their energy help stimulate economic growth.

Scenario 4—The world is divided into three rigid and distinct trading blocs, but political boundaries are more fragmented than ever. The European Union, including most of Europe and Russia, has a common currency and tight border controls. The Asia–Pacific region evolves into a trading bloc in response to the European Union, but it is weakened by internal political and economic differences. Mexico collapses under civil war. Canada breaks up after Quebec's withdrawal. The third trading bloc is centred on the Indian Ocean, with India, South Africa, Saudi Arabia, and Iran as the key members. Throughout the world, political conflicts and weaknesses allow widespread terrorism, organized crime, and environmental degradation.

Scenario 5—The world settles into small, powerful city-states. Civic pride blossoms, and governments use advanced technologies to create public works of an unprecedented scale and scope. Rural areas of the world are second class but have widespread virtual hookups. Europe fractionalizes into more than 50 countries; China, Russia, Brazil, and India devolve into black-market ethnic states. Gangs and militia in peripheral countries and old inner-city areas transform into political law-and-order machines.

Figure 12.1 Future scenarios In some ways, the future is already here, embedded in the world's institutional structures and the dynamics of its populations. However, there are some aspects of the future that we can only guess at. Given the impossibility of knowing precisely how the future will unfold, business strategists attempt to make decisions that play out well across several possible futures. To find the most robust strategy, several different scenarios are created, each representing a plausible outcome. (*Source:* L. Beach, "How to Build Scenarios." *Wired Scenarios* 1.01, October 1995, pp. 74–81; P. Schwartz, "The New World Disorder." *Wired Scenarios* 1.01, October 1995, pp. 104–106.)

and plastics, electrical engineering, aerospace industries, and electronics. In this short century, the modern world was established, along with its now-familiar landscapes and spatial structures—from the industrial landscapes of the core to the unintended metropolises of the periphery, from the voting blocs of the west to the newly independent nation-states of the south.

Looking around now, much of the established familiarity of the modern world and its geographies seems to be disappearing, about to be overwhelmed by a series of unexpected developments, or obscured by a sequence of unsettling juxtapositions. The United States is giving economic aid to Russia; Eastern European countries want to join NATO and the European Union; Germany has unified, but Czechoslovakia and Yugoslavia have disintegrated; Israel has established a fragile peace with Egypt and Jordan; South Africa has been transformed, through an unexpectedly peaceful revolution, to black majority rule. Meanwhile, Islamic terrorists shoot up tourist buses, bomb office buildings, and sabotage the World Trade towers; former communist Russian ultranationalists have become comradely with German neo-Nazis; Hindus, Sikhs, and Muslims are in open warfare in South Asia; and Somali pirater seize international shipping in the waters of the Arabian Sea and Indian Ocean.

In short, we have entered a period of transition since 1989. The economic and cultural flux of the world has provided some very colourful examples:

> McDonald's, Pizza Hut, and American dollars are everywhere. Overnight jet flights and international direct dialing to North America afford the basic infrastructure for South American narcocapitalism. . . . Parts of Africa are returning to a hunting and gathering economy. Russia's markets are often empty and its factories are idle, but billions in oil, metals, lumber, and weapons are smuggled, like dope from Bolivia or Burma [now Myanmar], to foreign markets through Kaliningrad. Moscow's GUM department store has a Benetton, while the city's nouveau riche mafia "entrepreneurs" ostentatiously zoom around in German BMWs and Mercedes Benzes, courtesy, in many cases, of lucrative car theft rings operating in Western Europe. Bloomingdale's sells Red Army watches at the costume jewelry counter. . . . Communist China's "military" industries are making millions selling knock-off running shoes to Singapore traders and reverse-engineered strategic rockets to Saudi princes.
>
> . . . Karaoke machines offer ancient Motown hits to American corporate managers, Hong Kong entrepreneurs, and German sex tourists in Thailand. Croatian-Canadian teenagers in Ontario hold car washes to buy weapons in South Africa for Zagreb's war efforts. . . . Global superband U2 entertains stadium audiences in Europe with channel surfing spectacles and live phone calls to the White House and trapped victims in Sarajevo. Meanwhile, Croatian, Moslem, and Serbian snipers listen to heavy metal on Sony Walkmans as they shoot up each other's families. Some of Iran's, Pakistan's, Libya's, and Mexico's largest urban populations are located in Paris, London, Milan, and Los Angeles. Disneyland now claims territory in Europe, Asia, and North America.[2]

These examples show that we cannot simply project our future geographies from the landscapes and spatial structures of the past. Rather, we must map them out from a combination of existing structures and budding trends. We have to anticipate, in other words, how the shreds of tradition and the strands of contemporary change will be rewoven into new landscapes and new spatial structures.

Although this is certainly a speculative and tricky undertaking, we can draw with a good deal of confidence on what we know about processes of geographical change and principles of spatial organization. The study of human geography has taught us to understand spatial change as a composite of local place-making processes (see Chapter 6) that are subject to certain principles of spatial organization and that operate within the dynamic framework of the world-system (Chapter 2).

---

[2]G. O'Tuathail and T. Luke, "Present at the (Dis)integration: Deterritorialization and Reterritorialization in the New Wor(l)d Order." *Annals of the Association of American Geographers* 84, 1994, pp. 381–382.

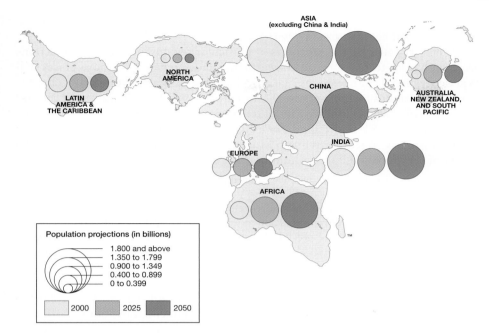

Figure 12.2   Population geography of the future   Population projections show a very marked disparity between world regions, with core countries and core regions growing very little in comparison with the periphery.   (*Source:* Map projection, Buckminster Fuller Institute and Dymaxion Map Design, Santa Barbara, CA. The word *Dymaxion* and the Fuller Projection Dymaxion™ Map design are trademarks of the Buckminster Fuller Institute, Santa Barbara, California, © 1938, 1967, & 1992. All rights reserved. Data from United Nations Population Division, *Long-Range World Population Projections, 1999 Revision.* New York: Population Division of the UN Department of Economic and Social Affairs, 1999.)

It has also taught us that many important dimensions exist to spatial organization and spatial change, from the demographic dimension (Chapter 3) to the urban (Chapters 10 and 11) and the cultural (Chapter 5).

As we look ahead to the future, we can appreciate that some dimensions of human geography are more certain than others. In some ways, the future is already here, embedded in the world's institutional structures and the dynamics of its populations. We know, for example, a good deal about the demographic trends of the next quarter-century, given present populations, birth and death rates, and so on (see Chapter 3; **Figure 12.2**). We also know a good deal about the distribution of environmental resources and constraints (Chapters 4 and 8), about the characteristics of local and regional economies (Chapter 7), and about the legal and political frameworks (Chapter 9) within which geographical change will probably take place.

However, we can only guess at some aspects of the future. Two of the most speculative realms are those of politics and technology. Although we can foresee some of the possibilities (maybe a spread and intensification of ethno-nationalism, perhaps a new railway era based on high-speed trains), politics and technology are both likely to spring surprises at any time. Such surprises (a political revolution in China? war between India and Pakistan? unanticipated breakthroughs in biotechnology?) can cause geographies to be rewritten suddenly and dramatically (as we have seen all too clearly since the events of 11 September 2001). As we review the prospects for geographical change, therefore, we must always be mindful that our prognoses are all open to the unexpected. As we shall see, this is perhaps our biggest cause for optimism.

GLOBAL OUTLOOK, LOCAL PROSPECTS

For many years now, such organizations as the United Nations and the World Bank have prepared forecasts of the world economy. These forecasts are based on economic models that take data on macro-economic variables (for example, trends in countries' gross domestic product, their imports and exports, their economic structure, their investment and savings performance, and their demographic dynamism) and use known relationships between and among these variables to predict future outcomes. The problem is that economic projection is an inexact science. Economic models are not able to take into account the changes brought about by major technological innovations, significant geopolitical shifts, governments' willingness and ability to develop strong economic policies, or the rather mysterious longer-term ups and downs that characterize the world economy.

When we focus on the prospects of particular regions and places, projections are even harder to make because we often cannot predict how those places will experience global change. Some places will be able to benefit from future changes in ways we cannot imagine at present; other areas will find changes spell the end for a particular way of life. We cannot tell. But, as geographers, we do know some important truths. We understand, for example, the importance of place. Thus, we are not surprised to read in William Mitchell's fascinating recent reflection on the effects of the global digital revolution on our cities, *e-topia*, that

> [i]n the twenty-first century, then, we can ground the condition of civilized urbanity less upon the accumulation of things and more upon the flow of information, less upon geographic centrality and more upon electronic connectivity, less upon expanding consumption of scarce resources and more upon intelligent management. . . . But the power of place will still prevail. As traditional locational imperatives weaken, we will gravitate to settings that offer particular cultural, scenic, and climatic attractions—those unique qualities that cannot be pumped through a wire—together with those face-to-face interactions we care most about.[3]

We also know that spatial inequalities are part and parcel of many of the processes shaping our social and economic world and we should not be surprised to see that these continue to act in the future. Certainly, we can expect that future geographies are structured by an even greater gap between the haves and have-not parts of the world. Perhaps ironically, in that his communiqués are issued via the internet (a medium that many have argued will act as a great leveller between peoples because it eliminates distance), Mexican Zapatist guerilla leader Subcomandante Marcos has described the opening up of the global economy as a death sentence for the poor. The gap between the world's core areas and the periphery has already begun to widen significantly. The United Nations has calculated that the ratio of GDP per capita (measured at constant prices and exchange rates) between the developed and developing areas of the world increased from 10:1 in 1970 to 12:1 in 1985, and 13:1 in 2000.

Economic disparities are no less marked if we look at the differences within individual countries. In fact, the existence of cores and peripheries at all scales is an aspect of the world-system model (see Chapter 2). Knowing this theoretically, however, does not make the plight of those affected any easier to bear. The situation of those who find themselves homeless and on the streets in Vancouver's Downtown Lower Eastside, the fear of environmental harm that affects those living beside the toxic Tar Ponds in Sydney (Nova Scotia), the poverty that characterizes many of Canada's Aboriginal peoples—these are but three examples among the many sad indictments of geography's ability to produce spatial inequalities in Canada.

The indications are that for many groups of people in Canada, these disparities are considerable, deeply entrenched, and likely to continue unless some fundamental steps are taken in the next few years. Writing in 2001, Evelyn Peters, a geographer at the University of Saskatchewan, observed that in 1981, the "average individual income for Registered Indians [that is, those registered according to the Indian Act] was 56.7 percent of that for all Canadians; in 1996, it was 59.2 percent."[4] (According to census statistics for 1996, the average annual income of Canadians

---

[3]William Mitchell, *e-topia: Urban Life, Jim—But Not As We Know It*. Cambridge, MA: Massachusetts Institute of Technology Press, 1999. The quotation is from p. 155.

[4]Evelyn Peters, "Geographies of Aboriginal People in Canada." *Canadian Geographer* 45, 2001, p. 139. As Peters herself cautions, data on income for Aboriginal people are affected by a general reluctance of Aboriginals to participate in the federal census (see Chapter 3). Although we cannot, therefore, insist on the precision of these estimates, it seems likely that the average income level discrepancies between the general and the Aboriginal population are too large to be wholly explained by incomplete data. The 2001 census data on personal income are available at **www.statcan.gc.ca**.

was $25 196, but among Aboriginal peoples in Canada, in that year, the equivalent figure was only $15 699.) Peters goes on to observe that "in 1981, 38 percent of the Registered Indian population 15 and over was employed, compared to 60 percent of the Canadian population. In 1996, 39.5 percent of the Registered Indians 15 and older were employed, compared to 58.9 percent of all Canadians."

There are, however, some signs for a cautious optimism. The *2002 Human Development Report,* released on 24 July 2002 by the United Nations Development Programme (UNDP), "singled out Canada for praise in dealing with income disparities"[5] according to press coverage in the *Globe and Mail* that day. The report noted that although incomes had increased over the last 20 years in the countries in the Organisation for Economic Co-operation and Development (OECD), the disparity between the rich and poor had also increased in most of these countries during that period. "However," as the *Globe and Mail* observes, "Canada and Denmark have bucked the trend by maintaining stable or slightly reduced inequalities." How was this achieved? The *2002 Human Development Report* notes, "[T]his was achieved primarily through fiscal policy and social transfers—indicating that with political will, nothing is inevitable about inequality increasing with rising incomes."

In spite of the globalization of the world-system (and in many ways *because* of it), much of the world has been all but written off by the bankers and corporate executives of the core. In many peripheral countries, 20 percent or more of all export earnings are swallowed up by debt service—the annual interest on international debts (**Figure 12.3**). In 1997, for example, 26 peripheral countries had total debts so large that they owed more than they produced. Guyana, with a debt of US$1.6 billion, a population of only 856 000, and a total gross national product (GNP) of US$502 million, had the greatest debt burden per person of any country. Practically none of this money is ever likely to be repaid, but so long as the American, European, and Japanese banks continue to receive interest on their loans, they will be satisfied. Indeed, core countries are doing extremely well from this aspect of international finance. In 1998, the world's core countries took in about US$275 billion in debt servicing while paying out a total of less than US$85 billion in new loans.

The huge dollar figures involved sometimes makes it hard to comprehend the real significance of international debt relief. However, we can more readily understand the effects of the problem if we consider how they touch individuals and the places they live. As an example, consider the January 2005 report in which Stephanie Nolan described the impact debt relief is having on one primary school in Tinde, Tanzania:[6]

> The Tinde Primary School would strike terror into the heart of any Canadian teacher, or indeed any parent. Students sit three to a rickety metre-wide wooden desk. There are 49 of them in the class, and one weary teacher—fighting her third bout of malaria in the past year. There are no brightly coloured alphabet letters on the walls, no bulletin board to show off new art projects. Students receive only four hours of instruction each day.
>
> Yet teachers at Tinde Primary are feeling rather good about the place. Yes, the average class has 48 students, with one flimsy paper textbook for every three students.

5United Nations Development Programme, *2002 Human Development Report*, 24 July 2002. Available online at **http://hdr.undp.org/en/reports/global/hdr2002**. Ingrid Peretz, "Canada Still Close to Top of UN Index." *Globe and Mail*, 24 July 2002, p. A10.

6Stephanie Nolan, "Reaping the Fruits of Debt Relief." *Globe and Mail*, 29 January 2005, pp. A1, A2. An excellent 29-page briefing paper on international debt relief from a Canadian think tank is John E. Serieux's *Reducing the Debt of the Poorest: Challenges and Opportunities*. Ottawa: North-South Institute, 1999. The latest developments on international debt relief can be found via the British group Jubilee Research (see **www.jubilee2000uk.org**) and from the World Bank's PovertyNet Newsletter (see **www.worldbank.org/poverty/newsl/**). Statistics can be found at the UN Statistics Division—Millennium Indicators Database (**http://mdgs.un.org/unsd/mdg/Default.aspx**) and the International Monetary Fund Fact Sheet (**www.imf.org/external/np/exr/facts/hipc.htm**).

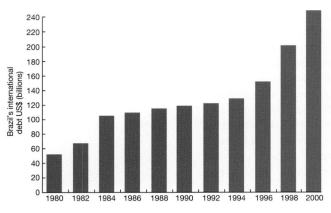

Brazil borrowed so much money in the 1970s and 1980s that it could no longer meet the interest payments. Between 1983 and 1989 the International Monetary Fund (IMF) bailed the country out but imposed austerity measures that were designed to curb imports. These included a 60 percent increase in gasoline prices and a reduction of the minimum wage to $50 a month, which gave workers half the purchasing power they had in 1940. Nevertheless, by 2002, the country's debt had reached nearly $228 billion, annual inflation rates in the 1990s having ranged between 500 percent and 2000 percent.

Mexico was forced to default on international debt repayments in 1982, triggering an international financial crisis that involved defaults the following year by Argentina, Brazil, Venezuela, the Philippines, Ghana, Nigeria, and many other peripheral countries. In 1996, Mexico was bailed out of another debt crisis by creditor countries, but was forced to devalue its currency, creating additional hardships for most of the population.

Since 1983, when a foreign exchange crisis left it unable to meet its debt repayments, the Philippine government has had to reschedule its debts several times with its creditor nations. By 2002 the Philippines had reduced its foreign debt to just over $59 billion, with a debt-service ratio of less than 12 percent of its GDP.

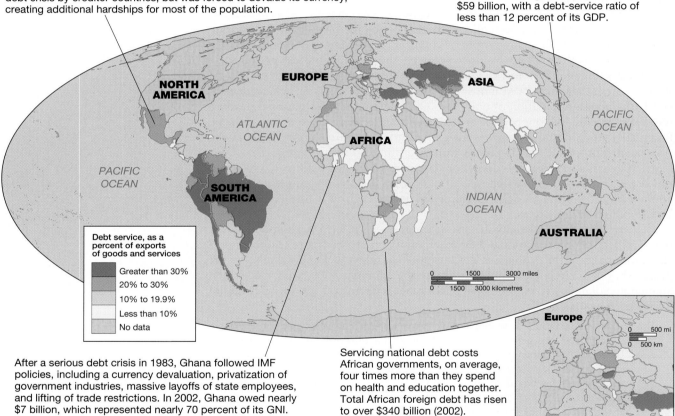

Debt service, as a percent of exports of goods and services

- Greater than 30%
- 20% to 30%
- 10% to 19.9%
- Less than 10%
- No data

After a serious debt crisis in 1983, Ghana followed IMF policies, including a currency devaluation, privatization of government industries, massive layoffs of state employees, and lifting of trade restrictions. In 2002, Ghana owed nearly $7 billion, which represented nearly 70 percent of its GNI.

Servicing national debt costs African governments, on average, four times more than they spend on health and education together. Total African foreign debt has risen to over $340 billion (2002).

Figure 12.3   The debt crisis   In some countries the annual interest on international debts (their "debt service") accounts for more than 20 percent of the annual value of their exports of goods and services. Many countries first got into debt trouble in the mid-1970s, when Western banks, faced with recession at home, offered low-interest loans to the governments of peripheral countries rather than being stuck with idle capital. When the world economy heated up again, interest rates rose and many countries found themselves facing a debt crisis. The World Bank and the International Monetary Fund (IMF), in tandem with Western governments, worked to prevent a global financial crisis by organizing and guaranteeing programs that eased poor countries' debt burdens. Western banks were encouraged to swap debt for equity stakes in nationalized industries, while debtor governments were persuaded to impose austere economic policies. These policies have helped ease the debt crisis, but often at the expense of severe hardship for ordinary people. In dark humour, the IMF became known among radical development theorists as "imposing misery and famine."

But three years ago it was 30 students to a book. The school's six classrooms and 23 teachers are double what it had. More than half of its students passed the national leaving exam in 2004, compared with 23 percent in 2001. What prompted this revolution in education? Debt Relief.

With an average annual per capita income of only US$290, Tanzania is one of the poorest nations in the world, and one with little ability to pay off its debt, which totalled almost US$7.3 billion in 1999. In that year, Tanzania paid $217 million simply to service the debt, an amount that was twice what the country spent on health care and one-quarter of its education spending. In 2005, however, the interest on Tanzania's debt will be about $65 million because of arrangements made under the World Bank's Heavily Indebted Poor Countries (HIPC) initiative. To qualify for HIPC relief and cut its annual debt repayment from 20 percent to 8.9 percent of government revenue, Tanzania pledged to use the money saved to increase education. In 2002, it was able to abolish primary school fees. The result was that 1.6 million more children were able to go to school for the first time that year.

Of course, much remains to be done. Primary schools are, as described by Stephanie Nolan, greatly underfunded; teachers are paid $90 a month and are in short supply; only 8 percent of children go on to secondary school because many cannot pay the fees (about $300 a year); and—most significantly of all—Tanzania still must make large interest repayments. Its debt has been reduced, not abolished.

Canada has taken a leadership role in the project to forgive the debts of the world's most indebted countries. Known as the Millennium or Jubilee debt relief plan, the idea was first proposed by a number of charitable organizations as a suitable way to usher in the new millennium. Unfortunately, however, because Canada is not a large lender, its debt forgiveness can achieve little on its own.

Write-Offs?

As for the countries being "written off," their future could be very bad, indeed. It is not just that they have already been dismissed by investors in the core or that their domestic economies are simply threadbare. They face unprecedented levels of demographic, environmental, economic, and societal stresses. In the worst-off regions—including much of West and Central Africa, for example—the events of the next 50 years are going to be played out from a starting point of scarce basic resources, serious environmental degradation, overpopulation, disease, unprovoked crime, refugee migrations, and criminal anarchy. African countries will be further disadvantaged because the prices of commodities produced there and in other peripheral locations have been dropping, while imported goods from the core have become more expensive. This means that Africa and many other peripheral countries have and will probably continue to have reduced purchasing power in the global marketplace because of the decline in the value of their exports. Continuing to disable the periphery's full participation in the global economy are the combined effects of external debt crisis, dwindling amounts of foreign aid, insufficient resources to purchase technology or develop indigenous technological innovations, and the high costs of marketing and transporting commodities.

Post-independence ideals of modernization and democracy now seem more remote than ever in these regions (**Figure 12.4**). Corrupt dictators, epitomized by the Democratic Republic of the Congo's former president Mobutu and Nigeria's former president General Abacha, have created "kleptocracies" (as in *kleptomania:* an irresistible desire to steal) in place of democracies. Of the estimated US$12.42 billion in oil revenues that came to Nigeria as a result of the Persian Gulf crisis of 1990 to 1991, for example, US$12.2 billion seems to have been clandestinely disbursed.

The U.S. State Department has estimated that during the 1990s, wars in Africa produced more than 8 million refugees and claimed 7 million to 8 million lives, including about 2 million children. Most conflicts in Africa, however, are civil wars that have become complicated and intractable as guerrilla groups have

Figure 12.4 UNDP aid, 2003
The United Nations Development Programme (UNDP) received many requests for aid in 2003. As this map shows, a large number were from countries of the periphery experiencing the pains of modernization and post-independence. (*Source:* United Nations Development Programme, *Annual Report 2004: 2015 Mobilizing* New York: UNDP, 2004. Available from **www.undp.org**.)

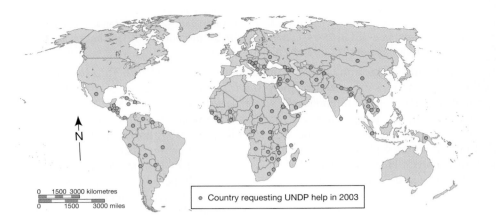

proliferated and divided into warring factions. Many of these wars are the result of the artificial boundaries created by the colonial powers (see Chapter 9), or the legacy of the political dependency Europe imposed on Africa as part of the emergence of the modern world-system (see Chapter 2).

Amid this chaos, disease has flourished. It is possible that parts of Africa may be more unhealthy today than they were a century ago. Malaria and tuberculosis are now a serious problem over much of sub-Saharan Africa (that part of Africa that lies south of the Sahara), while HIV/AIDS has become epidemic in many countries of that region. In 2007, according to the Joint United Nations Programme on HIV/AIDS (UNAIDS), in its *2008 Report on the Global AIDS Epidemic,* two-thirds (or 22 million) of all those living with HIV/AIDS in the world (33 million in 2007) lived in sub-Saharan Africa, and this region accounted for 72 percent (1.5 million) of all deaths caused by AIDS in 2007. The disease also exerts a terrible cost on those who survive: the number of children orphaned by the effects of the disease in this region of Africa continues to rise from approximately 2 million in 1995 to 12 million in 2007. Although UNAIDS was able to report that "most national epidemics have stabilized or begun to decline" across the region, this still could not be said for all parts of sub-Saharan Africa. In Kenya, for example, the prevalence rate of HIV in the adult population increased from 6.7 percent in 2003 to a figure that ranged between 7.1 and 8.5 percent in 2007.[7]

In the context of these difficulties, the agreement by the G8 countries, meeting at Kananaskis in Alberta from 26 to 27 June 2002, to the Africa Action Plan may be some grounds for optimism. This plan represents the G8 countries' response to the New Partnership for African Development (NEPAD), a program of action led by African countries and endorsed by the 53 member states of the Organization of African Unity. NEPAD emphasizes that economic aid should not be "imposed" by the West, as some commentators have described past attempts. Instead, the program "emphasizes African leadership and ownership of the development process and calls for a new global partnership based on shared responsibility and mutual interest."[8] In response to Western concerns that, in the past, economic aid has disappeared into the pockets of the rich and not reached those most in need, NEPAD recognizes that the new partnership must be based on issues of good government, human rights, and human security. Whether NEPAD will live up to these goals, it is still too early to say.

---

[7]Joint United Nations Programme on HIV/AIDS (UNAIDS) *2008 Report on the Global AIDS Epidemic.* Geneva: UNAIDS, 2008, pp. 5, 21 (available at **www.unaids.org**).

[8]A useful summary is provided in "A New Partnership for Africa's Development." *In Focus*, Department of Foreign Affairs and International Trade, 22 April 2002, available online at **www. dfait-maeci.gc.ca/trade/photos_pm_africas-en.asp**.

Overachievers

At the other end of the spectrum, the prospects for the core economies are bright, especially for large, core-based transnational corporations. With the end of the Cold War, new markets in east-central Europe have opened up to capitalist industry, along with more resources and a wider range of skilled and disciplined labour. New transport and communications technologies have already facilitated the beginnings of the globalization of production and the emergence of a global consumer culture. Top companies have reorganized themselves to take full advantage of this globalization. Reforms to the ground rules of international trade have removed many of the impediments to free-market growth, and a new, global financial system is now in place, ready to service the new global economy (see Chapter 7 for a full review of these developments).

An example of this is the World Trade Organization (WTO), an institution created in conjunction with GATT (the General Agreement on Trade and Tariffs), which is supranational in its scope. The WTO has begun to provide a system of regulations that supersedes national-level regulations and laws. In practice, this seems to mean that national restrictions over foreign corporations are increasingly subordinated to the new rules of the WTO. Proponents of the WTO argue that without such an organization, the terms of international trade are more likely to be set by powerful countries and transnational corporations at the expense of the weak. Subordinating powerful national interests to WTO-enforced free trade, they argue, will benefit less affluent countries by giving them free access to core-country markets and by requiring core countries to stop dumping the products of their subsidized agricultural sectors in peripheral markets. Critics of the WTO argue that the aims of the WTO have been shaped by international business and that the way that WTO negotiations take place—with dispute resolution panels made up of unelected bureaucrats rendering decisions in closed sessions—advances the interests of business, in general, and transnational corporations, in particular.

For the world-system core, therefore, the long-term question is not so much one of economic prosperity but of relative power and dominance. The same factors that will consolidate the advantages of the core as a whole—the end of the Cold War, the availability of advanced telecommunications, the transnational reorganization of industry and finance, the liberalization of trade, and the emergence of a global culture—will also open the way for a new geopolitical and geoeconomic order. This is likely to involve some new relationships among places, regions, and countries.

As we have suggested, the old order of the "short" twentieth century (1914–1989), dominated both economically and politically by the United States, is rapidly disappearing. In our present transitional phase, the new world order is up for grabs; we are coming to the end of a leadership cycle. This does not necessarily mean, however, that the United States will be unable to renew its position as the world's dominant power (see **Geography Matters 12.1—The Contenders**). As we saw in Chapter 2, Britain had two consecutive stints as the dominant world power—the hegemony that was able to impose its political view on the world and set the terms for a wide variety of economic and cultural practices.

Alternatively, we may not see the same kind of hegemonic power in the new world order of the twenty-first century; there may not be a new hegemony at all. Instead, the globalization of economics and culture may result in a polycentric network of nations, regions, and world cities bound together by flows of goods and capital. Order may come not from military strength rooted in national economic muscle, but from a mutual dependence on *trans*national production and marketing, with stability and regulation provided by powerful international institutions (such as the World Bank, the IMF, the World Trade Organization, the European Union, NATO, and the United Nations).

The Contenders

Because of the globalization of industry, finance, and culture and the dissolution of the Soviet Union—one of the cornerstones of the old world order—the world is currently in a state of transition. Looking ahead 25 to 50 years, several contenders exist for economic and political leadership.

China

Although China is currently not even part of the core of the world-system, many observers predict a "Pacific Destiny" for the twenty-first century. In this scenario, China will be the hub of a world economy whose centre of gravity is around the rim of the Pacific rather than the North Atlantic. China certainly has the potential to be a contender. It has a vast territory with a comprehensive resource base and a long history of political, cultural, and economic integration. It has the largest population of any country in the world (1.33 billion in 2007, according to UN estimates made in 2008)[9] and an economy that has been growing very rapidly. In the past 30 years, China has completely reorganized and revitalized its economy. China's increased participation in world trade has created an entirely new situation within the world economy, causing a deflationary trend in world prices for manufactured goods. Not only does the size of China's economy make it a major producer, but its huge labour force also guarantees that its wage levels will not approach Western levels for a long time. Overall, China's economy is already the fourth largest in the world after the European Union, the United States, and Japan.

Nevertheless, China must resolve a major feature of its contemporary human geography before it can emerge as a hegemonic power. This is the dramatically uneven development that has been a consequence of its economic reforms. The positive spiral of cumulative causation has affected only the larger cities and coastal regions, while the vast interior regions of the country have become increasingly impoverished. This, ironically, is the very geographical pattern of spatial polarization that motivated Chinese communists to revolt in the 1940s. Today, it is a source of potential unrest and of political instability among the central government, the provincial governments of the interior regions, and the provincial governments of the coastal regions.

China's rapid development raises many other issues. An increasing shortage of sufficient raw materials is leading China to invest heavily in overseas resources—its purchase of controlling interest in a number of Canada's mining corporations is but one example. China's rapid economic growth has fuelled a demand for food imports, and this is having an effect as far afield as the Brazilian Amazon, where substantial acreages of soya beans are now planted for the Chinese market.[10] Other examples include the Chinese government's support for countries with a record of human rights abuse because they offer the ability to supply China with oil (such as Somalia), and, critics argue, the continued occupation of areas such as Tibet because this enables the Chinese to control that country's abundant water supplies[11] (**Figure 12.1.1**).

Russia

Russia is the world's largest state by land area, with major reserves of important industrial raw materials and a pivotal strategic location in the centre of the Eurasian land mass. Now freed from the economic constraints of state socialism, Russia stands to benefit greatly by establishing economic linkages with the expanding world economy (**Figure 12.1.2**). With a population of 144 million in 2004, the Russian economy also has an ample labour force and a domestic market large enough to form the basis of a formidable economy. At present, though, the Russian economy is shrinking as it withdraws from the centrally planned model.

Nevertheless, Russia has to be a long-odds contender. The latter years of the Soviet system left Russian industry with obsolete technology and low-grade product lines, epitomized by its automobiles and civilian aircraft. As a result, the Russian economy now faces a massive task of modernization before it can approach its full potential. At the same time, there looms the equally massive task of renewing civil society and the institutions of business and democracy after 70 years of state socialism. Russia has been unable to create some of the essential pillars of a market economy. The institutional framework for the legal enforcement of private contracts and effective competition is still rudimentary. Another major weakness has been public finances. A system of fair and efficient

---

[10]Jonathan Watts, "A Hunger Eating Up the World." *Guardian Weekly*, 20–26 January 2006, p. 31.

[11]China's extensive economic involvement with Africa now includes ties with Mozambique, Zambia, the People's Republic of the Congo, and Equatorial Guinea; it imports substantial supplies of timber, copper, minerals and oil, respectively, from these countries (see Richard Behar, "Special Report: China Storms Africa." *Fast Company*, June 2008, available at **www.fastcompany.com/magazine/126/special-report-china-in-africa.html**).

---

[9]A very useful, up-to-date and reliable source for information of this sort is the website *UNdata*, maintained by the UN Statistics Division and found at **http://data.un.org**.

Figure 12.1.1 Challenges to Chinese rule This photograph, taken on 14 August 2008, shows Tibetan exiles demonstrating outside the Chinese Embassy in Kathmandu, Nepal. They demanded freedom for their homeland from Chinese rule and protested the 2008 Olympic Games being held in Beijing, China, despite that country's alleged violation of human rights in Tibet.

tax collection has yet to be put in place, while the relationship between federal and state taxes and spending has remained obscure. Meanwhile, real wages for most people have already fallen to 1950s levels, and life expectancies have fallen. These problems have serious implications for the future world order: a weak Russia is a provocation in Europe and throughout all of Eurasia. It tempts both the Americans and Europeans to overextend themselves geopolitically as the recent expansion of NATO eastwards illustrates.

The European Union

It is not stretching things too far to see a successful European Union as the main contender for world leadership (**Figure 12.1.3**). In geopolitical terms, the collapse of the Soviet Union has advanced the prospects of the European Union. The European Union (EU), which began in 1952 (the European Economic Community, or EEC), is now an *economic* union (with *integrated* economic policies among member states) and has moved a long way toward its goal of becoming a *supranational political union* (with a single set of institutions and policies).[12]

On 1 January 1999, a new unit of currency—the euro—officially came into being as the cornerstone of a move toward European Monetary Union (EMU). On that day, currency exchange rates were locked into place for 12 EU states—all except the United Kingdom, Denmark, and Sweden (which chose to stay out). The euro could well become a major reserve currency, enabling Europe to rival the United States in its capital and bond markets.

Figure 12.1.2 Post–Cold-War Russia In the new Russia, everyday street scenes betray the economic polarization and cultural tensions that have resulted from the "shock therapy" of competitive capitalist markets. Car dealerships selling U.S. imports; US$400-a-night luxury hotels; Western-style supermarkets selling Kellogg's Cornflakes, the Russian edition of *Playboy* magazine, and French mineral water; stores selling Reebok and Benetton products; and McDonald's and Pizza Hut restaurants stand in stark contrast to dull stores, street-corner booths, and grimy restaurants. These contrasts have become symbols for Russia's polarized politics, breeding a resentment among workers and pensioners that is exploited by nationalist politicians who want to restore Russia's superpower status through a self-reliant economy and renewed military strength. (*Source:* Les Stone/Corbis Sygma.)

[12]Information about the European Union is readily available from its statistical arm, Eurostat, and via its website, Europa (**http://europa.eu/index_en.htm**).

Figure 12.1.3   Headquarters of the European Union in Brussels
The European Union had its origins as an amalgamation in 1967 of
three institutions—Euratom, the European Coal and Steel Community, and the European Economic Community—which had been set
up in the 1950s to promote European economic integration. The
six original members—Belgium, France, Italy, Luxembourg, the
Netherlands, and West Germany—were joined in 1972 by
Denmark, the Republic of Ireland, and the United Kingdom. With
the addition of Greece in 1981, Portugal and Spain in 1984, Austria,
Sweden, and Finland in 1995, a further 10 countries in 2004, and
Bulgaria and Romania in 2007, the 27-member EU now has a
population and an economy significantly larger than those of
North America.

Collective success in the economic sphere could then spill
over into political and military cooperation. On the other
hand, EMU could lead to persistent stagnation in parts
of Europe if the EU fails to develop adequate mechanisms
for aid to disadvantaged regions. Extending the EU too
far too soon would risk destroying its own internal balance and cohesion. Nevertheless, successful enlargement,
combined with successful monetary union, would see
Europe poised either to challenge U.S. hegemony or to
become a senior partner among superpowers.

Japan

The rise of Japan since World War II to become the second-
largest national economy in the world has made it an obvious contender for the role of world leader in the first half
of the twenty-first century. Despite its limited resources
and the literal ruins of military defeat in 1945, it has
established competitive advantages in a wide range of

industrial and financial activities that now serve global
markets. The average annual income per household was
US$65 560 in 2007,[13] the highest of all the major core
countries. Japan is also the world's major creditor. Often
attributed to a system of informal alliances among politics,
business, and bureaucracy, the "Japanese miracle" includes
the key elements of the Ministry of Finance, the Ministry
of International Trade and Industry (MITI), and Nikkeiren,
the national business association. This system, sometimes
known as "Japan, Inc.," has systematically identified leading economic sectors and planned their success, first in
Japan and then at a global scale. The system is still in place,
and its success invites speculation that Japan will be the
nation-state best equipped to cope with a globalized world
economy.

Nevertheless, Japan faces several important handicaps
as a contender. First, it is heavily dependent on external
sources of raw materials. Japan is the number one importer
not only of basic raw materials (petroleum, iron ore, and
copper ore, for example) but also of agricultural goods.
Second, Japan is geographically isolated from its major
industrial markets and trading partners. Although the
Asian side of the Pacific Rim has great potential for
growth, Japan's investments and partnerships are oriented
overwhelmingly toward Europe and North America.
Third, Japan faces a demographic trap. With an aging population, a declining birth rate, and a resolute unwillingness to allow large-scale immigration, Japan will face a
serious labour shortage that can only be overcome by channelling more and more investment overseas.

The Japanese are the United States' major economic
rivals in Asia, and mutual commercial relations between
the two countries have been in deep conflict for many
years. Throughout the 1990s, Japan's economy experienced a prolonged crisis. In the future, Japan may have to
choose between dealing with neighbouring China either
as a possible military threat or as a colossal market to help
sustain its troubled economy. In the former case, Japan's
role could well become that of an "Asian Germany," an
advanced strategic base for American forces in a new, Eastern cold war with China. In the latter case, commercial
alliances with China would likely strengthen the
Asia–Pacific region as a contender for geopolitical
hegemony.

The United States

The United States is more than a contender: it is the reign-
ing hegemony. The U.S. economy is the largest in the
world, with a broad resource base; a large, well-trained,
and very sophisticated workforce; a domestic market

---

[13]Statistics Bureau, *Statistical Handbook of Japan*. Tokyo: Ministry of
Internal Affairs and Communication, 2007, available at
www.stat.go.jp/english/data/index.htm. This is a very useful set of
data and graphics on Japanese family budgets.

that has greater purchasing power than any other single country; and a high level of technological sophistication. The United States also has the most powerful and technologically sophisticated military apparatus, and it has the dominant voice and last word in international economic and political affairs. It is at least as well placed as its rivals to exploit the new technologies and new industries of a globalizing economy. It is also the only major contender for future world leadership with a global message: free markets, personal liberty, private property, electoral democracy, and mass consumption.

For the moment, however, the United States is a declining hegemony, at least in relative terms. Its economic dominance is no longer unquestioned in the way it was in the 1950s, 1960s, and 1970s. On some measures of economic development, the European Union has already overtaken the United States. More importantly, the globalization of the economy has severely constrained the ability of the United States to translate its economic might into the firm control of international financial markets that it used to enjoy.

Until the events of 11 September 2001 galvanized the Americans into a self-declared war against terrorism, the end of the Cold War, while a victory for the United States, robbed it of its image as Defender of the Free World and weakened the legitimacy of its role as global police officer. The absence of a Cold-War enemy and the globalization of economic affairs also made it much more difficult for the United States to identify and define the national interest. The hesitancy in U.S. policies toward Kosovo, East Timor, Somalia, Sudan, Bosnia, and Haiti in the 1990s was symptomatic of such problems. Since the events of 11 September 2001, the United States has turned to a more forward and aggressive policy, but as its invasions of Afghanistan in 2002 and Iraq in 2003 have shown, these actions have cost it world support.

In summary, while the United States must be considered the strongest contender, it is by no means a foregone conclusion that it will, in fact, become the leader for the next cycle of economic and political leadership. The United States has choices not unlike those faced by the British at the end of the nineteenth century: it can either oppose its rivals or accommodate them. It can oppose by pressing for a seamless global system that remains under its own hegemony, or it can try to accommodate by coaxing the others into a global sharing of power, with some mix of regional spheres of interest and collective world responsibilities.

RESOURCES, TECHNOLOGY, AND SPATIAL CHANGE

Many aspects of future geographies will depend on trends in the demand for particular resources and on the exploitation of new technologies. The evolution of the world's geographies has always been shaped by the availability of key resources and by the opportunities and constraints presented to different places and regions by successive technology systems. We should ask, therefore, what the future is likely to bring in terms of resource needs and technological shifts.

Resources and Development

The expansion of the world economy and the globalization of industry will undoubtedly boost the overall demand for raw materials of various kinds, and this will spur the development of some previously underexploited but resource-rich regions in Africa, Eurasia, and East Asia. Raw materials, however, will be only a fraction of future resource needs. The main issue, by far, will be energy resources. World energy consumption has been increasing steadily over the recent past (**Figure 12.5**). As the periphery is being industrialized and its population increases further, the global demand for energy will expand rapidly. Basic industrial development tends to be highly energy-intensive, however. The International Energy Agency (IEA), in its report *World Energy Outlook 2006*, has estimated that the world's total energy demands will increase by 50 percent from 2004 to 2030 (that is, from a total of 11 204 million barrels of oil equivalents [mboe] to one of 17 095 mboe, or an annual rate of increase of 1.5 percent). The IEA calculates that

Figure 12.5 Trends in energy consumption Global commercial energy consumption rose from less than 200 petajoules—10^{15} (1 quadrillion) joules—in 1970 to nearly 350 petajoules in 1997. (A *joule* is a unit of energy about equal to the force with which a grapefruit hits a table after being dropped from a height of about 10 centimetres). (*Source:* Data from United Nations Statistical Division, *1995 Energy Statistics Yearbook.* New York: United Nations, 1997.)

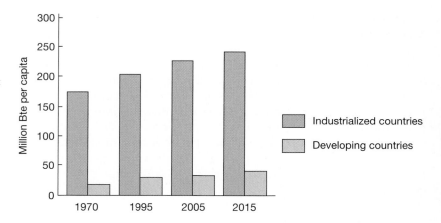

over 70 percent of this increase will be due to demands from developing countries—much of which (30 percent) will be accounted for by the predicted growth in China's energy needs as that country continues its rapid economic development (**Figure 12.6**).[14]

Although researchers at the IEA suggest that world energy resources are adequate to meet this level of future demand, the agency cautions that an additional global investment of over US$17 billion over the period 2004–2030 will be needed to ensure that all of the additional refineries, power stations, transmission lines, and such will have been constructed to meet that demand. Moreover, since over half of these additional costs will have to be spent to enable the developing countries meet their projected needs, it will prove difficult fully to meet total world energy needs by 2030 without extensive international cooperation, technology transfer from core countries to those of the periphery, and significant investment incentives (perhaps backed by the United Nations, or the European Union).[15]

For many countries of the developing world, the challenges of the future cannot be dealt with until the needs of the present are met. At present, according to

Figure 12.6 The changing face of China In a dramatic break with the past, many Chinese cities now bristle with high-rise towers and construction cranes. Cognac, laser-disk players, and wide-screen television sets line department-store shelves, and motorcycles jostle for space with foreign-brand automobiles.

[14]The International Energy Agency, *World Energy Outlook 2006.* Paris: International Energy Agency, 2006, pp. 37–38 and Table 2.1 on p. 66 (available at **www.iea.org/textbase/nppdf/free/2006/weo2006.pdf**).

[15]Dr F. Birol, *World Energy: Prospects and Challenges.* Paris: International Energy Agency, 2006, pp. 1–2 (available at **www.iea.org/textbase/publications/free_new_Desc.asp?PUBS_ID=1696**).

a 2007 report by the World Energy Council, almost 2 billion people do not have access to commercial forms of energy and a further billion only have access to periodic and unreliable forms of supply. "If about half of the world's population," the report observes, "continues in this condition, the world as a whole faces a significant threat to stability and the quality of life everywhere." Fortunately, the World Energy Council believes "with some confidence" that if the types of investments suggested by the IEA are made, it would be possible to halve the number of people without access to modern energy service by 2035, and to halve that figure again by 2050.[16]

Certainly, without higher rates of investment in exploration and extraction than at present, production will be slow to meet the escalating demand. The result might well be a temporary but significant increase in energy prices. This would have important geographical ramifications: companies would be forced to reconsider their operations seriously, core households would be forced to re-evaluate their residential preferences and commuting behaviours, and peripheral households would be forced further into poverty. If the oil-price crisis of 1973 is anything to go by (after crude oil prices had been quadrupled by the OPEC cartel), the outcome could be a significant revision of the patterns of industrial location and a substantial reorganization of the metropolitan form. Significantly higher energy costs may change the optimal location for many manufacturers, leading to deindustrialization in some regions and to new spirals of cumulative causation in others. Higher fuel costs will encourage some people to live nearer to their place of work, while other people will be able to take advantage of telecommuting to reduce personal transportation costs. It is also relevant to note that almost all of the increase in oil production over the next 15 or 20 years is likely to come from outside the core economies. This means that the world economy will become increasingly dependent on OPEC governments, which control over 70 percent of all proven oil reserves, most of them in the Middle East.

The increase in production costs are not, however, an unmitigated disaster, and certainly have a series of benefits for Canada. As we saw in Chapter 7, the rise in oil prices has now made Alberta's oil sands commercially viable and led to an economic boom in Fort McMurray, and in the province in general. That growth has also been able to absorb unemployed people from other parts of the country, as the migration of many from Newfoundland to the oil sands fields indicates. The rise in the value of the Canadian dollar from 2007 to 2008 (to reach over par with the American dollar) is mainly due to the Canadian economy being, like OPEC's, a petro-economy. Of course, these successes should not blind us to the downside, a major one being that the environmental damage caused by the oil sand upgraders are simply not factored into the current economic costs of production. It will be a heavy irony indeed if those people who have fled one environmental disaster (the collapse of the cod fisheries) find themselves embroiled in another.

In countries that can afford the costs of research and development, new materials will reduce the growth of demand both for energy and traditional raw materials, such as aluminum, copper, and tin. Japan, for instance, may be able to reduce motor vehicle fuel consumption by 15 percent (and thereby reduce its total fuel oil consumption by 3 percent) by using ceramics for major parts of engines. It may also be possible to substitute ceramics for expensive rare metals in creating heat-resistant materials. Improved engineering and product design will also make possible a reduced need for the input of some resources. The production of ethanol, for example, offers the possibility of creating biofuels from crops such as corn. Although these are a renewable resource and may produce less emissions of carbon dioxide than petroleum, their production threatens to lead to increases in

---

[16]World Energy Council, *Energy Policy Scenarios to 2050*. London: World Energy Council, November 2007, pp. 67 and 72, available at **www.worldenergy.org/publications/ energy_policy_scenarios_to_2050/default.asp.**

the cost of corn. Such increases may benefit producers (such as Canada's prairie grain farmers) at the cost of consumers (such as those who increasingly will find it hard to pay for their food supplies). In this respect, a statement in April 2008 at the meeting of world finance ministers and central bank governors who oversee the International Monetary Fund and the World Bank is significant. Noting that world agricultural prices had increased by 48 percent since the end of 2006, the managing director of IMF, Mr. Dominique Strauss-Kahn, observed that a number of government ministers who attended the meeting told him that using foodstuffs to make fuel amounted to a "crime against humanity."[17] As with earlier breakthroughs that produced steam energy, electricity, gasoline engines, and nuclear power, such advances would provide the catalyst for a major reorganization of the world's economic geographies.

New Technologies and Spatial Change

Just what new technologies are likely to have the most impact in reshaping human geographies? Given what we know about past processes of geographical change and principles of spatial organization, it is clear that changes in transportation technology are of fundamental importance (Chapter 2). Among the most important of the next generation of transportation technologies that will influence future geographies are high-speed rail systems, smart roads, smart cars, and the emergence of alternative energy sources. Several emerging industrial technologies also exist whose economic impact is likely to be so great that they will influence patterns of international, regional, and local development. Studies by the Organisation for Economic Co-operation and Development (OECD) and the United Nations have all identified biotechnology, materials technology, and information technology as the most critical areas for future economic development.

Transportation Technologies   On land, the most interesting developments seem likely to centre on new high-speed rail systems. Improved locomotive technologies and specially engineered tracks and rolling stock will make it possible to offer passenger rail services at speeds of 275 to 370 kilometres per hour (170 to 230 miles per hour). With shorter check-in times and in-town rail terminals, it will be quicker to travel between some cities by rail than by air. The most advanced plans are in Europe, where the European Union (EU) announced plans in 2005 for the development of a high-speed rail system as one of the major aspects of the EU's future transportation strategy known as the Trans-European Network (or TEN-T). This strategy calls for the completion of 20 000 kilometres of high-speed track by 2020 (**Figure 12.7**). An ambitious plan designed to meet a predicted doubling of Europe's transport needs between 2005 and 2020 by improving the EU's connections by road, rail, and sea, it is perhaps not surprising to hear that the EU itself estimates that the total projected costs of TEN-T would be of the order of $384 billion if all of its components were to be completed. However, because the difficulties of completing the high-speed rail component are immense, some commentators doubt that these goals can be fully realized, at least on the timescale envisaged. Just to complete the line between Lyon and Turin, for example, requires the completion of a 53 kilometre tunnel under the Alps, a construction project that will involve at least 10 years of work and the excavation of over 20 million cubic metres of rock.[18] Once completed, however, the geographical implications of these systems

---

[17]Kevin Carmichael, "Soaring Food Prices Now Top Threat, IMF Says," *Globe and Mail*, 14 April 2008, pp. A1, A7.

[18]Directorate-General for Energy and Transportation, "Trans-European Transport Network: TEN-T Priority Axes and Projects 2005." European Commission 2005, pp. 2 and 6 (available at **http://ec.europa.eu/ten/transport/projects/doc/2005_ten_t_en.pdf**). Regarding the Alpine tunnel, see Le Monde-Diplomatique, "Lyon-Turin, un projet de ferroutage controversé." *L'Atlas envionnement: analyses et solutions*. Paris: Le Monde diplomatique, 2008, pp. 80–81.

The Eurostar at Waterloo International Station, London.

Figure 12.7 High-speed rail in Europe Europe, with its relatively short distances between major cities, is ideally suited for rail travel and less suited, because of population densities and traffic congestion around airports, to air traffic. Allowing for check-in times and accessibility to terminals, it is already quicker to travel between many major European cities by rail than by air. The European Union plans to coordinate and subsidize a US$384-billion investment in 20 000 kilometres (almost 13 400 miles) of high-speed track, be phased in through 2020. High-speed rail routes will have only a few scheduled stops because the time penalties resulting from deceleration and acceleration undermine the advantages of high-speed travel. Places with no scheduled stops will be less accessible and so less attractive for economic development.

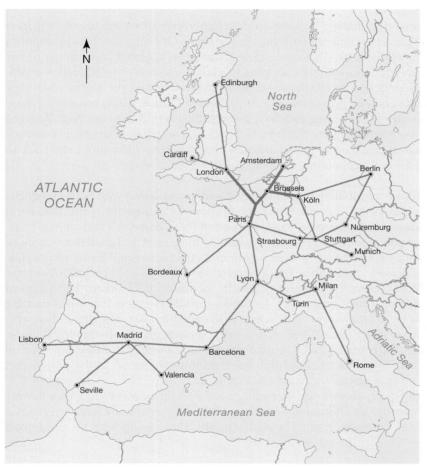

are significant. Quite simply, once the systems become commercially viable, places that are linked to them will be well situated to grow in future rounds of economic development; places that are not will probably be left behind.

The same significance will attach to *intelligent transportation systems (ITS)*, should they be developed from their current prototypes to become commercially viable. An ITS is a combination of so-called smart highways and smart cars. The basic ITS target concept is an interactive link of vehicle electronic systems with roadside sensors, satellites, and centralized traffic management systems. This linkage allows for real-time monitoring of traffic conditions and allows drivers to receive alternative route information via two-way communications, on-board video screens, and mapping systems. The next step would be completely automated highway systems, on which groups of vehicles would be guided automatically, in closely packed platoons, with virtually no active driver control. With fewer gridlocked roads, driving would be safer, less polluting, and more efficient. Metropolitan areas and interstate corridors that have the infrastructure of ITS technology will be at a significant advantage in attracting new industries and their workers. The first generation of smart cars, buses, and trucks, with on-board, microproccesor-based electronics, is already on the road, using route-planning software, Global Positioning Systems (GPS), fleet management systems software, and wireless communications.

At sea, no emerging technologies exist at present that might have an equivalent impact. In the air, however, a large untapped market encourages big investments in research and development. The new Airbus, produced by a consortium of European firms and unveiled in January 2005 can carry more than 500 passengers. Its size has already created a new hierarchy of world cities because only a very few can accommodate it.

The projected changes in transportation technology are enormous and will have profound impacts in both the core and the periphery. One question these innovations force us to ask is: how efficient do they allow us, as a global community, to be? For instance, does it make sense to consume large amounts of fossil fuels and generate more pollution to transport staple foodstuffs around the world when they could just as easily be grown locally? At present, in France, which possesses a long-established apple-producing industry, it is possible to find as many New Zealand apples as French ones in the markets. In Mongolia, where milk-producing animals are ubiquitous, the butter in the markets is imported from Germany. Does such an arrangement make economic, environmental, or social sense?

Biotechnology Although biotechnology is widely associated with both the genetic engineering of crops (through Green Revolution, such crops as hybrid rice, corn, wheat, lettuce, tomatoes, sugar cane, and cotton [see Chapter 8]) and with its pharmaceutical potential (through such products as Interferon and growth hormones), biotechnology is also likely to have a profound effect on animal husbandry, industrial production, renewable energy, waste recycling, and pollution control (**Figure 12.8**). Genetic engineering, or genetic modification, is already being applied quite widely in animal husbandry. Examples include Japanese fish farms that use cell fusion technology to produce algae in systems that are 350 times more efficient than are other methods of raising brine shrimp; genetically modified crops, such as canola, being routinely grown across the Canadian Prairies; rapeseed oil that has had a bay-tree gene spliced into it to improve its oil; and a potato that has been given a disease-resistant chicken gene.

The prospect, viewed optimistically, is for a scientific means to feed a hungry world efficiently. An additional advantage offered by genetically modified crops is that they can be engineered to be pest-resistant, thus saving both the dollar cost

Figure 12.8 Dangers of biotechnology In June 2000, the biotechnology giant Monsanto took a 69-year-old farmer, Percy Schmeiser, to federal court. Some genetically modified canola had been found on Schmeiser's farm in Bruno, Saskatchewan. Monsanto argued that he had not paid them for a licence to grow their herbicide-resistant variety. Schmeiser claimed windblown seeds from nearby farms where the genetically modified canola was growing had contaminated his crop. However, experts for Monsanto argued that this was not possible, and Schmeiser lost the case. In a 2008 judgment in a Civil Suit, Monsanto did agree to pay for the costs of removing genetically modified canola from Percy Schmeiser's fields.

and the environmental cost of pesticides (conventional farming uses five or more broad-spectrum pesticide applications on crops each year). The implications for agricultural productivity are profound, as are the implications for the geography of agriculture. If crops can be genetically engineered to withstand pests, cold climates, and other adverse conditions, the whole geography of production may change, bringing the prospect of orange groves and avocado orchards in temperate climates, among other strange scenarios.

Nevertheless, the future growth in the production of genetically modified food is by no means certain. A study carried out at Cornell University in 1999 found that the pollen produced by genetically engineered corn was lethal to the caterpillar of the popular Monarch butterfly. It was the first evidence that genetically engineered crops could have a long-term impact on biodiversity. The importance of this evidence, however, has since been debated by scientists since the results were obtained in a laboratory setting and do not reflect real-world conditions. In Europe and Japan, where consumers and their governments were already highly skeptical of genetically engineered foods ("frankenfoods"), the environmental lobby made genetically modified food a central issue in what promises to be one of the most critical cultural struggles of the early twenty-first century: local mobilization against transnational business (see **Geography Matters 12.2—Mobilization against Globalization**). Indeed, Europeans in general (perhaps because of the mad cow disease scare) have been far less trusting of genetically modified foods than Canadians have been.

In many European countries, supermarkets now voluntarily label genetically modified produce and promote organic lines, while several European governments have approved the compulsory labelling of products containing a significant percentage of genetically modified ingredients. In Canada in 2004 Monsanto quietly withdrew its plans to grow "Round Up Ready" wheat, a genetically modified crop it had been developing and testing in Canada for more than 20 years. It now seems likely that, in the near future at least, the commercial exploitation of genetic engineering will be slowed considerably by consumer resistance in the more affluent countries of the world. Meanwhile, more growth can be expected in industrial applications of biotechnology—enzymes, for example, that will be used as industrial catalysts in the microbial recovery of metals, in waste degradation, and in biomass fuels.

In geographical terms, we can expect the long-term economic benefits of biotechnology to be greatest in the countries and regions that can afford the costs of research and development and of installing and applying the new technologies. In this way, the core may gain control over crops that are currently exclusively produced in the periphery, and thereby continue to dominate world agriculture. Efforts to genetically engineer North American plant species to produce palm oil are underway, and carry with them the potential to rob many tropical producers of their monopoly of this crop. This is, of course, nothing more than a continuation of "ecological imperialism" in another guise, in this case using science to overcome biological barriers. On the other hand, one of the principal advantages of many applications of biotechnological innovations is that they are economic to use on a small scale, without large infrastructure requirements. This should facilitate their use in peripheral regions. There is the prospect (but by no means the certainty) that these applications could bring not only commercial success to peripheral regions but also help solve the problem of food shortages. Similarly, it is possible that biotechnology might reverse the environmental degradation of some parts of the world because it could provide economically viable ways of replacing chemical fertilizers and toxic sprays, recycling waste products, and cleaning up polluted water. One key benefit may well be the ability to biogenetically engineer plant species that are more salt-resistant than our current food crops. In this way, the increasing salinity of much of the world's irrigated lands (a major problem identified in Chapter 8 since it threatens to substantially reduce food production over large areas) could be rendered less problematic. It is also possible, unfortunately,

Mobilization against Globalization

Local mobilization against transnational business and the effects of economic globalization seems set to become an important cultural struggle in the early decades of the twenty-first century. Economic globalization is, in many ways, still in its beginning stages; but already, as we have seen in previous chapters, it has brought a great deal of change to the economic, cultural, and political geographies of places and regions throughout the world. A great deal of this change has been progressive, bringing increased overall levels of economic well-being, a strengthening of free enterprise and democracy, and an enriched flow of products, ideas, and culture among and between places and regions.

Inevitably though, as in previous epochs of economic change, economic globalization has also brought a round of "creative destruction" (see Chapter 7), as some places and regions have experienced disinvestment so that capital could be made available for more profitable investments elsewhere. Economic globalization has also undercut the power of national and local governments to regulate economic affairs and has erased a great deal of local diversity because of the economic success of global products: the "McDonaldization of everywhere."

Fundamental geographical differences—in climate, resources, culture, and so on—mean that economic globalization is variously embraced, modified, or resisted in different parts of the world. As we argued in Chapter 1, the more universal the diffusion of material culture and lifestyles, the more valuable regional and ethnic identities become; the faster the information highway takes people into cyberspace, the more they feel the need for a subjective setting—a specific place or community—that they can call their own; and the greater the integration of transnational governments and institutions, the more sensitive people have become to localized cleavages of race, ethnicity, and religion. In addition, there is in prospect a countermovement, a "mobilization against globalization," that could well affect the whole dynamic of economic globalization as it is played out over the next decade or two.

One form of this mobilization is exemplified by the efforts of some local communities to cope with the negative effects of creative destruction and deindustrialization. In Sheffield, England, for example, the merger of British Steel and the Dutch steelmaker Hoogovens in 1998 put many jobs in Sheffield in jeopardy when the city already had more than one-third of its jobless people on unemployment benefits for well over a year. In response to the employment crisis, the city established a Sheffield Employment Bond and raised £1.9 million from local investors. Some of the money raised will be used to build new houses, creating new jobs for the young trainee construction workers taken from the pool of the local unemployed. The remainder of the fund will be used as seed money to finance small businesses, such as bicycle workshops, mobile hairdressers, and neighbourhood cafés and bookshops.

Another form of mobilization is exemplified by activists who use the legal system to resist what they see as the undesirable local outcomes of transnational business practices. In the late 1990s, activists pursued transnational corporations, accusing them of helping to suppress human rights. For example, four U.S. retailers and clothing manufacturers, charged with unethical labour practices in a US$1-billion alien-tort suit that had been filed on behalf of some 50 000 garment workers in Saipan, agreed to settle in 1999. Although admitting no liability, Nordstrom, Gymboree, Cutter & Buck, and J. Crew agreed to pay US$1.25 million into a fund to support the independent monitoring of their overseas suppliers.

A third form of mobilization is old-fashioned popular protest. The most vivid examples are provided by French farmers who, in protest over trade-liberalization policies, regularly take to such tactics as blocking streets with tractors, produce, farmyard manure, or farm animals (**Figure 12.2.1**).

Figure 12.2.1 Local protest Globalization and transnational business often mean the downward convergence of wages and environmental standards, an undermining of democratic governance, and a general recoding of nearly all aspects of life on Earth to the language and logic of global markets. French farmers have been especially militant in protesting such outcomes, particularly when their livelihood and traditional farming practices have been threatened.

Finally, and perhaps most significantly in terms of future cultural struggles between local interests and transnational business interests, mobilization can be organized by coalitions of non-governmental agencies (NGOs). This form of mobilization against globalization became much more powerful in the 1990s as a result of the internet. Such groups as Kenya's Consumers' Information Network, Ecuador's Accion Ecologica, and Trinidad and Tobago's Caribbean Association for Feminist Research and Action are linked through scores of websites, blogs, and discussion groups to North American, European, and Asian counterparts. NGOs set the agenda for the Earth Summit in Rio in 1992 and lobbied governments to attend; they publicized the Chiapas rebellion in Mexico in 1994, thereby preventing the Mexican government from suppressing it violently. In 1997, a loose alliance of 350 NGOs from 23 countries set out to ban land mines; they soon persuaded 122 nations to sign on to a treaty. In 1998, another NGO alliance, this time reckoned to number 600 groups in nearly 70 countries, blocked a painstakingly negotiated treaty on international multilateral investment. In 1999, more than 775 NGOs registered with the World Trade Organization (WTO) and took more than 2000 observers to the WTO summit in Seattle, Washington. Recent protests against the WTO occurred in Quebec City (**Figure 12.2.2**).

These demonstrations against the WTO highlight some of the central issues surrounding economic globalization. Economic globalization may depend on free trade, but should the abolition of economic protectionism be accompanied by the abolition of social and environmental protection? The WTO's mandate is the "harmonization" of safety and environmental standards among member nations as well as the removal of tariffs and other barriers to free trade. Most people support free trade, but not if it harms public health or is based on child labour.

Increasingly, protests against globalization have been channelled through the World Social Forum (WSF). The WSF bills itself "not as a group [or] an organization." It is, according to its Charter of Principles,[19]

> an open meeting place for reflective thinking, democratic debate of ideas, formulation of proposals, free exchange of experiences and interlinking for effective action, by groups and movements of civil society that are opposed to neoliberalism and to domination of the world by capital and any form of imperialism, and are committed to building a planetary society directed towards fruitful relationships among Humankind and between it and the Earth.

Since its inception in 2001, the WSF has organized an annual world meeting to coincide with the date of the World Economic Forum. Every annual meeting is designed

Figure 12.2.2   Mobilization against globalization   The Third Summit of the Americas was held in Quebec City on 20–21 April 2001 to discuss the Free Trade Area of the Americas (FTAA). The summit was also the focus for a large gathering of people protesting against the FTAA, the WTO, and the general effects of globalization. Anticipating this, the site of the meeting was cordoned off by police. Much of the protest was peaceful, but a few individuals (equipped with their own masks to escape the effects of tear gas) were prepared to express themselves more violently.

to promote the creation of alternatives to globalization through open discussion. The January 2005 meeting was held in Porto Alegre, Brazil, and was attended by more than 100 000 people from more than 5700 organizations (including social movements, non-governmental organizations [NGOs], and human rights organizations) from more than 100 countries. Its four-day agenda included 2000 seminars and discussions arranged around the 11 themes of permanent autonomy, diversity, arts and creativity, communication, the environment, alternative democracies, peace and demilitarization, sovereign economies, human rights and dignity, ethics, and spirituality.

In 2006, the WSF event was decentralized and held in three cities: Bamako (Mali, Africa), Caracas (Venezuela, South America), and Karachi (Pakistan, Asia). It included more than 20 themes, some of which were specific to the host country, including war, safety, and peace; aggression against rural societies; culture, media and communication; international order and international institutions; international trade, debt, and social and economic policies; natural resources: rights, control, privatization, and transboundary disputes; social justice, human rights, and governance; and state and religion, pluralism and fundamentalism.

Using its annual meeting to gain publicity for its concerns, the internet to promote worldwide debate, and locally organized regional meetings to increase open discussion, the WSF provides a model of how democratic protest groups may mobilize against globalization in the future.

---

[19]World Social Forum, *Charter of Principles*. Approved and adopted in Sao Paulo, 9 April 2001, and approved with modifications by the WSF International Council on 10 June 2001. Available online at **www.worldsocialforum.org**. Details on future annual meetings can also be found on this site.

that natural genetic diversity will be reduced as native seeds are replaced by clones and as locally adapted forms of agriculture are replaced by industrialized ones. Farmers lose control over their own crops if they are forced to buy GMO seeds every year rather than save a portion of their harvest to sow next year. The result could very easily be the disappearance of thousands of plant varieties and with them the sources of natural resistance to genetically adapted pests.

Materials Technologies   Materials technologies include new metal alloys, specialty polymers, plastic-coated metals, elastothermoplastics, laminated glass, and fibre-reinforced ceramics. They are important because they can replace scarce natural resources, reduce the quantity of raw materials used in many industrial processes, reduce the weight and size of many finished products, increase the performance of many products, produce less waste, and allow for the commercial development of entirely new products.

Unlike biotechnology, applications of materials technologies will require a fairly close association with an expensive infrastructure of high-tech industry. As a result, their immediate geographical impact is likely to be much more localized within the core regions of the world-system. Peripheral regions and countries that are currently heavily dependent on the production and export of traditional raw materials—such as Guinea and Jamaica (bauxite), Zambia and the Democratic Republic of Congo (formerly Zaire) (copper), Bolivia (tin), and Peru (zinc)—will probably be at the wrong end of the creative destruction prompted by these new technologies. In other words, as new materials technologies reduce the demand for traditional raw materials, production and employment in the latter will decline, and investors will probably withdraw from producer regions to reinvest their capital in more profitable ventures elsewhere. In contrast, some peripheral regions and countries will benefit from the increasing demand for rare earth metals. Brazil, Nigeria, and the Democratic Republic of the Congo, for example, together account for almost 90 percent of the world's production of niobium (used with titanium in making superconductive materials); Brazil, Malaysia, Thailand, Mozambique, and Nigeria together account for about 75 percent of the world's production of tantalum (used in making capacitors that store and regulate the flow of electricity in electronic components). As one of the developed nations that most depends on the exploitation of raw materials, Canada must watch these new developments carefully. As was the case with the development of uranium and asbestos, the chances are that Canada will possess reserves of many materials required by new technology, but it would be wise to investigate the potential side effects of their use before proceeding with development.

Information Technologies   Information technologies include all of the components of information-based, computer-driven, and communications-related activities—a wide array of technologies that includes both hardware (silicon chips, microelectronics, computers, satellites, and so on) and the software that makes it operate. In addition to telematics—the automation of telecommunications and the linkage of computers by data transmission—information technologies include developments as diverse as real-time monitoring of traffic bottlenecks, computer-controlled manufacturing, chemical and biological sensors of effluent streams, 24-hour data-retrieval systems, bar-coded retail inventory control, telemetry systems for tracking parcels and packages, and geographic information systems. Information technologies have already found widespread applications in retailing, finance, banking, business management, and public administration; yet, it is estimated that even in the more developed countries, only about one-third of the benefits to be derived from information-technology-based innovations have so far been realized.

As we have seen in earlier chapters, information technologies have already transformed certain aspects of economic geography. In employment and production, an overall concentration exists in core countries, where the detailed geography of

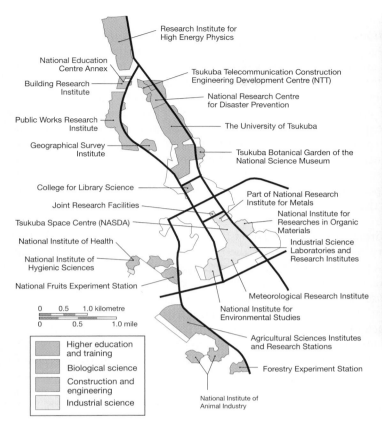

Figure 12.9 Technopolis cities Tsukuba Science City, about 65 kilometres (40 miles) northeast of Tokyo, has served as a model for the Japanese "Technopolis" program, which is a government-sponsored attempt to create a series of high-tech complexes to serve Japanese industry. Tsukuba was part of a strategic urban plan for the Tokyo metropolitan area, designed to exploit geographical principles of localization and agglomeration to foster Japanese high-tech industry. Although construction began only in the early 1970s, Tsukuba now has a population of over 180 000, of whom more than 12 000 are scientific researchers. The Technopolis program was master-planned by the Japanese Ministry of International Trade and Industry (MITI), and its 26 high-tech complexes will be the cornerstone of future high-tech development in Japan. Each technopole, or high-tech growth-pole settlement, is designed as a garden-city type setting for research universities, science centres, industrial research parks, joint research and development consortia, venture capital foundations, office complexes, international convention centres, and residential new towns. (*Source:* Map redrawn with permission from J.L. Bloom and S. Asano, "Tsukuba Science City," *Science*, 212. Copyright © 1981, American Association for the Advancement of Science.)

information technologies takes the form of highly localized agglomerations of activity. Examples include "Silicon Valley" (Santa Clara County) in California, the "high-tech" area west of Ottawa, and around the edges of the Osaka and Tokyo metropolitan areas in Japan (**Figure 12.9**). In addition, routine production, testing, and assembly functions have been decentralized to semiperipheral countries—Hong Kong, Singapore, Taiwan, and South Korea, in particular.

Future geographies of production and employment in information technologies will almost certainly follow the same pattern: most research and development and high-end production will be localized within core countries, and most routine functions will be decentralized to peripheral and semiperipheral countries, such as China, Indonesia, the Philippines, Sri Lanka, and Thailand. That is not to say that exceptions will not occur. India, for instance, has begun to carve a successful niche in software development, mainly because of the Indian government's provision of generous tax breaks and liberal foreign-exchange regulations for the industry. "Silicon Plateau" around Bangalore has more than 100 export-oriented software companies that are able to draw on a relatively cheap but highly educated labour pool. "Multimedia Super Corridor" outside Kuala Lumpur, Malaysia, is emerging as a result of tax breaks that have attracted key investments from Microsoft, Sun Microsystems, Nippon Telegraph, and IBM.

Of most interest to geographers are the spatial effects of information technologies' *applications*. As we have seen in previous chapters, information technologies have already had an enormous impact in facilitating the globalization of industry, finance, and culture. At local and regional scales, while they have been instrumental in decentralizing jobs and residences, their impact has been very uneven. Computers, for example, are mainly used in peripheral countries for standard functions of inventory control, accounting, and payroll; and even so, they remain much too expensive for widespread use in homes, small businesses, and local governments. We can expect future impacts of information technologies to exhibit the same unevenness. Although the world will certainly shrink even further, a marked lag will occur in the diffusion of information technologies to many peripheral regions, thus perpetuating and even accentuating the digital divide between the "fast world" and the "slow world."

Cyberspace and Virtual Geography   For fast-world countries, such as Canada, the internet poses very real challenges. On the one hand, the obvious potential for Canadian business to defeat the "friction of distance" in cyberspace, and so compete on level terms in the global marketplace, is a compelling argument. On the other hand, because Canadians themselves are able to participate in e-commerce, much business that would have originally been done with local stores takes place in cyberspace, much of it with American businesses. In this way, the virtual geography of this country has been fundamentally reconfigured. The way in which Amazon.com has affected the business of many local bookstores across this country is but one example of this process, we are now much "nearer" book warehouses in the virtual world of that company than we are to book stores physically down the street and able to access a far greater inventory. In 2000, more than half of Canadian purchases over the internet were from foreign sites.

In effect, e-commerce is not supplementing but competing with Canadian business. As geographer Donald Janelle has recently noted, "even within a country such as Canada, both peripheral and central regions could be impacted adversely. . . . The global centralization of internet technology may favour accumulation of capital at the upper levels in the global urban hierarchy and drain the time and income resources from local regions."[20] Ironically, we may find that the internet is a technology that is unable to liberate Canada's peripheries and only serves to maintain this country's dependent position in the world-system.

Few areas are more peripheral than many of Canada's northern Aboriginal communities, and we can hypothesize that if anywhere were to benefit from a technology that "defeated distance," it would be in those remote places. The actual evidence is, however (as we might expect), a little less clear. For example, Ioana Radu's fascinating recent study of internet use among the James Bay Cree of Nemaska, Quebec, has concluded that the technology is not actively being used for e-commerce or for job searches. Out of the sample of teenagers that she interviewed, "30 percent accessed information on online purchases but did not buy anything and 10 percent looked for employment opportunities."[21]

What Radu did find was that most teenagers were using the internet to keep in touch with family members, many of whom were far from Nemaska. As one of her respondents said, email is important "so you can communicate with friends and family anytime wherever they are." This finding contradicts the view that the internet is ultimately an isolating technology since we use it alone.

---

[20]Donald Janelle, "Globalization, the Internet Economy, and Canada," *Canadian Geographer* 45, 2001, p. 52.

[21]Ioana Radu, *Download in Progress . . . Offline Meets Online @ Nemaska.James Bay: The Use of Information and Communication Technologies among the Youth of a Remote Cree Community.* Unpublished Master's Thesis in Public Policy and Public Administration (Geography Option), Concordia University, 2004. The quotation is from p. 122.

Whatever purpose it is used for, if the internet is ever to be of much benefit to Canada's peripheral communities, Radu's work shows that fundamental issues of access need to be addressed. According to her research, only 20 percent of respondents in Nemaska have a computer at home, and more than 50 percent of respondents rely on access at school or the band council office. But these premises are open only at specific times, the computers do not always work properly, few people have enough training to fix the systems, and even these facilities are not as accessible as they could be. Certainly, Industry Canada's 1997 commitment to connect everyone in Canada to the internet, as part of the federal government's Information Highway policy, has been rendered less effective because it overlooked many of the important details that underlie its overall plans.

As we have already seen from this discussion, and from examples considered in earlier chapters, geographers have already devoted their attention to some of the many implications of cyberspace and virtual geography (see, for example, Figure 1.3.9 on the spatial structure of the internet itself, and Figure 2.25 on global internet connectivity). Thus, cyberspace has its own geography, its "core" and its "periphery" of user access, its central nodes and its principal routes. Beyond this, whole imaginary worlds have been created that exist only in a virtual "reality," with their own geographies, and these may be visited at will. Increasingly, access to GPS and wi-fi links enable the interface between that virtual reality and the physical reality to be achieved effortlessly. This will enable spatial information about specific locations to be acquired in real time; heritage enthusiasts will thus be able to receive information over the web about events that took place in a location while physically passing the spot, and restaurant-goers will soon be able to read menus and reviews online before entering the establishment of choice and ordering.

Cyberspace, of course, intersects with other spaces, and if we now turn our attention to its impact on economic space, we can consider the influence of computer gaming giant Ubisoft and its role as an economic rejuvenator in Montreal (**Figure 12.10**). Founded as a subsidiary of the French parent firm, Ubisoft Montreal established itself in that city in 1997, with the financial backing of the Quebec provincial government. Located in abandoned factory buildings towards the northern parts of Montreal, Ubisoft now employs over 1600 people at its "campus" on St. Laurent Boulevard and has been responsible for the rejuvenation of much of

Figure 12.10 Ubisoft The computer game business has expanded enormously in recent years, allowing many to compete with each other in cyberspace. Ubisoft, a leading player in this new industry, has rejuvenated old industrial buildings and created hundreds of high-tech jobs in Montreal.

the surrounding area. In an almost textbook example of Richard Florida's "creative city," highly paid and highly skilled computer programmers and game testers have bought up lofts and condominiums in the immediate vicinity and have also encouraged a resurgence of nearby stores and restaurants. In early 2007, the company announced its intention to invest $451 million over the next six years, and to add a further 1400 employees to its payroll, developments which, if they take place, will make the Montreal facility the world's largest computer game development centre by the year 2013.

Further advances in computational capacity, telematics, GIS, cellphones, and computer-driven surveillance will mean that many of the complex, hard-to-manage aspects of society, such as street crime and traffic, will increasingly be subject to automated surveillance and management systems. These developments will bring new ethical challenges. The RCMP's desire to install video surveillance cameras on Kelowna's main street has prompted Canada's privacy commissioner to use a court injunction to prevent public space from being monitored in this way. The commissioner has argued that in this case, the profound challenge to the control of public space outweighs any crime-prevention goal. New buildings, from individual houses to mega-developments, will be designed and tested in virtual space; and more environments will be "smart." These same technologies will also likely increase the gap between the haves and the have-nots within the fast world. Robotics and computers have already displaced millions of workers in the fast world. As the Information Revolution unfolds and matures, further changes in labour markets can be expected, creating high-wage jobs for those equipped to participate in new, knowledge-based industries. On the other hand, there is no reason to expect any expansion in jobs for unskilled or poorly educated workers. The net result is likely to be an increase in socioeconomic polarization.

ADJUSTING TO THE FUTURE

The immediate future will be characterized by a phase of geopolitical and geo-economic transition; by the continued overall expansion of the world economy; and by the continued globalization of industry, finance, and culture. In this future, new technologies—various transport technologies, biotechnology, materials technology, and especially information technologies—will be influential in shaping the opportunities and constraints for local, regional, and international development. The processes of change involved in shaping this kind of future will inevitably bring critical issues, conflicts, and threats. We can already identify what several of these might involve: dilemmas of scale, boundaries, and territories; fault lines of cultural dissonance; and the sustainability of development.

Scale and Territory

The globalization of the economy is undermining the status of the territorial nation-state as the chief regulating mechanism of both the global and local dimensions of the world-system. This is not to say that nation-states are about to become outmoded. In the future, a strong logic will continue to exist for the territorial powers of nation-states as we discussed in Chapter 9, but the states themselves will become increasingly permeable to flows of capital and information. Although capital, knowledge, entrepreneurship, management, and consumer tastes will continue to globalize, governments will be locked into their nineteenth-century quilt of territories and institutions.

Without strong nation-states—or some alternative—some important aspects of geographical change will escape the authority of national governments. Consider three examples:

■ Commercial information, patents, stocks, bonds, electronic cash transfers, and property deeds will flow in increasing volume across national boundaries, virtually unchecked and unchallenged by national governments and their agencies.

- Localities will be drawn more and more into dealing directly with overseas investors in their attempts to promote local development through their own "municipal foreign policy."
- Stealthy, temporary, "virtual states" will emerge illegally from clandestine alliances of political and military leaders and senior government officers to take advantage of the paralysis of national sovereignty.

These are propective changes at a time when the end of the Cold War has left an enormous zone of geopolitical uncertainty. The balance of power that stabilized international politics for 40 years has gone, and its sudden disappearance has revealed the precariousness of many domestic political systems. Previously held together by a common enemy, they are now especially vulnerable to internal economic, ethnic, and cultural divisions.

Some of the consequences are fairly predictable. The nation-states of the world-system core, unable to manage national economies and protect their populations from the winds of global change, will have to cope with severe economic slumps (rather than minor recessions) and persistent problems of poverty, unemployment, and homelessness. Social-democratic parties in many countries, deprived of their main means of satisfying their liberal supporters—effective national strategies for social and economic management—will lose their appeal, leaving electorates to fragment and polarize around xenophobia, racism, family values, personal freedoms, and green politics. Because nation-building had always promoted the idea of a national society and a "national culture," the permeability of nation-states also raises the prospect of national identities leaking away into local (or, via cyberspace, transnational) lifestyle communities: software clubs, multi-user dungeons, ecologists, hockey fans, fundamentalists, neo-Nazis, and so on.

Some of the consequences of weak nation-states are, in fact, already beginning to appear. To stem economic leaks and gain some control over the globalizing economy, these nation-states are forming economic blocs, such as the North American Free Trade Agreement (NAFTA) and the European Union. Meanwhile, as we saw in Chapter 9, many of the same nation-states are accommodating internal cultural cleavages by decentralizing their governmental structures. In other cases, governments are dismantling expensive social welfare programs to open up previously publicly operated industries to the private sector—often to transnational corporations. For example, Canada's federal and provincial or territorial governments may have to rethink social programs in the name of global economic competition.

Often regarded as a public-sector success story, Canada's social welfare system is now under threat from powerful corporate interests, in the form of the Business Council on National Issues (now known as the Canadian Council of Chief Executives), who have campaigned to privatize and deregulate the government sector. Deregulation would mean the loss or reduction of public control over the environment, transportation, and energy resources, as well as the dismantling of universal social programs, including unemployment insurance, social assistance, health care, and pensions. Canadians have begun to organize through coalitions of volunteer and nonprofit groups, such as the Council of Canadians. This alliance, which has few funds and no official standing, has managed, by an adroit use of the internet and political theatre, to stir up latent public concern that privatization, deregulation, and trade liberalization could reduce nation-state governments to branch plants of transnational corporations. Democratic action, via Canada's political parties at the federal and provincial or territorial levels, provides another avenue for citizens to participate in the country's future direction.

If first reactions are anything to go by, the consequences of globalization will be much more dramatic in the world's peripheral regions. However strong governments may be in their apparatus of domestic power, they will be next to helpless in the face of acute environmental stress, increased cultural friction, escalating poverty and disease, and growing migrations of refugees. In these situations, it is

Figure 12.11 Militia factions and road warriors In some parts of Africa, civil war and the breakdown of law and order have, from time to time, left some areas under the control of various private armies, armed gangs, and militarized factions. Some of this conflict is a direct legacy of inter-ethnic tensions created under nineteenth- and early twentieth-century colonialism. The photograph shows Ethiopian militia in position opposite the Eritrean army. (*Source:* Patrick Robert/Corbis Sygma.)

possible that people will seek liberation through violence (**Figure 12.11**). The question may be not so much whether war and violence will exist within the periphery, but who will fight whom and for what purpose?

This is how one commentator sees the probable outcome:

> Future wars will be those of communal survival, aggravated or, in many cases, caused by environmental scarcity. These wars will be subnational, meaning that it will be hard for states and local governments to protect their own citizens physically. This is how many states will ultimately die. As state power fades—and with it the state's ability to help weaker groups within society, not to mention other states—peoples and cultures around the world will be thrown back upon their own strengths and weaknesses, with fewer equalizing mechanisms to protect them.[22]

With nation-states weakened through the transnational flow of capital, goods, and services, and the distinction between criminal violence and "legitimate" war blurred, the power of international drug cartels, local mafias, road-warrior platoons, popular militias, guerrilla factions, and private local armies will create the possibility of borderless territories that wax and wane in an ever-mutating space of chaos. Future maps of parts of the world periphery may have to be drawn without clear boundaries, just as medieval maps and the maps of European explorers were. If this sounds far-fetched, consider this: since the 1990s, in such countries as Afghanistan, Lebanon, Liberia, Sri Lanka, Somalia, Rwanda, Peru, and Colombia, civil wars, armed insurrections, and criminal violence made it difficult to be certain of which group or government controlled what territory. The clearly defined boundaries of international treaties and school atlases have already been rendered as fiction by de facto buffer zones in a few places: the Kurdish and Azeri buffer "states" between Turkey and Iran, for example, and the Turkic Uighur buffer territory between central Asia and China.

Cultural Dissonance

At one level, globalization has brought a homogenization of culture through the language of consumer goods. This is the level of "Planet Reebok," where material cultures are enmeshed by 747s, CNN, music video channels, cellphones, and the internet; and swamped by Coca-Cola and formula-driven Hollywood movies. Furthermore, sociologists have recognized that a distinctive culture of "global metropolitanism" is emerging among the self-consciously transnational upper-middle classes. This is simply homogenized culture at a higher plane of consumption (French wines instead of Budweiser, BMWs instead of Hondas, and so on). The members of this new culture are people who hold international conference calls, send and receive text messages, make decisions and transact investments that are transnational in scope, edit the news, design and market international products, and travel the world for business and pleasure.

These trends are transcending some of the traditional cultural differences around the world. We can, perhaps, more easily identify with people who use the same products, listen to the same music, and appreciate the same sports stars that we do. In the process, however, sociocultural cleavages are opening up between the haves of the fast world and the have-nots of the slow world. By focusing people's attention on material consumption, these trends are also obscuring the emergence of new fault lines—between previously compatible cultural groups and between ideologically divergent civilizations.

Several reasons account for the appearance of these new fault lines. One is the release of pressure brought about by the end of the Cold War. The evaporation of external threats has allowed people to focus on other perceived threats and intrusions. Another is the globalization of culture itself. The more people's lives are homogenized through their jobs and their material culture, the more many of them want to revive subjectivity, reconstruct we/us feelings, and re-establish a distinctive

---

[22]R.D. Kaplan, "The Coming Anarchy." *Atlantic Monthly*, February 1994, p. 74.

Figure 12.12   The shape of things to come? Economic and social polarizations in the cities of the world's core can lead to significant change in the urban landscape. Increased electronic surveillance is now a feature of many public and private spaces, and the use of private security personnel has become an aspect of urban living in some wealthy neighbourhoods. "Gated communities" such as the one shown in this photograph, may protect their inhabitants but they do so by excluding other residents of the city, and create clearly visible physical barriers in the urban fabric.

cultural identity. In the slow world of have-nots, a different set of processes is at work, however. The juxtaposition of poverty, environmental stress, and crowded living conditions alongside the materialism of Planet Reebok creates a fertile climate for gangsterism. The same juxtaposition also provides the ideal circumstance for the spread and intensification of religious fundamentalism. This, perhaps more than anything else, represents a source of serious potential cultural dissonance.

The overall result is that cultural fault lines are opening up at every geographical scale. This poses the prospect of some very problematic dimensions of future geographies. The prospect at the metropolitan scale is one of fragmented and polarized communities, with outright cultural conflict suppressed only through electronic surveillance and the "militarization" of urban space via security posts and the "hardened" urban design using fences and gated streets (**Figure 12.12**). This, of course, presupposes a certain level of affluence to meet the costs of keeping the peace across economic and cultural fault lines. In the unintended metropolises of the periphery, where unprecedented numbers of migrants and refugees will be thrown together, there is the genuine prospect of anarchy and intercommunal violence—unless, that is, intergroup differences can be submerged in a common cause, such as religious fundamentalism.

At the regional scale, the prospect is one of increasing ethnic rivalry, parochialism, and insularity. Examples of these phenomena can be found throughout the world. Canada is faced by the possibility of separation from the French-speaking Québécois. In Europe, examples are the secessionism (from Spain) of the Basques, and, more recently, outright war among the Serbs, Croats, and Bosnians. In South Asia, examples are provided by the recurring hostility between Hindus and Muslims throughout the Indian subcontinent and between the Hindu Tamils and Buddhist Sinhalese of Sri Lanka. In Africa, a long list of ethnic rivalry, parochialism, and insularity includes the continuing and bloody conflict between the Hutus and the Tutsis in Rwanda, Burundi, northeast Democratic Republic of the Congo (formerly Zaire), and western Tanzania. Where the future brings prosperity, tensions and hostilities such as these will probably be muted; where it brings economic hardship or decline, they will undoubtedly intensify.

The prospect at the global scale is of a rising consciousness of people's identities in terms of their broader historical, geographical, and racial "civilizations". Given the steep economic differences that will almost certainly persist between the world's core regions and the periphery, this conjures up the prospect of an overt "West (and Japan) versus the Rest" scenario for international relations.

Sustainability

The same West-versus-the-Rest theme emerges in discussions of the environmental issues that will face us in the future. Even climatic change, an inherently global problem, seems to pose its greatest threats to poorer, peripheral countries, as we saw in Chapter 4. Global climate change is causing sea levels to rise (as polar ice caps melt) and has increased the frequency of violent tornadoes and hurricanes (as weather patterns have become unstable). During the twentieth century, sea level rose by 20 centimetres (7.9 inches), and a 1999 report by Britain's Meteorological Office warned that flooding will increase more than nine-fold over the next century, with four-fifths of the increase coming in south and southeast Asia. Such a rise in sea level is potentially disastrous for some countries. If current trends continue, by 2050 the Maldives will be permanently flooded. The fate of these islands in the Indian Ocean is an indicator of what could happen elsewhere. About 70 percent of Bangladesh, for example, is at sea level, while much of Egypt's most fertile land, in the Nile delta, is also at sea level. Meanwhile, extensive regions of Africa, Asia, and Latin America are so marginal for agriculture that further drought could prove disastrous. In contrast, farmers in much of Europe and North America would welcome a local rise in mean temperatures because it would extend their options for the kinds of crops that they could profitably raise. However, we have seen how a rise in temperature in the Canadian Prairies has also increased the number of pests present. Concerns such as these have led many Canadians to take active steps to reduce their own impact on climate change by a variety of initiatives, including recycling and energy conservation schemes, as discussed in more detail in **Human Geography and Climate Change 12.3—Climate Change and Social Action.**

Future trends will only intensify these contrasts between the rich and poor regions. We know enough about the growth of population and the changing geography of economic development to be able to calculate with some confidence that the air and water pollution generated by low-income countries will more than double in the next 15 years. We know, in short, that environmental problems will be inseparable from processes of demographic change, economic development, and human welfare. In addition, it is becoming clear that environmental problems are going to be increasingly enmeshed in matters of national security and regional conflict. For this reason, the Canadian government increasingly talks in terms of **human security**, a concept that includes environmental sustainability and population-carrying capacity. The spatial *interdependence* of economic, environmental, and social problems means that some parts of the world are ecological time bombs. The prospect of civil unrest and mass migrations resulting from the pressures of rapidly growing populations, deforestation, soil erosion, water depletion, air pollution, disease epidemics, and intractable poverty is real. These spectres are alarming not only for the peoples of the affected regions but also for their neighbours.

Such images are also alarming for the peoples of rich and far-away countries, whose continued prosperity will depend on processes of globalization that are not disrupted by large-scale environmental disasters, unmanageable mass migrations, or the breakdown of stability in the world-system as a whole.

All this has given some momentum to the notion of sustainable development. **Sustainable development** is a vision of development that seeks a balance among economic growth, environmental impacts, and social equity. In practice, sustainable development means that economic growth and change should occur only when the impacts on the environment are benign or manageable and when the impacts (both costs and benefits) on society are fairly distributed across classes and regions. Sustainable development is geared to meeting the needs of the present without compromising the ability of future generations to meet their needs. It envisages a future when improvements to the quality of human life are achieved within the carrying capacity of local and regional ecosystems. **Carrying capacity** is the maximum number of users that can be sustained over the long term by a given set of natural resources.

human security: a concept that includes environmental sustainability and population-carrying capacity in the measure of a country's ability to promote and defend its citizens' interests

sustainable development: a vision of development that seeks a balance among economic growth, environmental impacts, and social equity

carrying capacity: the maximum number of users that can be sustained over the long term by a given set of natural resources

Climate Change and Social Actions

Every day, Canadians engage in activities that place pressure on the environment. Once relatively low priority, attitudes toward climate change have shifted dramatically since the millennium. A 2007 Angus Reid poll, which questioned Canadians from across the country about climate change, found that approximately three-quarters of Canadians are convinced global warming is real, with nearly 50 percent believing that climate change will affect their lives and the lives of future generations.[23] The same pole also found that 30 percent of Canadians feel national leaders should pay as much attention to climate change as health care.

Canadians have responded to climate change in a number of ways. For instance, Statistics Canada reports that the residential recycling rate, or the amount diverted from landfills as a proportion of waste generated, increased from 19 percent in 2000 to 27 percent in 2004 (**Figure 12.3.1**).[24] Increased awareness, access to recycling programs, and an increased range of recyclable products has likely helped this change. Although waste production is a small part of global greenhouse gas emissions, landfill sites produce methane, a greenhouse gas. Recycling also reduces environmental pollution, reduces energy consumption, and conserves materials.[25] Canadians have also responded to climate change by increasingly purchasing such things as compact fluorescent light bulbs and/or programmable thermostats, although most Canadians continue to commute to work alone in a car or truck.[26]

The impetus of climate change has spurred other groups to action as well. For instance, Toronto Community Housing pledged to reduce its greenhouse gas emissions 40 percent by 2020[27] (based on 2000 emission levels) through the installation of low flush toilets and showers, improving windows and doors, using energy efficient appliances and lights, and installing high-efficiency boilers. The housing authority also increased its recycling programs, aiming to increase recycling rates that are notoriously low in multi-family dwellings and high-rises. Interestingly, the incentive to "go green" wasn't ethical, but economic, as the changes produced savings in electricity and water costs, money that could then be used for other repairs or projects.

While public opinion polls such as the Angus Reid poll have consistently shown that a significant percentage of

Figure 12.3.1 Recycling Municipalities have increasingly promoted recycling initiatives. In addition to saving landfill space, recycling reduces greenhouse gas production by reducing demand for new products.

consumers favour environmentally conscious products and companies, consumers' efforts to switch to such products in real life have remained limited. This finding underscores a larger problem: despite the desire for green products, interest has not yet translated into large-scale shifts in consumer preferences and purchases. For instance, **green marketing**, or the marketing and sale of products that are presumed to be environmentally safe, still represents a niche market. Barriers to the broader adoption of green products and services include premium prices, low familiarity or lack of knowledge of green products, limited selection, and issues of product standards (i.e., "how green is green?"). Many consumers are fearful of **greenwashing**, a term used to describe the act of misleading consumers regarding the environmental benefits of a product or service or the environmental practices of a company. At the same time, Canadians typically don't want to pay more for green products or other solutions.[28]

Despite its problems, green products are gaining increased attention, provided they achieve the same outcome as traditional products. Most major automotive manufacturers, for example, are actively selling or developing hybrid vehicles. Sales of hybrids have grown, representing

---

[23]Angus Reid Polling Strategies. *Canadians and Global Warming: Reshaping Canadian Society.* 2007. www.angusreidstrategies.com.

[24]Statistics Canada, *Envirostats* 1(1), 2007.

[25]Intergovernmental Panel on Climate Change, *Climate Change 2007.* www.ipcc.ch.

[26]Statistics Canada, *Envirostats* 1(1), 2007.

[27]Catherine Porter, "Recycling and Energy Savings at Forefront." *Futurewatch,* 2008, www.torontohousing.ca/media_centre/news/20080106/toronto_community_housing_leads_green_push.

green marketing: the marketing and sale of products that are presumed to be environmentally safe

greenwashing: a term used to describe the act of misleading consumers regarding the environmental benefits of a product or service or the environmental practices of a company

---

[28]Martin Mittelstaedt, "Taking the Blame for Eco-woes." *Globe and Mail,* 24 April 2008, p. A5.

2.2 percent of the U.S. market share in 2007. Although still small, the growth of this sector represents a combination of increased consumer preference for hybrid vehicles, rising gas prices, new government legislation, tax benefits that favour fuel efficient vehicles, and a sense that the technology has been around long enough to trust.[29] Green marketing is also increasingly visibly in sales promotions, as manufacturers emphasize fuel efficiency and their drive to go green. At the same time, consumers continue to buy large vehicles, citing preference for performance, although this behaviour was changing as gas prices soared in 2008.

Attempts to encourage green consumers reflect marketing techniques that aim to make consumers aware of options. The ENERGY STAR label, for example, promotes energy efficient consumer products and is easily identifiable. More broadly, campaigns have targeted changing social attitudes toward climate change. The rather provocative title of Canada's "Flick off" campaign (**www.flickoff. org**) has taken the message of climate change and action steps aimed at reducing energy use to Canadian youth. Marketers have increasingly turned to online social networks to pitch their sales, with different networks providing opportunities for users to connect and share. For example, interactive websites may allow people to link and arrange carpools or reuse goods. Likewise, shopping sites may allow people to connect and share green products and their reviews. At the same time, marketers are able to directly target and engage consumers by placing advertisements in social networks. Facebook, for instance, announced in 2008 that marketers will be able to directly target members with advertisements based on the member's profile, social connections, and recent online activities.

The greening of the Canadian consumer is a slow and ongoing process, but one that is likely to gather momentum in coming years as consumers are presented with new products and options, and as consumers increasingly demand greener products. Concurrently, recycling and reusing options, along with the incorporation of other green practices, will facilitate a greener society. Economic incentives will likely be important in driving change, much like the case of Toronto Community Housing. However, as the Intergovernmental Panel on Climate Change notes, governments will need to be more involved in the mitigation of climate change to ensure that longer-term benefits are realized.[30]

[29]Dee-Ann Durbin, "US Hybrid Sales up in 2007." *Globe and Mail*, 21 April 2008, p. E10.

[30]IPCC, *Climate Change 2007*.

Sustainable development means using renewable natural resources in a manner that does not eliminate or degrade them—by making greater use, for example, of solar and geothermal energy and by greater use of recycled materials. It means managing economic systems so that all resources—physical and human—are used optimally. It means regulating economic systems so that the benefits of development are distributed more equitably (if only to prevent poverty from causing environmental degradation). It also means organizing societies so that improved education, health care, and social welfare can contribute to environmental awareness and sensitivity and an improved quality of life.

A final and more radical aspect of sustainable development is—as we saw in Chapter 8 with the notion of the 100-mile diet in Vancouver—a move away from wholesale globalization toward increased "localization": a desire to return to a more locally based economy where production, consumption, and decision making can be oriented to local needs and conditions. Thus, peripheral countries, as well as workers and citizens throughout many parts of the core, are demanding a reinstatement of control over the economic events and institutions that directly shape their lives.

Put this way, sustainable development sounds eminently sensible yet impossibly Utopian. The first widespread discussion of sustainability took place in the early 1990s and culminated in the "Earth Summit" (the United Nations Conference on Environment and Development) in Rio de Janeiro in 1992. Attended by 128 heads of state, it attracted intense media attention. At the conference, many examples were described of successful sustainable development programs at the local level. Some of these examples centred on the use of renewable sources of energy, as in the creation of small hydroelectric power stations to modernize Nepalese villages. Most examples, however, centred on sustainable agricultural practices for peripheral countries, including the use of intensive agricultural features, such as raised fields and terraces in Peru's Titicaca Basin, techniques that had been successfully used in this difficult agricultural environment for centuries, before European colonization. After the United Nations conference, however, many observers commented bitterly on the deep conflict of interest between core countries and peripheral countries that was exposed by the summit. Without radical and widespread changes in value systems and unprecedented changes in political will, "sustainable development" will remain an embarrassing contradiction in terms. Certainly, until the core countries radically cut back their levels of consumption, we will not have seriously met the needs of a sustainable future.

Recent developments regarding the Kyoto Protocol also give grounds for concern (see Chapter 4). The Protocol is an agreement that requires the industrialized countries to reduce their greenhouse gas emissions by 8 percent of their 1990 levels by 2012. However, the inability of many developed nations (including Canada) to fulfill their commitments, the failure of others even to ratify the treaty (such as the United States), and the continued increase of emission in countries outside of the agreement (such as India and China) render the Kyoto Protocol a largely ineffective agreement. Certainly, any future treaty must have far more political heft.

We cannot just wait to see what the future will hold. If we are to have a better future (and if we are to *deserve* a better future), we must use our understanding of the world—and of geographical patterns and processes—to work toward more desirable outcomes. No discipline is more relevant to the ideal of sustainable development than geography. Where else, as British geographer W.M. Adams has observed, can the science of the environment (physical geography) be combined with an understanding of economic, technological, social, political, and cultural change (human geography)? What other discipline offers insights into environmental change, and who but geographers can cope with the diversity of environments and the sheer range of scales at which it is necessary to manage global change?

Those of us in the richer countries of the world have a special responsibility for leadership in sustainable development because our present affluence is based on a cumulative past (and present) exploitation of the world's resources that is disproportionate to our numbers. We also happen to have the financial, technical, and human resources to enable us to take the lead in developing cleaner, less resource-intensive technologies in transforming our economies to protect and work with natural systems, in providing more equitable access to economic opportunities and social services, and in supporting the technological and political frameworks necessary for sustainable development in poor countries. We cannot do it all at once, but we will certainly deserve the scorn and resentment of future generations if we do not try.

CONCLUSION

It is clear that the beginning of the twenty-first century is going to be a period of fluid and transitional relationships among places, regions, and nations. Nevertheless, we know enough about contemporary patterns and trends, as well as geographical processes, to be able to map out some plausible scenarios for the future. However, we can only guess at some aspects of the future. Two of the most speculative realms are those of politics and technology.

The future of the worst-off peripheral regions could be very bad, indeed. They face unprecedented levels of demographic, environmental, and societal stress, with the events of the next 50 years being played out from a starting point of scarce basic resources, serious environmental degradation, overpopulation, disease, unprovoked crime, refugee migrations, and criminal anarchy.

For the world-system core, however, the long-term question is one of relative power and dominance. The same factors that consolidate the advantages of the core as a whole—the end of the Cold War, the availability of advanced telecommunications, the transnational reorganization of industry and finance, the liberalization of trade, and the emergence of a global culture—will also open the possibility of a new geopolitical and geoeconomic order, within which the economic and political relationships among core countries might change substantially.

Many aspects of future geographies will depend on trends in demand for resources and on the exploitation of new technologies. The expansion of the world economy and the globalization of industry will undoubtedly boost the overall demand for raw materials of various kinds, and this will spur the development of previously underexploited but resource-rich regions in Africa, Eurasia, and East Asia. Raw materials will be only a fraction of future resource needs, however; the main issue, by far, will be energy resources.

It also appears that the present phase of globalization has the potential to create such disparities between the haves and the have-nots (as well as between the core and the periphery) that social unrest will ensue. The evidence of increasing dissatisfaction with the contemporary distribution of wealth both within and between the core and the periphery is widespread. In Russia, where public demonstrations against the government have been outlawed for decades, the new Russians are taking to the streets to protest government policies that favour transnational economic development at the expense of workers' minimum wages. In India, farmers damaged a KFC restaurant for its role in dislocating the domestic poultry industry. In Mexico, industrial workers in transnational plants are challenging the absence of health and safety regulations that leave some exposed to harmful chemicals.

At the same time that protests against globalization and new geographies are being waged, the products of a global economy and culture are being widely embraced. The market for blue contact lenses is growing in such unlikely places as Bangkok and Nairobi; plastic surgery to reshape eyes is increasing in many Asian countries. Highway systems, airports, and container facilities are springing up throughout the periphery.

In short, future geographies are being negotiated at this very moment—from the boardrooms of transnational corporations to the huts of remote villagers. The outcomes of these negotiations are still in the making as we, in our daily lives, make seemingly insignificant decisions about what to wear, what to eat, where to work, how to travel, and how to entertain ourselves. These decisions help to either support or undermine the larger forces at work in the global economy, such as where to build factories, what products to make, or how to package and deliver them to the consumer. In short, future geographies can be very much shaped by us through our understanding of the relatedness of people, places, and regions in a globalized economy.

MAIN POINTS REVISITED

- **In some ways, the future is already here, embedded in the world's institutional structures and in the dynamics of its populations.**

  We know, for example, a good deal about the demographic trends of the next quarter-century, given present populations and birth and death rates. We also know a good deal about the distribution of environmental resources and constraints, the characteristics of local and regional economies, and the legal and political frameworks within which geographical change will probably take place.

- **New and emerging technologies that are likely to have the most impact in reshaping human geographies include advanced transportation technologies, biotechnology, materials technologies, and information technologies.**

  The evolution of the world's geographies has always been shaped by the opportunities and constraints presented to different places and regions by successive technology systems. Many aspects of future geographies will depend on trends in the demand for particular resources and on the exploitation of these new technologies.

- **We must not underestimate the scope and impact of future environmental change in shaping future geographies.**

  Future environmental changes are very hard to predict. However, it is becoming clear that we should—at the very least—consider the possibility of such changes when discussing future geographies and expect some of these changes (such as climate change) to be extremely unpredictable in terms of their local impacts.

- **The changes involved in shaping future geographies will inevitably bring some critical issues, conflicts, and threats, including important geographical issues that centre on scale, boundaries, and territories; on cultural dissonance; and on the sustainability of development.**

  Many of these issues stem from the globalization of the economy, which is undermining the status of the territorial nation-state as the chief regulating mechanism of both global and local dimensions of the world-system. The implications for peripheral places and regions are dismal: no matter how strong governments may be in their apparatus of domestic power, they will be next to helpless in the face of acute environmental stress, increased cultural friction, escalating poverty and disease, and growing migrations of refugees.

Key Terms

carrying capacity   (p. 546)   **greenwashing**   (p. 547)   **sustainable development**   (p. 546)
green marketing   (p. 547)   **human security**   (p. 546)

Additional Reading

Agnew, J., and S. Corbridge. *Mastering Space: Hegemony, Territory, and International Political Economy.* New York: Routledge, 1995.

Atkinson, R.D. "Technological Change and Cities," *Cityscape: A Journal of Policy Development and Research* 3(3), 1998, 129–170.

Berry, B.J.L. *Long-Wave Rhythms in Economic Development and Political Behavior.* Baltimore: Johns Hopkins University Press, 1991.

Castells, M. *End of Millennium. Vol. 3. The Information Age: Economy, Society and Culture.* Oxford: Blackwell, 1998.

Coates, J.F., J.B. Mahaffie, and A. Hines. *2025: Scenarios of U.S. and Global Society Reshaped by Science and Technology.* Greensboro, NC: Oakhill Press, 1997.

De Alcantara, C.H. (ed.). *Social Futures, Global Visions.* Oxford: Blackwell, 1996.

Diamond, J. *Collapse: How Societies Choose to Fail or Succeed.* New York: Viking Penguin, 2005.

Hammond, A. *Which World? Scenarios for the 21st Century.* Washington, DC: Island Press, 1998.

Huntington, S. "The Clash of Civilizations?" *Foreign Affairs* 72, 1993, 22–49.

Janelle, D. "Globalization, the Internet Economy and Canada," *Canadian Geographer* 45, 2001, 48–53.

Johnston, R.J., P. J. Taylor, and M. Watts (eds.). *Geographies of Global Change.* Cambridge, MA: Blackwell, 1995.

Kaplan, R.D. "The Coming Anarchy," *Atlantic Monthly*, February 1994, 44–76.

Leamer, E.E., and M. Storpes. "The Economic Geography of the Internet Age," *Journal of International Business Studies* 32(4), 2001, 641–665.

Lemmen, D., F. Warren, E. Bush, and J. Lacroix (eds.). *From Impacts to Adaptation: Canada in a Changing Climate 2007.* Ottawa: Natural Resources Canada, 2007, available at **http://adaptation. nrcan.gc.ca/.**

Nash, A. "Environmental Refugees: Consequences and Policies from a Western Perspective," *Discrete Dynamics in Nature and Society* 3, 1999, 227–238.

O'Tuathail, G., and T. Luke. "Present at the (Dis)integration: Deterritorialization and Reterritorialization in the New Wor(l)d Order," *Annals of the Association of American Geographers* 84, 1994, 381–398.

Sassen, S. *Globalization and Its Discontents.* New York: New Press, 1998.

Slaymaker, O. "Why So Much Concern about Climate Change and So Little Attention to Land Use Change?" *Canadian Geographer* 45, 2001, 71–78.

Thurow, L. *Head to Head: The Coming Economic Battle among Japan, Europe, and America.* New York: William Morrow, 1992.

United Nations. *Global Outlook 2000: An Economic, Social, and Environmental Perspective.* New York: United Nations Publications, 1990.

United Nations Development Programme (UNDP). *UNDP Report 2004.* New York: UNDP, 2004.

Wallace, I. "Sustaining Geography; Sustainable Geographies: The Linked Challenge," *Canadian Geographer* 46, 2002, 98–107.

World Commission on Environment and Development. *Our Common Future.* New York: Oxford University Press, 1987.

Exercises

Here you will find exercises and activities for each chapter. Unplugged exercises help you review chapter discussions, and pose ideas for your own human geography research. On the Companion Website exercises will require you have access to the internet.

Unplugged

1. Using census data, construct a population pyramid (see Chapter 3) for any county or city with which you are familiar. What does this tell you about the future population of the locality?

2. Drawing on what you know about the geography of this locality and its regional, national, and global contexts, construct two scenarios of about 200 words each (see Figure 12.1 for brief examples) for the future, each based on different assumptions about resources and technology.

3. Write a short essay (500 words, or two double-spaced, typed pages) in which you outline the possible effects of economic globalization on a particular place or region with which you are familiar.

On the Companion Website

This book has its own Companion Website where you will find additional resources—maps, photographs, data—as well as exercises and activities that relate to each chapter. To complete the Companion Website exercises, go to **www.pearsoned.ca/ knox.** The following is a summary of the types of exercises created for this chapter.

1. The exercises for this chapter focus on future geographies and how they may reshape our socioeconomic landscape. The internet allows us to survey new and changing geographies, such as those of AIDS, biogenetics, citizenship, social relationships, geopolitical alliances, and more. Through our study exercises, we speculate on the changing geography of production and the power of the internet to democratize.

2. The Audio Interview, Interview with Quentin Chiotti, that accompanies this chapter has been conducted to highlight some of the future environmental challenges discussed in this chapter. In addition, you will hear why a geographical education better enables us to understand such problems—which are often of a scientific or public policy nature. You will find a link to the Audio Interview, interview summary, and questions on the Companion Website for this chapter.

Glossary

A

accessibility: the opportunity for contact or interaction from a given point or location in relation to other locations

acid rain: the wet deposition of acids on Earth created by the natural cleansing properties of the atmosphere

administrative record linkage: the linking together of a number of different government databases to build one database with much more detailed information on each individual

aesthetic: culturally determined standard of beauty and good taste

age–sex pyramid: a representation of the population based on its composition according to age and sex

agglomeration diseconomies: the negative economic effects of urbanization and the local concentration of industry

agglomeration effects: cost advantages that accrue to individual firms because of their location among functionally related activities

aging: a term used to describe the effects of an increasing proportion of older age groups on the population

agrarian: referring to the culture of agricultural communities and the type of tenure system that determines access to land and the kind of cultivation practices employed there

agribusiness: a set of economic and political relationships that organizes agro-food production from the development of seeds to the retailing and consumption of the agricultural product

agricultural industrialization: the process whereby the farm has moved from being the centrepiece of agricultural production to becoming one part of an integrated string of vertically organized industrial processes including production, storage, processing, distribution, marketing, and retailing

agriculture: a science, an art, and a business directed at the cultivation of crops and the raising of livestock for sustenance and profit

allophone: a person whose mother tongue is neither English nor French

ancillary activities: such activities as maintenance, repair, security, and haulage services that serve a variety of industries

anglophone: a person whose mother tongue is English

animistic perspective on nature: the view that natural phenomena–both animate and inanimate–possess an indwelling spirit or consciousness

areal units: spatial units of measurement, such as a city block or province, used for recording statistics

B

baby boom: the increased number of births in the two decades following World War II

backwash effects: the negative impacts on a region (or regions) of the economic growth of some other region

basic functions: economic activities that provide income from sales to customers beyond city limits

Beaux Arts: a style of urban design that sought to combine the best elements of all of the classic architectural styles

biofuels: fuels made from plant material including corn, soy, and sugar cane

biotechnology: a technique that uses living organisms (or parts of organisms) to make or modify products, to improve plants and animals, or to develop micro-organisms for specific uses

brownfield site: abandoned, idle, or underused industrial and commercial land on which redevelopment is hindered by the effects of contamination

Buddhist perspective on nature: the view that nothing exists in and of itself and everything is part of a natural, complex, and dynamic totality of mutuality and interdependence

C

carbon benefit: the reduction in carbon dioxide emissions for the same quantity of fuel

carbon neutral: any carbon released upon burning is equivalent to the carbon absorbed when the plants grew.

carbon tax: a tax on emissions of CO_2 and other greenhouse gases

carrying capacity: the maximum number of users that can be sustained over the long term by a given set of natural resources

cartography: the body of practical and theoretical knowledge about making distinctive visual representations of Earth's surface in the form of maps

census: the count of the number of people in a country, region, or city

central business district (CBD): the central nucleus of commercial land uses in a city

central place theory: a theory that seeks to explain the relative size and spacing of towns and cities as a function of people's shopping behaviours

central places: settlements in which certain products and services are available to consumers

centrality: the functional dominance of cities within an urban system

centrifugal forces: forces that can lead to the disintegration of the state

centripetal forces: forces that integrate the state

chemical farming: the application of synthetic fertilizers to the soil and herbicides, fungicides, and pesticides to crops to enhance yields

City Beautiful movement: an attempt to remake cities in ways that would reflect the higher values of society, using neo-classical architecture, grandiose street plans, parks, and inspirational monuments and statues

cognitive distance: the distance that people perceive to exist in a given situation

cognitive images (mental maps): psychological representations of locations that are created from people's individual ideas and impressions of these locations

cognitive space: space defined and measured in terms of the nature and degree of people's values, feelings, beliefs, and perceptions about locations, districts, and regions

cohort: a group of individuals who share a common temporal demographic experience

colonial cities: cities that were deliberately established or developed as administrative or commercial centres by colonial or imperial powers

colonialism: the establishment and maintenance of political and legal domination by a state over a separate and alien society

commercial agriculture: farming primarily for sale, not for direct consumption

commodity chains: networks of labour and production processes beginning with the extraction or production of raw materials and ending with the delivery of a finished commodity

confederation: a grouping of independent jurisdictions, such as provinces, into a larger unit that is given separate powers

conformal projections: map projections on which compass bearings are rendered accurately

congregation: the territorial and residential clustering of specific groups or subgroups of people

conservation: the view that natural resources should be used wisely and that society's effects on the natural world should represent stewardship, not exploitation

core regions: regions that dominate trade, control the most advanced technologies, and have high levels of productivity within diversified economies

cosmopolitanism: an intellectual and aesthetic openness toward divergent experiences, images, and products from different cultures

counterurbanization: the net loss of population from cities to smaller towns and rural areas

creative destruction: the withdrawal of investments from activities (and regions) that yield low rates of profit to reinvest in new activities (and new places)

crude birth rate (CBR): the ratio of the number of live births in a single year for every thousand people in the population

crude death rate (CDR): the number of deaths in a single year for every thousand people in the population

crude density (arithmetic density): the total number of people divided by the total land area

cultural adaptation: the use of complex strategies by human groups to live successfully as part of a natural system

cultural ecology: the study of the relationship between a cultural group and its natural environment

cultural geography: study of the ways in which space, place, and landscape shape culture at the same time that culture shapes space, place, and landscape

cultural hearth: the geographic origin or source of innovations, ideas, or ideologies (term coined by geographer Carl Sauer)

cultural landscape: a characteristic and tangible outcome of the complex interactions between a human group and a natural environment

cultural nationalism: an effort to protect regional and national cultures from the homogenizing impacts of globalization

cultural region: the area within which a particular cultural system prevails

cultural system: a collection of interacting elements that, taken together, shape a group's collective identity

cultural trait: a single aspect of the complex of routine practices that constitute a particular cultural group

culture: a shared set of meanings that are lived through the material and symbolic practices of everyday life

cumulative causation: a spiral buildup of advantages that occurs in specific geographical settings as a result of the development of external economies, agglomeration effects, and localization economies

cycle of poverty: transmission of poverty and deprivation from one generation to another through a combination of domestic circumstances and local neighbourhood conditions

D

decolonization: the acquisition of control by colonized peoples over their own territory

deep ecology: an approach to nature revolving around two key components: self-realization and biospherical egalitarianism

deforestation: the removal of trees from a forested area without adequate replanting

deindustrialization: a relative decline in industrial employment in core regions

democratic rule: a system in which public policies and officials are directly chosen by popular vote

demographic collapse: phenomenon of near genocide of indigenous populations

demographic transition: the replacement of high birth and death rates by low birth and death rates

demography: the study of the characteristics of human populations

dependency ratio: the measure of the economic impact of the young and old on the more economically productive members of the population

derelict landscapes: landscapes that have experienced abandonment, misuse, disinvestment, or vandalism

desertification: the degradation of land cover and damage to the soil and water in grasslands and arid and semi-arid lands

dialects: regional variations from standard language, in terms of accent, vocabulary, and grammar

diaspora: a spatial dispersion of a previously homogeneous group

diasporic community: a group made up of emigrants from a particular homeland who maintain their cultural, political, and economic ties with each other, despite having been dispersed across many countries

digital divide: inequality of access to telecommunications and information technology, particularly the internet

distance-decay function: the rate at which a particular activity or process diminishes with increasing distance

division of labour: the specialization of different people, regions, or countries in particular kinds of economic activities

domino theory: the belief that if one country in a region chose or was forced to accept a communist political and economic system, then neighbouring countries would be irresistibly susceptible to falling to communism

doubling time: the measure of how long it will take the population of an area to grow to twice its current size

dualism: the juxtaposition in geographical space of the formal and informal sectors of the economy

E

East–West divide: communist and noncommunist countries, respectively

ecofeminism: the view that patriarchal ideology is at the centre of our present environmental malaise

ecological footprint: a measure of the biologically productive land area needed to support a country by providing for its needs and absorbing its wastes

ecological imperialism: introduction of exotic plants and animals into new ecosystems

eco-migration: a population movement caused by the degradation of land and essential natural resources

economic base: set of manufacturing, processing, trading, or service activities that serve markets beyond the city

economies of scale: cost advantages to manufacturers that accrue from high-volume production, since the average cost of production falls with increasing output

ecosystem: a community of different species interacting with one another and with the larger physical environment that surrounds them

ecotourism: an activity which, in addition to following the goals of "sustainable tourism," also (1) contributes to the conservation of an area's natural and cultural heritage; (2) includes local indigenous communities in its planning; (3) interprets the natural and cultural heritage of the destination to the visitor; and (4) is aimed at small-sized groups

ecumene: the total habitable area of a country. Since it depends on the prevailing technology, the available ecumene varies over time. It is an important concept in Canada's case, since the ecumene is so much less than the country's total area.

edge cities: nodal concentrations of shopping and office space that are situated on the outer fringes of metropolitan areas, typically near major highway intersections

emigration: a movement in which a person *leaves* a country

Enlightenment: an eighteenth-century European movement that sought to replace ideas of authority or explanation drawn from God with those that individual humans could establish through their own reason

environmental determinism: a doctrine holding that human activities are controlled by the environment

environmental ethics: a philosophical perspective on nature that prescribes moral principles as guidance for our treatment of it

environmental justice: movement reflecting a growing political consciousness, largely among the world's poor, that their immediate environs are far more toxic than those in wealthier neighbourhoods

environmental refugee: people who have been physically displaced from their homes and livelihoods by the effects of climate change

environmental scarcity: a scarcity of renewable natural resources that, if not addressed by technological, social, or economic means, may cause social disruption or violent conflict

epidemiological transition: a theory stating that the prevailing forms of illness changed from infectious to degenerative types as the demographic transition occurred

equal-area (equivalent) projections: map projections that portray areas on Earth's surface in their true proportions

ethnicity: a socially created system of rules about who belongs and who does not belong to a particular group based on actual or perceived commonality

ethnocentrism: the attitude that a person's own race and culture are superior to those of others

ethology: the scientific study of the formation and evolution of human customs and beliefs

export-processing zones (EPZs): small areas within which especially favourable investment and trading conditions are created by governments to attract export-oriented industries

external arena: regions of the world not yet absorbed into the modern world-system

external economies: cost savings that result from circumstances beyond a firm's own organization and methods of production

F

family reconstitution: the process of reconstructing individual and family life histories by linking together separately recorded birth, marriage, and death data

fast world: people, places, and regions directly involved, as producers and consumers, in transnational industry, modern telecommunications, materialistic consumption, and international news and entertainment

federal state: a form of government in which powers are divided between the federal government and smaller units of government (such as provinces) within the country

feminist geography: a field that examines the extent to which women and men experience spaces and places differently and to show how these differences themselves are part of the social construction of gender as well as that of place

fertility: the childbearing performance of individuals, couples, groups, or populations

fishing capacity: the ability of a fleet to catch fish, most easily measured by counting the number of boats in a fishing fleet

food chain: five central and connected sectors (inputs, production, product processing, distribution, and consumption) with four contextual elements acting as external mediating forces (the state, international trade, the physical environment, and credit and finance)

food manufacturing: adding value to agricultural products through a range of treatments—such as processing, canning, refining, packing, and packaging—that occur off the farm and before they reach the market

food regime: the specific set of links that exist between food production and consumption as well as capital investment and accumulation opportunities

forced migration: the movement by an individual against his or her will

foreign direct investment: overseas business investments made by private companies

francophone: a person whose mother tongue is French

friction of distance: the deterrent or inhibiting effect of distance on human activity

G

Garden City movement: an attempt to plan cities in ways that combined the benefits of urban living with the spaciousness and environmental quality of rural life

gateway city: a city that serves as a link between one country or region and others because of its physical situation

gender: category reflecting the social differences between men and women rather than the anatomical differences that are related to sex

genre de vie: a functionally organized way of life that is seen to be characteristic of a particular cultural group

gentrification: the movement into older, centrally located working-class neighbourhoods by higher-income households seeking the character and convenience of less-expensive and well-located residences

geodemographic analysis: the practice of assessing the location and composition of particular populations

geodemographic research: investigation using census data and commercial data (such as sales data and property records) about the populations of small districts to create profiles of those populations for market research

geographic information system (GIS): an organized collection of computer hardware, software, and geographical data that is designed to capture, store, update, manipulate, and display spatially referenced information

geographical path dependence: the historical relationship between the present activities associated with a place and the past experiences of that place

geopolitics: the state's power to control space or territory and shape the foreign policy of individual states and international political relations

gerrymandering: the practice of redistricting for partisan purposes

global change: combination of political, economic, social, historical, and environmental problems at the world scale

Global Positioning System (GPS): a system of satellites that orbit Earth on precisely predictable paths, broadcasting highly accurate time and locational information

globalization: the increasing interconnectedness of different parts of the world through common processes of economic, environmental, political, and cultural change

globalized agriculture: a system of food production increasingly dependent on an economy and a set of regulatory practices that are global in scope and organization

green marketing: the marketing and sale of products that are presumed to be environmentally safe

Green Revolution: the export of a technological package of fertilizers and high-yielding seeds, from the core to the periphery, to increase global agricultural productivity

greenwashing: term used to describe the act of misleading consumers regarding the environmental benefits of a product or service or the environmental practices of a company

gross domestic product (GDP): an estimate of the total value of all materials, foodstuffs, goods, and services produced by a country in a particular year

gross migration: the total number of migrants moving into and out of a place, region, or country

gross national income (GNI): similar to GDP, but also includes the value of income from abroad and excludes the taxes and wages a country pays to outside interests

gross national product (GNP): similar to GDP, but also includes the value of income from abroad

growth poles: economic activities that are deliberately organized around one or more high-growth industries

guest workers: individuals who migrate temporarily to take jobs in other countries

H

hegemony: domination over the world economy exercised by one national state in a particular historical epoch through a combination of economic, military, financial, and cultural means

hinterland: the sphere of economic influence of a town or city

historical geography: the geography of the past

home language: the language most often spoken at home by an individual (as defined by Statistics Canada)

human geography: the study of the spatial organization of human activity and of people's relationships with their environments

human security: a concept that includes environmental sustainability and population-carrying capacity in the measure of a country's ability to promote and defend its citizens' interests

humanistic approach: places the individual—especially individual values, meaning systems, intentions, and conscious acts—at the centre of analysis

hunting and gathering: activities whereby people feed themselves through killing wild animals and fish and gathering fruits, roots, nuts, and other edible plants

I

imagined community: a group of people who believe that they share a common bond and thus are part of the same nation

immigration: a movement in which a person *arrives in* another country

imperialism: the extension of the power of a nation through direct or indirect control of the economic and political life of other territories

import substitution: the process by which domestic producers provide goods or services that formerly were bought from foreign producers

infant mortality rate: the annual number of deaths of infants under one year of age compared with the total number of live births for that same year

informal sector: economic activities that take place beyond official record and are not subject to formalized systems of regulation or remuneration

infrastructure (fixed social capital): the underlying framework of services and amenities needed to facilitate productive activity

initial advantage: the critical importance of an early start in economic development; a special case of external economies

intensive subsistence agriculture: practice that involves the effective and efficient use—usually through a considerable expenditure of human labour and application of fertilizer—of a small parcel of land to maximize crop yield

internal migration: a move within a particular country or region

international migration: a move from one country to another

international organization: a group that includes two or more states seeking political or economic cooperation with each other

invasion and succession: a process of neighbourhood change whereby one social or ethnic group succeeds another

Islamic perspective on nature: the view that the heavens and Earth were made for human purposes

isolate: a language that has no known relationship with any other and cannot be assigned to a language family

isotropic surface: a hypothetical, uniform plane—flat and with no variations in its physical attributes

J

Judeo-Christian perspective on nature: the view that nature was created by God and is subject to God in the same way that a child is subject to parents

L

landscape as text: the idea that landscapes can be read and written by groups and individuals

language: a means of communicating ideas or feelings by means of a conventionalized system of signs, gestures, marks, or articulate vocal sounds

language branch: a collection of languages that possess a definite common origin but have split into individual languages

language family: a collection of individual languages believed to be related in their prehistoric origin

language group: a collection of several individual languages that are part of a language branch, share a common origin, and have similar grammar and vocabulary

language shift: an indicator of the number of people who adopt a new language, usually measured by the difference between mother tongue and home language populations

latitude: the angular distance of a point on Earth's surface, *measured north or south* from the equator, which is 0°

law of diminishing returns: the tendency for productivity to decline, after a certain point, with the continued application of capital or labour or both to a given resource base

leadership cycles: periods of international power established by individual states through economic, political, and military competition

life expectancy: the average number of years an individual can expect to live

localization economies: cost savings that accrue to particular industries as a result of clustering together at a specific location

longitude: the angular distance of a point on Earth's surface, *measured east or west* from the prime meridian (the line that passes through both poles and through Greenwich, England, and that has the value of 0°)

M

map projection: a systematic rendering on a flat surface of the geographic coordinates of the features found on Earth's surface

masculinism: the assumption that the world is, and should be, shaped mainly by men for men

maximum sustainable yield (MSY): the equilibrium between a fish population's biological productivity and the level of fishing effort; theoretically, the MSY for a fish stock is the largest number that can be caught while ensuring that enough remain for a productive fishery next year

mechanization: the replacement of human farm labour with machines

medical geography: that part of geography that considers patterns of health and the spread of diseases

megacities: very large cities characterized by high centrality within their national economy

metropolitanism: the process by which the economic growth of a city enables it to attain a position of national dominance and, in so doing, creates the geographical structure of a metropolis and hinterland

middle cohort: members of the population 15 to 64 years of age who are considered economically active and productive

migration: a long-distance move to a new location

mini-system: a society with a single cultural base and a reciprocal social economy

minority groups: population subgroups that are seen—or that see themselves—as somehow different from the general population

mobility: the ability to move, either permanently or temporarily

model: often described as a theory or concept, a model is best thought of as "a simplification of reality" designed to help generalize our understanding of a particular process or set of phenomena; it can take the form of a diagram, equation, or simple verbal statement (such as a law), and may be used as a summary of past and present behaviour or to predict future events

modern movement: the idea that buildings and cities should be designed and run as machines are

modernism: a forward-looking view of the world that emphasizes reason, scientific rationality, creativity, novelty, and progress

mother tongue: the first language learned at home in childhood and still understood by the individual at the time of the census (as defined by Statistics Canada)

N

nation: a group of people often sharing common elements of culture, such as religion or language, or a history or political identity

nationalism: the feeling of belonging to a nation as well as the belief that a nation has a natural right to determine its own affairs

nation-state: an ideal form consisting of a homogeneous group of people governed by their own state

natural decrease: the difference between the CDR and the CBR, which is the deficit of births relative to deaths

natural increase: the difference between the CBR and the CDR, which is the surplus of births over deaths

nature: a social creation as well as the physical universe that includes human beings

neo-colonialism: economic and political strategies by which powerful states in core economies indirectly maintain or extend their influence over other areas or people

net migration: the gain or loss in the total population of a particular area as a result of migration

nonbasic functions: economic activities that serve a city's own population

North–South divide: the differentiation made between the colonizing states of the Northern Hemisphere and the formerly colonized states of the Southern Hemisphere

O

official languages: languages (in Canada, English and French) in which the government has a legal obligation to conduct its affairs, and in which the public has the right to receive federal services

offshore financial centres: islands or micro-states that have become specialized nodes in the geography of worldwide financial flows

oil sands: a mixture of bitumen (a type of oil), sand, clay, and water

old-age cohort: members of the population 65 years of age and older who are considered beyond their economically active and productive years

ordinary landscapes (vernacular landscapes): the everyday landscapes that people create in the course of their lives

overurbanization: a condition in which cities grow more rapidly than the jobs and housing they can sustain

P

Paleolithic period: the period when chipped-stone tools first began to be used

participation rate: the proportion of a cohort or group that becomes involved in a specific activity, such as attending an educational institution

pastoralism: subsistence activity that involves the breeding and herding of animals to satisfy the human needs of food, shelter, and clothing

peripheral regions: regions with dependent and disadvantageous trading relationships, obsolete technologies, and undeveloped or narrowly specialized economies with low levels of productivity

picturesque: a landscape design inspired by eighteenth-century landscape painters in the Romantic tradition

place: a concept with two levels of meaning: (1) an objective location that has both uniqueness and interdependence with other places; (2) a subjective social and cultural construct—somewhere that has personal meaning for individuals or groups

place making: any activity, deliberate or unintentional, that enables space to acquire meaning

plantations: large landholdings that usually specialize in the production of one particular crop for market

political ecology: an approach to cultural geography that studies human–environment relationships through the relationships of patterns of resource use to political and economic forces

postcolonialism: a broad set of artistic, political, and research approaches that examine the consequences of the end of European colonialism

postmodern urban design: a style characterized by a diversity of architectural styles and elements, often combined in the same building or project

postmodernism: a view of the world that emphasizes an openness to a range of perspectives in social inquiry, artistic expression, and political empowerment

preservation: an approach to nature advocating that certain habitats, species, and resources should remain off-limits to human use, regardless of whether the use maintains or depletes the resource in question

primacy: a condition in which the population of the largest city in an urban system is disproportionately large in relation to the second- and third-largest cities in that system

primary activities: economic activities that are concerned directly with natural resources of any kind

producer services: services that enhance the productivity or efficiency of other firms' activities or that enable them to maintain specialized roles

proxemics: the study of the social and cultural meanings that people give to personal space

pull factors: forces of attraction that influence migrants to move to a particular location

push factors: events and conditions that impel an individual to move away from a location

Q

quaternary activities: economic activities that deal with the handling and processing of knowledge and information

R

race: problematic classification of human beings based on skin colour and other physical characteristics

range: the maximum distance that consumers will normally travel to obtain a particular product or service

rank-size rule: a statistical regularity in city-size distributions of countries and regions

reapportionment: the process of allocating electoral seats to geographical areas

redistricting: the defining and redefining of territorial district boundaries

region: a larger-sized territory that encompasses many places, all or most of which share similar attributes in comparison with the attributes of places elsewhere

regional geography: the study of the ways in which unique combinations of environmental and human factors produce territories with distinctive landscapes and cultural attributes

regionalism: a feeling of collective identity based on a population's politico-territorial identification within a state or across state boundaries

religion: belief system and a set of practices that recognize the existence of a power higher than humans

remote sensing: the collection of information about parts of Earth's surface by means of aerial photography or satellite imagery designed to record data on visible, infrared, and microwave sensor systems

reserves: that part of a resource that is currently exploitable under prevailing technologies and economic demand

resources: that part of the total stock that is considered to be useful to humans in some way

romanticism: the philosophy that emphasizes interdependence and relatedness between humans and nature

S

sacred space: an area recognized by individuals or groups as worthy of special attention as a site of special religious experiences or events

scale: the general concept that there are various scales of analysis (local, regional, national, global), that they are linked, and that processes operating at one scale can have significance at other scales

secondary activities: economic activities that process, transform, fabricate, or assemble the raw materials derived from primary activities, or that reassemble, refinish, or package manufactured goods

segregation: the spatial separation of specific population subgroups within a wider population

self-determination: the right of a group with a distinctive politico-territorial identity to determine its own destiny, at least in part, through the control of its own territory

semiotics: the practice of writing and reading signs

semiperipheral regions: regions that are able to exploit peripheral regions but are themselves exploited and dominated by core regions

sense of place: feelings evoked among people as a result of the experiences and memories that they associate with a place and the symbolism they attach to it

shifting cultivation: a system in which farmers aim to maintain soil fertility by rotating the fields within which cultivation occurs

shock city: a city that is seen as the embodiment of surprising and disturbing changes in economic, social, and cultural lives

siltation: the buildup of sand and clay in a natural or artificial waterway

site: the physical attributes of a location—its terrain, soil, vegetation, and water sources, for example

situation: the location of a place relative to other places and human activities

slow world: people, places, and regions whose participation in transnational industry, modern telecommunications, materialistic consumption, and international news and entertainment is limited

society: sum of the inventions, institutions, and relationships created and reproduced by human beings across particular places and times

sovereignty: the exercise of state power over people and territory, recognized by other states and codified by international law

spatial diffusion: the way that things spread through space and over time

spatial justice: the fairness of the distribution of society's burdens and benefits, taking into account spatial variations in people's needs and in their contributions to the production of wealth and social well-being

spread effects: the positive impacts on a region (or regions) of the economic growth of some other region

squatter settlements: residential developments on land that is neither owned nor rented by its occupants

staples thesis: a proposition arguing that the export of Canada's natural resources, or staples, had a pervasive impact on this country, one consequence being that Canada became locked into dependency as a resource hinterland for more advanced economies

staples trap: an over-reliance on the export of staples makes an economy (national or regional) vulnerable to fluctuations in world prices and without alternatives when resource depletion occurs

states: independent political units with territorial boundaries that are internationally recognized by other political units

subaltern theory: a theory examining the ways in which the colonized margin is culturally dominated by the colonizing centre

sublime: a landscape so impressive that it inspires awe or wonder

subsistence agriculture: farming for direct consumption by the producers, not for sale

supranational organizations: collections of individual states with a common goal that may be economic and/or political in nature; such organizations diminish, to some extent, individual state sovereignty in favour of the group interests of the membership

sustainable development: a vision of development that seeks a balance among economic growth, environmental impacts, and social equity

swidden: land that is cleared using the slash-and-burn process and is ready for cultivation

symbolic landscapes: representations of particular values or aspirations that the builders and financiers of those landscapes want to impart to a larger public

T

Taoist perspective on nature: the view that nature should be valued for its own sake, not for how it might be exploited

technology: physical objects or artifacts, activities or processes, and knowledge or know-how

technology systems: clusters of interrelated energy, transportation, and production technologies that dominate economic activity for several decades at a time

territorial organization: a system of government formally structured by area, not by social groups

territoriality: the persistent attachment of individuals or peoples to a specific location or territory

territory: the delimited area over which a state exercises control and that is recognized by other states

tertiary activities: economic activities involving the sale and exchange of goods and services

threshold: the minimum market size required to make the sale of a particular product or service profitable

topological space: the connections between, or connectivity of, particular points in space

topophilia: the emotions and meanings associated with particular places that have become significant to individuals

total fertility rate (TFR): the average number of children a woman will have throughout the years that demographers have identified as her childbearing years, approximately ages 15 through 49

total stock: the entire amount of energy and matter on Earth, much of which is either inaccessible or unusable by humans

transhumance: the movement of herds according to seasonal rhythms: warmer, lowland areas in the winter and cooler, highland areas in the summer

transnational communities: international communities of peoples across international boundaries

transnational corporations: companies with investments and activities that span international boundaries and with subsidiary companies, factories, offices, or facilities in several countries

U

underclass: a subset of the poor, isolated from mainstream values and the formal labour market

underemployment: the state of working less than full time, even though the people concerned would prefer to work more hours

unitary state: a form of government in which power is concentrated in the central government

urban ecology: the social and demographic composition of city districts and neighbourhoods

urban form: the physical structure and organization of cities

urban heat island: an effect resulting from the absorption and radiation of thermal energy by buildings and roads, together with the heat generated by urban living, which causes the average city to be warmer than its surrounding countryside

urban system: an interdependent set of urban settlements within a specified region

urbanism: the way of life, attitudes, values, and patterns of behaviour fostered by urban settings

urbanization economies: external economies that accrue to producers because of the package of infrastructure, ancillary activities, labour, and markets typically associated with urban settings

utility: the usefulness of a specific place or location to a particular person or group

V

visualization: a computer-assisted representation of spatial data, often involving three-dimensional images and innovative perspectives, that reveals spatial patterns and relationships more effectively

vital records: information about births, deaths, marriages, divorces, and the incidences of certain infectious diseases

voluntary migration: the movement by an individual based on choice

vulnerable populations: populations that include common characteristics making them more susceptible to health problems and failing to get the health care they need, including the very young, the old, and those with existing health conditions

W

world cities: cities in which a disproportionate part of the world's most important businesses—economic, political, and cultural—are conducted

world-empire: mini-systems that have been absorbed into a common political system while retaining their fundamental cultural differences

world-system: an interdependent system of countries linked by economic and political competition

Y

youth cohort: members of the population who are less than 15 years of age and generally considered to be too young to be fully active in the labour force

Z

zone in transition: area of mixed commercial and residential land uses surrounding the central business district (CBD)

Photo Credits

Frontmatter

Page v: Ravi Kumar Publishing, Paris, France; page vii (top and bottom) Alan E. Nash; page viii: © Dick Hemingway; pages ix to xiii: (all) Alan E. Nash.

Chapter 1

Page 1: Library of Congress; page 4: photograph by Pierre Dunnigan, courtesy of *Canadian Geographic*; page 5: (left) photography by Rolf & Debra Kraiker, (right) reproduction authorized by the Library of Parliament/reproduction autorisee par la Bibliotheque du Parlement, photographer: Tom Littlemore; page 8: The Cartography Office, Department of Geography, University of Toronto, photograph by Don Hall; page 10: courtesy of Mille Porsild, www.polarhusky.com; page 12: Alan E. Nash; page 17: (top) Library of Congress, (bottom) the Granger collection; page 20: (top) Mike Yamashita/Woodfin Camp & Associates, (bottom left) Van Bucher/Photo Researchers, Inc., (bottom right) Steve McCurry/Magnum Photos, Inc.; page 25: (top) courtesy of *The Canadian Geographer*, (bottom) *The Canadian Geographer* 49(3), Fall 2005. Reprinted with the permission of Blackwell Publishing; page 27: provided courtesy of CCRS, Natural Resources, Canada; page 37: Paul L. Knox; page 46: Alan E. Nash.

Chapter 2

Page 50: Robert Holmes Photography; page 56: Alan E. Nash; page 59: (top) Alan E. Nash, (middle right) Brian Brake/Photo Researchers, Inc., (bottom) Macduff Everton/Swanstock, Inc., (middle left) Alan E. Nash; page 60: F.A.O. Food and Agriculture Organization of the United Nations; page 62: Champlain's Astrolabe, artifact #989.56.1, image S94-37602, courtesy of the Canadian Museum of Civilization Library; page 63: (top and bottom) Alan E. Nash: page 64: The New York Public Library; page 65: Library of Congress; page 66: Stevens/SIPA Press; page 70: (top and bottom) Alan E. Nash; page 72: Library of Congress; page 78: Alex S. MacLean/Peter Arnold, Inc.; page 79: Philippe Brylak/Liaison Agency, Inc.

Chapter 3

Page 88: © Dick Hemingway; page 117: (left and right): Lisa Harmatuk/Dick Hemingway Photos; page 121: © Benoit Aquin; page 126: J.C. Aunos/Liaison Agency, Inc.; page 128: Alan E. Nash; page 131: Shutterstock.

Chapter 4

Page 138: Marcus G. Martin www.photobirder.com; page 142: (top) Douglas Brooker/Swanstock, Inc., (bottom) Erich Hartmann/Magnum Photos, Inc.; page 143: (left) Peter Menzel/Material World, (right) Miguel Luis Fairbanks/Material World; page 146: Robert "Skip" Saunders, Nuxalk; page 148: Alan E. Nash; page 150: CP Archive Photo; page 151: Jean Clottes/Corbis Sygma; page 152: Bryan & Cherry Alexander; page 156: Alan E. Nash; page 157: Alan E. Nash; page 158: Alan E. Nash; page 166: H. Schwarzach/Argus Fotoarchive/Peter Arnold, Inc.; page 167: © 2005, The Pembina Institute, Photographer: David Dodge. With permission.; page 171: Bouygues Construction; page 174: © Dick Hemingway; page 177: (top) © Galen Rowell/Corbis, (bottom) Neil Smith; page 178: Data available from U.S. Geological Survey, EROS Data Center, Sioux Falls, SD; page 181: Alan E. Nash; page 182: CP/Nick Procaylo; page 183: (top) Medio Images/Maxximages.com, (bottom) Alan E. Nash; page 185: Photocanada.com; page 188: (left and right) Alan E. Nash; page 190: AP Photo; page 192: (left) © David Noton/Masterfile, (right) © Frederic Larson/San Francisco Chronicle/Corbis; page 193: (top) Mark Segal/Maxximages.com, (bottom) CP/David J. Phillip.

Chapter 5

Page 196: Alan E. Nash; page 197: Ravi Kumar Publishing, Paris, France; page 199: (top) Yellow Dog Prods/The Image Bank, (bottom) Alan E. Nash; page 200: University of California, Berkeley; page 201 and page 202: *All Possible Worlds: A History of Geographical Ideas* 2/e, Preston E. James/Geoffrey W. James; page 203: Alan E. Nash; page 204: Alan E. Nash; page 205: Alan E. Nash; page 211: Alan E. Nash; page 213: Alan E. Nash; page 214: (top and bottom) Alan E. Nash; page 216: Paul Chelsey/Photographers/ Aspen, Inc.; page 219: Alan E. Nash; page 220: Alan E. Nash; page 225: Alan E. Nash; page 229: Alan E. Nash; page 232: Robert Fried Photography; page 233: Reprinted with the permission of the *Globe and Mail*; page 235: Alan E. Nash; page 237: Bob Krist/CORBIS. All rights reserved; page 239: Alan E. Nash; page 241: (top) Sallie A. Marston, (bottom) Serge Dedina; page 243: Alan E. Nash; page 244: Patrick Doherty/The Image Bank.

Chapter 6

Page 250: Philip A. Jones; page 253: Corel; page 254: U.S. Department of Agriculture; page 256: Alan E. Nash; page 258: (top) Philip A. Jones, (bottom) Alan E. Nash; page 259: (top and bottom) Alan E. Nash; page 260: (left and right) Alan E. Nash; page 261: © Scott Tysick/Masterfile; page 262: Jon Arnold Images Ltd / Alamy; page 263: IFA Bilderteam/Maxximages.com; page 264: (top) courtesy of Royal LePage Lakes of Muskoka Realty Inc., (bottom) Paul L. Knox; page 266: Mike Yamashita/Woodfin Camp & Associates; page 267: (top and bottom) Alan E. Nash; page 270: CP/Richard Buchan; page 271: Mark Mainwring—Mainframe.org; page 272: courtesy of Stefan D. Bruda; page 274: Alan E. Nash; page 275: Paul L. Knox; page 280: Bernard Boutrit/Woodfin Camp & Associates; page 281: (left and right) Shutterstock; page 282: Mike Yamashita/Corbis; page 283: Alex S. MacLean/Landslides; page 287: Alan E. Nash.

Chapter 7

Page 294: Alan E. Nash; page 302: Lou Linwei/Alamy; page 308: Alan E. Nash; page 316: Alan E. Nash; page 318: Alan E. Nash; page 320: Alan E. Nash; page 321: courtesy of City of Fort McMurray; page 326: © BMP Stock; page 327: © Vince Streano/CORBIS. All Rights Reserved; page 329: Alan E. Nash; page 340: Alan E. Nash; page 342: Shutterstock; page 345: Alan E. Nash; page 346: Photocanada.com.

Chapter 8

Page 350: Alan E. Nash; page 353: F.A.O. Food and Agriculture Organization of the United Nations; page 354: F.A.O. Food and Agriculture Organization of the United Nations; page 355: (left) Curt Carnemark/World Bank Photo Library, (right) James P. Blair/National Geographic Society; page 356: (top) Alan E. Nash, (bottom) F.A.O. Food and Agriculture Organization of the United Nations; page 358: (top) Alan E. Nash, (bottom) Wolfgang Kaehler/Wolfgang Kaehler Photography; page 364: CP/Larry MacDougal; page 365: (top and bottom) Alan E. Nash; page 368: Alan E. Nash; page 369: Alan E. Nash; page 370: AP Wide World Photos; page 378: F.A.O. Food and Agriculture Organization of the United Nations; page 379: F.A.O. Food and Agriculture Organization of the United Nations; page 381: (top) Agricultural Research Service—USDA, (bottom) L. Kiff/Visuals Unlimited; page 382: EOS Data Center, U.S. Geological Survey.

Chapter 9

Page 388: Alan E. Nash; page 393: (top left) Sarah Leen/Matrix International, Inc., (top right) Raymond Gehman/Corbis, (bottom left) Paul L. Knox, (bottom right) Alan E. Nash; page 394: (left) Ahn Young-Joon/AP Wide World Photos, (right) AP/Wide World Photos; page 394: (bottom) Unknown/National Archives of Canada/ C-073304; page 395: (left and right) Alan E. Nash; page 399: (top) courtesy of Blue Quills First Nations College, (bottom) Alan E. Nash; page 400: Alan E. Nash; page 404: Alan E. Nash; page 411: Hulton Deutsch Collection/Corbis; page 412: Thomas Coe/Agence France Presse; page 423: Sallie A. Marston; page 427: CP/© Matthew Fearn/PA Photos Limited.

Chapter 10

Page 434: Georg Gerster/Photo Researchers, Inc.; page 435: Wendy Stone/CORBIS. All Rights Reserved; page 441: (top) Anthony Miles/Bruce Coleman Inc., (bottom) Guido Rossi/The Image Bank; page 442: (top) Alan E. Nash, (bottom) courtesy of Melinda Gibson; page 443: Macduff Everton/ Swanstock, Inc.; page 444: (middle) Stephanie Colasanti/Corbis, (top, bottom left and right) Paul L. Knox; page 447: (top right) Topham Picture Source, (bottom left) Library of Congress, (top left, middle, bottom right) Paul L. Knox; page 448: (top left) Stock Montage, Inc./Historical Pictures Collection, (top middle, top right) Library of Congress, (bottom) Paul L. Knox; page 449: Paul L. Knox; page 455: (top left) J. Pavlovsky/Corbis Sygma, (top right) Joe Viesti/The Viesti Collection, (middle) Macduff Everton/Swanstock, Inc., (bottom right) Lee Foster/Alamy, (bottom left) Katsumi Kasahara/AP/Wide World Photos, The Image Bank; page 464: Alan E. Nash.

Chapter 11

Page 468: Mike Grandmaison; page 470: Design Pics Inc./Alamy; page 471: (top) Alan E. Nash, (bottom) © Dick Hemingway; page 472: (top) Alan E. Nash, (bottom) Stepane Compoint/Corbis Sygma; page 479: Craftsmen at work on the model of the National Capital Plan, ca. 1949 © Library and Archives Canada. Reproduced with the permission of the Minister of Public Works and Government Services Canada (2005). Source: Library and Archives Canada/ Credit: Malak/Malak collection/PA-145870; page 481: Alan E. Nash; page 484: Ken Hugill/Alamy; page 485: Alan E. Nash; page 487: Paul L. Knox; page 488: (all) Paul L. Knox; page 489: (top left) © John Elk/Stock Boston/PNI, (bottom) Dinodia/Omni-Photo Communications, Inc.; page 490: from S. Lowder, *Inside Third World Cities*. London: Croom Helm, 1986; page 492: (top left) Chromosohm/Sohm/Photo Researchers, Inc., (top right) Wolfgang Kaehler Photography, (bottom) Aerial/Terrestrial Photography; page 493: Stock Montage, Inc./Historical Pictures Collection; page 494: Yann Artus-Bertrand/Photo Researchers, Inc.; page 496: Alan E. Nash; page 498: (top) F.A.O. Food and Agriculture Organization of the United Nations, (bottom) AP Wide World Photos; page 499: (top) Daniel Laine/CORBIS All Rights Reserved, (middle) James Marshall/Bettmann/CORBIS All Rights Reserved, (bottom) William Campbell/Corbis Sygma. All Rights Reserved; page 502: U.S. Department of Housing and Urban Development; page 503: courtesy of Yee-Guan Wong; page 506: (left) Matsumoto/Corbis Sygma, (right) Paul L. Knox; page 508: (top left) World Bank Photo Library, (top right) Huffman/World Bank Photo Library, (bottom left) Paul L. Knox, (bottom right) Alain Evrard/Photo Researchers, Inc.; page 509: (left) World Bank Photo Library, (right) Curt Carnemark/World Bank Photo Library; page 51: Ted Spiegel/Black Star.

Chapter 12

Page 514: Alan E. Nash; page 517: (top left) Allan Tannenbaum/ Corbis Sygma, (top middle) Nina Berman/SIPA Press, (top right) Pat & Tom Leeson/Photo Researchers, Inc., (bottom left) Moe Doiron/ Corbis Sygma, (bottom right) Noel Quido Liaison Agency, Inc.; page 527: (top) AP Photo, (bottom) Les Stone/ Corbis Sygma; page 528: Van Parys/Corbis Sygma; page 530: Eugene Hoshiko/AP/ Wide World Photos; page 533: Max Nash/AP/Wide World Photos; page 534: CP/Saskatoon Star Phoenix/Peter Wilson; page 536: Tschaen/SIPA Press; page 537: CP Photo/Paul Chiasson; page 539: David A. Harvey/National Geographic Society; page 541: Alan E. Nash; page 544: Patrick Robert/Corbis Sygma; page 545: Shutterstock; page 547: © Dick Hemingway.

Index